Handbook of
Business Mathematics

Second Edition

WILLIAM R. MINRATH

Vice-President, D. Van Nostrand Co., Inc.

D. VAN NOSTRAND COMPANY, INC.

PRINCETON, NEW JERSEY

TORONTO   **LONDON**

VAN NOSTRAND REGIONAL OFFICES: *New York, Chicago, San Francisco*

D. VAN NOSTRAND COMPANY, LTD., *London*

D. VAN NOSTRAND COMPANY (Canada), LTD., *Toronto*

PRINTED IN THE UNITED STATES OF AMERICA

PREFACE

This book has been prepared to provide methods for application of mathematics in solving practical business problems. To facilitate the use of these methods, and of the book as a whole, they have been organized both for reference and for study.

To this end the methods are applied to the solution of representative problems in the various phases of business mathematics. These problems are worked in full detail, both by formulas and by tables, which are given right at the points where they are needed. Thus the user of the book can refer to the discussion of any problem to find both of the methods of solving it, accompanied by the necessary formulas and tables. Moreover, those wishing to familiarize themselves with the principles of business mathematics will find that the derivations of the formulas and the methods of computing the tables are fully explained.

The first section presents the basic mathematical concepts and methods that are required in business mathematics. They are primarily algebraic, although the necessary foundation in arithmetic has been included, as well as the elements of the calculus, which is used more and more widely in current business applications.

The second part of this book deals with the methods of business mathematics—those computations that enter, to a greater or less degree, into the everyday operation of virtually every business. They include commercial discount, bank discount, simple interest, compound interest, annuities, depreciation and amortization.

The third section of this book is devoted to the more specific applications, in such fields as real estate, stocks and bonds, insurance and instalment loans. Also included are discussions of the interpretation of financial statements, the evaluation of securities and other topics of general importance. This third section contains chapters dealing with the more recent developments, including the calculating machines and computers, as well as the subjects of operations research and the theory of games in their specific application to business problems.

The broad coverage of this book has been made possible by contribu-

iii

tions of much valuable reference material. Particular acknowledgment is due to Dr. M. R. Neifeld, Vice President of the Beneficial Finance System, for the report, "Rate Sections in Collateral Statutes"; to Mr. John F. McGee, of Arthur D. Little, Inc., for the article, "Operations Research as Applied to Marketing Problems"; to Mr. M. L. Vidale and Mr. H. R. Wolfe, of Arthur D. Little, Inc., for the article, "An Operations-Research Study of Sales in Response to Advertising"; to Mr. Gifford H. Symonds and the Esso Standard Oil Company, for the article, "A Crude Allocation Problem"; and to Professor James R. Jackson, Director of the Management Sciences Research Project at the University of California, Los Angeles, for the article, "Business Gaming For General Management Education." Acknowledgment is also due to Professor Rolf Wubbels of New York University, for his many helpful suggestions and contributions, and to the manufacturers of the business machines, who kindly supplied photographs and advice.

September, 1959
Princeton, New Jersey

W. R. M.

PREFACE TO SECOND EDITION

Since the publication of the First Edition, the changes in business methods, as they affect various of the topics treated in this book, have obviously made its revision necessary. They include new depreciation methods, the new Commissioners' Standard Ordinary Table for computing life insurance and annuity figures, and new averages of security prices. Outstanding among these changes, however, is the effect upon business methods, extending from routine operation to decision-making and policy-making, of the automatic computer, especially the digital computer. As a result, the corresponding portion of this book has been revised to provide more specific information. Sincere acknowledgement is made to those readers who have kindly brought to the author's attention minor errors in the previous edition. The continued cooperation of the readers of this Second Edition will be sincerely appreciated.

January, 1967
Princeton, New Jersey

W. R. M.

CONTENTS

TABLES

Chapter 1

FRACTIONS, DECIMALS AND PERCENTAGES

Fractions, decimals and percentages enter into business mathematics, not only because of their direct use in making calculations, but also because of their use in certain specific applications. For example, in the conversion of fractions to decimals it is often necessary to decide the number of significant figures to which the decimal should be computed. Therefore, this chapter includes a general discussion of significant figures in their relation to business calculations. Another example is the use of percentages in computing commercial discounts, which is presented at length in Chapter 10 on the basis of the fundamental treatment of percentage in this first chapter.

Fractions

A proper fraction is one or more of the equal integral parts of a unit. An improper fraction is a quantity greater than unity that is written in fractional form. This form used in writing fractions consists of two numbers separated by a line which may be either horizontal or diagonal. The number above or before the line is called the numerator of the fraction; while the number below or after the line is called the denominator of the fraction. Thus in the fraction $\frac{2}{3}$, the number 2 is the numerator, and the number 3 is the denominator. One arithmetical meaning of this fraction is that a single unit which may be an object or entity of any kind, such as a dollar or a sum of money, has been divided into three parts and this fraction represents two of those three parts.

Prior to a discussion of the arithmetical operations—addition, subtraction, multiplication and division of fractions—there is a basic principle to be explained. This principle can be stated as: multiplication or division of both the numerator and denominator of a fraction by the same number does not change the value of the fraction. As an example, consider the fraction $\frac{2}{3}$. If both numerator and denominator are multiplied by 2, a

1

process which gives the new fraction $\frac{4}{6}$, the value of the fraction has not been changed. For the same reason if both the numerator and denominator of a fraction are divided by the same number, the value of the fraction is unchanged. For example, if both numerator and denominator of the fraction $\frac{12}{144}$ are divided by 12, the resulting fraction $\frac{1}{12}$ has the same value as $\frac{12}{144}$. This process of division of the numerator and denominator of a fraction by the same number is called reduction, or reduction to lower terms, and is of great usefulness in making calculations with fractions.

In general a fraction can be reduced to lower terms if its numerator and denominator have a common divisor. In the case of improper fractions, that common divisor may be the denominator itself. For example, in the fraction $\frac{12}{4}$ both numerator and denominator are divisible by 4, yielding the equivalent fraction $\frac{3}{1}$, which is 3. This particular operation of dividing both numerator and denominator by the same number gives directly another definition of a fraction. A fraction is an indicated division. This concept can be extended to improper fractions in which the numerator is not exactly divisible by the denominator. For example, the fraction $\frac{14}{4}$ gives, as its equal, the mixed number $3\frac{1}{2}$.

To generalize this method, any improper fraction can be reduced to a whole or mixed number by the ordinary rule for division. This rule for improper fractions is: divide the numerator by the denominator after first reducing to lower terms, and if there is a remainder write it over the denominator as a new fraction. The quotient of this division, or if there is a remainder, the quotient and the remainder fraction, is the equivalent reduced value of the improper fraction.

Addition and Subtraction of Fractions

If two fractions have the same denominator, their sum is a new fraction formed by adding the numerators and placing them over the same denominator. For example, the sum of fractions $\frac{3}{12}$ and $\frac{5}{12}$ is found by adding the numerators $(3 + 5)$ and placing their sum (8) over the denominator as the new fraction $\frac{8}{12}$, which reduces by the method explained in the preceding section to $\frac{2}{3}$.

Similarly, if two fractions have the same denominator, the difference between the first fraction and the second is found by subtracting from the numerator of the first fraction, the numerator of the second, and placing the difference over the denominator as a new fraction. For example, the difference between the fractions $\frac{5}{12}$ and $\frac{3}{12}$ is found by performing the subtraction $(5 - 3)$ and placing the difference (2) over the denominator to form the new fraction $\frac{2}{12}$. This fraction then reduces to $\frac{1}{6}$.

If the fractions which are to be added or subtracted do not have the same denominator, find their least common denominator (that is, the smallest number which is evenly divisible by the denominators of all the fractions). Then convert each of the fractions to a new fraction having this denominator, whereupon the rule previously given can be followed.

For example, to add the fractions $\frac{1}{3}$, $\frac{5}{8}$ and $\frac{3}{4}$, the first step is to find their least common denominator, which is 24 (the smallest number that is evenly divisible by 3, 4 and 8). Therefore, $\frac{1}{3}$ becomes $\frac{1}{3} \times \frac{8}{8} = \frac{8}{24}$; $\frac{5}{8}$ becomes $\frac{5}{8} \times \frac{3}{3} = \frac{15}{24}$ and $\frac{3}{4}$ becomes $\frac{3}{4} \times \frac{6}{6} = \frac{18}{24}$. Therefore, the addition $\frac{1}{3} + \frac{5}{8} + \frac{3}{4}$ becomes $\frac{8}{24} + \frac{15}{24} + \frac{18}{24} = \frac{41}{24} = 1\frac{17}{24}$.

As an example of the subtraction of fractions which do not have the same denominator, find the value of $\frac{2}{5} - \frac{3}{8}$. Here the least common denominator of 5 and 8 is 40, so that $\frac{2}{5}$ becomes $\frac{2}{5} \times \frac{8}{8} = \frac{16}{40}$; and $\frac{3}{8}$ becomes $\frac{3}{8} \times \frac{5}{5} = \frac{15}{40}$. Therefore the subtraction, $\frac{2}{5} - \frac{3}{8}$ becomes $\frac{16}{40} - \frac{15}{40} = \frac{1}{40}$.

To add or subtract mixed numbers, the whole number parts are added or subtracted in the usual manner, and the fractional parts are added or subtracted according to the rule just given and illustrated. If the fractional part of the subtrahend is greater than that of the minuend, one unit is "borrowed" from the whole number part of the minuend as in ordinary subtraction, and added to the fractional part of the minuend. This 1 and fraction are then expressed as an improper fraction and the fractional part of the subtrahend subtracted as before. In subtracting the whole number parts it must then be remembered that the minuend has been decreased by 1. These operations are illustrated in the following example:

$$9\frac{2}{9} - 3\frac{17}{27} = 9\frac{6}{27} - 3\frac{17}{27} = 8\frac{33}{27} - 3\frac{17}{27} = 5\frac{16}{27}.$$

Multiplication and Division of Fractions

To multiply a fraction by a whole number, multiply the numerator by the number, and take the product as the numerator of the result, the denominator of the result being the same as the denominator of the fraction before multiplication. For example, $3 \times \frac{2}{9} = \frac{6}{9}$, which reduces to $\frac{1}{3}$. Again, $5 \times \frac{5}{6} = \frac{25}{6}$ which is equal to the mixed number $4\frac{1}{6}$.

To divide a fraction by a whole number, multiply the denominator of the fraction by the number, and take the product as the denominator of the result, the numerator of the result being the same as the numerator of the fraction before multiplication. For example, to divide $\frac{2}{9}$ by 3, find the new denominator by multiplying the original denominator (9) by the divisor (3), and take the product (27) as the denominator of the resulting fraction. Since the numerator is the same as that in the original fraction it is 2. Therefore, the result of $\frac{2}{9} \div 3 = \frac{2}{27}$.

In order to apply the rules for multiplication or division of fractions by whole numbers to mixed numbers, multiply or divide the integral and fractional parts of the mixed number separately and add the results, or first reduce the mixed number to an improper fraction and then apply the rule directly. For example, to multiply $2\frac{1}{4}$ by 3, one can compute separately $3 \times 2 = 6$ and $3 \times \frac{1}{4}$ (by the rule above) $= \frac{3}{4}$, so that the desired product is $6 + \frac{3}{4} = 6\frac{3}{4}$. To multiply the mixed number by reduction to an improper fraction, write $2\frac{1}{4} = \frac{9}{4}$, then $3 \times \frac{9}{4} = \frac{27}{4}$, which reduces to $6\frac{3}{4}$. In the case of division, to divide $6\frac{1}{2}$ by 3, one can compute separately $6 \div 3 = 2$ and $\frac{1}{2} \div 3$ (by the rule above) $= \frac{1}{6}$. Therefore $6\frac{1}{2} \div 3 = 2 + \frac{1}{6} = 2\frac{1}{6}$. To divide the mixed number $6\frac{1}{2}$ by reduction to an improper fraction, write $6\frac{1}{2} = \frac{13}{2}$, and $\frac{13}{2} \div 3 = \frac{13}{6}$, which reduces to the mixed number $2\frac{1}{6}$.

To multiply a fraction by a fraction, multiply the numerators to obtain the numerator of the new fraction, and multiply the denominators to obtain the denominator of the new fraction. In other words, the product of the numerators is the numerator of the product fraction, and the product of the denominators is the denominator of the product fraction.

Examples. To find $\frac{2}{3} \times \frac{3}{4}$, the product of the numerators is $2 \times 3 = 6$, while the product of the denominators is $3 \times 4 = 12$. Therefore the product fraction is $\frac{6}{12}$, which reduces to $\frac{1}{2}$.

To find $\frac{3}{7} \times \frac{21}{25}$, the product of the numerators is $3 \times 21 = 63$, while the product of the denominators is $7 \times 25 = 175$. Therefore the product fraction is $\frac{63}{175}$.

To find $\frac{1}{7} \times \frac{3}{4}$, the product of the numerators is $1 \times 3 = 3$, while the product of the denominators is $7 \times 4 = 28$. Therefore the product fraction is $\frac{3}{28}$.

To divide a fraction by a fraction, remember that division is the inverse process to multiplication. This fact is given, not as a mathematical proof of the validity of the method of dividing fractions by fractions, but as a convenient aid to remembering that method, which may be stated as follows: To divide a fraction or a whole number by a fraction, invert the divisor fraction and multiply.

For example, to find $\frac{5}{12} \div \frac{2}{3}$, invert the division fraction ($\frac{2}{3}$) to obtain $\frac{3}{2}$, and multiply. Thus $\frac{5}{12} \div \frac{2}{3} = \frac{5}{12} \times \frac{3}{2} = \frac{15}{24}$, which reduces to $\frac{5}{8}$.

To find $\frac{5}{12} \div \frac{1}{3}$, invert the division fraction ($\frac{1}{3}$) to obtain $\frac{3}{1}$, and multiply. Thus $\frac{5}{12} \div \frac{1}{3} = \frac{5}{12} \times \frac{3}{1} = \frac{15}{12}$, which reduces to $1\frac{1}{4}$.

To find $4 \div \frac{7}{8}$, invert the division fraction ($\frac{7}{8}$) to obtain $\frac{8}{7}$, and multiply. Thus $4 \div \frac{7}{8} = 4 \times \frac{8}{7} = \frac{32}{7}$, which reduces to $4\frac{4}{7}$.

To find $7\frac{1}{4} \div \frac{3}{8}$, express the mixed number ($7\frac{1}{4}$) as an improper fraction ($\frac{29}{4}$); invert the division fraction ($\frac{3}{8}$) to obtain ($\frac{8}{3}$) and multiply. Thus $7\frac{1}{4} \div \frac{3}{8} = \frac{29}{4} \times \frac{8}{3} = \frac{29}{1} \times \frac{2}{3} = \frac{58}{3}$, which reduces to $19\frac{1}{3}$.

Note the step in performing the multiplication $\frac{29}{4} \times \frac{8}{3}$, whereby it was equated to $\frac{29}{1} \times \frac{2}{3}$ before multiplying. This step consisted of eliminating the factor 4 from the numerator of one fraction and the denominator of the other, thereby reducing the work of multiplication. This particular time-saving step is called cancellation of a common factor, and is justified by the principle that a quantity is unchanged by its multiplication and its division by the same number; therefore both operations can be omitted, as is done when a factor common to numerator and denominator is cancelled.

Decimal Fractions (Decimals)

A decimal fraction is a fraction having as its denominator the number 10 or a multiple of 10 by itself. Thus $\frac{3}{10}$ and $\frac{7}{1000}$ are decimal fractions. Decimal fractions can be written without their denominators by the use of the decimal point. If the denominator of the decimal fraction is 10, and the numerator consists of a single integer, place a decimal point before that integer; thus $\frac{3}{10}$ is also written .3. If the denominator of the decimal fraction is 100 and the numerator is a number between 10 and 99, inclusive, place the decimal point before that number, thus $\frac{39}{100}$ becomes .39. Note that in this last case, both digits of the number are placed to the right of the decimal point. If the numerator is a single digit (a number between 1 and 9 inclusive) and the denominator is 100, place a decimal point followed by a zero before the numerator; thus $\frac{9}{100}$ becomes the decimal .09. This method is extended to decimal fractions having denominators of 1000, 10,000 and higher multiples of ten by itself, by the rule that the number of places to the right of the decimal point must be equal to the multiple of 10 in the denominator. Thus if the denominator is 10 (10×1), the decimal point is placed so that there is one figure of the numerator to the right of the point; if the denominator is 100 (10×10), the decimal point is placed so that there are two figures of the numerator to the right of the point; if the denominator is 1000 ($10 \times 10 \times 10$), the decimal point is placed so that there are three figures from the numerator to the right of the point, and so on to higher multiples of 10 by itself. If there are not enough figures in the numerator to furnish the required number of figures to the right of the decimal point, the necessary number of zeros are placed between the decimal point and the numerator.

Examples of the application of this rule are:

$$\frac{3}{10} = .3$$
$$\frac{23}{10} = 2.3$$
$$\frac{3}{100} = .03$$
$$\frac{31}{100} = .31$$
$$\frac{315}{100} = 3.15$$
$$\frac{3}{1000} = .003$$
$$\frac{31}{1000} = .031$$
$$\frac{315}{1000} = .315$$
$$\frac{3157}{1000} = 3.157$$

Decimals are named according to their denominators, thus $\frac{3}{10}$ (or .3) is called "3 tenths"; $\frac{31}{100}$ (or .31) is called "31 hundredths"; $\frac{31}{1000}$ or (.031) is called "31 thousandths," etc.

Addition and Subtraction of Decimals

In adding and subtracting decimals, the numbers are written one below the other with their decimal points in line and the addition or subtraction is then carried out in the usual way, the same as for other numbers.   In the sum or remainder, the decimal point is placed in line with the decimal points above.

As an illustration, add 1254.62, 129.36, 26375.8, 4.753, 18.9654.   This addition is written and carried out below.   The sum is "27,783 and 4,984 ten-thousandths."

$$1254.62$$
$$129.36$$
$$26375.8$$
$$4.753$$
$$\underline{18.9654}$$
$$27783.4984$$

The subtraction 42.963 − 18.356 is performed as follows:

$$42.963$$
$$\underline{18.356}$$
$$24.607$$

and the remainder is "24 and 607 thousandths."

If the decimal fractional parts of the minuend and subtrahend do not have the same number of decimal places to the right of the decimal point, the blank places are considered as ciphers (zeros).   As examples, the subtraction 976.5928 − 854.937 is performed as at the left below; the subtraction 12.283 − 10.2617 is carried out at the right:

976.5928	12.283
854.937	10.2617
121.6558	2.0213

From these illustrations it is clear that addition and subtraction of decimals give no trouble when the numbers are written with decimal points in line, one below the other.

Multiplication of Decimals

In multiplying two decimal numbers, they are written without regard to the position of either of their decimal points and the multiplication is carried out exactly as in the case of ordinary whole numbers.   The position of the decimal point in the product is then determined by the following rule:

The number of figures to the right of the decimal point in the product of two decimal numbers equals the sum of the numbers of figures to the right of the decimal points in multiplicand and multiplier.

The use of this rule is illustrated in the following multiplication: $263.42 \times 12.4 = 3266.408$.

$$
\begin{array}{r}
263.42 \\
12.4 \\
\hline
105368 \\
52684 \\
26342 \\
\hline
3266.408
\end{array}
$$

There are two figures to the right of the decimal point in the multiplicand (.42) and one in the multiplier (.4). In the product, therefore, according to the rule, there are $2 + 1 = 3$ figures and so the decimal point is placed before the 4.

As a second example, multiply the two decimal fractions: $.1468 \times .463$. Here there are four figures to the right of the decimal point in the multiplicand (.1468) and three in the multiplier (.463). In the product, therefore, there must be $4 + 3 = 7$ figures to the right of the decimal point. But the product as found in the usual way contains only 6 figures (679684). A cipher is, therefore, added before these six figures to give the required seven figures to the right of the decimal point, and the decimal point is placed before the cipher (zero). The product is, therefore, .0679684. That is,

$$.1468 \times .463 = .0679684.$$

Division of Decimals

Division of one decimal number by another is carried out without regard to the position of either of their decimal points in exactly the same manner as for whole numbers. The position of the decimal point in the quotient is then determined by the following rule:

Subtract the number of places to the right of the decimal point in the divisor from the number in the dividend. The remainder is the number of figures to the right of the decimal point in the quotient.

The application of this rule is illustrated by the following division: $679.684 \div 14.68$. Division of 679684 by 1468 without regard to the decimal point gives (463). There are three decimal places in the dividend (.684) and two in the divisor (.68). The number of decimal places in the quotient is, therefore, $3 - 2 = 1$ and the decimal point is placed before the last figure.

$$1468)679684(463$$

$\underline{5872}$	Since there is one decimal place
9248	in the result, its value is 46.3.
$\underline{8808}$	
4404	
$\underline{4404}$	

As in multiplication, this rule for division applies without exception to either decimal fractions or mixed decimal numbers.

If a division involving decimals does not give an exact quotient, the remainder is not taken as the numerator of a fraction to form a part of the quotient as in the division of whole numbers, but a cipher (zero) is added to the remainder to form a new partial dividend and the division is continued. This process is repeated until the quotient is exact, or as long as desired if the quotient does not come out exact. In this way the remainder fraction is automatically converted into a decimal fraction and included as a part of the remainder. Each added cipher (zero) is counted as a decimal place in the dividend, and the rule applied as usual. This procedure is illustrated by the following example: $8293.7 \div 32.74$.

$$3274)829370000(253320$$

$\underline{6548}$	Since there are three decimal places
17457	in the result, its value is 253.320.
$\underline{16370}$	
10870	
$\underline{9822}$	
10480	
$\underline{9822}$	
6580	
$\underline{6548}$	
320	

The last remainder is 32 and when a cipher (zero) is added the partial dividend is 320. But 3274 will not go into 320 a whole number of times, so the next figure in the quotient is a cipher (zero). The division gives no indication that it would yield an exact result by carrying it further, therefore it is discontinued when the number of figures in the quotient is approximately equal to or one greater than the number in the dividend. (Computations of this type are discussed more fully later in this chapter, under the heading "Significant Figures.") Now apply the rule to locate the decimal point in the quotient. After the last figure, 7, in the dividend was used, four ciphers were used to form partial dividends. These four ciphers, together with the original decimal figure (.7) make five decimal places (.70000) in the dividend, while there are two in the divisor (.74). There are, therefore, $5 - 2 = 3$ decimal places in the quotient, and the decimal point is placed before the second 3, giving as quotient 253.320.

Conversion of Common Fractions into Decimals

In division of decimals it was seen that a smaller number may be divided by a larger, the quotient being a decimal fraction. Thus, by carrying out the division in the usual manner by long division, it is found that $5 \div 8 = .625$. But, since a common fraction indicates division, the numerator being the dividend and the denominator the divisor, the fraction $\frac{5}{8}$ means the same as $5 \div 8$. That is, $\frac{5}{8} = .625$, which states that the common fraction is equivalent to a decimal fraction. The same is true of any common fraction. This means that any common fraction can be expressed as, or converted into, a decimal fraction. Since any common fraction is an indicated division, the method of conversion is plain: simply divide the numerator by the denominator by long division and follow the usual rules for decimal points.

In short, the rule for converting a common fraction to a decimal is to divide the numerator by the denominator, continuing the division until the quotient comes out exact, or failing that, until as many decimal places have been found as is desired or required. The quotient is the equivalent decimal fraction. As an example, convert the common fraction $\frac{21}{25}$ to a decimal. Then the division is:

```
25)2100(84
   200      Since there are two decimal places
   ───
   100      in the result, its value is .84.
   100
   ───
```

The equivalent decimal fraction is thus .84, exactly. As another example, convert the common fraction $\frac{21}{23}$ to a decimal. Then the division is:

```
23)21000000(913043
   207          Since there are six decimal places
   ───
    30          in the result, its value is .913043.
    23
    ──
    70
    69
    ──
    100
     92
    ───
     80
     69
     ──
```

Here it is to be noted that the division does not come out exactly. The number of figures to which it should be computed naturally depends upon the particular calculation being made, a subject which is discussed in the next section on significant figures.

Significant Figures in Business Mathematics

Significant figures can be defined mathematically as those figures in a number which are unchanged by multiplication or division by 10 or a multiple of 10 by itself. Thus, the numbers 311 and .00311 have three figures and five figures respectively, but both have only three significant figures. In the division given at the end of the preceding paragraph the number 253.320 had six significant figures and the division by which this number was obtained as a quotient did not come out exactly, but was discontinued at six significant figures, although the divisor had four significant figures, and the dividend five significant figures.

However, in business mathematics it is not feasible to determine so casually the number of significant figures to which computations must be made. The difficulty arises from the fact that it is customary in business to make computations wherever possible so that they are accurate within $.01. Therefore, if one is computing a table of percentages, discounts, interest or any other relationship in business mathematics, the number of significant figures required for accuracy to $.01 depends upon the total sum of money involved. This situation is clearly illustrated by the following questions. How many significant figures should be given in a table of the decimal values of common fractions if the maximum sum involved in the computation is $100? Again, how many significant figures should such a table have if the maximum sum involved in the computation is $1,000,000? To answer these questions take the common fraction $\frac{21}{23}$, and find its decimal value necessary to compute $\frac{21}{23}$ of $100, accurate to within $.01, and then perform the same calculation for $1,000,000.

At this point it is well to recall that the standard practice in both pure mathematics and business is to round off figures, where necessary, by increasing by one the terminal digit of a number whenever the following digit is 5 or greater. For example, the value of the number 1.5678 to four significant figures is taken as 1.568, not 1.567; but the value of the number 1.5674 to four significant figures is 1.567.

In this particular problem the common fraction $\frac{21}{23}$ is equivalent (to 9 places of decimals) to .913043478. If this figure is to be used as a multiplying factor to determine $\frac{21}{23}$ of $100, a result correct to the penny is obtained by using only the four significant figures .9130, because .9130 × $100 = $91.30, while the addition of the fifth significant figure does not change the amount of money in the result, since .91304 × $100 = $91.30.

(It is standard business practice to drop, in final calculations, fractional sums of less than $\frac{1}{2}\cent$.)   On the other hand to find $\frac{21}{23}$ of $1,000,000, so that the result is accurate within $.01, it is necessary to use eight significant figures in the decimal value of that percentage, since .91304348 × 1,000,000 = $913,043.48.   Observe that the error that would result from the use of only four significant figures (that is, .9130 instead of .91304348) is $43.48.

It follows from the foregoing example that the safe rule in performing calculations involving money, as most business computations do, is to use the number of significant figures in the computing factors that are required in the final result.   For example, in making calculations involving sums between $10 and $100, the desired accuracy to $.01 requires four significant figures.   Therefore, as demonstrated in the above example involving $100, the use of factors to four significant figures (or for safety, to five significant figures) gives the desired accuracy to within $.01 in the result.   On the other hand in making calculations involving sums between $100,000 and $1,000,000, the desired accuracy to $.01 requires eight significant figures. Therefore, as demonstrated in the above example involving $1,000,000, the use of factors to eight significant figures (or for safety, nine significant figures) gives the desired accuracy to within $.01 in the final result that is obtained.

For this reason the tables for making compound interest and annuity calculations in this book have been given to eight significant figures.   This number of figures is possible for these particular tables because their values are given, in keeping with business practice, for only a limited number of interest rates.   On the other hand the tables of logarithms, of commercial discounts and of bank discounts have been given only to six significant figures.   The reason for limiting these particular tables is because (1) the tables of logarithms in this book are for 4-figure numbers to six places— increasing the number of significant figures to 7 would be useless unless the logarithms were given for 5-figure numbers, which would require ten times as many pages and (2) because commercial discounts are commonly applied to invoices, which in the main represent smaller sums than those entering into other types of computations.   However, for all the problems throughout this book methods of solution by formula as well as by table are developed, so that the calculations can always be made directly in cases where the number of significant figures desired in the result exceed those given in the tables.

Still another reason for limiting the number of significant figures in the tables is the necessity for constantly dropping those which are beyond the number required in the particular problem.   To understand this process consider the following question: What is the product of the numbers 234.76 and 11.529 if they are accurate to five significant figures?

$$
\begin{array}{r}
234.76 \\
11.529 \\
\hline
211284 \\
46952 \\
117380 \\
23476 \\
23476 \\
\hline
2706.54804
\end{array}
$$

While the product of the above multiplication is 2706.54804, the factors entering into that product are accurate only to five significant figures. Therefore, the product is also accurate only to five significant figures, and the result of this multiplication should be written 2706.5.

As stated above, where computations are to be made involving money, the number of significant figures necessary to give a result accurate to the penny is the controlling requirement. If that number of significant figures is not known in advance, then it is well to carry enough significant figures in the factors to make sure that the work need not be repeated. It is also to be noted that throughout the example calculations in this book, which in many cases involve figures taken from tables, the tabular values are used in the early steps in the computation of the problem, even though they frequently have unnecessary significant figures, so that the reader can readily follow the manner of choosing these figures from the tables.

Conversion of Common Fractions to Decimals—Tabular Method

Earlier in this chapter the method of converting common fractions to decimals was explained. It consisted of dividing the numerator by the denominator by long division, followed by proper placement of the decimal point. It is often possible to save time in effecting this conversion by the use of Table I given on pages 13–22. As will be seen by reference to this table, it gives the reciprocals of the numbers from 1 to 999; in other words, it gives the decimal fractions equivalent to the common fractions $\frac{1}{2}$, $\frac{1}{3}$, $\frac{1}{4}$ .... $\frac{1}{999}$. In order to convert the common fraction $\frac{34}{257}$ to a decimal, find from the table the decimal equivalent of the fraction $\frac{1}{257}$. It is .0038911. Therefore, $\frac{34}{257}$ is $34 \times .0038911 = .1322974$.

While the use of this table for converting common fractions to decimals does not eliminate the work entirely, it does have the advantage of permitting this calculation to be made by the multiplication of a tabulated value instead of by division. This alternative is useful in manual computation, because multiplication can be done faster than division. It is also of advantage in computations made with the many types of desk calculating machines on which multiplication can be performed much more readily than addition (see Chapter 21 on The Role of Machines in Business

TABLE 1—DECIMAL VALUES OF COMMON FRACTIONS

Fraction	Decimal	Fraction	Decimal	Fraction	Decimal
1 - 2	0.5	1 - 36	0.0277778	1 - 70	0.0142857
1 - 3	0.3333333	1 - 37	0.0270270	1 - 71	0.0140845
1 - 4	0.25	1 - 38	0.0263158	1 - 72	0.0138889
1 - 5	0.2	1 - 39	0.0256410	1 - 73	0.0136986
1 - 6	0.1666667	1 - 40	0.025	1 - 74	0.0135135
1 - 7	0.1428571	1 - 41	0.0243902	1 - 75	0.0133333
1 - 8	0.125	1 - 42	0.0238095	1 - 76	0.0131579
1 - 9	0.1111111	1 - 43	0.0232558	1 - 77	0.0129870
1 - 10	0.1	1 - 44	0.0227273	1 - 78	0.0128205
1 - 11	0.0909091	1 - 45	0.0222222	1 - 79	0.0126582
1 - 12	0.8333333	1 - 46	0.0217391	1 - 80	0.0125
1 - 13	0.0769231	1 - 47	0.0212766	1 - 81	0.0123457
1 - 14	0.0714286	1 - 48	0.0208333	1 - 82	0.0121951
1 - 15	0.0666667	1 - 49	0.0204082	1 - 83	0.0120482
1 - 16	0.0625	1 - 50	0.02	1 - 84	0.0119048
1 - 17	0.0588235	1 - 51	0.0196078	1 - 85	0.0117647
1 - 18	0.0555556	1 - 52	0.0192308	1 - 86	0.0116279
1 - 19	0.0526316	1 - 53	0.0188679	1 - 87	0.0114943
1 - 20	0.05	1 - 54	0.0185185	1 - 88	0.0113636
1 - 21	0.0476190	1 - 55	0.0181818	1 - 89	0.0112360
1 - 22	0.0454545	1 - 56	0.0178571	1 - 90	0.0111111
1 - 23	0.0434783	1 - 57	0.0175439	1 - 91	0.0109890
1 - 24	0.0416667	1 - 58	0.0172414	1 - 92	0.0108696
1 - 25	0.04	1 - 59	0.0169492	1 - 93	0.0107527
1 - 26	0.0384615	1 - 60	0.0166667	1 - 94	0.0106383
1 - 27	0.0370370	1 - 61	0.0163934	1 - 95	0.0105263
1 - 28	0.0357143	1 - 62	0.0161290	1 - 96	0.0104167
1 - 29	0.0344828	1 - 63	0.0158730	1 - 97	0.0103093
1 - 30	0.0333333	1 - 64	0.0156250	1 - 98	0.0102041
1 - 31	0.0322581	1 - 65	0.0153846	1 - 99	0.0101010
1 - 32	0.03125	1 - 66	0.0151515	1 - 100	0.01
1 - 33	0.0303030	1 - 67	0.0149254	1 - 101	0.0099010
1 - 34	0.0294118	1 - 68	0.0147059	1 - 102	0.0098039
1 - 35	0.0285714	1 - 69	0.0144928	1 - 103	0.0097087

13

TABLE 1—DECIMAL VALUES OF COMMON FRACTIONS (Cont.)

Fraction	Decimal	Fraction	Decimal	Fraction	Decimal
1 - 104	0.0096154	1 - 138	0.0072464	1 - 172	0.0058140
1 — 105	0.0095238	1 - 139	0.0071942	1 - 173	0.0057803
1 - 106	0.0094340	1 - 140	0.0071429	1 - 174	0.0057471
1 - 107	0.0093458	1 - 141	0.0070922	1 - 175	0.0057143
1 - 108	0.0092593	1 - 142	0.0070423	1 - 176	0.0056818
1 - 109	0.0091743	1 - 143	0.0069930	1 - 177	0.0056497
1 - 110	0.0090909	1 - 144	0.0069444	1 - 178	0.0056180
1 - 111	0.0090090	1 - 145	0.0068966	1 - 179	0.0055866
1 - 112	0.0089286	1 - 146	0.0068493	1 - 180	0.0055556
1 - 113	0.0088496	1 - 147	0.0068027	1 - 181	0.0055249
1 - 114	0.0087719	1 - 148	0.0067568	1 - 182	0.0054945
1 - 115	0.0086957	1 - 149	0.0067114	1 - 183	0.0054645
1 - 116	0.0086207	1 - 150	0.0066667	1 - 184	0.0054348
1 - 117	0.0085470	1 - 151	0.0066225	1 - 185	0.0054054
1 - 118	0.0084746	1 - 152	0.0065789	1 - 186	0.0053763
1 - 119	0.0084034	1 - 153	0.0065359	1 - 187	0.0053476
1 - 120	0.0083333	1 - 154	0.0064935	1 - 188	0.0053191
1 - 121	0.0082645	1 - 155	0.0064516	1 - 189	0.0052910
1 - 122	0.0081967	1 - 156	0.0064103	1 - 190	0.0052632
1 - 123	0.0081301	1 - 157	0.0063694	1 - 191	0.0052356
1 - 124	0.0080645	1 - 158	0.0063291	1 - 192	0.0052083
1 - 125	0.008	1 - 159	0.0062893	1 - 193	0.0051813
1 - 126	0.0079365	1 - 160	0.00625	1 - 194	0.0051546
1 - 127	0.0078740	1 - 161	0.0062112	1 - 195	0.0051282
1 - 128	0.0078125	1 - 162	0.0061728	1 - 196	0.0051020
1 - 129	0.0077519	1 - 163	0.0061350	1 - 197	0.0050761
1 - 130	0.0076923	1 - 164	0.0060976	1 - 198	0.0050505
1 - 131	0.0076336	1 - 165	0.0060606	1 - 199	0.0050251
1 - 132	0.0075758	1 - 166	0.0060241	1 - 200	0.005
1 - 133	0.0075188	1 - 167	0.0059880	1 - 201	0.0049751
1 - 134	0.0074627	1 - 168	0.0059524	1 - 202	0.0049505
1 - 135	0.0074074	1 - 169	0.0059172	1 - 203	0.0049261
1 - 136	0.0073529	1 - 170	0.0058823	1 - 204	0.0049020
1 - 137	0.0072993	1 - 171	0.0058480	1 - 205	0.0048780

TABLE 1—DECIMAL VALUES OF COMMON FRACTIONS (Cont.)

Fraction	Decimal	Fraction	Decimal	Fraction	Decimal
1 - 206	0.0048544	1 - 240	0.0041667	1 - 274	0.0036496
1 - 207	0.0048309	1 - 241	0.0041494	1 - 275	0.0036364
1 - 208	0.0048077	1 - 242	0.0041322	1 - 276	0.0036232
1 - 209	0.0047847	1 - 243	0.0041152	1 - 277	0.0036101
1 - 210	0.0047619	1 - 244	0.0040984	1 - 278	0.0035971
1 - 211	0.0047393	1 - 245	0.0040816	1 - 279	0.0035842
1 - 212	0.0047170	1 - 246	0.0040650	1 - 280	0.0035714
1 - 213	0.0046948	1 - 247	0.0040486	1 - 281	0.0035587
1 - 214	0.0046729	1 - 248	0.0040323	1 - 282	0.0035461
1 - 215	0.0046512	1 - 249	0.0040161	1 - 283	0.0035336
1 - 216	0.0046296	1 - 250	0.004	1 - 284	0.0035211
1 - 217	0.0046083	1 - 251	0.0039841	1 - 285	0.0035088
1 - 218	0.0045872	1 - 252	0.0039683	1 - 286	0.0034965
1 - 219	0.0045662	1 - 253	0.0039526	1 - 287	0.0034843
1 - 220	0.0045455	1 - 254	0.0039370	1 - 288	0.0034722
1 - 221	0.0045249	1 - 255	0.0039216	1 - 289	0.0034602
1 - 222	0.0045045	1 - 256	0.0039063	1 - 290	0.0034483
1 - 223	0.0044843	1 - 257	0.0038911	1 - 291	0.0034364
1 - 224	0.0044643	1 - 258	0.0038760	1 - 292	0.0034247
1 - 225	0.0044444	1 - 259	0.0038610	1 - 293	0.0034130
1 - 226	0.0044248	1 - 260	0.0038462	1 - 294	0.0034014
1 - 227	0.0044053	1 - 261	0.0038314	1 - 295	0.0033898
1 - 228	0.0043860	1 - 262	0.0038168	1 - 296	0.0033784
1 - 229	0.0043668	1 - 263	0.0038023	1 - 297	0.0033670
1 - 230	0.0043478	1 - 264	0.0037879	1 - 298	0.0033557
1 - 231	0.0043290	1 - 265	0.0037736	1 - 299	0.0033445
1 - 232	0.0043103	1 - 266	0.0037594	1 - 300	0.0033333
1 - 233]	0.0042918	1 - 267	0.0037453	1 - 301	0.0033223
1 - 234	0.0042735	1 - 268	0.0037313	1 - 302	0.0033113
1 - 235	0.0042553	1 - 269	0.0037175	1 - 303	0.0033003
1 - 236	0.0042373	1 - 270	0.0037037	1 - 304	0.0032895
1 - 237	0.0042194	1 - 271	0.0036900	1 - 305	0.0032787
1 - 238	0.0042017	1 - 272	0.0036765	1 - 306	0.0032680
1 - 239	0.0041841	1 - 273	0.0036630	1 - 307	0.0032573

TABLE 1—DECIMAL VALUES OF COMMON FRACTIONS (Cont.)

Fraction	Decimal	Fraction	Decimal	Fraction	Decimal
1 - 308	0.0032468	1 - 342	0.0029240	1 - 376	0.0026596
1 - 309	0.0032362	1 - 343	0.0029155	1 - 377	0.0026525
1 - 310	0.0032258	1 - 344	0.0029070	1 - 378	0.0026455
1 - 311	0.0032154	1 - 345	0.0028986	1 - 379	0.0026385
1 - 312	0.0032051	1 - 346	0.0028902	1 - 380	0.0026316
1 - 313	0.0031949	1 - 347	0.0028818	1 - 381	0.0026247
1 - 314	0.0031847	1 - 348	0.0028736	1 - 382	0.0026178
1 - 315	0.0031746	1 - 349	0.0028653	1 - 383	0.0026110
1 - 316	0.0031646	1 - 350	0.0028571	1 - 384	0.0026042
1 - 317	0.0031546	1 - 351	0.0028490	1 - 385	0.0025974
1 - 318	0.0031447	1 - 352	0.0028409	1 - 386	0.0025907
1 - 319	0.0031348	1 - 353	0.0028329	1 - 387	0.0025840
1 - 320	0.0031250	1 - 354	0.0028249	1 - 388	0.0025773
1 - 321	0.0031153	1 - 355	0.0028169	1 - 389	0.0025707
1 - 322	0.0031056	1 - 356	0.0028090	1 - 390	0.0025641
1 - 323	0.0030960	1 - 357	0.0028011	1 - 391	0.0025575
1 - 324	0.0030864	1 - 358	0.0027933	1 - 392	0.0025510
1 - 325	0.0030769	1 - 359	0.0027855	1 - 393	0.0025445
1 - 326	0.0030675	1 - 360	0.0027778	1 - 394	0.0025381
1 - 327	0.0030581	1 - 361	0.0027701	1 - 395	0.0025316
1 - 328	0.0030488	1 - 362	0.0027624	1 - 396	0.0025253
1 - 329	0.0030395	1 - 363	0.0027548	1 - 397	0.0025189
1 - 330	0.0030303	1 - 364	0.0027473	1 - 398	0.0025126
1 - 331	0.0030211	1 - 365	0.0027397	1 - 399	0.0025063
1 - 332	0.0030120	1 - 366	0.0027322	1 - 400	0.0025
1 - 333	0.0030030	1 - 367	0.0027248	1 - 401	0.0024938
1 - 334	0.0029940	1 - 368	0.0027174	1 - 402	0.0024876
1 - 335	0.0029851	1 - 369	0.0027100	1 - 403	0.0024814
1 - 336	0.0029762	1 - 370	0.0027027	1 - 404	0.0024752
1 - 337	0.0029674	1 - 371	0.0026954	1 - 405	0.0024691
1 - 338	0.0029586	1 - 372	0.0026882	1 - 406	0.0024631
1 - 339	0.0029499	1 - 373	0.0026810	1 - 407	0.0024570
1 - 340	0.0029412	1 - 374	0.0026738	1 - 408	0.0024510
1 - 341	0.0029326	1 - 375	0.0026667	1 - 409	0.0024450

TABLE 1—DECIMAL VALUES OF COMMON FRACTIONS (Cont.)

Fraction	Decimal	Fraction	Decimal	Fraction	Decimal
1 - 410	0.0024390	1 - 444	0.0022523	1 - 478	0.0020921
1 - 411	0.0024331	1 - 445	0.0022472	1 - 479	0.0020877
1 - 412	0.0024272	1 - 446	0.0022422	1 - 480	0.0020833
1 - 413	0.0024213	1 - 447	0.0022371	1 - 481	0.0020790
1 - 414	0.0024155	1 - 448	0.0022321	1 - 482	0.0020747
1 - 415	0.0024096	1 - 449	0.0022272	1 - 483	0.0020704
1 - 416	0.0024038	1 - 450	0.0022222	1 - 484	0.0020661
1 - 417	0.0023981	1 - 451	0.0022173	1 - 485	0.0020619
1 - 418	0.0023923	1 - 452	0.0022124	1 - 486	0.0020576
1 - 419	0.0023866	1 - 453	0.0022075	1 - 487	0.0020534
1 - 420	0.0023810	1 - 454	0.0022026	1 - 488	0.0020492
1 - 421	0.0023753	1 - 455	0.0021978	1 - 489	0.0020450
1 - 422	0.0023697	1 - 456	0.0021930	1 - 490	0.0020408
1 - 423	0.0023641	1 - 457	0.0021882	1 - 491	0.0020367
1 - 424	0.0023585	1 - 458	0.0021834	1 - 492	0.0020325
1 - 425	0.0023529	1 - 459	0.0021786	1 - 493	0.0020284
1 - 426	0.0023474	1 - 460	0.0021739	1 - 494	0.0020243
1 - 427	0.0023419	1 - 461	0.0021692	1 - 495	0.0020202
1 - 428	0.0023364	1 - 462	0.0021645	1 - 496	0.0020161
1 - 429	0.0023310	1 - 463	0.0021598	1 - 497	0.0020121
1 - 430	0.0023256	1 - 464	0.0021552	1 - 498	0.0020080
1 - 431	0.0023202	1 - 465	0.0021505	1 - 499	0.0020040
1 - 432	0.0023148	1 - 466	0.0021459	1 - 500	0.002
1 - 433	0.0023095	1 - 467	0.0021413	1 - 501	0.0019960
1 - 434	0.0023041	1 - 468	0.0021368	1 - 502	0.0019920
1 - 435	0.0022989	1 - 469	0.0021322	1 - 503	0.0019881
1 - 436	0.0022936	1 - 470	0.0021277	1 - 504	0.0019841
1 - 437	0.0022883	1 - 471	0.0021231	1 - 505	0.0019802
1 - 438	0.0022831	1 - 472	0.0021186	1 - 506	0.0019763
1 - 439	0.0022779	1 - 473	0.0021142	1 - 507	0.0019724
1 - 440	0.0022727	1 - 474	0.0021097	1 - 508	0.0019685
1 - 441	0.0022676	1 - 475	0.0021053	1 - 509	0.0019646
1 - 442	0.0022624	1 - 476	0.0021008	1 - 510	0.0019608
1 - 443	0.0022573	1 - 477	0.0020964	1 - 511	0.0019569

TABLE 1—DECIMAL VALUES OF COMMON FRACTIONS (Cont.)

Fraction	Decimal	Fraction	Decimal	Fraction	Decimal
1 - 512	0.0019531	1 - 546	0.0018315	1 - 580	0.0017241
1 - 513	0.0019493	1 - 547	0.0018282	1 - 581	0.0017212
1 - 514	0.0019455	1 - 548	0.0018248	1 - 582	0.0017182
1 - 515	0.0019417	1 - 549	0.0018215	1 - 583	0.0017153
1 - 516	0.0019380	1 - 550	0.0018182	1 - 584	0.0017123
1 - 517	0.0019342	1 - 551	0.0018149	1 - 585	0.0017094
1 - 518	0.0019305	1 - 552	0.0018116	1 - 586	0.0017065
1 - 519	0.0019268	1 - 553	0.0018083	1 - 587	0.0017036
1 - 520	0.0019231	1 - 554	0.0018051	1 - 588	0.0017007
1 - 521	0.0019194	1 - 555	0.0018018	1 - 589	0.0016978
1 - 522	0.0019157	1 - 556	0.0017986	1 - 590	0.0016949
1 - 523	0.0019120	1 - 557	0.0017953	1 - 591	0.0016920
1 - 524	0.0019084	1 - 558	0.0017921	1 - 592	0.0016892
1 - 525	0.0019048	1 - 559	0.0017889	1 - 593	0.0016863
1 - 526	0.0019011	1 - 560	0.0017857	1 - 594	0.0016835
1 - 527	0.0018975	1 - 561	0.0017825	1 - 595	0.0016807
1 - 528	0.0018939	1 - 562	0.0017794	1 - 596	0.0016779
1 - 529	0.0018904	1 - 563	0.0017762	1 - 597	0.0016750
1 - 530	0.0018868	1 - 564	0.0017731	1 - 598	0.0016722
1 - 531	0.0018832	1 - 565	0.0017699	1 - 599	0.0016694
1 - 532	0.0018797	1 - 566	0.0017668	1 - 600	0.0016667
1 - 533	0.0018762	1 - 567	0.0017637	1 - 601	0.0016639
1 - 534	0.0018727	1 - 568	0.0017606	1 - 602	0.0016611
1 - 535	0.0018692	1 - 569	0.0017575	1 - 603	0.0016584
1 - 536	0.0018657	1 - 570	0.0017544	1 - 604	0.0016556
1 - 537	0.0018622	1 - 571	0.0017513	1 - 605	0.0016529
1 - 538	0.0018587	1 - 572	0.0017483	1 - 606	0.0016502
1 - 539	0.0018553	1 - 573	0.0017452	1 - 607	0.0016474
1 - 540	0.0018519	1 - 574	0.0017422	1 - 608	0.0016447
1 - 541	0.0018484	1 - 575	0.0017391	1 - 609	0.0016420
1 - 542	0.0018450	1 - 576	0.0017361	1 - 610	0.0016393
1 - 543	0.0018416	1 - 577	0.0017331	1 - 611	0.0016367
1 - 544	0.0018382	1 - 578	0.0017301	1 - 612	0.0016340
1 - 545	0.0018349	1 - 579	0.0017271	1 - 613	0.0016313

TABLE 1—DECIMAL VALUES OF COMMON FRACTIONS (Cont.)

Fraction	Decimal	Fraction	Decimal	Fraction	Decimal
1 - 614	0.0016287	1 - 648	0.0015432	1 - 682	0.0014663
1 - 615	0.0016260	1 - 649	0.0015408	1 - 683	0.0014641
1 - 616	0.0016234	1 - 650	0.0015385	1 - 684	0.0014620
1 - 617	0.0016207	1 - 651	0.0015361	1 - 685	0.0014599
1 - 618	0.0016181	1 - 652	0.0015337	1 - 686	0.0014577
1 - 619	0.0016155	1 - 653	0.0015314	1 - 687	0.0014556
1 - 620	0.0016129	1 - 654	0.0015291	1 - 688	0.0014535
1 - 621	0.0016103	1 - 655	0.0015267	1 - 689	0.0014514
1 - 622	0.0016077	1 - 656	0.0015244	1 - 690	0.0014493
1 - 623	0.0016051	1 - 657	0.0015221	1 - 691	0.0014472
1 - 624	0.0016026	1 - 658	0.0015198	1 - 692	0.0014451
1 - 625	0.0016000	1 - 659	0.0015175	1 - 693	0.0014430
1 - 626	0.0015974	1 - 660	0.0015152	1 - 694	0.0014409
1 - 627	0.0015949	1 - 661	0.0015129	1 - 695	0.0014388
1 - 628	0.0015924	1 - 662	0.0015106	1 - 696	0.0014368
1 - 629	0.0015898	1 - 663	0.0015083	1 - 697	0.0014347
1 - 630	0.0015873	1 - 664	0.0015060	1 - 698	0.0014327
1 - 631	0.0015848	1 - 665	0.0015038	1 - 699	0.0014306
1 - 632	0.0015823	1 - 666	0.0015015	1 - 700	0.0014286
1 - 633	0.0015798	1 - 667	0.0014993	1 - 701	0.0014265
1 - 634	0.0015773	1 - 668	0.0014970	1 - 702	0.0014245
1 - 635	0.0015748	1 - 669	0.0014948	1 - 703	0.0014225
1 - 636	0.0015723	1 - 670	0.0014925	1 - 704	0.0014205
1 - 637	0.0015699	1 - 671	0.0014903	1 - 705	0.0014184
1 - 638	0.0015674	1 - 672	0.0014881	1 - 706	0.0014164
1 - 639	0.0015649	1 - 673	0.0014859	1 - 707	0.0014144
1 - 640	0.0015625	1 - 674	0.0014837	1 - 708	0.0014124
1 - 641	0.0015601	1 - 675	0.0014815	1 - 709	0.0014104
1 - 642	0.0015576	1 - 676	0.0014793	1 - 710	0.0014085
1 - 643	0.0015552	1 - 677	0.0014771	1 - 711	0.0014065
1 - 644	0.0015528	1 - 678	0.0014749	1 - 712	0.0014045
1 - 645	0.0015504	1 - 679	0.0014728	1 - 713	0.0014025
1 - 646	0.0015480	1 - 680	0.0014706	1 - 714	0.0014006
1 - 647	0.0015456	1 - 681	0.0014684	1 - 715	0.0013986

TABLE 1—DECIMAL VALUES OF COMMON FRACTIONS (Cont.)

Fraction	Decimal	Fraction	Decimal	Fraction	Decimal
1 - 716	0.0013966	1 - 750	0.0013333	1 - 784	0.0012755
1 - 717	0.0013947	1 - 751	0.0013316	1 - 785	0.0012739
1 - 718	0.0013928	1 - 752	0.0013298	1 - 786	0.0012723
1 - 719	0.0013908	1 - 753	0.0013280	1 - 787	0.0012706
1 - 720	0.0013889	1 - 754	0.0013263	1 - 788	0.0012690
1 - 721	0.0013870	1 - 755	0.0013245	1 - 789	0.0012674
1 - 722	0.0013850	1 - 756	0.0013228	1 - 790	0.0012658
1 - 723	0.0013831	1 - 757	0.0013210	1 - 791	0.0012642
1 - 724	0.0013812	1 - 758	0.0013193	1 - 792	0.0012626
1 - 725	0.0013793	1 - 759	0.0013175	1 - 793	0.0012610
1 - 726	0.0013774	1 - 760	0.0013158	1 - 794	0.0012594
1 - 727	0.0013755	1 - 761	0.0013141	1 - 795	0.0012579
1 - 728	0.0013736	1 - 762	0.0013123	1 - 796	0.0012563
1 - 729	0.0013717	1 - 763	0.0013106	1 - 797	0.0012547
1 - 730	0.0013699	1 - 764	0.0013089	1 - 798	0.0012531
1 - 731	0.0013680	1 - 765	0.0013072	1 - 799	0.0012516
1 - 732	0.0013661	1 - 766	0.0013055	1 - 800	0.0012500
1 - 733	0.0013643	1 - 767	0.0013038	1 - 801	0.0012484
1 - 734	0.0013624	1 - 768	0.0013021	1 - 802	0.0012469
1 - 735	0.0013605	1 - 769	0.0013004	1 - 803	0.0012453
1 - 736	0.0013587	1 - 770	0.0012987	1 - 804	0.0012438
1 - 737	0.0013569	1 - 771	0.0012970	1 - 805	0.0012422
1 - 738	0.0013550	1 - 772	0.0012953	1 - 806	0.0012407
1 - 739	0.0013532	1 - 773	0.0012937	1 - 807	0.0012392
1 - 740	0.0013514	1 - 774	0.0012920	1 - 808	0.0012376
1 - 741	0.0013495	1 - 775	0.0012903	1 - 809	0.0012361
1 - 742	0.0013477	1 - 776	0.0012887	1 - 810	0.0012346
1 - 743	0.0013459	1 - 777	0.0012870	1 - 811	0.0012330
1 - 744	0.0013441	1 - 778	0.0012853	1 - 812	0.0012315
1 - 745	0.0013423	1 - 779	0.0012837	1 - 813	0.0012300
1 - 746	0.0013405	1 - 780	0.0012821	1 - 814	0.0012285
1 - 747	0.0013387	1 - 781	0.0012804	1 - 815	0.0012270
1 - 748	0.0013369	1 - 782	0.0012788	1 - 816	0.0012255
1 - 749	0.0013351	1 - 783	0.0012771	1 - 817	0.0012240

TABLE 1—DECIMAL VALUES OF COMMON FRACTIONS (Cont.)

Fraction	Decimal	Fraction	Decimal	Fraction	Decimal
1 - 818	0.0012225	1 - 852	0.0011737	1 - 886	0.0011287
1 - 819	0.0012210	1 - 853	0.0011723	1 - 887	0.0011274
1 - 820	0.0012195	1 - 854	0.0011710	1 - 888	0.0011261
1 - 821	0.0012180	1 - 855	0.0011696	1 - 889	0.0011249
1 - 822	0.0012165	1 - 856	0.0011682	1 - 890	0.0011236
1 - 823	0.0012151	1 - 857	0.0011669	1 - 891	0.0011223
1 - 824	0.0012136	1 - 858	0.0011655	1 - 892	0.0011211
1 - 825	0.0012121	1 - 859	0.0011641	1 - 893	0.0011198
1 - 826	0.0012107	1 - 860	0.0011628	1 - 894	0.0011186
1 - 827	0.0012092	1 - 861	0.0011614	1 - 895	0.0011173
1 - 828	0.0012077	1 - 862	0.0011601	1 - 896	0.0011161
1 - 829	0.0012063	1 - 863	0.0011587	1 - 897	0.0011148
1 - 830	0.0012048	1 - 864	0.0011574	1 - 898	0.0011136
1 - 831	0.0012034	1 - 865	0.0011561	1 - 899	0.0011123
1 - 832	0.0012019	1 - 866	0.0011547	1 - 900	0.0011111
1 - 833	0.0012005	1 - 867	0.0011534	1 - 901	0.0011099
1 - 834	0.0011990	1 - 868	0.0011521	1 - 902	0.0011086
1 - 835	0.0011976	1 - 869	0.0011507	1 - 903	0.0011074
1 - 836	0.0011962	1 - 870	0.0011494	1 - 904	0.0011062
1 - 837	0.0011947	1 - 871	0.0011481	1 - 905	0.0011050
1 - 838	0.0011933	1 - 872	0.0011468	1 - 906	0.0011038
1 - 839	0.0011919	1 - 873	0.0011455	1 - 907	0.0011025
1 - 840	0.0011905	1 - 874	0.0011442	1 - 908	0.0011013
1 - 841	0.0011891	1 - 875	0.0011429	1 - 909	0.0011001
1 - 842	0.0011876	1 - 876	0.0011416	1 - 910	0.0010989
1 - 843	0.0011862	1 - 877	0.0011403	1 - 911	0.0010977
1 - 844	0.0011848	1 - 878	0.0011390	1 - 912	0.0010965
1 - 845	0.0011834	1 - 879	0.0011377	1 - 913	0.0010953
1 - 846	0.0011820	1 - 880	0.0011364	1 - 914	0.0010941
1 - 847	0.0011806	1 - 881	0.0011351	1 - 915	0.0010929
1 - 848	0.0011792	1 - 882	0.0011338	1 - 916	0.0010917
1 - 849	0.0011779	1 - 883	0.0011325	1 - 917	0.0010905
1 - 850	0.0011765	1 - 884	0.0011312	1 - 918	0.0010893
1 - 851	0.0011751	1 - 885	0.0011299	1 - 919	0.0010881

TABLE 1—DECIMAL VALUES OF COMMON FRACTIONS (Cont.)

Fraction	Decimal	Fraction	Decimal	Fraction	Decimal
1 - 920	0.0010870	1 - 947	0.0010560	1 - 974	0.0010267
1 - 921	0.0010858	1 - 948	0.0010549	1 - 975	0.0010256
1 - 922	0.0010846	1 - 949	0.0010537	1 - 976	0.0010246
1 - 923	0.0010834	1 - 950	0.0010526	1 - 977	0.0010235
1 - 924	0.0010823	1 - 951	0.0010515	1 - 978	0.0010225
1 - 925	0.0010811	1 - 952	0.0010504	1 - 979	0.0010215
1 - 926	0.0010799	1 - 953	0.0010493	1 - 980	0.0010204
1 - 927	0.0010787	1 - 954	0.0010482	1 - 981	0.0010194
1 - 928	0.0010776	1 - 955	0.0010471	1 - 982	0.0010183
1 - 929	0.0010764	1 - 956	0.0010460	1 - 983	0.0010173
1 - 930	0.0010753	1 - 957	0.0010449	1 - 984	0.0010163
1 - 931	0.0010741	1 - 958	0.0010438	1 - 985	0.0010152
1 - 932	0.0010730	1 - 959	0.0010428	1 - 986	0.0010142
1 - 933	0.0010718	1 - 960	0.0010417	1 - 987	0.0010132
1 - 934	0.0010707	1 - 961	0.0010406	1 - 988	0.0010121
1 - 935	0.0010695	1 - 962	0.0010395	1 - 989	0.0010111
1 - 936	0.0010684	1 - 963	0.0010384	1 - 990	0.0010101
1 - 937	0.0010672	1 - 964	0.0010373	1 - 991	0.0010091
1 - 938	0.0010661	1 - 965	0.0010363	1 - 992	0.0010081
1 - 939	0.0010650	1 - 966	0.0010352	1 - 993	0.0010070
1 - 940	0.0010638	1 - 967	0.0010341	1 - 994	0.0010060
1 - 941	0.0010627	1 - 968	0.0010331	1 - 995	0.0010050
1 - 942	0.0010616	1 - 969	0.0010320	1 - 996	0.0010040
1 - 943	0.0010604	1 - 970	0.0010309	1 - 997	0.0010030
1 - 944	0.0010593	1 - 971	0.0010299	1 - 998	0.0010020
1 - 945	0.0010582	1 - 972	0.0010288	1 - 999	0.0010010
1 - 946	0.0010571	1 - 973	0.0010277		

Mathematics). In fact, the use of tables of reciprocals on these smaller office machines is not restricted to the conversion of fractions into decimals. For by using this table, division by any number from 2 to 999 may be performed by looking up the reciprocal of that number (that is, the fraction having the number in its denominator and 1 in its numerator) in the table and multiplying by it. For example, to find $378 \div 463$, look up the reciprocal of 463 in the table. It is given there as .0021598. Then multiply .0021598 by 378, obtaining .8164044, which is the result of the division of 378 by 463. Since the figure in the table had five significant figures, the result should be written .81640.

Conversion of Decimals to Common Fractions

In order to reduce a decimal to a common fraction, reverse the process by which the common fraction is obtained from a decimal. That is, write the decimal (omitting the decimal point), as the numerator of the fraction and take as the denominator of the fraction the numbers 10, 100, 1,000 etc. according to the number of decimal places in the given decimal; then reduce this fraction to its lowest terms. For example, in converting the decimal .75 to a fraction, the figure 75 becomes the numerator of the fraction, and, since there are two places in the decimal, 100 becomes the denominator, so that the equivalent common fraction is $\frac{75}{100}$, which reduces to $\frac{3}{4}$. To convert the decimal .00064 to a common fraction take 64 as the numerator and 100,000 as the denominator (since there are five decimal places in the given decimal and since $10 \times 10 \times 10 \times 10 \times 10 = 100,000$). Therefore, the equivalent common fraction is $\frac{64}{100,000}$ which reduces to $\frac{2}{3125}$.

Percentage

The word percent is derived from the Latin *per centum*, which means by the hundred. It is an expression of a number of parts per hundred of any entity or quantity. For example, 3 percent means 3 out of every hundred, the 3 being of the same nature as the hundred, as 3 men out of every hundred men, 3 books out of every hundred books, or 3 dollars out of every hundred dollars.

From the foregoing definition of percent, and the definition of a common fraction given earlier in this chapter, it follows that 3 percent, or three out of every hundred, is equal to the fraction $\frac{3}{100}$. Furthermore, from the definition of a decimal fraction, or from the relationship between common fractions and decimal fractions, it follows that 3 percent $= \frac{3}{100} = .03$.

When any fractional part of an entity or total is stated in parts per hundred or percent, it is designated as the percentage of the entity or total. There is a distinction between the terms "percent" and "percentage" that is often important to keep in mind. Percent is an abstract fractional number, while percentage is the particular portion of an entity or quantity corresponding to the percent. Thus 25 percent of $1000.00 is the percentage of $1000.00 amounting to $250.00. Similarly 25 percent of 40 books is the percentage, 10 books; 25% of 120 horses is the percentage, 30 horses, etc.

Moreover, percentage also designates the method of calculation by the hundreds in any branch of arithmetic. Thus if one quarter of a sum is spent, it is $\frac{1}{4} = \frac{25}{100} = 25$ percent depleted; if the interest charged on money is 3 cents per dollar (100 cents) it is called 3 percent interest. The basis, or base, of the calculation is the entity or total considered as a whole, and the percentage is computed on it.

The term percent is usually represented by the symbol %, which is a shortened form of $\overline{100}$. Thus, $\frac{25}{100} = 25\%$ or 25 percent.

Expression of Fractions and Decimals as Percents

Since percent is the number of parts per hundred, any part of an entity or total, expressed as a decimal fraction, can be converted to percent by multiplying by 100 and adding the % sign. And, as has been shown in the discussion of decimals, multiplication by 100 is effected by moving the decimal point 2 places to the right. Therefore, to convert a decimal to a percent, move the decimal point 2 places to the right and add the % sign. Thus $.42 = 42\%$; $.0071 = .71\%$; $.03062 = 3.062\%$; $4.145 = 414.5\%$. Note from the last example that the rule for decimals can be extended to mixed decimal numbers, yielding percents greater than 100%. Such values have meaning by extension of the concept of percent as parts per hundred to apply to more than one entity or total so divided. Thus 210% of $1.00 is $\frac{210}{100}$ of $1.00 = 2.10.

To convert a common fraction to a percent, the simple rule is first to convert the common fraction to a decimal fraction by the method explained earlier in this chapter, and then to convert the decimal to a percent. Thus to express $\frac{3}{50}$ to a percent, divide 3 by 50, obtaining the decimal .06. Then convert the decimal .06 to a percent by the rule of the preceding paragraph, that is, by moving the decimal point 2 places to the right and adding the sign %, so $.06 = 6\%$. Therefore, the overall process becomes $\frac{3}{50} = .06 = 6\%$.

Other examples are $\frac{3}{125} = .024 = 2.4\%$; $\frac{4}{12} = .333 = 33.3\%$ (this is a non-terminating decimal and is carried out to the desired number of significant figures). Also $\frac{66}{120} = .55 = 55\%$; and $\frac{17}{8} = 2\frac{1}{8} = 2.125 = 212.5\%$.

Expression of Percent as a Decimal or a Common Fraction

To express a percent as a decimal, reverse the process of converting a decimal to a percent. That is, remove the % sign and move the decimal point 2 places to the left. Thus, to convert 16% to a decimal, remove the % sign and move the decimal point from its position in 16. to .16. Other examples are 74% = .74; 7% = .07; .013% = .00013; 215% = 2.15.

To express a percent as a common fraction, remove % sign and write the percent number as a numerator with 100 as a denominator; then reduce the resulting fraction to its lowest terms. Thus, to convert 4% to a fraction, write $\frac{4}{100}$, which reduces to $\frac{1}{25}$. Similarly, $32\% = \frac{32}{100} = \frac{8}{25}$; $.08\% = \frac{.08}{100} = \frac{8}{10.000} = \frac{1}{1250}$. From the last of these examples, note that to convert decimal percentages to fractions, it is necessary to multiply the numerator and the denominator of the fraction by a power of ten (that is, 10, 100, 1000, etc.) that is sufficient to change the numerator from a decimal to a whole number.

Chapter 2

ALGEBRAIC NUMBERS
AND FUNDAMENTAL OPERATIONS

The treatment of algebra in this and the following chapters has been developed with particular reference to the role of algebra in business mathematics. Therefore, while the discussion starts from the fundamental concepts, the examples illustrating them have been chosen from business situations. Moreover the topics emphasized are those which occur most extensively in the relationships used in the computation of compound interest, annuities and the other basic calculations of business mathematics. These computations are, in turn, used in calculations arising in work with securities, mortgages, insurance, instalment loans and many other practical business activities.

Algebraic Symbols

Elementary algebra is generalized arithmetic. One of the most familiar ways in which it generalizes is by using symbols, especially letters. Consider an extremely simple example, the calculation of the total cost of a quantity of articles of which the unit price is known, that is, the cost of 60 suits costing \$50.00 each. The total cost is found, of course, by multiplying the number of suits (60) by the unit price (\$50.00), to obtain the total (\$3000.00), as

$$60 \times \$50.00 = \$3000.00,$$

by the rule: Number of suits $\times$ Unit cost = Total cost.
This rule can be abbreviated by using the first letter of each word as follows:

$$N \times U = T,$$

and the use of the letters has truly generalized the rule, which now applies not only to suits, but to hats or coats or ties or automobiles or to any other article of which the number and unit cost is known, and the total cost is sought.

26

The letters used in algebra to represent numbers are called algebraic symbols. Since numbers may be added, subtracted, multiplied and divided, these operations can also be performed on the letters which represent them. Thus if the letter a represents the number 164, the operation of adding 164 to 164 may be performed in two ways,

$$164 + 164 = 328$$

or $$a + a = 2a; 2 \times 164 = 328.$$

There are advantages in so using letters to represent numbers, as is evident in cases where the numbers are not explicitly stated. For example, consider the following problem: the sum of two numbers is 45, and their difference is 5, what are the numbers? By using letters to represent the unknown numbers this problem is easily solved. Let x be the larger of the two numbers and y the smaller, then the problem becomes:

Given
$$x + y = 45$$
$$x - y = 5$$

To find x and y.

Now, if the two equations are added,

$$
\begin{aligned}
x + y &= 45 \\
\underline{x - y} &= \underline{5} \\
2x &= 50,
\end{aligned}
$$

since $x + x = 2x$; $y - y = 0$, and $45 + 5 = 50$.

Therefore $x = \frac{50}{2} = 25$, and since $x + y = 45$, then $y = 20$. So the two numbers are 25 and 20.

The solution to the foregoing problem illustrates an important point in algebra. It is that two algebraic equations may be added, just as two symbols may be added. The addition of equations is permissible because of the application of the axiom, "when equals are added to equals, the sums are equal." That is, since $x + y$ is equal to 45, and $x - y$ is equal to 5, then by addition of equations $x + y + x - y = 45 + 5$, giving $2x = 50$ and $x = 25$.

Negative Numbers

Just as algebra generalizes the numbers of arithmetic by using letters to represent them as explained in the preceding paragraph, so it generalizes the processes of arithmetic by using new kinds of numbers. One class of these new numbers is the negative numbers. They can be approached logically from the idea of a scale having a "zero-point." For example, the Centigrade temperature scale was established by taking 0° as the temperature of melting ice and 100° as the temperature of boiling water at standard pressure. Therefore temperatures lower than that of melting ice are designated by negative numbers, such as −15°C., −34°C., etc. Another example of the use of negative numbers occurs in altitude measurements, which are made from a zero point known as mean sea level. A height of 100 feet above mean sea level would be expressed as +100 feet (or as 100 feet, since positive numbers are understood when no sign is given), while altitudes below sea level are measured downward from it, and designated by negative numbers. Thus −25 feet means 25 feet below mean sea level. Since negative numbers are widely used in making algebraic calculations, their properties are important, and are discussed in the following paragraphs.

Addition of Negative Numbers

To add negative numbers to other negative numbers, simply find their total, just as if they were ordinary (positive) numbers. For example, to add the negative numbers −10 and −20, simply write them in column and find their total, as follows,

$$\begin{array}{r} -10 \\ -20 \\ \hline -30 \end{array}$$

The same process is followed for more than two negative numbers. For example, to find the sum of −8, −6, −15 and −34, write and add;

$$\begin{array}{r} -\ 8 \\ -\ 6 \\ -15 \\ -34 \\ \hline -63. \end{array}$$

Thus, the rule for the addition of negative numbers is: Add the negative numbers just as if they were regular (positive) numbers, keeping the minus sign before the total.

Addition of Negative and Positive Numbers

The meaning of the addition of a positive number and a negative number can be seen from an example using money. Suppose a man having $20.00 pays a bill of $10.00. How much does he have left? If the debt is represented as the negative number −$10.00, and the original cash as +$20.00, then the sum of +$20.00 and −$10.00 is seen to be $20.00 − $10.00, which is +$10.00, or simply $10.00, since numbers without signs are assumed to be positive. To take a less trivial example, suppose a balance sheet shows the following items only:

Cash, $10,000; Accounts Receivable, $40,000; Accounts Payable,

$25,000; Notes Receivable, $10,000; Notes Payable, $15,000. What is the net worth?

Representing assets as positive numbers of dollars, and liabilities as negative numbers of dollars, these figures could be written as: +$10,000; +$40,000; −$25,000; +$10,000; and −$15,000. The net worth would then be the sum of these five numbers, three of which are positive and two, negative. To find this sum, the rule is: Write the positive numbers in one column and the negative numbers in another column; then add the columns; disregard the signs of the totals and subtract the smaller total from the larger, attaching to the result the sign (+ or −) of the larger.

This is a long rule, but it is not difficult to apply, as is evident on finishing the example:

Assets		*Liabilities*	
Cash......................	+$10,000.	Accounts Payable.......	−$25,000.
Accounts Receivable........	+ 40,000.	Notes Payable..........	− 15,000.
Notes Receivable...........	+ 10,000.		
Total Assets...............	+$60,000.	Total Liabilities........	−$40,000.

Net worth = the sum of +$60,000, and −$40,000, which is +$20,000, (obtained by subtracting the smaller total, −$40,000, from the larger total, +$60,000, and attaching to the remainder, $20,000, the sign of the larger, so the result is +$20,000.)

The foregoing method of computing net worth may seem artificial when compared with the conventional process of subtracting total liabilities from total assets. The advantage of the method used, however, is that it introduces the systematic procedure for handling negative numbers, which is useful when working with algebraic numbers. Consider the following problem:

Find the sum of the expressions: $a + 2b - c$; $a - b + 3c$ and $3a - c$. The rule to be followed here is a simple extension of the rule given earlier for positive and negative numbers, whereby each kind was added in separate columns. In other words, like was added to like. The same rule is followed with literal numbers (i.e. letters which represent numbers). Therefore the problem given above is solved as follows:

$$
\begin{array}{rrr}
+a & +2b & -c \\
+a & -b & +3c \\
+3a & & -c \\
\hline
+5a & +b & +c
\end{array}
$$

The result is, therefore, $5a + b + c$.

Note that the work was simplified by putting positive and negative numbers in the same column. In this way, the operations of adding positive and negative numbers can be combined so that instead of listing the above $-c$ and $-c$ in one column, and the $+3c$ in another, all the c-terms were written in one column. However, the method remains unchanged, since the $-c$ and $-c$ are added mentally to give $-2c$, and the sum of this total and the positive c-term total ($+3c$) are added mentally by disregarding the signs, subtracting the smaller ($-2c$) from the larger ($+3c$), and attaching to the result (c) the sign of the larger, which is $+$.

At this point, it is pertinent to discuss the meaning of the algebraic terms that combine figures and letters without signs between them, such as $2b$ and $3c$. They have been treated as 2 b's and 3 c's, that is as $b + b$ or $c + c + c$, which indeed they are. However, these expressions mean the same as $2 \times b$ and $3 \times c$. In other words, an immediate gain by the use in algebra of letters to represent numbers is that the use of the multiplication sign is unnecessary, for whenever two or more letters, or two or more letters and a number, stand side by side without signs between them, the multiplication sign is understood.

Thus $2a$ means $2 \times a$; ab means $a \times b$; $3ac$ means $3 \times a \times c$; and $-3ac$ means $-(3 \times a \times c)$. The parentheses mean that the minus sign applies to the product of $3 \times a \times c$.

Subtraction of Algebraic Numbers

Subtraction is the reverse of addition. Therefore a short rule for performing the operation is: "Change the sign of the quantity to be subtracted, and add." In dealing with positive quantities only, this rule is scarcely necessary, since the result of subtracting $+4$ from $+6$, or $+4ab$ from $+6ab$ is so familiar from arithmetical experience as to require no special rule. But arithmetical experience does not extend to negative numbers, and for them the rule is necessary. For the result of subtracting -4 from $+6$ is $+10$, and the result of the subtraction of $-4ab$ from $+6ab$ is $+10ab$, results which follow from changing the sign of the -4 to $+4$, and the sign of the $-4ab$ to $+4ab$, and then adding the $+4$ to the $+6$ to obtain $+10$, and adding the $+4ab$ to the $+6ab$ to obtain $+10ab$. To appreciate why the subtraction of a negative number results in an increase, consider the balance sheet situation, where liabilities were designated as negative numbers. If a subtraction is made from liabilities, such as Accounts Payable, the result is obviously an addition to net worth.

The rule also indicates that subtraction of negative quantities from negative quantities gives a negative remainder that is smaller than the subtrahend, or zero, or a positive remainder.

Consider another example of algebraic subtraction, that is, to subtract $3a - b$ from $7a + 4b$. In this case the entity to be subtracted is the expression $3a - b$, therefore the correct procedure in following the rule "Change the sign of the quantity to be subtracted, and add" applies to both the $3a$ and the $-b$, which become $-3a$ and $+b$. Thus the process is performed as follows:

I. Write the quantity from which the
    subtraction is to be made $+7a$ $+4b$
II. Write the quantity to be subtracted,
    with signs changed $-3a$ $+b$
III. Add to obtain the result $\overline{+4a}$ $\overline{+5b,}$

which is written $4a + 5b$, as the initial sign is taken as $+$ unless written $-$.

Expressions in algebra which are to be treated as a unit are usually enclosed in parentheses, ( ), brackets, [ ], braces { }, etc. Thus the above example could have been written as $7a + 4b - (3a - b)$, to show that the subtraction to be performed was of the entire expression $(3a - b)$. This is accomplished, as shown above, by applying the sign outside the parentheses to each term. If the sign outside is $+$, the signs of the terms inside are unchanged, but if it is $-$, these signs are reversed, so that $-(3a - b)$ becomes $-3a + b$.

Another situation in algebraic subtraction arises when the expression to be subtracted contains terms not present in the expression from which they are to be subtracted. For example, subtract $4a - 5ab + 7b$ from $6a + 3ac - 7c$. The operation is performed as follows:

I. Write the quantity from which
    the subtraction is to be
    performed $6a + 3ac - 7c$
II. Write the quantity to be sub-
    tracted, with signs changed,
    and with like terms in column $-4a$ $+5ab - 7b$
III. Add to obtain the result. $\overline{2a + 3ac - 7c + 5ab - 7b}$

Multiplication and Division of Algebraic Numbers

The rule for multiplication and division of algebraic numbers is to perform these operations without regard to the signs, then if the numbers have like signs, affix a plus sign to the product or quotient; if unlike, affix a minus sign to the product or quotient.

For example, $(+2) \times (+2) = +4$
and $(+4) \div (+2) = +2.$

The numbers have like signs so the product or quotient is plus.

$$(+2) \times (-2) = -4$$
$$(+4) \div (-2) = -2.$$

The numbers have unlike signs, so the product or quotient is minus.

$$(-2) \times (-2) = +4$$
$$(-4) \div (-2) = +2.$$

The numbers have like signs, so the product or quotient is plus.

Before beginning the discussion of the multiplication and division of literal numbers, recall the earlier statement that in algebra the multiplication sign is usually omitted, so that $2a$ means $2 \times a$; $16ay$ means $16 \times a \times y$; and that $16(a + y)$ means $16 \times (a + y)$, which is the same as $16 \times a + 16 \times y$. Moreover, in algebra the division sign is usually replaced by the fraction line, thus $\frac{a}{2}$ or $a/2$ is used instead of $a \div 2$, and $\frac{a}{b}$ or a/b is used instead of $a \div b$.

In discussing multiplication, it is logical to begin by considering the multiplication of expressions having only one term. The terms of an expression are the parts which are separated by plus or minus signs. Thus the expression $3abcd$ has only one term, while the expression $2 + a$ has two terms, and $3a + b - c$ has three terms. The word used to designate expressions with only one term is monomial, that for those having two terms is binomial, etc. Any expression with two or more terms is called a polynomial. Thus, the discussion of multiplication begins with the multiplication of monomials.

It has already been shown that an algebraic symbol can be multiplied by an ordinary number, i.e., that 2 times $a = 2a$. Similarly, two symbols can be multiplied, thus a times $b = ab$, and by the rule of signs given previously, $-a$ times $b = -ab$.

An algebraic term of wide usefulness is "coefficient," which denotes each of the letters or numbers forming a term. Thus the term $3abc$ has the four coefficients, 3, a, b and c, while the term xy has two coefficients, x and y. Coefficients are also designated as numerical coefficients, such as the 3 in the example, and as literal coefficients, such as the a, b, c, x and y.

The rule for the multiplication of monomials is: (1) multiply the numerical coefficients to form the numerical coefficient of the product, (2) multiply the literal coefficients to form the literal part of the product, (3) use the algebraic rule of signs (like signs give plus products, unlike, minus), and (4) if the same letter occurs more than once in a product it is not repeated, but followed by a small superscript number, called an exponent.

Example 1. To multiply $6ab$ by $4cd$.

(1) Multiply the numerical coefficients

$$6 \times 4 = 24.$$

(2) Multiply the literal coefficients

$$ab \times cd = abcd.$$

(3) Use the algebraic rule of signs

Like signs (both $+$) therefore the product is $+$.

Then from (1), (2) and (3), the product is $+24abcd$.

Example 2.   To multiply $6ab$ by $-5cy$.
(1) Multiply the numerical coefficients

$$6 \times 5 = 30.$$

(2) Multiply the literal coefficients

$$ab \times cy = abcy.$$

(3) Use the algebraic rule of signs

Unlike signs ($+$ and $-$), therefore the product is $-$.

Then from (1), (2) and (3), the product is $-30abcy$.

Example 3.   To multiply $6ab$ by $-5ay$.
(1) Multiply the numerical coefficients

$$6 \times 5 = 30.$$

(2) Multiply the literal coefficients

$$ab \times ay = aaby.$$

(3) Use the algebraic rule of signs

Unlike signs ($+$ and $-$), therefore the product is $-$.

(4) The same letter occurs twice, so write it with an exponent, that is, use a^2 instead of aa.

Then from (1), (2), (3) and (4), the product is $-30a^2by$.

Example 4.   To multiply $6a^2b$ by $-5a^3y$.
(1) Multiply the numerical coefficients

$$6 \times 5 = 30.$$

(2) and (4) Multiply the literal coefficients,

$$a^2b \times a^3y = a^2ba^3y = a^5by.$$

(From this example, it is seen that in multiplication, exponents are added, $a^3 \times a^2$ giving a^5.   The reason for this procedure can be seen at once if a^3 is written in its other form $a \times a \times a$, and a^2 as $a \times a$; whence their product is $a \times a \times a \times a \times a$, or a^5.)

(3) Use the algebraic rule of signs

Unlike signs ($+$ and $-$), therefore the product is $-$.

Then from (1), (2), (3) and (4), the product is $-30a^5by$.

Multiplication of Polynomials

Consider a binomial (that is, a polynomial of two terms) such as $2 + a$, that is to be multiplied by 5.   The procedure is to multiply each of the two terms separately, that is, to multiply first the 2 by 5, obtaining 10, and then the a by 5, obtaining $5a$, so that the result is $10 + 5a$.

Similarly, $5(a + b) = 5a + 5b$, since as stated earlier, writing two expressions together indicates multiplication, and in this case the expressions are 5 and $(a + b)$.

Another example is $-5(a + b)$, which gives $[(-5 \times a) + (-5 \times b)] = -5a - 5b$. Still another example is $y(a + b) = ay + by$. This example illustrates the practice of arranging the letters in a term in alphabetical order; that is since in elementary algebra it does not matter in what order numbers are multiplied, then 2×3 has the same meaning as 3×2, and ay has the same algebraic meaning as ya, so that alphabetical order is used for uniformity and convenience.

Still another example of multiplication of a binomial is $-2xy(3a^2b - 6c)$. At this point it is well to recall the rule for multiplication of monomials, and to apply it successively to the multiplication of the two terms in the parentheses above.

Multiplier $-2xy$	First term $3a^2b$	Second term $-6c$
Step (1) Multiply numerical coefficients	$2 \times 3 = 6$	$2 \times 6 = 12$
Step (2) Multiply letters	$xy \times a^2b = a^2bxy$	$xy \times c = cxy$
Step (3) Use algebraic rule of signs	Signs are unlike, so result is $-$.	Signs are like (both $-$), so result is $+$.
Steps (1), (2) and (3)	$-6a^2bxy$	$+12cxy$

So the result is $-6a^2bxy + 12cxy$.

The examples above have dealt with the multiplication of binomials by monomials (single terms). A next step is the multiplication of binomials by binomials. The rule is to multiply each term by each term. Thus $(a + b)(c + d) = ac + ad + bc + bd$. To fix this rule in mind, try it on a numerical example. Thus 10 can be written $6 + 4$, and 12 can be written $9 + 3$. Then substitute these numbers for the $a + b$ and $c + d$ above, obtaining instead of $(10) \times (12)$, $(6 + 4) \times (9 + 3)$. Then multiplication of each term by each term yields $54 + 18 + 36 + 12$, which is 120, the same as is obtained from 10×12.

Another example of multiplication of binomials is $(3a + 2b)(3a - 4c)$. Here multiplying each term by each term yields $9a^2 - 12ac + 6ab - 8bc$. (The first term, the $9a^2$, results from the multiplication of $3a$ by $3a$, since as stated earlier in the chapter, the product of a number by itself is denoted by an exponent, in this case by ^{2}.)

The method of multiplying each term by each term extends to polynomials of any number of terms.

Thus, the multiplication of $(3a + 7b^2)$ and $(2a + 6b - 3c)$ yields $6a^2 + 18ab - 9ac + 14ab^2 + 42b^3 - 21b^2c$. In multiplying such polynomials having more than two terms, it is usual to take as multiplier the polynomial containing the smaller number of terms, and to write it below the multiplicand. Applying this arrangement to the multiplication above,

$$
\begin{array}{r}
2a + 6b - 3c \\
3a + 7b^2 \\
\hline
+14ab^2 + 42b^3 - 21b^2c \\
6a^2 + 18ab - 9ac \qquad\qquad\quad \\
\hline
6a^2 + 18ab - 9ac + 14ab^2 + 42b^3 - 14b^2c
\end{array}
$$

The rule for multiplication of polynomials is:

The product of any two polynomials is found by multiplying each term of one by each term of other and adding the results algebraically.

As another example, multiply $3a^4 + 2a^2b - 4b^2$ by $2a^2 - 5b$.

$$
\begin{array}{r}
3a^4 + 2a^2b - 4b^2 \\
2a^2 - 5b \\
\hline
-15a^4b - 10a^2b^2 + 20b^3 \\
6a^6 + 4a^4b - 8a^2b^2 \qquad\qquad \\
\hline
6a^6 - 11a^4b - 18a^2b^2 + 20b^3
\end{array}
$$

Note that multiplication starts with the right-hand term of the multiplier $(-5b)$, and is followed by the term to its left $(2a^2)$, and would continue to the left if there were more terms. In multiplying terms containing letters as above, this order is not essential, but has the convenience in that if the expressions to be multiplied are arranged in order of descending powers of the lowest letter of the alphabet appearing (in this case, a), then the product will come out in that order. The important consideration is always to place the same letter-combination in the same column for algebraic addition, remembering that a difference in exponents constitutes a different combination (that is a term consisting of a^2bc, with or without a numerical coefficient, can be added only to a term also consisting of a^2bc, with or without a numerical coefficient, and never by a term in ab^2c, for example).

As a further instance, consider the multiplication of two trinomials (that is, expressions consisting of three terms). As an example, multiply $a^3 - 6b + 4c$ by $3a^2c + 2ce + 4df$.

$$
\begin{array}{l}
a^3 - 6b + 4c \\
3a^2c + 2ce + 4df \\
\hline
\qquad\qquad\qquad\qquad\qquad\qquad 4a^3df - 24bdf + 16cdf \\
\qquad\qquad\qquad 2a^3ce - 12bce + 8c^2e \\
3a^5c - 18a^2bc + 12a^2c^2 \\
\hline
3a^5c - 18a^2bc + 12a^2c^2 + 2a^3ce - 12bce + 8c^2e + 4a^3df - 24bdf + 16cdf
\end{array}
$$

Rearranging in descending powers of a,

$$3a^5c + 2a^3ce + 4a^3df - 18a^2bc + 12a^2c^2 - 12bce - 24bdf + 8c^2e + 16cdf$$

Division of Monomials

Division is the inverse of multiplication. Thus, since $3 \times 2a = 6a$, therefore $6a \div 3 = 2a$. Similarly, since $-6 \times 2a = -12a$, then $-12a \div -6 = 2a$. Further, since $-6 \times -2a = 12a$, then $12a \div -6 = -2a$. From these examples comes directly the first part of the rule for dividing monomials: to divide a term consisting of numbers and letters, that is, a term consisting of letters with a numerical coefficient, by a number, divide the coefficient by the number, and apply the rule of signs. For example, $12a^2b \div -3 = -4a^2b$. This operation may also be done by factoring, that is, by separating the term to be divided (the dividend) into parts which give it upon multiplication. Thus, $12a^2b \div 3 = \dfrac{12a^2b}{3} = \dfrac{3 \times 4 \times a^2b}{3} = \dfrac{\cancel{3} \times 4 \times a^2b}{\cancel{3}} = 4a^2b$. The process used here is the cancellation of common factors from dividend and divisor. While this operation is not necessary in dividing the coefficient 12 by 3, it illustrates a principle of dividing widely useful in algebra.

For example, to divide $2ab$ by a, write $\dfrac{2ab}{a} = \dfrac{2\cancel{a}b}{\cancel{a}} = 2b$, remembering that the term $2ab$ consists of the factors 2; a; and b. To divide $3a^2cy$ by $-3a^2$ write $\dfrac{3a^2cy}{-3a^2} = \dfrac{\cancel{3a^2}cy}{-\cancel{3a^2}} = -cy$, the quotient, $-cy$, being negative by the rule of signs. Check this result by multiplying, using the rule that multiplication of terms with like signs (here both negative) gives a positive product.

Now suppose that one or more of the factors of dividend and divisor consist of the same letter with different exponents. Consider for example $\dfrac{2a^4b}{2a^2}$. Since a^2 is $a \times a$, and a^4 is $a \times a \times a \times a$, then $\dfrac{a^4}{a^2} = a \times a$ or a^2. In other words, the rule of division is to subtract the exponents of the same letter, just as the rule of multiplication is to add them.

As another example, divide $12a^7b$ by $-3a^3$. Write $\dfrac{12a^7b}{-3a^3}$. Then since $7 - 3 = 4$, then $a^7 \div a^3 = a^4$, and $\dfrac{12a^7b}{-3a^3} = -4a^4b$.

The rule for the division of monomials can be stated more fully as follows:

To find the quotient of two monomials, divide numerical coefficients to find the coefficient of the quotient, and cancel literal factors (letters) common to both dividend and divisor.   If the same letter appears as a factor of both dividend and divisor with different exponents, take the difference of these exponents as the exponent of the same letter of the quotient.   If this difference is negative, then that letter remains in the denominator of the quotient, with a positive exponent equal to the difference.   If any letter is present in the divisor only, it remains in the quotient.

The foregoing rule is long, and for that reason one aspect of it was not explained prior to its statement.   That aspect concerns the situations in which factors in the divisor are not contained in the dividend, or are smaller in the dividend than in the divisor.

For example, to divide a^2bc by bd, one writes $\dfrac{a^2bc}{bd} = \dfrac{a^2\cancel{b}c}{\cancel{b}d} = \dfrac{a^2c}{d}$.   The $\dfrac{a^2c}{d}$ is the final form in which the desired division can be expressed.   It is a fraction, like the numerical fractions of arithmetic.   Again, to divide a^2bc by $12b$, write $\dfrac{a^2bc}{12b} = \dfrac{a^2\cancel{b}c}{12\cancel{b}} = \dfrac{a^2c}{12}$, which again is the final form in which the desired division can be expressed.   Finally to divide a^2bc by a^5b, write $\dfrac{a^2bc}{a^5b} = \dfrac{aabc}{aaaaab} = \dfrac{\cancel{aa}b c}{\cancel{aa}aaa\cancel{b}} = \dfrac{c}{aaa} = \dfrac{c}{a^3}$; the final form of the desired division.   A further discussion of division by higher powers (exponents) of the same number or letter is given in Chapters 3 and 4.

Division of Polynomials

When division of polynomials is to be performed by short monomial divisors, the result can often be obtained by writing them as fractions and cancelling.   Thus, to divide $2ab + 3ac + ac^2$ by a, one can write

$$\frac{2ab + 3ac + ac^2}{a} = \frac{2\cancel{a}b + 3\cancel{a}c + \cancel{a}c^2}{\cancel{a}} = 2b + 3c + c^2.$$

As another example, to divide $2a^2b + 3axy + 6abd$ by $2ad$, write

$$\frac{2a^2b + 3axy + 6abd}{2ad} = \frac{2a^2b}{2ad} + \frac{3axy}{2ad} + \frac{6abd}{2ad}$$

$$= \frac{\cancel{2}a^{\cancel{2}}b}{\cancel{2}\cancel{a}d} + \frac{3\cancel{a}xy}{2\cancel{a}d} + \frac{^3\cancel{6}\cancel{a}b\cancel{d}}{\cancel{2}\cancel{a}\cancel{d}} = \frac{ab}{d} + \frac{3xy}{2d} + 3b.$$

For more complex cases of division, including most instances of division of polynomials by polynomials, a more extended form, similar to long division in arithmetic, is necessary.   For example, to divide the polynomial $6a^4b^2 + 7a^3b^3 + 4a^2b^4 + ab^5$ by the polynomial $2ab^2 + b^3$, write these expressions in the following form, and proceed as in the steps explained below:

$$3a^3 + 2a^2b + ab^2$$
$$2ab^2 + b^3 \overline{)6a^4b^2 + 7a^3b^3 + 4a^2b^4 + ab^5}$$
$$\underline{6a^4b^2 + 3a^3b^3}$$
$$4a^3b^3 + 4a^2b^4$$
$$\underline{4a^3b^3 + 2a^2b^4}$$
$$2a^2b^4 + ab^5$$
$$\underline{2a^2b^4 + ab^5}$$

(1) Divide the first term of the dividend ($6a^4b^2$) by the first term of the divisor ($2ab^2$) and write the result ($3a^3$) as the first term of the required quotient.

(2) Multiply the divisor ($2ab^2 + b^3$) by the quotient just obtained ($3a^3b$) and write the terms of their product ($6a^4b^2 + 3a^3b^3$) under the corresponding terms of the dividend.

(3) Subtract the terms just written from those above (obtaining $4a^3b^3$), and write after it enough terms remaining in the dividend to equal the number of terms in the divisor. (In this problem, bring down the term $4a^2b^4$ from the dividend, so the new "partial dividend" is $4a^3b^3 + 4a^2b^4$.)

(4) Divide the first term of this ($4a^3b^3$) by the first term of the divisor ($2ab^2$) and continue with steps (2), (3) and (4) as before.

(5) Repeat this process until there are no more terms in the dividend to bring down. If the last remainder is zero the division is complete and exact.

(6) If there is a remainder when there are no more terms in the dividend to bring down, write the divisor beneath it to form a fraction, and write this fraction as the last term of the quotient.

(7) All subtraction in the process is algebraic and in all division and multiplication the rules of signs apply.

As an example of division in which there is a remainder, consider the problem:

To divide $6a^4b^2 + 7a^3b^3 + 4a^2b^4 + 2ab^5$ by $2ab^2 + b^3$.

By following the steps given for the previous problem the resulting expressions are the same up to the last subtraction, where a difference appears:

$$3a^3 + 2a^2b + ab^2$$
$$2ab^2 + b^3 \overline{)6a^4b^2 + 7a^3b^3 + 4a^2b^4 + 2ab^5}$$
$$\underline{6a^4b^2 + 3a^3b^3}$$
$$4a^3b^3 + 4a^2b^4$$
$$\underline{4a^3b^3 + 2a^2b^4}$$
$$2a^2b^4 + 2ab^5$$
$$\underline{2a^2b^4 + \ ab^5}$$
$$ab^5$$

The remainder ab^5 is not divisible by $2ab^2 + b^3$, so this problem in division is said to leave a remainder, the fraction $ab^5/2ab^2 + b^3$. The result of the division is therefore;

$$3a^3 + 2a^2b + ab^2 + \frac{ab^5}{2ab^2 + b^3}.$$

The subject of algebraic fractions is treated in the next chapter.

Chapter 3

FACTORIZATION AND FRACTIONS

The operation of factoring in algebra is the same process as in arithmetic. In arithmetic the process is applied to numbers, and consists of finding other numbers which when multiplied yield a given number. Thus 3 and 4 are factors of 12, since $3 \times 4 = 12$. Arithmetic factoring was used in the previous chapter as a step in algebraic division.

As was also shown in the last chapter, algebraic factoring extends to literal numbers, and to expressions containing both figures and literal numbers, this process of separation into factors. Thus the expression $7ab^2c$ has the factors 7, a, b, b and c, since $7ab^2c$ is the product of those numbers. Again $a^2 + 2ab + b^2$ has the factors $(a + b)$ and $(a + b)$ since $(a + b) \times (a + b) = a^2 + 2ab + b^2$. That is, since an expression (no matter how it originates) is the product of its factors, factorization is the reverse of multiplication, that is, it is division. When one factor of an expression is known, another or others may be found by division. At this point, the methods of multiplication and division in Chapter 2 should be reviewed.

Monomial Factors of Polynomials

Inspection of polynomials frequently reveals the presence of monomial factors common to every term. Thus in the polynomial $ax^2 + abcxy + 6ay^2$, the monomial factor a is common to all terms of the polynomial. Therefore the latter can be factored into $a(x^2 + bcxy + 6y^2)$.

As another example, the polynomial $2ab - 10ac - 8a^2d - 2a$, has the common factor $2a$, so that it factors into $2a(b - 5c - 4ad - 1)$. It should also be noted that $-2a$ is also a factor of this polynomial, since the latter can be factored into $-2a$ and $(-b + 5c + 4ad + 1)$. Proof that these are factors of the original polynomial is obtained by multiplying them, observing the algebraic rule of signs ($+ \times +$ gives $+$; $+ \times -$ or $- \times +$ gives $-$; and $- \times -$ gives $+$).

Polynomials with Monomial Factors Common to Some Terms

As shown in the preceding paragraph, monomial factors common to each term of a polynomial are comparatively easy to find. In polynomials not having such factors or in the further factoring of polynomials from which the monomial factors have already been separated, the factoring operation is essentially a matter of repeated trial. One method of simplifying this search is to examine the polynomial expression to find and group together terms having common monomial factors. That is, even though there is no monomial factor common to *all* terms of the polynomial (as discussed in the previous paragraph), there may be monomial factors common to some of the terms.

Thus the polynomial

$$ax + 3bx + ay + 3by$$

permits its like terms to be grouped to give

$$ax + ay + 3bx + 3by,$$

from which it is apparent that the first two terms have the common monomial factor a, and the last two terms have the common monomial factor $3b$, so the polynomial can be written as

$$a(x + y) + 3b(x + y),$$

which can be further regrouped as $(a + 3b)(x + y)$, which is the factored form of the original polynomial, as can be checked by multiplying $(a + 3b)$ by $(x + y)$ to obtain the polynomial.

Another, and somewhat more complicated example of factoring by grouping of terms, is furnished by the polynomial

$$4x^2yz - 8b^2xz + abxy - 2ab^3 - 4c^2xy + 8b^2c^2.$$

By examining this polynomial closely, it is seen that the first two terms have the common monomial factor $4xz$, the third and fourth terms have the common monomial factor ab, and the last two terms have the common monomial factor $4c^2$. Then the polynomial can be rewritten as

$$4xz(xy - 2b^2) + ab(xy - 2b^2) - 4c^2(xy - 2b^2).$$

Since, after "factoring out" the monomial factors common to each. pair of terms, the other factor $(xy - 2b^2)$ is the same, therefore the polynomial can be factored into

$$(4xz + ab - 4c^2)(xy - 2b^2).$$

Note that in both this example and the preceding one, the "factoring out" (that is, division by) the monomial factor common to each group of terms gave the same other factor. This circumstance made possible the factor-

ing of the polynomial into two polynomials.   Now obviously not all polynomials have monomials that are common factors of their terms, and of
those, not all yield the same other factor.   However, there are other
polynomials which can be factored by using other methods.   To recognize
such other factorable polynomials, it is desirable to know certain common
types of products of multiplication of polynomials.   These are illustrated
by certain trinomials (that is, polynomials having three terms), which
are known to result from the same type of multiplication.

Trinomials

Consider the three trinomials that follow to determine their common
characteristics:

$$x^2 + 2xy + y^2$$
$$4x^2 + 12xy + 9y^2$$
$$4x^4 + 12x^2y^2 + 9y^4.$$

In each of these three trinomials the first and last terms are squares (that
is x^2 is the square of x, y^2 is the square of y, $4x^2$ is the square of $2x$, $9y^2$ is
the square of $3y$, $4x^4$ is the square of $2x^2$, and $9y^4$ is the square of $3y^2$).
Furthermore the middle term of each trinomial is twice the product of the
square roots of the first and last terms.   Thus $2xy$ is twice the product of
x and y, $12xy$ is twice the product of $2x$ and $3y$, and $12x^2y^2$ is twice the
product of $2x^2$ and $3y^2$.

Now, in all such cases the trinomial is a perfect square, that is, it is the
square of a binomial, as is seen by multiplication:

$x + y$	$2x + 3y$	$2x^2 + 3y^2$
$x + y$	$2x + 3y$	$2x^2 + 3y^2$
$x^2 + xy$	$4x + 6xy$	$4x^4 + 6x^2y^2$
$xy + y^2$	$6xy + 9y^2$	$6x^2y^2 + 9y^4$
$x^2 + 2xy + y^2$	$4x + 12xy + 9y^2$	$4x^4 + 12x^2y^2 + 9y^4$

Therefore the factoring operation is:

$$x^2 + 2xy + y^2 = (x + y)^2$$
$$4x^2 + 12xy + 9y^2 = (2x + 3y)^2$$
$$4x^4 + 12x^2y^2 + 9y^4 = (2x^2 + 3y^2)^2.$$

In the foregoing examples, the numbers were all positive, that is, the
perfect square was the square of a binomial sum.   However, by squaring
a binomial difference, it can be seen that certain characteristic trinomials
are obtained.

For example, multiply $(x - y)$ by $(x - y)$.

$$
\begin{array}{r}
x - y \\
x - y \\
\hline
x^2 - xy \\
- xy + y^2 \\
\hline
x^2 - 2xy + y^2
\end{array}
$$

The foregoing multiplication shows that the square of a binomial difference varies from the square of a binomial sum only in the sign of the second term. Therefore, just as

$$x^2 - 2xy + y^2 = (x - y)^2$$

so $$4x^2 - 12xy + y^2 = (2x - 3y)^2$$

and $$4x^4 - 12x^2y^2 + y^4 = (2x^2 - 3y^2)^2,$$

as can be shown by multiplying the factors.

Having considered the trinomials resulting from multiplying $(x + y)$ by itself, and $(x - y)$ by itself, now multiply $(x + y)$ by $(x - y)$ and $(2x^2 + 3y^2)$ by $(2x^2 - 3y^2)$

$$
\begin{array}{r}
x + y \\
x - y \\
\hline
x^2 + xy \\
- xy - y^2 \\
\hline
x^2 - y^2
\end{array}
\qquad
\begin{array}{r}
2x^2 + 3y^2 \\
2x^2 - 3y^2 \\
\hline
4x^4 + 6x^2y^2 \\
- 6x^2y^2 - 9y^2 \\
\hline
4x^4 - 9y^2
\end{array}
$$

The result in each case is the difference of two squares. (While this difference is not a trinomial term, it is included here because it follows in the logical development of this phase of factoring.)

Therefore, the difference of two squares is factorable into the product of two binomial terms, which are the sum and difference of their square roots.

$$x^2 - y^2 = (x + y)(x - y)$$

$$4x^4 - 9y^4 = (2x^2 + 3y^2)(2x^2 - 3y^2).$$

To return to the factoring of trinomials, obviously most trinomials are not perfect squares, and therefore cannot be factored by the methods given above. Therefore, it is fortunate that there is another method which applies to many other trinomials. To illustrate this method, multiply $(x + 5)$ by $(x + 4)$.

$$
\begin{array}{r}
x + 5 \\
x + 4 \\
\hline
x^2 + 5x \\
4x + 20 \\
\hline
x^2 + 9x + 20
\end{array}
$$

Since the trinomial $x^2 + 9x + 20$ is the product of $(x + 5)$ and $(x + 4)$, therefore those two terms are its factors. Now it is found on examination that the coefficient of x in the trinomial (i.e., 9) is the sum of the second terms in the factors (5 and 4), and the last term of the trinomial (i.e., 20) is the product of the second terms in the factors (5×4). Therefore the conclusion can be drawn that any trinomial of the form $x^2 + Mx + N$, where M and N do not contain x, and where M is the (algebraic) sum of two numbers whose product is N, that is, any trinomial which can be written in the form $x^2 + (a + b)x + ab$ is factorable, and its factors are $(x + a)$ and $(x + b)$.

As an example, consider the trinomial $x^2 + 11x + 30$. Is it factorable? To answer the question, consider the various pairs of numbers a and b whose total is eleven, beginning with 10 and 1, and continuing to 6 and 5. Do any two of them when multiplied give 30 as the product? By trying successively 10 and 1, 9 and 2, 8 and 3, 7 and 4, it is found that 6 and 5 have a sum of 11 and a product of 30. Therefore, in accordance with the rule, $x^2 + 11x + 30$ factors into $(x + 6)(x + 5)$, which can be confirmed by multiplication.

As another example, consider the trinomial $x^2 - 2x - 15$. Here, as before, if the expression is factorable, there must be two numbers a and b such that $a + b = -2$ and $ab = -15$. Since the product ab is negative, then a (or b) is negative, and since the sum is -2, the negative number is larger than the positive. Since -15 factors into -5 and $+3$, and the sum of -5 and $+3$ is -2, the trinomial

$$x^2 - 2x - 15 \text{ factors into } (x - 5)(x + 3).$$

A further extension of the number of trinomials factorable into products of binomials can be made by considering trinomials in which x^2 has a coefficient, that is, trinomials of the general form $Kx^2 + Mx + N$.

To approach this case of factoring, multiply two binomials of the general form $(ax + c)$ and $(bx + d)$,

$$
\begin{array}{l}
ax + c \\
\underline{bx + d} \\
abx^2 + bcx \\
 \underline{adx + cd} \\
abx^2 + (ad + bc)x + cd
\end{array}
$$

To explain the next step, it is desirable to have convenient words for describing the various products of a, b, c and d. Words often used for this purpose are "end product" and "cross product." That is, ab and cd are end products, since a and b, and c and d are at the same "end" of their respective binomials, while ad and bc are cross products. The rule for factoring a trinomial of the form $Kx^2 + Mx + N$ is that it may be factored if M (the coefficient of x) is the sum of two numbers such that they are the cross products of two pairs of numbers whose end products are K and N. Thus in the above multiplication the coefficient of x, which is $(ad + bc)$ is the sum of two numbers, ad and bc, which are the cross products of $a(x) + c$ and $b(x) + d$, these expressions having the end products $ab(x^2)$ and cd.

The application of this method to the factoring of a trinomial is given in the following example:

$$\text{Factor } 12x^2 + 53x + 56.$$

Here $12 = 4 \times 3$, $56 = 7 \times 8$ and $53 = (4 \times 8) + (3 \times 7)$. Hence, the factors are $(4x + 7)$ and $(3x + 8)$. Using the method of grouping, the coefficient 53 must be separated into two numbers such that they are the cross products of numbers whose end products are 12 and 56. These two numbers are 32 and 21. The arrangement of the terms is, therefore,

$$12x^2 + 32x + 21x + 56$$

$$(12x^2 + 32x) + (21x + 56)$$

or, $\qquad 4x(3x + 8) + 7(3x + 8).$

Therefore, $\qquad 12x^2 + 53x + 56 = (3x + 8)(4x + 7).$

Sums and Differences of Two Cubes

The factors of the sum and difference of two cubes are also frequently used, and are therefore noted below.

$$a^3 + b^3 = (a + b)(a^2 - ab + b^2)$$
$$a^3 - b^3 = (a - b)(a^2 + ab + b^2)$$

The factors of these two expressions are given here primarily because they occur quite frequently in some computations. They serve another purpose in that they illustrate the use of division in finding factors. Since the factors of an expression are defined as those quantities which yield the expression when multiplied, then if one factor is known, another or others may be found by division. For example, if one remembers or suspects that $(a + b)$ is a factor of $(a^3 + b^3)$, then the other factor can be found by dividing it by $(a + b)$:

$$
\begin{array}{r}
a^2 - ab + b^2 \\
a + b \overline{)a^3 + b^3} \\
\underline{a^3 + a^2b} \\
-a^2b \\
\underline{-a^2b - ab^2} \\
ab^2 + b^3 \\
\underline{ab^2 + b^3} \\
\end{array}
$$

Therefore $(a^3 + b^3) = (a + b)(a^2 - ab + b^2)$

At this point it is well to emphasize that many algebraic expressions are not factorable. Moreover, many that are factorable are not easy to factor. For that reason, it is well to acquire familiarity with the results of algebraic multiplications arising in particular kinds of work, so that when the converse process, factoring, is necessary, the factors may be recalled.

Fractions

In algebra, as in arithmetic, a fraction is an indicated division. Thus in arithmetic, the fraction $\frac{1}{2}$ may be converted into a decimal by performing the indicated division $\frac{1.0}{2}$ to obtain .5.

Many of the terms used in arithmetical work with fractions are also used in algebra. The number or expression above the line, that is, the dividend in the indicated division, is called the numerator, while the number or expression below the line, the divisor in the indicated division, is called the denominator. The terms proper and improper fraction are also used both in arithmetic and algebra, but with different meanings. In arithmetic, a proper fraction has a smaller numerator than denominator, while an improper fraction has a numerator equal to or greater than its denominator. In algebra, a proper fraction has a numerator of lower degree than its denominator, while an improper fraction has a numerator of equal or higher degree than its denominator.

The degree of a polynomial is the highest power of its variable, or in expressions containing more than one variable, the degree of its independent or first variable (x in expressions involving x and y or x, y, and z; a in expressions involving a, b, c . . ., etc.) These definitions are given at the beginning of this section because they are used in describing some of the operations with fractions.

Reduction to Lowest Terms

In working with fractions, it is usually convenient to reduce them to lowest terms. This operation is performed by factoring both numerator and denominator, then cancelling the common factors. Thus in arithmetic, the fraction $\frac{48}{144}$ factors into $\frac{3 \times 2 \times 2 \times 2 \times 2}{3 \times 3 \times 2 \times 2 \times 2 \times 2}$, which by cancellation of the common factors 3 and 2^4 from both numerator and denominator, reduces to $\frac{1}{3}$. Similarly in algebra, the fraction $\frac{x-2}{x^2-4}$ factors to $\frac{x-2}{(x+2)(x-2)}$, which by cancellation of $x-2$ from both numerator and denominator, reduces to $\frac{1}{x+2}$.

As another example, the fraction

$$\frac{a^2 - b^2}{a^3 + b^3} \text{ factors to } \frac{(a + b)(a - b)}{(a + b)(a^2 - ab + b^2)},$$

which by cancellation of $(a + b)$ from both numerator and denominator, reduces to $\dfrac{a - b}{a^2 - ab + b^2}$.

Reduction of Improper Fractions

Note that the examples in the preceding section were proper fractions. When improper fractions are reduced, they result in integral or mixed expressions, the latter being expressions consisting of both integral expressions and fractions. For example, $\dfrac{x^2 - 4}{x - 2}$ is an improper fraction, since the degree of the numerator is not less than the degree of the denominator, but is, in fact, higher. The fraction factors into $\dfrac{(x + 2)(x - 2)}{(x - 2)}$ which, by cancellation of the factor $x - 2$, that is common to both numerator and denominator, yields the integral expression $x + 2$. Another example is the fraction $\dfrac{a^3 + b^3}{a + b}$, which factors into $\dfrac{(a + b)(a^2 - ab + b^2)}{(a + b)}$ and by cancellation reduces to $a^2 - ab + b^2$, an integral expression. Of course, not all fractions have denominators that are contained exactly in their numerators, and such fractions reduce into mixed expressions, consisting of both integral expressions and fractions. Consider the fraction $\dfrac{a^3 + a + 27}{a + 3}$. To reduce this fraction, it is necessary to perform the indicated division, as follows:

$$
\begin{array}{r}
a^2 - 3a + 10 - 3/a + 3 \\
a + 3 \overline{)a^3 + a + 27} \\
\underline{a^3 + 3a^2} \\
-3a^2 + a \\
\underline{-3a^2 - 9a} \\
10a + 27 \\
\underline{10a + 30} \\
-3
\end{array}
$$

This division yields a mixed expression, since its remainder -3 is not divisible by $a + 3$, and so the reduction of the fraction yields the mixed expression $a^2 - 3a + 10 - \dfrac{3}{a + 3}$.

Note that in the foregoing example, the division was continued until the last subtraction yielded no term in a or a power of a. However, this is a special case, as is shown by the following example:

To reduce the fraction $\dfrac{a^4 + a^3 + 2a^2 + 5a + 24}{a^2 + 3}$, perform the indicated division:

$$
\begin{array}{r}
a^2 + a - 1 + (2a + 27)/(a^2 + 3) \\
a^2 + 3 \overline{)a^4 + a^3 + 2a^2 + 5a + 24} \\
\underline{a^4 \qquad\quad + 3a^2} \\
a^3 - \ a^2 + 5a \\
\underline{a^3 \qquad\quad + 3a} \\
- \ a^2 + 2a + 24 \\
\underline{- \ a^2 \qquad\quad - 3} \\
2a + 27
\end{array}
$$

Thus the reduced fraction is $a^2 + a - 1 + \dfrac{2a + 27}{a^2 + 3}$.

Note that the numerator of the remainder contains an a-term. This results from the rule in such cases, which is to continue the division until the remainder is of lower degree than the denominator, as in this case, a in $2a + 27$ is of lower degree (first) than a^2 (second degree) in $a^2 + 3$.

To check the result of the reduction of a fraction, multiply the integral part of the mixed number by the denominator of the fraction, and add the numerator, which should give the numerator of the original fraction. For example, this method of checking the reduction of the foregoing fraction is:

$$
\begin{array}{r}
a^2 + a - 1 \\
a^2 + 3 \\
\hline
a^4 + a^3 - \ a^2 \\
3a^2 + 3a - \ 3 \\
\hline
a^4 + a^3 + 2a^2 + 3a - \ 3 \\
2a + 27 \\
\hline
a^4 + a^3 + 2a^2 + 5a + 24
\end{array}
$$

Changing a Mixed Expression, or Two or More Fractions, into a Single Fraction

Note that the operation just performed resulted, not only in checking the correctness of the reduction of a fraction to its lowest terms, but also in producing a method for carrying out the inverse process, that is, for changing a mixed expression into a single fraction. Since this inverse process is necessary in various operations with fractions, it merits more extended treatment. Therefore, to restate clearly the nature of the process as a basis for its further extension, consider another example:

Express the mixed number $b + 2 + \dfrac{3a}{4x + y}$ as a fraction. The process is, of course, the same as that used in the previous example. That is, the integral part of the mixed expression is multiplied by the denominator of the fraction, and to the product is added the numerator of the fraction. Thus

$$
\begin{array}{ll}
b + 2 & \text{(integral part of mixed number)} \\
\underline{4x + y} & \text{(denominator of fraction)} \\
4bx + 8x
\end{array}
$$

$$
\begin{array}{ll}
\underline{ + by + 2y} & \\
4bx + 8x + by + 2y & \text{(product)} \\
\underline{ + 3a} & \\
4bx + 8x + by + 2y + 3a & \text{(numerator of new fraction)}
\end{array}
$$

The resulting new fraction is therefore:

$$\frac{4bx + 8x + by + 2y + 3a}{4x + y},$$

which may also be written in the factored form:

$$\frac{(4b + 8)x + (b + 2)y + 3a}{4x + y}.$$

The foregoing method for changing mixed expressions into single fractions is readily applied to mixed expressions having two or more fractions. Three cases are possible:

Case I. To change into a single fraction an expression containing an integral part and two or more fractions having the *same denominator*. The rule is to multiply, as before, the integral part of the expression by that denominator, and add to the product (algebraically) the numerators of all the fractions. For example, express as a single fraction the expression $5 + \dfrac{3x}{a + 2} + \dfrac{2y}{a + 2}$. Then as before

$$
\begin{array}{ll}
5 & \text{(integral part of expression)} \\
\underline{a + 2} & \text{(common denominator of fractions)} \\
5a + 10 & \text{(product)} \\
 + 3x & \text{(numerator of first fraction)} \\
\underline{ + 2y} & \text{(numerator of second fraction)} \\
5a + 10 + 3x + 2y & \text{(numerator of new fraction)}
\end{array}
$$

Giving $\quad \dfrac{5a + 10 + 3x + 2y}{a + 2}\quad$ (the single fraction sought).

Case II. To express as a single fraction an expression containing two or more fractions having different denominators without common factors. The rule is to multiply the integral part of the expression by the denominators of all of the fractions, to multiply the numerator of each fraction by the denominators of the other fractions, and to add (algebraically) these various products to form the numerator of the single fraction sought.   Its denominator is the product of the denominators of the fractions.   For example, change to a single fraction the expression

$$5 + \frac{3x}{a+2} + \frac{2y}{a+3}$$

5	(integral part of expression)
$\underline{a+2}$	(denominator of first fraction)
$5a + 10$	(product)
$\underline{a+3}$	(denominator of second fraction)
$5a^2 + 10a$	
$\underline{15a + 30}$	
$5a^2 + 25a + 30$	(final product from integral part of expression)
$3x$	(numerator of first fraction)
$\underline{a+3}$	(denominator of second fraction)
$3ax + 9x$	(product from numerator of first fraction)
$2y$	(numerator of second fraction)
$\underline{a+2}$	(denominator of first fraction)
$2ay + 4y$	(product from numerator of second fraction)

Then $5a^2 + 25a + 30 + 3ax + 9x + 2ay + 4y$ is the numerator of the new single fraction sought.

While

$a+2$	(denominator of first fraction)
$\underline{a+3}$	(denominator of second fraction)
$a^2 + 2a$	
$\underline{3a + 6}$	
$a^2 + 5a + 6$	(product from denominators of fractions)

Therefore $a^2 + 5a + 6$ is the denominator of the new single fraction sought. Therefore the single fraction sought is

$$\frac{5a^2 + 25a + 30 + 3ax + 9x + 2ay + 4y}{a^2 + 5a + 6},$$

which may also be written in the partially factored form and conventional order as

$$\frac{(3a + 9)x + (2a + 4)y + 5(a + 2)(a + 3)}{(a + 2)(a + 3)},$$

Case III. To express as a single fraction an expression containing two or more fractions having different denominators with common factors. The rule is to form a denominator for the new single fraction which is the least common denominator of the denominators of all the fractions.   Then the integral part of the mixed expression is multiplied by the new denominator, and to that product is added the product of the numerator of each fraction by the factors in the new denominator which are not present in the denominator of that fraction. For example, express as a single fraction

$$5 + \frac{3}{2a + 2b} + \frac{4}{a^2 - b^2};$$

after factoring, this expression becomes

$$5 + \frac{3}{2(a + b)} + \frac{4}{(a + b)(a - b)}.$$

The least common denominator of $2(a + b)$ and $(a + b)(a - b)$ is $2(a + b)(a - b)$, which is, therefore, the denominator of the new fraction.

Then
5	(integral part of expression)
$2(a + b)(a - b)$	(denominator of new single fraction)
$\overline{10(a + b)(a - b)}$	(product from integral part of expression)
3	(numerator of first fraction)
$a - b$	(factor(s) in new denominator not present in denominator of first fraction)
$\overline{3a - 3b}$	(product from numerator of first fraction)
4	(numerator of second fraction)
2	(factor(s) in new denominator not present in denominator of second fraction)
$\overline{8}$	(product from numerator of second fraction)

Then $10(a + b)(a - b) + 3a - 3b + 8$ is the sum of the above products, which is the numerator of the new single fraction sought. Since its denominator was found to be $2(a + b)(a - b)$, the new single fraction sought is

$$\frac{10(a + b)(a - b) + 3a - 3b + 8}{2(a + b)(a - b)},$$

which may be written in the non-factorial form

$$\frac{10a^2 + 3a - 3b - 10b^2 + 8}{2a^2 - 2b^2}.$$

Addition and Subtraction of Fractions

By reviewing the last three examples of changing mixed expressions into single fractions, they can be seen to involve addition of fractions. As another example of addition of fractions, consider the following:

$$\frac{5}{2(a + b)} + \frac{3}{a^2 - b^2}.$$

Here the denominator of the second fraction factors to give $(a + b)(a - b)$, while the denominator of the first fraction is $2(a + b)$, so that the denominator of the new single fraction is $2(a + b)(a - b)$ and the contributions to its numerator are

5	(numerator of first fraction)
$a - b$	(factor(s) in new denominator not present in denominator of first fraction)
$\overline{5a - 5b}$	(product from numerator of first fraction)
3	(numerator of second fraction)
2	(factor(s) in new denominator not present in denominator of second fraction)
$\overline{6}$	(product from numerator of second fraction)

Then	$(5a - 5b)$	$+$	6	is the numerator
	Product from numerator of first fraction	Sign of fraction	Product from numerator of second fraction	of the new single fraction sought.

This numerator is therefore $5a - 5b + 6$.

Since the denominator of the new single fraction sought is $2(a + b)(a - b)$ the result of the addition of the two fractions is

$$\frac{5a + 5b + 6}{2(a + b)(a - b)}$$

or,

$$\frac{5a + 5b + 6}{2(a^2 - b^2)}.$$

The practice of labelling every step in the addition of fractions is of advantage not only for demonstrating the method, but also for avoiding error in applying the rule of signs in algebraic subtraction.

Consider the subtraction,

$$\frac{4}{a} - \frac{6a}{a + 2} - \frac{5}{a^2 - 4}.$$

Since $a^2 - 4$ factors to $(a + 2)(a - 2)$ the least common denominator of the denominators of the three fractions is $a(a + 2)(a - 2)$. Therefore this is the denominator of the new single fraction sought. Its numerator is found by the usual steps,

4	(numerator of first fraction)
$(a + 2)(a - 2)$	(factors in new denominator not present in denominator of first fraction)
$\overline{4(a + 2)(a - 2) = 4a^2 - 16}$	(product from numerator of first fraction)

$6a$ (numerator of second fraction)

$a(a - 2)$ (factors in new denominator not present in denominator of second fraction)

$\overline{6a^2(a - 2)} = 6a^3 - 12a^2$ (product from numerator of second fraction)

5 (numerator of third fraction)

a (factor(s) in new denominator not present in denominator of third fraction)

$\overline{5a}$ (product from numerator of third fraction)

$(4a^2 - 16)$	$-$	$(6a^3 - 12a^2)$	$-$	$(5a)$
Product from numerator of first fraction	Sign of fraction	Product from numerator of second fraction	Sign of fraction	Product from numerator of third fraction

Thus the numerator is $4a^2 - 16 - 6a^3 + 12a^2 - 5a$ (Note that by the rule of signs the sign of the $12a^2$ term is plus).

Then, rearranging in order of descending powers of a, the numerator becomes $-6a^3 + 16a^2 - 5a - 16$.

Since the denominator was $a(a + 2)(a - 2) = a^3 - 4a$, the result of the subtraction of the fractions is $\dfrac{-6a^3 + 16a^2 - 5a - 16}{a^3 - 4a}$.

Multiplication of Fractions

To multiply a fraction by an integral expression, simply multiply the numerator of the fraction by the integral expression, the denominator being unchanged unless it has factors in common with the integral expression, in which case cancellation is performed.

For example

$$2 \times \frac{a + 1}{a - 2} = \frac{2(a + 1)}{a - 2} = \frac{2a + 2}{a - 2}.$$

Another example is

$$(a + b) \times \frac{a + 1}{a - 2} = \frac{(a + b)(a + 1)}{a - 2} = \frac{a^2 + a + ab + b}{a - 2}.$$

An example in which cancellation results is

$$(a^2 - b^2) \times \frac{a^3 + ab - b}{4(a + b)} = \frac{(a + b)(a - b)(a^3 + ab - b)}{4(a + b)}$$

$$= \frac{(a - b)(a^3 + ab - b)}{4} = \frac{a^4 - a^3b + a^2b - ab - ab^2 + b^2}{4}.$$

To multiply a fraction by a fraction, multiply the numerators, taking their product as the new numerator; and multiply the denominators, taking their product as the new denominator.

For example, to multiply $\dfrac{a + 4}{a - 6} \times \dfrac{a^2 - a + 4}{3a}$

$$\begin{array}{ll}
a + 4 & \text{(numerator of first fraction)} \\
\underline{a^2 - a + 4} & \text{(numerator of second fraction)} \\
a^3 + 4a^2 & \\
\quad - \ a^2 - 4a & \\
\qquad\quad \underline{4a + 16} & \\
a^3 + 3a^2 \qquad + 16 & \text{(numerator of resulting fraction)} \\
\end{array}$$

$$\begin{array}{ll}
a - 6 & \text{(denominator of first fraction)} \\
\underline{3a} & \text{(denominator of second fraction)} \\
3a^2 - 18a & \text{(denominator of resulting fraction)} \\
\end{array}$$

The resulting fraction is therefore

$$\frac{a^3 + 3a^2 + 16}{3a^2 - 18a}$$

In multiplication of fractions by fractions, as in multiplication of fractions by integral expressions, cancellation is done wherever possible.

For example, in the multiplication, $\dfrac{a^3 + b^3}{12a} \times \dfrac{3a + 3b}{a^2 + 2ab + b^2}$,

factoring shortens the work considerably,

for, $\qquad\qquad a^3 + b^3 = (a + b)(a^2 - ab + b^2)$

and $\qquad\qquad 3a + 3b = 3(a + b)$

and $\qquad\qquad a^2 + 2ab + b^2 = (a + b)^2$

Therefore

$$\frac{(a^3 + b^3)(3a + 3b)}{(12a)(a^2 + 2ab + b^2)} = \frac{(a + b)(a^2 - ab + b^2)(3)(a + b)}{12a(a + b)^2}$$

which by cancellation gives

$$\frac{a^2 - ab + b^2}{4a}$$

Division by Fractions

In Chapter 1 of this book, the division by fractions in arithmetic was shown to be identical with multiplication by the reciprocal of the fraction. There it was shown that $6 \div \frac{2}{3} = 6 \times \frac{3}{2} = \frac{18}{2} = 9$. The same process applies, of course, to algebraic numbers, where the rule for division by fractions is to invert the divisor fraction and multiply.

For example, to find $2a + b \div \dfrac{a^2}{a - b}$ simply invert the $\dfrac{a^2}{a - b} \Big($ thus obtaining $\dfrac{a - b}{a^2} \Big)$ and multiply:

$$(2a + b) \times \frac{a - b}{a^2} = \frac{(2a + b)(a - b)}{a^2} = \frac{2a^2 - ab - b^2}{a^2}.$$

As another example

$$\frac{1}{a} \div \frac{a^2 + b^2}{a + 3a^2} = \frac{1}{a} \times \frac{a(1 + 3a)}{a^2 + b^2} = \frac{1 + 3a}{a^2 + b^2}.$$

Chapter 4

EXPONENTS: POWERS AND ROOTS

The discussion in this chapter of exponents proceeds from the introductory treatment of positive whole number values and extends to various other values, including fractional and negative exponents. The need for this comprehensive treatment is apparent at once from the use of exponential expressions in the calculations of compound interest and present value which extend into the business mathematics of insurance, securities, amortization, depreciation and virtually all applications involving the use of money, especially for other than the shorter periods of time.

Positive Integral Exponents

In the previous chapter, exponents were introduced in terms of repeated multiplication. Thus, in the expression 3^2, the exponent 2 shows that the number 3 is to be multiplied by itself 2 times. That is

$3^2 = 3 \times 3 = 9$.   Similarly,
$3^3 = 3 \times 3 \times 3 = 27$
$3^4 = 3 \times 3 \times 3 \times 3 = 81$
$3^5 = 3 \times 3 \times 3 \times 3 \times 3 = 243$
$\vdots \qquad \vdots \qquad \vdots$
$3^m = 3 \times 3 \times 3 \ldots \ldots m$ times, where m is any positive integral number.

Now, exponents are used in the same way with the literal numbers of algebra. Thus,

$a^2 = a \times a$
$a^3 = a \times a \times a$
$a^4 = a \times a \times a \times a$
$a^5 = a \times a \times a \times a \times a$
$a^m = a \times a \times a \ldots m$ times, where m is any positive integral number.

The common algebraic term for a number or expression together with an

56

exponent is a "power." Thus 3^2 is the second power of 3, or 3 to the second power; a^5 is a to the fifth power; 3^m is 3 to the mth power.

It was also shown in the previous chapter that in multiplying a number which has an exponent, by the same number which also has an exponent, the method is to add the exponents.

$$(3^2) \times (3^3) = (3 \times 3) \times (3 \times 3 \times 3) = (9) \times (27) = 243$$

or $\quad (3^2) \times (3^3) = (3^5) = (3 \times 3 \times 3 \times 3 \times 3) = 243.$

In the same way, $a^2 \times a^3 = a^5$ or (using the dot as a multiplication sign in keeping with common practice), $a^2 \cdot a^3 = a^5$, or remembering that in algebra two quantities written together without any sign between are understood to be multiplied, $a^2 a^3 = a^5$.

This rule of multiplication (of powers of the same number or expression) by addition of exponents can be generalized to the form

$$a^m \times a^n = a^{m+n}, \quad \text{or} \quad a^m \cdot a^n = a^{m+n}, \quad \text{or} \quad a^m a^n = a^{m+n} \qquad (4\text{-}1)$$

One point to be remembered is represented by the multiplication $a + a^4$. In making this multiplication, remember that when no exponent is written, 1 is understood,

so $\qquad\qquad\qquad a \times a^4 = a^{1+4} = a^5.$

It was also pointed out in the previous chapter that just as multiplication (of the same number or letter) is carried out by *addition* of exponents, so *division* is performed by *subtraction* of exponents. Thus $a^5 \div a^3 = a^{5-3} = a^2$. To fix this rule in mind, write the division in the factorial form,

$$\frac{a^5}{a^3} = \frac{a \times a \times a \times a \times a}{a \times a \times a}, \quad \text{and cancel,}$$

$\dfrac{\cancel{a} \times \cancel{a} \times \cancel{a} \times a \times a}{\cancel{a} \times \cancel{a} \times \cancel{a}}, \quad$ leaving $a \times a$ or a^2 as the result.

This result can be demonstrated with numbers, as was done for multiplication, by writing

$$3^5 \div 3^3 = (3 \times 3 \times 3 \times 3 \times 3) \div (3 \times 3 \times 3) = (3 \times 3) = 9$$
$$= 343 \qquad\qquad\qquad \div 27 \qquad\qquad\qquad\qquad = 9.$$

The rule for division of powers (of the same number or expression) can be written in the general form,

$$\frac{a^m}{a^n} = a^{m-n} \qquad (4\text{-}2)$$

where m and n are any numbers.

Therefore $\qquad\qquad a^6 \div a^4 = a^{6-4} = a^2$
$$a^7 \div a^3 = a^{7-3} = a^4$$
$$3^3 \div 3^2 = 3^{3-2} = 3.$$

Special names that are widely used are the term square for the second power, and the term cube for the third power. This usage arises from the fact that the area of a *square* is the second power of the length of its edge, and the volume of a *cube* is the third power of the length of its edge.

Positive Integral Exponents Applied to Negative Numbers

Since algebraic numbers may be negative as well as positive, the powers of negative numbers enter into algebra. They are evaluated in the same way as any other powers by repeated multiplication. Thus

$$(-3)^2 = (-3) \times (-3) = +9.$$
$$(-3)^3 = (-3) \times (-3) \times (-3) = -27.$$
$$(-3)^4 = (-3) \times (-3) \times (-3) \times (-3) = +81.$$
$$(-3)^5 = (-3) \times (-3) \times (-3) \times (-3) \times (-3) = -243.$$

It is to be noted that *odd* powers of negative numbers are negative, while *even* powers are positive. This rule will be found useful in later sections of this chapter that deal with the converse problem to that of finding powers—which is that of finding roots, that is, of answering the question: "Of what number is 3125 the fourth power?" or "Of what number is 729 the third power?"

Negative Integral Exponents

From Formula (4-2) above, negative exponents result whenever the exponent of a number in the divisor is greater than the exponent of that number in the dividend. Since the rule for dividing a^m by a^n is $\dfrac{a^m}{a^n} = a^{m-n}$, then if, for example, m is 3 and n is 5, then $a^m \div a^n = \dfrac{a^m}{a^n} = a^{m-n} = a^{3-5} = a^{-2}$. What is the meaning of a^{-2}? A way of answering this question is to expand the terms, that is, to write

$$\frac{a^3}{a^5} = \frac{a \times a \times a}{a \times a \times a \times a \times a} \quad \text{and then to cancel,}$$

$$\frac{a^3}{a^5} = \frac{\cancel{a} \times \cancel{a} \times \cancel{a}}{\cancel{a} \times \cancel{a} \times \cancel{a} \times a \times a}, = \frac{1}{a \times a} = \frac{1}{a^2}.$$

Therefore
$$a^{-2} = \frac{1}{a^2}.$$

Or in general form

$$a^{-n} = \frac{1}{a^n}, \quad \text{where } n \text{ is any number.} \tag{4-3}$$

This rule states that multiplying by a number to a negative power is the same as dividing by that number raised to the corresponding positive power.

Thus $b \times a^{-2} = b \div a^2 \left(\text{or } \dfrac{b}{a^2} \right)$; again $b \times 5^{-2} = b \div 5^2 \left(\text{or } \dfrac{b}{5^2} = \dfrac{b}{25} \right)$. Therefore, if any number or letter appears with a negative exponent as a factor in the numerator of a fraction, then it may be moved to the denominator of the fraction by changing the sign of the exponent to plus. Thus, $5ax^{-2} = \dfrac{5a}{x^{+2}}$; or as another example $16ab + 10ay^{-4} = 16ab + \dfrac{10a}{y^4}$.

A consequence of the foregoing statement is its converse, that is, if the denominator of a fraction contains a factor with a negative exponent, the factor may be shifted to the numerator by changing the sign of the exponent to plus. Thus $\dfrac{b}{ca^{-2}} = \dfrac{a^2b}{c}$, or as another example $\dfrac{1}{x^{-3}} = x^3$.

A general statement for both positive and negative exponents is that any factor may be changed from numerator to denominator or *vice versa* by changing the sign of its exponent.

Zero Exponents

What is the meaning of a zero exponent? In other words, what is the value of a quantity which has an exponent of zero? The answer to this question follows directly from the relation expressed in Formula (4-2) for division of numbers with exponents that was given earlier in this chapter, which was

$$\frac{a^m}{a^n} = a^{m-n}$$

Now let $m = n$. For example let $a^m = 5^3$, and $a^n = 5^3$.

Then
$$\frac{a^m}{a^n} = \frac{5^3}{5^3} = \frac{125}{125} = 1.$$

But
$$\frac{a^m}{a^n} = a^{m-n} = 5^{3-3} = 5^0.$$

Therefore
$$5^0 = 1.$$

As another example, let $a^m = 4^2$ and $a^n = 4^2$.

Then
$$\frac{a^m}{a^n} = \frac{4^2}{4^2} = \frac{16}{16} = 1.$$

But
$$\frac{a^m}{a^n} = a^{m-n} = 4^{2-2} = 4^0.$$

Therefore
$$4^0 = 1.$$

From these two examples, the general rule can be induced that $a^0 = 1$, where a is any number or expression. In strict algebraic logic, this equality $a^0 = 1$ is the definition of zero power, but the above demonstration fixes it effectively in mind.

Powers of Powers

Up to this point, positive and negative exponents have been discussed only as applied to integral or literal numbers, such as to 3, 5, a or x, giving 3^2, 5^4, a^3, x^5, etc.; although the statement has been made that the zero power of any number or expression has the value of one.

To evaluate expressions containing exponents of numbers which already have exponents (that is, which are powers) consider the expression $(a^2)^3$. What is the value of this expression? It is easily found by "multiplying out," as was done in previous problems involving exponents. That is $(a^3)^2 = a^3 \times a^3$, and by Formula (4-1), $a^m \times a^n = a^{m+n}$.

Here m and n are both 3, so $a^3 \times a^3 = a^{3+3} = a^6$.

Therefore $$(a^3)^2 = a^6.$$

As another example, take $(a^5)^2$ which expands to $a^5 \times a^5 = a^{10}$.

This rule for evaluating powers of powers (of the same number or expression) by multiplication of exponents can be generalized to the form

$$(a^m)^n = a^{m \times n} = a^{mn} \qquad (4\text{-}4)$$

Powers of Products

To find the method of evaluating the power of a product, determine the value of $(ab)^2$. By definition of a power,

$$(ab)^2 = ab \times ab = a^2b^2.$$

As another example, determine the value of $(abc)^3$. By definition of a power,

$$(abc)^3 = abc \times abc \times abc = a^3b^3c^3.$$

The rule can be expressed in the general formula

$$(abc \ldots m)^n = a^n b^n c^n \ldots m^n, \qquad (4\text{-}5)$$

where m and n are any numbers and the general rule can be stated as: the power of a product is equal to the product of the corresponding powers of the factors of the product.

The above rule and formula can readily be extended to cover the power of a product of two or more powers, such as $(a^m b^n)^p$.

For by Formula (4-4),

$$(a^m)^p = a^{mp}, \quad \text{and} \quad (b^n)^p = b^{np}.$$

Therefore, $$(a^m b^n)^p = (a^{mp})(b^{np}) = a^{mp}b^{np}. \qquad (4\text{-}6)$$

Powers of Simple Fractions

A simple fraction may be defined as $\dfrac{a}{b}$, where both a and b are whole numbers. Then in accordance with the fundamental definition of an exponent:

$$\left(\frac{a}{b}\right)^2 = \frac{a}{b} \times \frac{a}{b} = \frac{a^2}{b^2}$$

and $\quad \left(\frac{a}{b}\right)^3 = \frac{a}{b} \times \frac{a}{b} \times \frac{a}{b} = \frac{a^3}{b^3},\quad$ and in general $\quad \left(\frac{a}{b}\right)^m = \frac{a^m}{b^m},\quad$ (4-7)

where m is any number.

1 he general rule is that the power of a fraction is the quotient of the corresponding powers of the numerator and denominator of the fraction.

Powers of Sums (and Differences)

Take the simplest algebraic expression involving a sum, $(a + b)$, and find $(a + b)^2$. According to the definition of an exponent, $(a + b)^2 = (a + b) \times (a + b)$

or
$$\begin{array}{r} a + b \\ a + b \\ \hline a^2 + ab \\ ab + b^2 \\ \hline a^2 + 2ab + b^2 \end{array}$$

Similarly $\quad (a + b)^3 = (a + b) \times (a + b) \times (a + b)$

$$\begin{array}{r} a + b \\ a + b \\ \hline a^2 + ab \\ ab + b^2 \\ \hline a^2 + 2ab + b^2 \\ a + b \\ \hline a^3 + 2a^2b + ab^2 \\ a^2b + 2ab^2 + b^3 \\ \hline a^3 + 3a^2b + 3ab^2 + b^3 \end{array}$$

The calculation of the power of a sum of two terms has been generalized for $(a + b)^n$, where n is any number. The method of expanding this expression for any value of n is discussed fully, under the heading, "The Binomial Theorem." in Chapter 7.

The powers of a difference, like those of a sum, are found by repeated multiplication,

$$(a - b)^2 = (a - b) \times (a - b) =$$

$$\begin{array}{r} a - b \\ a - b \\ \hline a^2 - ab \\ - ab + b^2 \\ \hline a^2 - 2ab + b^2 \end{array}$$

$$(a - b)^3 = (a - b) \times (a - b) \times (a - b) =$$

$$
\begin{array}{l}
a - b \\
\underline{a - b} \\
a^2 - ab \\
\underline{\quad - ab + b^2} \\
a^2 - 2ab + b^2 \\
\underline{\qquad\qquad a - b} \\
a^3 - 2a^2b + ab^2 \\
\underline{\quad\; - a^2b + 2ab^2 - b^3} \\
a^3 - 3a^2b + 3ab^2 - b^3
\end{array}
$$

Up to this point, the discussion has dealt only with binomial (two-term) expressions. However, the same method of finding powers by repeated multiplication applies to polynomials of any number of terms. Thus, find the value of $(3a - 2b + c^3 - 4d)^2$

$$
\begin{array}{l}
3a - 2b + c^3 - 4d \\
\underline{3a - 2b + c^3 - 4d} \\
9a^2 - \;\;6ab + 3ac^3 - 12ad \\
\quad\;\; - \;\;6ab \qquad\qquad\qquad + 4b^2 - 2bc^3 + \;\;8bd \\
\qquad\qquad\qquad 3ac^3 \qquad\qquad\qquad - 2bc^3 \qquad\qquad + c^6 - 4c^3d \\
\underline{\qquad\qquad\qquad\quad - 12ad \qquad\qquad\qquad\qquad + \;\;8bd \qquad\quad - 4c^3d + 16d^2} \\
9a^2 - 12ab + 6ac^3 - 24ad + 4b^2 - 4bc^3 + 16bd + c^6 - 8c^3d + 16d^2
\end{array}
$$

Note that in the above multiplication each partial product contained terms not present in the previous partial product. Such new terms are placed, of course, in new columns to the right.

Fractional Exponents and Roots

Up to this point the discussion of exponents has been restricted to those having integral (whole number) values. The discussion of fractional exponents may be commenced logically by asking the question; What is the meaning of $a^{\frac{1}{2}}$?

The algebraic answer to that question is that $a^{\frac{1}{2}}$ is equal to a number b such that $b^2 = a$.

The number b is called the second *root* (or the square root) of the number a, and the operation of finding a root of a number is the inverse of raising a number to a power. That is, the second root of a is the number b of which a is the second power.

To illustrate roots numerically, the following examples are given:

$$
\begin{array}{ll}
4^{\frac{1}{2}} = 2 & \text{(because } 2^2 = 4) \\
9^{\frac{1}{2}} = 3 & \text{(because } 3^2 = 9) \\
16^{\frac{1}{2}} = 4 & \text{(because } 4^2 = 16) \\
25^{\frac{1}{2}} = 5 & \text{(because } 5^2 = 25)
\end{array}
$$

In evaluating roots, certain general questions must be answered. First and foremost is the matter of the sign, whether plus or minus. Consider $4^{\frac{1}{2}}$ in light of the statement made above that the second root of a number a is the number b of which a is the second power. Then any number which, when raised to the second power, gives 4, is a second root of four. Therefore -2 is a second root of 4 as well as $+2$, because $(-2)^2 = 4$ just as $(+2)^2$ does. For that reason the complete expression of the foregoing roots, requires the use of the sign $\pm$ (plus or minus), expressing the fact that the roots sought may be either $+$ or $-$. Therefore, the complete statement of the four roots given above is as follows:

$$4^{\frac{1}{2}} = \pm 2 \quad \text{(because } (+2)^2 \text{ or } (-2)^2 \text{ both give } +4)$$

$$9^{\frac{1}{2}} = \pm 3 \quad \text{(because } (+3)^2 \text{ or } (-3)^2 \text{ both give } +9)$$

$$16^{\frac{1}{2}} = \pm 4 \quad \text{(because } (+4)^2 \text{ or } (-4)^2 \text{ both give } +16)$$

$$25^{\frac{1}{2}} = \pm 5 \quad \text{(because } (+5)^2 \text{ or } (-5)^2 \text{ both give } +25)$$

Instead of using a fractional exponent, roots are often indicated by the radical sign, $\sqrt{}$, with the number or expression whose root is to be taken written under the "bar", and the index of the root written in the "hook." Thus the second root (square root) of 4, may be written either $4^{\frac{1}{2}}$ or $\sqrt[2]{4}$, while the third root of 4 is written either $4^{\frac{1}{3}}$ or $\sqrt[3]{4}$. Both usages appear in mathematics—in fact the radical sign $\sqrt{}$ is so common that its use without an index number in the hook is understood to mean the second root (square root).

Thus, $4^{\frac{1}{2}}$ may be written $\sqrt[2]{4}$ or simply $\sqrt{4}$.

$9^{\frac{1}{2}}$ may be written $\sqrt[2]{9}$ or simply $\sqrt{9}$.

$16^{\frac{1}{2}}$ may be written $\sqrt[2]{16}$ or simply $\sqrt{16}$.

$25^{\frac{1}{2}}$ may be written $\sqrt[2]{25}$ or simply $\sqrt{25}$.

However the indices of higher roots must be designated, that is, the third root (cube root) of 27 must be written either as $27^{\frac{1}{3}}$ or $\sqrt[3]{27}$, and the fourth root of 64 must be written either as $64^{\frac{1}{4}}$ or $\sqrt[4]{64}$.

Roots higher than second roots are defined by the same process that applies to second roots.

For example, the third root of a ($a^{\frac{1}{3}}$ or $\sqrt[3]{a}$) is equal to a number b such that $b^3 = a$. The fourth root of a ($a^{\frac{1}{4}}$ or $\sqrt[4]{a}$) is a number b such that $b^4 = a$, and so on to roots higher than the fourth.

It was shown earlier in this chapter that the product of two integral powers of the same number is the power of that number obtained by adding the integral exponents, or by Formula (4-1), $a^m \times a^n = a^{m+n}$. The same rule applies to fractional exponents, that is,

$$a^{\frac{1}{2}} \times a^{\frac{1}{2}} = a^{\frac{1}{2}+\frac{1}{2}} = a$$

$$a^{\frac{1}{2}} \times a^{\frac{1}{3}} = a^{\frac{1}{2}+\frac{1}{3}} = a^{\frac{5}{6}}$$

$$a^{\frac{1}{4}} \times a^{\frac{1}{5}} = a^{\frac{1}{4}+\frac{1}{5}} = a^{\frac{9}{20}}.$$

Formula (4-1) also applies to negative fractional values of m and n, or to any combinations of integral and fractional exponents, positive or negative.

Thus, $a^{-2} \times a^{\frac{1}{4}} = a^{\frac{1}{4}-2} = a^{-\frac{7}{4}} = \dfrac{1}{a^{\frac{7}{4}}}$

$$a^{-\frac{1}{4}} \times a^{-\frac{1}{4}} = a^{-\frac{1}{4}-\frac{1}{4}} = a^{-\frac{1}{2}} = \dfrac{1}{a^{\frac{1}{2}}}$$

Not only Formula (4-1) and the rule it expresses, but all the other formulas derived earlier in this chapter for the integral exponents also apply to the fractional exponents. Thus, Rule and Formula (4-2), for division of powers, which was $\dfrac{a^m}{a^n} = a^{m-n}$, applies with equal validity to fractional exponents (roots) or to combinations of integral and fractional exponents (roots). Thus $\dfrac{a^{\frac{1}{2}}}{a^{\frac{1}{3}}} = a^{\frac{1}{2}-\frac{1}{3}} = a^{\frac{1}{6}}$. Rule and Formula (4-3) for negative exponents applies to fractional as well as integral exponents, thus $a^{-\frac{1}{2}} = \dfrac{1}{a^{\frac{1}{2}}}$. Rule and Formula (4-4), for evaluating the powers of powers by multiplication of exponents—that is $(a^m)^n = a^{mn}$, applies with equal validity to fractional powers (roots) or to combinations of fractional and integral powers, as is shown by the following examples:

$$(a^{\frac{1}{2}})^2 = a^{\frac{1}{2}\times 2} = a$$

$$(a^{\frac{1}{2}})^3 = a^{\frac{1}{2}\times 3} = a^{\frac{3}{2}}$$

$$(a^{\frac{1}{4}})^2 = a^{\frac{1}{4}\times 2} = a^{\frac{1}{2}}$$

$$(a^{-\frac{1}{2}})^2 = a^{-\frac{1}{2}\times 2} = a^{-1} = \dfrac{1}{a}$$

$$(a^{-\frac{1}{3}})^2 = a^{-\frac{1}{3}\times 2} = a^{-\frac{2}{3}} = \dfrac{1}{a^{\frac{2}{3}}}$$

$$(a^{\frac{1}{3}})^{\frac{1}{2}} = a^{\frac{1}{3}\times\frac{1}{2}} = a^{\frac{1}{6}}$$

To carry along the use of radical signs, so that the reader becomes accustomed to their use interchangeably with fractional exponents, the foregoing relations are repeated in that form:

$$(\sqrt{a})^2 = a^{\frac{1}{2}\times 2} = a$$

$$(\sqrt{a})^3 = a^{\frac{1}{2}\times 3} = \sqrt{a^3} = a^{\frac{3}{2}}$$

$$(\sqrt[4]{a})^2 = a^{\frac{1}{4}\times 2} = \sqrt{a} = a^{\frac{1}{2}}$$

$$\left(\frac{1}{\sqrt{a}}\right)^2 = a^{-\frac{1}{2}\times 2} = a^{-1} = \frac{1}{a}$$

$$\left(\frac{1}{\sqrt[3]{a}}\right)^2 = a^{-\frac{1}{3}\times 2} = a^{-\frac{2}{3}} = \frac{1}{a^{\frac{2}{3}}} = \frac{1}{\sqrt[3]{a^2}}$$

$$(\sqrt[3]{a})^{\frac{1}{2}} = a^{\frac{1}{3}\times\frac{1}{2}} = a^{\frac{1}{6}} = \sqrt[6]{a}$$

Remember that where the radical sign has no index number in its hook, the square root, $\sqrt[2]{}$ is understood.

Multiplication and Division of Radicals

Expressions containing numbers under the radical sign are often encountered in algebra. Where their roots are easily extracted, e.g., $\sqrt{16} = \pm 4$, the expressions can be evaluated by extracting the roots and working with the results, remembering that the sign of the latter is $\pm$. Even square roots that are not integral numbers, such as $\sqrt{5}$ and $\sqrt{12}$, can be extracted by the arithmetical method explained later in this chapter, while any numerical roots whatever can be evaluated by the logarithmic method of Chapter 6. However, the work is often materially shortened by carrying out indicated arithmetical operations before extracting the roots. Where radicals are to be multiplied apply Rule and Formula (4-5) in the reverse order. That is, reverse Formula (4-5) from its form $(abc\ldots m)^n = a^n b^n c^n \ldots m^n$, to the form

$$a^n b^n c^n \ldots m^n = (abc\ldots m)^n \tag{4-8}$$

Thus $\qquad 3^{\frac{1}{2}} \times 12^{\frac{1}{2}} = (3\times 12)^{\frac{1}{2}} = (36)^{\frac{1}{2}} = \pm 6$

or in radical notation,

$$\sqrt{3} \times \sqrt{12} = \sqrt{3\times 12} = \sqrt{36} = \pm 6.$$

The rule would also apply to cube roots,

$$\sqrt[3]{3} \times \sqrt[3]{12} = \sqrt[3]{36}$$

or to any higher roots, $\sqrt[n]{3} \times \sqrt[n]{12} = \sqrt[n]{36}$, provided that the indices of all the roots are the same (as shown here by using n for both) but not to roots with different indices. Thus $\sqrt[3]{3} \times \sqrt[4]{12}$ cannot be combined in this way.

To derive a formula for division of radicals, write the above Formula (4-8) for only two terms:

$$a^n b^n = (ab)^n$$

Substituting $\dfrac{1}{c}$ for b,

$$a^n \left(\frac{1}{c}\right)^n = \left(\frac{a}{c}\right)^n$$

or $$\frac{a^n}{c^n} = \left(\frac{a}{c}\right)^n \tag{4-9}$$

Thus $$\frac{\sqrt{99}}{\sqrt{11}} = \sqrt{\frac{99}{11}} = \sqrt{9} = \pm 3$$

and $$\frac{\sqrt[3]{88}}{\sqrt[3]{11}} = \sqrt[3]{\frac{88}{11}} = \sqrt[3]{8} = 2$$

and $$\frac{\sqrt[4]{128}}{\sqrt[4]{2}} = \sqrt[4]{\frac{128}{2}} = \sqrt[4]{64} = \pm\sqrt{8}.$$

Note that by performing the divisions or multiplications under the radical sign, that is, on terms having the same radical indices, the quotients or products obtained often have integral roots, so that their values are obtainable on inspection.

Reduction of Radicals

Another method of simplifying computations with radicals is the process of reduction, which is one of factoring. This method is particularly useful in handling series of radicals which are not perfect squares, but which can be expressed in terms of a single number under the radical sign.

Thus, to find the sum $\sqrt{24} + \sqrt{54}$ directly would require the extraction of two square roots, since neither number is a perfect square. However by factoring the numbers under the radical signs, it is found that $\sqrt{24} = \sqrt{4 \times 6}$, and that $\sqrt{54} = \sqrt{9 \times 6}$. Since both terms contain the product of the same number, 6, by perfect squares, 4 and 9, they can then be reduced:

$$\sqrt{24} = \sqrt{4 \times 6} = \sqrt{2^2 \times 6} = 2\sqrt{6}$$

$$\sqrt{56} = \sqrt{9 \times 6} = \sqrt{3^2 \times 6} = 3\sqrt{6}$$

so that $$\sqrt{24} + \sqrt{56} = 2\sqrt{6} + 3\sqrt{6} = 5\sqrt{6},$$

which requires the extraction of only one square root, instead of two.

Another application of this method of reduction occurs in cases where larger numbers are the product of two perfect squares but, because of their size, this fact is not apparent on inspection. Factoring the numbers brings to light the fact that they are products of perfect squares, and thus shortens the work. For example, the number under the radical $\sqrt{10816}$ is divisible by 8 twice, and thus factors into 64 and 169:

$$\sqrt{10816} = \sqrt{64 \times 169} = \sqrt{8^2 \times 13^2} = \sqrt{8^2} \times \sqrt{13^2} = \pm 8 \times 13$$
$$= \pm 104$$

While the foregoing methods are useful only when the numbers concerned may be resolved, partly or entirely, into numbers which are perfect squares, they are capable of extension to higher roots, provided that in those cases the numbers contain perfect powers as multiples.

Thus, $\qquad\qquad \sqrt[3]{8} = 2$, since $2 \times 2 \times 2 = 8$

and $\qquad\qquad \sqrt[3]{27} = 3$, since $3 \times 3 \times 3 = 27$.

Therefore the addition $\sqrt[3]{88} + \sqrt[3]{297}$ is simplified by factoring as follows:

$$\sqrt[3]{88} + \sqrt[3]{297} = \sqrt[3]{8 \times 11} + \sqrt[3]{27 \times 11} = \sqrt[3]{2^3 \times 11} + \sqrt[3]{3^3 \times 11}$$
$$= 2\sqrt[3]{11} + 3\sqrt[3]{11} = 5\sqrt[3]{11}.$$

As a further example, simplify $4\sqrt[3]{81} + \sqrt[3]{375} - 5\sqrt[3]{24}$.

On inspection it is found that each of the three quantities under the radical sign is the product of the number three and a perfect cube. That is, it factors as,

$$4\sqrt[3]{27 \times 3} + \sqrt[3]{125 \times 3} - 5\sqrt[3]{8 \times 3}$$
$$= 4\sqrt[3]{3^3 \times 3} + \sqrt[3]{5^3 \times 3} - 5\sqrt[3]{2^3 \times 3}$$
$$= 4 \times 3\sqrt[3]{3} + 5\sqrt[3]{3} - 5 \times 2\sqrt[3]{3}$$
$$= 12\sqrt[3]{3} + 5\sqrt[3]{3} - 10\sqrt[3]{3} = 7\sqrt[3]{3}.$$

Imaginary Numbers

It is to be noted that most integral numbers do not have integral roots. Thus $\sqrt{4} = \pm 2$; $\sqrt{9} = \pm 3$; $\sqrt{16} = \pm 4$, so that all numbers between 1 and 16 except 4 and 9 do not have integral, or even rational square roots (that is, their square roots do not yield terminating decimals), so they are expressed to whatever number of decimal places is required by the accuracy of the problem. (The evaluation of square roots is discussed later in this chapter, and that of other roots in Chapter 6.)

Similarly $\sqrt[3]{8} = 2$; $\sqrt[3]{27} = 3$; $\sqrt[3]{64} = 4$, and all numbers between 1 and 64 except 8 and 27 have irrational cube roots.

Also $\sqrt[4]{16} = \pm 2$; $\sqrt[4]{81} = \pm 3$; $\sqrt[4]{256} = \pm 4$, and all numbers between 1 and 256 except 16 and 81 have irrational fourth roots.

However, while the irrational roots cannot be found exactly, they can be expressed to as many decimal places as the accuracy of the calculation requires. There are other indicated roots, however, (an indicated root is any expression under a radical sign) which cannot be expressed in figures at all. They must always be expressed numerically, at least in part, as indicated roots, and for that reason bear the name imaginary roots, which was given to them by early mathematicians. This name is unfortunate, because these roots can be expressed by other than numerical methods, as for example, by graphical methods, and they are used in various types of calculations.

A major class of imaginary numbers is that of the even roots of negative numbers. By recalling the definition of the square root of a as the number b such that $b^2 = a$, it can be seen that there can be no numerical expression of $\sqrt{-4}$. $2^2 = +4$ and $(-2)^2 = +4$, therefore there is no positive or negative arithmetical number which when multiplied by itself gives -4.

The same statement can be made about any even root beyond the second. Thus $\sqrt[4]{16} = \pm 2$, since $2^4 = 16$ and $(-2)^4 = 16$ but there is no expression in figures of the indicated root $\sqrt[4]{-16}$.

It is to be noted that odd roots of negative numbers do exist. Since

$$(-2) \times (-2) \times (-2) = -8, \quad \text{therefore} \quad \sqrt[3]{-8} = -2$$

Similarly

$$\sqrt[5]{-243} = -3; \quad \text{and} \quad \sqrt[7]{-128} = -2.$$

In working with indicated even roots of negative numbers, the methods of reduction of radicals, explained in the preceding section, are extremely useful. By those methods, the indicated square root of any negative number may be expressed as the product of the square root of a positive number and $\sqrt{-1}$.

Thus $\quad \sqrt{-36} = \sqrt{36 \times (-1)} = \sqrt{36} \times \sqrt{-1} = \pm 6\sqrt{-1}$

and $\quad \sqrt{-169} = \sqrt{169 \times (-1)} = \sqrt{169} \times \sqrt{-1} = \pm 13\sqrt{-1}$

$$\sqrt{-24} = \sqrt{24 \times (-1)} = \sqrt{4 \times 6 \times (-1)} = \pm 2\sqrt{6}\sqrt{-1}$$

the general expression being

$$\sqrt{-a} = \sqrt{a}\sqrt{-1}.$$

By this method, therefore, any imaginary number may be expressed as a multiple of the imaginary number $\sqrt{-1}$. The number $\sqrt{-1}$, is, therefore, called the imaginary unit. Since it is much used in higher mathematics a single symbol is chosen to represent it, according to the usual method of algebra. This symbol is the letter i, the initial letter of the word "imaginary," (sometimes j is used). The symbol i, defined as $i = \sqrt{-1}$, is subject to all the usual rules of algebra.

A number which is the algebraic sum of a real number and an imaginary number is called a complex number. Thus, $4 + \sqrt{-3}$, or $4 + \sqrt{3}\sqrt{-1}$, or $4 + \sqrt{3}i$ is a complex number. So are $5 - 3i$; $-272 + 33i$; $2x - 3yi$; $a + ib$, etc. The usual algebraic symbol for any complex number is $a + ib$, or $x + iy$, where a,b, and x,y are positive or negative real numbers and $i = \sqrt{-1}$. Thus a complex number is, in general, a binomial. All the rules for addition, subtraction, multiplication, division, factorization, involution (expansion to powers) and evolution (extraction of roots) apply to complex binomials as to any other binomial, due allowance being made for the properties of i, as is shown below.

Properties of the Imaginary Unit

Since by definition the imaginary unit is $i = \sqrt{-1}$, then $i^2 = (\sqrt{-1})^2 = -1$. Then $i^3 = i^2 \times i = (-1) \times i = -i$, and $i^4 = (i^2)^2 = (-1)^2 = +1$. As i is raised to successive higher powers, $i^5 = i^4 \times i = (+1) \times i = +i$, $i^6 = -1$, $i^7 = -i$, $i^8 = +1$, etc. Thus, the values of powers of i repeat themselves in groups of four. That is, every fourth successive power of i is the same. This appears more clearly on tabulating these results, as follows:

$$
\begin{array}{lll}
i = +i & i^5 = +i & \cdots \cdots \\
i^2 = -1 & i^6 = -1 & \cdots \cdots \quad (4\text{-}10) \\
i^3 = -i & i^7 = -i & \cdots \cdots \\
i^4 = +1 & i^8 = +1 & \cdots \cdots
\end{array}
$$

From this table of powers of i, it is seen that all even powers of i are ± 1 and all odd powers of i are $\pm i$. Therefore, if in any algebraic operation any number is multiplied or divided by any even power of i, the symbol i with its exponent may be omitted and the number preceded simply by a plus or a minus sign, and if multiplied or divided by an odd power of i, the exponent of i may be omitted and the proper sign placed before it. Similarly, if powers of i appear alone as terms of a polynomial, they may be replaced by 1 or i with the proper sign.

Consider next the fraction or number $\dfrac{1}{i}$. Now, in algebra, as in arithmetic, the multiplication of both numerator and denominator of a fraction by the same number does not change the value of the fraction. One can, therefore, write $\dfrac{1}{i} = \dfrac{1 \times i}{i \times i} = \dfrac{i}{i^2}$.

But, $i^2 = -1$ and hence $\dfrac{i}{i^2} = \dfrac{i}{-1} = -i.$

that is, $\dfrac{1}{i} = -i$ (4-11)

and also, $i = -\dfrac{1}{i}.$

These relations show that in any expression i may be shifted from denominator to numerator, and vice versa, simply by changing the sign of the expression, or, division by i is the same as multiplication by $-i$ and vice versa.

Addition and Subtraction of Complex Numbers

Let $a + ib$ and $c + id$ represent two complex numbers. The sum of the two is then

$$(a + ib) + (c + id) = a + c + ib + id,$$

or, taking out the common factor i in the last two terms,

$$(a + ib) + (c + id) = (a + c) + i(b + d) \qquad (4\text{-}12)$$

Similarly, $\quad (a + ib) - (c + id) = (a - c) + i(b - d)$

The sum (or difference) of two complex numbers is, therefore, another complex number whose real part is the sum (or difference) of the real parts of the two numbers and whose imaginary part is the sum (or difference) of their imaginary parts.

Since a complex number is composed of two parts which are always distinct, it cannot be zero unless both parts are separately equal to zero. This is an important property of complex numbers, which leads directly to still another important attribute of them.

Suppose two complex numbers are equal; then the difference between them is zero. That is, if $a + ib$ and $c + id$ are two complex numbers, and if

$$a + ib = c + id,$$

then $\quad (a + ib) - (c + id) = 0.$

But, according to Formula (4-12) this difference is $(a - c) + i(b - d).$

Therefore, $\quad (a - c) + i(b - d) = 0.$

This is a complex number whose real part is $a - c$ and whose imaginary part is $b - d$, and it is equal to zero. But for this complex number to be equal to zero its real and imaginary parts are each equal to zero, as seen above.

Therefore, $\quad a - c = 0, \quad \text{and} \quad b - d = 0.$

But, when the difference between two numbers is zero, they are equal.

Therefore, $a = c$, and $b = d$.

Now a,c and b,d are the real and imaginary parts of the two original equal complex numbers, and they are, respectively, equal. This gives, therefore, the important result that "If two complex numbers are equal, their real parts must be equal and their imaginary parts equal."

Extraction of Roots—Arithmetical Method

The arithmetical method of extraction of the roots of numbers may be described clearly by reference to the algebraic expansion of the power of a binomial. While the general treatment of this expansion, which is called the Binomial Theorem, is given in Chapter 7, its second and third power expressions are sufficient for the present purpose, since the arithmetical method of root extraction is used primarily for extracting square roots, and occasionally for extracting cube roots. Therefore, the former process is explained below, and the extraction of higher roots is performed by the use of logarithms, by the method explained in Chapter 6.

The general expression for the second power of a binomial is $(a + b)^2 = (a + b)(a + b) = a^2 + 2ab + b^2$. The last of these relationships is the basis of the arithmetic method of extracting square roots, as is shown by the following example:

Extract the square root of 716,638.

(1) The first step is to divide the number into groups of two digits, starting from the decimal point and moving to the left (for numbers greater than 1), resulting in the arrangement 71 66 38.

(2) The next step is to find by trial a number a such that a is the maximum number whose square is contained in the left-hand group of digits. (If the total number of digits is even, as in the present case, there are 2 digits in the left-hand group; if it is odd, there is only one digit.) In this example, a is 8, since $8^2 = 64$, which is contained in the first group of digits, and $9^2 = 81$, which is not.

$$\sqrt{71\ 66\ 38.} \quad \overline{(846.5} \quad \text{(Step 7)}$$

(Step 2)	$\underline{64}$
(Step 3)	$\overline{766}$
(Step 4)	$\underline{656}$
(Step 5)	11038
(Step 6)	$\underline{10116}$
(Step 8)	92200
(Step 9)	84625

(3) Write this figure 8 as the first figure of the desired result, subtract its square (64) from the first group of digits (71), and bring down to the remainder (7) the next group of digits (66), forming the partial dividend 766.

(4) Find a number b such that the expression $20\,ab + b^2$ has the maximum value that is contained in the partial dividend 766. Since a was found to be 8, b must be 4, for $20 \times 8 \times 4 + 4^2 = 656$, while $20 \times 8 \times 5 + 5^2 = 825$. Write 656 below 766 to be subtracted, and write the value of b (4) as the second figure of the desired result.

(5) Subtract 656 from 766, and bring down to that remainder the next group of digits (38) forming the partial dividend 11038.

(6) Find a number b such that the expression $20\,ab + b^2$ has the maximum value that is contained in the partial dividend 11038. *Note that a in this step is now 84.* Then b for this step is 6, since $20\,ab + b^2$ is here $20 \times 84 \times 6 + 6^2 = 10116$, while if b were 7, $20\,ab + b^2$ would be $20 \times 84 \times 7 + 7^2 = 11809$, which is not contained in the partial dividend 11038. Write 10116 below 11038, and write the value of b (6) as the third figure of the desired result.

(7) Place the decimal point after the third figure of the desired result, for in square root there is one significant figure in the result for every group of figures obtained by separation of the original number from right to left in groups of two digits (with one digit in the left-hand group if the total number of digits is odd).

(8) Note that since the last value of $2\,ob + b^2$ is not contained exactly in the last partial dividend, there is a remainder. The square root is therefore greater than 846, but less than 847. Its value can be found as exactly as required by bringing down zeros, in groups of two, for each decimal place desired in the final result. Thus for one decimal place, subtract 10116 from 11038, obtaining 922, and bring down 00, forming the partial dividend 92200.

(9) Now proceed as before, taking a as 846, and finding the maximum value of b that makes $20\,ab + b^2$ less than 92200. It is 5, for $20 \times 846 \times 5 + 5^2 = 84625$, which is contained in 92200, while $20 \times 846 \times 6 + 6^2 = 101569$, which is not.

Therefore the square root of 716,638 to one place of decimals is 846.5.

The foregoing presentation of the arithmetical method of computing square root has been expressed in terms of the binomial expansion $(a + b)^2 = a^2 + 2\,ab + b^2$, because that method can be extended to any root. For example, since $(a + b)^3 = a^3 + 3a^2b + 3ab^2 + b^3$, that formula can be made the basis of a similar method for extracting cube roots of numbers. The differences are that the digits in the original number are divided into groups of three instead of two as in the extraction of square roots, and that the formula for computing the digits after the first in the result is

300 a^2b + 30 ab^2 + b^3. In view, however, of the amount of arithmetical work in making this calculation, this arithmetical method is rarely used for cube roots, and never for higher roots. Instead the logarithmic method, which is fully explained in Chapter 6, is far preferable.

Since square roots occur quite frequently in mathematical work and cube roots are also encountered, Table 2 is included in this chapter. It gives the square roots and cube roots of the numbers from 1 to 999.

TABLE 2—SQUARE ROOTS AND CUBE ROOTS

Number	Square Root	Cube Root	Number	Square Root	Cube Root
1	1	1	50	7.07107	3.68403
2	1.41421	1.25992	51	7.14143	3.70843
3	1.73205	1.44225	52	7.21110	3.73251
4	2	1.58740	53	7.28011	3.75629
5	2.23607	1.70998	54	7.34847	3.77976
6	2.44949	1.81712	55	7.41620	3.80295
7	2.64575	1.91293	56	7.48331	3.82586
8	2.82843	2	57	7.54983	3.84852
9	3	2.08008	58	7.61577	3.87088
10	3.16228	2.15443	59	7.68115	3.89300
11	3.31662	2.22398	60	7.74597	3.91487
12	3.46410	2.28943	61	7.81025	3.93650
13	3.60555	2.35133	62	7.87401	3.95789
14	3.74166	2.41014	63	7.93725	3.97906
15	3.87298	2.46621	64	8	4
16	4	2.51984	65	8.06226	4.02073
17	4.12311	2.57128	66	8.12404	4.04124
18	4.24264	2.62074	67	8.18535	4.06155
19	4.35890	2.66840	68	8.24621	4.08166
20	4.47214	2.71442	69	8.30662	4.10157
21	4.58258	2.75892	70	8.36660	4.12129
22	4.69042	2.80204	71	8.42615	4.14082
23	4.79583	2.84387	72	8.48528	4.16017
24	4.89898	2.88450	73	8.54400	4.17934
25	5	2.92402	74	8.60233	4.19834
26	5.09902	2.96250	75	8.66025	4.21716
27	5.19615	3	76	8.71780	4.23582
28	5.29150	3.03659	77	8.77496	4.25432
29	5.38516	3.07232	78	8.83176	4.27266
30	5.47723	3.10723	79	8.88819	4.29084
31	5.56776	3.14138	80	8.94427	4.30887
32	5.65685	3.17480	81	9	4.32675
33	5.74456	3.20753	82	9.05539	4.34448
34	5.83095	3.23961	83	9.11043	4.36207
35	5.91608	3.27107	84	9.16515	4.37952
36	6	3.30193	85	9.21954	4.39683
37	6.08276	3.33222	86	9.27362	4.41400
38	6.16441	3.36198	87	9.32738	4.43105
39	6.24500	3.39121	88	9.38083	4.44797
40	6.32456	3.41995	89	9.43398	4.46475
41	6.40312	3.44822	90	9.48683	4.48140
42	6.48074	3.47603	91	9.53939	4.49794
43	6.55744	3.50340	92	9.59166	4.51436
44	6.63325	3.53035	93	9.64365	4.53065
45	6.70820	3.55689	94	9.69536	4.54684
46	6.78233	3.58305	95	9.74679	4.56290
47	6.85565	3.60883	96	9.79796	4.57886
48	6.92820	3.63424	97	9.84886	4.59470
49	7	3.65931	98	9.89949	4.61044

TABLE 2—SQUARE ROOTS AND CUBE ROOTS (Cont.)

Number	Square Root	Cube Root		Number	Square Root	Cube Root
99	9.94987	4.62607		148	12.16553	5.28957
100	10	4.64159		149	12.20656	5.30146
101	10.04988	4.65701		150	12.24745	5.31329
102	10.09950	4.67233		151	12.28821	5.32507
103	10.14889	4.68755		152	12.32883	5.33680
104	10.19804	4.70267		153	12.36932	5.34848
105	10.24695	4.71769		154	12.40967	5.36011
106	10.29563	4.73262		155	12.44990	5.37169
107	10.34408	4.74746		156	12.49000	5.38321
108	10.39230	4.76220		157	12.52996	5.39469
109	10.44031	4.77686		158	12.56981	5.40612
110	10.48809	4.79142		159	12.60952	5.41750
111	10.53565	4.80590		160	12.64911	5.42884
112	10.58301	4.82028		161	12.68858	5.44012
113	10.63015	4.83459		162	12.72792	5.45136
114	10.67708	4.84881		163	12.76715	5.46256
115	10.72381	4.86294		164	12.80625	5.47370
116	10.77033	4.87700		165	12.84523	5.48481
117	10.81665	4.89097		166	12.88410	5.49586
118	10.86278	4.90487		167	12.92285	5.50688
119	10.90871	4.91868		168	12.96148	5.51785
120	10.95445	4.93242		169	13	5.52877
121	11	4.94609		170	13.03840	5.53966
122	11.04536	4.95968		171	13.07670	5.55050
123	11.09054	4.97319		172	13.11488	5.56130
124	11.13553	4.98663		173	13.15295	5.57205
125	11.18034	5		174	13.19091	5.58277
126	11.22497	5.01330		175	13.22876	5.59344
127	11.26943	5.02653		176	13.26650	5.60408
128	11.31371	5.03968		177	13.30413	5.61467
129	11.35782	5.05277		178	13.34165	5.62523
130	11.40175	5.06580		179	13.37909	5.63574
131	11.44552	5.07875		180	13.41641	5.64622
132	11.48913	5.09164		181	13.45362	5.65665
133	11.53256	5.10447		182	13.49074	5.66705
134	11.57584	5.11723		183	13.52775	5.67741
135	11.61895	5.12993		184	13.56466	5.68773
136	11.66190	5.14256		185	13.60147	5.69802
137	11.70470	5.15514		186	13.63818	5.70827
138	11.74734	5.16765		187	13.67479	5.71848
139	11.78983	5.18010		188	13.71131	5.72865
140	11.83216	5.19249		189	13.74773	5.73879
141	11.87434	5.20483		190	13.78405	5.74890
142	11.91638	5.21710		191	13.82028	5.75897
143	11.95826	5.22932		192	13.85641	5.76900
144	12	5.24148		193	13.89244	5.77900
145	12.04159	5.25359		194	13.92839	5.78896
146	12.08305	5.26564		195	13.96424	5.79889
147	12.12436	5.27763		196	14	5.80879

TABLE 2—SQUARE ROOTS AND CUBE ROOTS (Cont.)

Number	Square Root	Cube Root	Number	Square Root	Cube Root
197	14.03567	5.81865	246	15.68439	6.26583
198	14.07125	5.82848	247	15.71623	6.27431
199	14.10674	5.83827	248	15.74802	6.28276
			249	15.77973	6.29119
200	14.14214	5.84804			
201	14.17745	5.85777	250	15.81139	6.29961
202	14.21267	5.86747	251	15.84298	6.30799
203	14.24781	5.87713	252	15.87451	6.31636
204	14.28286	5.88677	253	15.90597	6.32470
205	14.31782	5.89637	254	15.93738	6.33303
206	14.35270	5.90594	255	15.96872	6.34133
207	14.38749	5.91548	256	16	6.34960
208	14.42221	5.92499	257	16.03122	6.35786
209	14.45683	5.93447	258	16.06238	6.36610
			259	16.09348	6.37431
210	14.49138	5.94392			
211	14.52584	5.95334	260	16.12452	6.38250
212	14.56022	5.96273	261	16.15549	6.39068
213	14.59452	5.97209	262	16.18641	6.39883
214	14.62874	5.98142	263	16.21727	6.40696
215	14.66288	5.99073	264	16.24808	6.41507
216	14.69694	6	265	16.27882	6.42316
217	14.73092	6.00925	266	16.30951	6.43123
218	14.76482	6.01846	267	16.34013	6.43928
219	14.79865	6.02765	268	16.37071	6.44731
			269	16.40122	6.45531
220	14.83240	6.03681			
221	14.86607	6.04594	270	16.43168	6.46330
222	14.89966	6.05505	271	16.46208	6.47127
223	14.93318	6.06413	272	16.49242	6.47922
224	14.96663	6.07318	273	16.52271	6.48715
225	15	6.08220	274	16.55295	6.49507
226	15.03330	6.09120	275	16.58312	6.50296
227	15.06652	6.10017	276	16.61325	6.51083
228	15.09967	6.10911	277	16.64332	6.51868
229	15.13275	6.11803	278	16.67333	6.52652
			279	16.70329	6.53434
230	15.16575	6.12693			
231	15.19868	6.13579	280	16.73320	6.54213
232	15.23155	6.14463	281	16.76305	6.54991
233	15.26434	6.15345	282	16.79286	6.55767
234	15.29706	6.16224	283	16.82260	6.56541
235	15.32971	6.17101	284	16.85230	6.57314
236	15.36229	6.17975	285	16.88194	6.58084
237	15.39480	6.18846	286	16.91153	6.58853
238	15.42725	6.19715	287	16.94107	6.59620
239	15.45962	6.20582	288	16.97056	6.60385
			289	17	6.61149
240	15.49193	6.21447			
241	15.52417	6.22308	290	17.02939	6.61911
242	15.55635	6.23168	291	17.05872	6.62671
243	15.58846	6.24025	292	17.08801	6.63429
244	15.62050	6.24880	293	17.11724	6.64185
245	15.65248	6.25732	294	17.14643	6.64940

TABLE 2—SQUARE ROOTS AND CUBE ROOTS (Cont.)

Number	Square Root	Cube Root		Number	Square Root	Cube Root
295	17.17556	6.65693		344	18.54724	7.00680
296	17.20465	6.66444		345	18.57418	7.01358
297	17.23369	6.67194		346	18.60108	7.02035
298	17.26268	6.67942		347	18.62794	7.02711
299	17.29162	6.68688		348	18.65476	7.03385
				349	18.68154	7.04059
300	17.32051	6.69433				
301	17.34935	6.70176		350	18.70829	7.04730
302	17.37815	6.70917		351	18.73499	7.05400
303	17.40690	6.71657		352	18.76166	7.06070
304	17.43560	6.72395		353	18.78829	7.06738
305	17.46425	6.73132		354	18.81489	7.07404
306	17.49286	6.73866		355	18.84144	7.08070
307	17.52142	6.74600		356	18.86796	7.08734
308	17.54993	6.75331		357	18.89444	7.09397
309	17.57840	6.76061		358	18.92089	7.10059
				359	18.94730	7.10719
310	17.60682	6.76790				
311	17.63519	6.77517		360	18.97367	7.11379
312	17.66352	6.78242		361	19	7.12037
313	17.69181	6.78966		362	19.02630	7.12694
314	17.72005	6.79688		363	19.05256	7.13349
315	17.74824	6.80409		364	19.07878	7.14004
316	17.77639	6.81128		365	19.10497	7.14657
317	17.80449	6.81846		366	19.13113	7.15309
318	17.83255	6.82562		367	19.15724	7.15960
319	17.86057	6.83277		368	19.18333	7.16610
				369	19.20937	7.17258
320	17.88854	6.83990				
321	17.91647	6.84702		370	19.23538	7.17905
322	17.94436	6.85412		371	19.26136	7.18552
323	17.97220	6.86121		372	19.28720	7.19197
324	18	6.86829		373	19.31321	7.19841
325	18.02776	6.87534		374	19.33908	7.20483
326	18.05547	6.88239		375	19.36492	7.21125
327	18.08314	6.88942		376	19.39072	7.21765
328	18.11077	6.89643		377	19.41649	7.22405
329	18.13836	6.90344		378	19.44222	7.23043
				379	19.46792	7.23680
330	18.16590	6.91042				
331	18.19341	6.91740		380	19.49359	7.24316
332	18.22087	6.92436		381	19.51922	7.24950
333	18.24829	6.93131		382	19.54482	7.25584
334	18.27567	6.93823		383	19.57039	7.26217
335	18.30301	6.94515		384	19.59592	7.26848
336	18.33030	6.95205		385	19.62142	7.27479
337	18.35756	6.95894		386	19.64688	7.28108
338	18.38478	6.96582		387	19.67232	7.28736
339	18.41195	6.97268		388	19.69772	7.29363
				389	19.72308	7.29989
340	18.43909	6.97953				
341	18.46619	6.98637		390	19.74842	7.30614
342	18.49324	6.99319		391	19.77372	7.31238
343	18.52026	7		392	19.79899	7.31861

TABLE 2—SQUARE ROOTS AND CUBE ROOTS (Cont.)

Number	Square Root	Cube Root	Number	Square Root	Cube Root
393	19.82423	7.32483	442	21.02380	7.61741
394	19.84943	7.33104	443	21.04757	7.62315
395	19.87461	7.33723	444	21.07131	7.62888
396	19.89975	7.34342	445	21.09502	7.63461
397	19.92486	7.34960	446	21.11871	7.64032
398	19.94994	7.35576	447	21.14237	7.64603
399	19.97498	7.36192	448	21.16601	7.65172
			449	21.18962	7.65741
400	20	7.36806			
401	20.02498	7.37420	450	21.21320	7.66309
402	20.04994	7.38032	451	21.23676	7.66877
403	20.07486	7.38644	452	21.26029	7.67443
404	20.09975	7.39254	453	21.28380	7.68009
405	20.12461	7.39864	454	21.30728	7.68573
406	20.14944	7.40472	455	21.33073	7.69137
407	20.17424	7.41080	456	21.35416	7.69700
408	20.19901	7.41686	457	21.37756	7.70262
409	20.22375	7.42291	458	21.40093	7.70824
			459	21.42429	7.71384
410	20.24846	7.42896			
411	20.27313	7.43499	460	21.44761	7.71944
412	20.29778	7.44102	461	21.47091	7.72503
413	20.32240	7.44703	462	21.49419	7.73061
414	20.34699	7.45304	463	21.51743	7.73619
415	20.37155	7.45904	464	21.54066	7.74175
416	20.39608	7.46502	465	21.56386	7.74731
417	20.42058	7.47100	466	21.58703	7.75286
418	20.44505	7.47697	467	21.61018	7.75840
419	20.46949	7.48292	468	21.63331	7.76394
			469	21.65641	7.76946
420	20.49390	7.48887			
421	20.51828	7.49481	470	21.67948	7.77498
422	20.54264	7.50074	471	21.70253	7.78049
423	20.56696	7.50666	472	21.72556	7.78599
424	20.59126	7.51257	473	21.74856	7.79149
425	20.61553	7.51847	474	21.77154	7.79697
426	20.63977	7.52437	475	21.79449	7.80245
427	20.66398	7.53025	476	21.81742	7.80793
428	20.68816	7.53612	477	21.84033	7.81339
429	20.71232	7.54199	478	21.86321	7.81885
			479	21.88607	7.82429
430	20.73644	7.54784			
431	20.76054	7.55369	480	21.90890	7.82974
432	20.78461	7.55953	481	21.93171	7.83517
433	20.80865	7.56535	482	21.95450	7.84059
434	20.83267	7.57117	483	21.97726	7.84601
435	20.85665	7.57698	484	22	7.85142
436	20.88061	7.58279	485	22.02272	7.85683
437	20.90455	7.58858	486	22.04541	7.86222
438	20.92845	7.59436	487	22.06808	7.86761
439	20.95233	7.60014	488	22.09072	7.87299
			489	22.11334	7.87837
440	20.97618	7.60590			
441	21	7.61166	490	22.13594	7.88374

TABLE 2—SQUARE ROOTS AND CUBE ROOTS (Cont.)

Number	Square Root	Cube Root	Number	Square Root	Cube Root
491	22.15852	7.88909	540	23.23790	8.14325
492	22.18107	7.89445	541	23.25941	8.14828
493	22.20360	7.89979	542	23.28089	8.15329
494	22.22611	7.90513	543	23.30236	8.15831
495	22.24860	7.91046	544	23.32381	8.16331
496	22.27106	7.91578	545	23.34524	8.16831
497	22.29350	7.92110	546	23.36664	8.17330
498	22.31591	7.92641	547	23.38803	8.17829
499	22.33831	7.93171	548	23.40940	8.18327
			549	23.43075	8.18824
500	22.36068	7.93701			
501	22.38303	7.94229	550	23.45208	8.19321
502	22.40536	7.94757	551	23.47339	8.19818
503	22.42766	7.95285	552	23.49468	8.20313
504	22.44994	7.95811	553	23.51595	8.20808
505	22.47221	7.96337	554	23.53720	8.21303
506	22.49444	7.96863	555	23.55844	8.21797
507	22.51666	7.97387	556	23.57965	8.22290
508	22.53886	7.97911	557	23.60085	8.22783
509	22.56103	7.98434	558	23.62202	8.23275
			559	23.64318	8.23766
510	22.58318	7.98957			
511	22.60531	7.99479	560	23.66432	8.24257
512	22.62742	8	561	23.68544	8.24747
513	22.64950	8.00520	562	23.70654	8.25237
514	22.67157	8.01040	563	23.72762	8.25726
515	22.69361	8.01559	564	23.74868	8.26215
516	22.71563	8.02078	565	23.76973	8.26703
517	22.73763	8.02596	566	23.79075	8.27190
518	22.75961	8.03113	567	23.81176	8.27677
519	22.78157	8.03629	568	23.83275	8.28163
			569	23.85372	8.28649
520	22.80351	8.04145			
521	22.82542	8.04660	570	23.87467	8.29134
522	22.84732	8.05175	571	23.89561	8.29619
523	22.86919	8.05689	572	23.91652	8.30103
524	22.89105	8.06202	573	23.93742	8.30587
525	22.91288	8.06714	574	23.95830	8.31069
526	22.93469	8.07226	575	23.97916	8.31552
527	22.95648	8.07737	576	24	8.32034
528	22.97825	8.08248	577	24.02082	8.32515
529	23	8.08758	578	24.04163	8.32995
			579	24.06242	8.33476
530	23.02173	8.09267			
531	23.04344	8.09776	580	24.08319	8.33955
532	23.06513	8.10284	581	24.10394	8.34434
533	23.08679	8.10791	582	24.12468	8.34913
534	23.10844	8.11298	583	24.14539	8.35390
535	23.13007	8.11804	584	24.16609	8.35868
536	23.15167	8.12310	585	24.18677	8.36345
537	23.17326	8.12814	586	24.20744	8.36821
538	23.19483	8.13319	587	24.22808	8.37297
539	23.21637	8.13822	588	24.24871	8.37772

TABLE 2—SQUARE ROOTS AND CUBE ROOTS (Cont.)

Number	Square Root	Cube Root	Number	Square Root	Cube Root
589	24.26932	8.38247	637	25.23886	8.60425
			638	25.25866	8.60875
590	24.28992	8.38721	639	25.27845	8.61325
591	24.31049	8.39194			
592	24.33105	8.39667	640	25.29822	8.61774
593	24.35159	8.40140	641	25.31798	8.62222
594	24.37212	8.40612	642	25.33772	8.62671
595	24.39262	8.41083	643	25.35744	8.63118
596	24.41311	8.41554	644	25.37716	8.63566
597	24.43358	8.42025	645	25.39685	8.64012
598	24.45404	8.42494	646	25.41653	8.64459
599	24.47448	8.42964	647	25.43619	8.64904
			648	25.45584	8.65350
600	24.49490	8.43433	649	25.47548	8.65795
601	24.51530	8.43901			
602	24.53569	8.44369	650	25.49510	8.66239
603	24.55606	8.44836	651	25.51470	8.66683
604	24.57641	8.45303	652	25.53429	8.67127
605	24.59675	8.45769	653	25.55386	8.67570
606	24.61707	8.46235	654	25.57342	8.68012
607	24.63737	8.46700	655	25.59297	8.68455
608	24.65766	8.47165	656	25.61250	8.68896
609	24.67793	8.47629	657	25.63201	8.69338
			658	25.65151	8.69778
610	24.69818	8.48093	659	25.67100	8.70219
611	24.71841	8.48556			
612	24.73863	8.49018	660	25.69047	8.70659
613	24.75884	8.49481	661	25.70992	8.71098
614	24.77902	8.49942	662	25.72936	8.71537
615	24.79919	8.50404	663	25.74879	8.71976
616	24.81935	8.50864	664	25.76820	8.72414
617	24.83948	8.51324	665	25.78749	8.72852
618	24.85961	8.51784	666	25.80698	8.73289
619	24.87971	8.52243	667	25.82634	8.73726
			668	25.84570	8.74162
620	24.89980	8.52702	669	25.86503	8.74598
621	24.91987	8.53160			
622	24.93993	8.53618	670	25.88436	8.75034
623	24.95997	8.54075	671	25.90367	8.75469
624	24.97999	8.54532	672	25.92296	8.75904
625	25	8.54988	673	25.94224	8.76338
626	25.01999	8.55444	674	25.96151	8.76772
627	25.03997	8.55899	675	25.98076	8.77205
628	25.05993	8.56354	676	26	8.77638
629	25.07987	8.56808	677	26.01922	8.78071
			678	26.03843	8.78503
630	25.09980	8.57262	679	26.05763	8.78935
631	25.11971	8.57715			
632	25.13961	8.58168	680	26.07681	8.79366
633	25.15949	8.58622	681	26.09598	8.79797
634	25.17936	8.59072	682	26.11513	8.80227
635	25.19921	8.59524	683	26.13427	8.80657
636	25.21904	8.59975	684	26.15339	8.81087

TABLE 2—SQUARE ROOTS AND CUBE ROOTS (Cont.)

Number	Square Root	Cube Root	Number	Square Root	Cube Root
685	26.17250	8.81516	733	27.07397	9.01643
686	26.19160	8.81945	734	27.09243	9.02053
687	26.21068	8.82373	735	27.11088	9.02462
688	26.22975	8.82801	736	27.12932	9.02871
689	26.24881	8.83229	737	27.14771	9.03280
690	26.26785	8.83656	738	27.16616	9.03689
691	26.28688	8.84082	739	27.18455	9.04097
692	26.30589	8.84509	740	27.20291	9.04504
693	26.32489	8.84934	741	27.22132	9.04911
694	26.34388	8.85360	742	27.23968	9.05318
695	26.36285	8.85785	743	27.25803	9.05725
696	26.38181	8.86210	744	27.27636	9.06131
697	26.40076	8.86634	745	27.29469	9.06537
698	26.41969	8.87058	746	27.31300	9.06942
699	26.43861	8.87481	747	27.33130	9.07347
700	26.45751	8.87904	748	27.34959	9.07752
701	26.47640	8.88327	749	27.36786	9.08156
702	26.49528	8.88749	750	27.38613	9.08560
703	26.51415	8.89171	751	27.40438	9.08964
704	26.53300	8.89592	752	27.42262	9.09367
705	26.55184	8.90013	753	27.44085	9.09770
706	26.57066	8.90434	754	27.45906	9.10173
707	26.58947	8.90854	755	27.47726	9.10575
708	26.60817	8.91274	756	27.49545	9.10977
709	26.62705	8.91693	757	27.51363	9.11378
710	26.64583	8.92112	758	27.53180	9.11779
711	26.66458	8.92531	759	27.54995	9.12180
712	26.68333	8.92949	760	27.56810	9.12581
713	26.70206	8.93367	761	27.58623	9.12981
714	26.72078	8.93784	762	27.60435	9.13380
715	26.73948	8.94201	763	27.62245	9.13780
716	26.75818	8.94618	764	27.64055	9.14179
717	26.77686	8.95034	765	27.65863	9.14577
718	26.79552	8.95450	766	27.67671	9.14976
719	26.81418	8.95866	767	27.69476	9.15374
720	26.83282	8.96281	768	27.71281	9.15771
721	26.85144	8.96696	769	27.73085	9.16169
722	26.87006	8.97110	770	27.74887	9.16566
723	26.88866	8.97524	771	27.76689	9.16962
724	26.90725	8.97938	772	27.78489	9.17359
725	26.92582	8.98351	773	27.80288	9.17754
726	26.94439	8.98764	774	27.82086	9.18150
727	26.96294	8.99176	775	27.83882	9.18545
728	26.98148	8.99589	776	27.85678	9.18940
729	27	9	777	27.87472	9.19335
730	27.01851	9.00411	778	27.89265	9.19729
731	27.03701	9.00822	779	27.91057	9.20123
732	27.05550	9.01233	780	27.92848	9.20516

TABLE 2—SQUARE ROOTS AND CUBE ROOTS (Cont.)

Number	Square Root	Cube Root	Number	Square Root	Cube Root
781	27.94638	9.20910	830	28.80972	9.39780
782	27.96426	9.21303	831	28.82707	9.40157
783	27.98214	9.21695	832	28.84441	9.40534
784	28	9.22087	833	28.86174	9.40911
785	28.01785	9.22479	834	28.87906	9.41287
786	28.03569	9.22871	835	28.89637	9.41663
787	28.05352	9.23262	836	28.91366	9.42039
788	28.07134	9.22653	837	28.93095	9.42414
789	28.08914	9.24043	838	28.94823	9.42789
790	28.10694	9.24434	839	28.96550	9.43164
791	28.12472	9.24823	840	28.98275	9.43538
792	28.14249	9.25213	841	29	9.43913
793	28.16026	9.25602	842	29.01724	9.44287
794	28.17801	9.25991	843	29.03446	9.44661
795	28.19574	9.26380	844	29.05168	9.45034
796	28.21347	9.26768	845	29.06888	9.45407
797	28.23119	9.27156	846	29.08608	9.45780
798	28.24889	9.27544	847	29.10326	9.46152
799	28.26659	9.27931	848	29.12044	9.46525
800	28.28427	9.28318	849	29.13760	9.46897
801	28.30194	9.28704	850	29.15476	9.47268
802	28.31960	9.29091	851	29.17190	9.47640
803	28.33725	9.29477	852	29.18904	9.48011
804	28.35489	9.29862	853	29.20616	9.48381
805	28.37252	9.30248	854	29.22328	9.48752
806	28.39014	9.30633	855	29.24038	9.49122
807	28.40775	9.31018	856	29.25748	9.49492
808	28.42534	9.31402	857	29.27456	9.49861
809	28.44293	9.31786	858	29.29164	9.50231
810	28.46050	9.32170	859	29.30870	9.50600
811	28.47806	9.32553	860	29.32576	9.50969
812	28.49561	9.32936	861	29.34280	9.51337
813	28.51315	9.33319	862	29.35984	9.51705
814	28.53069	9.33702	863	29.37686	9.52073
815	28.54820	9.34084	864	29.39388	9.52441
816	28.56571	9.34466	865	29.41088	9.52808
817	28.58321	9.34847	866	29.42788	9.53175
818	28.60070	9.35229	867	29.44486	9.53542
819	28.61818	9.35610	868	29.46184	9.53908
820	28.63564	9.35990	869	29.47881	9.54274
821	28.65310	9.36370	870	29.49576	9.54640
822	28.67054	9.36751	871	29.51271	9.55006
823	28.68798	9.37130	872	29.52965	9.55371
824	28.70540	9.37510	873	29.54657	9.55736
825	28.72281	9.37889	874	29.56349	9.56101
826	28.74022	9.38268	875	29.58040	9.56466
827	28.75761	9.38646	876	29.59730	9.56830
828	28.77499	9.39024	877	29.61419	9.57194
829	28.79236	9.39402	878	29.63106	9.57557

TABLE 2—SQUARE ROOTS AND CUBE ROOTS (Cont.)

Number	Square Root	Cube Root	Number	Square Root	Cube Root
879	29.64793	9.57921	927	30.44667	9.75049
880	29.66479	9.58284	928	30.46309	9.75400
881	29.68164	9.58647	929	30.47950	9.75750
882	29.69848	9.59009	930	30.49590	9.76100
883	29.71532	9.59372	931	30.51229	9.76450
884	29.73214	9.59734	932	30.52868	9.76799
885	29.74895	9.60095	933	30.54505	9.77148
886	29.76575	9.60457	934	30.56141	9.77497
887	29.78255	9.60818	935	30.57777	9.77846
888	29.79933	9.61179	936	30.59412	9.78295
889	29.81610	9.61540	937	30.61046	9.78543
890	29.83287	9.61900	938	30.62679	9.78891
891	29.84962	9.62260	939	30.64311	9.79239
892	29.86637	9.62620	940	30.65942	9.79586
893	29.88311	9.62980	941	30.67572	9.79933
894	29.89983	9.63339	942	30.69202	9.80280
895	29.91655	9.63698	943	30.70831	9.80627
896	29.93326	9.64057	944	30.72458	9.80974
897	29.94996	9.64415	945	30.74085	9.81320
898	29.96665	9.64774	946	30.75711	9.81666
899	29.98333	9.65132	947	30.77337	9.82012
900	30	9.65489	948	30.78961	9.82357
901	30.01666	9.65847	949	30.80584	9.82703
902	30.03331	9.66204	950	30.82207	9.83048
903	30.04996	9.66561	951	30.83829	9.83392
904	30.06659	9.66918	952	30.85450	9.83737
805	30.08322	9.67274	953	30.87070	9.84081
806	30.09983	9.67630	954	30.88689	9.84425
907	30.11644	9.67986	955	30.90307	9.84769
908	30.13304	9.68342	956	30.91925	9.85113
909	30.14963	9.68697	957	30.93542	9.85456
910	30.16621	9.69052	958	30.95158	9.85799
911	30.18278	9.69407	959	30.96773	9.86142
912	30.19934	9.69762	960	30.98387	9.86485
913	30.21589	9.70116	961	31	9.86827
914	30.23243	9.70470	962	31.01612	9.87169
915	30.24897	9.70824	963	31.03224	9.87511
916	30.26549	9.71177	964	31.04835	9.87853
917	30.28201	9.71531	965	31.06445	9.88195
918	30.29851	9.71884	966	31.08054	9.88536
919	30.31501	9.72236	967	31.09662	9.88877
920	30.33150	9.72589	968	31.11270	9.89217
921	30.34798	9.72941	969	31.12876	9.89558
922	30.36445	9.73293	970	31.14482	9.89898
923	30.38092	9.73645	971	31.16087	9.90238
924	30.39737	9.73996	972	31.17691	9.90578
925	30.41381	9.74348	973	31.19295	9.90918
926	30.43025	9.74699	974	31.20897	9.91257

TABLE 2—SQUARE ROOTS AND CUBE ROOTS (Cont.)

Number	Square Root	Cube Root	Number	Square Root	Cube Root
975	31.22499	9.91596	988	31.43247	9.95984
976	31.24100	9.91935	989	31.44837	9.96320
977	31.25700	9.92274	990	31.46427	9.96655
978	31.27299	9.92612	991	31.48015	9.96991
979	31.28898	9.92950	992	31.49603	9.97326
980	31.30495	9.93288	993	31.51190	9.97661
981	31.32092	9.93626	994	31.52777	9.97996
982	31.33688	9.93964	995	31.54362	9.98331
983	31.35283	9.94301	996	31.55947	9.98665
984	31.36877	9.94638	997	31.57531	9.98999
985	31.38471	9.94975	998	31.59114	9.99333
986	31.40064	9.95311	999	31.60696	9.99667
987	31.41656	9.95648			

Chapter 5

EQUATIONS

An algebraic equation contains a sign of equality, and *one or more* unknown terms. All equations contain the sign of equality, but not all expressions containing that sign are equations. When the two members (that is, the two expressions connected by the sign of equality) are equal for all values of their unknown terms, the complete statement is an identity, rather than an equation. Thus $x^2 - a^2 = (a - x)(a + x)$ is an identity, since it is true for any values of the letters x and a. (Sometimes the symbol $\equiv$ is used for identities, to avoid possible confusion.) On the other hand, the statement $2x - 3 = 5$, is an equation or a conditional equality, since it is true only for one value of x, namely 4.

Other equations may be satisfied by more than one value of their unknown terms: for example the equation $x^2 = 4$, as shown in Chapter 4, is satisfied by values of x of $+2$ or -2. However, no matter how many values of the unknown term or terms may satisfy the equation, these values are always definitely restricted within the particular classes of numbers concerned.

The process of finding the value of the unknown term(s) which satisfy an equation is called solving the equation or, particularly if it is of higher degree than the first in one or more unknown terms, of finding its roots.

When a solution of an equation has been found, it can be tested for correctness by substituting it in place of the symbol in the equation. If the equation is then a true statement, the solution is correct. Thus, $x = 2$ is the correct solution of the equation $4x + 1 = 8x - 7$, because the substitution of the value 2 for x in the equation gives $4(2) + 1 = 8(2) - 7$, or $8 + 1 = 16 - 7$, that is, $9 = 9$, which is an identity. The solution is therefore correct and by this procedure it is said to be verified or checked.

The two parts of an equation which are connected by the sign of equality ($=$) are called the members, or sides of the equation. The one on the left-hand side of the equation is called the left or first member, and that on the right is the right or second member.   Thus, in the equation above, $4x + 1$ is the first and $8x - 7$ the second member.

Properties of Equations

If any two quantities are equal, and each is increased or decreased by the same amount, the results are still equal.   Of course, neither is the same as at first, but the two results are still equal.   Thus if

$$(4x + 1) = (8x - 7)$$

then also

$$(4x + 1) + 3 = (8x - 7) + 3$$

for if $x = 2$ the equation as first written is equivalent to $9 = 9$, and the second to $9 + 3 = 9 + 3$, or $12 = 12$, which is, of course, true.   Similarly, if $3y - 2 = 7$, then also $(3y - 2) - 5 = 7 - 5$.

Thus, it is seen that the same number, and also the same expression, may be added or subtracted on both sides of an equation without changing the equality.   This fact is sometimes generalized by saying that:

If equals are added to equals the sums are equal, and if equals are subtracted from equals, the remainders are equal.

If two quantities or algebraic expressions are equal and both are exactly doubled, it is obvious that the two new quantities or expressions so obtained are also equal to each other, and, similarly, both may be exactly halved with equal results.   In the same way both members of an equation may be multiplied or divided by any number without destroying the equality.   Thus, in the case of the equation

$$4x + 1 = 8x - 7,$$

then

$$2(4x + 1) = 2(8x - 7)$$

and

$$\frac{4x + 1}{3} = \frac{8x - 7}{3}.$$

These results may be generalized by saying that:

If equals are multiplied or divided by equals, the results are equal.

If both members of an equation are multiplied or divided by the same number, the equation is said to be multiplied or divided by that number.

If two numbers or algebraic expressions are equal, they, of course, have the same square roots and their squares are also the same, and, any other roots or powers of them are the same.   This means that both members of an equation may be raised to any power or have the same root extracted and the results obtained will be equal.   Thus, equal powers and roots of equals are equal.

Applications of the above properties of equations extend throughout

algebraic operations. To see one such application, consider the equation
$$3x + 4 = 7x - 8$$
and subtract 4 from both sides. Then
$$3x + 4 - 4 = 7x - 8 - 4$$
or
$$3x = (7x - 8) - 4.$$
This equation now differs from the original in that the 4 which was on the left side at first seems to have been transferred to the right side and written with its original plus sign changed to minus.

Again, add 8 to both sides of the original equation
$$3x + 4 = 7x - 8.$$
This gives
$$3x + 4 + 8 = 7x - 8 + 8,$$
or
$$(3x + 4) + 8 = 7x.$$
Here the 8 has, in effect, been transposed from the right side of the original equation and its sign has been changed from minus to plus.

Thus, it appears that the process of adding or subtracting a certain term on both sides of an equation at the same time is the same as simply shifting the equivalent of that term from the side it was originally on to the other side, and changing its sign. This is indeed the case, and the process is called transposition of terms. This yields, therefore, the important result that:

Any term in either member of an equation may be transposed to the opposite member provided its sign is changed.

In the equation
$$4y + 7 = 14 - 3y$$
transpose the term $-3y$. The result is
$$4y + 7 + 3y = 14.$$
Then in this equation, transpose the 7,
$$4y + 3y = 14 - 7,$$
or
$$7y = 7.$$
Both these transpositions might have been made at once. In fact, if care is used, the transposition and subsequent combination of terms may often be performed mentally and by inspection, and the final result written down at once. Thus, in the equation
$$4y - 3 = 2x + 2,$$
by transposition of terms $2x$ and -3, and combining the 2 and 3, there is obtained

$$4y - 2x = 5.$$

The operation of transposition is used frequently in solving equations.

Equations in One Unknown to First Degree

The rule for solving simple equations in one unknown to the first degree may be stated in three steps, as follows:

A. Transpose the terms of the equation so that all the terms containing the unknown quantity are on the left side of the sign of equality, and all terms not containing it are on the right side of that sign.

B. Combine the terms on each side of the sign of equality into single terms.

C. Divide both sides of the equation by the coefficient of the unknown quantity. This operation leaves only the unknown quantity on the left side of the equation, so that the term on the right is its value.

For example, to solve the equation

$$-2x + 8 = 15 - x - 3x.$$

Step A. Transpose the $+8$ to the right side of the equation, where it appears as -8, and transpose the terms $-x$, $-3x$ from the right side to the left side of the equation, where they appear as $+x$, $+3x$. The equation now becomes: $-2x + x + 3x = 15 - 8$.

Step B. Add algebraically the terms on each side of the equation, obtaining $2x = 15 - 8 = 7$.

Step C. Therefore $x = \frac{7}{2} = 3.5$.

As another example, solve the equation $7x - (x + 3) + 12 = x - 4(x - 3)$. Here, the presence of the parentheses introduces expressions that combine terms in x and terms not containing x. It follows, therefore, that these parentheses must be cleared, i.e., the operations they indicate must be performed, before the necessary transpositions (Step A) can be made.

So, clearing of parentheses, this equation becomes,

$$7x - x - 3 + 12 = x - 4x + 12$$

Step A. Transpose the terms in x to the left side of the equation, and the numerical terms to the right side, obtaining

$$7x - x - x + 4x = 3 - 12 + 12$$

Step B. Combine the terms on each side of the equation obtaining

$$9x = 3$$

Step C. Divide the right side of the equation by the coefficient of x, obtaining

$$x = \tfrac{3}{9} = \tfrac{1}{3}.$$

As another example, solve the equation

$$4x + 12 - a = x - 5(a + 2b - x).$$

Here, as in the preceding example, the first step is to clear the parentheses, yielding $4x + 12 - a = x - 5a - 10b + 5x.$

Step A. Transpose the terms in x to the left side of the equation, and the terms in a and b, as well as the numerical term, to the right side of the equation, obtaining

$$4x - x - 5x = -12 + a - 5a - 10b$$

Step B. Here there are literal as well as numerical terms on the right side of the equation, so the conventional practice in algebra is to rearrange them in alphabetical order (after adding them) with the term consisting only of numbers coming last, obtaining

$$-2x = -4a - 10b - 12$$

Step C. Divide by the coefficient of x (which is -2), obtaining

$$x = 2a + 5b + 6.$$

As another example, solve the equation

$$6 + \frac{x}{2} - 9 = \frac{7x}{4 + a}.$$

Here, the fractions, like the parentheses in the preceding example, obviously must be cleared before transposition can be done. The method of clearing fractions consists of (1) finding the least common denominator of the fractions present, and (2) multiplying all the terms of the expression by this least common denominator. In the given equation, the denominators of the two fractions present are 2 and $4 + a$; therefore their least common denominator is $2(4 + a)$.

Therefore the term 6 in the original equation is multiplied by $2(4 + a)$ to give $48 + 12a$. The term $\frac{x}{2}$ is multiplied by $2(4 + a)$ to give $4x + ax$. The term -9 is multiplied by $2(4 + a)$ to give $-72 - 18a$. The term $\frac{7x}{4 + a}$ is multiplied by $2(4 + a)$ to give $14x$. Therefore, the given equation is transformed into $48 + 12a + 4x + ax - 72 - 18a = 14x.$

Step A. Transpose the terms in x to the left side of the equation, and the others to the right side, to obtain $4x - 14x + ax = -48 - 12a + 72 + 18a$

Step B. Group terms to obtain, $-10x + ax = 6a + 24$

Step C. The two resulting terms in x must be factored to give the coefficient of x.   That is $-10x + ax = x(-10 + a) = x(a - 10)$.   Then dividing by the coefficient of x

$$x = \frac{6a + 24}{a - 10} \quad \text{or} \quad \frac{6(a + 4)}{a - 10}.$$

Simultaneous Equations of First Degree in Two Unknowns

The equation in the preceding problem could not be solved numerically, because the value of the symbol a was not given.   However, the use of the letter a implies that the quantity it denotes is known, in accordance with the algebraic practice of restricting the use of the early letters of the alphabet to quantities which are known for the particular calculations. Such literal numbers $(a,b,c \ldots)$ are called known quantities to distinguish them from the unknowns x,y,z (or u,v,w, if more than three unknowns are involved).

Therefore, it is conventional practice in algebra to denote the second unknown by the letter y.

Now consider a simple equation in two unknowns, such as $x + y = 10$. Here it is obvious that there are an unlimited number of values of x and y which will satisfy this equation; including integral, fractional (or mixed), negative and irrational numbers.   (Thus if $x = 2$, $y = 8$; if $x = \sqrt{2}$, $y = 10 - \sqrt{2}$; if $x = 20$, $y = -10$.)   Therefore the term "unknowns" is no longer strictly applicable to x and y, and they are more consistently denoted by the term "variables."

However, if there are two equations involving x and y to the first degree, they can be solved for a single pair of values of x and y that satisfy them both.   (An important exception is the case in which both rearrange to give the same equation, as $3x = 9 - 6y$ gives $x + 2y = 3$, and is therefore the same equation.)   Consider for example, the equations,

$$5x + 4y = 23$$
$$3x - y = 7$$

These two equations can be solved for x and y in more than one way. One of these methods of solution is the method of elimination by comparison.

Solution of First Degree Simultaneous Equations in Two Unknowns by Method of Comparison

The basis of this method is (A) to solve both equations for one of the unknowns in terms of the other; then (B) to equate these two values, and to solve the resulting equation for the single unknown it contains; and finally (C) to substitute this value in one or the other of the derived equa-

tions of (A), and to solve the resulting equation for the other unknown.
This method is applied to the equations in the above example as follows:

Step A. $$5x + 4y = 23$$

Therefore $$5x = 23 - 4y$$

Therefore $$x = \frac{23 - 4y}{5}$$

$$3x - y = 7$$

Therefore $$3x = 7 + y$$

Therefore $$x = \frac{7 + y}{3}$$

Step B. $$\frac{23 - 4y}{5} = \frac{7 + y}{3}$$

Therefore $$3(23 - 4y) = 5(7 + y)$$
and $$69 - 12y = 35 + 5y$$
Therefore $$-17y = -34$$
and $$y = \tfrac{34}{17} = 2$$

Step C. The first of the two derived equations above is

$$x = \frac{23 - 4y}{5}$$

Therefore $$x = \frac{23 - (4 \times 2)}{5}$$

or $$x = \frac{23 - 8}{5} = 3.$$

The solution of the pair of first degree equations in x and y is, therefore,

$$x = 3 \text{ and } y = 2$$

Since these first degree equations in two (or more) unknowns are satisfied by the same values of their unknowns, and are solved together by the
same series of steps, they are called simultaneous equations. A second
method of solving simultaneous equations, that is closely related to the
foregoing comparison method, is the method of substitution.

Solution of First Degree Simultaneous Equations in Two Unknowns by Method of Substitution

The basis of this method is (A) to solve one equation for one unknown
in terms of the other; then (B) to substitute that value in the other equation, which is then solved for the single unknown remaining; then to substitute this value in the derived equation of (A). For example, solve the
following equations by substitution:

$$3x + 8y = 26$$
$$6x - y = 9.5$$

Step A.

$$3x + 8y = 26$$

Therefore

$$3x = 26 - 8y$$

$$x = \frac{26 - 8y}{3}$$

Step B.

$$6x - y = 9.5$$

Substituting,

$$6\left(\frac{26 - 8y}{3}\right) - y = 9.5$$

$$52 - 16y - y = 9.5$$

$$-17y = -42.5$$

$$y = 2.5$$

Step C.

$$x = \frac{26 - 8y}{3}$$

$$x = \frac{26 - (8 \times 2.5)}{3}$$

$$x = \frac{26 - 20}{3} = 2.$$

Therefore the solution is $x = 2$; $y = 2.5$.

A third method of solving simultaneous equations is the method of subtraction (or addition).

Solution of First Degree Simultaneous Equations in Two Unknowns by the Method of Subtraction (or Addition)

The basis of this method is (A) to multiply the second equation by a number that will make the coefficient of y (or x) the same as it is in the first equation. Then (B) subtraction of this second derived equation from the first equation will yield an equation in one unknown, provided that the coefficients of y have the same sign. If not, add the equations instead of subtracting them. Finally (C) solve the resulting equation in one unknown, and (D) substitute back to evaluate the other unknown.

For example, solve the following equations by subtraction,

$$3x + 2y = 16$$
$$7x + y = 19$$

Step A. Multiply the second equation by 2, obtaining $14x + 2y = 38$.

Step B. Subtract this derived second equation from the first equation as follows:

$$3x + 2y = 16$$
$$\underline{14x + 2y = 38}$$
$$-11x = -22$$

Step C. $ x = 2.$

Step D. $ 3(2) + 2y = 16$

$$6 + 2y = 16$$

$$2y = 10$$

$$y = 5$$

Therefore the solution is $x = 2;\ y = 5.$

A fourth method of solving simultaneous equations is the method of multiplication and subtraction.

Solution of First Degree Simultaneous Equations in Two Unknowns by the Method of Multiplication and Subtraction

The basis of this method is to eliminate one unknown by (A) multiplying the equations by quantities that yield a new pair of equations in which the coefficients of one of the unknowns are the same. Then (B) subtract the equations to obtain a derived equation in one unknown. Solve (C) for this unknown and substitute back (D) to find the other.

For example, solve the following equations by multiplication and subtraction.

$$2x + 7y = 57$$

$$3x + 4y = 40$$

Step A. Multiply the first equation by 4 and the second by 7, obtaining

$$8x + 28y = 228$$

$$21x + 28y = 280$$

Step B. Subtract these equations,

$$8x + 28y = 228$$
$$\underline{21x + 28y = 280}$$
$$-13x = -52$$

Step C. Therefore $ x = 4.$

Step D. Substitute in first original equation

$$8 + 7y = 57$$

Therefore $ 7y = 49$

$$y = 7$$

And the solution is $x = 4;\ y = 7.$

As another example, solve the following equations by multiplication and subtraction

$$2x + 3y = 28$$

$$4x - 2y = 8$$

Step A. Multiply the first equation by -2, and the second equation by 3, obtaining

$$-4x - 6y = -56$$

$$12x - 6y = 24$$

Step B. Subtract these equations,

$$\begin{array}{r} -4x - 6y = -56 \\ 12x - 6y = 24 \\ \hline -16x = -80 \end{array}$$

Step C. Therefore $\qquad\qquad\qquad x = \dfrac{-80}{-16} = 5.$

Step D. Substituting in first original equation

$$10 + 3y = 28$$

Therefore $\qquad\qquad\qquad\qquad y = 6.$

And the solution is $x = 5; y = 6$.

This method of solving two first degree simultaneous equations leads to a general method which can be applied by formula. It is called the method of determinants.

Method of Determinants for Solving Two First Degree Simultaneous Equations in Two Unknowns

As an approach to this method, derive a general solution by repeating the method of multiplication and subtraction, and by using literal algebraic numbers for the coefficients of x and y, and for the constant terms.

Consider the equations

$$a_1x + b_1y = k_1$$

$$a_2x + b_2y = k_2$$

in which a_1 and a_2 are coefficients of x in the two equations; b_1 and b_2, those of y, and k_1 and k_2 the constant terms.

(The subscript numbers are used merely to differentiate, thus a_1 and a_2, b_1 and b_2 and k_1 and k_2 are merely a differentiating notation. Always be sure to distinguish between subscript numbers and superscripts, such as the figures ^{2} in a^2 or x^2 which are *exponents*, as explained in Chapter 4.)

Now recall that in *Step A* of the examples in the previous solution, the first equation was multiplied by b_2 and the second equation was multiplied by b_1 (that is, by the coefficients of y) giving

Step A.
$$b_2a_1x + b_2b_1y = b_2k_1 \qquad (1)$$
$$b_1a_2x + b_1b_2y = b_1k_2 \qquad (2)$$

Step B. Since $b_2b_1y = b_1b_2y$, subtracting equation (2) from equation (1) gives

$$b_2a_1x - b_1a_2x = b_2k_1 - b_1k_2$$

Then by factoring the right-hand member, there is obtained

$$(b_2a_1 - b_1a_2)x = b_2k_1 - b_1k_2$$

Step C. Transposing gives

$$x = \frac{b_2k_1 - b_1k_2}{b_2a_1 - b_1a_2}$$

or by writing the terms in the denominator in alphabetical order,

$$x = \frac{b_2k_1 - b_1k_2}{a_1b_2 - a_2b_1} \qquad (5\text{-}1)$$

If the terms in x are eliminated from both equations by multiplying the first by a_2 and the second by a_1, and subtracting, the result for y is

$$y = \frac{a_1k_1 - a_2k_1}{a_1b_2 - a_2b_1} \qquad (5\text{-}2)$$

Now note that the denominators in both (5-1) and (5-2) are identical and that they are the cross-products of the coefficients of x and y in the two equations. That is, (the product of the coefficient of x in the first equation multiplied by the coefficient of y in the second equation) minus (the product of the coefficient of x in the second equation by the coefficient of y in the first equation). This cross-product difference is expressed by the symbol $\begin{vmatrix} a_1 & b_1 \\ a_2 & b_2 \end{vmatrix}$ and when so expressed is called a determinant.

The order of expansion of the determinant can be remembered by drawing the diagonals as shown below to connect the factors of the prod-

$$\begin{vmatrix} a_1 & b_1 \\ a_2 & b_2 \end{vmatrix}$$

ucts, noting that the line from the upper left to lower right indicates the first product, and the line from lower left to upper right, the second product.

Note also that the numerator of (5-1) may be written

$$\begin{vmatrix} k_1 & b_1 \\ k_2 & b_2 \end{vmatrix}$$

and that the numerator of (5-2) may be written

$$\begin{vmatrix} a_1 & k_1 \\ a_2 & k_2 \end{vmatrix}$$

To repeat the foregoing relations all together, the value of x as stated in this way is,

$$x = \frac{\begin{vmatrix} k_1 & b_1 \\ k_2 & b_2 \end{vmatrix}}{\begin{vmatrix} a_1 & b_1 \\ a_2 & b_2 \end{vmatrix}} \qquad (5\text{-}3)$$

which expands to

$$x = \frac{k_1 b_2 - k_2 b_1}{a_1 b_2 - a_2 b_1},$$

while the value of y as stated in this way is,

$$y = \frac{\begin{vmatrix} a_1 & k_1 \\ a_2 & k_2 \end{vmatrix}}{\begin{vmatrix} a_1 & b_1 \\ a_2 & b_2 \end{vmatrix}} \qquad (5\text{-}4)$$

which expands to

$$y = \frac{a_1 k_2 - a_2 k_1}{a_1 b_2 - a_2 b_1}$$

Now solve by this method the equations

$$2x + 3y = 41$$

$$4x - 2y = 10$$

Now here a_1 is 2; b_1 is 3; k_1 is 41; a_2 is 4; b_2 is -2; and k_2 is 10. Substituting the above figures,

$$x = \frac{\begin{vmatrix} 41 & 3 \\ 10 & -2 \end{vmatrix}}{\begin{vmatrix} 2 & 3 \\ 4 & -2 \end{vmatrix}}$$

which expands to

$$x = \frac{(41 \cdot -2) - (10 \cdot 3)}{(2 \cdot -2) - (4 \cdot 3)} = \frac{-82 - 30}{-4 - 12} = \frac{-112}{-16}$$

Thus,

$$x = \frac{-112}{-16} = 7.$$

$$y = \frac{\begin{vmatrix} 2 & 41 \\ 4 & 10 \end{vmatrix}}{\begin{vmatrix} 2 & 3 \\ 4 & -2 \end{vmatrix}}$$

which expands to

$$y = \frac{(2 \cdot 10) - (4 \cdot 41)}{(2 \cdot -2) - (4 \cdot 3)} = \frac{20 - 164}{-4 - 12} = \frac{-144}{-16}$$

Thus, $y = \dfrac{-144}{-16} = 9.$

Note that the denominators of the expressions for x and y are identical, being the determinant of their coefficients in the two equations, and that it need be computed only once.

For simple equations such as those in the foregoing example, the use of determinants may not be more direct than the other methods previously described. However, where the coefficients of the unknowns, or the constant terms, are decimals, fractions or more complicated quantities, this method is clearly of advantage.

Consider the equations

$$2x + 1.5y = 18.45$$
$$5x - 4y = 12.8$$

Here by Formula (5-3)

$$x = \frac{\begin{vmatrix} 18.45 & 1.5 \\ 12.8 & -4 \end{vmatrix}}{\begin{vmatrix} 2 & 1.5 \\ 5 & -4 \end{vmatrix}}$$

which expands to

$$x = \frac{(18.45 \cdot -4) - (12.8 \cdot 1.5)}{(2 \cdot -4) - (5 \cdot 1.5)} = \frac{-73.8 - 19.2}{-8 - 7.5} = \frac{-93.0}{-15.5}$$

Thus $x = 6.$

While by Formula (5-4)

$$y = \frac{\begin{vmatrix} 2 & 18.45 \\ 5 & 12.8 \end{vmatrix}}{-15.5^{*}}$$

Then expanding,

$$y = \frac{(2 \cdot 12.8) - (5 \cdot 18.45)}{-15.5} = \frac{25.6 - 92.25}{-15.5} = \frac{-66.65}{-15.5}$$

Thus $y = 4.3.$

Equations in Three Unknowns to First Degree

Another advantage of the method of solving simultaneous equations by determinants lies in its ready extension to first degree equations con-

---

* (The value of the denominator is, as stated above, the same for y as for x, and the latter value was found above to be -15.5).

taining three unknowns. To obtain single values for three unknowns, there must be three equations. While their solution can be effected by modifications of any of the methods explained and illustrated for equations in two unknowns, the use of determinants materially simplifies the work.

Method of Determinants for Solving Three First Degree Simultaneous Equations in Three Unknowns

The derivation of the determinants for solving three first degree equations in three unknowns follows the same method as that explained previously for two equations in two unknowns. Therefore it is not detailed here, but only the results are given. They are:

Consider the general first degree equations in three variables,

$$a_1x + b_1y + c_1z = k_1$$
$$a_2x + b_2y + c_2z = k_2$$
$$a_3x + b_3y + c_3z = k_3$$

The determinant method for solving them yields

$$x = \frac{\begin{vmatrix} k_1 & b_1 & c_1 \\ k_2 & b_2 & c_2 \\ k_3 & b_3 & c_3 \end{vmatrix}}{\begin{vmatrix} a_1 & b_1 & c_1 \\ a_2 & b_2 & c_2 \\ a_3 & b_3 & c_3 \end{vmatrix}} \qquad (5\text{-}5)$$

and its method of cross-multiplication is, for the determinant in the numerator,

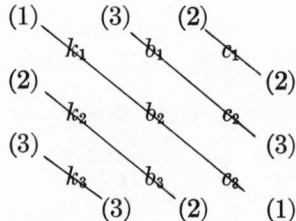

to obtain three additive terms, followed by

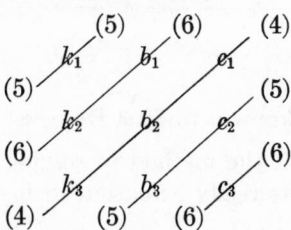

to obtain three subtractive terms.

In these diagrams, the elements to be multiplied are connected by lines, and each group is designated by a figure. Thus (1) ... (1), (2) ... (2) and (3) ... (3) denote in each case the three elements which are multiplied to obtain the three additive products; while (4) ... (4), (5) ... (5) and (6) ... (6) denote in each case the three elements which are multiplied to obtain the three products to be subtracted. Therefore this operation produces, from the determinant in the numerator of x, the following expression:

$$(k_1 b_2 c_3 + k_2 b_3 c_1 + k_3 b_1 c_2) - (k_3 b_2 c_1 + k_1 b_3 c_2 + k_2 b_1 c_3).$$

The determinant in the denominator of x is evaluated by multiplying the terms in precisely the same order as was done with the determinant in the numerator of x. Therefore this process yields the following expression:

$$(a_1 b_2 c_3 + a_2 b_3 c_1 + a_3 b_1 c_2) - (a_3 b_2 c_1 + a_1 b_3 c_2 + a_2 b_1 c_3).$$

Note also that, whereas the determinants arising in solving two equations in two unknowns have four elements and expand to two products, the determinants arising from three equations in three unknowns have nine elements and expand to six products.

From the expressions for the two determinants which were evaluated above, x becomes,

$$x = \frac{(k_1 b_2 c_3 + k_2 b_3 c_1 + k_3 b_1 c_2) - (k_3 b_2 c_1 + k_1 b_3 c_2 + k_2 b_1 c_3)}{(a_1 b_2 c_3 + a_2 b_3 c_1 + a_3 b_1 c_2) - (a_3 b_2 c_1 + a_1 b_3 c_2 + a_2 b_1 c_3)}$$

Also

$$y = \frac{\begin{vmatrix} a_1 & k_1 & c_1 \\ a_2 & k_2 & c_2 \\ a_3 & k_3 & c_3 \end{vmatrix}}{\begin{vmatrix} a_1 & b_1 & c_1 \\ a_2 & b_2 & c_2 \\ a_3 & b_3 & c_3 \end{vmatrix}} \tag{5-6}$$

which expands to

$$y = \frac{(a_1 k_2 c_3 + a_2 k_3 c_1 + a_3 k_1 c_2) - (a_3 k_2 c_1 + a_1 k_3 c_2 + a_2 k_1 c_3)}{(a_1 b_2 c_3 + a_2 b_3 c_1 + a_3 b_1 c_2) - (a_3 b_2 c_1 + a_1 b_3 c_2 + a_2 b_1 c_3)}$$

Also

$$z = \frac{\begin{vmatrix} a_1 & b_1 & k_1 \\ a_2 & b_2 & k_2 \\ a_3 & b_3 & k_3 \end{vmatrix}}{\begin{vmatrix} a_1 & b_1 & c_1 \\ a_2 & b_2 & c_2 \\ a_3 & b_3 & c_3 \end{vmatrix}} \tag{5-7}$$

which expands to

$$z = \frac{(a_1b_2k_3 + a_2b_3k_1 + a_3b_1k_2) - (a_3b_2k_1 + a_1b_3k_2 + a_2b_1k_3)}{(a_1b_2c_3 + a_2b_3c_1 + a_3b_1c_2) - (a_3b_2c_1 + a_1b_3c_2 + a_2b_1c_3)}$$

To apply this method to a problem, solve the equations

$$2x + 2y + 3z = 22$$
$$2x - 4y + 3z = 4$$
$$3x + 6y - 2z = 16$$

Here a_1 is 2, b_1 is 2; c_1 is 3, k_1 is 22; a_2 is 2; b_2 is -4; c_2 is 3; k_2 is 4; a_3 is 3; b_3 is 6; c_3 is -2; k_3 is 16.

Here

$$x = \frac{\begin{vmatrix} 22 & 2 & 3 \\ 4 & -4 & 3 \\ 16 & 6 & -2 \end{vmatrix}}{\begin{vmatrix} 2 & 2 & 3 \\ 2 & -4 & 3 \\ 3 & 6 & -2 \end{vmatrix}}$$

which expands to

$$x = \frac{(22 \cdot -4 \cdot -2 + 4 \cdot 6 \cdot 3 + 16 \cdot 2 \cdot 3) - (16 \cdot -4 \cdot 3 + 22 \cdot 6 \cdot 3 + 4 \cdot 2 \cdot -2)}{(2 \cdot -4 \cdot -2 + 2 \cdot 6 \cdot 3 + 3 \cdot 2 \cdot 3) - (3 \cdot -4 \cdot 3 + 2 \cdot 6 \cdot 3 + 2 \cdot 2 \cdot -2)}$$

Multiplying

$$\frac{(176 + 72 + 96) - (-192 + 396 - 16)}{(16 + 36 + 18) - (-36 + 36 - 8)}$$

Thus

$$x = \frac{344 - 188}{70 - (-8)} = \frac{156}{78} = 2.$$

Similarly, by applying the determinant formula to calculation of y, remembering that its denominator is the same as that for x,

$$y = \frac{\begin{vmatrix} 2 & 22 & 3 \\ 2 & 4 & 3 \\ 3 & 16 & -2 \end{vmatrix}}{78}$$

which expands to

$$y = \frac{(2 \cdot 4 \cdot -2 + 2 \cdot 16 \cdot 3 + 3 \cdot 22 \cdot 3) - (3 \cdot 4 \cdot 3 + 2 \cdot 16 \cdot 3 + 2 \cdot 22 \cdot -2)}{78}$$

multiplying

$$y = \frac{(-16 + 96 + 198) - (36 + 96 - 88)}{78}$$

Thus

$$y = \frac{278 - 44}{78} = \frac{234}{78} = 3.$$

The value of z could also be found by applying the determinant formula stated above. However, time can usually be saved by substituting the values of x and y already found in one of the equations. Thus, since x has been found to have a value of 2, and y a value of 3, the equation $2x + 2y + 3x = 22$ becomes $4 + 6 + 3z = 22$, whence $3z = 12$, and z has a value of 4. These calculations are then checked by substituting for the values found for x, y, and z in the two other equations.

The evaluation of determinants of higher order than the third requires application of the general rule, or of a method based on it other than merely drawing the diagonals as was done above. The general rule is: To find the value of a determinant of nth order, form all the n-factor products possible by taking one factor from each row and column (this is $1 \times 2 = 2$ products for a second order determinant, and $1 \times 2 \times 3 = 6$ products for a third order determinant, as has already been shown, and $1 \times 2 \times 3 \times \cdots \times n$ products for an nth order determinant.) Then apply algebraically to each product, a plus or minus sign according to whether the number of one-step moves necessary to arrange the subscripts (denoting the row of each factor) in numerical order are even or odd. For example, $c_3 d_1 b_2 a_4$ would be multiplied by $+1$ because an even number (2) of one-step moves (to $d_1 c_3 b_2 a_4$, then to $d_1 b_2 c_3 a_4$) is necessary to put the subscripts in numerical order, while $c_1 d_3 b_2 a_4$ would be multiplied by -1 because an odd number (1) of one-step moves (to $c_1 b_2 d_3 a_4$) is necessary to put the subscripts in numerical order.

In concluding the discussion of solution of simultaneous equations by determinants, it should be pointed out that under some conditions the determinant in the denominator has a value of zero. Since this is the determinant of the coefficients of the unknowns, the zero value means that these coefficients have either the same values in two or more equations, or a multiple of the same values. In this case the equations in question are identical, such as are the pair of equations $x + y = 4$; $2x + 2y = 8$, and therefore have an unlimited number of solutions, or else they are inconsistent, such as $x + y = 4$; $x + y = 5$, in which case, of course, there cannot be found a single pair of values which satisfies the equations.

Equations in One Unknown to Second Degree

A second degree equation is often called a quadratic equation. A second degree, or quadratic equation in one unknown, has its unknown present to the power two, and not higher. It may also contain terms having the unknown to the first power and constant terms.

Consider the quadratic equation $x^2 - 4 = 0$, in which there is no term containing the unknown to the first power.

By transposition, this equation becomes $x^2 = 4$, which has as its roots

$x = 2$ and $x = -2$. That is, either $x = 2$ or $x = -2$ will satisfy this equation, since by substituting the roots for x, $(2)^2 = 4$; and $(-2)^2 = 4$.

This property of yielding two roots is possessed by all second degree equations in one unknown. (In fact, it can be shown that algebraic equations in one unknown have a number of roots equal to their degree; thus third degree equations in one unknown have three roots; fourth degree equations in one unknown have four roots, etc. In some cases, however, equations have two or more identical roots.)

However, the roots of an equation are not necessarily real, or all real. For example, the equation $x^2 + 4 = 0$, which transposes to give $x^2 = -4$, has as its roots $+2\sqrt{-1}$ and $-2\sqrt{-1}$, since $(+2\sqrt{-1})^2 = -4$; and $(-2\sqrt{-1})^2 = -4$, and thus both of the roots belong to the class of imaginary numbers discussed in Chapter 4.

As a further example of a quadratic equation without a first-power term in its unknown, consider the equation, $3x^2 - 4 = 0$. Here by transposition and division,

$$x^2 = \frac{4}{3}, \quad \text{hence} \quad x = \pm\sqrt{\frac{4}{3}} = \pm\frac{\sqrt{4}}{\sqrt{3}} = \pm\frac{2}{\sqrt{3}} = \pm\frac{2\sqrt{3}}{3}.$$

In expressing these particular roots, the conventional practice in algebra is to restrict the use of irrational numbers, wherever possible, to numerators of fractions. Therefore, the expression $\pm\frac{2}{\sqrt{3}}$ is multiplied by $\frac{\sqrt{3}}{\sqrt{3}}$, which does not change its value, so that it becomes $\pm\frac{2\sqrt{3}}{3}$, and the algebraic statement of the roots of the equation $3x - 4 = 0$ is thus $\pm\frac{2\sqrt{3}}{3}$.

From the foregoing simple example, a general formula for determining the roots of a quadratic equation in one unknown may be derived, for the case in which there is no first power term containing the variable.

Let the general equation be $ax^2 + k = 0$, then $ax^2 = -k$, and $x^2 = -\frac{k}{a}$, yielding $x = +\sqrt{-\frac{k}{a}}$ and $x = -\sqrt{-\frac{k}{a}}$ $\left(\text{which may also be written} \right.$ $x = \pm\sqrt{-\frac{k}{a}}\bigg).$ (5-8)

As an example of the use of the formula, find the roots of the quadratic equation

$$8x^2 - 58 = 5x^2 - 10.$$

By transposing all terms to the right-hand side of the equation,

$$3x^2 - 48 = 0.$$

Thus 3 is the coefficient of x^2, which becomes a in the formula, and -48 is the constant term, which becomes k in the formula.

Substituting these values in Formula (5-8), $x = \pm\sqrt{-\dfrac{k}{a}}$, there is obtained

$$x = \pm\sqrt{-\left(\frac{-48}{3}\right)}$$

thus

$$x = \pm\sqrt{-(-16)} = \pm\sqrt{16} = \pm4.$$

In the quadratic equations that arise in business mathematics and other fields of application, the conditions of the problem often show which one of the two roots is the root sought. In scientific and engineering applications this statement is also true, but with the added qualification that in those applications, negative and even imaginary roots often describe a real situation.

Up to this point, the discussion has been restricted to quadratic equations without terms containing the variable to the first power. Consider now complete quadratic equations in one variable, that is, equations having one (or more) terms containing a variable to the second power, one (or more) terms containing that variable to the first power, and one (or more) constant terms.

For example, consider the equation

$$2x^2 + 12x - 14 = 0.$$

A general method for solving such complete quadratic equations is known as the method of completing the square. It consists of the following steps:

Step A. Divide the equation by the coefficient of the second power of the variable. In the example, the coefficient of x^2 is 2. The equation then becomes $x^2 + 6x - 7 = 0$.

Step B. Transpose the constant term (which in this derived equation is 7). The equation becomes $x^2 + 6x = 7$.

Step C. Add to both members of this equation the square of half the coefficient of the first power of the unknown. (In the above derived equation, the coefficient of x is 6. One-half of 6 is 3, and the square of 3 is 9.) The equation then becomes $x^2 + 6x + 9 = 7 + 9 = 16$.

Step D. Take the square root of both members of the derived equation.

(The square root of $x^2 + 6x + 9$ is $x + 3$, because $(x + 3)^2 = x^2 + 6x + 9$. The square root of 16 is ± 4.)

The result of Step D is therefore: $x + 3 = \pm 4$.

Step E. Solve the resulting simple equation. (Transpose the 3 above to the other side of the equation.)

Thus $x = \pm 4 - 3$.

Thus the roots of the equation are $x = 1; x = -7$.

As a second example of the solution of quadratic equations, consider the equation

$$2x^2 + 12x + 24 = 0.$$

The steps indicated above then yield the following results:

Step A. $x^2 + 6x + 12 = 0$

Step B. $x^2 + 6x = -12$

Step C. $x^2 + 6x + 9 = -12 + 9 = -3$

Step D. $x + 3 = \pm\sqrt{-3} = \pm\sqrt{3}\sqrt{-1}$

Step E. $x = \pm\sqrt{3}\sqrt{-1} - 3$, which can also be written $x = \pm\sqrt{3}i - 3$.

This equation thus has no real roots, that is, its solution is in terms of a complex number. As explained in Chapter 4, complex numbers enter into many phases of calculations and analyses, both in pure mathematics and applied mathematics. The conditions under which quadratic equations yield complex number solutions are evident from the general quadratic formula, which is now derived.

The general quadratic equation is

$$ax^2 + bx + c = 0.$$

Then the results of the steps described above are as follows:

Step A. Divide by coefficient of x^2, obtaining

$$x^2 + \frac{b}{a}x + \frac{c}{a} = 0.$$

Step B. Transpose term not containing x, obtaining

$$x^2 + \frac{b}{a}x = -\frac{c}{a}$$

Step C. Add square of one-half coefficient of x, obtaining

$$x^2 + \frac{b}{a}x + \left(\frac{b}{2a}\right)^2 = \left(\frac{b}{2a}\right)^2 - \frac{c}{a}$$

which becomes, on squaring terms in parentheses,

$$x^2 + \frac{b}{a}x + \frac{b^2}{4a^2} = \frac{b^2}{4a^2} - \frac{c}{a}$$

Step D. Take square root of both sides, obtaining

$$x + \frac{b}{2a} = \pm\sqrt{\frac{b^2}{4a^2} - \frac{c}{a}}$$

which becomes, by clearing of fractions under the radical sign,

$$x + \frac{b}{2a} = \pm\sqrt{\frac{b^2 - 4ac}{4a^2}} = \pm\frac{\sqrt{b^2 - 4ac}}{2a}$$

Step E. Transposing,

$$x = -\frac{b}{2a} \pm \frac{\sqrt{b^2 - 4ac}}{2a}$$

thus

$$x = \frac{-b \pm \sqrt{b^2 - 4ac}}{2a} \qquad (5\text{-}9)$$

As an example of the use of this formula, consider the equation

$$2x^2 + x - 105 = 0.$$

In this equation a is 2, b is 1 and c is -105.

Therefore, on substituting

$$x = \frac{-1 \pm \sqrt{(1)^2 - 4 \cdot 2 \cdot -105}}{2 \cdot 2}$$

or

$$x = \frac{-1 \pm \sqrt{1 + 840}}{4}$$

Thus

$$x = \frac{-1 \pm \sqrt{841}}{4}$$

$$x = \frac{-1 \pm 29}{4} = \frac{28}{4} \quad \text{or} \quad \frac{-30}{4} = 7 \quad \text{or} \quad -7.5$$

As another example, consider the equation

$$4x^2 + 8x + 9 = 0$$

Here a is 4, b is 8 and c is 9. Therefore, on substituting

$$x = \frac{-8 \pm \sqrt{(8)^2 - 4 \cdot 4 \cdot 9}}{2 \cdot 4}$$

or

$$x = \frac{-8 \pm \sqrt{64 - 144}}{8}$$

or

$$x = -1 \pm \frac{\sqrt{-80}}{8}$$

or $\quad x = -1 \pm \dfrac{4\sqrt{-5}}{8} = -1 \pm \dfrac{\sqrt{5}\sqrt{-1}}{2};\quad$ or $\quad x = -1 \pm \dfrac{\sqrt{5}i}{2}$

Thus since the expression under the radical sign is negative, the roots are complex. Since the sign of the quantity under the radical determines the nature of the roots, it is called the discriminant of the quadratic equation. If the discriminant is negative the roots are complex; if it is positive and a perfect square (provided that a, b, and c are rational) the roots are integers (whole numbers) or common fractions (ratios of whole numbers) and if it is positive and not a perfect square, the roots are irrational.

Solution of Equations by Factoring

The method of solving quadratic equations just discussed, that is, the method of completing the square, is general. In contrast, the method of factoring is not general, since it applies only to equations which can be factored into terms which have a value of zero selectively on substitution of particular values of the unknown. However, the factoring method has the advantage that it is not limited to equations of the second degree.

To apply the method first to second degree (quadratic) equations, consider the equation

$$x^2 + 13x + 40 = 0.$$

In accordance with the factoring methods explained in Chapter 3, the factors of $x^2 + 13x + 40$ are $(x + 8)(x + 5)$, as can be checked at once by multiplication.

Therefore $(x + 8)(x + 5) = 0$.

Since the product of these two factors is zero, the quadratic equation is satisfied if either factor is zero.

The first factor, $(x + 8)$, becomes zero if $x = -8$. The second factor, $(x + 5)$, becomes zero if $x = -5$. Therefore the solutions of the quadratic equation are $x = -8$; $x = -5$.

Now, the quadratic equation could, of course, have been solved instead by the general method of completing the square, and thus the factoring method offers no advantages for such equations, except sometimes, as in this case, some shortening of the arithmetical work.

However, consider the cubic equation $x^3 - 1 = 0$. It was shown in Chapter 4 that the factors of this expression $x^3 - 1$ are $(x - 1)(x^2 + x + 1)$, whence the equation becomes

$$(x - 1)(x^2 + x + 1) = 0.$$

Now by setting the first factor $(x - 1) = 0$, there is obtained at once the first root $x = 1$. The other two roots (since third-degree equations in one unknown have three roots) are found by setting the other factor equal to zero, and solving that equation

$$x^2 + x + 1 = 0.$$

Since this equation is not factorable, use Formula (5-9) for solution by completing the square

$$x = \frac{-b \pm \sqrt{b^2 - 4ac}}{2a}$$

In the equation, $x^2 + x + 1 = 0$, a is 1, b is 1, and c is 1. Substituting in the formula,

$$x = \frac{-1 \pm \sqrt{1 - 4}}{2} = \frac{-1 \pm \sqrt{3}\sqrt{-1}}{2}$$

Therefore the three roots of the equation are $x = 1$; $x = \dfrac{-1 + \sqrt{3}\sqrt{-1}}{2}$;

$$x = \frac{-1 - \sqrt{3}\sqrt{-1}}{2}.$$

In addition to factoring methods, there are general algebraic methods for solving third-degree (cubic) and (fourth-degree) quartic equations. Since these algebraic methods are somewhat lengthy, such equations are often solved by graphical methods, as explained in Chapter 8, by approximation methods, or by combinations of the two. The use of approximation methods has increased markedly with the growing availability of computers. (See Chapter 21.)

Chapter 6

CALCULATING WITH LOGARITHMS

Logarithms are used for two purposes that are different in effect but closely related in nature. Their first purpose is to shorten and reduce the work of arithmetical calculations by transforming multiplication into addition, division into subtraction, and calculation of powers or roots into multiplication or division. The second advantage of the use of logarithms is that by so shortening the work of arithmetic, they make possible computations which could not be done otherwise except by the use of calculating machines. For it was explained earlier in this book that extraction of integral roots other than the second is extremely laborious by the methods of arithmetic; while the computation of other fractional or negative powers is practically impossible. By the use of logarithms these calculations become simple and straightforward, as is shown in this present chapter.

A logarithm is an exponent. It is given another name because it is used for a special purpose, to shorten the work in computation with numbers. The method by which this result is accomplished follows, as stated above, from the properties of exponents, which were treated in Chapter 4.

There it was explained that the exponent of a number may be integral or fractional, positive or negative. For example, in $10^2 = 100$, the exponent of ten is integral and positive; in $10^{\frac{1}{2}} = \sqrt{10} = 3.162 \ldots$, the exponent is fractional and positive; in $10^{-2} = \dfrac{1}{10^2} = .01$; the exponent is integral and negative, while in $10^{-\frac{1}{2}} = \dfrac{1}{10^{\frac{1}{2}}} = \dfrac{1}{\sqrt{10}} = \dfrac{\sqrt{10}}{10} = .3162 \ldots$, the exponent is fractional and negative.

The point is, however, that for every exponent of a given number, there is a corresponding number which is the value of the number raised to the power of the exponent.

In calculating with exponents, there are a few special terms used to designate the various numbers involved. They are conveniently defined with respect to the basic relationship as follows:

Let that relationship, which has been exemplified by $10^2 = 100$, be generalized to $a^n = N$. Then n, the exponent of a, is called the *logarithm* of the *number* N to the *base, a*. In the specific example, 2 is the *logarithm* of the *number* 100 to the *base* 10. Instead of writing $a^n = N$, the relationship may also be written in the form $\log_a N$, the *logarithm* to the *base a* of the *number N*. The specific example would appear in this form as $\log_{10} 100$, which is equal to 2. In the case where a logarithm is a mixed number, it is always expressed as a whole number followed by the decimal, rather than by a fraction. Thus the accepted form in which to write the logarithm having a value of one and one-half is 1.5 and not $1\frac{1}{2}$. For example, the logarithm to base 10 of 500 ($\log_{10} 500$) is $2.699 \ldots$. The series of dots following the logarithm denotes continuation, because very few logarithms have exact values (i.e., they are irrational numbers). Therefore, they are computed and used to as many decimal places as the accuracy of the work requires.

Their method of calculation, while a straightforward mathematical process, is not given in this book. Knowledge of it is not required in business mathematics, where logarithms are taken from tables, such as Table 3 in this chapter.

The Logarithm of a Product

By definition the logarithm of a number N to base 10 (or $\log_{10} N$) is equal to a number n such that $10^n = N$. Consider another number M, which has a logarithm to base 10 (or $\log_{10} M$) equal to a number m.

That is, $N = 10^n$, where $n = \log_{10} N$, and $M = 10^m$, where $m = \log_{10} M$. Since by Formula (4-1) Chapter 4,

$$10^n \times 10^m = 10^{n+m}$$

Then, $$N \times M = 10^{n+m}$$

Therefore $$\log_{10} (N \times M) = \log_{10} N + \log_{10} M. \qquad (6\text{-}1)$$

Stating this relationship in words, the logarithm of the product of two numbers to a given base is equal to the sum of the logarithms of the numbers to that base.

This relationship can be further generalized to "the logarithm of the product of any numbers is equal to the sum of their individual logarithms, if all are taken to the same base."

Obviously this relationship provides a means whereby the work in the multiplication of numbers can be greatly reduced. For by determining the logarithms, to the same base, of all the numbers to be multiplied and adding them together, then the number of which their sum is the logarithm (that is, the anti-logarithm of their sum), is the product of the numbers. Thus, by the use of logarithms, multiplication is transformed into addition, a much more rapid operation.

Logarithms Having Integral (Whole Number) Values

In any system of logarithms, that is, using any number as a base, there are few whole number (or rational number) logarithms, as stated above. Consider the logarithms to base 10, which are those used in business mathematics.

The integral and zero logarithms to base 10 have the following values:

$$\log_{10} 1 = 0, \text{ since } 10^0 = 1$$

$$\log_{10} 10 = 1, \text{ since } 10^1 = 10$$

$$\log_{10} 100 = 2, \text{ since } 10^2 = 100$$

$$\log_{10} 1000 = 3, \text{ since } 10^3 = 1000$$

$$\log_{10} 10,000 = 4, \text{ since } 10^4 = 10,000$$

And so on up.

$$\text{Also } \log_{10} 0.1 = -1, \text{ since } 10^{-1} = \frac{1}{10^1} = 0.1$$

$$\log_{10} .01 = -2, \text{ since } 10^{-2} = \frac{1}{10^2} = 0.001$$

$$\log_{10} .001 = -3, \text{ since } 10^{-3} = \frac{1}{10^3} = 0.001$$

$$\log_{10} .0001 = -4, \text{ since } 10^{-4} = \frac{1}{10^4} = 0.0001$$

And so on down.

Note that as negative logarithms increase in numerical value, the numbers they represent grow smaller and smaller, but never reach zero. Thus there are no logarithms of negative numbers, since no exponent of a positive number (and bases of logarithms are always positive) yields a negative value of the power.

The logarithms to base 10 of all the numbers between those given in the above list are decimal numbers or mixed decimal numbers. Their values are given or may be computed from Table 3 in this chapter as explained below.

The Logarithmic Table

To understand the nature of this table, turn to it and examine a typical value. For example, at the top of Page 119, the figure 520 in the N. column indicates that the figures in that row are the logarithms of numbers whose first three figures are 520. The numbers above the table, ranging from 0 to 9, designate the fourth place of the number, so that the number in the 520 row that is below 4 in the top row, this number being 716337, is the logarithm of 5204. Now the question that arises immediately is: where should one place the decimal point in these numbers and their logarithms? In other words, is the figure 716337, that is given in the table, the logarithm of 520.4 or 52.04 or 5.204?

The answer to this question is that 716337 is not the logarithm, but that .716337 is the mantissa of the logarithm. The word mantissa is a special term designating the decimal part of a logarithm, while the integral part is called the characteristic. Thus, the logarithms of 5204 and 52.04 have the same decimal part (mantissa), which is the figure given in the table, 716337, but the (complete) logarithm of 5204 is 3.716337, where 3 is the characteristic and .716337 is the mantissa, while the (complete) logarithm of 52.04 is 1.716337, where 1 is the characteristic and .716337 is the mantissa. The number 5.204 has a characteristic of 0, and a mantissa of .716337, so that the logarithm in this case is the mantissa alone.

The above relationship between numbers and their logarithms has been stated without evidence or justification. However, it is easy to justify by using the values of the numbers having integral logarithms, given on Page 110, and the rule for obtaining the logarithm of a product. Thus, it was shown on Page 110 that:

$$\log_{10} 10 = 1$$
$$\log_{10} 100 = 2$$
$$\log_{10} 1000 = 3$$

Now, as stated on Page 109, the logarithm of a product is equal to the sum of the logarithms of its factors.

Therefore since log 5.204 is .716337, and log 10 is 1,

then log 52.04 (= 5.204 × 10) is .716337 + 1 = 1.716337.
Also since log 5.204 is .716337 and log 100 is 2, then log 520.4 (= 5.204 × 100) is .716337 + 2 = 2.716337.

In other words, the values given in the table of logarithms become, by placing a decimal point before them, the logarithms of the numbers from 1 to 10, even though the logarithms in Table 3 are designated by the use of numbers in the hundreds in its first column.

For example, the logarithm of the number 6.154 is found by locating the number 615 in the first column of the table (the N. column) where it occurs on Page 120, and then moving across the 615 row to the column headed by the number 4; then the value in that space, which is 789157, gives .789157 as the logarithm of 6.154. As another example, the loga-

TABLE 3—LOGARITHMS

N.	0	1	2	3	4	5	6	7	8	9	D
100	000000	000434	000868	001301	001734	002166	002598	003029	003461	003891	432
1	4321	4751	5181	5609	6038	6466	6894	7321	7748	8174	428
2	8600	9026	9451	9876	010300	010724	011147	011570	011993	012415	424
3	012837	013259	013680	014100	4521	4940	5360	5779	6197	6616	420
4	7033	7451	7868	8284	8700	9116	9532	9947	020361	020775	416
105	021189	021603	022016	022428	022841	023252	023664	024075	4486	4896	412
6	5306	5715	6125	6533	6942	7350	7757	8164	8571	8978	408
7	9384	9789	030195	030600	031004	031408	031812	032216	032619	033021	404
8	033424	033826	4227	4628	5029	5430	5830	6230	6629	7028	400
9	7426	7825	8223	8620	9017	9414	9811	040207	040602	040998	397
110	041393	041787	042182	042576	042969	043362	043755	044148	044540	044932	393
1	5323	5714	6105	6495	6885	7275	7664	8053	8442	8830	390
2	9218	9606	9993	050380	050766	051153	051538	051924	052309	052694	386
3	053078	053463	053846	4230	4613	4996	5378	5760	6142	6524	383
4	6905	7286	7666	8046	8426	8805	9185	9563	9942	060320	379
115	060698	061075	061452	061829	062206	062582	062958	063333	063709	4083	376
6	4458	4832	5206	5580	5953	6326	6699	7071	7443	7815	373
7	8186	8557	8928	9298	9668	070038	070407	070776	071145	071514	370
8	071882	072250	072617	072985	073352	3718	4085	4451	4816	5182	366
9	5547	5912	6276	6640	7004	7368	7731	8094	8457	8819	363
120	079181	079543	079904	080266	080626	080987	081347	081707	082067	082426	360
1	082785	083144	083503	3861	4219	4576	4934	5291	5647	6004	357
2	6360	6716	7071	7426	7781	8136	8490	8845	9198	9552	355
3	9905	090258	090611	090963	091315	091667	092018	092370	092721	093071	352
4	093422	3772	4122	4471	4820	5169	5518	5866	6215	6562	349
125	6910	7257	7604	7951	8298	8644	8990	9335	9681	100026	346
6	100371	100715	101059	101403	101747	102091	102434	102777	103119	3462	343
7	3804	4146	4487	4828	5169	5510	5851	6191	6531	6871	341
8	7210	7549	7888	8227	8565	8903	9241	9579	9916	110253	338
9	110590	110926	111263	111599	111934	112270	112605	112940	113275	3609	335
130	113943	114277	114611	114944	115278	115611	115943	116276	116608	116940	333
1	7271	7603	7934	8265	8595	8926	9256	9586	9915	120245	330
2	120574	120903	121231	121560	121888	122216	122544	122871	123198	3525	328
3	3852	4178	4504	4830	5156	5481	5806	6131	6456	6781	325
4	7105	7429	7753	8076	8399	8722	9045	9368	9690	130012	323
135	130334	130655	130977	131298	131619	131939	132260	132580	132900	3219	321
6	3539	3858	4177	4496	4814	5133	5451	5769	6086	6403	318
7	6721	7037	7354	7671	7987	8303	8618	8934	9249	9564	316
8	9879	140194	140508	140822	141136	141450	141763	142076	142389	142702	314
9	143015	3327	3639	3951	4263	4574	4885	5196	5507	5818	311
140	146128	146438	146748	147058	147367	147676	147985	148294	148603	148911	309
1	9219	9527	9835	150142	150449	150756	151063	151370	151676	151982	307
2	152288	152594	152900	3205	3510	3815	4120	4424	4728	5032	305
3	5336	5640	5943	6246	6549	6852	7154	7457	7759	8061	303
4	8362	8664	8965	9266	9567	9868	160168	160469	160769	161068	301
145	161368	161667	161967	162266	162564	162863	3161	3460	3758	4055	299
6	4353	4650	4947	5244	5541	5838	6134	6430	6726	7022	297
7	7317	7613	7908	8203	8497	8792	9086	9380	9674	9968	295
8	170262	170555	170848	171141	171434	171726	172019	172311	172603	172895	293
9	3186	3478	3769	4060	4351	4641	4932	5222	5512	5802	291
150	176091	176381	176670	176959	177248	177536	177825	178113	178401	178689	289
1	8977	9264	9552	9839	180126	180413	180699	180986	181272	181558	287
2	181844	182129	182415	182700	2985	3270	3555	3839	4123	4407	285
3	4691	4975	5259	5542	5825	6108	6391	6674	6956	7239	283
4	7521	7803	8084	8366	8647	8928	9209	9490	9771	190051	281
155	190332	190612	190892	191171	191451	191730	192010	192289	192567	2846	279
6	3125	3403	3681	3959	4237	4514	4792	5069	5346	5623	278
7	5900	6176	6453	6729	7005	7281	7556	7832	8107	8382	276
8	8657	8932	9206	9481	9755	200029	200303	200577	200850	201124	274
9	201397	201670	201943	202216	202488	2761	3033	3305	3577	3848	272
N.	0	1	2	3	4	5	6	7	8	9	D

TABLE 3—LOGARITHMS (Cont.)

N.	0	1	2	3	4	5	6	7	8	9	D.
160	204120	204391	204663	204934	205204	205475	205746	206016	206286	206556	271
1	6826	7096	7365	7634	7904	8173	8441	8710	8979	9247	269
2	9515	9783	210051	210319	210586	210853	211121	211388	211654	211921	267
3	212188	212454	2720	2986	3252	3518	3783	4049	4314	4579	266
4	4844	5109	5373	5638	5902	6166	6430	6694	6957	7221	264
165	7484	7747	8010	8273	8536	8798	9060	9323	9585	9846	262
6	220108	220370	220631	220892	221153	221414	221675	221936	222196	222456	261
7	2716	2976	3236	3496	3755	4015	4274	4533	4792	5051	259
8	5309	5568	5826	6084	6342	6600	6858	7115	7372	7630	258
9	7887	8144	8400	8657	8913	9170	9426	9682	9938	230193	256
170	230449	230704	230960	231215	231470	231724	231979	232234	232488	232742	255
1	2996	3250	3504	3757	4011	4264	4517	4770	5023	5276	253
2	5528	5781	6033	6285	6537	6789	7041	7292	7544	7795	252
3	8046	8297	8548	8799	9049	9299	9550	9800	240050	240300	250
4	240549	240799	241048	241297	241546	241795	242044	242293	2541	2790	249
175	3038	3286	3534	3782	4030	4277	4525	4772	5019	5266	248
6	5513	5759	6006	6252	6499	6745	6991	7237	7482	7728	246
7	7973	8219	8464	8709	8954	9198	9443	9687	9932	250176	245
8	250420	250664	250908	251151	251395	251638	251881	252125	252368	2610	243
9	2853	3096	3338	3580	3822	4064	4306	4548	4790	5031	242
180	255273	255514	255755	255996	256237	256477	256718	256958	257198	257439	241
1	7679	7918	8158	8398	8637	8877	9116	9355	9594	9833	239
2	260071	260310	260548	260787	261025	261263	261501	261739	261976	262214	238
3	2451	2688	2925	3162	3399	3636	3873	4109	4346	4582	237
4	4818	5054	5290	5525	5761	5996	6232	6467	6702	6937	235
185	7172	7406	7641	7875	8110	8344	8578	8812	9046	9279	234
6	9513	9746	9980	270213	270446	270679	270912	271144	271377	271609	233
7	271842	272074	272306	2538	2770	3001	3233	3464	3696	3927	232
8	4158	4389	4620	4850	5081	5311	5542	5772	6002	6232	230
9	6462	6692	6921	7151	7380	7609	7838	8067	8296	8525	229
190	278754	278982	279211	279439	279667	279895	280123	280351	280578	280806	228
1	281033	281261	281488	281715	281942	282169	2396	2622	2849	3075	227
2	3301	3527	3753	3979	4205	4431	4656	4882	5107	5332	226
3	5557	5782	6007	6232	6456	6681	6905	7130	7354	7578	225
4	7802	8026	8249	8473	8696	8920	9143	9366	9589	9812	223
195	290035	290257	290480	290702	290925	291147	291369	291591	291813	292034	222
6	2256	2478	2699	2920	3141	3363	3584	3804	4025	4246	221
7	4466	4687	4907	5127	5347	5567	5787	6007	6226	6446	220
8	6665	6884	7104	7323	7542	7761	7979	8198	8416	8635	219
9	8853	9071	9289	9507	9725	9943	300161	300378	300595	300813	218
200	301030	301247	301464	301681	301898	302114	302331	302547	302764	302980	217
1	3196	3412	3628	3844	4059	4275	4491	4706	4921	5136	216
2	5351	5566	5781	5996	6211	6425	6639	6854	7068	7282	215
3	7496	7710	7924	8137	8351	8564	8778	8991	9204	9417	213
4	9630	9843	310056	310268	310481	310693	310906	311118	311330	311542	212
205	311754	311966	2177	2389	2600	2812	3023	3234	3445	3656	211
6	3867	4078	4289	4499	4710	4920	5130	5340	5551	5760	210
7	5970	6180	6390	6599	6809	7018	7227	7436	7646	7854	209
8	8063	8272	8481	8689	8898	9106	9314	9522	9730	9938	208
9	320146	320354	320562	320769	320977	321184	321391	321598	321805	322012	207
210	322219	322426	322633	322839	323046	323252	323458	323665	323872	324077	206
1	4282	4488	4694	4899	5105	5310	5516	5721	5926	6131	205
2	6336	6541	6745	6950	7155	7359	7563	7767	7972	8176	204
3	8380	8583	8787	8991	9194	9398	9601	9805	330008	330211	203
4	330414	330617	330819	331022	331225	331427	331630	331832	2034	2236	202
215	2438	2640	2842	3044	3246	3447	3649	3850	4051	4253	202
6	4454	4655	4856	5057	5257	5458	5658	5859	6059	6260	201
7	6460	6660	6860	7060	7260	7459	7659	7858	8058	8257	200
8	8456	8656	8855	9054	9253	9451	9650	9849	340047	340246	199
9	340444	340642	340841	341039	341237	341435	341632	341830	2028	2225	198
N.	0	1	2	3	4	5	6	7	8	9	D.

TABLE 3—LOGARITHMS (Cont.)

N.	0	1	2	3	4	5	6	7	8	9	D.
220	342423	342620	342817	343014	343212	343409	343606	343802	343999	344196	197
1	4392	4589	4785	4981	5178	5374	5570	5766	5962	6157	196
2	6353	6549	6744	6939	7135	7330	7525	7720	7915	8110	195
3	8305	8500	8694	8889	9083	9278	9472	9666	9860	350054	194
4	350248	350442	350636	350829	351023	351216	351410	351603	351796	1989	193
225	2183	2375	2568	2761	2954	3147	3339	3532	3724	3916	193
6	4108	4301	4493	4685	4876	5068	5260	5452	5643	5834	192
7	6026	6217	6408	6599	6790	6981	7172	7363	7554	7744	191
8	7935	8125	8316	8506	8696	8886	9076	9266	9456	9646	190
9	9835	360025	360215	360404	360593	360783	360972	361161	361350	361539	189
230	361728	361917	362105	362294	362482	362671	362859	363048	363236	363424	188
1	3612	3800	3988	4176	4363	4551	4739	4926	5113	5301	188
2	5488	5675	5862	6049	6236	6423	6610	6796	6983	7169	187
3	7356	7542	7729	7915	8101	8287	8473	8659	8845	9030	186
4	9216	9401	9587	9772	9958	370143	370328	370513	370698	370883	185
235	371068	371253	371437	371622	371806	1991	2175	2360	2544	2728	184
6	2912	3096	3280	3464	3647	3831	4015	4198	4382	4565	184
7	4748	4932	5115	5298	5481	5664	5846	6029	6212	6394	183
8	6577	6759	6942	7124	7306	7488	7670	7852	8034	8216	182
9	8398	8580	8761	8943	9124	9306	9487	9668	9849	380030	181
240	380211	380392	380573	380754	380934	381115	381296	381476	381656	381837	181
1	2017	2197	2377	2557	2737	2917	3097	3277	3456	3636	180
2	3815	3995	4174	4353	4533	4712	4891	5070	5249	5428	179
3	5606	5785	5964	6142	6321	6499	6677	6856	7034	7212	178
4	7390	7568	7746	7923	8101	8279	8456	8634	8811	8989	178
245	9166	9343	9520	9698	9875	390051	390228	390405	390582	390759	177
6	390935	391112	391288	391464	391641	1817	1993	2169	2345	2521	176
7	2697	2873	3048	3224	3400	3575	3751	3926	4101	4277	176
8	4452	4627	4802	4977	5152	5326	5501	5676	5850	6025	175
9	6199	6374	6548	6722	6896	7071	7245	7419	7592	7766	174
250	397940	398114	398287	398461	398634	398808	398981	399154	399328	399501	173
1	9674	9847	400020	400192	400365	400538	400711	400883	401056	401228	173
2	401401	401573	1745	1917	2089	2261	2433	2605	2777	2949	172
3	3121	3292	3464	3635	3807	3978	4149	4320	4492	4663	171
4	4834	5005	5176	5346	5517	5688	5858	6029	6199	6370	171
255	6540	6710	6881	7051	7221	7391	7561	7731	7901	8070	170
6	8240	8410	8579	8749	8918	9087	9257	9426	9595	9764	169
7	9933	410102	410271	410440	410609	410777	410964	411114	411283	411451	169
8	411620	1788	1956	2124	2293	2461	2629	2796	2964	3132	168
9	3300	3467	3635	3803	3970	4137	4305	4472	4639	4806	167
260	414973	415140	415307	415474	415641	415808	415974	416141	416308	416474	167
1	6641	6807	6973	7139	7306	7472	7638	7804	7970	8135	166
2	8301	8467	8633	8798	8964	9129	9295	9460	9625	9791	165
3	9956	420121	420286	420451	420616	420781	420945	421110	421275	421439	165
4	421604	1768	1933	2097	2261	2426	2590	2754	2918	3082	164
265	3246	3410	3574	3737	3901	4065	4228	4392	4555	4718	164
6	4882	5045	5208	5371	5534	5697	5860	6023	6186	6349	163
7	6511	6674	6836	6999	7161	7324	7486	7648	7811	7973	162
8	8135	8297	8459	8621	8783	8944	9106	9268	9429	9591	162
9	9752	9914	430075	430236	430398	430559	430720	430881	431042	431203	161
270	431364	431525	431685	431846	432007	432167	432328	432488	432649	432809	161
1	2969	3130	3290	3450	3610	3770	3930	4090	4249	4409	160
2	4569	4729	4888	5048	5207	5367	5526	5685	5844	6004	159
3	6163	6322	6481	6640	6799	6957	7116	7275	7433	7592	159
4	7751	7909	8067	8226	8384	8542	8701	8859	9017	9175	158
275	9333	9491	9648	9806	9964	440122	440279	440437	440594	440752	158
6	440909	441066	441224	441381	441538	1695	1852	2009	2166	2323	157
7	2480	2637	2793	2950	3106	3263	3419	3576	3732	3889	157
8	4045	4201	4357	4513	4669	4825	4981	5137	5293	5449	156
9	5604	5760	5915	6071	6226	6382	6537	6692	6848	7003	155
N.	0	1	2	3	4	5	6	7	8	9	D.

TABLE 3—LOGARITHMS (Cont.)

N.	0	1	2	3	4	5	6	7	8	9	D.
280	447158	447313	447468	447623	447778	447933	448088	448242	448397	448552	155
1	8706	8861	9015	9170	9324	9478	9633	9787	9941	450095	154
2	450249	450403	450557	450711	450865	451018	451172	451326	451479	1633	154
3	1786	1940	2093	2247	2400	2553	2706	2859	3012	3165	153
4	3318	3471	3624	3777	3930	4082	4235	4387	4540	4692	153
285	4845	4997	5150	5302	5454	5606	5758	5910	6062	6214	152
6	6366	6518	6670	6821	6973	7125	7276	7428	7579	7731	152
7	7882	8033	8184	8336	8487	8639	8789	8940	9091	9242	151
8	9392	9543	9694	9845	9995	460146	460296	460447	460597	460748	151
9	460898	461048	461198	461348	461499	1649	1799	1948	2098	2248	150
290	462398	462548	462697	462847	462997	463146	463296	463445	463594	463744	150
1	3893	4042	4191	4340	4490	4639	4788	4936	5085	5234	149
2	5383	5532	5680	5829	5977	6126	6274	6423	6571	6719	149
3	6868	7016	7164	7312	7460	7608	7756	7904	8052	8200	148
4	8347	8495	8643	8790	8938	9085	9233	9380	9527	9675	148
295	9822	9969	470116	470263	470410	470557	470704	470851	470998	471145	147
6	471292	471438	1585	1732	1878	2025	2171	2318	2464	2610	146
7	2756	2903	3049	3195	3341	3487	3633	3779	3925	4071	146
8	4216	4362	4508	4653	4799	4944	5090	5235	5381	5526	146
9	5671	5816	5962	6107	6252	6397	6542	6687	6832	6976	145
300	477121	477266	477411	477555	477700	477844	477989	478133	478278	478422	145
1	8566	8711	8855	8999	9143	9287	9431	9575	9719	9863	144
2	480007	480151	480294	480438	480582	480725	480869	481012	481156	481299	144
3	1443	1586	1729	1872	2016	2159	2302	2445	2588	2731	143
4	2874	3016	3159	3302	3445	3587	3730	3872	4015	4157	143
305	4300	4442	4585	4727	4869	5011	5153	5295	5437	5579	142
6	5721	5863	6005	6147	6289	6430	6572	6714	6855	6997	142
7	7138	7280	7421	7563	7704	7845	7986	8127	8269	8410	141
8	8551	8692	8833	8974	9114	9255	9396	9537	9677	9818	141
9	9958	490099	490239	490380	490520	490661	490801	490941	491081	491222	140
310	491362	491502	491642	491782	491922	492062	492201	492341	492481	492621	140
1	2760	2900	3040	3179	3319	3458	3597	3737	3876	4015	139
2	4155	4294	4433	4572	4711	4850	4989	5128	5267	5406	139
3	5544	5683	5822	5960	6099	6238	6376	6515	6653	6791	139
4	6930	7068	7206	7344	7483	7621	7759	7897	8035	8173	138
315	8311	8448	8586	8724	8862	8999	9137	9275	9412	9550	138
6	9687	9824	9962	500099	500236	500374	500511	500648	500785	500922	137
7	501059	501196	501333	1470	1607	1744	1880	2017	2154	2291	137
8	2427	2564	2700	2837	2973	3109	3246	3382	3518	3655	136
9	3791	3927	4063	4199	4335	4471	4607	4743	4878	5014	136
320	505150	505286	505421	505557	505693	505828	505964	506099	506234	506370	136
1	6505	6640	6776	6911	7046	7181	7316	7451	7586	7721	135
2	7856	7991	8126	8260	8395	8530	8664	8799	8934	9068	135
3	9203	9337	9471	9606	9740	9874	510009	510143	510277	510411	134
4	510545	510679	510813	510947	511081	511215	1349	1482	1616	1750	134
325	1883	2017	2151	2284	2418	2551	2684	2818	2951	3084	133
8	3218	3351	3484	3617	3750	3883	4016	4149	4282	4415	133
7	4548	4681	4813	4946	5079	5211	5344	5476	5609	5741	133
8	5874	6006	6139	6271	6403	6535	6668	6800	6932	7064	132
9	7196	7328	7460	7592	7724	7855	7987	8119	8251	8382	132
330	518514	518646	518777	518909	519040	519171	519303	519434	519566	519697	131
1	9828	9959	520090	520221	520353	520484	520615	520745	520876	521007	131
2	521138	521269	1400	1530	1661	1792	1922	2053	2183	2314	131
3	2444	2575	2705	2835	2966	3096	3226	3356	3486	3616	130
4	3746	3876	4006	4136	4266	4396	4526	4656	4785	4915	130
335	5045	5174	5304	5434	5563	5693	5822	5951	6081	6210	129
6	6339	6469	6598	6727	6856	6985	7114	7243	7372	7501	129
7	7630	7759	7888	8016	8145	8274	8402	8531	8660	8788	129
8	8917	9045	9174	9302	9430	9559	9687	9815	9943	530072	128
9	530200	530328	530456	530584	530712	530840	530968	531096	531223	1351	128
N.	0	1	2	3	4	5	6	7	8	9	D.

Table 3—Logarithms (Cont.)

N.	0	1	2	3	4	5	6	7	8	9	D.
340	531479	531607	531734	531862	531990	532117	532245	532372	532500	532627	128
1	2754	2882	3009	3136	3264	3391	3518	3645	3772	3899	127
2	4026	4153	4280	4407	4534	4661	4787	4914	5041	5167	127
3	5294	5421	5547	5674	5800	5927	6053	6180	6306	6432	126
4	6558	6685	6811	6937	7063	7189	7315	7441	7567	7693	126
345	7819	7945	8071	8197	8322	8448	8574	8699	8825	8951	126
6	9076	9202	9327	9452	9578	9703	9829	9954	540079	540204	125
7	540329	540455	540580	540705	540830	540955	541080	541205	1330	1454	125
8	1579	1704	1829	1953	2078	2203	2327	2452	2576	2701	125
9	2825	2950	3074	3199	3323	3447	3571	3696	3820	3944	124
350	544068	544192	544316	544440	544564	544688	544812	544936	545060	545183	124
1	5307	5431	5555	5678	5802	5925	6049	6172	6296	6419	124
2	6543	6666	6789	6913	7036	7159	7282	7405	7529	7652	123
3	7775	7898	8021	8144	8267	8389	8512	8635	8758	8881	123
4	9003	9126	9249	9371	9494	9616	9739	9861	9984	550106	123
355	550228	550351	550473	550595	550717	550840	550962	551084	551206	1328	122
6	1450	1572	1694	1816	1938	2060	2181	2303	2425	2547	122
7	2668	2790	2911	3033	3155	3276	3398	3519	3640	3762	121
8	3883	4004	4126	4247	4368	4489	4610	4731	4852	4973	121
9	5094	5215	5336	5457	5578	5699	5820	5940	6061	6182	121
360	556303	556423	556544	556664	556785	556905	557026	557146	557267	557387	120
1	7507	7627	7748	7868	7988	8108	8228	8349	8469	8589	120
2	8709	8829	8948	9068	9188	9308	9428	9548	9667	9787	120
3	9907	560026	560146	560265	560385	560504	560624	560743	560863	560982	119
4	561101	1221	1340	1459	1578	1698	1817	1936	2055	2174	119
365	2293	2412	2531	2650	2769	2887	3006	3125	3244	3362	119
6	3481	3600	3718	3837	3955	4074	4192	4311	4429	4548	119
7	4666	4784	4903	5021	5139	5257	5376	5494	5612	5730	118
8	5848	5966	6084	6202	6320	6437	6555	6673	6791	6909	118
9	7026	7144	7262	7379	7497	7614	7732	7849	7967	8084	118
370	568202	568319	568436	568554	568671	568788	568905	569023	569140	569257	117
1	9374	9491	9608	9725	9842	9959	570076	570193	570309	570426	117
2	570543	570660	570776	570893	571010	571126	1243	1359	1476	1592	117
3	1709	1825	1942	2058	2174	2291	2407	2523	2639	2755	116
4	2872	2988	3104	3220	3336	3452	3568	3684	3800	3915	116
375	4031	4147	4263	4379	4494	4610	4726	4841	4957	5072	116
6	5188	5303	5419	5534	5650	5765	5880	5996	6111	6226	115
7	6341	6457	6572	6687	6802	6917	7032	7147	7262	7377	115
8	7492	7607	7722	7836	7951	8066	8181	8295	8410	8525	115
9	8639	8754	8868	8983	9097	9212	9326	9441	9555	9669	114
380	579784	579898	580012	580126	580241	580355	580469	580583	580697	580811	114
1	580925	581039	1153	1267	1381	1495	1608	1722	1836	1950	114
2	2063	2177	2291	2404	2518	2631	2745	2858	2972	3085	114
3	3199	3312	3426	3539	3652	3765	3879	3992	4105	4218	113
4	4331	4444	4557	4670	4783	4896	5009	5122	5235	5348	113
385	5461	5574	5686	5799	5912	6024	6137	6250	6362	6475	113
6	6587	6700	6812	6925	7037	7149	7262	7374	7486	7599	112
7	7711	7823	7935	8047	8160	8272	8384	8496	8608	8720	112
8	8832	8944	9056	9167	9279	9391	9503	9615	9726	9838	112
9	9950	590061	590173	590284	590396	590507	590619	590730	590842	590953	112
390	591065	591176	591287	591399	591510	591621	591732	591843	591955	592066	111
1	2177	2288	2399	2510	2621	2732	2843	2954	3064	3175	111
2	3286	3397	3508	3618	3729	3840	3950	4061	4171	4282	111
3	4393	4503	4614	4724	4834	4945	5055	5165	5276	5380	110
4	5496	5606	5717	5827	5937	6047	6157	6267	6377	6487	110
395	6597	6707	6817	6927	7037	7146	7256	7366	7476	7586	110
6	7695	7805	7914	8024	8134	8243	8353	8462	8572	8681	110
7	8791	8900	9009	9119	9228	9337	9446	9556	9665	9774	109
8	9883	9992	600101	600210	600319	600428	600537	600646	600755	600864	109
9	600973	601082	1191	1299	1408	1517	1625	1734	1843	1951	109
N.	0	1	2	3	4	5	6	7	8	9	D.

TABLE 3—LOGARITHMS (Cont.)

N.	0	1	2	3	4	5	6	7	8	9	D.
400	602060	602169	602277	602386	602494	602603	602711	602819	602928	603036	108
1	3144	3253	3361	3469	3577	3686	3794	3902	4010	4118	108
2	4226	4334	4442	4550	4658	4766	4874	4982	5089	5197	108
3	5305	5413	5521	5628	5736	5844	5951	6059	6166	6274	108
4	6381	6489	6596	6704	6811	6919	7026	7183	7241	7348	107
405	7455	7562	7669	7777	7884	7991	8098	8205	8312	8419	107
6	8526	8633	8740	8847	8954	9061	9167	9274	9381	9488	107
7	9594	9701	9808	9914	610021	610128	610234	610341	610447	610554	107
8	610660	610767	610873	610979	1086	1192	1298	1405	1511	1617	106
9	1723	1829	1936	2042	2148	2254	2360	2466	2572	2678	106
410	612784	612890	612996	613102	613207	613313	613419	613525	613630	613736	106
1	3842	3947	4053	4159	4264	4370	4475	4581	4686	4792	106
2	4897	5003	5108	5213	5319	5424	5529	5634	5740	5845	105
3	5950	6055	6160	6265	6370	6476	6581	6686	6790	6895	105
4	7000	7105	7210	7315	7420	7525	7629	7734	7839	7943	105
415	8048	8153	8257	8362	8466	8571	8676	8780	8884	8989	105
6	9093	9198	9302	9406	9511	9615	9719	9824	9928	620032	104
7	620136	620240	620344	620448	620552	620656	620760	620864	620968	1072	104
8	1176	1280	1384	1488	1592	1695	1799	1903	2007	2110	104
9	2214	2318	2421	2525	2628	2732	2835	2939	3042	3146	104
420	623249	623353	623456	623559	623663	623766	623869	623973	624076	624179	103
1	4282	4385	4488	4591	4695	4798	4901	5004	5107	5210	103
2	5312	5415	5518	5621	5724	5827	5929	6032	6135	6238	103
3	6340	6443	6546	6648	6751	6853	6956	7058	7161	7263	103
4	7366	7468	7571	7673	7775	7878	7980	8082	8185	8287	102
425	8389	8491	8593	8695	8797	8900	9002	9104	9206	9308	102
6	9410	9512	9613	9715	9817	9919	630021	630123	630224	630326	102
7	630428	630530	630631	630733	630835	630936	1038	1139	1241	1342	102
8	1444	1545	1647	1748	1849	1951	2052	2153	2255	2356	101
9	2457	2559	2660	2761	2862	2963	3064	3165	3266	3367	101
430	633468	633569	633670	633771	633872	633973	634074	634175	634276	634376	101
1	4477	4578	4679	4779	4880	4981	5081	5182	5283	5383	101
2	5484	5584	5685	5785	5886	5986	6087	6187	6287	6388	100
3.	6488	6588	6688	6789	6889	6989	7089	7189	7290	7390	100
4	7490	7590	7690	7790	7890	7990	8090	8190	8290	8389	100
435	8489	8589	8689	8789	8888	8988	9088	9188	9287	9387	100
6	9486	9586	9686	9785	9885	9984	640084	640183	640283	640382	99
7	640481	640581	640680	640779	640879	640978	1077	1177	1276	1375	99
8	1474	1573	1672	1771	1871	1970	2069	2168	2267	2366	99
9	2465	2563	2662	2761	2860	2959	3058	3156	3255	3354	99
440	643453	643551	643650	643749	643847	643946	644044	644143	644242	644340	98
1	4439	4537	4636	4734	4832	4931	5029	5127	5226	5324	98
2	5422	5521	5619	5717	5815	5913	6011	6110	6208	6306	98
3	6404	6502	6600	6698	6796	6894	6992	7089	7187	7285	98
4	7383	7481	7579	7676	7774	7872	7969	8067	8165	8262	98
445	8360	8458	8555	8653	8750	8848	8945	9043	9140	9237	97
6	9335	9432	9530	9627	9724	9821	9919	650016	650113	650210	97
7	650308	650405	650502	650599	650696	650793	650890	0987	1084	1181	97
8	1278	1375	1472	1569	1666	1762	1859	1956	2053	2150	97
9	2246	2343	2440	2536	2633	2730	2826	2923	3019	3116	97
450	653213	653309	653405	653502	653598	653695	653791	653888	653984	654080	96
1	4177	4273	4369	4465	4562	4658	4754	4850	4946	5042	96
2	5138	5235	5331	5427	5523	5619	5715	5810	5906	6002	96
3	6098	6194	6290	6386	6482	6577	6673	6769	6864	6960	96
4	7056	7152	7247	7343	7438	7534	7629	7725	7820	7916	96
455	8011	8107	8202	8298	8393	8488	8584	8679	8774	8870	95
6	8965	9060	9155	9250	9346	9441	9536	9631	9726	9821	95
7	9916	660011	660106	660201	660296	660391	660486	660581	660676	660771	95
8	660865	0960	1055	1150	1245	1339	1434	1529	1623	1718	95
9	1813	1907	2002	2096	2191	2286	2380	2475	2569	2663	95
N.	0	1	2	3	4	5	6	7	8	9	D.

TABLE 3—LOGARITHMS (Cont.)

N.	0	1	2	3	4	5	6	7	8	9	D.
460	662758	662852	662947	663041	663135	663230	663324	663418	663512	663607	94
1	3701	3795	3889	3983	4078	4172	4266	4360	4454	4548	94
2	4642	4736	4830	4924	5018	5112	5206	5299	5393	5487	94
3	5581	5675	5769	5862	5956	6050	6143	6237	6331	6424	94
4	6518	6612	6705	6799	6892	6986	7079	7173	7266	7360	94
465	7453	7546	7640	7733	7826	7920	8013	8106	8199	8293	93
6	8386	8479	8572	8665	8759	8852	8945	9038	9131	9224	93
7	9317	9410	9503	9596	9689	9782	9875	9967	670060	670153	93
8	670246	670339	670431	670524	670617	670710	670802	670895	0988	1080	93
9	1173	1265	1358	1451	1543	1636	1728	1821	1913	2005	93
470	672098	672190	672283	672375	672467	672560	672652	672744	672836	672929	92
1	3021	3113	3205	3297	3390	3482	3574	3666	3758	3850	92
2	3942	4034	4126	4218	4310	4402	4494	4586	4677	4769	92
3	4861	4953	5045	5137	5228	5320	5412	5503	5595	5687	92
4	5778	5870	5962	6053	6145	6236	6328	6419	6511	6602	92
475	6694	6785	6876	6968	7059	7151	7242	7333	7424	7516	91
6	7607	7698	7789	7881	7972	8063	8154	8245	8336	8427	91
7	8518	8609	8700	8791	8882	8973	9064	9155	9246	9337	91
8	9428	9519	9610	9700	9791	9882	9973	680063	680154	680245	91
9	680336	680426	680517	680607	680698	680789	680879	0970	1060	1151	91
480	681241	681332	681422	681513	681603	681693	681784	681874	681964	682055	90
1	2145	2235	2326	2416	2506	2596	2686	2777	2867	2957	90
2	3047	3137	3227	3317	3407	3497	3587	3677	3767	3857	90
3	3947	4037	4127	4217	4307	4396	4486	4576	4666	4756	90
4	4845	4935	5025	5114	5204	5294	5383	5473	5563	5652	90
485	5742	5831	5921	6010	6100	6189	6279	6368	6458	6547	89
6	6636	6726	6815	6904	6994	7083	7172	7261	7351	7440	89
7	7529	7618	7707	7796	7886	7975	8064	8153	8242	8331	89
8	8420	8509	8598	8687	8776	8865	8953	9042	9131	9220	89
9	9309	9398	9486	9575	9664	9753	9841	9930	690019	690107	89
490	690196	690285	690373	690462	690550	690639	690728	690816	690905	690993	89
1	1081	1170	1258	1347	1435	1524	1612	1700	1789	1877	88
2	1965	2053	2142	2230	2318	2406	2494	2583	2671	2759	88
3	2847	2935	3023	3111	3199	3287	3375	3463	3551	3639	88
4	3727	3815	3903	3991	4078	4166	4254	4342	4430	4517	88
495	4605	4693	4781	4868	4956	5044	5131	5219	5307	5394	88
6	5482	5569	5657	5744	5832	5919	6007	6094	6182	6269	87
7	6356	6444	6531	6618	6706	6793	6880	6968	7055	7142	87
8	7229	7317	7404	7491	7578	7665	7752	7839	7926	8014	87
9	8101	8188	8275	8362	8449	8535	8622	8709	8796	8883	87
500	698970	699057	699144	699231	699317	699404	699491	699578	699664	699751	87
1	9838	9924	700011	700098	700184	700271	700358	700444	700531	700617	87
2	700704	700790	0877	0963	1050	1136	1222	1309	1395	1482	86
3	1568	1654	1741	1827	1913	1999	2086	2172	2258	2344	86
4	2431	2517	2603	2689	2775	2861	2947	3033	3119	3205	86
505	3291	3377	3463	3549	3635	3721	3807	3893	3979	4065	86
6	4151	4236	4322	4408	4494	4579	4665	4751	4837	4922	86
7	5008	5094	5179	5265	5350	5436	5522	5607	5693	5778	86
8	5864	5949	6085	6120	6206	6291	6376	6462	6547	6632	85
9	6718	6803	6888	6974	7059	7144	7229	7315	7400	7485	85
510	707570	707655	707740	707826	707911	707996	708081	708166	708251	708336	85
1	8421	8506	8591	8676	8761	8846	8931	9015	9100	9185	85
2	9270	9355	9440	9524	9609	9694	9779	9863	9948	710033	85
3	710117	710202	710287	710371	710456	710540	710625	710710	710794	0879	85
4	0963	1048	1132	1217	1301	1385	1470	1554	1639	1723	84
515	1807	1892	1976	2060	2144	2229	2313	2397	2481	2566	84
6	2650	2734	2818	2902	2986	3070	3154	3238	3323	3407	84
7	3491	3575	3659	3742	3826	3910	3994	4078	4162	4246	84
8	4330	4414	4497	4581	4665	4749	4833	4916	5000	5084	84
9	5167	5251	5335	5418	5502	5586	5669	5753	5836	5920	84
N.	0	1	2	3	4	5	6	7	8	9	D.

TABLE 3—LOGARITHMS (Cont.)

N.	0	1	2	3	4	5	6	7	8	9	D.
520	716003	716087	716170	716254	716337	716421	716504	716588	716671	716754	83
1	6838	6921	7004	7088	7171	7254	7338	7421	7504	7587	83
2	7671	7754	7837	7920	8003	8086	8169	8253	8336	8419	83
3	8502	8585	8668	8751	8834	8917	9000	9083	9165	9248	83
4	9331	9414	9497	9580	9663	9745	9828	9911	9994	720077	83
525	720159	720242	720325	720407	720490	720573	720655	720738	720821	0903	83
6	0986	1068	1151	1233	1316	1398	1481	1563	1646	1728	82
7	1811	1893	1975	2058	2140	2222	2305	2387	2469	2552	82
8	2634	2716	2798	2881	2963	3045	3127	3209	3291	3374	82
9	3456	3538	3620	3702	3784	3866	3948	4030	4112	4194	82
530	724276	724358	724440	724522	724604	724685	724767	724849	724931	725013	82
1	5095	5176	5258	5340	5422	5503	5585	5667	5748	5830	82
2	5912	5993	6075	6156	6238	6320	6401	6483	6564	6646	82
3	6727	6809	6890	6972	7053	7134	7216	7297	7379	7460	81
4	7541	7623	7704	7785	7866	7948	8029	8110	8191	8273	81
535	8354	8435	8516	8597	8678	8759	8841	8922	9003	9084	81
6	9165	9246	9327	9408	9489	9570	9651	9732	9813	9893	81
7	9974	730055	730136	730217	730298	730378	730459	730540	730621	730702	81
8	730782	0863	0944	1024	1105	1186	1266	1347	1428	1508	81
9	1589	1669	1750	1830	1911	1991	2072	2152	2233	2313	81
540	732394	732474	732555	732635	732715	732796	732876	732956	733037	733117	80
1	3197	3278	3358	3438	3518	3598	3679	3759	3839	3919	80
2	3999	4079	4160	4240	4320	4400	4480	4560	4640	4720	80
3	4800	4880	4960	5040	5120	5200	5279	5359	5439	5519	80
4	5599	5679	5759	5838	5918	5998	6078	6157	6237	6317	80
545	6397	6476	6556	6635	6715	6795	6874	6954	7034	7113	80
6	7193	7272	7352	7431	7511	7590	7670	7749	7829	7908	79
7	7987	8067	8146	8225	8305	8384	8463	8543	8622	8701	79
8	8781	8860	8939	9018	9097	9177	9256	9335	9414	9493	79
9	9572	9651	9731	9810	9889	9968	740047	740126	740205	740284	79
550	740363	740442	740521	740600	740678	740757	740836	740915	740994	741073	79
1	1152	1230	1309	1388	1467	1546	1624	1703	1782	1860	79
2	1939	2018	2090	2175	2254	2332	2411	2489	2568	2647	79
3	2725	2804	2882	2961	3039	3118	3196	3275	3353	3431	78
4	3510	3588	3667	3745	3823	3902	3980	4058	4136	4215	78
555	4293	4371	4449	4528	4606	4684	4762	4840	4919	4997	78
6	5075	5153	5231	5309	5387	5465	5543	5621	5699	5777	78
7	5855	5933	6011	6089	6167	6245	6323	6401	6479	6556	78
8	6634	6712	6790	6868	6945	7023	7101	7179	7256	7334	78
9	7412	7489	7567	7645	7722	7800	7878	7955	8033	8110	78
560	748188	748266	748343	748421	748498	748576	748653	748731	748808	748885	77
1	8963	9040	9118	9195	9272	9350	9427	9504	9582	9659	77
2	9736	9814	9891	9968	750045	750123	750200	750277	750354	750431	77
3	750508	750586	750663	750740	0817	0894	0971	1048	1125	1202	77
4	1279	1356	1433	1510	1587	1664	1741	1818	1895	1972	77
565	2048	2125	2202	2279	2356	2433	2509	2586	2663	2740	77
6	2816	2893	2970	3047	3123	3200	3277	3353	3430	3506	77
7	3583	3660	3736	3813	3889	3966	4042	4119	4195	4272	77
8	4348	4425	4501	4578	4654	4730	4807	4883	4960	5036	76
9	5112	5189	5265	5341	5417	5494	5570	5646	5722	5799	76
570	755875	755951	756027	756103	756180	756256	756332	756408	756484	756560	76
1	6636	6712	6788	6864	6940	7016	7092	7168	7244	7320	76
2	7396	7472	7548	7624	7700	7775	7851	7927	8003	8079	76
3	8155	8230	8306	8382	8458	8533	8609	8685	8761	8836	76
4	8912	8988	9063	9139	9214	9290	9366	9441	9517	9592	76
575	9668	9743	9819	9894	9970	760045	760121	760196	760272	760347	75
6	760422	760498	760573	760649	760724	0799	0875	0950	1025	1101	75
7	1176	1251	1326	1402	1477	1552	1627	1702	1778	1853	75
8	1928	2003	2078	2153	2228	2303	2378	2453	2529	2604	75
9	2679	2754	2829	2904	2978	3053	3128	3203	3278	3353	75
N.	0	1	2	3	4	5	6	7	8	9	D.

TABLE 3—LOGARITHMS (Cont.)

N.	0	1	2	3	4	5	6	7	8	9	D.
580	763428	763503	763578	763653	763727	763802	763877	763952	764027	764101	75
1	4176	4251	4326	4400	4475	4550	4624	4699	4774	4848	75
2	4923	4998	5072	5147	5221	5296	5370	5445	5520	5594	75
3	5669	5743	5818	5892	5966	6041	6115	6190	6264	6338	74
4	6413	6487	6562	6636	6710	6785	6859	6933	7007	7082	74
585	7156	7230	7304	7379	7453	7527	7601	7675	7749	7823	74
6	7898	7972	8046	8120	8194	8268	8342	8416	8490	8564	74
7	8638	8712	8786	8860	8934	9008	9082	9156	9230	9303	74
8	9377	9451	9525	9599	9673	9746	9820	9894	9968	770042	74
9	770115	770189	770263	770336	770410	770484	770557	770631	770705	0778	74
590	770852	770926	770999	771073	771146	771220	771293	771367	771440	771514	74
1	1587	1661	1734	1808	1881	1955	2028	2102	2175	2248	73
2	2322	2395	2468	2542	2615	2688	2762	2835	2908	2981	73
3	3055	3128	3201	3274	3348	3421	3494	3567	3640	3713	73
4	3786	3860	3933	4006	4079	4152	4225	4298	4371	4444	73
595	4517	4590	4663	4736	4809	4882	4955	5028	5100	5173	73
6	5246	5319	5392	5465	5538	5610	5683	5756	5829	5902	73
7	5974	6047	6120	6193	6265	6338	6411	6483	6556	6629	73
8	6701	6774	6846	6919	6992	7064	7137	7209	7282	7354	73
9	7427	7499	7572	7644	7717	7789	7862	7934	8006	8079	72
600	778151	778224	778296	778368	778441	778513	778585	778658	778730	778802	72
1	8874	8947	9019	9091	9163	9236	9308	9380	9452	9524	72
2	9596	9669	9741	9813	9885	9957	780029	780101	780173	780245	72
3	780317	780389	780461	780533	780605	780677	0749	0821	0893	0965	72
4	1037	1109	1181	1253	1324	1396	1468	1540	1612	1684	72
605	1755	1827	1899	1971	2042	2114	2186	2258	2329	2401	72
6	2473	2544	2616	2688	2759	2831	2902	2974	3046	3117	72
7	3189	3260	3332	3403	3475	3546	3618	3689	3761	3832	71
8	3904	3975	4046	4118	4189	4261	4332	4403	4475	4546	71
9	4617	4689	4760	4831	4902	4974	5045	5116	5187	5259	71
610	785330	785401	785472	785543	785615	785686	785757	785828	785899	785970	71
1	6041	6112	6183	6254	6325	6396	6467	6538	6609	6680	71
2	6751	6822	6893	6964	7035	7106	7177	7248	7319	7390	71
3	7460	7531	7602	7673	7744	7815	7885	7956	8027	8098	71
4	8168	8239	8310	8381	8451	8522	8593	8663	8734	8804	71
615	8875	8946	9016	9087	9157	9228	9299	9369	9440	9510	71
6	9581	9651	9722	9792	9863	9933	790004	790074	790144	790215	70
7	790285	790356	790426	790496	790567	790637	0707	0778	0848	0918	70
8	0988	1059	1129	1199	1269	1340	1410	1480	1550	1620	70
9	1691	1761	1831	1901	1971	2041	2111	2181	2252	2322	70
620	792392	792462	792532	792602	792672	792742	792812	792882	792952	793022	70
1	3092	3162	3231	3301	3371	3441	3511	3581	3651	3721	70
2	3790	3860	3930	4000	4070	4139	4209	4279	4349	4418	70
3	4488	4558	4627	4697	4767	4836	4906	4976	5045	5115	70
4	5185	5254	5324	5393	5463	5532	5602	5672	5741	5811	70
625	5880	5949	6019	6088	6158	6227	6297	6366	6436	6505	69
6	6574	6644	6713	6782	6852	6921	6990	7060	7129	7198	69
7	7268	7337	7406	7475	7545	7614	7683	7752	7821	7890	69
8	7960	8029	8098	8167	8236	8305	8374	8443	8513	8582	69
9	8651	8720	8789	8858	8927	8996	9065	9134	9203	9272	69
630	799341	799409	799478	799547	799616	799685	799754	799823	799892	799961	69
1	800029	800098	800167	800236	800305	800373	800442	800511	800580	800648	69
2	0717	0786	0854	0923	0992	1061	1129	1198	1266	1335	69
3	1404	1472	1541	1609	1678	1747	1815	1884	1952	2021	69
4	2089	2158	2226	2295	2363	2432	2500	2568	2637	2705	68
635	2774	2842	2910	2979	3047	3116	3184	3252	3321	3389	68
6	3457	3525	3594	3662	3730	3798	3867	3935	4003	4071	68
7	4139	4208	4276	4344	4412	4480	4548	4616	4685	4753	68
8	4821	4889	4957	5025	5093	5161	5229	5297	5365	5433	68
9	5501	5569	5637	5705	5773	5841	5908	5976	6044	6112	68
N.	0	1	2	3	4	5	6	7	8	9	D.

Table 3—Logarithms (Cont.)

N.	0	1	2	3	4	5	6	7	8	9	D.
640	806180	806248	806316	806384	806451	806519	806587	806655	806723	806790	68
1	6858	6926	6994	7061	7129	7197	7264	7332	7400	7467	68
2	7535	7603	7670	7738	7806	7873	7941	8008	8076	8143	68
3	8211	8279	8346	8414	8481	8549	8616	8684	8751	8818	67
4	8886	8953	9021	9088	9156	9223	9290	9358	9425	9492	67
645	9560	9627	9694	9762	9829	9896	9964	810031	810098	810165	67
6	810233	810300	810367	810434	810501	810569	810636	0703	0770	0837	67
7	0904	0971	1039	1106	1173	1240	1307	1374	1441	1508	67
8	1575	1642	1709	1776	1843	1910	1977	2044	2111	2178	67
9	2245	2312	2379	2445	2512	2579	2646	2713	2780	2847	67
650	812913	812980	813047	813114	813181	813247	813314	813381	813448	813514	67
1	3581	3648	3714	3781	3848	3914	3981	4048	4114	4181	67
2	4248	4314	4381	4447	4514	4581	4647	4714	4780	4847	67
3	4913	4980	5046	5113	5179	5246	5312	5378	5445	5511	66
4	5578	5644	5711	5777	5843	5910	5976	6042	6109	6175	66
655	6241	6308	6374	6440	6506	6573	6639	6705	6771	6838	66
6	6904	6970	7036	7102	7169	7235	7301	7367	7433	7499	66
7	7565	7631	7698	7764	7830	7896	7962	8028	8094	8160	66
8	8226	8292	8358	8424	8490	8556	8622	8688	8754	8820	66
9	8885	8951	9017	9083	9149	9215	9281	9346	9412	9478	66
660	819544	819610	819676	819741	819807	819873	819939	820004	820070	820136	66
1	820201	820267	820333	820399	820464	820530	820595	0661	0727	0792	66
2	0858	0924	0989	1055	1120	1186	1251	1317	1382	1448	66
3	1514	1579	1645	1710	1775	1841	1906	1972	2037	2103	65
4	2168	2233	2299	2364	2430	2495	2560	2626	2691	2756	65
665	2822	2887	2952	3018	3083	3148	3213	3279	3344	3409	65
6	3474	3539	3605	3670	3735	3800	3865	3930	3996	4061	65
7	4126	4191	4256	4321	4386	4451	4516	4581	4646	4711	65
8	4776	4841	4906	4971	5036	5101	5166	5231	5296	5361	65
9	5426	5491	5556	5621	5686	5751	5815	5880	5945	6010	65
670	826075	826140	826204	826269	826334	826399	826464	826528	826593	826658	65
1	6723	6787	6852	6917	6981	7046	7111	7175	7240	7305	65
2	7369	7434	7499	7563	7628	7692	7757	7821	7886	7951	65
3	8015	8080	8144	8209	8273	8338	8402	8467	8531	8595	64
4	8660	8724	8789	8853	8918	8982	9046	9111	9175	9239	64
675	9304	9368	9432	9497	9561	9625	9690	9754	9818	9882	64
6	9947	830011	830075	830139	830204	830268	830332	830396	830460	830525	64
7	830589	0653	0717	0781	0845	0909	0973	1037	1102	1166	64
8	1230	1294	1358	1422	1486	1550	1614	1678	1742	1806	64
9	1870	1934	1998	2062	2126	2189	2253	2317	2381	2445	64
680	832509	832573	832637	832700	832764	832828	832892	832956	833020	833083	64
1	3147	3211	3275	3338	3402	3466	3530	3593	3657	3721	64
2	3784	3848	3912	3975	4039	4103	4166	4230	4294	4357	64
3	4421	4484	4548	4611	4675	4739	4802	4866	4929	4993	64
4	5056	5120	5183	5247	5310	5373	5437	5500	5564	5627	63
685	5691	5754	5817	5881	5944	6007	6071	6134	6197	6261	63
6	6324	6387	6451	6514	6577	6641	6704	6767	6830	6894	63
7	6957	7020	7083	7146	7210	7273	7336	7399	7462	7525	63
8	7588	7652	7715	7778	7841	7904	7967	8030	8093	8156	63
9	8219	8282	8345	8408	8471	8534	8597	8660	8723	8786	63
690	838849	838912	838975	839038	839101	839164	839227	839289	839352	839415	63
1	9478	9541	9604	9667	9729	9792	9855	9918	9981	840043	63
2	840106	840169	840232	840294	840357	840420	840482	840545	840608	0671	63
3	0733	0796	0859	0921	0984	1046	1109	1172	1234	1297	63
4	1359	1422	1485	1547	1610	1672	1735	1797	1860	1922	63
695	1985	2047	2110	2172	2235	2297	2360	2422	2484	2547	62
6	2609	2672	2734	2796	2859	2921	2983	3046	3108	3170	62
7	3233	3295	3357	3420	3482	3544	3606	3669	3731	3793	62
8	3855	3918	3980	4042	4104	4166	4229	4291	4353	4415	62
9	4477	4539	4601	4664	4726	4788	4850	4912	4974	5036	62
N.	0	1	2	3	4	5	6	7	8	9	D.

TABLE 3—LOGARITHMS (Cont.)

N.	0	1	2	3	4	5	6	7	8	9	D.
700	845098	845160	845222	845284	845346	845408	845470	845532	845594	845656	62
1	5718	5780	5842	5904	5966	6028	6090	6151	6213	6275	62
2	6337	6399	6461	6523	6585	6646	6708	6770	6832	6894	62
3	6955	7017	7079	7141	7202	7264	7326	7388	7449	7511	62
4	7573	7634	7696	7758	7819	7881	7943	8004	8066	8128	62
705	8189	8251	8312	8374	8435	8497	8559	8620	8682	8743	62
6	8805	8866	8928	8989	9051	9112	9174	9235	9297	9358	61
7	9419	9481	9542	9604	9665	9726	9788	9849	9911	9972	61
8	850033	850095	850156	850217	850279	850340	850401	850462	850524	850585	61
9	0646	0707	0769	0830	0891	0952	1014	1075	1136	1197	61
710	851258	851320	851381	851442	851503	851564	851625	851686	851747	851809	61
1	1870	1931	1992	2053	2114	2175	2236	2297	2358	2419	61
2	2480	2541	2602	2663	2724	2785	2846	2907	2968	3029	61
3	3090	3150	3211	3272	3333	3394	3455	3516	3577	3637	61
4	3698	3759	3820	3881	3941	4002	4063	4124	4185	4245	61
715	4306	4367	4428	4488	4549	4610	4670	4731	4792	4852	61
6	4913	4974	5034	5095	5156	5216	5277	5337	5398	5459	61
7	5519	5580	5640	5701	5761	5822	5882	5943	6003	6064	61
8	6124	6185	6245	6306	6366	6427	6487	6548	6608	6668	60
9	6729	6789	6850	6910	6970	7031	7091	7152	7212	7272	60
720	857332	857393	857453	857513	857574	857634	857694	857755	857815	857875	60
1	7935	7995	8056	8116	8176	8236	8297	8357	8417	8477	60
2	8537	8597	8657	8718	8778	8838	8898	8958	9018	9078	60
3	9138	9198	9258	9318	9379	9439	9499	9559	9619	9679	60
4	9739	9799	9859	9918	9978	860038	860098	860158	860218	860278	60
725	860338	860398	860458	860518	860578	0637	0697	0757	0817	0877	60
6	0937	0996	1056	1116	1176	1236	1295	1355	1415	1475	60
7	1534	1594	1654	1714	1773	1833	1893	1952	2012	2072	60
8	2131	2191	2251	2310	2370	2430	2489	2549	2608	2668	60
9	2728	2787	2847	2906	2966	3025	3085	3144	3204	3263	60
730	863323	863382	863442	863501	863561	863620	863680	863739	863799	863858	59
1	3917	3977	4036	4096	4155	4214	4274	4333	4392	4452	59
2	4511	4570	4630	4689	4748	4808	4867	4926	4985	5045	59
3	5104	5163	5222	5282	5341	5400	5459	5519	5578	5637	59
4	5696	5755	5814	5874	5933	5992	6051	6110	6169	6228	59
735	6287	6346	6405	6465	6524	6583	6642	6701	6760	6819	59
6	6878	6937	6996	7055	7114	7173	7232	7291	7350	7409	59
7	7467	7526	7585	7644	7703	7762	7821	7880	7939	7998	59
8	8056	8115	8174	8233	8292	8350	8409	8468	8527	8586	59
9	8644	8703	8762	8821	8879	8938	8997	9056	9114	9173	59
740	869232	869290	869349	869408	869466	869525	869584	869642	869701	869760	59
1	9818	9877	9935	9994	870053	870111	870170	870228	870287	870345	59
2	870404	870462	870521	870579	0638	0696	0755	0813	0872	0930	58
3	0989	1047	1106	1164	1223	1281	1339	1398	1456	1515	58
4	1573	1631	1690	1748	1806	1865	1923	1981	2040	2098	58
745	2156	2215	2273	2331	2389	2448	2506	2564	2622	2681	58
6	2739	2797	2855	2913	2972	3030	3088	3146	3204	3262	58
7	3321	3379	3437	3495	3553	3611	3669	3727	3785	3844	58
8	3902	3960	4018	4076	4134	4192	4250	4308	4366	4424	58
9	4482	4540	4598	4656	4714	4772	4830	4888	4945	5003	58
750	875061	875119	875177	875235	875293	875351	875409	875466	875524	875582	58
1	5640	5698	5756	5813	5871	5929	5987	6045	6102	6160	58
2	6218	6276	6333	6391	6449	6507	6564	6622	6680	6737	58
3	6795	6853	6910	6968	7026	7083	7141	7199	7256	7314	58
4	7371	7429	7487	7544	7602	7659	7717	7774	7832	7889	58
755	7947	8004	8062	8119	8177	8234	8292	8349	8407	8464	57
6	8522	8579	8637	8694	8752	8809	8866	8924	8981	9039	57
7	9096	9153	9211	9268	9325	9383	9440	9497	9555	9612	57
8	9669	9726	9784	9841	9898	9956	880013	880070	880127	880185	57
9	880242	880299	880356	880413	880471	880528	0585	0642	0699	0756	57
N.	0	1	2	3	4	5	6	7	8	9	D.

TABLE 3—LOGARITHMS (Cont.)

N.	0	1	2	3	4	5	6	7	8	9	D.
760	880814	880871	880928	880985	881042	881099	881156	881213	881271	881328	57
1	1385	1442	1499	1556	1613	1670	1727	1784	1841	1898	57
2	1955	2012	2069	2126	2183	2240	2297	2354	2411	2468	57
3	2525	2581	2638	2695	2752	2809	2866	2923	2980	3037	57
4	3093	3150	3207	3264	3321	3377	3434	3491	3548	3605	57
765	3661	3718	3775	3832	3888	3945	4002	4059	4115	4172	57
6	4229	4285	4342	4399	4455	4512	4569	4625	4682	4739	57
7	4795	4852	4909	4965	5022	5078	5135	5192	5248	5305	57
8	5361	5418	5474	5531	5587	5644	5700	5757	5813	5870	57
9	5926	5983	6039	6096	6152	6209	6265	6321	6378	6434	56
770	886491	886547	886604	886660	886716	886773	886829	886885	886942	886998	56
1	7054	7111	7167	7223	7280	7336	7392	7449	7505	7561	56
2	7617	7674	7730	7786	7842	7898	7955	8011	8067	8123	56
3	8179	8236	8292	8348	8404	8460	8516	8573	8629	8685	56
4	8741	8797	8853	8909	8965	9021	9077	9134	9190	9246	56
775	9302	9358	9414	9470	9526	9582	9638	9694	9750	9806	56
6	9862	9918	9974	890030	890086	890141	890197	890253	890309	890365	56
7	890421	890477	890533	0589	0645	0700	0756	0812	0868	0924	56
8	0980	1035	1091	1147	1203	1259	1314	1370	1426	1482	56
9	1537	1593	1649	1705	1760	1816	1872	1928	1983	2039	56
780	892095	892150	892206	892262	892317	892373	892429	892484	892540	892595	56
1	2651	2707	2762	2818	2873	2929	2985	3040	3096	3151	56
2	3207	3262	3318	3373	3429	3484	3540	3595	3651	3706	56
3	3762	3817	3873	3928	3984	4039	4094	4150	4205	4261	55
4	4316	4371	4427	4482	4538	4593	4648	4704	4759	4814	55
785	4870	4925	4980	5036	5091	5146	5201	5257	5312	5367	55
6	5423	5478	5533	5588	5644	5699	5754	5809	5864	5920	55
7	5975	6030	6085	6140	6195	6251	6306	6361	6416	6471	55
8	6526	6581	6636	6692	6747	6802	6857	6912	6967	7022	55
9	7077	7132	7187	7242	7297	7352	7407	7462	7517	7572	55
790	897627	897682	897737	897792	897847	897902	897957	898012	898067	898122	55
1	8176	8231	8286	8341	8396	8451	8506	8561	8615	8670	55
2	8725	8780	8835	8890	8944	8999	9054	9109	9164	9218	55
3	9273	9328	9383	9437	9492	9547	9602	9656	9711	9766	55
4	9821	9875	9930	9985	900039	900094	900149	900203	900258	900312	55
795	900367	900422	900476	900531	0586	0640	0695	0749	0804	0859	55
6	0913	0968	1022	1077	1131	1186	1240	1295	1349	1404	55
7	1458	1513	1567	1622	1676	1731	1785	1840	1894	1948	54
8	2003	2057	2112	2166	2221	2275	2329	2384	2438	2492	54
9	2547	2601	2655	2710	2764	2818	2873	2927	2981	3036	54
800	903090	903144	903199	903253	903307	903361	903416	903470	903524	903578	54
1	3633	3687	3741	3795	3849	3904	3958	4012	4066	4120	54
2	4174	4229	4283	4337	4391	4445	4499	4553	4607	4661	54
3	4716	4770	4824	4878	4932	4986	5040	5094	5148	5202	54
4	5256	5310	5364	5418	5472	5526	5580	5634	5688	5742	54
805	5796	5850	5904	5958	6012	6066	6119	6173	6227	6281	54
6	6335	6389	6443	6497	6551	6604	6658	6712	6766	6820	54
7	6874	6927	6981	7035	7089	7143	7196	7250	7304	7358	54
8	7411	7465	7519	7573	7626	7680	7734	7787	7841	7895	54
9	7949	8002	8056	8110	8163	8217	8270	8324	8378	8431	54
810	908485	908539	908592	908646	908699	908753	908807	908860	908914	908967	54
1	9021	9074	9128	9181	9235	9239	9342	9396	9449	9503	54
2	9556	9610	9663	9716	9770	9823	9877	9930	9984	910037	53
3	910091	910144	910197	910251	910304	910358	910411	910464	910518	0571	53
4	0624	0678	0731	0784	0838	0891	0944	0998	1051	1104	53
815	1158	1211	1264	1317	1371	1424	1477	1530	1584	1637	53
6	1690	1743	1797	1850	1903	1956	2009	2063	2116	2169	53
7	2222	2275	2328	2381	2435	2488	2541	2594	2647	2700	53
8	2753	2806	2859	2913	2966	3019	3072	3125	3178	3231	53
9	3284	3337	3390	3443	3496	3549	3602	3655	3708	3761	53
N.	0	1	2	3	4	5	6	7	8	9	D.

TABLE 3—LOGARITHMS (Cont.)

N.	0	1	2	3	4	5	6	7	8	9	D.
820	913814	913867	913920	913973	914026	914079	914132	914184	914237	914290	53
1	4343	4396	4449	4502	4555	4608	4660	4713	4766	4819	53
2	4872	4925	4977	5030	5083	5136	5189	5241	5294	5347	53
3	5400	5453	5505	5558	5611	5664	5716	5769	5822	5875	53
4	5927	5980	6033	6085	6138	6191	6243	6296	6349	6401	53
825	6454	6507	6559	6612	6664	6717	6770	6822	6875	6927	53
6	6980	7033	7085	7138	7190	7243	7295	7348	7400	7453	53
7	7506	7558	7611	7663	7716	7768	7820	7873	7925	7978	52
8	8030	8083	8135	8188	8240	8293	8345	8397	8450	8502	52
9	8555	8607	8659	8712	8764	8816	8869	8921	8973	9026	52
830	919078	919130	919183	919235	919287	919340	919392	919444	919496	919549	52
1	9601	9653	9706	9758	9810	9862	9914	9967	920019	920071	52
2	920123	920176	920228	920280	920332	920384	920436	920489	0541	0593	52
3	0645	0697	0749	0801	0853	0906	0958	1010	1062	1114	52
4	1166	1218	1270	1322	1374	1426	1478	1530	1582	1634	52
835	1686	1738	1790	1842	1894	1946	1998	2050	2102	2154	52
6	2206	2258	2310	2362	2414	2466	2518	2570	2622	2674	52
7	2725	2777	2829	2881	2933	2985	3037	3089	3140	3192	52
8	3244	3296	3348	3399	3451	3503	3555	3607	3658	3710	52
9	3762	3814	3865	3917	3969	4021	4072	4124	4176	4228	52
840	924279	924331	924383	924434	924486	924538	924589	924641	924693	924744	52
1	4796	4848	4899	4951	5003	5054	5106	5157	5209	5261	52
2	5312	5364	5415	5467	5518	5570	5621	5673	5725	5776	52
3	5828	5879	5931	5982	6034	6085	6137	6188	6240	6291	51
4	6342	6394	6445	6497	6548	6600	6651	6702	6754	6805	51
845	6857	6908	6959	7011	7062	7114	7165	7216	7268	7319	51
6	7370	7422	7473	7524	7576	7627	7678	7730	7781	7832	51
7	7883	7935	7986	8037	8088	8140	8191	8242	8293	8345	51
8	8396	8447	8498	8549	8601	8652	8703	8754	8805	8857	51
9	8908	8959	9010	9061	9112	9163	9215	9266	9317	9368	51
850	929419	929470	929521	929572	929623	929674	929725	929776	929827	929879	51
1	9930	9981	930032	930083	930134	930185	930236	930287	930338	930389	51
2	930440	930491	0542	0592	0643	0694	0745	0796	0847	0898	51
3	0949	1000	1051	1102	1153	1204	1254	1305	1356	1407	51
4	1458	1509	1560	1610	1661	1712	1763	1814	1865	1915	51
855	1966	2017	2068	2118	2169	2220	2271	2322	2372	2423	51
6	2474	2524	2575	2626	2677	2727	2778	2829	2879	2930	51
7	2981	3031	3082	3133	3183	3234	3285	3335	3386	3437	51
8	3487	3538	3589	3639	3690	3740	3791	3841	3892	3943	51
9	3993	4044	4094	4145	4195	4246	4296	4347	4397	4448	51
860	934498	934549	934599	934650	934700	934751	934801	934852	934902	934953	50
1	5003	5054	5104	5154	5205	5255	5306	5356	5406	5457	50
2	5507	5558	5608	5658	5709	5759	5809	5860	5910	5960	50
3	6011	6061	6111	6162	6212	6262	6313	6363	6413	6463	50
4	6514	6564	6614	6665	6715	6765	6815	6865	6916	6966	50
865	7016	7066	7117	7167	7217	7267	7317	7367	7418	7468	50
6	7518	7568	7618	7668	7718	7769	7819	7869	7919	7969	50
7	8019	8069	8119	8169	8219	8269	8320	8370	8420	8470	50
8	8520	8570	8620	8670	8720	8770	8820	8870	8920	8970	50
9	9020	9070	9120	9170	9220	9270	9320	9369	9419	9469	50
870	939519	939569	939619	939669	939719	939769	939819	939869	939918	939968	50
1	940018	940068	940118	940168	940218	940267	940317	940367	940417	940467	50
2	0516	0566	0616	0666	0716	0765	0815	0865	0915	0964	50
3	1014	1064	1114	1163	1213	1263	1313	1362	1412	1462	50
4	1511	1561	1611	1660	1710	1760	1809	1859	1909	1958	50
875	2008	2058	2107	2157	2207	2256	2306	2355	2405	2455	50
6	2504	2554	2603	2653	2702	2752	2801	2851	2901	2950	50
7	3000	3049	3099	3148	3198	3247	3297	3346	3396	3445	49
8	3495	3544	3593	3643	3692	3742	3791	3841	3890	3939	49
9	3989	4038	4088	4137	4186	4236	4285	4335	4384	4433	49
N.	0	1	2	3	4	5	6	7	8	9	D.

TABLE 3—LOGARITHMS (Cont.)

N	0	1	2	3	4	5	6	7	8	9	D.
880	944483	944532	944581	944631	944680	944729	944779	944828	944877	944927	49
1	4976	5025	5074	5124	5173	5222	5272	5321	5370	5419	49
2	5469	5518	5567	5616	5665	5715	5764	5813	5862	5912	49
3	5961	6010	6059	6108	6157	6207	6256	6305	6354	6403	49
4	6452	6501	6551	6600	6649	6698	6747	6796	6845	6894	49
885	6943	6992	7041	7090	7140	7189	7238	7287	7336	7385	49
6	7434	7483	7532	7581	7630	7679	7728	7777	7826	7875	49
7	7924	7973	8022	8070	8119	8168	8217	8266	8315	8364	49
8	8413	8462	8511	8560	8609	8657	8706	8755	8804	8853	49
9	8902	8951	8999	9048	9097	9146	9195	9244	9292	9341	49
890	949390	949439	949488	949536	949585	949634	949683	949731	949780	949829	49
1	9878	9926	9975	950024	950073	950121	950170	950219	950267	950316	49
2	950365	950414	950462	0511	0560	0608	0657	0706	0754	0803	49
3	0851	0900	0949	0997	1046	1095	1143	1192	1240	1289	49
4	1338	1386	1435	1483	1532	1580	1629	1677	1726	1775	49
895	1823	1872	1920	1969	2017	2066	2114	2163	2211	2260	48
6	2308	2356	2405	2453	2502	2550	2599	2647	2696	2744	48
7	2792	2841	2889	2938	2986	3034	3083	3131	3180	3228	48
8	3276	3325	3373	3421	3470	3518	3566	3615	3663	3711	48
9	3760	3808	3856	3905	3953	4001	4049	4098	4146	4194	48
900	954243	954291	954339	954387	954435	954484	954532	954580	954628	954677	48
1	4725	4773	4821	4869	4918	4966	5014	5062	5110	5158	48
2	5207	5255	5303	5351	5399	5447	5495	5543	5592	5640	48
3	5688	5736	5784	5832	5880	5928	5976	6024	6072	6120	48
4	6168	6216	6265	6313	6361	6409	6457	6505	6553	6601	48
905	6649	6697	6745	6793	6840	6888	6936	6984	7032	7080	48
6	7128	7176	7224	7272	7320	7368	7416	7464	7512	7559	48
7	7607	7655	7703	7751	7799	7847	7894	7942	7990	8038	48
8	8086	8134	8181	8229	8277	8325	8373	8421	8468	8516	48
9	8564	8612	8659	8707	8755	8803	8850	8898	8946	8994	48
910	959041	959089	959137	959185	959232	959280	959328	959375	959423	959471	48
1	9518	9566	9614	9661	9709	9757	9804	9852	9900	9947	48
2	9995	960042	960090	960138	960185	960233	960281	960328	960376	960423	48
3	960471	0518	0566	0613	0661	0709	0756	0804	0851	0899	48
4	0946	0994	1041	1089	1136	1184	1231	1279	1326	1374	48
915	1421	1469	1516	1563	1611	1658	1706	1753	1801	1848	47
6	1895	1943	1990	2038	2085	2132	2180	2227	2275	2322	47
7	2369	2417	2464	2511	2559	2606	2653	2701	2748	2795	47
8	2843	2890	2937	2985	3032	3079	3126	3174	3221	3268	47
9	3316	3363	3410	3457	3504	3552	3599	3646	3693	3741	47
920	963788	963835	963882	963929	963977	964024	964071	964118	964165	964212	47
1	4260	4307	4354	4401	4448	4495	4542	4590	4637	4684	47
2	4731	4778	4825	4872	4919	4966	5013	5061	5108	5155	47
3	5202	5249	5296	5343	5390	5437	5484	5531	5578	5625	47
4	5672	5719	5766	5813	5860	5907	5954	6001	6048	6095	47
925	6142	6189	6236	6283	6329	6376	6423	6470	6517	6564	47
6	6611	6658	6705	6752	6799	6845	6892	6939	6986	7033	47
7	7080	7127	7173	7220	7267	7314	7361	7408	7454	7501	47
8	7548	7595	7642	7688	7735	7782	7829	7875	7922	7969	47
9	8016	8062	8109	8156	8203	8249	8296	8343	8390	8436	47
930	968483	968530	968576	968623	968670	968716	968763	968810	968856	968903	47
1	8950	8996	9043	9090	9136	9183	9229	9276	9323	9369	47
2	9416	9463	9509	9556	9602	9649	9695	9742	9789	9835	47
3	9882	9928	9975	970021	970068	970114	970161	970207	970254	970300	47
4	970347	970393	970440	0486	0533	0579	0626	0672	0719	0765	46
935	0812	0858	0904	0951	0997	1044	1090	1137	1183	1229	46
6	1276	1322	1369	1415	1461	1508	1554	1601	1647	1693	46
7	1740	1786	1832	1879	1925	1971	2018	2064	2110	2157	46
8	2203	2249	2295	2342	2388	2434	2481	2527	2573	2619	46
9	2666	2712	2758	2804	2851	2897	2943	2989	3035	3082	46
N.	0	1	2	3	4	5	6	7	8	9	D.

TABLE 3—LOGARITHMS (Cont.)

N.	0	1	2	3	4	5	6	7	8	9	D.
940	973128	973174	973220	973266	973313	973359	973405	973451	973497	973543	46
1	3590	3636	3682	3728	3774	3820	3866	3913	3959	4005	46
2	4051	4097	4143	4189	4235	4281	4327	4374	4420	4466	46
3	4512	4558	4604	4650	4696	4742	4788	4834	4880	4926	46
4	4972	5018	5064	5110	5156	5202	5248	5294	5340	5386	46
945	5432	5478	5524	5570	5616	5662	5707	5753	5799	5845	46
6	5891	5937	5983	6029	6075	6121	6167	6212	6258	6304	46
7	6350	6396	6442	6488	6533	6579	6625	6671	6717	6763	46
8	6808	6854	6900	6946	6992	7037	7083	7129	7175	7220	46
9	7266	7312	7358	7403	7449	7495	7541	7586	7632	7678	46
950	977724	977769	977815	977861	977906	977952	977998	978043	978089	978135	46
1	8181	8226	8272	8317	8363	8409	8454	8500	8546	8591	46
2	8637	8683	8728	8774	8819	8865	8911	8956	9002	9047	46
3	9093	9138	9184	9230	9275	9321	9366	9412	9457	9503	46
4	9548	9594	9639	9685	9730	9776	9821	9867	9912	9958	46
955	980003	980049	980094	980140	980185	980231	980276	980322	980367	980412	45
6	0458	0503	0549	0594	0640	0685	0730	0776	0821	0867	45
7	0912	0957	1003	1048	1093	1139	1184	1229	1275	1320	45
8	1366	1411	1456	1501	1547	1592	1637	1683	1728	1773	45
9	1819	1864	1909	1954	2000	2045	2090	2135	2181	2226	45
960	982271	982316	982362	982407	982452	982497	982543	982588	982633	982678	45
1	2723	2769	2814	2859	2904	2949	2994	3040	3085	3130	45
2	3175	3220	3265	3310	3356	3401	3446	3491	3536	3581	45
3	3626	3671	3716	3762	3807	3852	3897	3942	3987	4032	45
4	4077	4122	4167	4212	4257	4302	4347	4392	4437	4482	45
965	4527	4572	4617	4662	4707	4752	4797	4842	4887	4932	45
6	4977	5022	5067	5112	5157	5202	5247	5292	5337	5382	45
7	5426	5471	5516	5561	5606	5651	5696	5741	5786	5830	45
8	5875	5920	5965	6010	6055	6100	6144	6189	6234	6279	45
9	6324	6369	6413	6458	6503	6548	6593	6637	6682	6727	45
970	986772	986817	986861	986906	986951	986996	987040	987085	987130	987175	45
1	7219	7264	7309	7353	7398	7443	7488	7532	7577	7622	45
2	7666	7711	7756	7800	7845	7890	7934	7979	8024	8068	45
3	8113	8157	8202	8247	8291	8336	8381	8425	8470	8514	45
4	8559	8604	8648	8693	8737	8782	8826	8871	8916	8960	45
975	9005	9049	9094	9138	9183	9227	9272	9316	9361	9405	45
6	9450	9494	9539	9583	9628	9672	9717	9761	9806	9850	44
7	9895	9939	9983	990028	990072	990117	990161	990206	990250	990294	44
8	990339	990383	990428	0472	0516	0561	0605	0650	0694	0738	44
9	0783	0827	0871	0916	0960	1004	1049	1093	1137	1182	44
980	991226	991270	991315	991359	991403	991448	991492	991536	991580	991625	44
1	1669	1713	1758	1802	1846	1890	1935	1979	2023	2067	44
2	2111	2156	2200	2244	2288	2333	2377	2421	2465	2509	44
3	2554	2598	2642	2686	2730	2774	2819	2863	2907	2951	44
4	2995	3039	3083	3127	3172	3216	3260	3304	3348	3392	44
985	3436	3480	3524	3568	3613	3657	3701	3745	3789	3833	44
6	3877	3921	3965	4009	4053	4097	4141	4185	4229	4273	44
7	4317	4361	4405	4449	4493	4537	4581	4625	4669	4713	44
8	4757	4801	4845	4889	4933	4977	5021	5065	5108	5152	44
9	5196	5240	5284	5328	5372	5416	5460	5504	5547	5591	44
990	995635	995679	995723	995767	995811	995854	995898	995942	995986	996030	44
1	6074	6117	6161	6205	6249	6293	6337	6380	6424	6468	44
2	6512	6555	6599	6643	6687	6731	6774	6818	6862	6906	44
3	6949	6993	7037	7080	7124	7168	7212	7255	7299	7343	44
4	7386	7430	7474	7517	7561	7605	7648	7692	7736	7779	44
995	7823	7867	7910	7954	7998	8041	8085	8129	8172	8216	44
6	8259	8303	8347	8390	8434	8477	8521	8564	8608	8652	44
7	8695	8739	8782	8826	8869	8913	8956	9000	9043	9087	44
8	9131	9174	9218	9261	9305	9348	9392	9435	9479	9522	44
9	9565	9609	9652	9696	9739	9783	9826	9870	9913	9957	43
N.	0	1	2	3	4	5	6	7	8	9	D.

rithm of the number 6.35 is found by locating the number 635 in the first column of the table (the N. column) where it occurs on Page 120, and then moving to the next column (which is headed by the number 0) in the 635 row; then the value in that space, which is 802774, gives .802774 as the logarithm of 6.35.

Similarly, the values given in the table of logarithms become, by placing the number 1 followed by a decimal point, before them, the logarithms of the numbers from 10 to 100.

For example, the logarithm of the number 45.67 is found by locating the number 456 in the first column of the table (the N. column) where it occurs on Page 117, and then moving across the 456 row to the column headed by the number 7; then the value in that space, which is 659631, gives 1.659631 as the logarithm of 45.67.

A further example is the logarithm of the number 300 which is found by locating the number 300 in the first column of the table (the N. column) where it occurs on Page 115, and then moving to the next column (which is headed by the number 0) in the 300 row; then the value in that space, which is 477121, gives 2.477121 as the logarithm of 300.   Here the characteristic of the logarithm (the whole number part) is 2, since 300 is a number between 100 and 1000.   As another example, the logarithm of 3000 is 3.477121, which has the same mantissa as the logarithm of 300, but the characteristic 3 instead of 2, since all numbers between 1000 and 10,000 have the characteristic 3.

It can easily be inferred that the characteristics continue to increase in this way in order of the powers of ten by which the number in question must be divided to obtain a number between 1 and 10.   This can be stated more simply in the form that the characteristic of a logarithm is one less than the number of figures in the number that are to the *left* of the decimal point.

Up to this point, logarithms have been computed for numbers from 1 to 10, which have a characteristic of zero, and numbers from 10 to 100, 100 to 1000 etc., which have characteristics of 1, 2, etc.   The smaller numbers such as those from .1 to 1., .01 to .1, etc., also have logarithms, which, however, have negative characteristics.   The mathematical justification for these negative characteristics follows from the values of the numbers having integral logarithms given on Page 109, and the rule for obtaining the logarithm of a product.   Thus it was shown on Page 106, that

$$\log_{10} .1 = -1$$

$$\log_{10} .01 = -2$$

$$\log_{10} .001 = -3$$

Now as shown on Page 109, the logarithm of a product is equal to the sum of the logarithms of its factors.

Therefore, since log 5.204 has been found to be .716337, and log .1 is −1, then log .5204 (= 5.204 × .1) is equal to .716337 + (−1) which is written $\bar{1}$.716337, where the minus sign above the 1. shows that only the 1 − 1 (the characteristic of the logarithm) is negative, the mantissa being positive.

Also, since log 5.204 is .716337 and log .01 is −2, then log .05204 (= 5.204 × .01) .716337 + (−2) = $\bar{2}$.716337.

Also, since log 5.204 is .716337 and log .001 is −3, then log .005204 (= 5.204 × .001) = (.716337) + (−3) = $\bar{3}$.5204.

That is, negative logarithms consist of a negative characteristic, which is denoted by a minus sign over such characteristics, and a positive mantissa. This system for expressing logarithms, while inconsistent with other mathematical usage, has been adopted for convenience in calculation with logarithms. Its use permits the performance of a series of multiplications by arithmetical addition of their mantissas, since only the characteristics must be added algebraically.

As an example of finding the logarithms of numbers less than 1, consider the numbers .2165, .02165, and .002165.

The logarithms of these numbers are found by locating the number 216 in the first column of the table, where it occurs on Page 113, and then moving across the 216 row to the column headed by the number 5; then the value in that space, which is 335458, becomes, by placing a decimal point before it, the mantissa of all three of the logarithms sought. Their characteristics are respectively, −1 for .2165 (since this number lies between .1 and 1.); −2 for .02165 (since this number lies between .01 and .1); and −3 for .002165 (since this number lies between .001 and .01). Therefore,

$$\log .2165 = \bar{1}.335458$$

$$\log .02165 = \bar{2}.335458$$

$$\log .002165 = \bar{3}.335458$$

Up to this point, methods and examples have been given for finding logarithms of numbers both greater than 1 and less than 1, and having as many as four significant figures, this being the number of figures for which the values of the logarithms are stated in the table. Suppose, however, there are more than four significant figures in the number for which a logarithm is to be found. Then a further step is required, which can be demonstrated by examples.

Given the number 6.1836, to find its logarithm. Refer to Page 120 of Table 3, and locate 618 in the left-hand column. Then move across the

618 row to the column headed by 3 in the top row; the figure in this space, 791199, gives .791199 as the mantissa and also the logarithm of 6.183.   (It has no characteristic to be added, since 6.183 is between 1 and 10.)   Then move one space to the right to find the next greater logarithm in the table, that of the number 6.184, which is .791269.   Now subtract the smaller logarithm from the larger:

$$\log 6.184 = .791269$$
$$\log 6.183 = .791199$$
$$\text{Difference} \quad .000070$$

Now the logarithm of 6.1836 is greater than the logarithm of 6.183 by .6 of the difference between 6.183 and 6.184, which is .6 of .000070, or .000042. Therefore   log   6.1836 = log   6.183 + .000042 = .791199 + .000042 = .791241.

This process is called interpolation, and is so widely used that differences between successive logarithms in each row of the table are listed in the last column on each page, so that it is unnecessary to subtract successive logarithms to determine this difference.   (Thus, the last column of Page 120 contains the figure 70 on the line starting with 618.)

As an example of the use of these difference figures (note that the last column in the table is headed D. for Difference), find the logarithm of 436,519.

Refer to Page 117 of Table 3 and locate 436 in the left-hand column. Then move across the 436 row to the column headed by 5 in the top row; the figure in this space, 639984, gives .639984 as the mantissa of the logarithm of 4365.   Then the mantissa of the logarithm of 436519 is .639984 plus $\frac{19}{100}$ of the difference between successive logarithms, which is given in the last column of the table as 99.

$$\text{Since mantissa of } 4365 = .639984$$
$$\frac{19}{100} \text{ of } .000099 = .000019$$
$$\text{Then mantissa of } 436519 = .640003$$

Then log 436,519 which has six places to the left of the decimal point = 5.640003, by the rule for characteristics.

Note that in the foregoing examples, interpolation was carried out by multiplying the difference between successive logarithms by the excess of the number sought over that given in the table, divided by the power of 10 equal to the excess of significant figures in the number over those listed in the table, which is 4.   That is, the table gives mantissas directly to six places for numbers having four significant figures.   Therefore, in the example given of a number having five significant figures, the D. value in the table was multiplied by one-tenth of the fifth significant figure in the number, while in the example of a number having six significant figures, the D. value was multiplied by one-hundredth of the two-figure number formed by the fifth and sixth significant figures.

There is, however, a practical limit to which interpolation is meaningful—this limit being imposed by the number of significant figures in the mantissas (i.e. body of the table) themselves, which in this table is six significant figures. (Since mantissas of logarithms are irrational numbers, they must be tabulated to the number of significant figures required by the accuracy of the work in hand.) Since in this table they are given only to six significant figures, numbers given to more than six significant figures should be rounded off to that number before interpolation.

As an example, find the logarithm of 5275.4371. Since this number is given to eight significant figures, and the mantissas in the table only to six, round off the number to six significant figures, obtaining 5275.44. Then refer to Table 3 and locate 527 in the left-hand column. Then move across the 537 line to the column headed by 5 in the top row; the figure in this space is 722222, the mantissa of 5275. Then the mantissa of the logarithm of 5,275.44 is mantissa of $5275 = .722222 + \frac{44}{100}$ of .000082 (since 82 is given in last (D.) column of table) = .000036.

Therefore, the mantissa of 5275.44 = .722258
Then log 5275.44 = 3.722258.

The method of finding logarithms of numbers from a table may be summarized as follows:

(1) Round off the significant figures in the number to a value equal to the number of significant figures to which the mantissas of the logarithms are given in the table. (6 in this book.)

(2) Find in the left-hand column of the table the number corresponding to the left-hand significant figures of the number whose mantissa is sought. In this book, numbers are given in the left-hand column of the table to three significant figures, therefore the first three significant figures of the numbers are used.

(3) Move across the table to the column headed by the number corresponding to the next significant figure (in this book, the fourth) in the number whose mantissa is sought.

(4) To the value found in this space, add an amount proportional to the excess of the given number over the number tabulated. In this book the amount to be added is found by multiplying the difference between successive logarithms at that point (given in the last column of the table) by one-tenth the fifth significant figure in the number, or by one-hundredth

of the two-figure quantity composed of the fifth and sixth significant figures in the number.

(5) Add the characteristic to the mantissa to form the logarithm. The characteristic of the logarithm of any number greater than 1 is a positive number which is 1 less than the number of figures to the left of the decimal point in the number. The characteristic of the logarithm of any decimal fraction is a negative number which is 1 greater than the number of zeros immediately to the right of the decimal point. (Note that numbers between .1 and 1., which are decimal fractions with no zeros between the decimal point and the first number, have by this rule characteristics of −1.)

(6) Designate negative characteristics by writing minus signs above them.

Multiplication by Use of Logarithms

Earlier in this chapter, the relationship for the logarithms of a product was stated in the form "the logarithm of the product of any numbers is equal to the sum of their individual logarithms," or by Formula (6-1) as,

$$\log (N \times M) = \log N + \log M$$

From this relationship, the method of multiplication by use of logarithms can be stated as:

(1) Find the logarithms of the numbers
(2) Add them
(3) Find the number of which their sum is the logarithm.

For example, multiply 1225. by 204.6.

$$\begin{aligned}
\log\ 1225 &= 3.088136 \\
\log 204.6 &= \underline{2.310906} \\
&\ 5.399042
\end{aligned}$$

Now turn to the beginning of Table 3, and turn over its pages seeking initial mantissas (upper left-hand corner of page) less than and greater than 399042. The initial mantissa on Page 114 is 342423, and that on Page 115 is 447158, therefore the mantissa sought, 399042, is on Page 114. Examination of that page gives the closest values as 398981, the mantissa of 2506, and 399154, the mantissa of 2507. Then subtracting

$$\begin{aligned}
\text{Mantissa of number sought} &= .399042 \\
\text{Mantissa of 2506} &= \underline{.398981} \\
\text{Difference} &\ .000061
\end{aligned}$$

Since the difference between mantissas in this row of the table is shown in the last column as 173, the fifth and sixth digits in the number sought are found from the ratio $\frac{61}{173} = .34$, so that the digits of the number sought are $2506 + 000034 = 250634$. Moreover, the characteristic of its logarithm is 5, therefore the number is 250,634.

It is to be noted that actual multiplication of 1225 and 204.6 gives 250,635, so that the use of the table of six-place logarithms for four place numbers has introduced an error of 1 in the sixth place. This is to be expected, since the accuracy of any tabular method cannot be better, on average, than ± 1 in the last place. If a greater degree of accuracy is required, then tables computed to a greater number of places are required.

As another example, multiply 47,452 by .003711.

$$\begin{array}{l} \log 47{,}452 \ = 4.676254 \\ \log .003711 = \overline{3}.569491 \\ \hline \qquad\qquad\quad 2.245745 \end{array}$$

Note that the characteristics are added algebraically, that is, 1 (carried over from addition of mantissas) $+ 4 + (-3) = +2$.

Now refer to the beginning of Table 3, which is on Page 112, and turn its pages as before to find the page containing mantissa .245745. It is on Page 113, which has .204120 as its initial mantissa (upper left-hand corner). The closest values to .245745 are .245513, mantissa of 1760, and .245759, mantissa of 1761. Then subtracting

$$\begin{array}{ll} \text{Mantissa of number sought} & = .245745 \\ \text{Mantissa of 1760} & = .245513 \\ \hline \qquad\qquad\text{Difference} & .000232 \end{array}$$

Since the difference between mantissas in this row of the table is 246 (as shown in the last column) the fifth and sixth digits in the number sought are found from the ratio $\frac{232}{246} = 94$, so that the digits of the number sought are $1760 + 000094 = 176094$. Moreover, the characteristic of its logarithm is 2, therefore the number is 176.094. Note again that direct multiplication of the numbers 47,452 and .003711 gives 176.094372, and that the last three places are unobtainable with the six-place table used.

Where several logarithms having negative characteristics are to be added, an alternative method of writing them is often useful. In this method, instead of writing log .003711 in the form $\overline{3}.569491$, as was done in the above example, 10 is added to the characteristic and -10 is written after it, so the log .003711 becomes $7.569491 - 10$. This method has the advantage that by its use characteristics are always arithmetically additive, and so the chances of error are reduced.

As an example of the use of this method, multiply

$$(.00466) \times (12.52) \times (.00074) \times (136.)$$

$$
\begin{array}{lll}
\log .00466 = \bar{3}.668386 = & 7.668386 - 10 \\
\log 12.52 & = & 1.097604 \\
\log .00074 = \bar{4}.869232 = & 6.869232 - 10 \\
\log 136 & = & \underline{2.133539} \\
\text{Giving the sum} & & 17.768761 - 20
\end{array}
$$

Then $17.768761 - 20 = \bar{3}.768761$.

From Table 3, Page 120, .768761 is the mantissa of $5871 + \dfrac{0049}{74} = .587166$,

and since the characteristic of the logarithm is -3, the number is .00587166, the product of the four numbers.

Division by Use of Logarithms

The logarithm of a quotient is found, just as was the logarithm of a product, by use of the exponential relationship.

To find $\dfrac{M}{N}$, write $\qquad M = a^m$, so that $\log_a M = m$.

and $\qquad\qquad\qquad N = a^n$, so that $\log_a N = n$.

Then $\qquad\qquad\qquad\qquad \dfrac{M}{N} = \dfrac{a^m}{a^n}$

And by Formula (4-2) Chapter 4,

$$\frac{a^m}{a^n} = a^{m-n}$$

Therefore $\qquad\qquad\qquad \dfrac{M}{N} = a^{m-n}$

Therefore, $\qquad\qquad\qquad \log_a \dfrac{M}{N} = m - n$

and $\qquad\qquad\qquad \log_a \dfrac{M}{N} = \log_a M - \log_a N$

Therefore $\qquad\qquad\qquad \log_{10} \dfrac{M}{N} = \log_{10} M - \log_{10} N \qquad\qquad (6\text{-}2)$

Or in words, the logarithm of a quotient is the logarithm of its dividend minus the logarithm of its divisor.

For example, divide 964. by 282.

$$
\begin{array}{ll}
\text{From Table 3, } \log 964 = & 2.984077 \\
\text{From Table 3, } \log 282 = & \underline{2.450249} \\
\text{Difference} & .533828
\end{array}
$$

Now Table 3 gives 533772, the mantissa of 3418, and 533899, the mantissa of 3419, as the mantissas bracketing 533828, and 127 as the difference between them.

Therefore, subtracting

$$\begin{array}{ll} \text{Mantissa of number sought} = & .533828 \\ \text{Mantissa of 3418} \qquad\qquad = & .533772 \\ \hline \qquad\qquad\qquad \text{Difference} & .000056 \end{array}$$

Since D, the difference between mantissas in this row of the table, is 127, the fifth and sixth digits of the number sought are found from the ratio $\dfrac{56}{127} = .44$, so that the digits of the number sought are 341844, and since its characteristic is zero, the number is 3.41844.

If either the dividend or the divisor, or both, are numbers less than 1, which thus have negative characteristics, the method of adding 10 to the characteristic, and writing $-$ 10 after it, which was explained earlier in this chapter may be employed.

As an example, divide .6164 by .000561.

$$\begin{array}{lll} \text{From Table 3,} & \log .6164 = \bar{1}.789863 = & 9.789863 - 10 \\ \text{From Table 3,} & \log .000561 = \bar{4}.748963 = & 6.748963 - 10 \\ & \hline \text{Difference} & 3.040900 \end{array}$$

Now the mantissas in Table 3 bracketing 040900, are 040602, the mantissa of 1098, and 040998, the mantissa of 1099.

$$\begin{array}{ll} \text{Mantissa of number sought} = & .040900 \\ \text{Mantissa of 1098} \qquad\qquad = & .040602 \\ \hline \qquad\qquad\quad \text{Difference} & .000298 \end{array}$$

Since the difference between mantissas in this row of the table is shown in the last column as 397, the fifth and sixth digits of the number sought are found from the ratio $\dfrac{298}{397} = .75$, so that the digits of the number sought are 109875. Moreover, the characteristic of the logarithm is 3, therefore the number is 1098.75.

The method of adding 10 to characteristics to simplify calculations is often found useful in cases where the divisor is much larger than the dividend.

As an example, divide 2469 by 1,397,000.

$$\begin{array}{ll} \text{From Table 3,} & \log 2469 = 3.392521 \\ \text{From Table 3,} & \log 1,397,000 = 6.145196 \end{array}$$

Now the characteristic of the difference is $3 - 6 = -3$.

However, instead of subtracting directly, it is preferable to rewrite the

logarithm of the dividend, by adding 10 to its characteristic, and writing
− 10 after it, and then subtracting the logarithm of the divisor from the
logarithm of the dividend:

$$\begin{aligned}
\log 2469 \quad &= 13.392521 - 10 \\
\log 1{,}397{,}000 &= \underline{6.145196} \\
& 7.247325 - 10 = \overline{3}.247325
\end{aligned}$$

Then .247325 is found in Table 3, with interpolation, to be the mantissa
of 176736, so the number sought is .00176736, the quotient of 2469 by
1,397,000.

Use of Logarithms in Calculating Powers

As was stated in Chapter 4 on exponents, logarithms are of great usefulness in computing powers and roots of numbers, especially when those
roots or powers are fractional, decimal or mixed numbers. Since many
problems in business mathematics, especially in compound interest and
annuity calculations, involve fractional or decimal powers and roots, this
use of logarithms is particularly important.

The power of a number (A) is found by logarithms as follows,

Let $\log A = m$, where $A = a^m$

Since $A = a^m$, then $A^p = (a^m)^p$

Since by Formula (4-4), Chapter 4, $(a^m)^p = a^{mp}$

Then $A^p = a^{mp}$

Therefore $\log A^p = mp$

and substituting $\log A$ for m,

$$\log A^p = (\log A)p \text{ or } p \log A. \tag{6-3}$$

In words, the logarithm of a power of a number is equal to the logarithm
of the number multiplied by the exponent of that power.

Therefore, to find a given power of a number, multiply the logarithm
of the number by the exponent of the power, and then find the number
corresponding to the resulting logarithm.

As an example, find the fifth power of 132, that is, $(132)^5$.

From Table 3, the mantissa of $132 = .120574$.

Then, $\qquad\qquad\qquad \log 132 \quad = \quad 2.120574$

$$\underline{5}$$

And by Formula (6-3), $\quad \log (132)^5 = 10.602870$

From Table 3, and interpolation, .602870 is the mantissa of 400746.
Since the characteristic of the logarithm is 10, it has 10 + 1 places to the

left of the decimal point, therefore the number corresponding to the logarithm 10.602870 (its antilog) is 40,074,600,000, which is thus $(132)^5$.

As another example, find $(61.26)^{3.2}$

From Table 3, the mantissa of 61.26 = .787177

Therefore, $\quad\quad\quad$ log 61.26 $\quad$ = $\quad$ 1.787177

$$\frac{3.2}{}$$

3574354

$$\frac{5361531}{}$$

And by Formula (6-3), log $(61.26)^{3.2}$ = 5.7189664

Then from Table 3 and interpolation, .718966 is the mantissa of 523547. Since the characteristic of the logarithm is 5, the number has $5 + 1 = 6$ places to the left of the decimal point, therefore 5.718966 is antilog of 523,547, which thus is $(61.26)^{3.2}$.

As another example, find $(1.06)^{24}$.

From Table 3, the mantissa of 1.06 $\quad\quad$ = .025306

And since there is only one digit to the

left of the decimal point, log 1.06 is also = .025306

$$\frac{24}{}$$

101224

$$\frac{50612}{}$$

By Formula (6-3), log $(1.06)^{24}$ $\quad\quad\quad$ = .607344

Then for Table 3 and interpolation, .607344 is the mantissa of 404896. Since the characteristic of the logarithm is 0, the number has $0 + 1 = 1$ places to the left of the decimal point. Therefore .607344 is antilog 4.04896, which is thus $(1.06)^{24}$.

As another example, find $(.000346)^{1.4}$

From Table 3, the mantissa of 346 $\quad\quad$ = .539076

Therefore log .000346 $\quad\quad\quad\quad$ = $\bar{4}$.539076

Rewrite log .000346 by adding 10 to its characteristic and writing $-$ 10 after it,

Thus, log .000346 $\quad\quad\quad\quad\quad\quad$ = 6.539076 $-$ 10

$$\frac{1.4}{}$$

$$= 9.1547064 - 14$$

Then by Formula (6-3), log $(.000346)^{1.4}$ = $\bar{5}$.154706

Then from Table 3, and interpolation, .154706 is the mantissa of 142793. Since the characteristic of the logarithm is -5, the number of zeros to the right of the decimal point is $5 - 1 = 4$. Therefore, $\bar{5}$.154706 is antilog .0000142793, which is thus $(.000346)^{1.4}$.

If a number is to be raised to a negative power, its logarithm is multiplied algebraically by the negative exponent. If the characteristic and mantissa of its logarithm were both positive, then the result of the multiplication is to yield as product a logarithm in which both the characteristic and the mantissa are negative. In this case, 10 is added algebraically to the logarithm as a whole, and not to the characteristic only, and the −10 is written after the result, as usual. The algebraic addition of 10 is effected by subtracting the negative logarithm from 10.

The method is readily understood from an example. Thus, find the value of $(165)^{-2.3}$.

$$\begin{aligned}
\text{From Table 3, the mantissa of 165} \quad &= \quad .217484 \\
\text{Therefore, log 165} \quad &= \quad 2.217484 \\
&\quad \underline{ -2.3} \\
&\quad 6652452 \\
&\quad \underline{4434968} \\
\text{Then by Formula (6-3), log } (165)^{-2.3} &= \ -5.1002132
\end{aligned}$$

In the above expression, the minus sign applies to both characteristic and mantissa. Therefore, the entire expression is added algebraically to 10, giving

$$10 \ - \ 5.1002132 \ = \ 4.8997868$$

Then, $\log (165)^{-2.3} = 4.899787 - 10$

or $\log (165)^{-2.3} = \bar{6}.899787$

Then from Table 3, and interpolation, .899787 is the mantissa of 793938. Since the characteristic of the logarithm is −6. the number of zeros to the right of the decimal point is $6 - 1 = 5$. Therefore $\bar{6}.899787$ is antilog .00000793938, which is thus $(165)^{-2.3}$.

As a final example of calculating powers by the use of logarithms, find the value of $(.0246)^{-1.8}$.

From Table 3 the mantissa of 246 is .390935. Since there is one zero to the right of the decimal point, the characteristic of the logarithm is −2, therefore $\log .0246 = \bar{2}.390935$.

To multiply the negative characteristic and positive mantissa by the negative power, a convenient method is to perform the two multiplications separately, as

Characteristic	−2	Mantissa	.390935
Power	−1.8	Power	−1.8
Product	+3.6	Product	−.703683

Then $\log (.0246)^{-1.8} = 3.6 + (-.703683) = 2.896317$

Then from Table 3 and interpolation, .896317 is the mantissa of 787620. Since the characteristic of the logarithm is 2, the number of digits to the left of the decimal point is $2 + 1 = 3$, so the number is 787.620, which is thus found to be $(.0246)^{-1.8}$.

Calculation of Roots by Use of Logarithms

In the preceding section, it was shown that the logarithm of the power of a number was the product of the exponent of the power by the logarithm of the number, expressed symbolically in Formula (6-3) as $\log A^p = p \log A$.

Since a root is a fractional power, that is, since $\sqrt[p]{A} = A^{\frac{1}{p}}$ it follows that

$$\log A^{\frac{1}{p}} = \frac{1}{p} \log A = \frac{\log A}{p} \tag{6-4}$$

In other words, the logarithm of the root of a number is equal to the logarithm of the number divided by the index of the root. Therefore, to find a given root of a number, divide the logarithm of the number by the index of the root, and then find the number corresponding to the resulting logarithm.

As an example, find the cube root of 14569.42, that is, find $\sqrt[3]{14569.42}$. From Table 3 and interpolation, the mantissa of the number 145694 is .163442, therefore $\log 14{,}569.4 = 4.163442$, then $\log \sqrt[3]{14{,}569.4} = \dfrac{4.163442}{3}$ $= 1.387814$. Then, from Table 3 and interpolation, 387314 is the mantissa of the number 244238. Since the characteristic of the logarithm is 1, the number has $1 + 1 = 2$ places to the left of the decimal point, therefore the number is 24.4238, which is thus the cube root of 14,569.4. (Note that the digit 2, the seventh significant figure in the original number, cannot be used, since Table 3 gives mantissas only to six significant figures, as explained earlier in this chapter.)

As another example, find $\sqrt[1.67]{1742}$. From Table 3, the mantissa of 1742 is .241048; therefore $\log 1742 = 3.241048$.

Dividing by 1.67,

```
                1.940747
        1.67)3.241048
             167
             1571
             1503
              680
              668
             1248
             1169
              790
              668
             1220
             1169
```

Thus, log $\overset{1\cdot67}{\sqrt{}}\overline{1742}$ = 1.940747

Then from Table 3 and interpolation, .940747 is the mantissa of 872462. Since the characteristic of the logarithm is 1, the number has $1 + 1 = 2$ places to the left of the decimal point, therefore the number is 87.2462, which is thus $\overset{1\cdot67}{\sqrt{}}\ \overline{1742}$.

As another example, find $\overset{2\cdot4}{\sqrt{}}\overline{.00726}$.

From Table 3 the mantissa of 726 is .860937, then log .00726 = $\overline{3}.860937$ = 7.860937 − 10

Dividing by 2.4, $\dfrac{7.860937}{2.4}$ = 3.275390, and $\dfrac{10}{2.4}$ = 4.166667

Subtracting, 3.275390 − 4.166667 = $\overline{1}.108723$.

Thus log $\overset{2\cdot4}{\sqrt{}}\overline{.00726}$ = $\overline{1}.108723$

Then from Table 3 and interpolation, .108723 is the mantissa of 128447. Since the characteristic of the logarithm is −1 the number has $1 - 1 = 0$, zeros to the right of the decimal point, therefore the number is .128447, which is thus $\overset{2\cdot4}{\sqrt{}}\overline{.00746}$.

Chapter 7

SERIES AND PROGRESSIONS

A series is a succession of terms arranged in a definite order and related so that a general formula or law determines the formation of the terms. Series are widely used in mathematics, often for the purpose of facilitating or shortening calculations. Various types of series are used throughout this book; therefore the more important of these types of series are treated in this chapter, beginning with those used in arithmetic.

In the types of series used in arithmetic, the terms composing the series are numbers. If the series has a limited number of terms, the first and last of them are called the first term and the last term, respectively. The sum of all the terms is called the sum of the series. The formula or law by which the terms are formed is called the law of the series. Often this law is expressed as the relationship between successive terms, that is, it includes a statement of the first term, of the rule by which each additional term is formed from the preceding one, and of the last term. It is for this reason that such series, particularly when having numerical terms only, are called progressions.

Arithmetical Progression

A type of series which suggests itself at once is that in which the rule of formation of successive terms is additive, that is, in which each term is formed from the preceding one by addition, usually of the same quantity. When the terms of such a series are numbers, it is called an arithmetical progression. The number added to each term to form the next is called the common difference. The law of an arithmetical progression is, therefore, addition of the common difference. From that law, one can readily develop formulas relating the important elements (parts) of an arithmetical progression. In order to make these formulas general, that is, such that they can be used to calculate the elements of any arithmetical progression, their elements must be expressed in letters, so that the corresponding

140

elements of any such series can be substituted. That is, the following letter symbols are used for the elements already mentioned:

f, for the first term of the arithmetical progression,
l, for the last term of the arithmetical progression,
n, for the number of terms of the arithmetical progression,
d, for the common difference of the arithmetical progression,
S, for the sum of the arithmetical progression.

For example, consider the series of the consecutive odd numbers beginning with 3, and having 25 members. Then f is 3, d is 2 (since only the consecutive *odd* numbers are included) and n is 25. What is the last term?

The last term can be found by reasoning that since 3 is the first term, and there are 25 terms in all, then the common difference is added 24 times (that is, $25 - 1$ times) to form the last term, which is therefore,

$$3 + (24 \times 2) = 3 + 48 = 51.$$

Expressing this relationship in the letter symbols,

$$f + (n - 1) \times d = l$$
$$l = f + (n - 1) \times d \tag{7-1}$$

Or the relationship can be stated in words in the form: the last term of an arithmetical progression is equal to the first term, plus the common difference multiplied by one less than the number of terms.

This relationship can be transposed to give the relationship for finding the first term if the last term, the number of terms, and the common difference are known. The relationship thus becomes: the first term of an arithmetical progression is equal to the last term, minus the common difference multiplied by one less than the number of terms.

Expressed in symbols,

$$f = l - (n - 1) \times d. \tag{7-2}$$

As an example of the use of Formula (7-1), find the last term of the arithmetical progression whose first term is 5, common difference, 3, and number of terms, 10.

Substituting in Formula (7-1),

$$l = 5 + (10 - 1) \times 3 = 32.$$

As an example of the use of Formula (7-2), find the first term of an arithmetical progression whose last term is 62, common difference, 4, and number of terms, 12.

Substituting in Formula (7-2),

$$f = 62 - (12 - 1) \times 4 = 18.$$

Formula (7-1) can be modified to find the common difference if the first term, the last term and the number of terms are known, by reasoning that since the last term equals the first term plus the product, $(n - 1) \times d$, then the last term *minus* the first term equals that product, or in symbols $l - f = (n - 1) \times d$. Then since $(l - f)$ equals d *multiplied* by $(n - 1)$, therefore d equals $(l - f)$ divided by $(n - 1)$.

Thus the formula for the common difference becomes,

$$d = \frac{l - f}{n - 1} \tag{7-3}$$

This relationship can be stated in words as: the common difference of an arithmetical progression is equal to the difference of last and first terms, divided by one less than the number of terms.

Also, the relationship $l - f = (n - 1) \times d$ also can be used to find n, for from it,

$$n - 1 = (l - f) \div d = \frac{l - f}{d}, \quad \text{or} \quad n = \frac{l - f}{d} + 1, \tag{7-4}$$

which can be stated in words as: the number of terms in an arithmetical progression is equal to the difference between last term and first term, divided by the common difference, plus 1.

To find the sum of an arithmetical progression, a rule, and corresponding formula, can readily be developed by a mathematical device, that of adding the series term for term in inverse order. That is, write the terms of the arithmetical progression whose first term is 5, common difference, 3, and number of terms, 8. Then copy this series in reverse order, so that each term of the second row falls directly below a term in the first row, giving:

	5	8	11	14	17	20	23	26	= 124
(Reverse Order)	26	23	20	17	14	11	8	5	= 124
	31	31	31	31	31	31	31	31	= 248

Note that the sum of the series, as found directly by adding the eight terms, is 124. Note also that the sum of the doubled series is, naturally, twice 124 or 248. Note also that each term in the doubled series is 31, which is the sum of the first and the last terms, so that the sum of the doubled series is (the sum of first and last terms) $\times$ (number of terms in series). Therefore the sum of the undoubled series (that is, the series itself) is one-half the number of terms, multiplied by the sum of the first and last terms.

In symbols,

$$S = \frac{n}{2} \times (f + l) \tag{7-5}$$

Note that this formula requires a knowledge of n, f, and l. However, from formulas (7-1), (7-2) and (7-4), any one of these elements can be found, if the other two of them and d are known. Therefore, if there are given, for example, f, l, and d, one would first use the appropriate formula, in this case (Formula 7-4) to find the missing term (in this case, n), and then apply Formula (7-5).

For example, to find the sum of an arithmetical progression whose first term is 4, last term is 46, and common difference is 3, one would first find n by Formula (7-4).

$$n = \frac{l - f}{d} + 1$$

$$= \frac{46 - 4}{3} + 1 = 14 + 1 = 15.$$

Then apply Formula (7-5),

$$S = \frac{n}{2} \times (f + l)$$

Substituting,

$$S = \frac{15}{2} \times (4 + 46)$$

$$= 7\tfrac{1}{2} \times 50 = 375.$$

Geometrical Progression

A geometrical progression differs from an arithmetical progression in that each term is formed from the preceding one by multiplication instead of addition. The number by which each term is multiplied to form the next is called the common ratio. If the common ratio is a number greater than 1, each term is obviously greater than the preceding term, and the series or progression is called an *increasing* series. If the ratio is a number less than 1, that is, a fraction, each term is obviously less than the preceding, and the series is called a *decreasing* series. If the number of terms in a decreasing series is infinitely great, the last term is obviously indefinitely small, that is, it approaches zero as a limit (see Chapter 9). The sum of an infinite series of this kind is not infinitely great, but has a very definite value, as is shown later in the present chapter.

The elements of a geometrical progression and the letter symbols used to represent them are:

f, for the first term of the geometrical progression,
l, for the last term of the geometrical progression,
n, for the number of terms in the geometrical progression,
r, for the common ratio of the geometrical progression,
S, for the sum of the geometrical progression.

For example, consider a series of numbers beginning with 3, having a common ratio of 2, and having 6 terms in the series.   One can then find the last term by reasoning that since 3 is the first term, and there are 6 terms in all, then the first term, if multiplied by the common ratio (6-1) or 5 times, gives the last term.

That is, the last term = 3 (the first term) multiplied by the common ratio (r) raised to the fifth power, which is,

$$3 \times 2^5 = 3 \times 32 = 96.$$

Expressing this relationship in literal symbols,

$$l = f \times r^{n-1}, \tag{7-6}$$

This relationship for finding the last term of a geometrical progression can be stated in words as: The last term of a geometrical progression equals the first term multiplied by the common ratio raised to a power one less than the number of terms.

As an example of the use of Formula (7-6), find the last term of a geometrical progression whose first term is 6, whose common ratio is 3, and whose number of terms is 5.

Substituting in Formula (7-6),

$$l = 6 \times 3^{5-1} = 6 \times 3^4 = 6 \times 81 = 486.$$

This relationship can be transposed to give the relationship for finding the first term if the last term, number of terms and the common difference are known.   That relationship thus becomes: the first term of a geometrical progression equals the last term, divided by the common ratio raised to a power one less than the number of terms.

Expressed in symbols,

$$f = l \div r^{n-1} \tag{7-7}$$

Formula (7-6) can be modified to find the common ratio if the first term, the last term and the number of terms are known, by reasoning that since the last term equals the first term *multiplied* by r^{n-1}, then the last term divided by the first term equals r^{n-1}.   Then since $l \div f$ equals r raised to the $n - 1$ power, then r equals the $n - 1$ root of $l \div f$.   Thus the formula for the common ratio is,

$$r = \sqrt[n-1]{l/f} \tag{7-8}$$

This rule can be expressed in words as: To find the common ratio of a geometrical progression, divide the last term by the first, and extract the root that is 1 less than the number of terms.

The application of Formula (7-8), involving the operation of extraction of roots, is best performed by the use of logarithms (Chapter 6) as is shown in the following example: Find the common ratio of a geometrical progression whose first term is 3, last term, 960, and number of terms, 5.

Substituting in Formula (7-8),

$$r = \sqrt[4]{960 \div 3} = \sqrt[4]{320}.$$

Now by Chapter 6 and Table 3,

$$\log 320 \quad = 2.505150$$

$$\log \sqrt[4]{320} = 2.505150 \div 4 = .626288$$

From Table 3, .626288 = antilog 4.23 approximately.

Therefore, $\qquad r = 4.23$

A formula for n, in terms of f, l, and r can be derived as follows: Since by Formula (7-7),

$$f = l \div r^{n-1}$$

Then by transposition,

$$r^{n-1} = l/f$$

And, $\qquad \log r^{n-1} = \log l/f$

Then by Formula (6-3) of Chapter 6, $(n - 1) \log r = \log l/f$

$$n - 1 = \frac{\log l/f}{\log r} \qquad\qquad (7\text{-}9)$$

$$n = \frac{\log l/f}{\log r} + 1$$

This rule can be expressed in words as: To find the number of terms in a geometrical progression, divide the last term by the first, and find the logarithm of that quotient. Then divide that logarithm by the logarithm of the common ratio, and add 1 to the result.

As an example of the use of Formula (7-9), find the number of terms in a geometrical progression of which 4 is the first term, 9600 the last, and 7 is the common ratio.

Substituting

$$n = \frac{\log (9600 \div 4)}{\log 7} + 1$$

Then from Table 3, and Chapter 6,

$$\log (9600 \div 4) = \log 2400 = 3.380211.$$

And $\qquad\qquad \log 7 = .845098$

And $\qquad 3.380211 \div .845098 = 4.$ approximately.

Therefore the number of terms $= 4 + 1 = 5.$

As in the case of an arithmetical progression, the sum of a geometrical progression is commonly expressed in terms of the first term, the last term and the common ratio. If the number of terms is given instead of one of these three elements, the missing element can always be found by the use of Formulas (7-6), (7-7) or (7-8).

To derive the formula for the sum of a geometrical progression, consider the 4-term progression with first term 5 and ratio 4. The terms are then 5, 20, 80 and 320, and the sum is

$$5 + 20 + 80 + 320 = 425.$$

Multiply each term and the sum by the ratio, 4, giving

$$20 + 80 + \ 320 + 1280 = 1700, \text{4 times the sum,}$$

and subtract $5 + 20 + 80 + \ 320 \qquad\ = \ \ 425, \text{1 times the sum,}$

obtaining $\qquad\qquad\qquad\qquad \overline{1280 - 5} \ = 1275 \text{ 3 times the sum}$

But $\qquad\qquad 1280 = \text{(last term)} \times \text{(ratio)},$

$$5 = \text{first term,}$$

and $\qquad\qquad\qquad 3 = \text{(ratio)} - 1.$

Expressing this result in words: To find the sum of a geometrical progression, multiply the last term (greater extreme) by the ratio; from this product subtract the first term (lesser extreme), and divide the remainder by the ratio less 1.

In symbols:

$$S = [(l \times r) - f] \div (r - 1) \qquad\qquad (7\text{-}10)$$

As an example of the use of Formula (7-10), find the sum of a geometrical progression which has 3 as its first term; 7023 as its last term; and 7 as its common ratio.

Substituting in the formula $S = [(l \times r) - f] \div (r - 1)$

$$S = [(7023 \times 7) - 3] \div (7 - 1)$$

$$= (49161 - 3)/6$$

$$= 49158/6 = 8193.$$

A formula for S in terms of n, r and f can be derived by substituting in Formula (7-10) the value of l from Formula (7-6) giving

$$S = \frac{(fr^{n-1} \times r) - f}{r - 1}$$

$$S = \frac{f(r^n - 1)}{r - 1} \qquad\qquad (7\text{-}11)$$

In certain geometrical progressions, the common ratio, r, is less than 1, that is, it is a fraction or decimal. Formula (7-10) for the sum as well as the other formulas above, applies to those series, and requires only that care be taken in expressing the signs of the quantities obtained during the course of the calculation. Thus, in the series 16, 8, 4, 2, in which the first term is 16, the last term is 2, and the common ratio is $\frac{1}{2}$, using Formula (7-10), $S = [(l \times r) - f] \div (r - 1)$, and substituting, gives

$$S = [(2 \times \tfrac{1}{2}) - 16] \div (\tfrac{1}{2} - 1)$$

$$= (1 - 16) \div (\tfrac{1}{2} - 1)$$

$$= \frac{-15}{-\frac{1}{2}} = 30,$$

which can be verified by adding the four terms.

Values of r of less than unity appear in the "infinite" geometrical progressions that have finite sums. That is, a geometrical progression may continue indefinitely with no last term. If such a progression had a common ratio greater than 1, its sum would increase indefinitely with the number of terms, and have no limiting value. On the other hand, if a geometrical progression has a common ratio of less than 1, and continues indefinitely, then its last term is smaller than any assignable quantity, and may therefore be omitted from the formula for the sum of a geometrical progression.

Since Formula (7-10) for the sum of a geometrical progression is

$$S = [(l \times r) - f \div (r - 1)]$$

and in an infinite geometrical progression, l is smaller than any assignable quantity, then the product of l by r (r being less than 1) also becomes smaller than any assignable quantity. Therefore, the term $(l \times r)$ may be dropped from the formula, giving, for an infinite geometrical progression

$$S_\infty = \frac{-f}{r - 1} \quad \text{or} \quad \frac{f}{1 - r} \qquad (7\text{-}12)$$

As an example of the use of Formula (7-12), find the sum of the infinite geometrical series of which the first term is 16 and the common ratio is $\frac{1}{2}$.

Substituting,

$$S_\infty = \frac{16}{1 - \frac{1}{2}} = 32.$$

To appreciate how this infinite geometrical progression can have a sum of only 32, when the sum of its first five terms alone (16, 8, 4, 2 and 1) is 31, write a number of the following terms, such as $\frac{1}{2}$, $\frac{1}{4}$, $\frac{1}{8}$, $\frac{1}{16}$, and $\frac{1}{32}$, and note that the sum of the first two is $\frac{3}{4}$; that of the first three is $\frac{7}{8}$; that of the first four is $\frac{15}{16}$, and that of the first five is $\frac{31}{32}$. This sequence of sums approaches the value 1 in a way that suggests that 1 is the limiting value of the sum of the fractional terms in this series as their number increases indefinitely, and that the sum of the entire series is 1 plus the sum of the integral terms, a total of 32.

The Binomial Theorem

It was shown in Chapter 4 that,

$$(a + b)^2 = a^2 + 2ab + b^2$$

$$(a + b)^3 = a^3 + 3a^2b + 3ab^2 + b^3$$

These results were obtained by repeated multiplication by $(a + b)$. If the process is continued further it yields,

$$(a + b)^4 = a^4 + 4a^3b + 6a^2b^2 + 4ab^3 + b^4$$

$$(a + b)^5 = a^5 + 5a^4b + 10a^3b^2 + 10a^2b^3 + 5ab^4 + b^5$$

By comparing these consecutive expanded powers of the binomial, it can be seen that they show certain similarities. In each case the number of terms is 1 greater than the exponent of the binomial, the exponents of a decrease by 1 from term to term, while those of b increase in the same way, and the coefficients of the terms also exhibit a similarity in pattern. The existence of these similarities suggest the possibility of inducing a general formula for powers of the binomial, that is, for $(a + b)^n$. This formula has, in fact, been developed. It is called the binomial theorem and can be stated thus:

The first term in the expansion of $(a + b)^n$ is a^n; the second term has n for its coefficient, and its other factors are a^{n-1} and b; in subsequent terms the powers of a decrease by 1 for each term, and those of b increase by 1 for each term, while any coefficient can be obtained from the previous coefficient by multiplying the latter by the exponent of a in the previous term, and dividing it by the number of terms up to and including the previous term. The binomial theorem holds for any exponent whatever, with certain restrictions on a and b.

In view of the relative complexity of this statement, the use of a form of the general formula is a more direct route to its application. The formula can be written,

$$(a_1 + b)^n = a^n + na^{n-1}b + \frac{n(n-1)}{1 \times 2} a^{n-2}b^2 + \frac{n(n-1)(n-2)}{1 \times 2 \times 3} a^{n-3}b^3$$

$$+ \frac{n(n-1)(n-2)(n-3)}{1 \times 2 \times 3 \times 4} a^{n-4}b^4 \cdot \cdot \cdot b^n \qquad (7\text{-}13)$$

where the coefficient of each successive term is written by adding a numerical factor to the numerator and another to the denominator of the coefficient of the previous term (the factor added to the numerator being one less than the last previous factor, and the factor added to the denominator one greater). The powers of a decrease by 1 and those of b increase by 1 from term to term.

When the numerical value of n is a whole number, the number of terms is equal to $n + 1$. To demonstrate this statement, use the formula to find $(a + b)^2$.

Then since n is 2, a^n is a^2; na^{n-1} is $2a^{2-1}b = 2ab$; $\dfrac{n(n-1)}{1 \times 2} a^{n-2}b^2$ is

$\dfrac{2(2-1)}{1 \times 2} a^{2-2}b^2 = \dfrac{2(1)}{1 \times 2} a^0b^2 = \dfrac{2}{2} 1b^2 = b^2$; while $\dfrac{n(n-1)(n-2)}{1 \times 2 \times 3} a^{n-3}b^3 =$

$\dfrac{2(1)(0)}{1 \times 2 \times 3} a^{-1}b^3 = 0$ because zero is a multiplying factor in this term, which makes its value zero. Therefore, there are only three terms, and by gathering them, the result obtained is $(a + b)^2 = a^2 + 2ab + b^2$. Similarly, for $(a + b)^3$, application of the binomial formula yields only four terms in the expansion: for a^n is a^3; $na^{n-1}b$ is $3a^{3-1}b = 3a^2b$; $\dfrac{n(n-1)}{1 \times 2} a^{n-2}b^2$

$= \dfrac{3(3-1)}{1 \times 2} a^{3-1}b = \dfrac{3 \times 2}{1 \times 2} a^2b = 3a^2b$; $\dfrac{3(3-1)(3-2)}{1 \times 2 \times 3} a^{n-3}b^3 =$

$\dfrac{3(3-1)(3-2)}{1 \times 2 \times 3} a^{3-3}b^3 = \dfrac{3 \times 2 \times 1}{1 \times 2 \times 3} a^0b^3 = b^3$; $\dfrac{n(n-1)(n-2)(n-3)}{1 \times 2 \times 3 \times 4}$

$a^{n-4}b^4 = \dfrac{3(3-1)(3-2)(3-3)}{1 \times 2 \times 3 \times 4} a^{3-4}b^4 = \dfrac{3 \times 2 \times 1 \times 0}{1 \times 2 \times 3 \times 4} a^{-1}b^4 = 0$, because zero is a multiplying factor in this term, which makes its value zero. Therefore there are only four terms, and by gathering them, it is found that $(a + b)^3 = a^3 + 3a^2b + 3ab^2 + b^3$.

Therefore the binomial theorem is readily extended to any whole number value of n, yielding a number of terms one greater than n, since the terms higher than that all contain 0 factors which makes their value zero.

However, if n is fractional or negative, then subtraction from it of increasing integers never yields a zero factor. (For if n is $\frac{3}{2}$, $\frac{3}{2} - 1 = \frac{1}{2}$, $\frac{3}{2} - 2 = -\frac{1}{2}$, $\frac{3}{2} - 3 = -\frac{3}{2}$, etc.)

In such cases the succession of terms continues indefinitely, and becomes an infinite series. Even an infinite series may be, and in fact often is used in mathematical computations, as was the case with the infinite geometrical progression discussed earlier in this chapter. The requirement to be met is that its value must be convergent, that is, that the values of succeeding terms must decrease in such a way that the sum of a finite number of terms (and in practice, a reasonably small number of terms), must approach the exact value as closely as may be desired.

Thus to express the binomial expansion of $(a + b)^{\frac{1}{2}}$ in terms of the binomial theorem, a^n is $a^{\frac{1}{2}}$; $na^{n-1}b$ is $\dfrac{1}{2}a^{\frac{1}{2}-1}b = \dfrac{1}{2} a^{-\frac{1}{2}}b = \dfrac{1}{2a^{\frac{1}{2}}} b$; $\dfrac{n(n-1)}{1 \times 2}$

$$a^{n-2}b^2 \text{ is } \frac{\frac{1}{2}(\frac{1}{2} - 1)}{1 \times 2} \ a^{\frac{1}{2}-2}b^2 = \frac{-\frac{1}{4}}{2} \ a^{-\frac{3}{2}}b^2 = -\frac{1}{8a^{\frac{3}{2}}} \ b^2; \frac{n(n - 1)(n - 2)}{1 \times 2 \times 3} \ a^{n-3}b^3$$

$$= \frac{\frac{1}{2}(\frac{1}{2} - 1)(\frac{1}{2} - 2)}{1 \times 2 \times 3} \ a^{\frac{1}{2}-3}b^3 = \frac{\frac{1}{2}(-\frac{1}{2})(-\frac{3}{2})}{1 \times 2 \times 3} \ a^{-\frac{5}{2}}b^3 = \frac{\frac{3}{8}}{1 \times 2 \times 3} \frac{1}{a^{\frac{5}{2}}} \ b^3 =$$

$$\frac{1}{16a^{\frac{5}{2}}} \ b^3 \cdot \cdot \cdot \cdot$$ Whether this series is useful in calculating the values of the expansion for given values of a and b depends, as stated above, on how rapidly it converges, because the number of terms is infinite.

Chapter 8

GRAPHS AND FUNCTIONS

A graph may be defined as a picture of a relationship. In keeping with this definition, graphs are capable of showing at a glance a sequence of related values which constitute a mathematical relationship in its area of interest. Furthermore, by the use of graphs it is often possible to make mathematical calculations which by algebraic or analytical methods would be far more difficult and time-consuming. Both of these uses of graphs are explained in this chapter, in their application to business mathematics and business problems.

Among the simplest methods of graphical representation are the bar charts, pie charts, and other types of charts. In fact, such charts are often very useful in business control operations. One example is the Inventory coverage chart, given in Fig. 8-1, in which the amount of inventory of

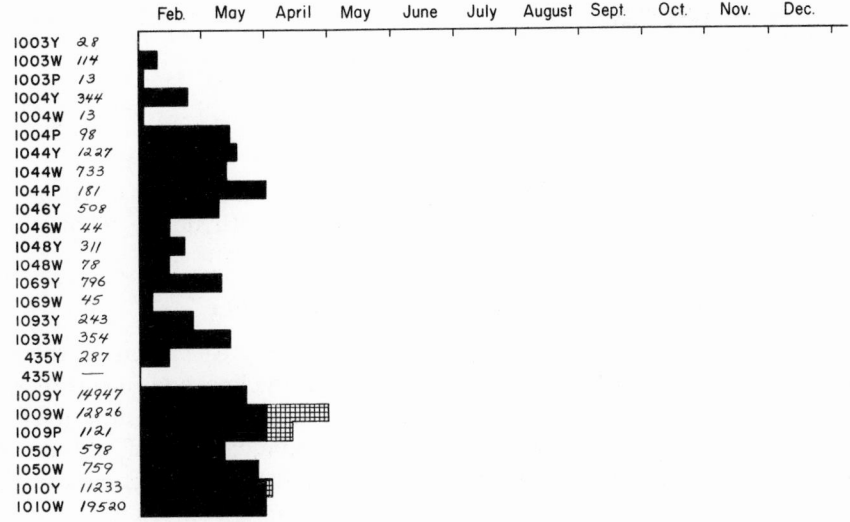

Figure 8-1. Inventory coverage chart.

each item carried in stock is divided by the average monthly sales (or projected monthly sales) and plotted against the time. Since in this particular business two months' supply is required of all items, the "bars" longer than that are cross-hatched.

Another example of a control bar chart is the Absenteeism chart shown in Fig. 8-2. Still another is the Production control chart shown in Fig. 8-3. The data reported on this particular chart is somewhat exceptional, since it shows the recovery period following a seasonal shutdown.

An especially valuable method of graphical representation is that using

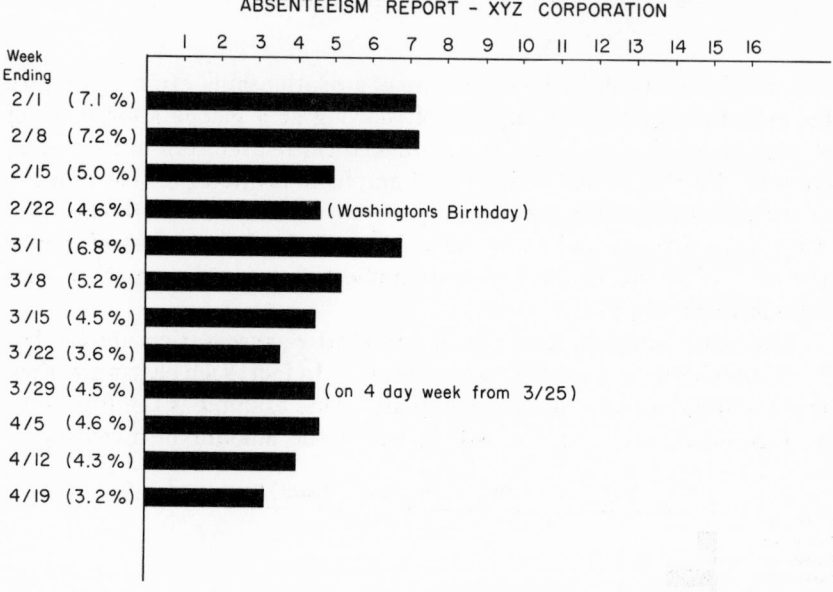

Figure 8-2.   Absenteeism chart.

rectangular coordinates. Its great advantage is its adaptability to mathematical analysis. It is, therefore, discussed at length in the following section.

Graphical Representation by Rectangular Coordinates

A number may be represented by a point on a line. An obvious method is to establish an O-point or origin somewhere on the line, and to choose a unit of length along the line to represent successive numbers in a given sequence. This method is convenient for the representation of algebraic numbers, since positive numbers can be measured in one direction away from the origin (O-point), while negative numbers are measured in the opposite direction.

Lines used to represent numbers are called axes. In the most commonly used system of graphical representation, the rectangular Cartesian system, the axes are straight lines that are mutually perpendicular at the origin. The X-axis is horizontal and in the plane of the paper; points to the right of the origin represent positive numbers, and those to the left, negative numbers. The Y-axis is vertical and in the plane of the paper; points upward from the origin represent positive numbers, and those downward from the origin, negative numbers. The Z-axis is perpendicular to the plane of the paper, points in the direction of advance of an ordinary (right-handed) screw into the paper from the origin represent negative

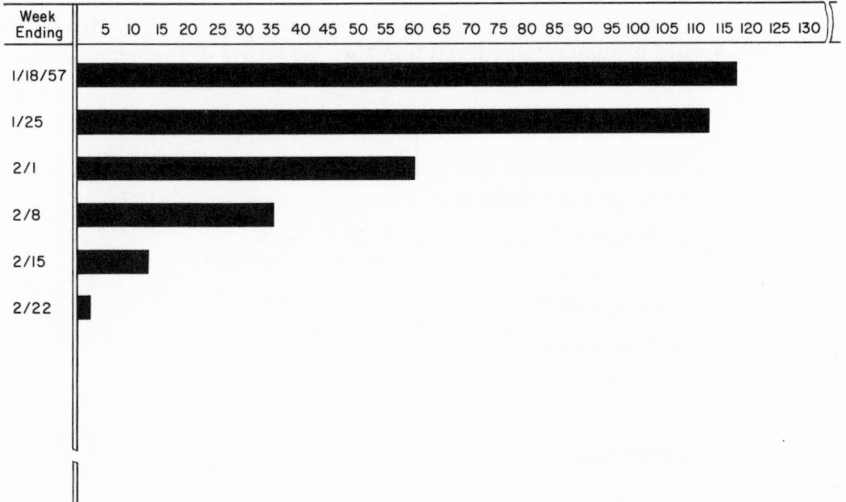

Figure 8-3. Production control chart. (Part orders open in factory older than 6 weeks.)

numbers, and those in the opposite direction, that is, from the plane of the paper toward the writer, positive numbers. In some systems, however, the Z-axis signs are reversed; that is not important here, because this chapter deals exclusively with 2-axis relationships, so that the Z-axis is not used.

The advantage of the graphical method is that it permits the representation of more than one number by a single point. Thus, using the X-axis and Y-axis only, each point on the paper represents two numbers. To illustrate the process, refer to Figure 8-4, which shows the representation of the numbers $+5$, -3 by the point P. The position of P is found (in mathematical terms, P is plotted) by marking off 5 equal, convenient units of distance along the X-axis in the positive direction (i.e. to the right of the origin), and 3 equal units of distance along the Y-axis in a negative direction, (i.e., downward from the origin). Then by projecting these points perpendicularly until the projecting lines (shown dotted in the figure) intersect, the position of P is found. Of course, the dotted lines need not actually be drawn; their position can be judged by applying a straight edge to the paper. Better still, a specially printed paper, on which are printed closely-spaced lines, can be used.

Some of the mathematical terms widely used in plotting coordinates are: abscissa, the number representing the horizontal distance of a point from the origin, which is the distance measured along the X-axis; ordinate, the number representing the vertical distance of a point from the origin, which is the distance measured along the Y-axis; coordinates, which are the abscissa and ordinate considered together, or either of them generically;

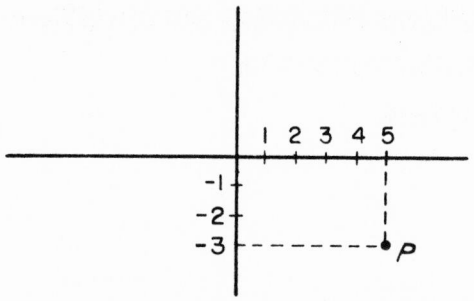

Figure 8-4.   Graphical representation of a pair of number (geometrically a point in a plane) in rectangular Cartesian System.

and coordinate paper, which is the paper already described that is printed with intersecting lines for use in plotting.

The fundamental significance of the coordinate method is, as stated above, that it permits the representation by a point of a pair of related numbers (or by the use of additional axes, of more than two related numbers). More than that, it permits the representation by a group of points of a group of pairs of related numbers. Thus, the annual gross sales of a business may be represented by a group of points, each of which is fixed by two numbers, one representing the year and the other the gross sales, as shown in Figure 8-5. Note that the choice of units on the coordinate paper has been made so as to present the data clearly (i.e. to spread it over a large area). Therefore the abscissas have been taken as 4 divisions per year, while the ordinates have been taken as $250,000 of gross sales per division.

Graphical Solution of Simultaneous Equations

Obviously, any collection of pairs of related numbers can be represented graphically by the method used in constructing Figure 8-5. Furthermore, a *continuous* relationship between two variables, can also be so represented.

For example, consider the equation $2x + 4y = 22$. By substituting the values 1, 2, 3, 4 · · · for x, we can determine the corresponding values

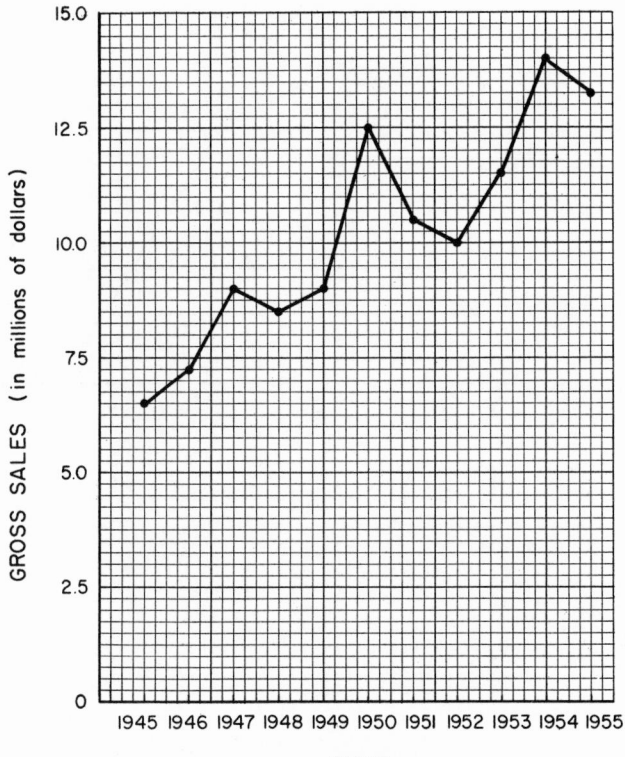

Figure 8-5.　Graphical representation of gross sales by years.

of y, which are 5, 4.5, 4, 3.5 · · · . These values can then be plotted on coordinate paper at the points 1, 5; 2, 4.5; 3, 4; 4, 3.5, as shown in graph #1 of Figure 8-6. Note that all four of the points fall on a straight line. This is characteristic of equations in which the variables are present only to first powers, and their graphs can therefore be plotted from any two points— that is, any two pairs of values of x and y that satisfy the equation.

Now, suppose that the equation $6x + 4y = 30$ be plotted on the same paper and, of course, to the same scale. The plotting may be effected, as stated above, from any two points. Thus from the equation, when $x = 1$, $y = 6$; and when $x = 5$, $y = 0$. Then by plotting these two points 1,6 and 5,0 and drawing a straight line through them, graph #2 is produced.

Note that graphs #1 and #2 intersect in the point 2,4.5; since this point

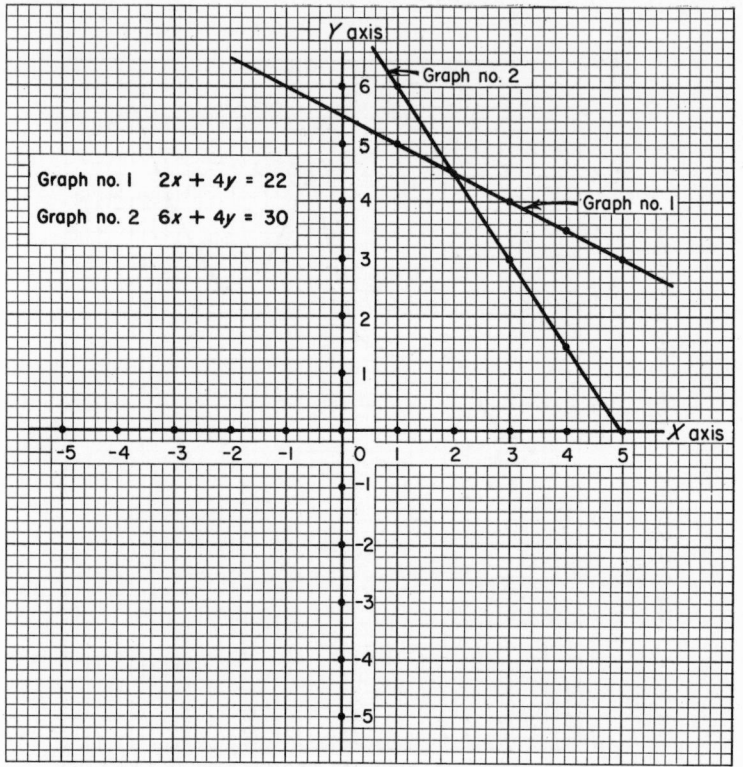

Figure 8-6.   Graphical solution of two first degree simultaneous equations in two variables.

lies on both graphs, its corresponding values of x and y satisfy both equations, and are therefore the solution of these two simultaneous equations.

Graphical Solution of Quadratic Equations in One Variable

To find the solution of a quadratic equation in one variable by graphical means, it must be expressed in terms of a second variable, that is, in explicit functional form. Thus the equation $x^2 + 3x - 18 = 0$, is a special value of the equation $x^2 + 3x - 18 = y$.   To obtain a solution of the former by graphical means, the latter is plotted, by substituting various values of x and computing the corresponding values of y.   A table of such values, so computed, is as follows:

$$y = x^2 + 3x - 18$$

x	y
-10	52
-9	36
-8	22
-7	10
-6	0
-5	-8
-4	-14
-3	-18
-2	-20
-1	-19
0	-18
1	-14
2	-8
3	0
4	10
5	22
6	36
7	52
8	70
9	90
10	112

Plotting the points representing the above values of x and corresponding values of y, gives the collection of points shown in Figure 8-7, on the following page.   These points are then connected by a smooth graph drawn through them, and the values of x at which this graph cuts the x-axis, that is, the values of x at which $y = 0$, obviously satisfy the original equation $x^2 + 3x - 18 = 0$, and are solutions of it, as may be found by substitution.   These values are $x = 3$ and $x = -6$.

Not all quadratic equations in x give graphs which cut the X-axis in two points, yielding two real roots.   Some such graphs are tangent to the X-axis (i.e., touch it) at one point only.   In that case, the two roots have the value of that point, i.e., they are equal.   Some graphs of quadratic equations do not touch the axis at all—in which case the roots are imaginary or complex.

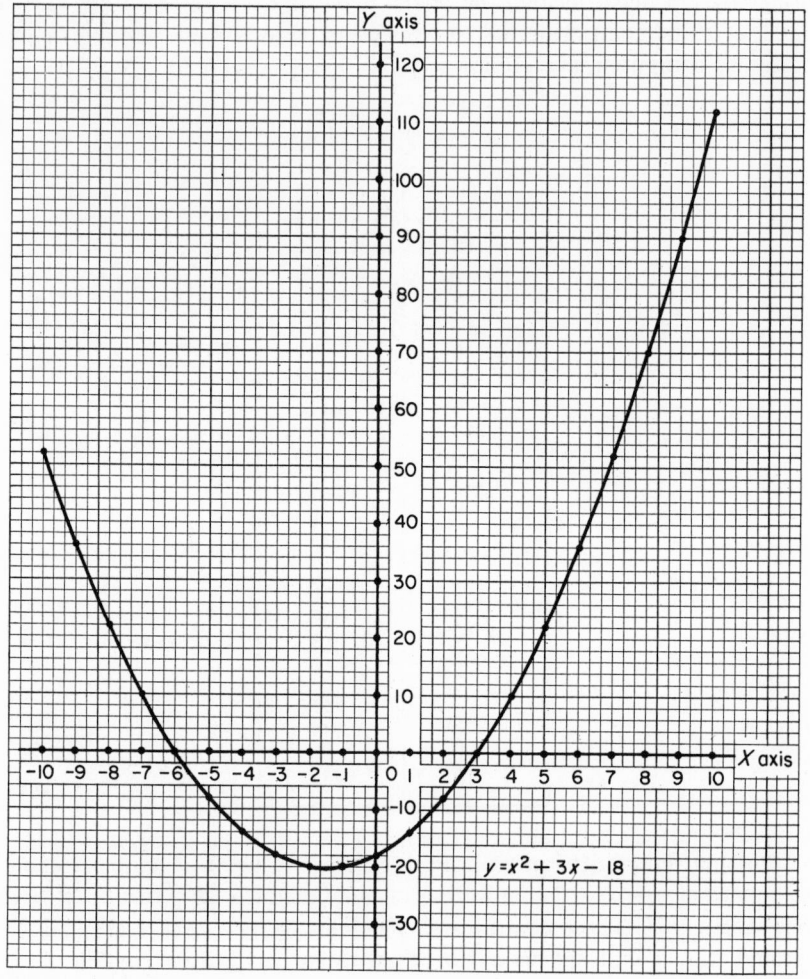

Figure 8-7.   Graphical solution of a second degree (quadratic) equation in one variable.

Graphical Solution of Simultaneous Quadratic Equations

Some simultaneous quadratic equations lend themselves readily to solution by graphical methods. Consider for example, the equations $y = x^2 - 2x - 3$ and $x^2 + y^2 = 16$. Now these equations yield the values of y corresponding to x values as shown in the following tabulations:

$$y = x^2 - 3x - 3 \qquad\qquad x^2 + y^2 = 16$$

x	y
-5	32
-4	21
-3	12
-2	5
-1	0
0	-3
1	-4
2	-3
3	0
4	5
5	12

x	y
-4	0
-3.5	± 1.94
-3	± 2.65
-2	± 3.46
-1	± 3.87
0	± 4
1	± 3.87
2	± 3.46
3	± 2.65
3.5	± 1.94
4	0

Plotting these values yields
Graph #1, Figure 8-8.

Plotting these values yields
Graph #2, Figure 8-8..

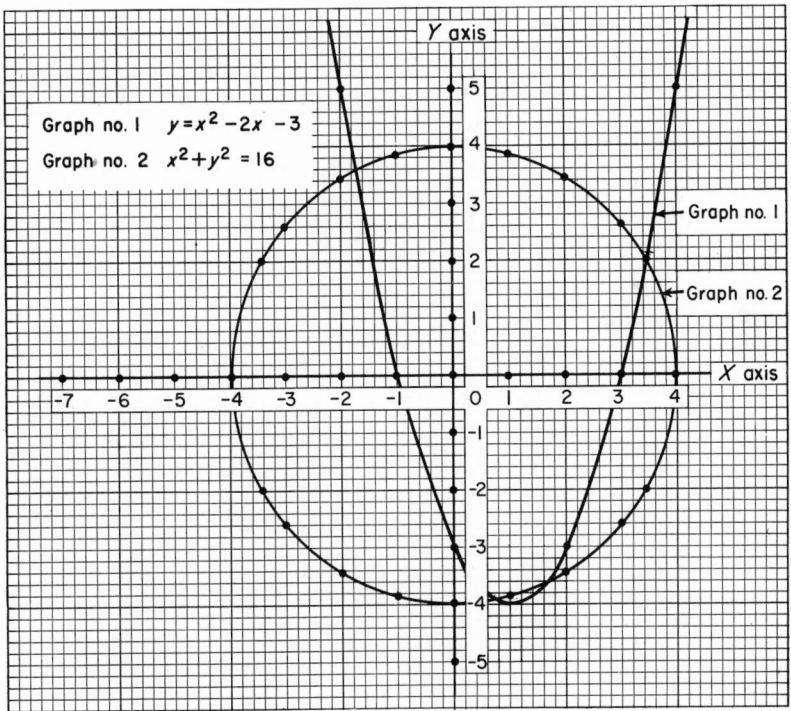

Figure 8-8. Graphical solution of two second degree (quadratic) simultaneous equations in two variables.

The values of x, y which satisfy both equations are found at the points of intersection of the graphs plotted in Figure 8-8 on page 159, which are $x = -1.75$, $y = 3.6$; $x = .7$, $y = -3.9$; $x = 1.6$, $y = -3.55$; $x = 3.45$, $y = 2$.

It should be noted, however, that the graphical method does not apply to all quadratic equations. Not only are some such equations more time-consuming to solve in this way than by algebraic methods, but others cannot be solved at all graphically. These include equations which have one or more imaginary roots. When such equations are plotted, the imaginary roots do not appear as intersections with axes, as was found to be the case with real roots, as in the example of the equation $x^2 + 3x - 18 = 0$.

Graphical Solution of Higher Equations

As stated in Chapter 5, the algebraic methods of solving equations of a power (of the variable or variables) higher than the second are beyond the scope of this book. However, such equations can frequently be solved by the graphical methods already discussed.

Consider the equation $x^3 - 4x^2 - 20x + 48 = 0$. By writing it as an explicit function of y, and substituting various values of x, the following values of x and y are obtained·

$$y = x^3 - 4x^2 - 20x + 48$$

x	y
-8	-560
-7	-351
-6	-192
-5	-77
-4	0
-3	45
-2	64
-1	63
0	48
1	25
2	0
3	-21
4	-32
5	-27
6	0
7	55
8	144

The graph of this function is plotted in Figure 8-9. From this the roots of the equation can be found from the values of x at the points where the graph cuts the X-axis, that is, where $y = 0$, giving the roots as $x = -4$, $x = 2$, and $x = 6$, which can be verified by substitution.

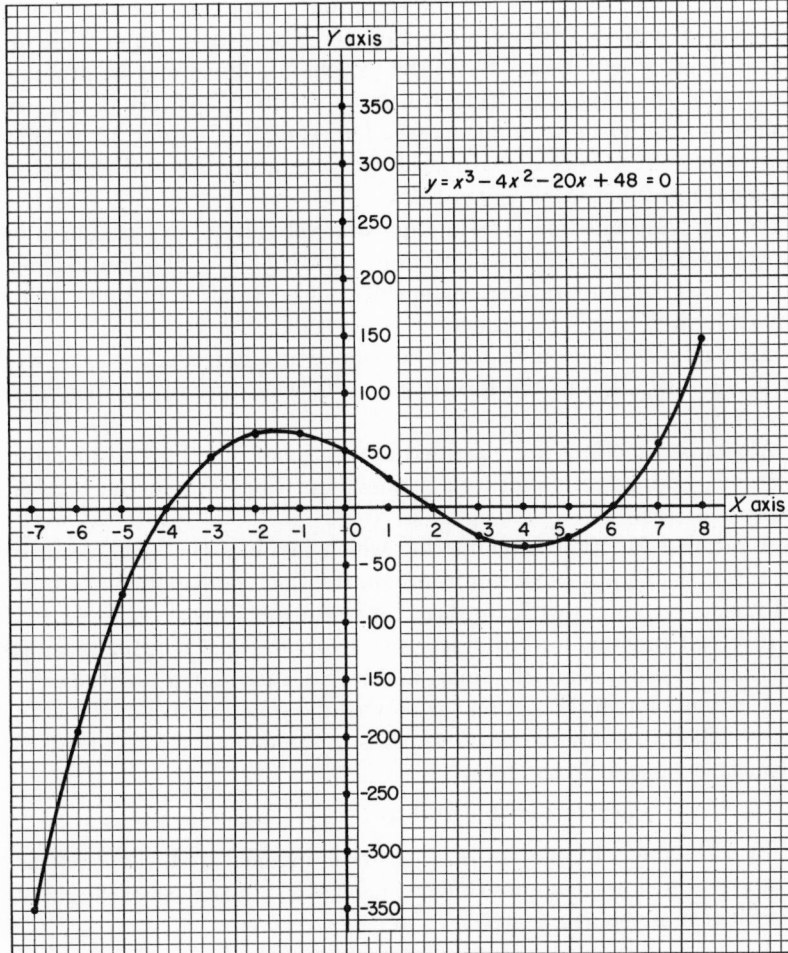

Figure 8-9. Graphical solution of a third degree (cubic) equation in one variable.

Now, it is to be noted that roots of equations are not necessarily integral, as they were in this case. They may be fractions, mixed numbers, irrational numbers or imaginary. In the last case, they cannot be found graphically, since there is no corresponding axial intersection. However, in all the other cases mentioned, the intersection does exist, and can be found graphically, to the degree of accuracy with which the graph is plotted.

Functions

In the foregoing discussion the equation giving y in terms of various powers of x, with or without a constant term, was called an explicit function, without a definition. Since the various functions play so prominent a part in mathematical analysis, which is used so extensively in the newer applications to business problems (see for example, Chapter 22 on Operations Research) a brief discussion of the general nature and character of mathematical functions is given below.

An algebraic function is a function which involves the variable in only the operations of addition, subtraction, multiplication, division, raising to powers with constant rational exponents, and extraction of roots (involution), a limited number of times.

An algebraic function may also be defined as a function $y = \phi(x)$ which satisfies an equation of the form $f(x,y) = 0$, where $f(x,y)$ is a polynomial in x and y.

Algebraic functions are classified into rational functions and irrational functions, and power functions; rational functions are further classified into sub-classes.

A rational function is a function which involves the variable in only the rational operations of addition, subtraction, multiplication, division and raising to powers with constant integral exponents.

Rational functions are divided into two sub-classes: rational integral functions or polynomial functions, and rational fractional functions.

A rational integral function (or polynomial function) is a rational function in which the variable never appears in the denominator of a fraction. It can be expressed in the form

$$P(x) = a_o x^n + a_1 x^{n-1} + \cdots + a_{n-1} x + a_n,$$

where x is the variable, n is a positive integer, and the coefficients $a_o, a_1 \cdots, a_n$ are constants (independent of x); in this case, the function is said to be of the nth degree.

A power function is an algebraic function of the form ax^n, where a and n are constants (independent of x) and x is the variable. It has a variable base x and a constant exponent n. The exponent may be a positive integer, or it may be a fraction or negative number, or even irrational.

A transcendental function is a function which is not an algebraic function. Among the transcendental functions are the following types: trigonometric functions, inverse trigonometric functions, exponential functions, hyperbolic functions, logarithmic functions, etc., etc.

If two variables are so related that to each value of one variable in a given range there correspond one or more values of the other variable, the second variable is called a function of the first variable.

The first variable is often called the independent variable and the function is sometimes called the dependent variable.

If one variable is so related to several variables that to each set of values of the last-mentioned variables there correspond one or more values of the first variable, the first variable is called a function of the other variables.

If a function is defined by a relation between the variables giving an equation expressing one variable directly in terms of the other without the necessity of solving the equation, the function so defined is called an explicit function.

If a function is defined by a relation between the variables given by an equation which must be solved in order to express one variable in terms of the other, the function so defined is called an implicit function.

If a variable y is an explicit function of another variable x, the function is often denoted in general by such symbols as $f(x)$, $F(x)$, $\phi(x)$, etc., and we write $y = f(x)$, etc. The symbol $f(a)$ then denotes the value of the function $f(x)$ for the value $x = a$.

A function of two variables, as x and y, may be represented in general by such symbols as $f(x,y)$, etc.; and similarly for functions of more than two variables.

A function which takes one value only, corresponding to any given value of the independent variable, is called a single-valued function.

A multiple-valued function is a function which takes more than one value corresponding to any given value of the independent variable.

A function of one variable $f(x)$ is said to be continuous at a value $x = c$ when $f(c)$ has a definite finite value which is equal to the limit of $f(x)$ when $x \rightarrow c$:

$$\lim_{x \to c} f(x) = f(c).$$

A function $f(x)$ is said to be continuous in an interval (a,b) when it is continuous at every point of the interval, it being sufficient at the end points that

$$\lim_{x \to a^+} f(x) = f(a),$$

and

$$\lim_{x \to b^-} f(x) = f(b).$$

Continuous functions are dealt with extensively in the calculus, and for that reason the subject of limits, and their notation, which is used in the above definitions, is treated in the next chapter.

Chapter 9

DIFFERENTIAL AND INTEGRAL CALCULUS

One of the most significant recent developments in business mathematics has been its widespread use of applications of the methods of the calculus. Chapter 22 on operations research indicates how extensively these methods are coming into use in modern managerial techniques. For that reason this present chapter has been added to explain briefly certain of the fundamental concepts and elementary methods of the calculus.

The purpose of this chapter is to introduce a single fundamental process from the calculus, and the inverse of that process, both of which occur frequently in certain of the methods and applications of business mathematics. The process is that of differentiation, and its inverse is integration; the two being among the most useful of all mathematical operations. As a background for the discussion of these processes, however, a few preliminary topics must first be discussed.

Limits

The concept of a limit has already been introduced in Chapter 7. There it was shown that an infinite geometric series, while having an indefinitely large (infinite) number of terms, also has a finite sum which can be evaluated. Thus the infinite series $1 + \left(\frac{1}{2}\right) + \left(\frac{1}{4}\right) + \cdots + \left(\frac{1}{2^n}\right)$, has a definite sum, which can be found by use of the general formula: $S = \frac{f - r^n}{1 - r}$; for by substituting and dividing:

$$S = \frac{1 - (\frac{1}{2})^n}{1 - \frac{1}{2}} = \frac{1 - (\frac{1}{2})^n}{\frac{1}{2}} = 2 - \frac{(\frac{1}{2})^n}{\frac{1}{2}} = 2 - \left(\frac{1}{2}\right)^{n-1} = 2 - \frac{1}{2^{n-1}}$$

Now if n, the number of terms, increases indefinitely, the term $\frac{1}{2^{n-1}}$ grows smaller and smaller, and therefore the difference between the number 2, and the number $2 - \dfrac{1}{2^{n-1}}$ becomes smaller and smaller. Consequently, the limiting value, or limit of S as n increases indefinitely, is 2, because by making n large enough, S can be made to approach 2 as closely as required.

The foregoing statement is a form of the fundamental theorem on limits, which can be stated more precisely as follows: If a variable steadily increases (or decreases) but never becomes greater (or less) than a fixed number A, then the variable approaches a limit which is not greater (or less) than A.

The concept of limits can be applied to a function. As shown in Chapter 8, the expression $y = f(x)$, denotes a relationship between the values assumed by a dependent variable y, and an independent variable x. Examples are $y = 2x^2 + 3x + 7$; $y = x^2 + 3 \log_{10} x$; $y = 4(3 + 7x)$; etc. In all such relationships, y is said to be a function of x. Whatever the nature of the function, if as x approaches a fixed value a, the difference between $f(x)$ and some fixed number b becomes and remains less than any preassigned constant however small, then the function $f(x)$ is said to approach the limit b, which is expressed symbolically as

$$\lim_{x \to a} f(x) = b$$

The concept of limits is used in differential calculus, which is primarily concerned with the problem of finding how a function varies in comparison with the independent variable(s)—e.g., where $y = f(x)$, how y varies with x. In general, a change in the value of the variable produces a change in its function. Any arbitrary change in an independent variable is called an increment in that variable—this increment being, for convenience, usually taken as positive. Corresponding to any increment of the independent variable, there is produced an increment of its function, these increments being denoted for $y = f(x)$ by the symbols Δx for the increment in the independent variable and Δy for the increment in its function.

Rate of Change of a Function—The Derivative

Now, these increments may be applied to the determination of the rate of change of a function. The particular functional graph chosen for the purpose is shown in Figure 9-1, but this derivation is general (within certain limiting conditions) and therefore it will be formulated for the general function $y = f(x)$.

If this function is continuous in the portion of interest, take a point P, having coordinates x,y. Now assign an increment Δx to x, and denote the corresponding increment of y by Δy. That is, there is a point P', having coordinates $x + \Delta x$, $y + \Delta y$. Moreover, since $y = f(x)$, then since P' is also on the graph of the function,

$$y + \Delta y = f(x + \Delta x)$$

The geometric meaning of these quantities can be seen by reference to Figure 9-1, where the points P (with coordinates x,y) and P' (with coordinates $x + \Delta x$, $y + \Delta x$) are shown, along with the lengths corresponding to Δx and Δy.

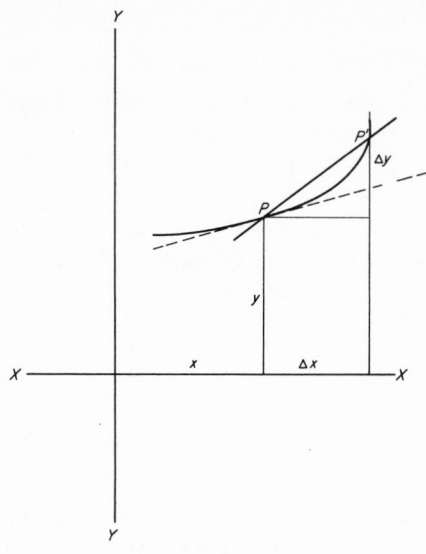

Figure 9-1. Geometrical meaning of the derivative.

Transposing y, we have

$$\Delta y = f(x + \Delta x) - y$$

Substituting $f(x)$ for y, we have

$$\Delta y = f(x + \Delta x) - f(x)$$

Dividing both sides by Δx, we have

$$\frac{\Delta y}{\Delta x} = \frac{f(x + \Delta x) - f(x)}{\Delta x} \quad (9\text{-}1)$$

Now the ratio $\frac{\Delta y}{\Delta x}$ can be seen by reference to Figure 9-1 to be the average rate of change of y with respect to x in the interval Δx; geometrically it is the slope, or inclination to the horizontal of the line PP'. (That is, if Δy is small for a given Δx the line has little slope; whereas if Δy is large relative to Δx, the line has a large slope.)

Now, let the increment Δx decrease toward a limiting value of 0. Then Δy will also approach its limiting value of zero, as can be seen from Figure 9-1 if P' is considered to approach P along the graph, which causes both Δx and Δy to decrease toward values of zero. Note, however, that the ratio $\frac{\Delta y}{\Delta x}$ does not usually approach zero as a limit as Δx and Δy do; this can be seen by following the changing slope of the line PP' as P' approaches P. Its limiting position when P' reaches P is the dashed line.

The limiting value of the ratio $\frac{\Delta y}{\Delta x}$ as x approaches 0 is called the derivative of y with respect to x and is denoted by the expression $\frac{dy}{dx}$. Its value in geometric terms is the slope of PP', the line tangent to the graph at P.

Its symbolic expression is

$$\frac{dy}{dx} = \lim_{\Delta x \to 0} \frac{\Delta y}{\Delta x} = \lim_{\Delta x \to 0} \frac{f(x + \Delta x) - f(x)}{\Delta x} \tag{9-2}$$

Note that $\frac{dy}{dx}$ as obtained here is a single quantity, (although there exists a class of quantities called differentials, such as dy and dx) just as Δx and Δy are single quantities. In fact the derivative $\frac{dy}{dx}$ is often represented by the symbol y'.

Moreover, since the derivative is also the slope of a function for given values of the variables, its magnitude is the rate of change of the function at that point with respect to the independent variable. This value is obviously important in all those problems where we are interested, not only in values at one point on a function, but also in its rate of change there. Therefore, we are interested in the determination of the value of the derivative for different functions, a process called differentiation.

Differentiation

A general method of differentiation of a function is shown by the following example,

Differentiate the function $y = x^2$

Adding the increments Δy and Δx gives

$$y + \Delta y = (x + \Delta x)^2$$

$$y + \Delta y = x^2 + 2x \, \Delta x + (\Delta x)^2$$

Since $y = x^2$, subtract y from the left side of the equality and x^2 from the right, giving

$$\Delta y = 2x \, \Delta x + (\Delta x)^2$$

Dividing through by Δx

$$\frac{\Delta y}{\Delta x} = 2x + \Delta x$$

Then the derivative, which is the limiting value of $\frac{\Delta y}{\Delta x}$ as Δy and Δx approach 0, is

$$\frac{dy}{dx} = \lim_{\Delta x \to 0} \frac{\Delta y}{\Delta x} = 2x. \tag{9-3}$$

To extend the process of differentiation, differentiate the function $y = x^3$.

Following the same steps as above, we have

$$y + \Delta y = (x + \Delta x)^3$$

$$y + \Delta y = x^3 + 3x^2 \, \Delta x + 3x(\Delta x)^2 + (\Delta x)^3$$

$$y = 3x^2 \, \Delta x + 3x(\Delta x)^2 + (\Delta x)^3$$

$$\frac{y}{\Delta x} = 3x^2 + 3x \, \Delta x + (\Delta x)^2$$

Then
$$\frac{dy}{dx} = \lim_{\Delta x \to 0} \frac{\Delta y}{\Delta x} = 3x^2 \qquad (9\text{-}4)$$

To extend the process of differentiation to x^n, where n is any positive integer, we write

$$y + \Delta y = (x + \Delta x)^n$$

And by the binomial theorem (Chapter 7)

$$y + \Delta y = x^n + nx^{n-1} \, \Delta x + \frac{n(n-1)}{2!} \, x^{n-2} \, (\Delta x)^2 \, \cdots \, (\Delta x)^n$$

$$\Delta y = nx^{n-1} \, \Delta x + \frac{n(n-1)}{2!} \, xn^{-2} \, (\Delta x)^2 \, \cdots \, (\Delta x)^n$$

$$\frac{\Delta y}{\Delta x} = nx^{n-1} + \frac{n(n-1)}{2!} \, x^{n-2} \, (\Delta x) \, \cdots \, (\Delta x)^{n-1}$$

Then
$$\frac{dy}{dx} = \lim_{\Delta x \to 0} \frac{\Delta y}{\Delta x} = nx^{n-1} \qquad (9\text{-}5)$$

because all terms but the first term contain Δx, or a multiple of it, as a factor, and therefore they all approach 0 as Δx does.

Note that the foregoing development of the concepts of functions and derivatives was applied to *variables*—the derivative of a *constant* is zero, since it does not vary.

To find the derivative of a sum, take y, z and w, all being functions of the independent variable x, and related by the equation $y = z + w$.

Then
$$y + \Delta y = (z + \Delta z) + (w + \Delta w)$$

$$\Delta y = \Delta z + \Delta w$$

$$\frac{\Delta y}{\Delta x} = \frac{\Delta z}{\Delta x} + \frac{\Delta w}{\Delta x}$$

Then
$$\frac{dy}{dx} = \lim_{\Delta x \to 0} = \frac{dz}{dx} + \frac{dw}{dx} \qquad (9\text{-}6)$$

Thus the derivative of the sum of two functions with respect to a common variable is the sum of their derivatives with respect to that variable.

To find the derivative of a product, take y, z and w, all being functions of the independent variable x, and related by the equation $y = zw$.

Then
$$y + \Delta y = (z + \Delta z)(w + \Delta w)$$
$$y + \Delta y = zw + z\Delta w + \Delta zw + \Delta z \, \Delta w$$
$$\Delta y = z\Delta w + \Delta zw + \Delta z \, \Delta w$$
$$\frac{\Delta y}{\Delta x} = z\frac{\Delta w}{\Delta x} + w\frac{\Delta z}{\Delta x} + \frac{\Delta z \, \Delta w}{\Delta x}$$

Then
$$\frac{dy}{dx} = \lim_{\Delta x \to 0} \frac{\Delta y}{\Delta x} = z\frac{dw}{dx} + w\frac{dz}{dx} \qquad (9\text{-}7)$$

Thus, the derivative of a product of two functions with respect to a common variable is the sum of the first function multiplied by the derivative of the second (with respect to the common variable) and the second function multiplied by the derivative of the first (with respect to the common variable).

Note that the product of a constant and a function of a variable has as its derivative only the product of the constant by the derivative of the function of the variable, since the derivative of the constant is zero. Thus, the derivative of $6x^2$ is

$$\frac{d6x^2}{dx} = 6\frac{dx^2}{dx} = 6(2x) = 12x.$$

To find the dividend of a quotient, take y, z and w, all being functions of the independent variable x, and related by the equation $y = \dfrac{z}{w}$

Then
$$y + \Delta y = \frac{z + \Delta z}{w + \Delta w}$$
$$\Delta y = \frac{z + \Delta z}{w + \Delta w} - \frac{z}{w}$$
$$\Delta y = \frac{wz + w\Delta z - zw - z\Delta w}{w(w + \Delta w)}$$
$$\Delta y = \frac{w\Delta z - z\Delta w}{w^2 + w\Delta w}$$
$$\frac{\Delta y}{\Delta x} = \frac{w\dfrac{\Delta z}{\Delta x} - z\dfrac{\Delta w}{\Delta x}}{w^2 + w\Delta w}$$

Then
$$\frac{dy}{dx} = \lim_{\Delta x \to 0} \frac{\Delta y}{\Delta x} = \frac{w\dfrac{dz}{dx} - z\dfrac{dw}{dx}}{w^2} \qquad (9\text{-}8)$$

Thus, the derivative with respect to a common variable of a quotient of two functions (i.e., of a fraction formed by two functions) is the ratio of (the denominator multiplied by the derivative of the numerator with respect to the common variable less the numerator multiplied by the derivative of the denominator with respect to the common variable) to the square of the denominator.

The foregoing relations cover many of the cases of differentiation that are likely to occur in business mathematics. One other is $\dfrac{d \log_{10} y}{dx}$, which has the value

$$\frac{dy}{dx} = \frac{.4343}{y} \tag{9-9}$$

There are, of course, many other types of functions for which derivatives exist, as well as others for which they do not. These subjects are, however, clearly beyond the scope of this book.

To show the application of the differentiation formulas, a few examples are given below:

Differentiate $3x^4 + 5x^3 - x^2 + 6x - 10 = 0$.
By Formula (9-6), the derivative of this expression is the sum of the derivatives of its terms, so

$$\frac{dy}{dx} = \frac{d3x^4}{dx} + \frac{d5x^3}{dx} - \frac{dx^2}{dx} + \frac{d6x}{dx}$$

Then by Formula (9-7),

$$\frac{dy}{dx} = 3(4x^3) + 5(3x^2) - 2x + 6$$

The required derivative is therefore

$$12x^3 + 15x^2 - 2x + 6.$$

Differentiate $4 \log_{10} 3x^3 - 5x^2$.
    By Formula (9-6)

$$\frac{dy}{dx} = \frac{d4 \log_{10} 3x^3}{dx} - \frac{d5x^2}{dx}$$

$$\frac{dy}{dx} = \frac{4 \, d \log_{10} 3x^3}{dx} - 5\frac{dx^2}{dx}$$

By Formula (9-9)

$$\frac{dy}{dx} = 4 \left(\frac{.4343}{3x^3} \right)\left(\frac{d3x^3}{dx} \right) - 5\frac{dx^2}{dx}$$

By Formula (9-5)

$$\frac{dy}{dx} = 4 \left(\frac{.4343}{3x^3} \right)(9x^2) - 5(2x)$$

The required derivative is therefore

$$\frac{5.2116}{x} - 10x$$

Differentiate $\dfrac{1 + x^2}{1 - 3x}$

By Formula (9-8)

$$\frac{dy}{dx} = \frac{(1 - 3x)\left(\dfrac{d(1 + x^2)}{dx}\right) - (1 + x^2)\left(\dfrac{d(1 - 3x)}{dx}\right)}{(1 - 3x)^2}$$

By Formula (9-5)

$$\frac{dy}{dx} = \frac{(1 - 3x)(2x) - (1 + x^2)(-3)}{(1 - 3x)^2}$$

Therefore, the required derivative is

$$\frac{2x}{1 - 3x} + \frac{3 + 3x^2}{(1 - 3x)^2}$$

Uses of Derivatives

The evaluation of a derivative for a particular value of the independent variable shows clearly one of its most important uses. For as explained at the beginning of this chapter, that evaluation gives the slope, or rate of change of the function at that value of x. Suppose that x is time, and the function represents the distance of a moving body. Then the derivative with respect to x is the rate of change of distance with time, which is the velocity. To take a business example, suppose that x is time and the function represents the depreciation of an asset (by any method, such as the constant ratio method, which does not give a straight line function). Then the derivative with respect to x is the rate at which the asset is depreciating.

As an example of such applications of the derivative, substitution in it of various values of x gives the corresponding rates of change of the function. Thus substituting values of 1,2,3,4,5 and 6 for x in the function differentiated in the first example solved above gives the following values:

Function: $3x^4 + 5x^3 - x^2 + 6x - 10 = 0$
Derivative: $12x^3 + 15x^2 - 2x + 6$

x	$\dfrac{dy}{dx}$
1	31.
2	158
3	459
4	1006
5	1871
6	3126

A special significance attaches to 0 values of the derivative. Since the derivative is the slope of the curve of the function, a zero value of the derivative means that the line representing the slope is parallel to the x-axis at that particular value of x. This often indicates that the function has a minimum or maximum value at that value of x. For increasing values of x, a maximum in the curve of the function means a change from positive to negative values of the derivative, and hence from increasing to decreasing rates of change (trends) of the function. Similarly, for decreasing values of x, a minimum in the curve of the function means a change from negative to positive values of the derivative, and hence from decreasing to increasing rates of change (trends) of the function.

Higher Derivatives

In concluding this discussion of derivatives, mention should be made of the existence of derivatives of derivatives, which are called second order derivatives; of derivatives of derivatives of derivatives, which are called third order derivatives, etc. The process of differentiation of a derivative of a given order to obtain the derivative of next higher order follows essentially the same procedure as that already described for first order differentiation. Thus, in the case of the first-order derivative whose values were tabulated above, $12x^3 + 15x^2 - 2x + 6$, the second-order derivative is $36x^2 + 30x - 2$, and is obtained by the procedure by which the first derivative was obtained from the original function.

The significance of a second-order derivative is that of a rate of change of a rate of change. This meaning can be clarified by the example of a moving object already cited. It was stated that if there is a known function representing the distance of a moving body for various values of the time, x, then if the function is represented by y, the first-order derivative, $\dfrac{dy}{dx}$, is the velocity of the body corresponding to various values of the time, x. Then the second-order derivative, which is symbolized by $\dfrac{d^2y}{dx^2}$ (note that these superscripts are not squares), or by y'', is the rate of change of velocity, which is acceleration.

Differentials

In the preceding sections, the derivative $\dfrac{dy}{dx}$ was treated as a single quantity, which was adequate there for the purpose of differentiation. However, dy and dx can also be considered separately, and when so considered they are called differentials. They are defined in the following way: Let

$y = f(x)$ be a function of one variable x, of which the derivative $\dfrac{dy}{dx}$ exists.

Then the differential of y is $dy = \dfrac{dy}{dx} dx$, where dx is an independent variable. Then dy is a function of the two variables x and dx, and equations involving it, or other differentials, are called differential equations. While this subject of differential equations is beyond the scope of this book, there is another operation in which differentials appear, that is treated next. That operation is integration.

Integration

Integration is the reverse process to differentiation. It consists of finding a function, or more exactly, of finding the variable part of a function, when its derivative is known, or when data is available from which its derivative may be calculated.

Thus, if the derivative $\dfrac{dy}{dx}$ of the function $y = f(x)$ is known, and the function y is required, the process is

$\dfrac{dy}{dx} = \phi(x)$, where $\phi(x)$ is a function of x or a constant obtained by differentiating y with respect to x.

Then $dy = \phi(x)dx$, (see discussion of differentials above).

Then $$\int dy = y = \int \phi(x)dx \qquad (9\text{-}10)$$

where the sign $\int$ denotes the process of integration to be performed.

For example, if it is required to integrate $2x$, write it in place of $\phi(x)$ in the above formula, obtaining

$$y = \int 2x\,dx$$

Now, since in Formula (9-3), the derivative $\dfrac{dy}{dx}$ of x^2 was found to be $2x$, and since integration is the reverse of differentiation, then the integral of $2x$ could be expected to be x^2. It is, but there is a further addition to be made. Since the derivative of a constant is zero (see note after Formula 9-6), then the derivative of x^2; or $x^2 + 5$; or x^2 plus any constant quantity, would also be $2x$. Therefore the integral of $2x$ is written $x^2 + C$, to show that there may be an added constant. For this reason, the integral now under discussion is called the indefinite integral; the definite integral is discussed later in this chapter.

Thus $y = \int 2x\,dx = x^2 + C$.

The method of integration applied to the expression $2x$ can be used generally. That is, to integrate a given expression, one can seek among the known derivatives one of that form, and take the function that was differentiated, or an obvious modification of it, as the integral sought.

For example, by Formula (9-5), nx^{n-1} is the differential of x^n, therefore the integral of any term consisting only of x or a power of x (with or without a constant coefficient), may be integrated by multiplying it by x, and dividing it by n.

Thus

$$\int x^5 dx = \frac{x^6}{6} + C; \int x^8 dx = \frac{x^9}{9} + C; \text{ and } \int 5x^3 dx = 5 \int x^3 dx = \frac{5x^4}{4} + C.$$

In the last example, note that a constant coefficient carries through unchanged.

Note also that the integral of a constant is the product of the constant by x, i.e. $\int 5dx = 5x + C$, since the derivative of $5x$ is 5.

While the method of integration by use of derivatives of known functions can be extended far beyond the use in that way of Formulas (9-3)-(9-9), and while tables of integrals are published for the same purpose, obviously no tables can be large enough to cover every expression to be integrated and every form in which it might be written. Therefore, other methods of integration are required.

Integration by Algebraic Simplification

Rather than being classed as a method of integration, this operation should preferably be treated as an essential preliminary, wherever applicable, to any use of tables of integrals. Occasions for its use arise, for example, from the fact that products and quotients can be changed into sums and differences by carrying out the indicated multiplications and divisions. As an illustration, consider the example

$$\int (x^2 + 3x)x \, dx.$$

This does not correspond to any of the standard forms, but by multiplication $(x^2 + 3x)x = x^3 + 3x^2$, and therefore $\int (x^2 + 3x)x \, dx$ becomes $\int x^3 dx + 3 \int x^2 dx = \frac{1}{4}x^4 + x^3 + C$. By the same method one can write

$$\int (ax + b)(x - c)dx = \int (ax^2 - acx + bx - bc)dx$$

$$= \int [ax^2 + (b - ac)x - bc]dx$$

$$= a \int x^2 dx + (b - ac) \int x dx - bc \int dx$$

$$= \tfrac{1}{3} a x^3 + \tfrac{1}{2}(b - ac)x^2 - bcx + C.$$

In evaluating the integral $\int \dfrac{x^3 - a^3}{x - a}\, dx$, one can, by division, write

$\dfrac{x^3 - a^3}{x - a} = x^2 + ax + a^2$ and the integral becomes

$$\int (x^2 + ax + a^2)dx = \int x^2 dx + a \int x dx + a^2 \int dx$$

$$= \tfrac{1}{3}x^3 + \tfrac{1}{2}ax^2 + a^2x + C.$$

In this case the quotient is exact, but in many cases it may not be so. Thus, in the case

$$\int \frac{2x^4 - 2x^3 - 4x^2 + x}{x + 3}\, dx$$

the denominator is not a factor of the numerator. The integration can be performed, however, by carrying out the indicated division as far as it will go, and forming a fraction of the remainder, as $2x^3 - 8x^2 + 20x - 61 + \dfrac{183}{x + 3}$, and when this is integrated term by term it gives

$$2 \int x^3 dx - 8 \int x^2 dx + 20 \int x dx - 61 \int dx + 183 \int \frac{dx}{x + 3}$$

$$= \tfrac{1}{2}x^4 - \tfrac{8}{3}x^3 + 10x^2 - 61x + 183 \log_{10}\left(\frac{1}{.4343}\right)(x + 3) + C.$$

Integration by Substitution

As an example of this method, consider the integral $\int x\sqrt{x^2 - a^2}\,dx$. This can be written $\int (x^2 - a^2)^{\frac{1}{2}}x\,dx$. Now

$$d(x^2 - a^2) = d(x^2) - d(a^2) = 2(x\,dx),$$

therefore $x\,dx = \tfrac{1}{2}d(x^2 - a^2)$. So let $x^2 - a^2 = z$ and we have

$$\int (x^2 - a^2)^{\frac{1}{2}}(x\,dx) = \int (z)^{\frac{1}{2}}\left(\frac{1}{2}\,dz\right) = \frac{1}{2} \int z^{\frac{1}{2}}dz = \frac{1}{2}\left(\frac{z^{\frac{3}{2}}}{\frac{3}{2}}\right) + C$$

or $\tfrac{1}{3}z^{\frac{3}{2}} + C$. Replacing in this the value of z the final result is

$$\tfrac{1}{3}(x^2 - a^2)^{\frac{3}{2}} + C, \quad \text{or} \quad \tfrac{1}{3}\sqrt{(x^2 - a^2)^3} + C.$$

The substitution used in this last example will always work in the case of the square root of a binomial in which one term is a constant and the other a power of the variable, provided the square root is multiplied by the variable raised to a power which is one less than the power under the radical.

Integration by Graphical Methods—The Definite Integral

Consider an expression of the form $y = f(x)$, where $f(x)$ is any continuous, single valued function of x. Then this function can be plotted graphically against corresponding values of x. Moreover, the area between the curve and the X-axis can be divided into rectangles of width dx and height y. The area of any one of these rectangles is $y\,dx$, where y is the value of y defined by the function at that point, that is, it is $y\,dx$. The area under the curve at that point differs from that under the rectangle by the amount of area between the flat top of the rectangle and the curve, or *vice versa*. Now consider that the length dx is infinitesimal in length, therefore the difference between the area of all the rectangles and the area under the curve is negligible. Since, however, integration is a process of summation, the integral $\int y\,dx$ is the total area under the curve.

Before substituting any given function $f(x)$ for y, it is necessary to recognize that continuous, single-valued functions extend indefinitely. Therefore, we are usually interested in the area under part of them only. That area can be found by evaluating the integral, substituting the bounding values and subtracting. The following example illustrates the process.

Find the area under the function $y = 4x^2$, from $x = 2$ to $x = 5$.

Then
$$A = \int_{2}^{5} 4x^2\,dx.$$

The numbers are used to denote the bounds within which the integral is to be evaluated, which is also called the range of integration. An integral so limited is called a definite integral, because no indefinite constant of integration is needed to define its value.

Then $A = \int_{2}^{5} 4x^2\,dx$, by Formula (9-5)

becomes
$$A = \tfrac{4}{3}x^3 \Big]_{2}^{5}$$
$$= \tfrac{4}{3}(5)^3 - \tfrac{4}{3}(2)^3$$
$$= 166\tfrac{2}{3} - 10\tfrac{2}{3} = 156.$$

The usefulness of the fact that the integral of an explicit function of one variable is the area under a curve (or that of a function of two variables is the volume under a surface) is not limited to area or volume determinations. For by measuring that area or volume, either by a method of averaging, by a planemeter or other methods, the numerical value of the integral may be determined.

Chapter 10

COMMERCIAL DISCOUNTS

Commercial discounts are deductions applied to the list price of articles sold. Many businesses, especially wholesalers and others selling for resale, wish to show on their invoices the established or recommended list price for resale to the consumer, and at the same time, of course, to bill the retailer or other purchaser correctly. This purpose is served by billing the merchandise at the list price, less the discount or discounts. Therefore the first part of this chapter deals with commercial discounts as applied to invoices.

A further use of discount computations occurs in the internal calculations of many types of business. For example, some retail stores and other resale operations give discounts to the consumer, often in the form of reduced prices, and so need to make calculations involving the discounts which they receive from their suppliers, the discounts which they give to their customers, and the relations among these figures. Such calculations are explained in the second part of this chapter.

Since discounts are commonly stated in percentages, and since discount computations are therefore percentage calculations, the reader is referred to Chapter 1 of this book for a discussion of the mathematics of percentage.

Discounts Applied to Invoices

The term *list price* originated from the practice of wholesalers and manufacturers of issuing a catalog in which prices were listed. Such prices were, and still are, intended to apply to retail or small-quantity sales. The retailer, or other business buying for resale or quantity use, receives a discount (or discounts) from this price, which is used to compute the net price, that is, the amount he actually pays. For example, if the list price of an article is $60.00 and the discount is 30%, the net price is $60.00 − (30% of $60.00) which is equal to $60.00 − $18.00 = $42.00. Since discounted invoices often involve multiples of the items, a more representative example would be 5 dozen hats at $14.00 per dozen less 30%, which is (5 × $14.00) less 30% = $70.00 − 30% of $70.00 = $49.00.

Deductions of a single discount are, as shown here, simple to compute. The calculations become somewhat more complicated when several discounts are to be applied. Such calculations arise in two situations.

The first instance of chain discounts is the practice by some wholesalers and manufacturers of granting a series of discounts. That is, they may sell merchandise to a retailer subject to successive trade discounts of 25%, 10% and 5%, or any other combination of two or more discounts.

The second instance of the occurrence of chain discounts is the use of cash discounts in addition to trade discounts. A cash discount is the percent of an invoice that may be deducted if the invoice is paid within a specified time. The rate of this discount is stated in the terms of the invoice, which include the cash discount and the number of days within which payment must be made if this discount is to be deducted. One rather common cash discount is: 2/10, n/30, (meaning that 2 percent of the total of the invoice may be deducted if it is paid within 10 days. If the invoice is not paid within 10 days, no cash discount is allowed, and the full amount must be paid within 30 days). Another, but less frequently used basis is: 5/30, n/60 (meaning that the five percent of the total of the invoice may be deducted if it is paid within 30 days. If it is not paid within 30 days, no cash discount is allowed and the full amount of the invoice must be paid within 60 days.).

Wherever two or more discounts, consisting of trade discounts or trade discounts plus cash discount, are to be calculated, there are obviously two possible methods of calculation which may be used. The first method is to multiply the total amount invoiced by the first discount, subtract the result from the total amount, thus obtaining the result of applying the first discount; then to multiply the amount remaining by the second discount, subtracting that product to obtain the second balance; continuing until all discounts have been applied.

For example, to find the net amount of an invoice for 40 dresses at $35.00 each, subject to trade discounts of 30% and 10%, and to a cash discount of 2%, the calculation is made by this method as follows:

40 dresses at $35.00 each..........................	$1,400.00
Amount of 30% discount is .30 × $1,400.00 = ...	420.00
Amount of invoice after 30% discount..............	$980.00
Amount of 10% discount is .10 × $980.00 = ...	98.00
Amount of invoice after 30% and 10% discounts.....	$882.00
Amount of 2% discount is .02 × $882.00 = ...	17.64
Amount of invoice after trade discounts of 30% and 10% and cash discount of 2%..............	$864.36

The second method of applying chain discounts to an invoice is to compute the result of applying those discounts to $1.00 and then to multiply the gross amount of the invoice by the remainder obtained by applying the successive discounts to $1.00. Thus, to solve the foregoing problem by this second method:

		$1.00
Amount of 30% discount is .30 × $1.00 = ...		.30
Amount left from $1.00 after 30% discount...........		$0.70
Amount of 10% discount is .10 × $0.70 = ...		0.07
Amount left from $1.00 after 30% and 10% discounts..		$0.63
Amount of 2% discount is .02 × $0.63 = ...		0.0126
Amount left from $1.00 after 30%, 10% and 2% discounts		$0.6174

Amount of $1,400.00 gross invoice after 30%, 10% and 2% discounts is ($1,400.00) × (0.6174) = $864.36.

The advantage of the second method is that it permits the construction of a table. For if the amount of a gross invoice of $1.00 is $0.6174 after deducting discounts of 30%, 10% and 2%, then the net amount of a gross invoice of any other number of dollars subject to these discounts can be found by multiplying the gross amount of that invoice by the number 0.6174.

The following fifteen pages in this book contain a table (Table 4) computed for various combinations of three discounts, showing the value of $1.00 after application of these discounts. The arrangement of Table 4 is:

Page 180 is for a first discount of 10%, second discounts ranging from 10% to 40%, and third discounts from $\frac{1}{2}$% to 25%.

Page 181 is for a first discount of $12\frac{1}{2}$%, second discounts ranging from 10% to 40%, and third discounts from $\frac{1}{2}$% to 25%.

The other pages have the same second and third discounts as the first and second pages, but first discounts as follows:

Page 182	First Discount	15%
Page 183	First Discount	$17\frac{1}{2}$%
Page 184	First Discount	20%
Page 185	First Discount	$22\frac{1}{2}$%
Page 186	First Discount	25%
Page 187	First Discount	$27\frac{1}{2}$%
Page 188	First Discount	30%
Page 189	First Discount	$33\frac{1}{3}$%
Page 190	First Discount	35%
Page 191	First Discount	$37\frac{1}{2}$%
Page 192	First Discount	40%
Page 193	First Discount	45%
Page 194	First Discount	50%

TABLE 4—DISCOUNTED VALUE OF $1.00

FIRST DISCOUNT 10%

Third Discount	Second Discount								
	0	10%	15%	20%	25%	30%	33-1/3%	35%	40%
0%	.90000	.81000	.76500	.72000	.67500	.63000	.60000	.58500	.54000
1/2%	.89550	.80595	.76118	.71640	.67163	.62685	.59700	.58208	.53730
1%	.89100	.80190	.75735	.71280	.66825	.62370	.59400	.57915	.53460
1-1/2%	.88650	.79785	.75353	.70920	.66488	.62055	.59100	.57623	.53190
2%	.88200	.79380	.74970	.70560	.66150	.61740	.58800	.57330	.52920
2-1/2%	.87750	.78975	.74588	.70200	.65813	.61425	.58500	.57038	.52650
3%	.87300	.78570	.74205	.69840	.65475	.61110	.58200	.56745	.52380
3-1/2%	.86850	.78165	.73823	.69480	.65138	.60795	.57900	.56453	.52110
4%	.86400	.77760	.73440	.69120	.64800	.60480	.57600	.56160	.51840
4-1/2%	.85950	.77355	.73058	.68760	.64463	.60165	.57300	.55868	.51570
5%	.85500	.76950	.72675	.68400	.64125	.59850	.57000	.55575	.51300
5-1/2%	.85050	.76545	.72293	.68040	.63788	.59535	.56700	.55283	.51030
6%	.84600	.76140	.71910	.67680	.63450	.59220	.56400	.54990	.50760
6-1/2%	.84150	.75735	.71528	.67320	.63112	.58905	.56100	.54698	.50490
7%	.83700	.75330	.71145	.66960	.62775	.58590	.55800	.54405	.50220
7-1/2%	.83250	.74925	.70763	.66600	.62438	.58275	.55500	.54113	.49950
8%	.82800	.74520	.70380	.66240	.62100	.57960	.55200	.53820	.49680
8-1/2%	.82350	.74115	.69998	.65880	.61763	.57645	.54900	.53528	.49410
9%	.81900	.73710	.69615	.65520	.61425	.57330	.54600	.53235	.49140
9-1/2%	.81450	.73305	.69233	.65160	.61088	.57015	.54300	.52943	.48870
10%	.81000	.72900	.68850	.64800	.60750	.56700	.54000	.52650	.48600
10-1/2%	.80550	.72495	.68468	.64440	.60413	.56385	.53700	.52358	.48330
11%	.80100	.72090	.68085	.64080	.60075	.56070	.53400	.52065	.48060
11-1/2%	.79650	.71685	.67703	.63720	.59738	.55755	.53100	.51773	.47790
12%	.79200	.71280	.67320	.63360	.59400	.55440	.52800	.51480	.47520
12-1/2%	.78750	.70875	.66938	.63000	.59063	.55125	.52500	.51188	.47250
13%	.78300	.70470	.66555	.62640	.58725	.54810	.52200	.50895	.46980
13-1/2%	.77850	.70065	.66173	.62280	.58388	.54495	.51900	.50603	.46710
14%	.77400	.69660	.65790	.61920	.58050	.54180	.51600	.50310	.46440
14-1/2%	.76950	.69255	.65408	.61560	.57713	.53865	.51300	.50018	.46170
15%	.76500	.68850	.65025	.61200	.57375	.53550	.51000	.49725	.45900
15-1/2%	.76050	.68445	.64643	.60840	.57038	.53235	.50700	.49433	.45630
16%	.75600	.68040	.64260	.60480	.56700	.52920	.50400	.49140	.45360
16-1/2%	.75150	.67635	.63878	.60120	.56363	.52605	.50100	.48848	.45090
17%	.74700	.67230	.63495	.59760	.56025	.52290	.49800	.48555	.44820
17-1/2%	.74250	.66825	.63113	.59400	.55688	.51975	.49500	.48263	.44550
18%	.73800	.66420	.62730	.59040	.55350	.51660	.49200	.47970	.44280
18-1/2%	.73350	.66015	.62348	.58680	.55013	.51345	.48900	.47678	.44010
19%	.72900	.65610	.61965	.58320	.54675	.51030	.48600	.47385	.43740
19-1/2%	.72450	.65205	.61583	.57960	.54338	.50715	.48300	.47093	.43470
20%	.72000	.64800	.61200	.57600	.54000	.50400	.48000	.46800	.43200
21%	.71100	.63990	.60435	.56880	.53325	.49770	.47400	.46215	.42660
22%	.70200	.63180	.59670	.56160	.52650	.49140	.46800	.45630	.42120
23%	.69300	.62370	.58905	.55440	.51975	.48510	.46200	.45045	.41580
24%	.68400	.61560	.58140	.54720	.51300	.47880	.45600	.44460	.41040
25%	.67500	.60750	.57375	.54000	.50625	.47250	.45000	.43875	.40500

TABLE 4—DISCOUNTED VALUE OF $1.00 (Cont.)

FIRST DISCOUNT 12-1/2%

Third Discount	Second Discount								
	0	10%	15%	20%	25%	30%	33-1/3%	35%	40%
0%	.87500	.78750	.74375	.70000	.65625	.61250	.58333	.56875	.52500
1/2%	.87063	.78356	.74003	.69650	.65297	.60944	.58042	.56591	.52238
1%	.86625	.77963	.73631	.69300	.64969	.60638	.57750	.56306	.51975
1-1/2%	.86188	.77569	.73259	.68950	.64641	.60331	.57458	.56022	.51713
2%	.85750	.77175	.72888	.68600	.64313	.60025	.57167	.55738	.51450
2-1/2%	.85313	.76781	.72516	.68250	.63984	.59719	.56875	.55453	.51188
3%	.84875	.76388	.72144	.67900	.63656	.59413	.56583	.55169	.50925
3-1/2%	.84438	.75994	.71772	.67550	.63328	.59106	.56292	.54884	.50663
4%	.84000	.75600	.71400	.67200	.63000	.58800	.56000	.54600	.50400
4-1/2%	.83563	.75206	.71028	.66850	.62672	.58494	.55708	.54316	.50138
5%	.83125	.74813	.70656	.66500	.62344	.58188	.55417	.54031	.49875
5-1/2%	.82688	.74419	.70284	.66150	.62016	.57881	.55125	.53747	.49613
6%	.82250	.74025	.69913	.65800	.61688	.57575	.54833	.53463	.49350
6-1/2%	.81813	.73631	.69541	.65450	.61359	.57269	.54542	.53178	.49088
7%	.81375	.73238	.69169	.65100	.61031	.56963	.54250	.52894	.48825
7-1/2%	.80938	.72844	.68797	.64750	.60703	.56656	.53958	.52609	.48563
8%	.80500	.72450	.68425	.64400	.60375	.56350	.53667	.52325	.48300
8-1/2%	.80063	.72056	.68053	.64050	.60047	.56044	.53375	.52041	.48038
9%	.79625	.71663	.67681	.63700	.59719	.55738	.53083	.51756	.47775
9-1/2%	.79188	.71269	.67309	.63350	.59391	.55431	.52792	.51472	.47513
10%	.78750	.70875	.66938	.63000	.59063	.55125	.52500	.51188	.47250
10-1/2%	.78313	.70481	.66566	.62650	.58734	.54819	.52208	.50903	.46988
11%	.77875	.70088	.66194	.62300	.58406	.54513	.51917	.50619	.46725
11-1/2%	.77438	.69694	.65822	.61950	.58078	.54206	.51625	.50334	.46463
12%	.77000	.69300	.65450	.61600	.57750	.53900	.51333	.50050	.46200
12-1/2%	.76563	.68906	.65078	.61250	.57422	.53594	.51042	.49766	.45938
13%	.76125	.68513	.64706	.60900	.57094	.53288	.50750	.49481	.45675
13-1/2%	.75688	.68119	.64334	.60550	.56766	.52981	.50458	.49197	.45413
14%	.75250	.67725	.63963	.60200	.56438	.52675	.50167	.48913	.45150
14-1/2%	.74813	.67331	.63591	.59850	.56109	.52369	.49875	.48628	.44888
15%	.74375	.66938	.63219	.59500	.55781	.52063	.49583	.48344	.44625
15-1/2%	.73938	.66544	.62847	.59150	.55453	.51756	.49292	.48059	.44363
16%	.73500	.66150	.62475	.58800	.55125	.51450	.49000	.47775	.44100
16-1/2%	.73063	.65756	.62103	.58450	.54797	.51144	.48708	.47491	.43838
17%	.72625	.65363	.61731	.58100	.54469	.50838	.48417	.47206	.43575
17-1/2%	.72188	.64969	.61359	.57750	.54141	.50531	.48125	.46922	.43313
18%	.71750	.64575	.60988	.57400	.53813	.50225	.47833	.46638	.43050
18-1/2%	.71313	.64181	.60616	.57050	.53484	.49919	.47542	.46353	.42788
19%	.70875	.63788	.60244	.56700	.53156	.49613	.47250	.46069	.42525
19-1/2%	.70438	.63394	.59872	.56350	.52828	.49306	.46958	.45784	.42263
20%	.70000	.63000	.59500	.56000	.52500	.49000	.46667	.45500	.42000
21%	.69125	.62213	.58756	.55300	.51844	.48388	.46083	.44931	.41475
22%	.68250	.61425	.58013	.54600	.51188	.47775	.45500	.44363	.40950
23%	.67375	.60638	.57269	.53900	.50531	.47163	.44917	.43794	.40425
24%	.66500	.59850	.56525	.53200	.49875	.46550	.44333	.43225	.39900
25%	.65625	.59063	.55781	.52500	.49219	.45938	.43750	.42656	.39375

TABLE 4—DISCOUNTED VALUE OF $1.00 (Cont.)

FIRST DISCOUNT 15%

Third Discount	Second Discount								
	0	10%	15%	20%	25%	30%	33-1/3%	35%	40%
0%	.85000	.76500	.72250	.68000	.63750	.59500	.56667	.55250	.51000
1/2%	.84575	.76118	.71889	.67660	.63431	.59203	.56383	.54974	.50745
1%	.84150	.75735	.71528	.67320	.63113	.58905	.56100	.54698	.50490
1-1/2%	.83725	.75353	.71166	.66980	.62794	.58608	.55817	.54421	.50235
2%	.83300	.74970	.70805	.66640	.62475	.58310	.55533	.54145	.49980
2-1/2%	.82875	.74588	.70444	.66300	.62156	.58013	.55250	.53869	.49725
3%	.82450	.74205	.70083	.65960	.61838	.57715	.54967	.53593	.49470
3-1/2%	.82025	.73823	.69721	.65620	.61519	.57418	.54683	.53316	.49215
4%	.81600	.73440	.69360	.65280	.61200	.57120	.54400	.53040	.48960
4-1/2%	.81175	.73058	.68999	.64940	.60881	.56823	.54117	.52764	.48705
5%	.80750	.72675	.68638	.64600	.60563	.56525	.53833	.52488	.48450
5-1/2%	.80325	.72293	.68276	.64260	.60244	.56228	.53550	.52221	.48195
6%	.79900	.71910	.67915	.63920	.59925	.55930	.53267	.51935	.47940
6-1/2%	.79475	.71528	.67554	.63580	.59606	.55633	.52983	.51659	.47685
7%	.79050	.71145	.67193	.63240	.59288	.55335	.52700	.51383	.47430
7-1/2%	.78625	.70763	.66831	.62900	.58969	.55038	.52417	.51106	.47175
8%	.78200	.70380	.66470	.62560	.58650	.54740	.52133	.50830	.46920
8-1/2%	.77775	.69998	.66109	.62220	.58331	.54443	.51850	.50554	.46665
9%	.77350	.69615	.65748	.61880	.58013	.54145	.51567	.50278	.46410
9-1/2%	.76925	.69233	.65386	.61540	.57694	.53848	.51283	.50001	.46155
10%	.76500	.68850	.65025	.61200	.57375	.53550	.51000	.49725	.45900
10-1/2%	.76075	.68468	.64664	.60860	.57056	.53253	.50717	.49449	.45645
11%	.75650	.68085	.64303	.60520	.56738	.52955	.50433	.49173	.45390
11-1/2%	.75225	.67703	.63941	.60180	.56419	.52658	.50150	.48896	.45135
12%	.74800	.67320	.63580	.59840	.56100	.52360	.49867	.48620	.44880
12-1/2%	.74375	.66938	.63219	.59500	.55781	.52063	.49583	.48344	.44625
13%	.73950	.66555	.62858	.59160	.55463	.51765	.49300	.48068	.44370
13-1/2%	.73525	.66173	.62496	.58820	.55144	.51468	.49017	.47791	.44115
14%	.73100	.65790	.62135	.58480	.54825	.51170	.48733	.47515	.43860
14-1/2%	.72675	.65408	.61774	.58140	.54506	.50873	.48450	.47239	.43605
15%	.72250	.65025	.61413	.57800	.54188	.50575	.48167	.46963	.43350
15-1/2%	.71825	.64643	.61051	.57460	.53869	.50278	.47883	.46686	.43095
16%	.71400	.64260	.60690	.57120	.53550	.49980	.47600	.46410	.42840
16-1/2%	.70975	.63878	.60329	.56780	.53231	.49683	.47317	.46134	.42585
17%	.70550	.63495	.59968	.56440	.52913	.49385	.47033	.45858	.42330
17-1/2%	.70125	.63113	.59606	.56100	.52594	.49088	.46750	.45581	.42075
18%	.69700	.62730	.59245	.55760	.52275	.48790	.46467	.45305	.41820
18-1/2%	.69275	.62348	.58884	.55420	.51956	.48493	.46183	.45029	.41565
19%	.68850	.61965	.58523	.55080	.51638	.48195	.45900	.44753	.41310
19-1/2%	.68425	.61583	.58161	.54740	.51319	.47898	.45617	.44476	.41055
20%	.68000	.61200	.57800	.54400	.51000	.47600	.45333	.44200	.40800
21%	.67150	.60435	.57078	.53720	.50363	.47005	.44767	.43648	.40290
22%	.66300	.59670	.56355	.53040	.49725	.46410	.44200	.43096	.39780
23%	.65450	.58905	.55633	.52360	.49088	.45815	.43633	.42543	.39270
24%	.64600	.58140	.54910	.51680	.48450	.45220	.43067	.41990	.38760
25%	.63750	.57375	.54188	.51000	.47813	.44625	.42500	.41438	.38250

TABLE 4—DISCOUNTED VALUE OF $1.00 (Cont.)

FIRST DISCOUNT 17-1/2%

Third Discount	Second Discount								
	0	10%	15%	20%	25%	30%	33-1/3%	35%	40%
0%	.82500	.74250	.70125	.66000	.61875	.57750	.55000	.53625	.49500
1/2%	.82088	.73879	.69774	.65670	.61566	.57461	.54725	.53357	.49253
1%	.81675	.73508	.69424	.65340	.61256	.57173	.54450	.53089	.49005
1-1/2%	.81263	.73136	.69073	.65010	.60947	.56884	.54175	.52821	.48758
2%	.80850	.72765	.68723	.64680	.60638	.56595	.53900	.52553	.48510
2-1/2%	.80438	.72394	.68372	.64350	.60328	.56306	.53625	.52284	.48263
3%	.80025	.72023	.68021	.64020	.60019	.56018	.53350	.52016	.48015
3-1/2%	.79613	.71651	.67671	.63690	.59709	.55729	.53075	.51748	.47768
4%	.79200	.71280	.67320	.63360	.59400	.55440	.52800	.51480	.47520
4-1/2%	.78788	.70909	.66969	.63030	.59091	.55151	.52525	.51212	.47273
5%	.78375	.70538	.66619	.62700	.58781	.54863	.52250	.50944	.47025
5-1/2%	.77963	.70166	.66268	.62370	.58472	.54574	.51975	.50676	.46778
6%	.77550	.69795	.65918	.62040	.58163	.54285	.51700	.50408	.46530
6-1/2%	.77138	.69424	.65567	.61710	.57853	.53996	.51425	.50139	.46283
7%	.76725	.69053	.65216	.61380	.57544	.53708	.51150	.49871	.46035
7-1/2%	.76313	.68681	.64866	.61050	.57234	.53419	.50875	.49603	.45788
8%	.75900	.68310	.64515	.60720	.56925	.53130	.50600	.49335	.45540
8-1/2%	.75488	.67939	.64164	.60390	.56616	.52841	.50325	.49067	.45293
9%	.75075	.67568	.63814	.60060	.56306	.52553	.50050	.48799	.45045
9-1/2%	.74663	.67196	.63463	.59730	.55997	.52264	.49775	.48531	.44798
10%	.74250	.66825	.63113	.59400	.55688	.51975	.49500	.48263	.44550
10-1/2%	.73838	.66454	.62762	.59070	.55378	.51686	.49225	.47994	.44303
11%	.73425	.66083	.62411	.58740	.55069	.51398	.48950	.47726	.44055
11-1/2%	.73013	.65711	.62061	.58410	.54759	.51109	.48675	.47458	.43808
12%	.72600	.65340	.61710	.58080	.54450	.50820	.48400	.47190	.43560
12-1/2%	.72188	.64969	.61359	.57750	.54141	.50531	.48125	.46922	.43313
13%	.71775	.64598	.61009	.57420	.53831	.50243	.47850	.46654	.43065
13-1/2%	.71363	.64226	.60658	.57090	.53522	.49954	.47575	.46386	.42818
14%	.70950	.63855	.60308	.56760	.53213	.49665	.47300	.46118	.42570
14-1/2%	.70538	.63484	.59957	.56430	.52903	.49376	.47025	.45849	.42323
15%	.70125	.63113	.59606	.56100	.52594	.49088	.46750	.45581	.42075
15-1/2%	.69713	.62741	.59256	.55770	.52284	.48799	.46475	.45313	.41828
16%	.69300	.62370	.58905	.55440	.51975	.48510	.46200	.45045	.41580
16-1/2%	.68888	.61999	.58554	.55110	.51666	.48221	.45925	.44777	.41333
17%	.68475	.61628	.58204	.54780	.51356	.47933	.45650	.44509	.41085
17-1/2%	.68063	.61256	.57853	.54450	.51047	.47644	.45375	.44241	.40838
18%	.67650	.60885	.57503	.54120	.50738	.47355	.45100	.43973	.40590
18-1/2%	.67238	.60514	.57152	.53790	.50428	.47066	.44825	.43704	.40343
19%	.66825	.60143	.56801	.53460	.50119	.46778	.44550	.43436	.40095
19-1/2%	.66413	.59771	.56451	.53130	.49809	.46489	.44275	.43168	.39848
20%	.66000	.59400	.56100	.52800	.49500	.46200	.44000	.42900	.39600
21%	.65175	.58658	.55399	.52140	.48881	.45623	.43050	.42364	.39105
22%	.64350	.57915	.54698	.51480	.48263	.45045	.42900	.41828	.38610
23%	.63525	.57173	.53996	.50820	.47644	.44468	.42350	.41291	.38115
24%	.62700	.56430	.53295	.50160	.47025	.43890	.41800	.40755	.37620
25%	.61875	.55688	.52594	.49500	.46406	.43313	.41250	.40219	.37125

183

TABLE 4—DISCOUNTED VALUE OF $1.00 (Cont.)

FIRST DISCOUNT 20%

Third Discount	Second Discount								
	0	10%	15%	20%	25%	30%	33-1/3%	35%	40%
0%	.80000	.72000	.68000	.64000	.60000	.56000	.53333	.52000	.48000
1/2%	.79600	.71640	.67660	.63680	.59700	.55720	.53067	.51740	.47760
1%	.79200	.71280	.67320	.63360	.59400	.55440	.52800	.51480	.47520
1-1/2%	.78800	.70920	.66980	.63040	.59100	.55160	.52533	.51220	.47280
2%	.78400	.70560	.66640	.62720	.58800	.54880	.52267	.50960	.47040
2-1/2%	.78000	.70200	.66300	.62400	.58500	.54600	.52000	.50700	.46800
3%	.77600	.69840	.65960	.62080	.58200	.54320	.51733	.50440	.46560
3-1/2%	.77200	.69480	.65620	.61760	.57900	.54040	.51467	.50180	.46320
4%	.76800	.69120	.65280	.61440	.57600	.53760	.51200	.49920	.46080
4-1/2%	.76400	.68760	.64940	.61120	.57300	.53480	.50933	.49660	.45840
5%	.76000	.68400	.64600	.60800	.57000	.53200	.50667	.49400	.45600
5-1/2%	.75600	.68040	.64260	.60480	.56700	.52920	.50400	.49140	.45360
6%	.75200	.67680	.63920	.60160	.56400	.52640	.50133	.48880	.45120
6-1/2%	.74800	.67320	.63580	.59840	.56100	.52360	.49867	.48620	.44880
7%	.74400	.66960	.63240	.59520	.55800	.52080	.49600	.48360	.44640
7-1/2%	.74000	.66600	.62900	.59200	.55500	.51800	.49333	.48100	.44400
8%	.73600	.66240	.62560	.58880	.55200	.51520	.49067	.47840	.44160
8-1/2%	.73200	.65880	.62220	.58560	.54900	.51240	.48800	.47580	.43920
9%	.72800	.65520	.61880	.58240	.54600	.50960	.48533	.47320	.43680
9-1/2%	.72400	.65160	.61540	.57920	.54300	.50680	.48267	.47060	.43440
10%	.72000	.64800	.61200	.57600	.54000	.50400	.48000	.46800	.43200
10-1/2%	.71600	.64440	.60860	.57280	.53700	.50120	.47733	.46540	.42960
11%	.71200	.64080	.60520	.56960	.53400	.49840	.47467	.46280	.42720
11-1/2%	.70800	.63720	.60180	.56640	.53100	.49560	.47200	.46020	.42480
12%	.70400	.63360	.59840	.56320	.52800	.49280	.46933	.45760	.42240
12-1/2%	.70000	.63000	.59500	.56000	.52500	.49000	.46667	.45500	.42000
13%	.69600	.62640	.59160	.55680	.52200	.48720	.46400	.45240	.41760
13-1/2%	.69200	.62280	.58820	.55360	.51900	.48440	.46133	.44980	.41520
14%	.68800	.61920	.58480	.55040	.51600	.48160	.45867	.44720	.41280
14-1/2%	.68400	.61560	.58140	.54720	.51300	.47880	.45600	.44460	.41040
15%	.68000	.61200	.57800	.54400	.51000	.47600	.45333	.44200	.40800
15-1/2%	.67600	.60840	.57460	.54080	.50700	.47320	.45067	.43940	.40560
16%	.67200	.60480	.57120	.53760	.50400	.47040	.44800	.43680	.40320
16-1/2%	.66800	.60120	.56780	.53440	.50100	.46760	.44533	.43420	.40080
17%	.66400	.59760	.56440	.53120	.49800	.46480	.44267	.43160	.39840
17-1/2%	.66000	.59400	.56100	.52800	.49500	.46200	.44000	.42900	.39600
18%	.65600	.59040	.55760	.52480	.49200	.45920	.43733	.42640	.39360
18-1/2%	.65200	.58680	.55420	.52160	.48900	.45640	.43467	.42380	.39120
19%	.64800	.58320	.55080	.51840	.48600	.45360	.43200	.42120	.38880
19-1/2%	.64400	.57960	.54740	.51520	.48300	.45080	.42933	.41860	.38640
20%	.64000	.57600	.54400	.51200	.48000	.44800	.42667	.41600	.38400
21%	.63200	.56880	.53720	.50560	.47400	.44240	.42133	.41080	.37920
22%	.62400	.56160	.53040	.49920	.46800	.43680	.41600	.40560	.37440
23%	.61600	.55440	.52360	.49280	.46200	.43120	.41067	.40040	.36960
24%	.60800	.54720	.51680	.48640	.45600	.42560	.40533	.39520	.36480
25%	.60000	.54000	.51000	.48000	.45000	.42000	.40000	.39000	.36000

TABLE 4—DISCOUNTED VALUE OF $1.00 (Cont.)

FIRST DISCOUNT 22-1/2%

Third D Discount	Second Discount								
	0	10%	15%	20%	25%	30%	33-1/3%	35%	40%
0%	.77500	.69750	.65875	.62000	.58125	.54250	.51667	.50375	.46500
1/2%	.77113	.69401	.65546	.61690	.57834	.53979	.51408	.50123	.46268
1%	.76725	.69053	.65216	.61380	.57544	.53708	.51150	.49871	.46035
1-1/2%	.76338	.68704	.64887	.61070	.57253	.53436	.50892	.49619	.45803
2%	.75950	.68355	.64558	.60760	.56963	.53165	.50633	.49368	.45570
2-1/2%	.75563	.68006	.64228	.60450	.56672	.52894	.50375	.49116	.45338
3%	.75175	.67658	.63899	.60140	.56381	.52623	.50117	.48864	.45105
3-1/2%	.74788	.67309	.63569	.59830	.56091	.52351	.49858	.48612	.44873
4%	.74400	.66960	.63240	.59520	.55800	.52080	.49600	.48360	.44640
4-1/2%	.74013	.66611	.62911	.59210	.55509	.51809	.49342	.48108	.44408
5%	.73625	.66263	.62581	.58900	.55219	.51538	.49083	.47856	.44175
5-1/2%	.73238	.65914	.62252	.58590	.54928	.51266	.48825	.47604	.43943
6%	.72850	.65565	.61923	.58280	.54638	.50995	.48567	.47353	.43710
6-1/2%	.72463	.65216	.61593	.57970	.54347	.50724	.48308	.47101	.43478
7%	.72075	.64868	.61264	.57660	.54056	.50453	.48050	.46849	.43245
7-1/2%	.71688	.64519	.60934	.57350	.53766	.50181	.47792	.46597	.43013
8%	.71300	.64170	.60605	.57040	.53475	.49910	.47533	.46345	.42780
8-1/2%	.70913	.63821	.60276	.56730	.53184	.49639	.47275	.46093	.42548
9%	.70525	.63473	.59946	.56420	.52894	.49368	.47017	.45841	.42315
9-1/2%	.70138	.63124	.59617	.56110	.52603	.49096	.46758	.45589	.42083
10%	.69750	.62775	.59288	.55800	.52313	.48825	.46500	.45338	.41850
10-1/2%	.69363	.62426	.58958	.55490	.52022	.48554	.46242	.45086	.41618
11%	.68975	.62078	.58629	.55180	.51731	.48283	.45983	.44834	.41385
11-1/2%	.68588	.61729	.58299	.54870	.51441	.48011	.45725	.44582	.41153
12%	.68200	.61380	.57970	.54560	.51150	.47740	.45467	.44330	.40920
12-1/2%	.67813	.61031	.57641	.54250	.50859	.47469	.45208	.44078	.40688
13%	.67425	.60683	.57311	.53940	.50569	.47198	.44950	.43826	.40455
13-1/2%	.67038	.60334	.56982	.53630	.50278	.46926	.44692	.43574	.40223
14%	.66650	.59985	.56653	.53320	.49988	.46655	.44433	.43323	.39990
14-1/2%	.66263	.59636	.56323	.53010	.49697	.46384	.44175	.43071	.39758
15%	.65875	.59288	.55994	.52700	.49406	.46113	.43917	.42819	.39525
15-1/2%	.65488	.58939	.55664	.52390	.49116	.45841	.43658	.42567	.39293
16%	.65100	.58590	.55335	.52080	.48825	.45570	.43400	.42315	.39060
16-1/2%	.64713	.58241	.55006	.51770	.48534	.45299	.43142	.42063	.38828
17%	.64325	.57893	.54676	.51460	.48244	.45028	.42883	.41811	.38595
17-1/2%	.63938	.57544	.54347	.51150	.47953	.44756	.42625	.41559	.38363
18%	.63550	.57195	.54018	.50840	.47663	.44485	.42367	.41308	.38130
18-1/2%	.63163	.56846	.53688	.50530	.47372	.44214	.42108	.41056	.37898
19%	.62775	.56498	.53359	.50220	.47081	.43943	.41850	.40804	.37665
19-1/2%	.62388	.56149	.53029	.49910	.46791	.43663	.41592	.40552	.37433
20%	.62000	.55800	.52700	.49600	.46500	.43400	.41333	.40300	.37200
21%	.61225	.55103	.52041	.48980	.45919	.42858	.40817	.39796	.36735
22%	.60450	.54405	.51383	.48360	.45338	.42315	.40300	.39293	.36270
23%	.59675	.53708	.50724	.47740	.44756	.41773	.39783	.38789	.35805
24%	.58900	.53010	.50065	.47120	.44175	.41230	.39267	.38285	.35340
25%	.58125	.52313	.49406	.46500	.43594	.40688	.38750	.37781	.34875

TABLE 4—DISCOUNTED VALUE OF $1.00 (Cont.)

FIRST DISCOUNT 25%

Third Discount	Second Discount								
	0	10%	15%	20%	25%	30%	33-1/3%	35%	40%
0%	.75000	.67500	.63750	.60000	.56250	.52500	.50000	.48750	.45000
1/2%	.74625	.67163	.63431	.59700	.55969	.52238	.49750	.48506	.44775
1%	.74250	.66825	.63113	.59400	.55688	.51975	.49500	.48263	.44550
1-1/2%	.73875	.66488	.62794	.59100	.55406	.51713	.49250	.48019	.44325
2%	.73500	.66150	.62475	.58800	.55125	.51450	.49000	.47775	.44100
2-1/2%	.73125	.65813	.62156	.58500	.54844	.51188	.48750	.47531	.43875
3%	.72750	.65475	.61838	.58200	.54563	.50925	.48500	.47288	.43650
3-1/2%	.72375	.65138	.61519	.57900	.54281	.50663	.48250	.47044	.43425
4%	.72000	.64800	.61200	.57600	.54000	.50400	.48000	.46800	.43200
4-1/2%	.71625	.64463	.60881	.57300	.53719	.50138	.47750	.46556	.42975
5%	.71250	.64125	.60563	.57000	.53438	.49875	.47500	.46313	.42750
5-1/2%	.70875	.63788	.60244	.56700	.53156	.49613	.47250	.46069	.42525
6%	.70500	.63450	.59925	.56400	.52875	.49350	.47000	.45825	.42300
6-1/2%	.70125	.63113	.59606	.56100	.52594	.49088	.46750	.45581	.42075
7%	.69750	.62775	.59288	.55800	.52313	.48825	.46500	.45338	.41850
7-1/2%	.69375	.62438	.58969	.55500	.52031	.48563	.46250	.45094	.41625
8%	.69000	.62100	.58650	.55200	.51750	.48300	.46000	.44850	.41400
8-1/2%	.68625	.61763	.58331	.54900	.51469	.48038	.45750	.44606	.41175
9%	.68250	.61425	.58013	.54600	.51188	.47775	.45500	.44363	.40950
9-1/2%	.67875	.61088	.57694	.54300	.50906	.47513	.45250	.44119	.40725
10%	.67500	.60750	.57375	.54000	.50625	.47250	.45000	.43875	.40500
10-1/2%	.67125	.60413	.57056	.53700	.50344	.46988	.44750	.43631	.40275
11%	.66750	.60075	.56738	.53400	.50063	.46725	.44500	.43388	.40050
11-1/2%	.66375	.59738	.56419	.53100	.49781	.46463	.44250	.43144	.39825
12%	.66000	.59400	.56100	.52800	.49500	.46200	.44000	.42900	.39600
12-1/2%	.65625	.59063	.55781	.52500	.49219	.45938	.43750	.42656	.39375
13%	.65250	.58725	.55463	.52200	.48938	.45675	.43500	.42413	.39150
13-1/2%	.64875	.58388	.55144	.51900	.48656	.45413	.43250	.42169	.38925
14%	.64500	.58050	.54825	.51600	.48375	.45150	.43000	.41925	.38700
14-1/2%	.64125	.57713	.54506	.51300	.48094	.44888	.42750	.41681	.38475
15%	.63750	.57375	.54188	.51000	.47813	.44625	.42500	.41438	.38250
15-1/2%	.63375	.57038	.53869	.50700	.47531	.44363	.42250	.41194	.38025
16%	.63000	.56700	.53550	.50400	.47250	.44100	.42000	.40950	.37800
16-1/2%	.62625	.56363	.53231	.50100	.46969	.43838	.41750	.40706	.37575
17%	.62250	.56025	.52913	.49800	.46688	.43575	.41500	.40463	.37350
17-1/2%	.61875	.55688	.52594	.49500	.46406	.43313	.41250	.40219	.37125
18%	.61500	.55350	.52275	.49200	.46125	.43050	.41000	.39975	.36900
18-1/2%	.61125	.55013	.51956	.48900	.45844	.42788	.40750	.39731	.36675
19%	.60750	.54675	.51638	.48600	.45563	.42525	.40500	.39488	.36450
19-1/2%	.60375	.54338	.51319	.48300	.45281	.42263	.40250	.39244	.36225
20%	.60000	.54000	.51000	.48000	.45000	.42000	.40000	.39000	.36000
21%	.59250	.53325	.50363	.47400	.44438	.41475	.39500	.38513	.35550
22%	.58500	.52650	.49725	.46800	.43875	.40950	.39000	.38025	.35100
23%	.57750	.51975	.49088	.46200	.43313	.40425	.38500	.37538	.34650
24%	.57000	.51300	.48450	.45600	.42750	.39900	.38000	.37050	.34200
25%	.56250	.50625	.47813	.45000	.42188	.39375	.37500	.36563	.33750

TABLE 4—DISCOUNTED VALUE OF $1.00 (Cont.)

FIRST DISCOUNT 27-1/2%

Third Discount	Second Discount								
	0	10%	15%	20%	25%	30%	33-1/3%	35%	40%
0%	.72500	.65250	.61625	.58000	.54375	.50750	.48333	.47125	.43500
1/2%	.72138	.64924	.61317	.57710	.54103	.50496	.48091	.46889	.43283
1%	.71775	.64598	.61009	.57420	.53831	.50243	.47850	.46654	.43065
1-1/2%	.71413	.64271	.60701	.57130	.53559	.49989	.47608	.46418	.42848
2%	.71050	.63945	.60393	.56840	.53288	.49735	.47366	.46183	.42630
2-1/2%	.70688	.63619	.60084	.56550	.53016	.49481	.47125	.45947	.42413
3%	.70325	.63293	.59776	.56260	.52744	.49228	.46883	.45711	.42195
3-1/2%	.69963	.62966	.59468	.55970	.52472	.48974	.46641	.45476	.41978
4%	.69600	.62640	.59160	.55680	.52200	.48720	.46400	.45240	.41760
4-1/2%	.69238	.62314	.58852	.55390	.51928	.48466	.46158	.45004	.41543
5%	.68875	.61988	.58544	.55100	.51656	.48213	.45916	.44769	.41325
5-1/2%	.68513	.61661	.58236	.54810	.51384	.47959	.45675	.44533	.41108
6%	.68150	.61335	.57928	.54520	.51113	.47705	.45433	.44298	.40890
6-1/2%	.67788	.61009	.57619	.54230	.50841	.47451	.45191	.44062	.40673
7%	.67425	.60683	.57311	.53940	.50569	.47198	.44950	.43826	.40455
7-1/2%	.67063	.60356	.57003	.53650	.50297	.46944	.44708	.43591	.40238
8%	.66700	.60030	.56695	.53360	.50025	.46690	.44466	.43355	.40020
8-1/2%	.66338	.59704	.56387	.53070	.49753	.46436	.44225	.43119	.39803
9%	.65975	.59378	.56079	.52780	.49481	.46183	.43983	.42884	.39585
9-1/2%	.65613	.59051	.55771	.52490	.49209	.45929	.43741	.42648	.39368
10%	.65250	.58725	.55463	.52200	.48938	.45675	.43500	.42413	.39150
10-1/2%	.64888	.58399	.55154	.51910	.48666	.45421	.43258	.42177	.38933
11%	.64525	.58073	.54846	.51620	.48394	.45168	.43016	.41941	.38715
11-1/2%	.64163	.57746	.54538	.51330	.48122	.44914	.42775	.41706	.38498
12%	.63800	.57420	.54230	.51040	.47850	.44660	.42533	.41470	.38280
12-1/2%	.63438	.57094	.53922	.50750	.47578	.44406	.42291	.41234	.38063
13%	.63075	.56768	.53614	.50460	.47306	.44153	.42050	.40999	.37845
13-1/2%	.62713	.56441	.53306	.50170	.47034	.43899	.41808	.40763	.37628
14%	.62350	.56115	.52998	.49880	.46763	.43645	.41566	.40528	.37410
14-1/2%	.61988	.55789	.52689	.49590	.46491	.43391	.41325	.40292	.37193
15%	.61625	.55463	.52381	.49300	.46219	.43138	.41083	.40056	.36975
15-1/2%	.61263	.55136	.52073	.49010	.45947	.42884	.40841	.39821	.36758
16%	.60900	.54810	.51765	.48720	.45675	.42630	.40600	.39585	.36540
16-1/2%	.60538	.54484	.51457	.48430	.45403	.42376	.40358	.39349	.36323
17%	.60175	.54158	.51149	.48140	.45131	.42123	.40116	.39114	.36105
17-1/2%	.59813	.53831	.50841	.47850	.44859	.41869	.39875	.38878	.35888
18%	.59450	.53505	.50533	.47560	.44588	.41615	.39633	.38643	.35670
18-1/2%	.59088	.53179	.50224	.47270	.44316	.41361	.39391	.38407	.35453
19%	.58725	.52853	.49916	.46980	.44044	.41108	.39150	.38171	.35235
19-1/2%	.58363	.52526	.49608	.46690	.43772	.40854	.38908	.37936	.35018
20%	.58000	.52200	.49300	.46400	.43500	.40600	.38666	.37700	.34800
21%	.57275	.51548	.48684	.45820	.42956	.40093	.38183	.37229	.34365
22%	.56550	.50895	.48068	.45240	.42413	.39585	.37700	.36758	.33930
23%	.55825	.50243	.47451	.44660	.41869	.39078	.37216	.36286	.33495
24%	.55100	.49590	.46835	.44080	.41325	.38570	.36733	.35815	.33060
25%	.54375	.48938	.46219	.43500	.40781	.38063	.36250	.35344	.32625

TABLE 4—DISCOUNTED VALUE OF $1.00 (Cont.)

FIRST DISCOUNT 30%

Third Discount	Second Discount								
	0	10%	15%	20%	25%	30%	33-1/3%	35%	40%
0%	.70000	.63000	.59500	.56000	.52500	.49000	.46667	.45500	.42000
1/2%	.69650	.62685	.59203	.55720	.52238	.48755	.46433	.45273	.41790
1%	.69300	.62370	.58905	.55440	.51975	.48510	.46200	.45045	.41580
1-1/2%	.68950	.62055	.58608	.55160	.51713	.48265	.45967	.44818	.41370
2%	.68600	.61740	.58310	.54880	.51450	.48020	.45733	.44590	.41160
2-1/2%	.68250	.61425	.58013	.54600	.51188	.47775	.45500	.44363	.40950
3%	.67900	.61110	.57715	.54320	.50925	.47530	.45267	.44135	.40740
3-1/2%	.67550	.60795	.57418	.54040	.50663	.47285	.45033	.43908	.40530
4%	.67200	.60480	.57120	.53760	.50400	.47040	.44800	.43680	.40320
4-1/2%	.66850	.60165	.56823	.53480	.50138	.46795	.44567	.43453	.40110
5%	.66500	.59850	.56525	.53200	.49875	.46550	.44333	.43225	.39900
5-1/2%	.66150	.59535	.56228	.52920	.49613	.46305	.44100	.42998	.39690
6%	.65800	.59220	.55930	.52640	.49350	.46060	.43867	.42770	.39480
6-1/2%	.65450	.58905	.55633	.52360	.49088	.45815	.43633	.42543	.39270
7%	.65100	.58590	.55335	.52080	.48825	.45570	.43400	.42315	.39060
7-1/2%	.64750	.58275	.55038	.51800	.48563	.45325	.43167	.42088	.38850
8%	.64400	.57960	.54740	.51520	.48300	.45080	.42933	.41860	.38640
8-1/2%	.64050	.57645	.54443	.51240	.48038	.44835	.42700	.41633	.38430
9%	.63700	.57330	.54145	.50960	.47775	.44590	.42467	.41405	.38220
9-1/2%	.63350	.57015	.53848	.50680	.47513	.44345	.42233	.41178	.38010
10%	.63000	.56700	.53550	.50400	.47250	.44100	.42000	.40950	.37800
10-1/2%	.62650	.56385	.53253	.50120	.46988	.43855	.41767	.40723	.37590
11%	.62300	.56070	.52955	.49840	.46725	.43610	.41533	.40495	.37380
11-1/2%	.61950	.55755	.52658	.49560	.46463	.43365	.41300	.40268	.37170
12%	.61600	.55440	.52360	.49280	.46200	.43120	.41067	.40040	.36960
12-1/2%	.61250	.55125	.52063	.49000	.45938	.42875	.40833	.39813	.36750
13%	.60900	.54180	.51765	.48720	.45675	.42630	.40600	.39585	.36540
13-1/2%	.60550	.54495	.51468	.48440	.45413	.42385	.40367	.39358	.36330
14%	.60200	.54810	.51170	.48160	.45150	.42140	.40133	.39130	.36120
14-1/2%	.59850	.53865	.50873	.47880	.44888	.41895	.39900	.38903	.35910
15%	.59500	.53550	.50575	.47600	.44625	.41650	.39667	.38675	.35700
15-1/2%	.59150	.53235	.50278	.47320	.44363	.41405	.39433	.38448	.35490
16%	.58800	.52920	.49980	.47040	.44100	.41160	.39200	.38220	.35280
16-1/2%	.58450	.52605	.49683	.46760	.43838	.40915	.38967	.37993	.35070
17%	.58100	.52290	.49385	.46480	.43575	.40670	.38733	.37765	.34860
17-1/2%	.57750	.51975	.49088	.46200	.43313	.40425	.38500	.37538	.34650
18%	.57400	.51660	.48790	.45920	.43050	.40180	.38267	.37310	.34440
18-1/2%	.57050	.51345	.48493	.45640	.42788	.39935	.38033	.37083	.34230
19%	.56700	.51030	.48195	.45360	.42525	.39690	.37800	.36855	.34020
19-1/2%	.56350	.50715	.47898	.45080	.42263	.39445	.37567	.36628	.33810
20%	.56000	.50400	.47600	.44800	.42000	.39200	.37333	.36400	.33600
21%	.55300	.49770	.47005	.44240	.41475	.38710	.36867	.35945	.33180
22%	.54600	.49140	.46410	.43680	.40950	.38220	.36400	.35490	.32760
23%	.53900	.48510	.45815	.43120	.40425	.37730	.35933	.35035	.32340
24%	.53200	.47880	.45220	.42560	.39900	.37240	.35467	.34580	.31920
25%	.52500	.47250	.44625	.42000	.39375	.36750	.35000	.34125	.31500

TABLE 4—DISCOUNTED VALUE OF $1.00 (Cont.)

FIRST DISCOUNT 33-1/3%

Third Discount	Second Discount								
	0	10%	15%	20%	25%	30%	33-1/3%	35%	40%
0%	.66667	.60000	.56667	.53333	.50000	.46667	.44444	.43333	.40000
1/2%	.66333	.59700	.56383	.53067	.49750	.46433	.44222	.43117	.39800
1%	.66000	.59400	.56100	.52800	.49500	.46200	.44000	.42900	.39600
1-1/2%	.65667	.59100	.55817	.52533	.49250	.45967	.43778	.42683	.39400
2%	.65333	.58800	.55533	.52267	.49000	.45733	.43556	.42467	.39200
2-1/2%	.65000	.58500	.55250	.52000	.48750	.45500	.43333	.42250	.39000
3%	.64667	.58200	.54967	.51733	.48500	.45267	.43111	.42033	.38800
3-1/2%	.64333	.57900	.54683	.51467	.48250	.45033	.42889	.41817	.38600
4%	.64000	.57600	.54400	.51200	.48000	.44800	.42667	.41600	.38400
4-1/2%	.63667	.57300	.54117	.50933	.47750	.44567	.42444	.41383	.38200
5%	.63333	.57000	.53833	.50667	.47500	.44333	.42222	.41167	.38000
5-1/2%	.63000	.56700	.53550	.50400	.47250	.44100	.42000	.40950	.37800
6%	.62667	.56400	.53267	.50133	.47000	.43867	.41778	.40733	.37600
6-1/2%	.62333	.56100	.52983	.49867	.46750	.43633	.41556	.40517	.37400
7%	.62000	.55800	.52700	.49600	.46500	.43400	.41333	.40300	.37200
7-1/2%	.61667	.55500	.52417	.49333	.46250	.43167	.41111	.40083	.37000
8%	.61333	.55200	.52133	.49067	.46000	.42933	.40889	.39867	.36800
8-1/2%	.61000	.54900	.51850	.48800	.45750	.42700	.40667	.39650	.36600
9%	.60667	.54600	.51567	.48533	.45500	.42467	.40444	.39433	.36400
9-1/2%	.60333	.54300	.51283	.48267	.45250	.42233	.40222	.39217	.36200
10%	.60000	.54000	.51000	.48000	.45000	.42000	.40000	.39000	.36000
10-1/2%	.59667	.53700	.50717	.47733	.44750	.41767	.39778	.38783	.35800
11%	.59333	.53400	.50433	.47467	.44500	.41533	.39556	.38567	.35600
11-1/2%	.59000	.53100	.50150	.47200	.44250	.41300	.39333	.38350	.35400
12%	.58667	.52800	.49867	.46933	.44000	.41067	.39111	.38133	.35200
12-1/2%	.58333	.52500	.49583	.46667	.43750	.40833	.38889	.37917	.35000
13%	.58000	.52200	.49300	.46400	.43500	.40600	.38667	.37700	.34800
13-1/2%	.57667	.51900	.49017	.46133	.43250	.40367	.38444	.37483	.34600
14%	.57333	.51600	.48733	.45867	.43000	.40133	.38222	.37267	.34400
14-1/2%	.57000	.51300	.48450	.45600	.42750	.39900	.38000	.37050	.34200
15%	.56667	.51000	.48167	.45333	.42500	.39667	.37778	.36833	.34000
15-1/2%	.56333	.50700	.47883	.45067	.42250	.39433	.37556	.36617	.33800
16%	.56000	.50400	.47600	.44800	.42000	.39200	.37333	.36400	.33600
16-1/2%	.55667	.50100	.47317	.44533	.41750	.38967	.37111	.36183	.33400
17%	.55333	.49800	.47033	.44267	.41500	.38733	.36889	.35967	.33200
17-1/2%	.55000	.49500	.46750	.44000	.41250	.38500	.36667	.35750	.33000
18%	.54667	.49200	.46467	.43733	.41000	.38267	.36444	.35533	.32800
18-1/2%	.54333	.48900	.46183	.43467	.40750	.38033	.36222	.35317	.32600
19%	.54000	.48600	.45900	.43200	.40500	.37800	.36000	.35100	.32400
19-1/2%	.53667	.48300	.45617	.42933	.40250	.37567	.35778	.34883	.32200
20%	.53333	.48000	.45333	.42667	.40000	.37333	.35556	.34667	.32000
21%	.52667	.47400	.44767	.42133	.39500	.36867	.35111	.34233	.31600
22%	.52000	.46800	.44200	.41600	.39000	.36400	.34667	.33800	.31200
23%	.51333	.46200	.43633	.41067	.38500	.35933	.34222	.33367	.30800
24%	.50667	.45600	.43067	.40533	.38000	.35467	.33778	.32933	.30400
25%	.50000	.45000	.42500	.40000	.37500	.35000	.33333	.32500	.30000

TABLE 4—DISCOUNTED VALUE OF $1.00 (Cont.)

FIRST DISCOUNT 35%

Third Discount	Second Discount								
	0	10%	15%	20%	25%	30%	33-1/3%	35%	40%
0%	.65000	.58500	.55250	.52000	.48750	.45500	.43333	.42250	.39000
1/2%	.64675	.58208	.54974	.51740	.48506	.45273	.43117	.42039	.38805
1%	.64350	.57915	.54698	.51480	.48263	.45045	.42900	.41828	.38610
1-1/2%	.64025	.57623	.54421	.51220	.48019	.44818	.42683	.41616	.38415
2%	.63700	.57330	.54145	.50960	.47775	.44590	.42467	.41405	.38220
2-1/2%	.63375	.57038	.53869	.50700	.47531	.44363	.42250	.41194	.38025
3%	.63050	.56745	.53593	.50440	.47288	.44135	.42033	.40983	.37830
3-1/2%	.62725	.56453	.53316	.50180	.47044	.43908	.41817	.40771	.37635
4%	.62400	.56160	.53040	.49920	.46800	.43680	.41600	.40560	.37440
4-1/2%	.62075	.55868	.52764	.49660	.46556	.43453	.41383	.40349	.37245
5%	.61750	.55575	.52488	.49400	.46313	.43225	.41167	.40138	.37050
5-1/2%	.61425	.55283	.52211	.49140	.46069	.42998	.40950	.39926	.36855
6%	.61100	.54990	.51935	.48880	.45825	.42770	.40733	.39715	.36660
6-1/2%	.60775	.54698	.51659	.48620	.45581	.42543	.40517	.39504	.36465
7%	.60450	.54405	.51383	.48360	.45338	.42315	.40300	.39293	.36270
7-1/2%	.60125	.54113	.51106	.48100	.45094	.42088	.40083	.39081	.36075
8%	.59800	.53820	.50830	.47840	.44850	.41860	.39867	.38870	.35880
8-1/2%	.59475	.53528	.50554	.47580	.44606	.41633	.39650	.38659	.35685
9%	.59150	.53235	.50278	.47320	.44363	.41405	.39433	.38448	.35490
9-1/2%	.58825	.52943	.50001	.47060	.44119	.41178	.39217	.38236	.35295
10%	.58500	.52650	.49725	.46800	.43875	.40950	.39000	.38025	.35100
10-1/2%	.58175	.52358	.49449	.46540	.43631	.40723	.38783	.37814	.34905
11%	.57850	.52065	.49173	.46280	.43388	.40495	.38567	.37603	.34710
11-1/2%	.57525	.51773	.48896	.46020	.43144	.40268	.38350	.37391	.34515
12%	.57200	.51480	.48620	.45760	.42900	.40040	.38133	.37180	.34320
12-1/2%	.56875	.51188	.48344	.45500	.42656	.39813	.37917	.36969	.34125
13%	.56550	.50895	.48068	.45240	.42413	.39585	.37700	.36758	.33930
13-1/2%	.56225	.50603	.47791	.44980	.42169	.39358	.37483	.36546	.33735
14%	.55900	.50310	.47515	.44720	.41925	.39130	.37267	.36335	.33540
14-1/2%	.55575	.50018	.47239	.44460	.41681	.38903	.37050	.36124	.33345
15%	.55250	.49725	.46963	.44200	.41438	.38675	.36833	.35913	.33150
15-1/2%	.54925	.49433	.46686	.43940	.41194	.38448	.36617	.35701	.32955
16%	.54600	.49140	.46410	.43680	.40950	.38220	.36400	.35490	.32760
16-1/2%	.54275	.48848	.46134	.43420	.40706	.37993	.36183	.35279	.32565
17%	.53950	.48555	.45858	.43160	.40463	.37765	.35967	.35068	.32370
17-1/2%	.53625	.48263	.45581	.42900	.40219	.37538	.35750	.34856	.32175
18%	.53300	.47970	.45305	.42640	.39975	.37310	.35533	.34645	.31980
18-1/2%	.52975	.47678	.45029	.42380	.39731	.37082	.35317	.34434	.31785
19%	.52650	.47385	.44753	.42120	.39488	.36855	.35010	.34223	.31590
19-1/2%	.52325	.47093	.44476	.41860	.39244	.36628	.34883	.34011	.31395
20%	.52000	.46800	.44200	.41600	.39000	.36400	.34667	.33800	.31200
21%	.51350	.46215	.43647	.41080	.38513	.35945	.34233	.33378	.30810
22%	.50700	.45630	.43095	.40560	.38025	.35490	.33710	.32956	.30420
23%	.50050	.45045	.42543	.40040	.37538	.35035	.33367	.32533	.30030
24%	.49400	.44460	.41990	.39520	.37050	.34580	.32933	.32110	.29640
25%	.48750	.43875	.41438	.39000	.36563	.34125	.32410	.31688	.29250

TABLE 4—DISCOUNTED VALUE OF $1.00 (Cont.)

FIRST DISCOUNT 37-1/2%

Third Discount	Second Discount								
	0	10%	15%	20%	25%	30%	33-1/3%	35%	40%
0%	.62500	.56250	.53125	.50000	.46875	.43750	.41667	.40625	.37500
1/2%	.62188	.55969	.52860	.49750	.46641	.43531	.41458	.40422	.37313
1%	.61875	.55688	.52594	.49500	.46406	.43313	.41250	.40219	.37125
1-1/2%	.61563	.55406	.52328	.49250	.46172	.43094	.41042	.40015	.36938
2%	.61250	.55125	.52063	.49000	.45938	.42875	.40833	.39813	.36750
2-1/2%	.60938	.54844	.51797	.48750	.45703	.42652	.40625	.39609	.36563
3%	.60625	.54563	.51531	.48500	.45469	.42438	.40417	.39406	.36375
3-1/2%	.60313	.54281	.51266	.48250	.45234	.42219	.40208	.39203	.36188
4%	.60000	.54000	.51000	.48000	.45000	.42000	.39910	.39000	.36000
4-1/2%	.59688	.53719	.50734	.47750	.44766	.41781	.39792	.38797	.35813
5%	.59375	.53438	.50469	.47500	.44531	.41563	.39583	.38594	.35625
5-1/2%	.59063	.53156	.50203	.47250	.44297	.41344	.39375	.38391	.35438
6%	.58750	.52875	.49938	.47000	.44063	.41125	.39167	.38188	.35250
6-1/2%	.58438	.52594	.49672	.46750	.43828	.40906	.38958	.37984	.35063
7%	.58125	.52313	.49406	.46500	.43594	.40688	.38750	.37781	.34875
7-1/2%	.57813	.52031	.49141	.46250	.43359	.40469	.38542	.37578	.34688
8%	.57500	.51750	.48875	.46000	.43125	.40250	.38333	.37375	.34500
8-1/2%	.57188	.51469	.48609	.45750	.42891	.40031	.38125	.37172	.34313
9%	.56875	.51188	.48344	.45500	.42656	.39813	.37917	.36969	.34125
9-1/2%	.56563	.50906	.48078	.45250	.42422	.39594	.37708	.36765	.33938
10%	.56250	.50625	.47813	.45000	.42188	.39375	.37500	.36563	.33750
10-1/2%	.55938	.50344	.47547	.44750	.41953	.39156	.37292	.36359	.33563
11%	.55625	.50063	.47281	.44500	.41719	.38938	.37083	.36156	.33375
11-1/2%	.55313	.49781	.47016	.44250	.41485	.38719	.36875	.35953	.33188
12%	.55000	.49500	.46750	.44000	.41250	.38500	.36667	.35750	.33000
12-1/2%	.54688	.49219	.46484	.43750	.41016	.38281	.36458	.35547	.32813
13%	.54375	.48938	.46219	.43500	.40781	.38063	.36250	.35344	.32625
13-1/2%	.54063	.48656	.45953	.43250	.40547	.37844	.36042	.35141	.32438
14%	.53750	.48375	.45688	.43000	.40313	.37625	.35833	.34938	.32250
14-1/2%	.53438	.48094	.45422	.42750	.40078	.37406	.35625	.34734	.32063
15%	.53125	.47813	.45156	.42500	.39844	.37188	.35417	.34531	.31875
15-1/2%	.52813	.47531	.44891	.42250	.39609	.36969	.35208	.34328	.31688
16%	.52500	.47250	.44625	.42000	.39375	.36750	.35000	.34125	.31500
16-1/2%	.52188	.46969	.44360	.41750	.39141	.36531	.34792	.33922	.31313
17%	.51875	.46688	.44094	.41500	.38906	.36313	.34583	.33719	.31125
17-1/2%	.51563	.46406	.43828	.41250	.38672	.36094	.34375	.33516	.30938
18%	.51250	.46125	.43563	.41000	.38438	.35875	.34167	.33313	.30750
18-1/2%	.50938	.45844	.43297	.40750	.38203	.35656	.33958	.33110	.30563
19%	.50625	.45563	.43031	.40500	.37969	.35438	.33750	.32906	.30375
19-1/2%	.50313	.45281	.42766	.40250	.37734	.35219	.33542	.32703	.30188
20%	.50000	.45000	.42500	.40000	.37500	.35000	.33333	.32500	.30000
21%	.49375	.44438	.41969	.39500	.37031	.34563	.32917	.32094	.29625
22%	.48750	.43875	.41438	.39000	.36563	.34125	.32500	.31688	.29250
23%	.48125	.43313	.40906	.38500	.36094	.33688	.32083	.31281	.28875
24%	.47500	.42750	.40375	.38000	.35625	.33250	.31667	.30875	.28500
25%	.46875	.42188	.39844	.37500	.35156	.32813	.31250	.30469	.28125

191

TABLE 4—DISCOUNTED VALUE OF $1.00 (Cont.)

FIRST DISCOUNT 40%

Third Discount	Second Discount								
	0	10%	15%	20%	25%	30%	33-1/3%	35%	40%
0%	.60000	.54000	.51000	.48000	.45000	.42000	.40000	.39000	.36000
1/2%	.59700	.53730	.50745	.47760	.44775	.41790	.39800	.38805	.35820
1%	.59400	.53460	.50490	.47520	.44550	.41580	.39600	.38610	.35640
1-1/2%	.59100	.53190	.50235	.47280	.44325	.41370	.39400	.38415	.35460
2%	.58800	.52920	.49980	.47040	.44100	.41160	.39200	.38220	.35280
2-1/2%	.58500	.52650	.49725	.46800	.43875	.40950	.39000	.38025	.35100
3%	.58200	.52380	.49470	.46560	.43650	.40740	.38800	.37830	.34920
3-1/2%	.57900	.52110	.49215	.46320	.43425	.40530	.38600	.37635	.34740
4%	.57600	.51840	.48960	.46080	.43200	.40320	.38400	.37440	.34560
4-1/2%	.57300	.51570	.48705	.45840	.42975	.40110	.38200	.37245	.34380
5%	.57000	.51300	.48450	.45600	.42750	.39900	.38000	.37050	.34200
5-1/2%	.56700	.51030	.48195	.45360	.42525	.39690	.37800	.36855	.34020
6%	.56400	.50760	.47940	.45120	.42300	.39480	.37600	.36660	.33840
6-1/2%	.56100	.50490	.47685	.44880	.42075	.39270	.37400	.36465	.33660
7%	.55800	.50220	.47430	.44640	.41850	.39060	.37200	.36270	.33480
7-1/2%	.55500	.49950	.47175	.44400	.41625	.38850	.37000	.36075	.33300
8%	.55200	.49680	.46920	.44160	.41400	.38640	.36800	.35880	.33120
8-1/2%	.54900	.49410	.46665	.43920	.41175	.38430	.36600	.35685	.32940
9%	.54600	.49140	.46410	.43680	.40950	.38220	.36400	.35490	.32760
9-1/2%	.54300	.48870	.46155	.43440	.40725	.38010	.36200	.35295	.32580
10%	.54000	.48600	.45900	.43200	.40500	.37800	.36000	.35100	.32400
10-1/2%	.53700	.48330	.45645	.42960	.40275	.37590	.35800	.34905	.32220
11%	.53400	.48060	.45390	.42720	.40050	.37380	.35600	.34710	.32040
11-1/2%	.53100	.47790	.45135	.42480	.39825	.37170	.35400	.34515	.31860
12%	.52800	.47520	.44880	.42240	.39600	.36960	.35200	.34320	.31680
12-1/2%	.52500	.47250	.44625	.42000	.39375	.36750	.35000	.34125	.31500
13%	.52200	.46980	.44370	.41760	.39150	.36540	.34800	.33930	.31320
13-1/2%	.51900	.46710	.44115	.41520	.38925	.36330	.34600	.33735	.31140
14%	.51600	.46440	.43860	.41280	.38700	.36120	.34400	.33540	.30960
14-1/2%	.51300	.46170	.43605	.41040	.38475	.35910	.34200	.33345	.30780
15%	.51000	.45900	.43350	.40800	.38250	.35700	.34000	.33150	.30600
15-1/2%	.50700	.45630	.43095	.40560	.38025	.35490	.33800	.32955	.30420
16%	.50400	.45360	.42840	.40320	.37800	.35280	.33600	.32760	.30240
16-1/2%	.50100	.45090	.42585	.40080	.37575	.35070	.33400	.32565	.30060
17%	.49800	.44820	.42330	.39840	.37350	.34860	.33200	.32370	.29880
17-1/2%	.49500	.44550	.42075	.39600	.37125	.34650	.33000	.32175	.29700
18%	.49200	.44280	.41820	.39360	.36900	.34440	.32800	.31980	.29520
18-1/2%	.48900	.44010	.41565	.39120	.36675	.34230	.32600	.31785	.29340
19%	.48600	.43740	.41310	.38880	.36450	.34020	.32400	.31590	.29160
19-1/2%	.48300	.43470	.41055	.38640	.36225	.33810	.32200	.31395	.28980
20%	.48000	.43200	.40800	.38400	.36000	.33600	.32000	.31200	.28800
21%	.47400	.42660	.40290	.37920	.35550	.33180	.31600	.30810	.28440
22%	.46800	.42120	.39780	.37440	.35100	.32760	.31200	.30420	.28080
23%	.46200	.41580	.39270	.36960	.34650	.32340	.30800	.30030	.27720
24%	.45600	.41040	.38760	.36480	.34200	.31920	.30400	.29640	.27360
25%	.45000	.40500	.38250	.36000	.33750	.31500	.30000	.29250	.27000

TABLE 4—DISCOUNTED VALUE OF $1.00 (Cont.)

FIRST DISCOUNT 45%

Third Discount	Second Discount								
	0	10%	15%	20%	25%	30%	33-1/3%	35%	40%
0%	.55000	.49500	.46750	.44000	.41250	.38500	.36667	.35750	.33000
1/2%	.54725	.49253	.46516	.43780	.41044	.38308	.36483	.35571	.32835
1%	.54450	.49005	.46283	.43560	.40838	.38115	.36300	.35393	.32670
1-1/2%	.54175	.48758	.46049	.43340	.40631	.37923	.36117	.35214	.32505
2%	.53900	.48510	.45815	.43120	.40425	.37730	.35933	.35035	.32340
2-1/2%	.53625	.48263	.45581	.42900	.40219	.37538	.35750	.34856	.32175
3%	.53350	.48015	.45348	.42680	.40013	.37345	.35567	.34678	.32010
3-1/2%	.53075	.47768	.45114	.42460	.39806	.37153	.35383	.34499	.31845
4%	.52800	.47520	.44880	.42240	.39600	.36960	.35200	.34320	.31680
4-1/2%	.52525	.47273	.44646	.42020	.39394	.36768	.35017	.34141	.31515
5%	.52250	.47025	.44413	.41800	.39188	.36575	.34833	.33963	.31350
5-1/2%	.51975	.46778	.44179	.41580	.38981	.36383	.34650	.33784	.31185
6%	.51700	.46530	.43945	.41360	.38775	.36190	.34467	.33605	.31020
6-1/2%	.51425	.46283	.43711	.41140	.38569	.35998	.34283	.33426	.30855
7%	.51150	.46035	.43478	.40920	.38363	.35805	.34100	.33248	.36090
7-1/2%	.50875	.45788	.43244	.40700	.38156	.35613	.33917	.33069	.30525
8%	.50600	.45540	.43010	.40480	.37950	.35420	.33733	.32890	.30360
8-1/2%	.50325	.45293	.42776	.40260	.37744	.35228	.33550	.32711	.30195
9%	.50050	.45045	.42543	.40040	.37538	.35035	.33367	.32533	.30030
9-1/2%	.49775	.44798	.42309	.39820	.37331	.34843	.33183	.32354	.29865
10%	.49500	.44550	.42075	.39600	.37125	.34650	.33000	.32175	.29700
10-1/2%	.49225	.44303	.41842	.39380	.36919	.34458	.32817	.31997	.29535
11%	.48950	.44055	.41608	.39160	.36713	.34265	.32633	.31818	.29370
11-1/2%	.48675	.43808	.41374	.38940	.36506	.34073	.32450	.31639	.29205
12%	.48400	.43560	.39930	.38720	.36300	.33880	.32267	.31460	.29040
12-1/2%	.48125	.43313	.40906	.38500	.36094	.33688	.32083	.31281	.28875
13%	.47850	.43065	.40673	.38280	.35888	.33495	.31900	.31103	.28710
13-1/2%	.47575	.42818	.40439	.38060	.35681	.33303	.31717	.30924	.28545
14%	.47300	.42570	.40205	.37840	.35475	.41710	.31533	.30745	.28380
14-1/2%	.47025	.42322	.39971	.37620	.35269	.32918	.31350	.30566	.28215
15%	.46750	.42075	.39738	.37400	.35063	.32725	.31167	.30388	.28050
15-1/2%	.46475	.41828	.39504	.37180	.34856	.32533	.30983	.30209	.27885
16%	.46200	.41580	.39270	.36960	.34650	.32340	.30800	.30030	.27720
16-1/2%	.45925	.41333	.39036	.36740	.34444	.32148	.30617	.29851	.27555
17%	.45650	.41085	.38803	.36520	.34238	.31955	.30433	.29673	.27390
17-1/2%	.45375	.40838	.38569	.36300	.34031	.31763	.30250	.29494	.27225
18%	.45100	.40590	.38335	.36080	.33825	.31570	.30067	.29315	.27060
18-1/2%	.44825	.40343	.38101	.35860	.33619	.31378	.29883	.29136	.26895
19%	.44550	.40095	.36754	.35640	.33413	.31185	.29700	.28958	.26730
19-1/2%	.44275	.39848	.37634	.35420	.33206	.30993	.29517	.28779	.26565
20%	.44000	.39600	.37400	.35200	.33000	.30800	.29333	.28600	.26400
21%	.43450	.39105	.36933	.34760	.32588	.30415	.28967	.28243	.26070
22%	.42900	.38610	.36465	.34320	.32175	.30030	.28600	.27885	.25740
23%	.42350	.38115	.35998	.33880	.31763	.29645	.28233	.27528	.25410
24%	.41800	.37620	.35530	.33440	.31350	.29260	.27867	.27170	.25080
25%	.41250	.37125	.35063	.33000	.30938	.28875	.27450	.26813	.24750

TABLE 4—DISCOUNTED VALUE OF $1.00 (Cont.)

FIRST DISCOUNT 50%

Third Discount	Second Discount								
	0	10%	15%	20%	25%	30%	33-1/3%	35%	40%
0%	.50000	.45000	.42500	.40000	.37500	.35000	.33333	.32500	.30000
1/2%	.49750	.44775	.42288	.39800	.37313	.34825	.33167	.32338	.29850
1%	.49500	.44550	.42075	.39600	.37125	.34650	.33000	.32175	.29700
1-1/2%	.49250	.44325	.41863	.39400	.36938	.34475	.32833	.32013	.29550
2%	.49000	.44100	.41650	.39200	.36750	.34300	.32667	.31850	.29400
2-1/2%	.48750	.43875	.41438	.39000	.36563	.34125	.32500	.31688	.29250
3%	.48500	.43650	.41225	.38800	.36375	.33950	.32333	.31525	.29100
3-1/2%	.48250	.43425	.41013	.38600	.36188	.33775	.32167	.31363	.28950
4%	.48000	.43200	.40800	.38400	.36000	.33600	.32000	.31200	.28800
4-1/2%	.47750	.42975	.40588	.38200	.35813	.33425	.31833	.31038	.28650
5%	.47500	.42750	.40375	.38000	.35625	.33250	.31667	.30875	.28500
5-1/2%	.47250	.42525	.40163	.37800	.35438	.33075	.31500	.30713	.28350
6%	.47000	.42300	.39950	.37600	.35250	.32900	.31333	.30550	.28200
6-1/2%	.46750	.42075	.39738	.37400	.35063	.32725	.31167	.30388	.28050
7%	.46500	.41850	.39525	.37200	.34875	.32550	.31000	.30225	.27900
7-1/2%	.46250	.41625	.39313	.37000	.34688	.32375	.30833	.30063	.27750
8%	.46000	.41400	.39100	.36800	.34500	.32200	.30667	.29900	.27600
8-1/2%	.45750	.41175	.38888	.36600	.34313	.32025	.30500	.29738	.27450
9%	.45500	.40950	.38675	.36400	.34125	.31850	.30333	.29575	.27300
9-1/2%	.45250	.40725	.38463	.36200	.33938	.31675	.30167	.29413	.27150
10%	.45000	.40500	.38250	.36000	.33750	.31500	.30000	.29250	.27000
10-1/2%	.44750	.40275	.38037	.35800	.33563	.31325	.29833	.29088	.26850
11%	.44500	.40050	.37825	.35600	.33375	.31150	.29667	.28925	.26700
11-1/2%	.44250	.39825	.37613	.35400	.33188	.30975	.29500	.28763	.26550
12%	.44000	.39600	.37400	.35200	.33000	.30800	.29333	.28600	.26400
12-1/2%	.43750	.39375	.37188	.35000	.32813	.30625	.29167	.28438	.26250
13%	.43500	.39150	.36975	.34800	.32625	.30450	.29000	.28275	.26100
13-1/2%	.43250	.38925	.36763	.34600	.32438	.30275	.28833	.28113	.25950
14%	.43000	.38700	.36550	.34400	.32250	.30100	.28667	.27950	.25800
14-1/2%	.42750	.38475	.36338	.34200	.32063	.29925	.28500	.27788	.25650
15%	.42500	.38250	.36125	.34000	.31875	.29750	.28333	.27625	.25500
15-1/2%	.42250	.38025	.35913	.33800	.31688	.29575	.28167	.27463	.25350
16%	.42000	.37800	.35700	.33600	.31500	.29400	.28000	.27300	.25200
16-1/2%	.41750	.37575	.35488	.33400	.31313	.29225	.27833	.27138	.25050
17%	.41500	.37350	.35275	.33200	.31125	.29050	.27667	.26975	.24900
17-1/2%	.41250	.37125	.35063	.33000	.30938	.28875	.27500	.26813	.24750
18%	.41000	.36900	.34850	.32800	.30750	.28700	.27333	.26650	.24600
18-1/2%	.40750	.36675	.34638	.32600	.30563	.28525	.27167	.26488	.24450
19%	.40500	.36450	.34425	.32400	.30375	.28350	.27000	.26325	.24300
19-1/2%	.40250	.36225	.34213	.32200	.30188	.28175	.26833	.26163	.24150
20%	.40000	.36000	.34000	.32000	.30000	.28000	.26667	.26000	.24000
21%	.39500	.35550	.33575	.31600	.29625	.27650	.26333	.25675	.23700
22%	.39000	.35100	.33150	.31200	.29250	.27300	.26000	.25350	.23400
23%	.38500	.34650	.32725	.30800	.28875	.26950	.25667	.25025	.23100
24%	.38000	.34200	.32300	.30400	.28500	.26600	.25333	.24700	.22800
25%	.37500	.33750	.31875	.30000	.28125	.26250	.25000	.24375	.22500

To use this table, find from the above list the page of Table 4 having the correct first discount. Turn to that page, and find the correct second discount in the first horizontal line at the top of the page, and hold a finger of your right hand on that figure. Then run a finger of your left hand down the first vertical column on the page until you find the correct third discount. Then the figure wanted.is in the space located by the vertical column down from your right-hand finger, and the horizontal line across from your left-hand finger.

For example, to obtain from the table the net amount of $642.50 subject to discounts of 25%, 10% and 2%, turn to Page 186, which gives the discounted values of $1.00 for invoices on which the first discount is 25%. Then find the correct second discount, 10% in the top horizontal column. Finally, find the correct third discount, 2%, in the left-hand vertical column, and follow that row to its intersection with the 10% second discount vertical column. The figure found in this way is $.6615, which is thus the value of $1.00 after discounts of 25%, 10% and 2%. Then by multiplying the gross amount of the invoice, $642.50, by .6615, the figure $425.01375 is obtained, which to the nearest cent is $425.01, the net amount of the invoice.

It should also be noted that the first column of discounts at the left of each page of the table, and the first row of discounts at the top of each page, are the values for 0%. This column and row are to facilitate making calculations in cases where fewer than three discounts apply. Thus, to find the net amount of a gross invoice of $862.25 subject to discounts of 30% and $1\frac{1}{2}$%, turn to Page 188, which is calculated for a first discount of 30%. Since there is no second discount of $1\frac{1}{2}$% given (first horizontal line at top of table), use the second discount column that is headed 0%, and run down it to the figure on the line with the third discount of $1\frac{1}{2}$%. This figure is $.6895, the amount of $1.00 after discounts of 30% and $1\frac{1}{2}$%. Multiply the gross amount of the invoice, $862.25, by the figure .6895, obtaining $594.521375, which to the nearest cent is $594.52, the net amount of the invoice.

Internal Discount Calculations

Determination of Selling Price. The theoretically ideal method of determining the selling price of an article or commodity would be to add to the cost of buying or producing that article, the cost of doing business in that article and the profit. For it is obvious that the cost of doing business varies from article to article and from commodity to commodity, due to differences in costs of selling, advertising, packaging, etc., as well as to differences in the share of the general overhead of the business (rent, light, administrative salaries, etc.) fairly chargeable to the particular commodity or article. Because, however, of the difficulty and bookkeeping cost of determining the variations in these costs from one article or commodity to another, many businesses use the same percentage of the cost price or of the selling price to cover their costs and profits on all their goods. This practice is particularly prevalent in general businesses reselling articles of many different kinds, where it would be impracticable to determine costs of handling each kind.

The element of confusion arising in calculations of selling price is due to the fact that some businesses express their increment in selling price over cost (which is called markup) in percentage of cost, which others use percentage of selling price.

Thus, when a business computes its percentage markup on cost, the relationship is

$$\text{Percentage Markup on Cost} = (100)\left(\frac{\text{Selling Price} - \text{Cost Price}}{\text{Cost Price}}\right)$$

(10-1)

Thus, if the selling price and cost price are known, the percentage markup on cost can be found directly from Formula 10-1. Thus, if the selling price is \$100.00 and the cost price is \$70.00, the percentage markup on cost is $100\frac{\$100 - 70}{70} = 42.8571\%$.

By rearrangement of this formula,

$$\text{Selling Price} = (\text{Cost Price})\left(\frac{100 + \text{Percentage Markup on Cost}}{100}\right)$$

(10-2)

Therefore, if the cost price of an article is \$60.00 and the percentage markup on cost is 40%, the selling price is $\$60.00\frac{100 + 40}{100} = (\$60.00) \times (1.40) = \$84.00$.

Finally, by again rearranging the formula,

$$\text{Cost Price} = \frac{(100 \times \text{Selling Price})}{(100 + \text{Percentage Markup on Cost})}$$

(10-3)

Therefore if the selling price of an article is \$100, and the percentage markup on cost is 30%, the cost price is $\frac{100 \times \$100}{100 + 30} = \$76.92$.

A series of formulas similar to those just developed for percentage markup on cost can also be derived for calculations in cases where the percentage markup is based on selling price. Thus,

$$\text{Percentage Markup on Selling Price} = 100\frac{(\text{Selling Price} - \text{Cost Price})}{(\text{Selling Price})}$$

(10-4)

If the selling price is \$100 and the cost price is \$70, the percentage markup on selling price is $\dfrac{\$100 - 70}{\$100} = \dfrac{\$30}{\$100} = 30\%$

By rearrangement of Formula (10-4)

Cost Price = (Selling Price)

$$- \text{(Selling Price)} \left(\frac{\text{Percentage Markup on Selling Price}}{100} \right)$$

$$\text{Cost Price} = \text{(Selling Price)} \left(1 - \frac{\text{Percentage Markup on Selling Price}}{100} \right)$$

$$(10\text{-}5)$$

Therefore, if the selling price is \$90, and the percentage markup on selling price is 25%, the cost price is $(\$90) \left(1 - \dfrac{25}{100} \right) = \$67.50.$

By again rearranging Formula (10-4),

$$\text{Selling Price} = \frac{(100) \times \text{(Cost Price)}}{(100 - \text{Percentage Markup on Selling Price})}$$

$$(10\text{-}6)$$

Therefore, if the cost price is \$60, and the percentage markup on selling price is 40%, the selling price is $\dfrac{(100) \times (\$60)}{100 - 40} = \$100.00.$

Formulas (10-1)-(10-3) relate cost, selling price and percentage markup on cost, while Formulas (10-4)-(10-6) relate cost, selling price and percentage markup on selling price.   Thus to find any one of the three quantities, percentage markup on cost, selling price or cost price, if the other two are known, use the correct formula (10-1), (10-2) or (10-3). Similarly, to find any one of the three quantities, percentage markup on selling price, cost or selling price, knowing the other two, use the corresponding formula from the three (10-4), (10-5) and (10-6).

It is often useful to have a relationship between the percentage markup on cost and the percentage markup on selling price.   Such a relationship may be derived as follows:

The actual (not percentage) markup is the difference between selling price and cost price.   That is

Markup = Selling Price − Cost Price or, using symbols for brevity, $M = P_s - P_c,$

Transposing M and P_c,

$$P_c = P_s - M \qquad\qquad\qquad\qquad\text{(a)}$$

Then by transposing both sides of the equation,

$$\frac{1}{P_c} = \frac{1}{P_s - M} \qquad\qquad\qquad\qquad\text{(b)}$$

Multiplying the equals by M,

$$\frac{M}{P_c} = \frac{M}{P_s - M} \tag{c}$$

Now divide both numerator and denominator of second term by P_s,

$$\frac{M}{P_s - M} = \frac{\dfrac{M}{P_s}}{\dfrac{P_s - M}{P_s}} = \frac{\dfrac{M}{P_s}}{1 - \dfrac{M}{P_s}} \tag{d}$$

Now multiply numerator and denominator of (d) by 100,

$$\frac{\dfrac{M}{P_s}}{1 - \dfrac{M}{P_s}} = \frac{100 \dfrac{M}{P_s}}{100 - 100 \dfrac{M}{P_s}} \tag{e}$$

Now substitute final value of second term (e) in (c),

$$\frac{M}{P_c} = \frac{100 \dfrac{M}{P_s}}{100 - 100 \dfrac{M}{P_s}} \tag{f}$$

Now multiply both sides by 100,

$$100 \frac{M}{P_c} = 100 \left(\frac{100 \dfrac{M}{P_s}}{100 - 100 \dfrac{M}{P_s}} \right) \tag{g}$$

But $100 \dfrac{M}{P_c}$ is percent markup on cost and $100 \dfrac{M}{P_s}$ is percent markup on selling price. Therefore,

Percent Markup on Cost

$$= 100 \left(\frac{\text{Percent Markup on Selling Price}}{100 - \text{Percent Markup on Selling Price}} \right) \tag{10-7}$$

For example, if it is known that an article is priced at a 25% markup on selling price, its percent markup on cost is: $100 \left(\dfrac{25}{100 - 25} \right) = 100 \left(\dfrac{25}{75} \right) = 33\frac{1}{3}\%$. By a similar derivation, it is shown that

Percent Markup on Selling Price

$$= 100 \frac{\text{Percent Markup on Cost}}{100 + \text{Percent Markup on Cost}} \tag{10-8}$$

Thus if it is known that an article is priced at a 40% markup on cost, then its markup on selling price is $100\left(\dfrac{40}{100+40}\right) = 100\left(\dfrac{40}{140}\right) = 28\tfrac{4}{7}\%$.

Many businesses, especially merchandising business, determine their selling prices on the basis of the markup on selling price (which they call the "margin"). For convenience in making such calculations, Table 4a is given, in which percent markups on cost are given for known percent markups on selling price. To compute the selling price of an article, when its cost and percent markup on selling price are known, simply look up the percent markup on cost for the known percent markup on selling price, and add the given percent of the cost price to the cost price. Thus this table is equivalent to Formula (10-7) above.

Suppose that an article costs $1.20 and that the markup on selling price (margin) is 20 percent. Refer to Table 4a. Find 20 percent markup on selling price in the column headed "Percent Markup on Selling Price." The percentage markup on cost is the corresponding percent in the column headed "Percent Markup on Cost Price," and is 25 percent. To determine the selling price, multiply the cost price, $1.20, by 125 percent, obtaining $1.50.

Into many commercial discount calculations, various combinations of discounts enter. In making such calculations, great care should be taken to designate every figure explicitly and to proceed systematically, using wherever possible the shortened methods already given in this chapter.

To illustrate what is meant by explicit designation, consider the case of a resale business which purchases goods at a discount, (or series of discounts) and lists them in a catalog which is subject to sales discounts. This situation introduces seven elements, which may be designated as follows:

1. Purchase list price
2.   Less Purchase discounts
3. Cost Price
4.   Plus Overall Markup
5. Sales list price
6.   Less sales discounts
7. Selling price.

In most instances, the purchase list price and purchase discounts are known, so that the cost price can be calculated, as stated above, by the methods already explained earlier in this chapter. What remains to be explained, therefore, are the calculations from the cost price (#3 in the above list), of items #4, #5, #6 and #7, which follow cost price, #3, in the above tabulation.

TABLE 4a—PERCENTAGE MARKUP ON COST PRICE FOR GIVEN PERCENTAGE MARKUP ON SELLING PRICE
MARK-UP TABLE

Percent Mark-Up on Selling Price	Percent Mark-Up on Cost Price	Percent Mark-Up on Selling Price	Percent Mark-Up on Cost Price
4.8	5.0	25.0	33.3
5.0	5.3	26.0	35.0
6.0	6.4	27.0	37.0
7.0	7.5	27.3	37.5
8.0	8.7	28.0	39.0
9.0	10.0	28.5	40.0
10.0	11.1	29.0	40.9
10.7	12.0	30.0	42.9
11.0	12.4	31.0	45.0
11.1	12.5	32.0	47.1
12.0	13.6	33.3	50.0
12.5	14.3	34.0	51.5
13.0	15.0	35.0	53.9
14.0	16.3	35.5	55.0
15.0	17.7	36.0	56.3
16.0	19.1	37.0	58.8
16.7	20.0	37.5	60.0
17.0	20.5	38.0	61.3
17.5	21.2	39.0	64.0
18.0	22.0	39.5	65.5
18.5	22.7	40.0	66.7
19.0	23.5	41.0	70.0
20.0	25.0	42.0	72.4
21.0	26.6	42.8	75.0
22.0	28.2	44.4	80.0
22.5	29.0	46.1	85.0
23.1	30.0	48.7	95.0
24.0	31.6	50.0	100.0

These calculations can, of course, be made directly and simply if the overall markup, (#4) and the sales discounts (#6) are fixed and known for the particular business. Frequently, however, the known quantity is the percent markup, based on cost price or selling price, which is used to compute selling price (#7) directly from cost price (#3) by the formulas given earlier in this chapter. Then the sales list price (#5) is figured back from the selling price (#7) by applying the known sales discounts.

This process is illustrated by the following example—If the cost price of an article to a merchant is $40.00, its percent markup on cost is 30%, and the merchant gives a sales discount of 10%, what should be his (sales) list price?

To take the first step in solving this problem, use the Formula (10-2), which is:

$$\text{Selling Price} = (\text{Cost Price}) \frac{(100 + \text{Percent Markup on Cost})}{100}$$

Substituting, $\quad$ Selling Price $= \$40.00 \dfrac{100 + 30}{100} = \$40.00 \dfrac{130}{100} = \$52.00$

Since this selling price is #7 in the above tabulation, and it was obtained after a sales discount (#6) of 10% of the list price (#5), therefore #7 is 90% of #5. Therefore the list price should be $\dfrac{\$52.00}{.90} = \$57.77\frac{7}{9}$. This figure is often increased to the next "round" figure, the definition of a "round" figure depending upon the pricing policy of the business. Thus the list price might be $57.80, or $58.00, or even $60.00.

A further question that carries this particular example a step further is: If the merchant "rounds off" the price at $57.80, what is the overall markup and what is the percent overall markup on cost?

Since the list price (#5) in the foregoing example is $57.80, and the cost price (#3 in the tabulation) was stated to be $40.00, the overall markup (#4) is #5 − #3 or $57.80 − 40.00 = $17.80, and the percent overall markup on cost is $(100) \dfrac{\$17.80}{\$40.00} = 44.5\%$.

Another example is: A merchant purchases an article at a purchase list price of $90.00, less purchase discounts of 25%, 10% and 5%. If he gives a sales discount of 10%, and his percent markup based on selling price is 30%, what should be his approximate list price, and what is his overall markup and his percent overall markup on cost?

The cost of the article can be found by use of the multiple discount tables in this book. Refer to Table 4, turning to the page for first discounts of 25%. Then the second column of figures in that table is for a second discount of 10%, and the eleventh row of figures is for a third discount of

5%. The figure in the space at the intersection of the second column and the eleventh row is .64125, which is the value of $1.00 after discounts of 25%, 10% and 5%.

Multiply .64125 by $90.00 to find the cost price of the article—the product of this multiplication is $57.7125, which to the nearest cent is $57.71. Since the percent markup on selling price is given as 30%, then use the Formula (10-6), which gives selling price if cost price and percent markup on selling price are known. This formula is—

$$\text{Selling Price} = \frac{(100) \times (\text{Cost Price})}{(100 - \text{Percent Markup on Selling Price})}$$

Substituting,

$$\text{Selling Price} = \frac{(100)(\$57.71)}{(100 - 30)} = \frac{\$5771.}{70} = \$82.443,$$

which to the nearest cent is #82.44.

This selling price corresponds to the #7 in the foregoing tabulation. Since item #5, the sales list price, is to be subject to a discount of 10% to give #7, then the sales list price is $82.44/.90 = $91.60, sales list price.

To find the overall markup (#4) subtract the cost price from the sales list price. Thus $91.60 − $57.71 = $33.89, overall markup.

Finally the percent overall markup on cost is $(100) \dfrac{\text{Overall markup}}{\text{Cost}}$

$$= (100) \frac{\$33.89}{\$57.71} = 58.7\%.$$

Throughout the calculations made in this chapter, a single basic figure has been used, which was either the percent markup on cost or the percent markup on selling price. The assumption in the use of one of these figures, as already stated, is that a business engaged in the resale of articles purchased may apply in all cases a single percent figure to calculate selling price from cost—this figure to include all the expenses of the business and the profit.

In many instances, however, the costs of selling, and even the correct share of the overhead of the business, varies from one type of merchandise to another. In such cases, the correct percent markup should, if possible, be calculated for the particular type of article, using actual cost accounting figures.

It is also to be noted that the single percent markup figure contains the profit as well as the expenses of the business. However, due to competition, a business should be able to vary its profit margin on some of its merchandise so that it can reduce its selling prices and profit on those items on which the competition is most keen. The need for relatively lower profit margins and prices is often made evident, not so much by observing competitors' prices, as by reduced inventory turnover. The maintainance of the rate of merchandise turnover is of critical importance if the business is to remain in a healthy financial condition; for that reason the subject is discussed at length in Chapter 18, under the section heading, "Financial Statements and Their Interpretation."

Therefore, to obtain the desired close control over pricing, the use of two, instead of one, percent markup figures is often preferable. One of these figures is based upon the expenses of the business, and the other, upon the profit. This method of calculating prices is illustrated by the following example.

The manufacturing cost of an article is $26.00. What should be the manufacturer's list price if he is selling at a discount of 40% from list, if his total non-manufacturing costs are 32% of sales, and if his profit is to be 5% of sales (Selling Price)? What list price for 10% profit? What list price for 15% profit?

The percent markup on selling price is total non-manufacturing costs plus profit = $32\% + P\%$.

Since the cost price is known ($26.00), use Formula (10-6), which gives selling price in terms of cost price and percent markup on selling price. This formula is:

$$\text{Selling Price} = \frac{(100) \times (\text{Cost Price})}{(100 - \text{Percent Markup on Selling Price})}$$

Substituting,

$$\text{Selling Price} = \frac{(100)(\$26.00)}{100 - (32 + P)}$$

Now the discount from list price is 40%, therefore the selling price = 60% of list price, or the list price $= \frac{100\%}{60}$ (Selling Price).

Substituting,

$$\text{List Price} = \frac{(100)(100)(\$26.00)}{60[100 - (32 + P)]}$$

or

$$\text{List Price} = \frac{(100)^2(\$26.00)}{60(100 - 32 - P)}$$

By substituting successively values of 5, 10, and 15 for P in formula, the list prices are found to be $68.78; $74.71 and $81.76, which may be rounded off to $68.80; $74.75; and $81.80. By setting up this type of formula, the manufacturer can determine the profit percents obtainable at various list prices, so that he can readily determine the profit percent available to him in relation to competitive list prices.

Chapter 11

SIMPLE INTEREST

Interest is income received for the use of capital. Both interest and capital are, in this relationship, usually expressed in money. The amount of the capital is called the principal. The basis for calculating the amount of interest to be paid for a given amount of capital, is the interest rate per unit time, which is usually expressed as in hundredths of the principal, or percentage. When no unit of time is specified, it is understood to be a year.

The term simple interest denotes interest computed on the original principal only. If the interest is added periodically to the principal, and then the interest for the following period is computed on the total, then the sum by which the original principal is increased at the end of the total time is called compound interest. Compound interest is treated in Chapter 13, the present chapter being concerned with simple interest.

Computing Simple Interest

The interest rate is the interest earned per unit principal per unit time. Thus, if simple interest is computed at a rate of 4% (per year), the amount of interest per year for each dollar of principal is 4% of $1.00, which is $0.04 (4 cents). Consequently the simple interest for one year on $50.00 at 4% (per year) is 50 × $.04 = $2.00, and the simple interest for two years on $50.00 at 4% (per year) is 2 × $2.00 = $4.00. This relationship may be stated in words as:

Simple Interest = Principal × Rate per Unit time

× Number of Units of Time

or it may be expressed by the formula

$$I = Prn, \tag{11-1}$$

where I is the interest on a principal P at an interest rate of r per year for n years. As stated above the interest rate is expressed as a decimal; for example, a 4% interest rate is substituted for r in the decimal form .04.

Then the total amount of principal and interest after n years is the sum of principal and interest, or as expressed symbolically by formula,

$$S = P + I \tag{11-2}$$

As an example, to compute the simple interest and total sum of a principal of \$6,700.00 at an interest rate of 5.5% per year for 4 years:

P is \$6,700.00; r is .055; and n is 4.

Therefore $I = Prn = (\$6,700.00)(.055)(4.) = \$1,474.00$, the interest.

And $S = P + I = \$6,700.00 + \$1,474.00 = \$8,174.00$, the total sum.

Ordinary and Exact Simple Interest

Most business calculations involving simple interest cover periods of time of less than one year. They are often for periods of months or even days. This fact gives rise to two methods of computing simple interest which are called ordinary interest and exact interest.

Ordinary interest is calculated upon the basis of a 360-day year consisting of twelve months of thirty days each. Exact interest, as the term indicates, is based upon the actual number of days in the period, which is 365 days in a year, except in leap years when it is 366 days. As stated in words:

Ordinary Simple Interest = (Principal)(interest rate per year) $\left(\dfrac{\text{Time in days}}{360}\right)$ or it may be expressed symbolically by the formula,

$$I_{or} = \frac{Prt}{360} \tag{11-3}$$

while the statement for exact simple interest is:

Exact Simple Interest = (Principal) (Interest rate per year) $\left(\dfrac{\text{Time in days}}{365^*}\right)$ or it may be expressed symbolically by the formula,

$$I_{ex} = \frac{Prt}{365^*} \tag{11-4}$$

As an example, compute the ordinary simple interest and the exact simple interest (the year not being a leap year) on \$5,000.00 at 4% for 60 days. Substituting in Formula (11-3)

Ordinary simple interest $= \dfrac{(\$5,000.00)(.04)(60)}{360} = \$33.33.$

Substituting in Formula (11-4)

Exact simple interest $= \dfrac{(\$5,000.00)(.04)(60)}{365} = \$32.88.$

Another useful relationship is that between ordinary simple interest

* In leap years, 366 is used.

and exact simple interest. Since ordinary simple interest $= \dfrac{Prt}{360}$, while

exact simple interest $= \dfrac{Prt}{365*}$.

$$\frac{\text{Ordinary Simple Interest}}{\text{Exact Simple Interest}} = \frac{\dfrac{Prt}{360}}{\dfrac{Prt}{365*}} = \frac{365*}{360}$$

Therefore,

$$\text{Ordinary Simple Interest} = (\text{Exact Simple Interest})\,\frac{365*}{360} \quad (11\text{-}5)$$

while

$$\text{Exact Simple Interest} = (\text{Ordinary Simple Interest})\,\frac{360}{365*} \quad (11\text{-}6)$$

For example, consider the following problem;

If the ordinary simple interest on $10,000.00 for 90 days at 5% is $125.00, what is the exact simple interest?

Using formula (11-6), and assuming a non-leap year for exact simple interest,

$$\text{Exact Simple Interest} = (\text{Ordinary Simple Interest})\,\frac{360}{365} = (\$125.00)$$

$\dfrac{360}{365} = \$123.29$.

Exact simple interest is less than ordinary simple interest, as is apparent from Formulas (11-5) and (11-6).

Computing Exact Simple Interest

In the example of the computation of exact simple interest given earlier in this chapter, the number of days in the interest period was given. Frequently, however, interest computations involve dates, from which it is necessary to compute the number of days. For calculating exact simple interest the general practice is to use the exact time, excluding the first day (i.e., the day of the first date) and including the last day (i.e., the day of the last date). Thus to determine the exact time from April 12 to July 15, write:

Days left in April	$30 - 12 = 18$
Days in May	31
Days in June	30
Days in July	15
	Exact time 94 days

The computation of exact time can also be made from tables, the only complication being the need for two such tables, one for years that are not leap years, and the other for leap years.   The two such tables are Tables 5 and 6, respectively on Pages 208 and 209.

To use these tables, note that they are constructed by assigning consecutive integral numbers to the days in the year.   Thus, in Table 5, (for non-leap years) April 12 has a day-number of 102 and July 15, a day number of 196.   Therefore, the exact time from April 12 to July 15 is $196 - 102 = 94$ days, as was determined above by direct counting.   Note also that in Table 6 for leap years, April 12 has a day-number of 103 and July 15, a day-number of 197.   Therefore, the exact time is $197 - 103 = 94$ days.   Thus, the elapsed time is the same in a non-leap year and a leap year if the time period does not include February 29.

If the period extends over a year end, simply add 365 to the second day-number, being sure to use the leap-year table (Table 6) to find this second day-number if it falls after February 28 in a leap year.   For example, to find the exact time from November 15 to March 15 in a non-leap year, use Table 5, finding 319 for November 15, and 74 for March 15.   The exact time is then $74 + 365 - 319 = 120$ days.   On the other hand, if the March 15 date was in a leap year, the day-number for that date would be found in Table 6, and is 75.   Then the exact time is $75 + 365 - 319 = 121$ days.

Having determined the exact time by the direct counting method or by Tables 5 or 6, the exact simple interest may be computed by Formula (11-4) given earlier in this chapter.   That formula is

$$I_{ex} = \frac{Prt}{365*} \qquad (*366 \text{ for leap years})$$

For example, to find the exact simple interest on $6,000.00 at 5% from April 10 to August 25 in a year that is not a leap year, proceed as follows:

Look up the dates in Table 5.   The day-numbers are 100 and 237, so the exact time is 137 days.   Substituting in Formula (11-4),

$$I_{ex} = \frac{Prt}{365} = \frac{(\$6,000.00)(.05)137}{365} = \$112.60$$

Another method of computing exact simple interest is by the use of tables.   Table 7 gives the exact simple interest on $1.00 for various rates, ranging from 1% to $8\frac{1}{2}\%$, for interest periods terminating after February 28 in years that are not leap years.   In this table, amounts of exact simple interest are given for 1-10 days, in multiples of one day, and for 10 to 100 days in multiples of 10 days; and then for 200 days and 300 days.

An example of the use of this table (Pages 211-213) is the following:
Find the exact simple interest at 5% for 137 days on $6,000.00 in a

TABLE 5—FOR COMPUTING EXACT TIME (IN DAYS) BETWEEN DATES.
Use this table for years that are not leap years

Day of Month	January	February	March	April	May	June	July	August	September	October	November	December
1	1	32	60	91	121	152	182	213	244	274	305	335
2	2	33	61	92	122	153	183	214	245	275	306	336
3	3	34	62	93	123	154	184	215	246	276	307	337
4	4	35	63	94	124	155	185	216	247	277	308	338
5	5	36	64	95	125	156	186	217	248	278	309	339
6	6	37	65	96	126	157	187	218	249	279	310	340
7	7	38	66	97	127	158	188	219	250	280	311	341
8	8	39	67	98	128	159	189	220	251	281	312	342
9	9	40	68	99	129	160	190	221	252	282	313	343
10	10	41	69	100	130	161	191	222	253	283	314	344
11	11	42	70	101	131	162	192	223	254	284	315	345
12	12	43	71	102	132	163	193	224	255	285	316	346
13	13	44	72	103	133	164	194	225	256	286	317	347
14	14	45	73	104	134	165	195	226	257	287	318	348
15	15	46	74	105	135	166	196	227	258	288	319	349
16	16	47	75	106	136	167	197	228	259	289	320	350
17	17	48	76	107	137	168	198	229	260	290	321	351
18	18	49	77	108	138	169	199	230	261	291	322	352
19	19	50	78	109	139	170	200	231	262	292	323	353
20	20	51	79	110	140	171	201	232	263	293	324	354
21	21	52	80	111	141	172	202	233	264	294	325	355
22	22	53	81	112	142	173	203	234	265	295	326	356
23	23	54	82	113	143	174	204	235	266	296	327	357
24	24	55	83	114	144	175	205	236	267	297	328	358
25	25	56	84	115	145	176	206	237	268	298	329	359
26	26	57	85	116	146	177	207	238	269	299	330	360
27	27	58	86	117	147	178	208	239	270	300	331	361
28	28	59	87	118	148	179	209	240	271	301	332	362
29	29	..	88	119	149	180	210	241	272	302	333	363
30	30	..	89	120	150	181	211	242	273	303	334	364
31	31	..	90	...	151	...	212	243.	...	304	...	365

TABLE 6—FOR COMPUTING EXACT TIME (IN DAYS) BETWEEN DATES.
Use this table for leap years

Day of Month	January	February	March	April	May	June	July	August	September	October	November	December
1	1	32	61	92	122	153	183	214	245	275	306	336
2	2	33	62	93	123	154	184	215	246	276	307	337
3	3	34	63	94	124	155	185	216	247	277	308	338
4	4	35	64	95	125	156	186	217	248	278	309	339
5	5	36	65	96	126	157	187	218	249	279	310	340
6	6	37	66	97	127	158	188	219	250	280	311	341
7	7	38	67	98	128	159	189	220	251	281	312	342
8	8	39	68	99	129	160	190	221	252	282	313	343
9	9	40	69	100	130	161	191	222	253	283	314	344
10	10	41	70	101	131	162	192	223	254	284	315	345
11	11	42	71	102	132	163	193	224	255	285	316	346
12	12	43	72	103	133	164	194	225	256	286	317	347
13	13	44	73	104	134	165	195	226	257	287	318	348
14	14	45	74	105	135	166	196	227	258	288	319	349
15	15	46	75	106	136	167	197	228	259	289	320	350
16	16	47	76	107	137	168	198	229	260	290	321	351
17	17	48	77	108	138	169	199	230	261	291	322	352
18	18	49	78	109	139	170	200	231	262	292	323	353
19	19	50	79	110	140	171	201	232	263	293	324	354
20	20	51	80	111	141	172	202	233	264	294	325	355
21	21	52	81	112	142	173	203	234	265	295	326	356
22	22	53	82	113	143	174	204	235	266	296	327	357
23	23	54	83	114	144	175	205	236	267	297	328	358
24	24	55	84	115	145	176	206	237	268	298	329	359
25	25	56	85	116	146	177	207	238	269	299	330	360
26	26	57	86	117	147	178	208	239	270	300	331	361
27	27	58	87	118	148	179	209	240	271	301	332	362
28	28	59	88	119	149	180	210	241	272	302	333	363
29	29	60	89	120	150	181	211	242	273	303	334	364
30	30	. .	90	121	151	182	212	243	274	304	335	365
31	31	. .	91	. . .	152	. . .	213	244	. . .	305	. . .	366

year that is not a leap year. Turn to Table 7, and obtain the following figures:

Interest on $1.00 at 5% for 100 days = $.0136986
Interest on $1.00 at 5% for 30 days = .0041096
Interest on $1.00 at 5% for   7 days = .0009589
                                 Total $.0187671
                             Principal $6,000.00
Interest on $6,000.00 for 137 days $ 112.60

Table 8 gives the exact simple interest for various rates, ranging from 1% to $8\frac{1}{2}$%, for interest periods terminating after February 28 in leap years. In this table, amounts of exact simple interest are given for 1-10 days, in multiples of one day; for 10-100 days, in multiples of 10 days; and then for 200 and 300 days, for leap years.

An example of the use of Table 8 for exact simple interest for leap years is the following:

Find the exact simple interest at 5% for 95 days on $6,000.00 in a leap year. Turn to Table 8 (Pages 214-216), and obtain the following figures:

Interest on $1.00 at 5% for 90 days = $.0122951
Interest on $1.00 at 5% for 5 days = .0006831
                                Total $.0129782
                            Principal $6,000.00
Interest on $6,000.00 for 95 days $ 77.87

Computing Ordinary Simple Interest

Ordinary simple interest is, as stated earlier in this chapter, computed upon the basis of a year of 360 days, by the Formula (11-3), $I_{or} = Prt/360$. The time may be exact, in which case it is computed, as explained earlier in this chapter, either by counting days, or by use of Tables 5 or 6. The computation of ordinary interest for exact time is known as the banker's method. Another method of computing ordinary simple interest involves the use of approximate time, which treats each month as consisting of 30 days.

As an illustration of these two methods, consider the following problem: Compute the ordinary interest on $6,000.00 at 5% from February 10 to November 5, in a year that is not a leap year, by both exact time and approximate time.

The exact time is found from Table 5 (since the year is not a leap year), where February 10 has a day-number of 41 and November 5 a day-number of 309, so that the exact time is 268 days. Then, substituting in Formula (11-3),

$$I_{or} = \frac{Prt}{360} = \frac{(\$6,000.00)(.05)(268)}{360} = \$223.33 \text{ ordinary interest for}$$
$$\text{exact time.}$$

TABLE 7—EXACT SIMPLE INTEREST ON $1.00
(non-leap years)

Exact Simple Interest at 1%

Days	Interest	Days	Interest
1	.0000274	10	.0002740
2	.0000548	20	.0005480
3	.0000822	30	.0008220
4	.0001096	40	.0010959
5	.0001370	50	.0013699
6	.0001644	60	.0016338
7	.0001918	70	.0019178
8	.0002192	80	.0021918
9	.0002466	90	.0024658
10	.0002740	100	.0027397
		200	.0054795
		300	.0082192

Exact Simple Interest at 2-1/2%

Days	Interest	Days	Interest
1	.0000685	10	.0006849
2	.0001370	20	.0013699
3	.0002055	30	.0020548
4	.0002740	40	.0027397
5	.0003425	50	.0034247
6	.0004110	60	.0041096
7	.0004795	70	.0047945
8	.0005480	80	.0054795
9	.0006164	90	.0061644
10	.0006849	100	.0068493
		200	.0136986
		300	.0205479

Exact Simple Interest at 1-1/2%

Days	Interest	Days	Interest
1	.0000411	10	.0004110
2	.0000822	20	.0008219
3	.0001233	30	.0012329
4	.0001644	40	.0016438
5	.0002055	50	.0020548
6	.0002466	60	.0024658
7	.0002877	70	.0028767
8	.0003288	80	.0032877
9	.0003699	90	.0036986
10	.0004110	100	.0041096
		200	.0082192
		300	.0123288

Exact Simple Interest at 3%

Days	Interest	Days	Interest
1	.0000822	10	.0008219
2	.0001644	20	.0016438
3	.0002466	30	.0024658
4	.0003288	40	.0032877
5	.0004110	50	.0041096
6	.0004932	60	.0049315
7	.0005753	70	.0057534
8	.0006575	80	.0065753
9	.0007397	90	.0073973
10	.0008219	100	.0082192
		200	.0164384
		300	.0246575

Exact Simple Interest at 2%

Days	Interest	Days	Interest
1	.0000548	10	.0005480
2	.0001096	20	.0010959
3	.0001644	30	.0016438
4	.0002192	40	.0021918
5	.0002740	50	.0027397
6	.0003288	60	.0032877
7	.0003836	70	.0038356
8	.0004384	80	.0043836
9	.0004932	90	.0049315
10	.0005480	100	.0054795
		200	.0109589
		300	.0164384

Exact Simple Interest at 3-1/2%

Days	Interest	Days	Interest
1	.0000959	10	.0009589
2	.0001918	20	.0019178
3	.0002877	30	.0028767
4	.0003836	40	.0038356
5	.0004795	50	.0047945
6	.0005753	60	.0057534
7	.0006712	70	.0067123
8	.0007671	80	.0076712
9	.0008630	90	.0086301
10	.0009589	100	.0095890
		200	.0191781
		300	.0287671

TABLE 7—EXACT SIMPLE INTEREST ON $1.00 (Cont.)
(*non-leap years*)

Exact Simple Interest at 4%

Days	Interest	Days	Interest
1	.0001096	10	.0010959
2	.0002192	20	.0021918
3	.0003288	30	.0032877
4	.0004384	40	.0043836
5	.0005480	50	.0054795
6	.0006575	60	.0065753
7	.0007671	70	.0076712
8	.0008767	80	.0087671
9	.0009863	90	.0098630
10	.0010959	100	.0109589
		200	.0219178
		300	.0328767

Exact Simple Interest at 5-1/2%

Days	Interest	Days	Interest
1	.0001507	10	.0015069
2	.0003014	20	.0030137
3	.0004521	30	.0045205
4	.0006027	40	.0060274
5	.0007534	50	.0075342
6	.0009041	60	.0090411
7	.0010548	70	.0105479
8	.0012055	80	.0120548
9	.0013562	90	.0135616
10	.0015069	100	.0150685
		200	.0301370
		300	.0452055

Exact Simple Interest at 4-1/2%

Days	Interest	Days	Interest
1	.0001233	10	.0012329
2	.0002466	20	.0024658
3	.0003699	30	.0036986
4	.0004932	40	.0049315
5	.0006164	50	.0061644
6	.0007397	60	.0073973
7	.0008630	70	.0086301
8	.0009863	80	.0098630
9	.0011096	90	.0010959
10	.0012329	100	.0123288
		200	.0246575
		300	.0369863

Exact Simple Interest at 6%

Days	Interest	Days	Interest
1	.0001644	10	.0016438
2	.0003288	20	.0032876
3	.0004932	30	.0049315
4	.0006575	40	.0065753
5	.0008219	50	.0082192
6	.0009863	60	.0098630
7	.0011507	70	.0115068
8	.0013151	80	.0131507
9	.0014795	90	.0147945
10	.0016438	100	.0164384
		200	.0328767
		300	.0493151

Exact Simple Interest at 5%

Days	Interest	Days	Interest
1	.0001370	10	.0013699
2	.0002739	20	.0027397
3	.0004110	30	.0041096
4	.0005480	40	.0054795
5	.0006849	50	.0068493
6	.0008219	60	.0082192
7	.0009589	70	.0095890
8	.0010959	80	.0109589
9	.0012329	90	.0123288
10	.0013699	100	.0136986
		200	.0273973
		300	.0410959

Exact Simple Interest at 6-1/2%

Days	Interest	Days	Interest
1	.0001781	10	.0017808
2	.0003562	20	.0035616
3	.0005343	30	.0053425
4	.0007123	40	.0071233
5	.0008904	50	.0089041
6	.0010685	60	.0106849
7	.0012466	70	.0124658
8	.0014247	80	.0142466
9	.0016027	90	.0160274
10	.0017808	100	.0178082
		200	.0356164
		300	.0534246

TABLE 7—EXACT SIMPLE INTEREST ON $1.00 (Cont.)
(*non-leap years*)

Exact Simple Interest at 7%

Days	Interest	Days	Interest
1	.0001918	10	.0019178
2	.0003836	20	.0038356
3	.0005753	30	.0057534
4	.0007671	40	.0076712
5	.0009589	50	.0095890
6	.0011507	60	.0115068
7	.0013435	70	.0134247
8	.0015343	80	.0153425
9	.0017260	90	.0172603
10	.0019178	100	.0191781
		200	.0383562
		300	.0575343

Exact Simple Interest at 8%

Days	Interest	Days	Interest
1	.0002192	10	.0021918
2	.0004384	20	.0043836
3	.0006575	30	.0065753
4	.0008767	40	.0087671
5	.0010969	50	.0109590
6	.0013151	60	.0131507
7	.0015343	70	.0153425
8	.0017534	80	.0175342
9	.0019726	90	.0197260
10	.0021918	100	.0219178
		200	.0438356
		300	.0657534

Exact Simple Interest at 7-1/2%

Days	Interest	Days	Interest
1	.0002055	10	.0020548
2	.0004110	20	.0041096
3	.0006164	30	.0061644
4	.0008219	40	.0082192
5	.0010274	50	.0102740
6	.0012329	60	.0123288
7	.0014384	70	.0143836
8	.0016438	80	.0164384
9	.0018493	90	.0184932
10	.0020548	100	.0205479
		200	.0410959
		300	.0616438

Exact Simple Interest at 8-1/2%

Days	Interest	Days	Interest
1	.0002329	10	.0023288
2	.0004658	20	.0046575
3	.0006986	30	.0069863
4	.0009315	40	.0093151
5	.0011644	50	.0116438
6	.0013973	60	.0139726
7	.0016301	70	.0163014
8	.0018630	80	.0186301
9	.0020959	90	.0209589
10	.0023288	100	.0232877
		200	.0465753
		300	.0698630

TABLE 8—EXACT SIMPLE INTEREST ON $1.00
(leap years)

Exact Simple Interest at 1%

Days	Interest	Days	Interest
1	.0000273	10	.0002732
2	.0000546	20	.0005464
3	.0000820	30	.0008197
4	.0001093	40	.0010929
5	.0001366	50	.0013661
6	.0001639	60	.0016393
7	.0001913	70	.0019126
8	.0002186	80	.0021858
9	.0002459	90	.0024590
10	.0002732	100	.0027322
		200	.0054645
		300	.0081967

Exact Simple Interest at 2-1/2%

Days	Interest	Days	Interest
1	.0000683	10	.0006831
2	.0001366	20	.0013661
3	.0002049	30	.0020492
4	.0002732	40	.0027322
5	.0003415	50	.0034153
6	.0004098	60	.0040984
7	.0004781	70	.0047814
8	.0005465	80	.0054645
9	.0006148	90	.0061475
10	.0006831	100	.0068306
		200	.0136612
		300	.0204918

Exact Simple Interest at 1-1/2%

Days	Interest	Days	Interest
1	.0000410	10	.0004098
2	.0000820	20	.0008197
3	.0001230	30	.0012295
4	.0001639	40	.0016393
5	.0002049	50	.0020492
6	.0002459	60	.0024590
7	.0002869	70	.0028689
8	.0003279	80	.0032787
9	.0003689	90	.0036885
10	.0004098	100	.0040984
		200	.0081967
		300	.0122951

Exact Simple Interest at 3%

Days	Interest	Days	Interest
1	.0000820	10	.0008197
2	.0001639	20	.0016393
3	.0002459	30	.0024590
4	.0003279	40	.0032787
5	.0004098	50	.0040984
6	.0004918	60	.0049180
7	.0005738	70	.0057377
8	.0006557	80	.0065574
9	.0007377	90	.0073770
10	.0008197	100	.0081967
		200	.0163934
		300	.0245902

Exact Simple Interest at 2%

Days	Interest	Days	Interest
1	.0000547	10	.0005465
2	.0001093	20	.0010929
3	.0001639	30	.0016393
4	.0002186	40	.0021858
5	.0002732	50	.0027322
6	.0003278	60	.0032787
7	.0003825	70	.0038251
8	.0004372	80	.0043716
9	.0004918	90	.0049180
10	.0005465	100	.0054645
		200	.0109290
		300	.0163934

Exact Simple Interest at 3-1/2%

Days	Interest	Days	Interest
1	.0000956	10	.0009563
2	.0001913	20	.0019126
3	.0002869	30	.0028689
4	.0003825	40	.0038251
5	.0004781	50	.0047814
6	.0005738	60	.0057377
7	.0006694	70	.0066940
8	.0007650	80	.0076503
9	.0008607	90	.0086066
10	.0009563	100	.0095628
		200	.0191257
		300	.0286885

TABLE 8—EXACT SIMPLE INTEREST ON $1.00 (Cont.)
(*leap years*)

Exact Simple Interest at 4%

Days	Interest	Days	Interest
1	.0001093	10	.0010929
2	.0002186	20	.0021858
3	.0003279	30	.0032787
4	.0004372	40	.0043716
5	.0005465	50	.0054645
6	.0006557	60	.0065574
7	.0007650	70	.0076503
8	.0008743	80	.0087432
9	.0009836	90	.0098361
10	.0010929	100	.0109290
		200	.0218579
		300	.0327869

Exact Simple Interest at 5-1/2%

Days	Interest	Days	Interest
1	.0001503	10	.0015027
2	.0003006	20	.0030055
3	.0004508	30	.0045082
4	.0006011	40	.0060109
5	.0007514	50	.0075137
6	.0009016	60	.0090164
7	.0010519	70	.0105191
8	.0012022	80	.0120219
9	.0013525	90	.0135246
10	.0015027	100	.0150273
		200	.0300546
		300	.0450819

Exact Simple Interest at 4-1/2%

Days	Interest	Days	Interest
1	.0001230	10	.0012295
2	.0002459	20	.0024590
3	.0003689	30	.0036885
4	.0004918	40	.0049180
5	.0006148	50	.0061475
6	.0007377	60	.0073770
7	.0008607	70	.0086066
8	.0009836	80	.0098361
9	.0011066	90	.0110656
10	.0012295	100	.0122951
		200	.0245902
		300	.0368852

Exact Simple Interest at 6%

Days	Interest	Days	Interest
1	.0001639	10	.0016393
2	.0003279	20	.0032787
3	.0004918	30	.0049180
4	.0006557	40	.0065574
5	.0008197	50	.0081967
6	.0009836	60	.0098361
7	.0011475	70	.0114754
8	.0013115	80	.0311147
9	.0014754	90	.0147541
10	.0016393	100	.0163934
		200	.0327869
		300	.0491803

Exact Simple Interest at 5%

Days	Interest	Days	Interest
1	.0001366	10	.0013661
2	.0002732	20	.0027322
3	.0004098	30	.0040984
4	.0005465	40	.0054645
5	.0006831	50	.0068306
6	.0008197	60	.0081967
7	.0009563	70	.0095628
8	.0010929	80	.0109290
9	.0012295	90	.0122951
10	.0013661	100	.0136612
		200	.0273224
		300	.0409836

Exact Simple Interest at 6-1/2%

Days	Interest	Days	Interest
1	.0001776	10	.0017760
2	.0003552	20	.0035519
3	.0005328	30	.0053279
4	.0007104	40	.0071038
5	.0008880	50	.0088798
6	.0010656	60	.0106557
7	.0012432	70	.0124317
8	.0014208	80	.0142076
9	.0015984	90	.0159836
10	.0017760	100	.0177596
		200	.0355191
		300	.0532787

TABLE 8—EXACT SIMPLE INTEREST ON $1.00 (Cont.)
(*leap years*)

Exact Simple Interest at 7%

Days	Interest	Days	Interest
1	.0001913	10	.0019126
2	.0003825	20	.0038251
3	.0005738	30	.0057377
4	.0007650	40	.0076503
5	.0009563	50	.0095629
6	.0011475	60	.0114754
7	.0013388	70	.0133880
8	.0015301	80	.0153005
9	.0017213	90	.0172131
10	.0019126	100	.0191257
		200	.0382514
		300	.0573771

Exact Simple Interest at 8%

Days	Interest	Days	Interest
1	.0002186	10	.0021858
2	.0004372	20	.0043716
3	.0006557	30	.0065574
4	.0008743	40	.0087432
5	.0010929	50	.0109290
6	.0013115	60	.0131148
7	.0015301	70	.0153005
8	.0017486	80	.0174863
9	.0019672	90	.0196721
10	.0021858	100	.0218579
		200	.0437158
		300	.0655738

Exact Simple Interest at 7-1/2%

Days	Interest	Days	Interest
1	.0002049	10	.0020492
2	.0004098	20	.0040984
3	.0006148	30	.0061475
4	.0008197	40	.0081967
5	.0010246	50	.0102459
6	.0012295	60	.0122951
7	.0014344	70	.0143442
8	.0016393	80	.0163934
9	.0018443	90	.0184426
10	.0020492	100	.0204918
		200	.0409836
		300	.0614754

Exact Simple Interest at 8-1/2%

Days	Interest	Days	Interest
1	.0002322	10	.0023224
2	.0004645	20	.0046448
3	.0006967	30	.0069672
4	.0009290	40	.0092896
5	.0011612	50	.0116120
6	.0013934	60	.0139344
7	.0016257	70	.0162568
8	.0018579	80	.0185792
9	.0020902	90	.0209016
10	.0023224	100	.0232240
		200	.0464481
		300	.0696721

The approximate time is found as follows:

	Month	Day
November 5 is	11	5
February 10 is	2	10
	8	25

This subtraction is done by carrying 30 days from the months column, leaving 10 months, and then subtracting in both columns, obtaining 8 months 25 days, or 265 days. Then, substituting in the formula:

$$I_{or} = \frac{Prt}{360} = \frac{(\$6,000.00)(.05)(265)}{360} = \$220.83 \text{ ordinary interest for approximate time.}$$

Another method of computing ordinary simple interest is by the use of tables. Table 9 gives the ordinary simple interest on $1.00 at various rates ranging from 1% to $8\frac{1}{2}$%. In this table amounts of interest are given for 1-10 days, in multiples of one day; and for 10 to 100 days, in multiples of 10 days, and for 200 days and 300 days. For example, to compute the ordinary interest on $6,000.00 at 5% for 265 days, turn to Table 9 (Pages 218-220), and obtain the following figures:

Interest on $1.00 at 5% for 200 days.........	$.0277778
Interest on $1.00 at 5% for 60 days.........	.0083333
Interest on $1.00 at 5% for 5 days.........	.0006944
Total...............................	$.0368055
Principal............................	$6,000.00
Interest on $6,000.00 for 265 days..........	$ 220.83

Present Value

Up to this point, the calculations in this chapter have been interest calculations—that is, the principal, interest rate and time have been known, and the interest has been calculated. However, some business problems require the calculation of another of these quantities, which can be found by simple algebraic manipulation of the basic interest formulas.

To find the principal which, at a given rate of interest for a given fractional period, will produce a given sum, the following derivation is used (Note that in this usage, the principal is called the present value):

$$I = \frac{Prt}{T}, \text{ (where } I \text{ is interest, } P \text{ is principal, } r \text{ is periodic rate, } t \text{ is time,}$$

and T is the time per rate period).

Then the total sum (principal plus interest) after time t is:

$$S = P + I = P + \frac{Prt}{T} = P\left(1 + \frac{rt}{T}\right) \tag{11-7}$$

so that the (principal) present value is, by transposition of Formula (11-7)

TABLE 9—ORDINARY SIMPLE INTEREST ON $1.00

Ordinary Simple Interest at 1%

Days	Interest	Days	Interest
1	.0000278	10	.0002778
2	.0000556	20	.0005556
3	.0000833	30	.0008333
4	.0001111	40	.0011111
5	.0001389	50	.0013889
6	.0001667	60	.0016667
7	.0001944	70	.0019444
8	.0002222	80	.0022222
9	.0002500	90	.0025000
10	.0002778	100	.0027778
		200	.0055556
		300	.0083333

Ordinary Simple Interest at 2-1/2%

Days	Interest	Days	Interest
1	.0000694	10	.0006944
2	.0001389	20	.0013889
3	.0002083	30	.0020833
4	.0002778	40	.0027778
5	.0003472	50	.0034722
6	.0004167	60	.0041667
7	.0004861	70	.0048611
8	.0005556	80	.0055556
9	.0006250	90	.0062500
10	.0006944	100	.0069444
		200	.0138889
		300	.0208333

Ordinary Simple Interest at 1-1/2%

Days	Interest	Days	Interest
1	.0000417	10	.0004167
2	.0000833	20	.0008333
3	.0001250	30	.0012500
4	.0001667	40	.0016667
5	.0002083	50	.0020833
6	.0002500	60	.0025000
7	.0002917	70	.0029167
8	.0003333	80	.0033333
9	.0003750	90	.0037500
10	.0004167	100	.0041667
		200	.0083333
		300	.0125000

Ordinary Simple Interest at 3%

Days	Interest	Days	Interest
1	.0000833	10	.0008333
2	.0001667	20	.0016667
3	.0002500	30	.0025000
4	.0003333	40	.0033333
5	.0004167	50	.0041667
6	.0005000	60	.0050000
7	.0005833	70	.0058333
8	.0006667	80	.0066667
9	.0007500	90	.0075000
10	.0008333	100	.0083333
		200	.0166667
		300	.0250000

Ordinary Simple Interest at 2%

Days	Interest	Days	Interest
1	.0000556	10	.0005556
2	.0001111	20	.0011111
3	.0001667	30	.0016667
4	.0002222	40	.0022222
5	.0002778	50	.0027778
6	.0003333	60	.0033333
7	.0003889	70	.0038889
8	.0004444	80	.0044444
9	.0005000	90	.0050000
10	.0005556	100	.0055556
		200	.0111111
		300	.0166667

Ordinary Simple Interest at 3-1/2%

Days	Interest	Days	Interest
1	.0000972	10	.0009722
2	.0001944	20	.0019444
3	.0002917	30	.0029167
4	.0003889	40	.0038889
5	.0004861	50	.0048611
6	.0005833	60	.0058333
7	.0006806	70	.0068056
8	.0007778	80	.0077778
9	.0008750	90	.0087500
10	.0009722	100	.0097222
		200	.0194444
		300	.0291667

TABLE 9—ORDINARY SIMPLE INTEREST ON $1.00 (Cont.)

Ordinary Simple Interest at 4%

Days	Interest	Days	Interest
1	.0001111	10	.0011111
2	.0002222	20	.0022222
3	.0003333	30	.0033333
4	.0004444	40	.0044444
5	.0005556	50	.0055556
6	.0006667	60	.0066667
7	.0007778	70	.0077778
8	.0008889	80	.0088889
9	.0010000	90	.0100000
10	.0011111	100	.0111111
		200	.0222222
		300	.0333333

Ordinary Simple Interest at 5-1/2%

Days	Interest	Days	Interest
1	.0001528	10	.0015278
2	.0003056	20	.0030556
3	.0004583	30	.0045833
4	.0006111	40	.0061111
5	.0007639	50	.0076389
6	.0009167	60	.0091667
7	.0010694	70	.0106944
8	.0012222	80	.0122222
9	.0013750	90	.0137500
10	.0015278	100	.0152778
		200	.0305556
		300	.0458333

Ordinary Simple Interest at 4-1/2%

Days	Interest	Days	Interest
1	.0001250	10	.0012500
2	.0002500	20	.0025000
3	.0003750	30	.0037500
4	.0005000	40	.0050000
5	.0006250	50	.0062500
6	.0007500	60	.0075000
7	.0008750	70	.0087500
8	.0010000	80	.0100000
9	.0011250	90	.0112500
10	.0012500	100	.0125000
		200	.0250000
		300	.0375000

Ordinary Simple Interest at 6%

Days	Interest	Days	Interest
1	.0001667	10	.0016667
2	.0003333	20	.0033333
3	.0005000	30	.0050000
4	.0006667	40	.0066667
5	.0008333	50	.0083333
6	.0010000	60	.0100000
7	.0011667	70	.0116667
8	.0013333	80	.0133333
9	.0015000	90	.0150000
10	.0016667	100	.0166667
		200	.0333333
		300	.0500000

Ordinary Simple Interest at 5%

Days	Interest	Days	Interest
1	.0001389	10	.0013889
2	.0002778	20	.0027778
3	.0004167	30	.0041667
4	.0005556	40	.0055556
5	.0006944	50	.0069444
6	.0008333	60	.0083333
7	.0009722	70	.0097222
8	.0011111	80	.0111111
9	.0012500	90	.0125000
10	.0013889	100	.0138889
		200	.0277778
		300	.0416667

Ordinary Simple Interest at 6-1/2%

Days	Interest	Days	Interest
1	.0001806	10	.0018056
2	.0003611	20	.0036111
3	.0005417	30	.0054167
4	.0007222	40	.0072222
5	.0009028	50	.0090278
6	.0010833	60	.0108333
7	.0012639	70	.0126389
8	.0014444	80	.0144444
9	.0016250	90	.0162500
10	.0018056	100	.0180556
		200	.0361111
		300	.0541667

TABLE 9—ORDINARY SIMPLE INTEREST ON $1.00 (Cont.)

Ordinary Simple Interest at 7%

Days	Interest	Days	Interest
1	.0001944	10	.0019444
2	.0003889	20	.0038889
3	.0005832	30	.0058333
4	.0007778	40	.0077778
5	.0009722	50	.0097222
6	.0011667	60	.0116667
7	.0013611	70	.0136111
8	.0015556	80	.0155556
9	.0017500	90	.0175000
10	.0019444	100	.0194444
		200	.0388889
		300	.0583333

Ordinary Simple Interest at 8%

Days	Interest	Days	Interest
1	.0002222	10	.0022222
2	.0004444	20	.0044444
3	.0006667	30	.0066667
4	.0008889	40	.0088889
5	.0011111	50	.0111111
6	.0013333	60	.0133333
7	.0015556	70	.0155556
8	.0017778	80	.0177778
9	.0020000	90	.0200000
10	.0022222	100	.0222222
		200	.0444444
		300	.0666667

Ordinary Simple Interest at 7-1/2%

Days	Interest	Days	Interest
1	.0002083	10	.0020833
2	.0004167	20	.0041667
3	.0006250	30	.0062500
4	.0008333	40	.0083333
5	.0010417	50	.0104167
6	.0012500	60	.0125000
7	.0014583	70	.0145833
8	.0016667	80	.0166667
9	.0018750	90	.0187500
10	.0020833	100	.0208333
		200	.0416667
		300	.0625000

Ordinary Simple Interest at 8-1/2%

Days	Interest	Days	Interest
1	.0002361	10	.0023611
2	.0004722	20	.0047222
3	.0007083	30	.0070833
4	.0009444	40	.0094444
5	.0011806	50	.0118056
6	.0014167	60	.0141667
7	.0016528	70	.0165278
8	.0018889	80	.0188889
9	.0021250	90	.0212500
10	.0023611	100	.0236111
		200	.0472222
		300	.0708333

$$P = \frac{S}{1 + \dfrac{rt}{T}} \tag{11-8}$$

As an example of the use of Formula (11-8), consider the following problem: What principal must be invested at 5% simple interest to produce $3,000.00 in 90 days, in other words, what is the present value of $3,000.00 to be paid in 90 days at 5% interest?

To substitute in Formula (11-8), S is $3,000.00, r is .05, t is 90 and T is 360, since in calculations of present value at simple interest ordinary simple interest is generally used.

Then, $P = \dfrac{\$3,000.00}{1 + \dfrac{(.05)(90)}{360}}$

Therefore $P = \dfrac{\$3,000.00}{1.0125} = \$2,962.63$, present value.

It is also possible to find the value of $\dfrac{rt}{T}$ by the use of tables, since this figure is equal to the interest on $1.00 for the given rate and time.

For example, to find the present value of $3,000.00 to be paid in 127 days with simple interest at 5%. Turn to Table 9, and obtain the following figures,

Interest on $1.00 at 5% for 100 days........... $.0138889
Interest on $1.00 at 5% for 20 days........... .0027778
Interest on $1.00 at 5% for   7 days........... .0009722
Interest on $1.00 at 5% for 127 days........... $.0176389

Substituting this value for $\dfrac{rt}{T}$, in Formula (11-8), $P = \dfrac{\$3,000.00}{1 + .0176389}$

Thus $P = \dfrac{3,000.00}{1.0176389} = \$2,948.00$, the present value.

A somewhat more complicated problem in present value arises when two interest rates are involved. As an illustration, consider the problem: What is the present value at exact time, on April 1 in a non-leap year, of $3,000.00 borrowed on March 1 and payable with 6% interest on November 1, if the interest rate is recalculated to a call money rate of 3%?

The method of solving this type of problem is to compute the total sum of principal plus 6% interest from March 1 to November 1, and then compute the principal which would yield this total sum if placed at 3% interest from April 1 to November 1.

Since exact time is used, find from Table 5 (for exact time in non-leap year)

Exact time from March 1 to November 1, 305 − 60 = 245 days

Exact time from April 1 to November 1, 305 − 91 = 214 days.

Then to find the total sum due on November 1, use Table 9. Where r is .06 and t is 245 days, the interest on $1.00 for 245 days at 6% is

Interest on $1.00 at 6% for 200 days............	$.0333333
Interest on $1.00 at 6% for 40 days............	.0066667
Interest on $1.00 at 6% for 5 days............	.0008333
Interest on $1.00 at 6% for 245 days............	$.0408333

Then by Formula (11-7), $S = P\left(1 + \dfrac{rt}{T}\right)$

Substituting S = $3,000.00 (1.0408333) = $3,122.50.

Then to find present value of $3,122.50 payable November 1, on April 1 at 3%, a period computed above to be 214 days, from Table 9, the interest on $1.00 for 214 days at 3% is

Interest on $1.00 at 3% for 200 days............	$.0166667
Interest on $1.00 at 3% for 10 days............	.0008333
Interest on $1.00 at 3% for 4 days............	.0003333
Interest on $1.00 at 3% for 214 days............	$.0178333

Then by Formula (11-8), $P = \dfrac{S}{1 + \dfrac{rt}{T}}$

Substituting values of S, $3,122.50; $\dfrac{rt}{T}$, $.0178333

$$P = \frac{\$3,122.50}{1 + .0178333}$$

$$P = \frac{\$3,122.50}{1.0178333} = \$3,067.79, \text{ the present value on April 1.}$$

In concluding the discussion of present value at simple interest, it is to be noted that for longer periods, the present value, just as the total sum yielded by a principal, is computed at compound interest, which is treated in Chapter 13. The determination of whether simple or compound interest applies is usually stated or is obvious from the circumstances. Occasionally, however, confusion may be possible, and in such cases, the question of whether simple or compound interest applies should be settled by agreement.

Chapter 12

BANK DISCOUNT

Commercial paper is a general name for a number of types of evidence of indebtedness which include promissory notes, drafts and trade acceptances. They invariably carry a date of issuance, and also a date of maturity or due date (except in the case of sight drafts, which are due on presentation.)

Discount is a charge made for payment before due date. This charge is deducted from the maturity value to determine the proceeds, which is the amount paid on the date of discount. Bank discount is this charge calculated at simple interest on the maturity value for the time from date of discount to date of maturity.

For example, for a trade acceptance without interest for $5,000.00 (maturity value) due in 3 months, the proceeds if discounted at 5% are

$$\$5,000.00 - (\$5,000.00)(.05)(\tfrac{3}{12}) =$$
$$\$5,000.00 - \$62.50 = \$4,937.50$$

This example illustrates the fundamental difference between conventional interest, such as that on a savings account, which is computed (and credited) at the end of the interest period on the principal at the beginning of the period (provided it is not reduced during the period), and bank discount, which is computed (and deducted) at the beginning of the discount period from the amount due at the end of the period.

Note also that in the above example the statement of the problem contained the words "without interest." This condition is by no means always applicable to commercial paper, which frequently stipulates a rate of interest, especially for promissory notes. Therefore, discount calculations are conveniently discussed separately for non-interest-bearing and interest-bearing commercial paper.

Non-Interest-Bearing Commercial Paper

In the above example, the proceeds of a commercial obligation (a trade acceptance) were computed by subtracting the discount from the value at maturity; the discount being found by multiplying the maturity value by the discount rate, and then by time factor, which is the number of days or months in the discount period divided by the number of days or months in the discount rate period.

Expressed symbolically, the discount on a non-interest-bearing note is

$$D = Mr\frac{t}{T},\qquad(12\text{-}1)$$

and the proceeds are $P = M - D = M - Mr\dfrac{t}{T} = M\left(1 - r\dfrac{t}{T}\right)$ (12-2)

where D is the discount, M is the maturity value, r is the discount rate, and $\dfrac{t}{T}$ is the time factor, in which t is the number of months or days in the discount period, and T is the corresponding number of months or days in the rate period, which is one year unless otherwise stated.

To apply formulas (12-1) and (12-2) find the discount and proceeds of the following note, if it is discounted on the date of making (March 1).

| $3000.00 | New York, March 1, 19— |

Sixty days after date I promise to pay to the order of

Roberts Motors, Inc.

Three thousand $\frac{00}{100}$ .... Dollars

Value received   Harvey Jones

Then to substitute in Formula (12-1) $D = Mr\dfrac{t}{T}$; M, the maturity value, is $3,000.00; r is $6\% = .06$; t is the discount period $= 60$ days; T is the rate period, 1 year.

Then $D = (\$3{,}000.00)(.06)(\frac{60}{360})$

or $D = \$30.00.$

And by Formula (12-2), $P = M - D$

or $P = \$3{,}000.00 - \$30.00 = \$2{,}970.00.$

Bank discount can also be computed by tables. For this purpose, use Table 9, Ordinary Simple Interest on $1.00, which is given in Chapter 11. Comparison of Formula (12-2) above with the Formula (11-3) in Chapter 11 for ordinary simple interest, shows that they contain the same factors, $rt/360$. The difference between ordinary simple interest and discount is that in the former the principal is multiplied by rt/T to obtain the interest, while in the latter the maturity value is multiplied by rt/T to obtain the discount.

Therefore, Table 9 in Chapter 11 can be used to obtain the bank discount on $1.00 at a given rate for a given number of days. Thus, for the promissory note discussed above, reference to that table gives the interest on $1.00 at 6% for 60 days as $.01. Therefore, since the formula is the same, the discount on $1.00 for the same rate and period is also $.01, and the discount on $3,000.00 is therefore ($3,000.00)(.01) = $30.00.

Accordingly, the tabular method of making bank discount calculations is to use Table 9 to compute the discount on $1.00, and then to multiply the figure obtained by the maturity value.

As an example of this tabular method, find the bank discount at 5% on a promissory note having a maturity value of $2,680.00 for a discount period of 115 days, by proceeding as follows:

Refer to Table 9, to find the ordinary simple interest of $1.00 at 5% for the period. The values in this table are:

$$\begin{array}{ll}\text{Interest on \$1.00 at 5\% for 100 days} & \text{\$.0138889} \\ \text{Interest on \$1.00 at 5\% for } 10 \text{ days} & .0013889 \\ \underline{\text{Interest on \$1.00 at 5\% for } 5 \text{ days}} & \underline{.0006444} \\ \text{Interest on \$1.00 at 5\% for 115 days} & \text{\$.0159222} \end{array}$$

Therefore, discount on a maturity value of $2,680.00 at 5% for 115 days

$= (.0159222)(\$2,680.00) = \$42.67.$

Then by Formula (12-2), $P = M - D$, or

Proceeds = Maturity Value − Discount = $2,680.00 − $42.67

= $2,637.33.

Frequently, the number of days in the discount period is not stated explicitly. This situation arises when a date of payment is stipulated in the commercial paper. Consider, for example, the following trade acceptance:

New York, May 1, 1957

To Jones and Co. of 1120 Spruce St., Chicago, Ill. _____

    on October 10, 1957, pay to the order of

            Smith and Co. of 1275 Elm St., Chicago, Ill. _____

Three thousand $\tfrac{00}{100}$.. Dollars

    This obligation arises by purchase of merchandise from the drawer. The drawer may accept this bill payable at any bank or trust company that he may designate.

Accepted at   _____
Date of Acceptance _____
Payable at   _____   Signed _____
Signature of Buyer _____
For the Bank   _____

If this trade acceptance were discounted on May 1, 1957, the term of discount would be the exact time from May 1 to October 10 as defined in Chapter 11. It can be calculated, therefore, by the method given there, or by the use of Table 5 in Chapter 11. Since in that table May 1 has a day-number of 121, and October 10, a day-number of 283, the discount period is therefore $283 - 121 = 162$ days. Then, to compute the discount on this trade acceptance at 6% by Table 9 as before, find the following values from that Table:

Interest on \$1.00 at 6% for 100 days........ \$.0166667
Interest on \$1.00 at 6% for 60 days........ .0100000
Interest on \$1.00 at 6% for   2 days........ .0003333
Interest on \$1.00 at 6% for 162 days........ \$.0270000

Therefore, discount on maturity value of \$3,000.00 at 6% for 162 days

$$= (\$3,000.00)(.027) = \$81.00$$

And by Formula (12-2), $P = M - D$, therefore,

Proceeds = \$3,000.00 - \$81.00 = \$2,919.00.

Another type of situation in which the number of days in the discount period must be computed is when the paper is not discounted on its date of issuance. That is, a promissory note dated January 15, 1959, due in six months, may be discounted at any time during that interval (which is called its term). Therefore, the term of discount may be different from the term of the paper.

Consider a promissory note made by Jones & Co. in favor of Brown and Co. in the maturity value of \$3,000.00, dated March 31, 1952, and due in six months. If it is discounted at 5% on May 15, 1952, what are the discount and proceeds?

The first step is to determine the due date. The standard practice in the case of a paper whose term is stated in months is to take as its due date the same day of the month as that of the date of issuance. Thus, a note dated January 5, with a stated term of six months, is due July 5; a note dated March 20, with a stated term of three months, is due June 20. A complication that often arises is in cases where there is no day in the due month corresponding to the day of issuance. Thus, the note in the above example is dated March 31, 1952, and the sixth month following is September which has only 30 days. In such cases, the due date is taken as the last day in the month due, which in this example would be September 30, 1952.

It should also be noted that if the due date falls on a non-business day, the note is due on the next following business day.

To proceed with the above example, the due date has been determined to be September 30, 1952. The maturity value was given as $3,000.00, and the date of discount as May 15, 1952.

Then from Table 6, Chapter 11, the day-number of May 15, 1952 is 136, and the day-number of September 30 is 274, so that the discount period is 274 − 136 = 138 days. Then using Table 9, Chapter 11,

Interest on $1.00 at 5% for 100 days....... $.0138889
Interest on $1.00 at 5% for 30 days........ .0041667
Interest on $1.00 at 5% for   8 days........ .0011111
Interest on $1.00 at 5% for 138 days....... $.0191667

Therefore, discount on maturity value of $3,000.00 at 6% for 138 days
= ($3,000.00)(.0191667) = $57.50
And by Formula (12-2), $P = M - D$ = $3,000.00 − $57.50 = $2,942.50

Exchange

One other deduction that may be made in discounting a note is *exchange*, which is a collection charge on out-of-town notes. It is usually relatively small, on the order of $\frac{1}{8}$ to $\frac{1}{4}$% of the maturity value, or $1.00 to $2.00 flat. It is subtracted from the maturity value, just as is the discount, in order to arrive at the proceeds.

Interest-Bearing Commercial Paper

In the foregoing section on non-interest-bearing commercial paper, the maturity value was the same as the face value, that is, the same as the value shown on the face of the paper. However, if a note or other commercial paper stipulates that it bears interest, then the amount of that interest must be added to the face value to obtain the maturity value, before computing the discount.

An example of an interest-bearing note is the following:

$5000.00	New York, March 1, 1951
Ninety days after date I promise to pay to the order of	
Brown and Co.	
Five thousand $\frac{00}{100}$.. Dollars	
at 5% interest from date	
Value received	Jones and Co.
	per Robert Waters, Treasurer

What is the maturity value of this note, and what are its proceeds if discounted April 1 at 6%?

First determine the due date, which is March 1 + 90 days. Using Table 5, Chapter 11, the day-number of March 1 is 60; 60 + 90 = 150, which is found from that Table to be the day-number of May 30, which is thus the due date. Now from Table 5, the day-number of April 1, the date of discount, is 91. The discount period is therefore 150 − 91 = 59 days.

Now, the formula for computing the maturity value of an interest bearing note from its face value is the same as Formula (11-3) Chapter 11 (since it also effects the addition of simple interest). The difference is only in the replacement of the principal by the face value, and of the total sum by the maturity value. This formula is, therefore,

$$M = F + Fr_1\frac{t_1}{T_1} = F\left(1 + r_1\frac{t_1}{T_1}\right) \tag{12-3}$$

where M is maturity value, F is face value, r_1 is the interest rate specified in the note, t_1, is the term of the note, and T_1, is the interest rate period, expressed in the same units as t_1. (T_1 is 12 or 360, depending on whether t_1 is known in months or days.)

Substituting the values from the problem stated above in Formula (12-3).

$$M = (\$5,000.00)[1 + (.05)(\tfrac{90}{360})]$$
$$= (\$5,000.00)(1 + .0125) = \$5,062.50.$$

Then to find by formula the proceeds of this note from its maturity value, use Formula (12-2),

$$P = M - D = M\left(1 - r\frac{t}{T}\right),$$

and in this problem M has just been found to be \$5,062.50, r was stated to be 6% = .06, t was found to be 59 days, and T is 360 days.

Substituting,

$$\text{Proceeds} = (\$5,062.50)(1 - .06 \times \tfrac{59}{360})$$
$$= (\$5,062.50)(.990167) = \$5,012.72$$

To derive a single formula for computing the proceeds of an interest-bearing note, substitute Formula (12-3) in Formula (12-2), obtaining

$$P = M\left(1 - r\frac{t}{T}\right) = F\left(1 + r_1\frac{t_1}{T_1}\right)\left(1 - r\frac{t}{T}\right) \tag{12-4}$$

where P is the proceeds, F is the face value, r_1 is the interest rate specified in the note, t_1 is the term of the note, T_1 is 12 or 360, depending on whether t_1 is stated in months or days, r is the discount rate, t is the discount period, and T is 12 or 360, depending on whether t is stated in months or days.

Thus, to solve the foregoing problem by this formula, the substitution becomes

$$P_r = (\$5,000.00)[1 + (.05)(\tfrac{90}{360})][1 - (.06)(\tfrac{59}{360})]$$
$$= (\$5,000.00)[1.0125][.990167] = \$5,012.72$$

To illustrate the computation of the proceeds of interest-bearing paper, by the use of tables, consider the following promissory note:

$4620.00   New York, April 10, 1950

On September 20, I promise to pay to the order of

Robertson and Green
_____

Four Thousand Six Hundred Twenty and $\tfrac{00}{100}$.................. Dollars

at 5% interest from date.

Value received   Charles Paulson

---

which is discounted at 6% on May 17.   What are the proceeds?

In Table 5, April 10 has a day-number of 100; May 17, a day-number of 137, and September 20, a day-number of 263.

Therefore, the term of the note = 263 − 100 = 163 days
And the discount period = 263 − 137 = 126 days
Then from Table 9, Chapter 11,

Interest on $1.00 at 5% for 100 days........................... $.0138889
Interest on $1.00 at 5% for   60 days........................... .0083333
Interest on $1.00 at 5% for   3 days........................... .0004167
Interest on $1.00 at 5% for 163 days........................... $.0226389
Interest = (Face Value) × (.0226389) = ($4,620.00)(.0226389) = $104.59
Maturity Value = Face Value + Interest = $4,620.00 + $104.59 = $4,724.59

Then, again from Table 9, Chapter 11,

Interest on $1.00 at 6% for 100 days....................... $.0166667
Interest on $1.00 at 6% for   20 days....................... .0033333
Interest on $1.00 at 6% for   6 days....................... .0010000
Interest on $1.00 at 6% for 126 days....................... $.0210000
Discount = (Maturity Value)(.021) = ($4,724.59)(.021) = $99.22
Proceeds = Maturity Value − Discount = $4,724.59 − 99.22 = $4,625.37

Calculation of Face Value

The discount calculations up to this point have been concerned with finding the proceeds of commercial paper for which the maturity value or face value is known.   Often, however, the information known is the proceeds, and it is required to find the face value of a note or other commercial paper that will yield those proceeds on discount. Business situations from which such calculations arise are, for example, (1) the payment of an outstanding obligation by a note; (2), the borrowing of a sum on a discount basis to pay an outstanding obligation. In such cases, it is desirable to have a formula giving M in terms of P. Such a formula is derived readily from Formula (12-2), by the transposition,

Since by Formula 12-2,

$$P = M \left(1 - r\frac{t}{T} \right)$$

Then
$$M = \frac{P}{1 - r\dfrac{t}{T}} \qquad (12\text{-}5)$$

As an example of the use of this formula consider this problem: What should be the face value of a 90-day note which is to yield \$3,840.00 when discounted at 6% on date of issue?

Since the note bears no interest, the face value is the maturity value, as explained earlier in this chapter. Therefore, Formula 12-5 will give the desired information, and for substitution in it, P is \$3,840.00, r is .06, t is 90 days and T is 360 days. Then, on substituting,

$$M = \frac{3,840.00}{1 - (.06)(\frac{90}{360})} = \frac{3,840.00}{.985} = \$3,898.48, \text{ face value.}$$

The formula for the maturity value of an interest-bearing note is derived readily from Formula (12-4), by the transposition:

Since by Formula (12-4), $P = F \left(1 + r_1\frac{t_1}{T_1} \right)\left(1 - r\frac{t}{T} \right)$

Then
$$F = \frac{P}{\left(1 + r_1\dfrac{t_1}{T_1} \right)\left(1 - r\dfrac{t}{T} \right)} \qquad (12\text{-}6)$$

The use of this formula is exemplified by the problem:

What should be the face value of 90-day note bearing 5% interest to yield \$3,840.00 when discounted at 6% on day of making?

For substitution in the formula, P is \$3,840.00, r_1 is .05, t_1 is 90 days, T_1 is 360 days, r_2 is .06, t_2 is 90 days, and T_2 is 360 days.

Substituting,
$$F = \frac{\$3,840.00}{(1 + .05\frac{90}{360})(1 - .06\frac{90}{360})}$$

Then,
$$F = \frac{\$3,840.00}{(1.0125)(.985)}$$

$$F = \frac{\$3,840.00}{.9973125} = \$3,850.35$$

Just as in the problems given earlier in this chapter in which the proceeds were to be found, so in these problems in maturity values, the interest term and discount period may not be given directly, but may need to be found from dates of issuance, maturity and discount. However, the use of Tables 5 and 6 is still the same, and therefore examples of such calculations are not necessary.

However, problems in computing maturity value occur often enough so that the time-saving to be effected by tabular computation justifies the use of special tables for the purpose. The nature and use of these tables can best be illustrated by an introductory example.

What is the difference in interest charges between $1.00 borrowed for 1 year at 6% per year interest, and $1.00 obtained as the proceeds of a note for 1 year discounted at 6%?

In the first case, by Formula (11-3), Chapter 11,

$$I = Pr\frac{t}{T}$$

$$\text{Interest} = (\$1.00)(.06)(\tfrac{1}{1}) = .06$$

In the second case, by Formula (12-5),

$$\text{Maturity Value} = M = \frac{P}{1 - r\dfrac{t}{T}}$$

$$= \frac{\$1.00}{1 - (.06)(\tfrac{1}{1})}$$

$$= \frac{\$1.00}{.94} = \$1.0638$$

$$\text{Giving interest of } \$1.0638 - \$1.00 = \$ .0638$$

From this example, it is apparent that the cost of borrowing money by discounting paper at a given rate is greater than borrowing money at interest at the same rate. Moreover, the standard banking practice is to charge for borrowed money, especially for short terms, at the discount rate rather than at the interest rate. (Long term loans are discussed in Chapter 13, while installment loans are treated in Chapter 19.) In view of this wide-spread practice, it is desirable to have methods of computation, both by formulas and tables, of the interest rates that are equivalent to given discount rates. Thus the calculation made above shows that the simple interest rate that is equivalent to a discount rate of 6% is 6.38%.

A general formula for finding interest rates equivalent to discount rates may be derived as follows:

From Formula (11-7), Chapter 11,

$$S = P\left(1 + r\frac{t}{T}\right),$$

where S is the total sum from a principal P at a periodic interest rate r per period T, for time t.

Now from Formula (12-5),

$$M = \frac{P}{1 - r_d \dfrac{t}{T}}$$

where M is the maturity value of a note having proceeds P at discount rate r_d per period T for time t.

Now to find the interest rate equivalent to a given discount rate, equate the above values of S and M, obtaining

$$P\left(1 + r\frac{t}{T}\right) = \frac{P}{1 - r_d \dfrac{t}{T}}$$

Therefore

$$1 + r\frac{t}{T} = \frac{1}{1 - r_d \dfrac{t}{T}}$$

Then

$$r\frac{t}{T} = \frac{1}{1 - r_d \dfrac{t}{T}} - 1$$

Clearing of fractions in the right-hand term

$$r\frac{t}{T} = \frac{1 - 1 + r_d \dfrac{t}{T}}{1 - r_d \dfrac{t}{T}} = \frac{r_d \dfrac{t}{T}}{1 - r_d \dfrac{t}{T}}$$

Dividing by $\dfrac{t}{T}$,

$$r = \frac{r_d}{1 - r_d \dfrac{t}{T}} \qquad\qquad (12\text{-}7)$$

that is, the interest rate equivalent to a given discount rate is equal to the discount rate, divided by 1 minus the product of the discount rate and the number of interest periods, or the fractional period.

To apply this formula, find the interest rate equivalent to a discount rate of 6% for 1 year.

In this case, $r_d = .06$, $\dfrac{t}{T} = 1$, so on substituting

$$r = \frac{.06}{1 - (.06)(1)} = \frac{.06}{.94} = .0638 = 6.38\%$$

As another example, find the interest rate equivalent to a 6% discount rate for two months.

Here, $$r = \frac{.06}{1 - (.06)(\frac{2}{12})} = \frac{.06}{.99} = 6.0606\%$$

From these two examples, it is evident that the interest rate corresponding to a given discount rate increases with the length of the period. Therefore, tables for computing maturity values corresponding to $1.00 of proceeds for given discount rates (or, what is the same, total sums to repay loans at discounted rates) cannot be constructed for use by addition of time periods, as was done with simple interest tables. They are therefore constructed for use by interpolation, as shown below.

Table 10 gives the maturity value for $1.00 of proceeds discounted at various rates from 1% to $8\frac{1}{2}\%$ for ten-day periods from 10 days to 360 days, which is the same as the total sum yielded by $1.00 of principal for those periods at discount rates (instead of interest rates) ranging from 1% to $8\frac{1}{2}\%$. The method of using Table 10 is illustrated by the following problems.

What is the face value of a 180-day non-interest bearing note, which Charles Smith gives to the Dalson Lumber Company to pay a bill in net amount of $3,275.65, for discount on date of note at 6%?

Since the note bears no interest, its face value is the same as its maturity value. From Table 10, the maturity value per $1.00 of proceeds at 6% discount for 180 days is $1.030928. Therefore, to yield $3,275.65 of proceeds the note must have a maturity value, which in this case is the face value, of ($3,275.65) × ($1.030928) = $3,376.96.

Robert Jones obtains $450.00 from a bank by making a note at the discount rate of 6%. What is the face value of the note, if due in 90 days?

From Table 10, the maturity value per $1.00 of proceeds at 6% discount for 90 days is $1,015228. Therefore the face value of the note is

($450.00) × ($1.015228) = $4,568.53.

On March 10, 1951, Charles D. Adams gives a note due November 1, 1951 to the H. D. Simmons Co. in satisfaction of a debt of $3,614.60, the note being for discount at 6%. What is the face value of the note?

From Table 5, Chapter 11, the day-numbers of March 10 and November 1 are 69 and 305. Therefore the period of the note is 305 − 69 = 236 days. Then from Table 10,

Maturity value at 6% of $1.00 for 240 days is $1.041667
Maturity value at 6% of $1.00 for 230 days is   <u>1.039861</u>
Difference $ .001806

For 6 days, take $\frac{6}{10}$ of $.001806 = $001084 (Continued on Page 239)

TABLE 10—MATURITY VALUE PER $1.00 OF PROCEEDS

(Discounted at 1% per Year)

Time (days)	Maturity Value	Time (days)	Maturity Value	Time (days)	Maturity Value
10	1.000277	130	1.003624	250	1.006994
20	1.000556	140	1.003904	260	1.007276
30	1.000834	150	1.004185	270	1.007556
40	1.001111	160	1.004465	280	1.007840
50	1.001391	170	1.004746	290	1.008123
60	1.001670	180	1.005025	300	1.008403
70	1.001949	190	1.005307	310	1.008685
80	1.002227	200	1.005586	320	1.008969
90	1.002506	210	1.005867	330	1.009252
100	1.002785	220	1.006149	340	1.009535
110	1.003064	230	1.006430	350	1.009818
120	1.003344	240	1.006712	360	1.010101

Maturity Value per $1.00 of Proceeds
(Discounted at 1-1/2% per Year)

Time (days)	Maturity Value	Time (days)	Maturity Value	Time (days)	Maturity Value
10	1.000416	130	1.005447	250	1.010528
20	1.000834	140	1.005868	260	1.010954
30	1.001251	150	1.006291	270	1.011380
40	1.001670	160	1.006713	280	1.011807
50	1.002089	170	1.007137	290	1.012234
60	1.002506	180	1.007559	300	1.012658
70	1.002927	190	1.007982	310	1.013085
80	1.003347	200	1.008403	320	1.013514
90	1.003767	210	1.008827	330	1.013942
100	1.004184	220	1.009252	340	1.014371
110	1.004604	230	1.009677	350	1.014800
120	1.005025	240	1.010101	360	1.015228

Maturity Value per $1.00 of Proceeds
(Discounted at 2% per Year)

Time (days)	Maturity Value	Time (days)	Maturity Value	Time (days)	Maturity Value
10	1.000555	130	1.007274	250	1.014084
20	1.001111	140	1.007838	260	1.014656
30	1.001669	150	1.008403	270	1.015228
40	1.002228	160	1.008968	280	1.015801
50	1.002785	170	1.009534	290	1.016374
60	1.003345	180	1.010101	300	1.016949
70	1.003904	190	1.010668	310	1.017524
80	1.004464	200	1.011236	320	1.018098
90	1.005025	210	1.011804	330	1.018675
100	1.005586	220	1.012373	340	1.019252
110	1.006148	230	1.012933	350	1.019830
120	1.006711	240	1.013513	360	1.020408

TABLE 10—MATURITY VALUE PER $1.00 OF PROCEEDS (Cont.)

(Discounted at 2-1/2% per Year)

Time (days)	Maturity Value	Time (days)	Maturity Value	Time (days)	Maturity Value
10	1.000694	130	1.009110	250	1.017667
20	1.001389	140	1.009817	260	1.018387
30	1.002086	150	1.010526	270	1.019108
40	1.002785	160	1.011235	280	1.019830
50	1.003483	170	1.011946	290	1.020552
60	1.004183	180	1.012658	300	1.021276
70	1.004884	190	1.013370	310	1.022001
80	1.005586	200	1.014084	320	1.022727
90	1.006289	210	1.014799	330	1.023454
100	1.006993	220	1.015514	340	1.024182
110	1.007697	230	1.016230	350	1.024911
120	1.008403	240	1.016947	360	1.025641

Maturity Value per $1.00 of Proceeds
(Discounted at 3% per Year)

Time (days)	Maturity Value	Time (days)	Maturity Value	Time (days)	Maturity Value
10	1.000834	130	1.010951	250	1.021276
20	1.001669	140	1.011804	260	1.022146
30	1.002506	150	1.012658	270	1.023017
40	1.003344	160	1.013513	280	1.023889
50	1.004183	170	1.014370	290	1.024765
60	1.005025	180	1.015228	300	1.025641
70	1.005866	190	1.016088	310	1.026518
80	1.006711	200	1.016949	320	1.027397
90	1.007556	210	1.017811	330	1.028277
100	1.008403	220	1.018675	340	1.029159
110	1.009251	230	1.019541	350	1.030042
120	1.010101	240	1.020408	360	1.030928

Maturity Value per $1.00 of Proceeds
(Discounted at 3-1/2% per Year)

Time (days)	Maturity Value	Time (days)	Maturity Value	Time (days)	Maturity Value
10	1.000973	130	1.012800	250	1.024911
20	1.001948	140	1.013798	260	1.025933
30	1.002925	150	1.014799	270	1.026957
40	1.003904	160	1.015801	280	1.027984
50	1.004884	170	1.016805	290	1.029012
60	1.005867	180	1.017811	300	1.030042
70	1.006853	190	1.018819	310	1.031075
80	1.007838	200	1.019830	320	1.032110
90	1.008827	210	1.020842	330	1.033146
100	1.009817	220	1.021856	340	1.034185
110	1.010810	230	1.022872	350	1.035226
120	1.011804	240	1.023890	360	1.036269

TABLE 10—MATURITY VALUE PER $1.00 OF PROCEEDS (Cont.)

(Discounted at 4% per Year)

Time (days)	Maturity Value	Time (days)	Maturity Value	Time (days)	Maturity Value
10	1.001112	130	1.014654	250	1.028570
20	1.002226	140	1.015800	260	1.029747
30	1.003344	150	1.016948	270	1.030928
40	1.004463	160	1.018098	280	1.032108
50	1.005586	170	1.019251	290	1.033293
60	1.006710	180	1.020408	300	1.034482
70	1.007837	190	1.021565	310	1.035672
80	1.008967	200	1.022727	320	1.036865
90	1.010099	210	1.023890	330	1.038061
100	1.011235	220	1.025056	340	1.039260
110	1.012373	230	1.026225	350	1.040461
120	1.013513	240	1.027396	360	1.041665

Maturity Value per $1.00 of Proceeds
(Discounted at 4-1/2% per Year)

Time (days)	Maturity Value	Time (days)	Maturity Value	Time (days)	Maturity Value
10	1.001251	130	1.016518	250	1.032258
20	1.002506	140	1.017812	260	1.033590
30	1.003764	150	1.019108	270	1.034929
40	1.005025	160	1.020408	280	1.036261
50	1.006289	170	1.021711	290	1.037613
60	1.007556	180	1.023018	300	1.038961
70	1.008827	190	1.024328	310	1.040312
80	1.010101	200	1.025641	320	1.041667
90	1.011378	210	1.026958	330	1.043025
100	1.012658	220	1.028278	340	1.044386
110	1.013942	230	1.029601	350	1.045752
120	1.015228	240	1.030928	360	1.047120

Maturity Value per $1.00 of Proceeds
(Discounted at 5% per Year)

Time (days)	Maturity Value	Time (days)	Maturity Value	Time (days)	Maturity Value
10	1.001390	130	1.018388	250	1.035971
20	1.002785	140	1.019830	260	1.037464
30	1.004184	150	1.021277	270	1.038961
40	1.005587	160	1.022727	280	1.040462
50	1.006993	170	1.024182	290	1.041968
60	1.008404	180	1.025641	300	1.043478
70	1.009818	190	1.027104	310	1.044993
80	1.011236	200	1.028571	320	1.046511
90	1.012659	210	1.030042	330	1.048035
100	1.014084	220	1.031519	340	1.049563
110	1.015515	230	1.032999	350	1.051095
120	1.016949	240	1.034483	360	1.052632

TABLE 10—MATURITY VALUE PER $1.00 OF PROCEEDS (Cont.)

(Discounted at 5-1/2% per Year)

Time (days)	Maturity Value	Time (days)	Maturity Value	Time (days)	Maturity Value
10	1.001531	130	1.020263	250	1.039711
20	1.003064	140	1.021856	260	1.041365
30	1.004604	150	1.023454	270	1.043024
40	1.006148	160	1.025056	280	1.044689
50	1.007697	170	1.026664	290	1.046359
60	1.009251	180	1.028277	300	1.048034
70	1.010810	190	1.029895	310	1.049715
80	1.012373	200	1.031518	320	1.051401
90	1.013941	210	1.033146	330	1.053093
100	1.015514	220	1.034780	340	1.054790
110	1.017092	230	1.036418	350	1.056491
120	1.018675	240	1.038062	360	1.058201

Maturity Value per $1.00 of Proceeds
(Discounted at 6% per Year)

Time (days)	Maturity Value	Time (days)	Maturity Value	Time (days)	Maturity Value
10	1.001669	130	1.022146	250	1.043478
20	1.003344	140	1.023889	260	1.045296
30	1.005025	150	1.025641	270	1.047120
40	1.006711	160	1.027397	280	1.048951
50	1.008403	170	1.029159	290	1.050788
60	1.010101	180	1.030928	300	1.052631
70	1.011804	190	1.032702	310	1.054481
80	1.013513	200	1.034482	320	1.056338
90	1.015228	210	1.036269	330	1.058201
100	1.016949	220	1.038062	340	1.060070
110	1.018675	230	1.039861	350	1.061946
120	1.020408	240	1.041667	360	1.063830

Maturity Value per $1.00 of Proceeds
(Discounted at 6-1/2% per Year)

Time (days)	Maturity Value	Time (days)	Maturity Value	Time (days)	Maturity Value
10	1.001808	130	1.024036	250	1.047261
20	1.003624	140	1.026001	260	1.049257
30	1.005446	150	1.027837	270	1.051247
40	1.007264	160	1.029748	280	1.053246
50	1.009110	170	1.031666	290	1.055253
60	1.010941	180	1.033591	300	1.057268
70	1.012804	190	1.035149	310	1.059290
80	1.014656	200	1.037464	320	1.061320
90	1.016518	210	1.039410	330	1.063358
100	1.018387	220	1.041365	340	1.065413
110	1.020263	230	1.043326	350	1.067457
120	1.022146	240	1.045296	360	1.069518

TABLE 10—MATURITY VALUE PER $1.00 OF PROCEEDS (Cont.)

(Discounted at 7% per Year)

Time (days)	Maturity Value	Time (days)	Maturity Value	Time (days)	Maturity Value
10	1.001948	130	1.025933	250	1.051093
20	1.003904	140	1.027984	260	1.053247
30	1.005867	150	1.030042	270	1.055408
40	1.007838	160	1.032110	280	1.057579
50	1.009817	170	1.034185	290	1.059758
60	1.011804	180	1.036269	300	1.061946
70	1.013798	190	1.038361	310	1.064144
80	1.015801	200	1.040462	320	1.066350
90	1.017811	210	1.042571	330	1.068566
100	1.019830	220	1.044689	340	1.070791
110	1.021856	230	1.046815	350	1.073025
120	1.023890	240	1.048949	360	1.075268

Maturity Value per $1.00 of Proceeds
(Discounted at 7-1/2% per Year)

Time (days)	Maturity Value	Time (days)	Maturity Value	Time (days)	Maturity Value
10	1.002087	130	1.027837	250	1.054944
20	1.004184	140	1.030042	260	1.057268
30	1.006289	150	1.032258	270	1.059602
40	1.008403	160	1.034482	280	1.061946
50	1.010526	170	1.036743	290	1.064301
60	1.012658	180	1.038961	300	1.066667
70	1.014799	190	1.041214	310	1.069042
80	1.016949	200	1.043478	320	1.071428
90	1.019108	210	1.045751	330	1.073825
100	1.021276	220	1.048034	340	1.076233
110	1.023454	230	1.050328	350	1.078651
120	1.025641	240	1.052631	360	1.081081

Maturity Value per $1.00 of Proceeds
(Discounted at 8% per Year)

Time (days)	Maturity Value	Time (days)	Maturity Value	Time (days)	Maturity Value
10	1.002227	130	1.029748	250	1.058823
20	1.004464	140	1.032110	260	1.061320
30	1.006711	150	1.034482	270	1.063829
40	1.008958	160	1.036866	280	1.066350
50	1.011235	170	1.039260	290	1.068883
60	1.013513	180	1.041666	300	1.071428
70	1.015801	190	1.044083	310	1.073985
80	1.018099	200	1.046511	320	1.076555
90	1.020408	210	1.048951	330	1.079136
100	1.022727	220	1.051401	340	1.081730
110	1.025056	230	1.053864	350	1.084337
120	1.027397	240	1.056338	360	1.086956

TABLE 10—MATURITY VALUE PER $1.00 OF PROCEEDS (Cont.)

(Discounted at 8-1/2% per Year)

Time (days)	Maturity Value	Time (days)	Maturity Value	Time (days)	Maturity Value
10	1.002366	130	1.031666	250	1.062730
20	1.004744	140	1.034185	260	1.065403
30	1.007133	150	1.036717	270	1.068090
40	1.009534	160	1.039260	280	1.070791
50	1.011306	170	1.041817	290	1.073505
60	1.014370	180	1.044386	300	1.076233
70	1.016805	190	1.046968	310	1.078974
80	1.019252	200	1.049562	320	1.081730
90	1.021711	210	1.052170	330	1.084501
100	1.024182	220	1.054790	340	1.087284
110	1.026664	230	1.057424	350	1.090083
120	1.029159	240	1.060070	360	1.092896

Then add this value to that for 230 days ($1.039861). Therefore, the maturity value at 6% for $1.00 for 236 days = $1.039861 + $.001084 = $1.040945

Therefore, face value of the note is ($3,614.60) × (1.040945) = $3,762.59.

Partial Payments

The term partial payments, as used in this section, refers to partial payments on commercial paper. They are not to be confused with partial payments made on installment plan purchases, which are treated in Chapter 19.

The calculation that arises most frequently in regard to partial payments on commercial paper is the method of crediting interest on the partial payment or payments. While the interest may be calculated on exact or ordinary basis and for exact or approximate time, the general practice today is to use ordinary interest for approximate time. There are, however, two methods of computing this interest when partial payments are made, the U. S. Rule, which is used in U. S. Government accounting, and the Merchant's Rule, which is common in commercial practice. The U. S. Rule is also used most commonly on longer term (over 1 year) payment periods, while the Merchant's Rule is used most widely for shorter periods.

The U. S. Rule depends on the relation between the payment and the accrued interest. If the payment exceeds the accrued interest, the payment is subtracted from the total sum of principal and accrued interest, and the remainder is continued at interest until the next sufficient payment is made, or until the entire debt is paid.

If the payment does not exceed the accrued interest, no change is made in principal or interest, and the payment is carried forward as a credit, but without interest, until the debt is paid; or until another partial payment is made such that the interest to its date is less than the sum of two payments, in which case they are subtracted from total principal and interest.

The application of the U. S. Rule is shown in the calculation of the balance due at maturity of the following obligation: Charles Smith borrowed $3,000.00 on January 1, 1951 on a note due January 1, 1954 and bearing 6% interest. On July 1, 1951 he paid $50.00 on account; on October 1, 1951 he made another payment of $300.00; and he then made a third payment of $200.00 on July 1, 1953. What is the balance due at maturity?

The calculations are as follows:

Original face of note, January 1, 1951	$3,000.00
Interest on $3,000.00 from January 1 to July 1, 1951 (6 months) at 6%.	90.00
This interest is greater than July 1 payment of $50.00, so that payment is carried forward.	
Interest on $3,000.00 from January 1, 1951 to October 1, 1951 (9 months) at 6%	135.00
This interest is less than total of July 1 payment of $50.00 plus October 1 payment of $300.00 so the total of these two payments is deducted from total of face and interest.	3,135.00
Less	350.00
New balance as of October 1, 1951	$2,785.00
Interest on $2,785.00 from October 1, 1951 to July 1, 1953 (1 year 9 months) at 6%.	292.43
This interest is greater than July 1, 1953 payment of $200.00, so that payment is carried forward	
Interest on $2,785.00 from October 1, 1951 to January 1, 1954 at 6%	375.98
Total balance and interest	3,160.98
Less payment carried forward	200.00
Balance due January 1, 1954	2,960.98

The Merchant's Rule computes interest separately on face value of the obligation, and on payments, and subtracts at the end of the period the total of payments and their interest from face value and interest. The period is the term of the obligation, unless that is greater than one year, in which case the computation of interest, and subtraction of payments and their interest is made annually.

Two examples serve to illustrate the application of the Merchant's Rule.

What is the balance due on maturity of a note for $2,100.00 at 5% interest, dated September 1, 1951 and due March 18, 1952, if a payment of $300.00 was made on November 12, 1951?

The calculations are as follows:

Original face of note September 1, 1951.......................... $2,100.00
Ordinary Interest at 5% from September 1, 1951 to March 18, 1952
  (6 mo. 17 days)... 57.46
Maturity Value... $2,157.46
Payment on Account November 12, 1931.................. $300.00
Ordinary Interest at 5% from November 12, 1951 to March 18,
  1952 (4 mo. 6 days).................................. 5.25
  Total payment and interest................................ 305.25
  Balance due at maturity.................................. $1,852.21

Another example is:

What is the balance due on maturity of a note for $3,200.00 at 6% interest, dated September 1, 1954 and due April 26, 1956, if a payment of $400.00 was made on October 1, 1954?

The calculations are as follows:

Original face of note September 1, 1954.......................... $3,200.00
Interest at 6% from September 1, 1954 to September 1, 1955 (1 year).. 192.00
Value on September 1, 1955................................... $3,392.00
Payment of $400.00 October 1, 1954...................... $400.00
Interest on payment at 6% from October 1, 1954 to September 1, 1955 (11 months)........................... 22.00
  Total payment and interest................................ $ 422.00
  Balance due September 1, 1955............................. $2,970.00
Interest on balance at 6% from September 1, 1955 to April 25, 1956
  (7 months, 25 days)... 116.33
  Maturity balance due...................................... $3,086.33

Equation of Value

In repeated business transactions between the same parties, there are occasions in which it is desired to exchange debts, that is, to change payment dates and amounts. The equation of value is a method of effecting such changes upon an equitable basis. Its character and use is best explained by an example.

As of January 1, A owes B $400.00 payable March 1 and $500.00 due September 1. However, A wishes to change the payment dates to the quarter-dates, April 1 and July 1, and to make equal payments on those dates. What is the amount of those payments at 6% simple interest?

To set up the equation of value, choose a single date to which to calculate all payments. Such a date is called the focal date. For convenience in computation, it is usually taken as the date of the last payment. In this example, that date would be September 1.

Then the amount that would be due September 1 on the first debt owed is the amount of that debt ($400.00), plus interest on it from its due date (March 1) to the focal date (September 1), a period of 6 months. The total amount would be $400.00 + ($400.00)$(\frac{1}{2})$(.06) = $400.00(1 + .03)$ = $412.00.

The amount that would be due September 1 on the second debt owed is the amount of that debt ($500.00) plus the interest from its due date (September 1) to the focal date (September 1), which is 0. Therefore the total amount is $500.00.

The amount to be credited to the payer (A) on the first new payment is the amount of that payment x, plus interest from the date of payment (April 1) to the focal date (September 1), period of 5 months. The amount would be payment + interest = $x[1 + (\frac{5}{12})(.06).]$

The amount to be credited to the payer (A) on the second new payment is the amount of that payment x, plus interest from the date of payment (July 1) to the focal date (September 1), a period of 2 months. The amount would be payment + interest = $x[1 + (\frac{2}{12})(.06).]$

Then writing the equation of value between amount due and amounts credited,

$$\$412.00 + 500.00 = x[1 + (\tfrac{5}{12})(.06)] + x[1 + (\tfrac{2}{12})(.06)]$$

Then $\qquad$ $\$912.00 = x + .025x + x + .01x$

$$\$912.00 = 2.035x$$

$$x = \frac{912.00}{2.035} = \$448.16, \text{ the amount of each of}$$

the two payments to be made April 1 and July 1.

Another type of problem using the equation of value is to find, instead of exchange payments, the exchange date, that is, the date on which a number of debts may be satisfied by a single payment of their sum. This date is called the equated date.

Consider the problem: A owes B $300.00 payable March 1, $400.00 payable April 1, and $700.00 payable September 1. What is the date on which these three debts can be satisfied by payment of their sum (the equated date)?

Here again the focal date is conveniently chosen as the date of the last payment due (September 1). The equated date is taken as x days before the focal date.

Then the amount that would be due on the focal date (September 1) on the first debt owed is amount of that debt ($300.00) plus interest on it from its due date (March 1) to (September 1), a period of 6 months. The amount would be ($300.00)$(1 + \frac{6}{12}r)$ where r is the annual interest rate.

The amount that would be due on the focal date (September 1) on the second debt owed is the amount of that debt ($400.00) plus interest from its due date (April 1) to (September 1) a period of 5 months. The amount would be ($400.00)$(1 + \frac{5}{12}r)$.

The amount that would be due on the focal date (September 1) on the third debt owed which is due September 1, is the amount of that debt ($700.00).

The amount due on the focal date (September 1) to satisfy all three debts by a single payment of their sum is the amount of that sum ($1,400.00) plus interest from its date of payment (September $1 - x$) to September 1, a period of x days. The amount is $\$1,400.00 \left(1 + \dfrac{x}{360} r\right)$.

Then writing the equation of value between amounts due and amount credited,

$$(\$300.00)(1 + \tfrac{6}{12}r) + (\$400.00)(1 + \tfrac{5}{12}r) + \$700.00$$

$$= (1,400.00) \left(1 + \dfrac{x}{360} r\right)$$

which becomes,

$$\$300.00 + \$150.00r + \$400.00 + \$166.67r + \$700.00$$

$$= \$1,400.00 + \$1,400.00 \dfrac{x}{360} r$$

Adding terms,

$$\$1,400.00 + 316.67r = \$1,400.00 + 3.89rx$$

Therefore, $\qquad x = \dfrac{316.67r}{3.89r} = 81.4$ days.

Therefore equated date is 81 days before September 1. From Table 5, Chapter 11, day-number of September 1 is 244; $244 - 81 = 163$; and again from Table 5, 163 is the day-number of June 12, the equated date.

Chapter 13

COMPOUND INTEREST

In the calculations of simple interest in Chapter 11, the assumption was made that the interest was paid when due. Thus, even when the duration of the debt was greater than one interest period, its principal amount was not increased by the interest. On the other hand, in compound interest the interest is added to the principal to form a new principal, and it is on this new principal that the interest for the following period is computed. The original principal is therefore said to be compounded, and the difference between the total amount at the end of a stated number of such periods (which is called the compound amount) and the original principal, is compound interest.

Consider a savings bank which pays interest at an annual rate of $r\%$, but compounds it quarterly. Then the interest added at the end of the first quarter to the principal at the beginning of that quarter, assuming no deposits or withdrawals during that quarter is $P \times \frac{r}{4}$, and the new principal at the end of that quarter is $P\left(1 + \frac{r}{4}\right)$. Then, in the second quarter, the interest earned on that new principal is $\left[P\left(1 + \frac{r}{4}\right)\right] \times \frac{r}{4}$, and the new principal (compound amount) at the end of the second quarter is $\left[P\left(1 + \frac{r}{4}\right)\right]\left(1 + \frac{r}{4}\right) = P\left(1 + \frac{r}{4}\right)^2$, again assuming no deposits or withdrawals during the quarter. By continuing this line of reasoning, the compound amount at the end of the third quarter is $P\left(1 + \frac{r}{4}\right)^3$; that at the end of the fourth quarter is $P\left(1 + \frac{r}{4}\right)^4$, and that at the end of the nth quarter is $P\left(1 + \frac{r}{4}\right)^n$.

244

This formula can be further generalized to the form:

$$S = P(1 + i)^n \tag{13-1}$$

where S is the compound amount after compounding interest on the original principal P, for n periods at an interest rate of i per period. The interest rate per period, i is defined by the relationship

$$i = \frac{r}{m} \tag{13-2}$$

where i is the interest rate per period, r is the annual interest rate, and m is the number of interest periods per year, or in other words, the number of times annually that interest is compounded. Note that if interest is compounded annually $m = 1$, and $i = r$.

By the definition of compound interest, the amount of compound interest is given by the formula,

$$I = S - P = P(1 + i)^n - P = P[(1 + i)^n - 1] \tag{13-3}$$

These three formulas, (13-1), (13-2) and (13-3) are basic in the solution of problems in compound interest. Since, however, the direct evaluation of the term $(1 + i)^n$ requires repeated multiplications, the work is materially shortened by the use of logarithms. Thus, by taking logarithms of both sides of Formula (13-1), there results $\log S = \log P (1 + i)^n$

which by Formula (6-1) in Chapter 6, becomes

$$\log S = \log P + \log (1 + i)^n$$

which by Formula (6-3) in Chapter 6, becomes

$$\log S = \log P + n \log (1 + i) \tag{13-4}$$

As an example of compound interest calculation by formulas, find the compound amount of, and the compound interest on, \$3,650.00 at $2\frac{1}{2}\%$ annual interest rate, compounded quarterly for 3 years.

By Formula (13-2), $i = \frac{r}{m}$, where r is .025 and m is 4,

Substituting, $i = \frac{.025}{4} = .00625$

By Formula (13-4), $\log S = \log P + n \log (1 + i)$
where P is \$3,650.00, n is $4 \times 3 = 12$, and i is .00625
Substituting, $\log S = \log (\$3,650.00) + 12 \log (1 + .00625)$

From Table 3, Chapter 6, and rule for characteristics,

$$\log 1.00625 = .002706$$
Therefore $12 \times \log (1.00625) = 12(.002706) = .032472$

From Table 3, Chapter 6, and rule for characteristics

$$\log 3{,}650 = 3.562293$$

Therefore, $\log 3{,}650 + 12 \log (1.00625)$ $= 3.594765$

Therefore S is antilog 3.594765, which by Table 3 is \$3,933.37, the compound amount sought.

And by Formula (13-3), the compound interest is \$3,933.37 − \$3,650.00 = \$283.37.

As another example of compound interest calculation by formula, find the amount to be repaid on a loan of \$875.00, at $4\frac{1}{2}\%$ interest compounded monthly for 9 years.

By Formula (13-2), $i = \dfrac{r}{m}$ where r is .045 and m is 12.

Substituting in the formula, $i = \dfrac{.045}{12} = .00375$

By Formula (13-4), $\log S = \log P + n \log (1 + i)$ where P is \$875.00, n is $9 \times 12 = 108$, and i is .00375.

Substituting, $\log S = \log (\$875.00) + 12 \log (1 + .00375)$

From Table 3, Chapter 6, and rule for characteristics,

$$\log 1.00375 = .001625$$

Therefore $108 (\log 1.00375) = 108(.001625) = .175500$

From Table 3, Chapter 6, and rule for characteristics,

$$\log 875. = \underline{2.942008}$$

Therefore $\log 875. + 108 (\log 1.00375)$ $= 3.117508$

Thus, S is antilog 3.117508 which by Table 3 is \$1,310.71, the amount sought.

Computing Compound Interest by Tables

From Formula 13-1, $S = P(1 + i)^n$, it is obvious that if P is \$1.00, then S is the compound amount resulting from compounding \$1.00 for n interest periods at the rate per period, i. This value of S for a principal of \$1.00 is commonly denoted by a lower case letter s. By tabulating such values of s for various numbers of interest periods, and interest rates per period, it is possible to compute the compound amount for any sum— by multiplying that sum by the tabulated value of s for the corresponding n and i. These values are given in Table 11, on Pages 247-263 in this book.

Note that this table gives values of s on \$1.00 for periods from 1 to 150 in number at periodic rates ranging from $\frac{1}{4}\%$ to $1\frac{1}{8}\%$, and for periods from 1 to 100 in number at periodic rates ranging from $1\frac{1}{4}\%$ to $6\frac{1}{2}\%$. Note also that the interest rate per period is obtained (as in Formula 13-2)

n	$\frac{1}{4}\%$	$\frac{7}{24}\%$	$\frac{1}{3}\%$	$\frac{5}{12}\%$	n
1	1.0025 0000	1.0029 1667	1.0033 3333	1.0041 6667	1
2	1.0050 0625	1.0058 4184	1.0066 7778	1.0083 5069	2
3	1.0075 1877	1.0087 7555	1.0100 3337	1.0125 5216	3
4	1.0100 3756	1.0117 1781	1.0134 0015	1.0167 7112	4
5	1.0125 6266	1.0146 6865	1.0167 7815	1.0210 0767	5
6	1.0150 9406	1.0176 2810	1.0201 6741	1.0252 6187	6
7	1.0176 3180	1.0205 9618	1.0235 6797	1.0295 3379	7
8	1.0201 7588	1.0235 7292	1.0269 7986	1.0338 2352	8
9	1.0227 2632	1.0265 5834	1.0304 0313	1.0381 3111	9
10	1.0252 8313	1.0295 5247	1.0338 3780	1.0424 5666	10
11	1.0278 4634	1.0325 5533	1.0372 8393	1.0468 0023	11
12	1.0304 1596	1.0355 6695	1.0407 4154	1.0511 6190	12
13	1.0329 9200	1.0385 8736	1.0442 1068	1.0555 4174	13
14	1.0355 7448	1.0416 1657	1.0476 9138	1.0599 3983	14
15	1.0381 6341	1.0446 5462	1.0511 8369	1.0643 5625	15
16	1.0407 5882	1.0477 0153	1.0546 8763	1.0687 9106	16
17	1.0433 6072	1.0507 5732	1.0582 0326	1.0732 4436	17
18	1.0459 6912	1.0538 2203	1.0617 3060	1.0777 1621	18
19	1.0485 8404	1.0568 9568	1.0652 6971	1.0822 0670	19
20	1.0512 0550	1.0599 7829	1.0688 2060	1.0867 1589	20
21	1.0538 3352	1.0630 6990	1 0723 8334	1.0912 4387	21
22	1.0564 6810	1.0661 7052	1.0759 5795	1.0957 9072	22
23	1.0591 0927	1.0692 8018	1.0795 4448	1.1003 5652	23
24	1 0617 5704	1.0723 9891	1.0831 4296	1.1049 4134	24
25	1.0644 1144	1.0755 2674	1.0867 5344	1.1095 4526	25
26	1.0670 7247	1.0786 6370	1.0903 7595	1.1141 6836	26
27	1.0697 4015	1.0818 0980	1.0940 1053	1.1188 1073	27
28	1.0724 1450	1.0849 6508	1.0976 5724	1.1234 7244	28
29	1.0750 9553	1.0881 2956	1.1013 1609	1.1281 5358	29
30	1.0777 8327	1.0913 0327	1 1049 8715	1.1328 5422	30
31	1.0804 7773	1.0944 8624	1.1086 7044	1.1375 7444	31
32	1.0831 7892	1.0976 7849	1.1123 6601	1.1423 1434	32
33	1.0858 8687	1.1008 8005	1.1160 7389	1.1470 7398	33
34	1.0886 0159	1.1040 9095	1.1197 9414	1.1518 5346	34
35	1.0913 2309	1.1073 1122	1.1235 2679	1.1566 5284	35
36	1.0940 5140	1.1105 4088	1 1272 7187	1.1614 7223	36
37	1.0967 8653	1.1137 7995	1.1310 2945	1.1663 1170	37
38	1.0995 2850	1.1170 2848	1.1347 9955	1.1711 7133	38
39	1.1022 7732	1.1202 8648	1.1385 8221	1.1760 5121	39
40	1.1050 3301	1.1235 5398	1.1423 7748	1.1809 5142	40
41	1.1077 9559	1.1268 3101	1.1461 8541	1.1858 7206	41
42	1.1105 6508	1.1301 1760	1.1500 0603	1.1908 1319	42
43	1.1133 4149	1.1334 1378	1.1538 3938	1.1957 7491	43
44	1.1161 2485	1.1367 1957	1.1576 8551	1.2007 5731	44
45	1.1189 1516	1.1400 3500	1.1615 4446	1.2057 6046	45
46	1.1217 1245	1.1433 6010	1.1654 1628	1.2107 8446	46
47	1.1245 1673	1.1466 9490	1.1693 0100	1.2158 2940	47
48	1.1273 2802	1.1500 3943	1.1731 9867	1.2208 9536	48
49	1.1301 4634	1.1533 9371	1.1771 0933	1.2259 8242	49
50	1.1329 7171	1.1567 5778	1.1810 3303	1.2310 9068	50

n	$\frac{1}{4}\%$	$\frac{7}{24}\%$	$\frac{1}{3}\%$	$\frac{5}{12}\%$	n
51	1.1358 0414	1.1601 3165	1.1849 6981	1.2362 2002	51
52	1.1386 4365	1.1635 1537	1.1889 1971	1.2413 7114	52
53	1.1414 9026	1.1669 0896	1.1928 8277	1.2465 4352	53
54	1.1443 4398	1.1703 1244	1.1968 5905	1.2517 3745	54
55	1.1472 0484	1.1737 2585	1.2008 4858	1.2569 5302	55
56	1.1500 7285	1.1771 4922	1.2048 5141	1.2621 9033	56
57	1.1529 4804	1.1805 8257	1.2088 6758	1.2674 4946	57
58	1.1558 3041	1.1840 2594	1.2128 9714	1.2727 3050	58
59	1.1587 1998	1.1874 7935	1.2169 4013	1.2780 3354	59
60	1.1616 1678	1.1909 4283	1.2209 9659	1.2833 5868	60
61	1.1645 2082	1.1944 1641	1.2250 6658	1.2887 0601	61
62	1.1674 3213	1.1979 0013	1.2291 5014	1.2940 7561	62
63	1.1703 5071	1.2013 ?400	1.2332 4730	1.2994 6760	63
64	1.1732 7658	1.2048 9b.	1.2373 5813	1.3048 8204	64
65	1.1762 0977	1.2084 1235	1.2414 8266	1.3103 1905	65
66	1.1791 5030	1.2119 3689	1.2456 2093	1.3157 7872	66
67	1.1820 9817	1.2154 7171	1.2497 7300	1.3212 6113	67
68	1.1850 5342	1.2190 1683	1.2539 3891	1.3267 6638	68
69	1.1880 1605	1.2225 7230	1.2581 1871	1.3322 9458	69
70	1.1909 8609	1.2261 3813	1.2623 1244	1.3378 4580	70
71	1.1939 6356	1.2297 1437	1.2665 2015	1.3434 2016	71
72	1.1969 4847	1.2333 0104	1.2707 4188	1.3490 1774	72
73	1.1999 4084	1.2368 9816	1.2749 7769	1.3546 3865	73
74	1.2029 4069	1.2405 0578	1.2792 2761	1.3602 8298	74
75	1.2059 4804	1.2441 2393	1.2834 9170	1.3659 5082	75
76	1,2089 6291	1.2477 5262	1.2877 7001	1.3716 4229	76
77	1.2119 8532	1.2513 9190	1.2920 6258	1.3773 5746	77
78	1.2150 1528	1.2550 4179	1.2963 6945	1.3830 9645	78
79	1.2180 5282	1.2587 0233	1.3006 9068	1.3888 5935	79
80	1.2210 9795	1.2623 7355	1.3050 2632	1.3946 4627	80
81	1.2241 5070	1.2660 5547	1.3093 7641	1.4004 5729	81
82	1.2272 1108	1.2697 4813	1.3137 4099	1.4062 9253	82
83	1.2302 7910	1.2734 5156	1.3181 2013	1.4121 5209	83
84	1.2333 5480	1.2771 6580	1.3225 1386	1.4180 3605	84
85	1.2364 3819	1.2808 9086	1.3269 2224	1.4239 4454	85
86	1.2395 2928	1.2846 2680	1.3313 4532	1.4298 7764	86
87	1.2426 2811	1.2883 7362	1.3357 8314	1.4358 3546	87
88	1.2457 3468	1.2921 3138	1.3402 3575	1.4418 1811	88
89	1.2488 4901	1.2959 0010	1.3447 0320	1.4478 2568	89
90	1.2519 7114	1.2996 7980	1.3491 8554	1.4538 5829	90
91	1.2551 0106	1.3034 7054	1.3536 8283	1.4599 1603	91
92	1.2582 3882	1.3072 7233	1.3581 9510	1.4659 9902	92
93	1.2613 8441	1.3110 8520	1.3627 2242	1.4721 0735	93
94	1.2645 3787	1.3149 0920	1.3672 6483	1.4782 4113	94
95	1.2676 9922	1.3187 4435	1.3718 2238	1.4844 0047	95
96	1.2708 6847	1.3225 9069	1.3763 9512	1.4905 8547	96
97	1.2740 4564	1.3264 4825	1.3809 8310	1.4967 9624	97
98	1.2772 3075	1.3303 1706	1.3855 8638	1.5030 3289	98
99	1.2804 2383	1.3341 9715	1.3902 0500	1.5092 9553	99
100	1.2836 2489	1.3380 8856	1.3948 3902	1.5155 8426	100

n	$\frac{1}{4}\%$	$\frac{7}{24}\%$	$\frac{1}{3}\%$	$\frac{5}{12}\%$	n
101	1.2868 3395	1.3419 9131	1.3994 8848	1.5218 9919	101
102	1.2900 5104	1.3459 0546	1.4041 5344	1.5282 4044	102
103	1.2932 7616	1.3498 3101	1.5346 0811	1.5346 0811	103
104	1.2965 0935	1.3537 6802	1.4135 3007	1.5410 0231	104
105	1.2997 5063	1.3577 1651	1.4182 4183	1.5474 2315	105
106	1.3030 0000	1.3616 7652	1.4229 6931	1.5538 7075	106
107	1.3062 5750	1.3656 4807	1.4277 1254	1.5603 4521	107
108	1.3095 2315	1.3696 3121	1.4324 7158	1.5668 4665	108
109	1.3127 9696	1.3736 2597	1.4372 4649	1.5733 7518	109
110	1.3160 7895	1.3776 3238	1.4420 3731	1.5799 3091	110
111	1.3193 6915	1.3816 5047	1.4468 4410	1.5865 1395	111
112	1.3226 6757	1.3856 8029	1.4516 6691	1.5931 2443	112
113	1.3259 7424	1.3897 2186	1.4565 0580	1.5997 6245	113
114	1.3292 8917	1.3937 7521	1.4613 6082	1.6064 2812	114
115	1.3326 1240	1.3978 4039	1.4662 3202	1.6131 2157	115
116	1.3359 4393	1.4019 1742	1.4711 1946	1.6198 4291	116
117	1.3392 8379	1.4060 0635	1.4760 2320	1.6265 9226	117
118	1.3426 3200	1.4101 0720	1.4809 4327	1.6333 6973	118
119	1.3459 8858	1.4142 2001	1.4858 7979	1.6401 7543	119
120	1.3493 5355	1.4183 4482	1.4908 3268	1.6470 0950	120
121	1,3527 2693	1.4224 8166	1.4958 0212	1.6538 7204	121
122	1.3561 0875	1.4266 3057	1.5007 8813	1.6607 6317	122
123	1.3594 9902	1.4307 9157	1.5057 9076	1.6676 8302	123
124	1.3628 9777	1.4349 6471	1.5108 1006	1.6746 3170	124
125	1.3663 0501	1.4391 5003	1.5158 4609	1.6816 0933	125
126	1.3697 2077	1.4433 4755	1.5208 9892	1.6886 1603	126
127	1.3731 4508	1.4475 5731	1.5259 6858	1.6956 5193	127
128	1.3765 7794	1.4517 7935	1.5310 5514	1.7027 1715	128
129	1.3800 1938	1.4560 1371	1.5361 5866	1.7098 1181	129
130	1.3834 6943	1.4602 6042	1.5412 7919	1.7169 3602	130
131	1.3869 2811	1.4645 1951	1.5464 1678	1.7240 8992	131
132	1.3903 9543	1.4687 9103	1.5515 7151	1.7312 7363	132
133	1.3938 7142	1.4730 7500	1.5567 4341	1.7384 8727	133
134	1.3973 5609	1.4773 7147	1.5619 3256	1.7457 3097	134
135	1.4008 4948	1.4816 8047	1.5671 3900	1.7530 0485	135
136	1.4043 5161	1.4860 0204	1.5723 6279	1.7603 0903	136
137	1.4078 6249	1.4903 3621	1.5776 0400	1.7676 4365	137
138	1.4113 8214	1.4946 8302	1.5828 6268	1.7750 0884	138
139	1.4149 1060	1.4990 4252	1.5881 3889	1.7824 0471	139
140	1.4184 4787	1.5034 1472	1.5934 3269	1.7898 3139	140
141	1.4219 9399	1.5077 9968	1.5987 4413	1.7972 8902	141
142	1.4255 4898	1.5121 9743	1.6040 7328	1.8047 7773	142
143	1.4291 1285	1.5166 0801	1.6094 2019	1.8122 9763	143
144	1.4326 8563	1.5210 3145	1.6147 8492	1.8198 4887	144
145	1.4362 6735	1.5254 6779	1.6201 6754	1.8274 3158	145
146	1.4398 5802	1.5299 1707	1.6255 6810	1.8350 4588	146
147	1.4434 5766	1.5343 7933	1.6309 8666	1.8426 9190	147
148	1.4470 6631	1.5388 5460	1.6364 2328	1.8503 6978	148
149	1.4506 8397	1.5433 4293	1.6418 7802	1.8580 7966	149
150	1.4543 1068	1.5478 4434	1.6473 5095	1.8658 2166	150

n	$\frac{1}{2}\%$	$\frac{7}{12}\%$	$\frac{5}{8}\%$	$\frac{2}{3}\%$	n
1	1.0050 0000	1.0058 3333	1.0062 5000	1.0066 6667	1
2	1.0100 2500	1.0117 0069	1.0125 3906	1.0133 7778	2
3	1.0150 7513	1.0176 0228	1.0188 6743	1.0201 3363	3
4	1.0201 5050	1.0235 3830	1.0252 3535	1.0269 3452	4
5	1.0252 5125	1.0295 0894	1.0316 4307	1.0337 8075	5
6	1.0303 7751	1.0355 1440	1.0380 9084	1.0406 7262	6
7	1.0355 2940	1.0415 5490	1.0445 7891	1.0476 1044	7
8	1.0407 0704	1.0476 3064	1.0511 0753	1.0545 9451	8
9	1.0459 1058	1.0537 4182	1.0576 7695	1.0616 2514	9
10	1.0511 4013	1.0598 8865	1.0642 8743	1.0687 0264	10
11	1.0563 9583	1.0660 7133	1.0709 3923	1.0758 2732	11
12	1.0616 7781	1.0722 9008	1.0776 3260	1.0829 9951	12
13	1.0669 8620	1.0785 4511	1.0843 6780	1.0902 1950	13
14	1.0723 2113	1.0848 3662	1.0911 4510	1.0974 8763	14
15	1.0776 8274	1.0911 6483	1.0979 6476	1.1048 0422	15
16	1.0830 7115	1.0975 2996	1.1048 2704	1.1121 6958	16
17	1.0884 8651	1.1039 3222	1.1117 3221	1.1195 8404	17
18	1.0939 2894	1 1103 7182	1.1186 8053	1.1270 4794	18
19	1.0993 9858	1.1168 4899	1.1256 7229	1.1345 6159	19
20	1.1048 9558	1.1233 6395	1.1327 0774	1.1421 2533	20
21	1.1104 2006	1.1299 1690	1.1397 8716	1 1497 3950	21
22	1.1159 7216	1.1365 0808	1.1469 1083	1.1574 0443	22
23	1.1215 5202	1.1431 3771	1.1540 7902	1.1651 2046	23
24	1.1271 5978	1.1498 0602	1.1612 9202	1.1728 8793	24
25	1.1327 9558	1.1565 1322	1.1685 5009	1.1807 0718	25
26	1 1384 5955	1.1632 5955	1.1758 5353	1.1885 7857	26
27	1.1441 5185	1.1700 4523	1.1832 0262	1.1965 0242	27
28	1.1498 7261	1.1768 7049	1.1905 9763	1.2044 7911	28
29	1.1556 2197	1.1837 3557	1.1980 3887	1.2125 0897	29
30	1.1614 0008	1.1906 4069	1.2055 2661	1.2205 9236	30
31	1.1672 0708	1.1975 8610	1.2130 6115	1.2287 2964	31
32	1.1730 4312	1.2045 7202	1.2206 4278	1.2369 2117	32
33	1.1789 0833	1.2115 9869	1.2282 7180	1.2451 6731	33
34	1.1848 0288	1.2186 6634	1.2359 4850	1.2534 6843	34
35	1 1907 2689	1.2257 7523	1.2436 7318	1.2618 2489	35
36	1 1966 8052	1.2329 2559	1.2514 4614	1.2702 3705	36
37	1.2026 6393	1.2401 1765	1.2592 6767	1.2787 0530	37
38	1.2086 7725	1.2473 5167	1.2671 3810	1.2872 3000	38
39	1.2147 2063	1.2546 2789	1.2750 5771	1.2958 1153	39
40	1.2207 9424	1.2619 4655	1.2830 2682	1.3044 5028	40
41	1.2268 9821	1.2693 0791	1.2910 4574	1.3131 4661	41
42	1.2330 3270	1.2767 1220	1.2991 1477	1.3219 0092	42
43	1.2391 9786	1.2841 5969	1.3072 3424	1.3307 1360	43
44	1.2453 9385	1.2916 5062	1.3154 0446	1.3395 8502	44
45	1.2516 2082	1.2991 8525	1.3236 2573	1.3485 1559	45
46	1.2578 7892	1.3067 6383	1.3318 9839	1.3575 0569	46
47	1.2641 6832	1.3143 8662	1.3402 2276	1.3665 5573	47
48	1.2704 8916	1.3220 5388	1.3485 9915	1.3756 6610	48
49	1.2768 4161	1.3297 6586	1.3570 2790	1.3848 3721	49
50	1.2832 2581	1.3375 2283	1.3655 0932	1.3940 6946	50

n	$\frac{1}{2}\%$	$\frac{7}{12}\%$	$\frac{5}{8}\%$	$\frac{2}{3}\%$	n
51	1.2896 4194	1.3453 2504	1.3740 4375	1.4033 6325	51
52	1.2960 9015	1.3531 7277	1.3826 3153	1.4127 1901	52
53	1.3025 7060	1.3610 6628	1.3912 7297	1.4221 3713	53
54	1.3090 8346	1.3690 0583	1.3999 6843	1.4316 1805	54
55	1.3156 2887	1.3769 9170	1.4087 1823	1.4411 6217	55
56	1.3222 0702	1.3850 2415	1.4175 2272	1.4507 6992	56
57	1.3288 1805	1.3931 0346	1.4263 8224	1.4604 4172	57
58	1.3354 6214	1.4012 2990	1.4352 9713	1.4701 7799	58
59	1.3421 3946	1.4094 0374	1.4442 6773	1.4799 7918	59
60	1.3488 5015	1.4176 2526	1.4532 9441	1.4898 4571	60
61	1.3555 9440	1.4258 9474	1.4623 7750	1.4997 7801	51
62	1.3623 7238	1.4342 1246	1.4715 1736	1.5097 7653	62
63	1.3691 8424	1.4425 7870	1.4807 1434	1.5198 4171	63
64	1.3760 3016	1.4509 9374	1.4899 6881	1.5299 7399	64
65	1.3829 1031	1.4594 5787	1.4992 8111	1.5401 7381	65
66	1.3898 2486	1.4679 7138	1.5086 5162	1.5504 4164	66
67	1.3967 7399	1.4765 3454	1.5180 8069	1.5607 7792	67
68	1.4037 5785	1.4851 4766	1.5275 6869	1.5711 9310	68
69	1.4107 7664	1.4938 1102	1.5371 1600	1.5816 5766	69
70	1.4178 3053	1.5025 2492	1.5467 2297	1.5922 0204	70
71	1.4249 1968	1.5112 8965	1.5563 8999	1.6028 1672	71
72	1.4320 4428	1.5201 0550	1.5661 1743	1.6135 0217	72
73	1.4392 0450	1.5289 7279	1.5759 0566	1.6242 5885	73
74	1.4464 0052	1.5378 9179	1.5857 5507	1.6350 8724	74
75	1.4536 3252	1.5468 6283	1.5956 6604	1.6459 8782	75
76	1.4609 0069	1.5558 8620	1.6056 3896	1.6569 6107	76
77	1.4682 0519	1.5649 6220	1.6156 7420	1.6680 0748	77
78	1.4755 4622	1.5740 9115	1.6257 7216	1.6791 2753	78
79	1.4829 2395	1.5832 7334	1.6359 3324	1.6903 2172	79
80	1.4903 3857	1.5925 0910	1.6461 5782	1.7015 9053	80
81	1.4977 9026	1.6017 9874	1.6564 4631	1.7129 3446	81
82	1.5052 7921	1.6111 4257	1.6667 9910	1.7243 5403	82
83	1.5128 0561	1.6205 4090	1.6772 1659	1.7358 4972	83
84	1.5203 6964	1.6299 9405	1.6876 9920	1.7474 2205	84
85	1.5279 7148	1.6395 0235	1.6982 4732	1.7590 7153	85
86	1.5356 1134	1.6490 6612	1.7088 6136	1.7707 9868	86
87	1.5432 8940	1.6586 8567	1.7195 4175	1.7826 0400	87
88	1.5510 0585	1.6683 6134	1.7302 8888	1.7944 8803	88
89	1.5587 6087	1.6780 9344	1.7411 0319	1.8064 5128	89
90	1.5665 5468	1.6878 8232	1.7519 8508	1.8184 9429	90
91	1.5743 8745	1.6977 2830	1.7629 3499	1.8306 1758	91
92	1.5822 5939	1.7076 3172	1.7739 5333	1.8428 2170	92
93	1.5901 7069	1.7175 9290	1.7850 4054	1.8551 0718	93
94	1.5981 2154	1.7276 1219	1.7961 9704	1.8674 7456	94
95	1.6061 1215	1.7376 8993	1.8074 2328	1.8799 2439	95
96	1.6141 4271	1.7478 2646	1.8187 1967	1.8924 5722	96
97	1.6222 1342	1.7580 2211	1.8300 8667	1.9050 7360	97
98	1.6303 2449	1.7682 7724	1.8415 2471	1.9177 7409	98
99	1.6384 7611	1.7785 9219	1.8530 3424	1.9305 5925	99
100	1.6466 6849	1.7889 6731	1.8646 1570	1.9434 2965	100

251

n	$\frac{1}{2}\%$	$\frac{7}{12}\%$	$\frac{5}{8}\%$	$\frac{2}{3}\%$	u
101	1.6549 0183	1.7994 0295	1.8762 6955	1.9563 8585	101
102	1.6631 7634	1.8098 9947	1.8879 9624	1.9694 2842	102
103	1.6714 9223	1.8204 5722	1.8997 9621	1.9825 5794	103
104	1.6798 4969	1.8310 7655	1.9116 6994	1.9957 7499	104
105	1.6882 4894	1.8417 5783	1.9236 1788	2.0090 8016	105
106	1.6966 9018	1.8525 0142	1.9356 4049	2.0224 7403	106
107	1.7051 7363	1.8633 0768	1.9477 3824	2.0359 5719	107
108	1.7136 9950	1.8741 7697	1.9599 1161	2.0495 3024	108
109	1.7222 6800	1.8851 0967	1.9721 6105	2.0631 9377	109
110	1.7308 7934	1.8961 0614	1.9844 8706	2.0769 4840	110
111	1.7395 3373	1.9071 6676	1.9968 9010	2.0907 9472	111
112	1.7482 3140	1.9182 9190	2.0093 7067	2.1047 3335	112
113	1.7569 7256	1.9294 8194	2.0219 2923	2.1187 6491	113
114	1.7657 5742	1.9407 3725	2.0345 6629	2.1328 9000	114
115	1.7745 8621	1.9520 5822	2.0472 8233	2.1471 0927	115
116	1.7834 5914	1.9634 4522	2.0600 7785	2.1614 2333	116
117	1.7923 7644	1.9748 9865	2.0729 5333	2.1758 3282	117
118	1.8013 3832	1.9864 1890	2.0859 0929	2.1903 3837	118
119	1.8103 4501	1.9980 0634	2.0989 4622	2.2049 4063	119
120	1.8193 9673	2.0096 6138	2.1120 6464	2.2196 4023	120
121	1.8284 9372	2.0213 8440	2.1252 6504	2.2344 3784	121
122	1.8376 3619	2.0331 7581	2.1385 4795	2.2493 3409	122
123	1.8468 2437	2.0450 3600	2.1519 1387	2.2643 2965	123
124	1.8560 5849	2.0569 6538	2.1653 6333	2.2794 2518	124
125	1.8653 3878	2.0689 6434	2.1788 9685	2.2946 2135	125
126	1.8746 6548	2.0810 3330	2.1925 1496	2.3099 1882	126
127	1.8840 3880	2.0931 7266	2.2062 1818	2.3253 1828	127
128	1.8934 5900	2.1053 8284	2.2200 0704	2.3408 2040	128
129	1.9029 2629	2.1176 6424	2.2338 8209	2.3564 2587	129
130	1.9124 4092	2.1300 1728	2.2478 4385	2.3721 3538	130
131	1.9220 0313	2.1424 4238	2.2618 9287	2.3879 4962	131
132	1.9316 1314	2.1549 3996	2.2760 2970	2.4038 6928	132
133	1.9412 7121	2.1675 1044	2.2902 5489	2.4198 9507	133
134	1.9509 7757	2.1801 5425	2.3045 6898	2.4360 2771	134
135	1.9607 3245	2.1928 7182	2.3189 7254	2.4522 6789	135
136	1.9705 3612	2.2056 6357	2.3334 6612	2.4686 1635	136
137	1.9803 8880	2.2185 2994	2.3480 5028	2.4850 7379	137
138	1.9902 9074	2.2314 7137	2.3627 2559	2.5016 4095	138
139	2.0002 4219	2.2444 8828	2.3774 9263	2.5183 1855	139
140	2.0102 4340	2.2575 8113	2.3923 5196	2.5351 0734	140
141	2.0202 9462	2.2707 5036	2.4073 0416	2.5520 0806	141
142	2.0303 9609	2.2839 9640	2.4223 4981	2.5690 2145	142
143	2.0405 4808	2.2973 1971	2.4374 8950	2.5861 4826	143
144	2.0507 5082	2.3107 2074	2.4527 2380	2.6033 8924	144
145	2.0610 0457	2.3241 9995	2.4680 5333	2.6207 4517	145
146	2.0713 0959	2.3377 5778	2.4834 7866	2.6382 1681	146
147	2.0816 6614	2.3513 9470	2.4990 0040	2.6558 0492	147
148	2.0920 7447	2.3651 1117	2.5146 1916	2.6735 1028	148
149	2.1025 3484	2.3789 0765	2.5303 3553	2.6913 3369	149
150	2.1130 4752	2.3927 8461	2.5461 5012	2.7092 7591	150

TABLE 11—COMPOUND AMOUNT OF $1.00 WITH INTEREST COMPOUNDED FOR n PERIODS AT RATE PER PERIOD, i. (Cont.)

n	¾%	⅞%	1%	1⅛%	n
1	1.0075 0000	1.0087 5000	1.0100 0000	1.0112 5000	1
2	1.0150 5625	1 0175 7656	1.0201 0000	1.0226 2656	2
3	1.0226 6917	1.0264 8036	1.0303 0100	1.0341 3111	3
4	1.0303 3919	1.0354 6206	1.0406 0401	1.0457 6509	4
5	1.0380 6673	1.0445 2235	1.0510 1005	1.0575 2994	5
6	1.0458 5224	1.0536 6192	1.0615 2015	1.0694 2716	6
7	1.0536 9613	1.0628 8147	1.0721 3535	1.0814 5821	7
8	1.0615 9885	1.0721 8168	1.0828 5671	1.0936 2462	8
9	1.0695 6084	1.0815 6327	1.0936 8527	1.1059 2789	9
10	1.0775 8255	1.0910 2695	1.1046 2213	1.1183 6958	10
11	1.0856 6441	1.1005 7343	1.1156 6835	1.1309 5124	11
12	1.0938 0690	1.1102 0345	1.1268 2503	1.1436 7444	12
13	1.1020 1045	1.1199 1773	1.1380 9328	1.1565 4078	13
14	1.1102 7553	1.1297 1701	1.1494 7421	1.1695 5186	14
15	1.1186 0259	1.1396 0203	1.1609 6896	1.1827 0932	15
16	1.1269 9211	1.1495 7355	1.1725 7864	1.1960 1480	16
17	1.1354 4455	1.1596 3232	1.1843 0443	1.2094 6997	17
18	1.1439 6039	1.1697 7910	1.1961 4748	1.2230 7650	18
19	1.1525 4009	1.1800 1467	1.2081 0895	1.2368 3611	19
20	1.1611 8414	1.1903 3980	1.2201 9004	1.2507 5052	20
21	1.1698 9302	1.2007 5527	1.2323 9194	1.2648 2146	21
22	1.1786 6722	1.2112 6188	1.2447 1586	1.2790 5071	22
23	1.1875 0723	1.2218 6042	1.2571 6302	1.2934 4003	23
24	1.1964 1353	1.2325 5170	1.2697 3465	1.3079 9123	24
25	1.2053 8663	1.2433 3653	1.2824 3200	1.3227 0613	25
26	1.2144 2703	1.2542 1572	1.2952 5631	1.3375 8657	26
27	1.2235 3523	1.2651 9011	1.3082 0888	1.3526 3442	27
28	1.2327 1175	1.2762 6052	1.3212 9097	1.3678 5156	28
29	1.2419 5709	1.2874 2780	1.3345 0388	1.3832 3989	29
30	1.2512 7176	1.2986 9280	1.3478 4892	1.3988 0134	30
31	1.2606 5630	1.3100 5636	1.3613 2740	1.4145 3785	31
32	1.2701 1122	1.3215 1935	1.3749 4068	1.4304 5140	32
33	1.2796 3706	1.3330 8265	1.3886 9009	1.4465 4398	33
34	1.2892 3434	1.3447 4712	1.4025 7699	1.4628 1760	34
35	1.2989 0359	1.3565 1366	1.4166 0276	1.4792 7430	35
36	1.3086 4537	1.3683 8315	1.4307 6878	1.4959 1613	36
37	1.3184 6021	1.3803 5650	1.4450 7647	1.5127 4519	37
38	1.3283 4866	1.3924 3462	1.4595 2724	1.5297 6357	38
39	1.3383 1128	1.4046 1843	1.4741 2251	1.5469 7341	39
40	1.3483 4861	1.4169 0884	1.4888 6373	1.5643 7687	40
41	1.3584 6123	1.4293 0679	1.5037 5237	1.5819 7611	41
42	1.3686 4969	1.4418 1322	1.5187 8989	1.5997 7334	42
43	1.3789 1456	1.4544 2909	1.5339 7779	1.6177 7079	43
44	1.3892 5642	1.4671 5534	1.5493 1757	1.6359 7071	44
45	1.3996 7584	1.4799 9295	1.5648 1075	1.6543 7538	45
46	1.4101 7341	1.4929 4289	1.5804 5885	1.6729 8710	46
47	1.4207 4971	1.5060 0614	1.5962 6344	1.6918 0821	47
48	1.4314 0533	1.5191 8370	1.6122 2608	1.7108 4105	48
49	1.4421 4087	1.5324 7655	1.6283 4834	1.7300 8801	49
50	1.4529 5693	1.5458 8572	1.6446 3182	1.7495 5150	50

n	$\frac{3}{4}\%$	$\frac{7}{8}\%$	1%	$1\frac{1}{8}\%$	n
51	1.4638 5411	1.5594 1222	1.6610 7814	1.7692 3395	51
52	1.4748 3301	1.5730 5708	1.6776 8892	1.7891 3784	52
53	1.4858 9426	1.5868 2133	1.6944 6581	1.8092 6564	53
54	1.4970 3847	1.6007 0602	1.7114 1047	1.8296 1988	54
55	1.5082 6626	1.6147 1219	1.7285 2457	1.8502 0310	55
56	1.5195 7825	1.6288 4093	1.7458 0982	1.8710 1788	56
57	1.5309 7509	1.6430 9328	1.7632 6792	1.8920 6684	57
58	1.5424 5740	1.6574 7035	1.7809 0060	1.9133 5259	58
59	1.5540 2583	1.6719 7322	1.7987 0960	1.9348 7780	59
60	1.5656 8103	1.6866 0298	1.8166 9670	1.9566 4518	60
61	1.5774 2363	1.7013 6076	1.8348 6367	1.9786 5744	61
62	1.5892 5431	1.7162 4766	1.8532 1230	2.0009 1733	62
63	1.6011 7372	1.7312 6483	1.8717 4443	2.0234 2765	63
64	1.6131 8252	1.7464 1340	1.8904 6187	2.0461 9121	64
65	1.6252 8139	1.7616 9452	1.9093 6649	2.0692 1087	65
66	1.6374 7100	1.7771 0934	1.9284 6015	2.0924 8949	66
67	1.6497 5203	1.7926 5905	1.9477 4475	2.1160 2999	67
68	1.6621 2517	1.8083 4482	1.9672 2220	2.1398 3533	68
69	1.6745 9111	1.8241 6783	1.9868 9442	2.1639 0848	69
70	1.6871 5055	1.8401 2930	2.0067 6337	2.1882 5245	70
71	1.6998 0418	1.8562 3043	2.0268 3100	2.2128 7029	71
72	1.7125 5271	1.8724 7245	2.0470 9931	2.2377 6508	72
73	1.7253 9685	1.8888 5658	2.0675 7031	2.2629 3994	73
74	1.7383 3733	1.9053 8408	2.0882 4601	2.2883 9801	74
75	1.7513 7486	1.9220 5619	2.1091 2847	2.3141 4249	75
76	1.7645 1017	1.9388 7418	2.1302 1975	2.3401 7659	76
77	1.7777 4400	1.9558 3933	2.1515 2195	2.3665 0358	77
78	1.7910 7708	1.9729 5292	2.1730 3717	2.3931 2675	78
79	1.8045 1015	1.9902 1626	2.1947 6754	2.4200 4942	79
80	1.8180 4398	2.0076 3066	2.2167 1522	2.4472 7498	80
81	1.8316 7931	2.0251 9742	2.2388 8237	2.4748 0682	81
82	1.8454 1691	2.0429 1790	2.2612 7119	2.5026 4840	82
83	1.8592 5753	2.0607 9343	2.2838 8390	2.5308 0319	83
84	1.8732 0196	2.0788 2537	2.3067 2274	2.5592 7473	84
85	1.8872 5098	2.0970 1510	2.3297 8997	2.5880 6657	85
86	1.9014 0536	2.1153 6398	2.3530 8787	2.6171 8232	86
87	1.9156 6590	2.1338 7341	2.3766 1875	2.6466 2562	87
88	1.9300 3339	2.1525 4481	2.4003 8494	2.6764 0016	88
89	1.9445 0865	2.1713 7957	2.4243 8879	2.7065 0966	89
90	1.9590 9246	2.1903 7914	2.4486 3267	2.7369 5789	90
91	1.9737 8565	2.2095 4496	2.4731 1900	2.7677 4867	91
92	1.9885 8905	2.2288 7848	2.4978 5019	2.7988 8584	92
93	2.0035 0346	2.2483 8117	2.5228 2869	2.8303 7331	93
94	2.0185 2974	2.2680 5450	2.5480 5698	2.8622 1501	94
95	2.0336 6871	2.2878 9998	2.5735 3755	2.8944 1492	95
96	2.0489 2123	2.3079 1910	2.5992 7293	2.9269 7709	96
97	2.0642 8814	2.3281 1340	2.6252 6565	2.9599 0559	97
98	2.0797 7030	2.3484 8439	2.6515 1831	2.9932 0452	98
99	2.0953 6858	2.3690 3363	2.6780 3349	3.0268 7807	99
100	2.1110 8384	2.3897 6267	2.7048 1383	3.0609 3045	100

n	$\frac{3}{4}\%$	$\frac{7}{8}\%$	1%	$1\frac{1}{8}\%$	n
101	2.1269 1697	2.4106 7309	2.7318 6197	3.0953 6592	101
102	2.1428 6885	2.4317 6648	2.7591 8059	3.1301 8879	102
103	2.1589 4036	2.4530 4444	2.7867 7239	3.1654 0341	103
104	2.1751 3242	2.4745 0858	2.8146 4012	3.2010 1420	104
105	2.1914 4591	2.4961 6053	2.8427 8652	3.2370 2561	105
106	2.2078 8175	2.5180 0193	2.8712 1438	3.2734 4215	106
107	2.2244 4087	2.5400 3445	2.8999 2653	3.3102 6837	107
108	2.2411 2417	2.5622 5975	2.9289 2579	3.3475 0889	108
109	2.2579 3260	2.5846 7953	2.9582 1505	3.3851 6836	109
110	2.2748 6710	2.6072 9547	2.9877 9720	3.4232 5151	110
111	2.2919 2860	2.6301 0931	3.0176 7517	3.4617 6309	111
112	2.3091 1807	2.6531 2276	3.0478 5192	3.5007 0792	112
113	2.3264 3645	2.6763 3759	3.0783 3044	3.5400 9089	113
114	2.3438 8472	2.6997 5554	3.1091 1375	3.5799 1691	114
115	2.3614 6386	2.7233 7840	3.1402 0489	3.6201 9097	115
116	2.3791 7484	2.7472 0796	3.1716 0693	3.6609 1812	116
117	2.3970 1865	2.7712 4603	3.2033 2300	3.7021 0345	117
118	2.4149 9629	2.7954 9444	3.2353 5623	3.7437 5212	118
119	2.4331 0876	2.8199 5501	3.2677 0980	3.7858 6933	119
120	2.4513 5708	2.8446 2962	3.3003 8689	3.8284 6036	120
121	2.4697 4226	2.8695 2013	3.3333 9076	3.8715 3054	121
122	2.4882 6532	2.8946 2843	3.3667 2467	3.9150 8525	122
123	2.5069 2731	2.9199 5643	3.4003 9192	3.9591 2996	123
124	2.5257 2927	2.9455 0605	3.4343 9584	4.0036 7018	124
125	2.5446 7224	2.9712 7922	3.4687 3980	4.0487 1147	125
126	2.5637 5728	2.9972 7792	3.5034 2719	4.0942 5947	126
127	2.5829 8546	3.0235 0410	3.5384 6147	4.1403 1989	127
128	2.6023 5785	3.0499 5976	3.5738 4608	4.1868 9849	128
129	2.6218 7553	3.0766 4691	3.6095 8454	4.2340 0110	129
130	2.6415 3960	3.1035 6757	3.6456 8039	4.2816 3361	130
131	2.6613 5115	3.1307 2378	3.6821 3719	4.3298 0199	131
132	2.6813 1128	3.1581 1762	3.7189 5856	4.3785 1226	132
133	2.7014 2112	3.1857 5115	3.7561 4815	4.4277 7052	133
134	2.7216 8177	3.2136 2647	3.7937 0963	4.4775 8294	134
135	2.7420 9439	3.2417 4570	3.8316 4673	4.5279 5575	135
136	2.7626 6009	3.2701 1098	3.8699 6319	4.5788 9525	136
137	2.7833 8005	3.2987 2445	3.9086 6282	4.6304 0782	137
138	2.8042 5540	3.3275 8829	3.9477 4945	4.6824 9991	138
139	2.8252 8731	3.3567 0468	3.9872 2695	4.7351 7803	139
140	2.8464 7697	3.3860 7585	4.0270 9922	4.7884 4879	140
141	2.8678 2554	3.4157 0401	4.0673 7021	4.8423 1883	141
142	2.8893 3424	3.4455 9142	4.1080 4391	4.8967 9492	142
143	2.9110 0424	3.4757 4035	4.1491 2435	4.9518 8386	143
144	2.9328 3677	3.5061 5308	4.1906 1559	5.0075 9256	144
145	2.9548 3305	3.5368 3192	4.2325 2175	5.0639 2797	145
146	2.9769 9430	3.5677 7919	4.2748 4697	5.1208 9716	146
147	2.9993 2175	3.5989 9726	4.3175 9544	5.1785 0726	147
148	3.0218 1667	3.6304 8849	4.3607 7139	5.2367 6546	148
149	3.0444 8029	3.6622 5526	4.4043 7910	5.2956 7908	149
150	3.0673 1389	3.6943 0000	4.4484 2290	5.3552 5546	150

n	$1\frac{1}{4}\%$	$1\frac{3}{8}\%$	$1\frac{1}{2}\%$	$1\frac{3}{4}\%$	n
1	1.0125 0000	1.0137 5000	1.0150 0000	1.0175 0000	1
2	1.0251 5625	1.0276 8906	1.0302 2500	1.0353 0625	2
3	1.0379 7070	1.0418 1979	1.0456 7838	1.0534 2411	3
4	1.0509 4534	1.0561 4481	1.0613 6355	1.0718 5903	4
5	1.0640 8215	1.0706 6680	1.0772 8400	1.0906 1656	5
6	1.0773 8318	1.0853 8847	1.0934 4326	1.1097 0235	6
7	1.0908 5047	1.1003 1256	1.1098 4491	1.1291 2215	7
8	1.1044 8610	1.1154 4186	1.1264 9259	1.1488 8178	8
9	1.1182 9218	1.1307 7918	1.1433 8998	1.1689 8721	9
10	1.1322 7083	1.1463 2740	1.1605 4083	1.1894 4449	10
11	1.1464 2422	1.1620 8940	1.1779 4894	1.2102 5977	11
12	1.1607 5452	1.1780 6813	1.1956 1817	1.2314 3931	12
13	1.1752 6395	1.1942 6656	1.2135 5244	1.2529 8950	13
14	1.1899 5475	1.2106 8773	1.2317 5573	1.2749 1682	14
15	1.2048 2918	1.2273 3469	1.2502 3207	1.2972 2786	15
16	1.2198 8955	1.2442 1054	1.2689 8555	1.3199 2935	16
17	1.2351 3817	1.2613 1843	1.2880 2033	1.3430 2811	17
18	1.2505 7739	1.2786 6156	1.3073 4064	1.3665 3111	18
19	1.2662 0961	1.2962 4316	1.3269 5075	1.3904 4540	19
20	1.2820 3723	1.3140 6650	1.3468 5501	1.4147 7820	20
21	1.2980 6270	1.3321 3492	1.3670 5783	1.4395 3681	21
22	1.3142 8848	1.3504 5177	1.3875 6370	1.4647 2871	22
23	1.3307 1709	1.3690 2048	1.4083 7715	1.4903 6146	23
24	1.3473 5105	1.3878 4451	1.4295 0281	1.5164 4279	24
25	1.3641 9294	1.4069 2738	1.4509 4535	1.5429 8054	25
26	1.3812 4535	1.4262 7263	1.4727 0953	1.5699 8269	26
27	1.3985 1092	1.4458 8388	1.4948 0018	1.5974 5739	27
28	1.4159 9230	1.4657 6478	1.5172 2218	1.6254 1290	28
29	1.4336 9221	1.4859 1905	1.5399 8051	1.6538 5762	29
30	1.4516 1336	1.5063 5043	1.5630 8022	1.6828 0013	30
31	1.4697 5853	1.5270 6275	1.5865 2642	1.7122 4913	31
32	1.4881 3051	1.5480 5986	1.6103 2432	1.7422 1349	32
33	1.5067 3214	1.5693 4569	1.6344 7918	1.7727 0223	33
34	1.5255 6629	1.5909 2419	1.6589 9637	1.8037 2452	34
35	1.5446 3587	1.6127 9940	1.6838 8132	1.8352 8970	35
36	1.5639 4382	1.6349 7539	1.7091 3954	1.8674 0727	36
37	1.5834 9312	1.6574 5630	1.7347 7663	1.9000 8689	37
38	1.6032 8678	1.6802 4633	1.7607 9828	1.9333 3841	38
39	1.6233 2787	1.7033 4971	1.7872 1025	1.9671 7184	39
40	1.6436 1946	1.7267 7077	1.8140 1841	2.0015 9734	40
41	1.6641 6471	1.7505 1387	1.8412 2868	2.0366 2530	41
42	1.6849 6677	1.7745 8343	1.8688 4712	2.0722 6624	42
43	1.7060 2885	1.7989 8396	1.8968 7982	2.1085 3090	43
44	1.7273 5421	1.8237 1999	1.9253 3302	2.1454 3019	44
45	1.7489 4614	1.8487 9614	1.9542 1301	2.1829 7522	45
46	1.7708 0797	1.8742 1708	1.9835 2621	2.2211 7728	46
47	1.7929 4306	1.8999 8757	2.0132 7910	2.2600 4789	47
48	1.8153 5485	1.9261 1240	2.0434 7829	2.2995 9872	48
49	1.8380 4679	1.9525 9644	2.0741 3046	2.3398 4170	49
50	1.8610 2237	1.9794 4464	2.1052 4242	2.3807 8893	50

n	$1\frac{1}{4}\%$	$1\frac{3}{8}\%$	$1\frac{1}{2}\%$	$1\frac{3}{4}\%$	n
51	1.8842 8515	2.0066 6201	2.1368 2106	2.4224 5274	51
52	1.9078 3872	2.0342 5361	2.1688 7337	2.4648 4566	52
53	1.9316 8670	2.0622 2460	2.2014 0647	2.5079 8046	53
54	1.9558 3279	2.0905 8019	2.2344 2757	2.5518 7012	54
55	1.9802 8070	2.1193 2566	2.2679 4398	2.5965 2785	55
56	2.0050 3420	2.1484 6639	2.3019 6314	2.6419 6708	56
57	2.0300 9713	2.1780 0780	2.3364 9259	2.6882 0151	57
58	2.0554 7335	2.2079 5541	2.3715 3998	2.7352 4503	58
59	2.0811 6676	2.2383 1480	2.4071 1308	2.7831 1182	59
60	2.1071 8135	2.2690 9163	2.4432 1978	2.8318 1628	60
61	2.1335 2111	2.3002 9164	2.4798 6807	2.8813 7306	61
62	2.1601 9013	2.3319 2065	2.5170 6609	2.9317 9709	62
63	2.1871 9250	2.3639 8456	2.5548 2208	2.9831 0354	63
64	2.2145 3241	2.3964 8934	2.5931 4442	3.0343 0785	64
65	2.2422 1407	2.4294 4107	2.6320 4158	3.0884 2574	65
66	2.2702 4174	2.4628 4589	2.6715 2221	3.1424 7319	66
67	2.2986 1976	2.4967 1002	2.7115 9504	3.1974 6647	67
68	2.3273 5251	2.5310 3978	2.7522 6896	3.2534 2213	68
69	2.3564 4442	2.5658 4158	2.7935 5300	3.3103 5702	69
70	2.3858 9997	2.6011 2190	2.8354 5629	3.3682 8827	70
71	2.4157 2372	2.6368 8732	2.8779 8814	3.4272 3331	71
72	2.4459 2027	2.6731 4453	2.9211 5796	3.4872 0990	72
73	2.4764 9427	2.7099 0026	2.9649 7533	3.5482 3607	73
74	2.5074 5045	2.7471 6139	3.0094 4996	3.6103 3020	74
75	2.5387 9358	2.7849 3486	3.0545 9171	3.6735 1098	75
76	2.5705 2850	2.8232 2771	3.1004 1059	3.7377 9742	76
77	2.6026 6011	2.8620 4710	3.1469 1674	3.8032 0888	77
78	2.6351 9336	2.9014 0024	3.1941 2050	3.8697 6503	78
79	2.6681 3327	2.9412 9450	3.2420 3230	3.9374 8592	79
80	2.7014 8494	2.9817 3730	3.2906 6279	4.0063 9192	80
81	2.7352 5350	3.0227 3618	3.3400 2273	4.0765 0378	81
82	2.7694 4417	3.0642 9881	3.3901 2307	4.1478 4260	82
83	2.8040 6222	3.1064 3291	3.4409 7492	4.2204 2984	83
84	2.8391 1300	3.1491 4637	3.4925 8954	4.2942 8737	84
85	2.8746 0191	3.1924 4713	3.5449 7838	4.3694 3740	85
86	2.9105 3444	3.2363 4328	3.5981 5306	4.4459 0255	86
87	2.9469 1612	3.2808 4300	3.6521 2535	4.5237 0584	87
88	2.9837 5257	3.3259 5459	3.7069 0723	4.6028 7070	88
89	3.0210 4948	3.3716 8646	3.7625 1084	4.6834 2093	89
90	3.0588 1260	3.4180 4715	3.8189 4851	4.7653 8080	90
91	3.0970 4775	3.4650 4530	3.8762 3273	4.8487 7496	91
92	3.1357 6085	3.5126 8967	3.9343 7622	4.9336 2853	92
93	3.1749 5786	3.5609 8916	3.9933 9187	5.0199 6703	93
94	3.2146 4483	3.6099 5276	·4.0532 9275	5.1078 1645	94
95	3.2548 2789	3.6595 8961	4.1140 9214	5.1972 0324	95
96	3.2955 1324	3.7099 0897	4.1758 0352	5.2881 5429	96
97	3.3367 0716	3.7609 2021	4.2384 4057	5.3806 9699	97
98	3.3784 1600	3.8126 3287	4.3020 1718	5.4748 5919	98
99	3.4206 4620	3.8650 5657	4.3665 4744	5.5706 6923	99
100	3.4634 0427	3.9182 0110	4.4320 4565	5.6681 5594	100

n	2%	2¼%	2½%	2¾%	n
1	1.0200 0000	1.0225 0000	1.0250 0000	1.0275 0000	1
2	1.0404 0000	1.0455 0625	1.0506 2500	1.0557 5625	2
3	1.0612 0800	1.0690 3014	1.0768 9063	1.0847 8955	3
4	1.0824 3216	1.0930 8332	1.1038 1289	1.1146 2126	4
5	1.1040 8080	1.1176 7769	1.1314 0821	1.1452 7334	5
6	1.1261 6242	1.1428 2544	1.1596 9342	1.1767 6836	6
7	1.1486 8567	1.1685 3901	1.1886 8575	1.2091 2949	7
8	1.1716 5938	1.1948 3114	1.2184 0290	1.2423 8055	8
9	1.1950 9257	1.2217 1484	1.2488 6297	1.2765 4602	9
10	1.2189 9442	1.2492 0343	1.2800 8454	1.3116 5103	10
11	1.2433 7431	1.2773 1050	1.3120 8666	1.3477 2144	11
12	1.2682 4179	1.3060 4999	1.3448 8882	1.3847 8378	12
13	1.2936 0663	1.3354 3611	1.3785 1104	1.4228 6533	13
14	1.3194 7876	1.3654 8343	1.4129 7382	1.4619 9413	14
15	1.3458 6834	1.3962 0680	1.4482 9817	1.5021 9896	15
16	1.3727 8571	1.4276 2146	1.4845 0562	1.5435 0944	16
17	1.4002 4142	1.4597 4294	1.5216 1826	1.5859 5595	17
18	1.4282 4625	1.4925 8716	1.5596 5872	1.6295 6973	18
19	1.4568 1117	1.5261 7037	1.5986 5019	1.6743 8290	19
20	1.4859 4740	1.5605 0920	1.6386 1644	1.7204 2843	20
21	1.5156 6634	1.5956 2066	1.6795 8185	1.7677 4021	21
22	1.5459 7967	1.6315 2212	1.7215 7140	1.8163 5307	22
23	1.5768 9926	1.6682 3137	1.7646 1068	1.8663 0278	23
24	1.6084 3725	1.7057 6658	1.8087 2595	1.9176 2610	24
25	1.6406 0599	1.7441 4632	1.8539 4410	1.9703 6082	25
26	1.6734 1811	1.7833 8962	1.9002 9270	2.0245 4575	26
27	1.7068 8648	1.8235 1588	1.9478 0002	2.0802 2075	27
28	1.7410 2421	1.8645 4499	1.9964 9502	2.1374 2682	28
29	1.7758 4469	1.9064 9725	2.0464 0739	2.1962 0606	29
30	1.8113 6158	1.9493 9344	2.0975 6758	2.2566 0173	30
31	1.8475 8882	1.9932 5479	2.1500 0677	2.3186 5828	31
32	1.8845 4059	2.0381 0303	2.2037 5694	2.3824 2138	32
33	1.9222 3140	2.0839 6034	2.2588 5086	2.4479 3797	33
34	1.9606 7603	2.1308 4945	2.3153 2213	2.5152 5626	34
35	1.9998 8955	2.1787 9356	2.3732 0519	2.5844 2581	35
36	2.0398 8734	2.2278 1642	2.4325 3532	2.6554 9752	36
37	2.0806 8509	2.2779 4229	2.4933 4870	2.7285 2370	37
38	2.1222 9879	2.3291 9599	2.5556 8242	2.8035 5810	38
39	2.1647 4477	2.3816 0290	2.6195 7448	2.8806 5595	39
40	2.2080 3966	2.4351 8897	2.6850 6384	2.9598 7399	40
41	2.2522 0046	2.4899 8072	2.7521 9043	3.0412 7052	41
42	2.2972 4447	2.5460 0528	2.8209 9520	3.1249 0546	42
43	2.3431 8936	2.6032 9040	2.8915 2008	3.2108 4036	43
44	2.3900 5314	2.6618 6444	2.9638 0808	3.2991 3847	44
45	2.4378 5421	2.7217 5639	3.0379 0328	3.3898 6478	45
46	2.4866 1129	2.7829 9590	3.1138 5086	3.4830 8606	46
47	2.5363 4351	2.8456 1331	3.1916 9713	3.5788 7093	47
48	2.5870 7039	2.9096 3961	3.2714 8956	3.6772 8988	48
49	2.6388 1179	2.9751 0650	3.3532 7680	3.7784 1535	49
50	2.6915 8803	3.0420 4640	3.4371 0872	3.8823 2177	50

n	2%	2¼%	2½%	2¾%	n
51	2.7454 1979	3.1104 9244	3.5230 3644	3.9890 8562	51
52	2.8003 2819	3.1804 7852	3.6111 1235	4.0987 8547	52
53	2.8563 3475	3.2520 3929	3.7013 9016	4.2115 0208	53
54	2.9134 6144	3.3252 1017	3.7939 2491	4.3273 1838	54
55	2.9717 3067	3.4000 2740	3.8887 7303	4.4463 1964	55
56	3.0311 6529	3.4765 2802	3.9859 9236	4.5685 9343	56
57	3.0917 8859	3.5547 4990	4.0856 4217	4.6942 2975	57
58	3.1536 2436	3.6347 3177	4.1877 8322	4.8233 2107	58
59	3.2166 9685	3.7165 1324	4.2924 7780	4.9559 6239	59
60	3.2810 3079	3.8001 3479	4.3997 8975	5.0922 5136	60
61	3.3466 5140	3.8856 3782	4.5097 8449	5.2322 8827	61
62	3.4135 8443	3.9730 6467	4.6225 2910	5.3761 7620	62
63	3.4818 5612	4.0624 5862	4.7380 9233	5.5240 2105	63
64	3.5514 9324	4.1538 6394	4.8565 4464	5.6759 3162	64
65	3.6225 2311	4.2473 2588	4.9779 5826	5.8320 1974	65
66	3.6949 7357	4.3428 9071	5.1024 0721	5.9924 0029	66
67	3.7688 7304	4.4406 0576	5.2299 6739	6.1571 9130	67
68	3.8442 5050	4.5405 1939	5.3607 1658	6.3265 1406	68
69	3.9211 3551	4.6426 8107	5.4947 3449	6.5004 9319	69
70	3.9995 5822	4.7471 4140	5.6321 0286	6.6792 5676	70
71	4.0795 4939	4.8539 5208	5.7729 0543	6.8629 3632	71
72	4.1611 4038	4.9631 6600	5.9172 2806	7.0516 6706	72
73	4.2443 6318	5.0748 3723	6.0651 5876	7.2455 8791	73
74	4.3292 5045	5.1890 2107	6.2167 8773	7.4448 4158	74
75	4.4158 3546	5.3057 7405	6.3722 0743	7.6495 7472	75
76	4.5041 5216	5.4251 5396	6.5315 1261	7.8599 3802	76
77	4.5942 3521	5.5472 1993	6.6948 0043	8.0760 8632	77
78	4.6861 1991	5.6720 3237	6.8621 7044	8.2981 7869	78
79	4.7798 4231	5.7996 5310	7.0337 2470	8.5263 7861	79
80	4.8754 3916	5.9301 4530	7.2095 6782	8.7608 5402	80
81	4.9729 4794	6.0635 7357	7.3898 0701	9.0017 7751	81
82	5.0724 0690	6.2000 0397	7.5745 5219	9.2493 2639	82
83	5.1738 5504	6.3395 0406	7.7639 1599	9.5036 8286	83
84	5.2773 3214	6.4821 4290	7.9580 1389	9.7650 3414	84
85	5.3828 7878	6.6279 9112	8.1569 6424	10.0335 7258	85
86	5.4905 3636	6.7771 2092	8.3608 8834	10.3094 9583	86
87	5.6003 4708	6.9296 0614	8.5699 1055	10.5930 0696	87
88	5.7123 5402	7.0855 2228	8.7841 5832	10.8843 1465	88
89	5.8266 0110	7.2449 4653	9.0037 6228	11.1836 3331	89
90	5.9431 3313	7.4079 5782	9.2288 5633	11.4911 8322	90
91	6.0619 9579	7.5746 3688	9.4595 7774	11.8071 9076	91
92	6.1832 3570	7.7450 6621	9.6960 6718	12.1318 8851	92
93	6.3069 0042	7.9193 3020	9.9384 6886	12.4655 1544	93
94	6.4330 3843	8.0975 1512	10.1869 3058	12.8083 1711	94
95	6.5616 9920	8.2797 0921	10.4416 0385	13.1605 4584	95
96	6.6929 3318	8.4660 0267	10.7026 4395	13.5224 6085	96
97	6.8267 9184	8.6564 8773	10.9702 1004	13.8943 2852	97
98	6.9633 2768	8.8512 5871	11.2444 6530	14.2764 2255	98
99	7.1025 9423	9.0504 1203	11.5255 7693	14.6690 2417	99
100	7.2446 4612	9.2540 4630	11.8137 1635	15.0724 2234	100

TABLE 11—COMPOUND AMOUNT OF $1.00 WITH INTEREST COMPOUNDED FOR n
PERIODS AT RATE PER PERIOD, i. (Cont.)

n	3%	3½%	4%	4½%	n
1	1.0300 0000	1.0350 0000	1.0400 0000	1.0450 0000	1
2	1.0609 0000	1.0712 2500	1.0816 0000	1.0920 2500	2
3	1.0927 2700	1.1087 1788	1.1248 6400	1.1411 6613	3
4	1.1255 0881	1.1475 2300	1.1698 5856	1.1925 1860	4
5	1.1592 7407	1.1876 8631	1.2166 5290	1.2461 8194	5
6	1.1940 5230	1.2292 5533	1.2653 1902	1.3022 6012	6
7	1.2298 7387	1.2722 7926	1.3159 3178	1.3608 6183	7
8	1.2667 7008	1.3168 0904	1.3685 6905	1.4221 0061	8
9	1.3047 7318	1.3628 9735	1.4233 1181	1.4860 9514	9
10	1.3439 1638	1.4105 9876	1.4802 4428	1.5529 6942	10
11	1.3842 3387	1.4599 6972	1.5394 5406	1.6228 5305	11
12	1.4257 6089	1.5110 6866	1.6010 3222	1.6958 8143	12
13	1.4685 3371	1.5639 5606	1.6650 7351	1.7721 9610	13
14	1.5125 8972	1.6186 9452	1.7316 7645	1.8519 4492	14
15	1.5579 6742	1.6753 4883	1.8009 4351	1.9352 8244	15
16	1.6047 0644	1.7339 8604	1.8729 8125	2.0223 7015	16
17	1.6528 4763	1.7946 7555	1.9479 0050	2.1133 7681	17
18	1.7024 3306	1.8574 8920	2.0258 1652	2.2084 7877	18
19	1.7535 0605	1.9225 0132	2.1068 4918	2.3078 6031	19
20	1.8061 1123	1.9897 8886	2.1911 2314	2.4117 1402	20
21	1.8602 9457	2.0594 3147	2.2787 6807	2.5202 4116	21
22	1.9161 0341	2.1315 1158	2.3699 1879	2.6336 5201	22
23	1.9735 8651	2.2061 1448	2.4647 1554	2.7521 6635	23
24	2.0327 9411	2.2833 2849	2.5633 0416	2.8760 1383	24
25	2.0937 7793	2.3632 4498	2.6658 3633	3.0054 3446	25
26	2.1565 9127	2.4459 5856	2.7724 6978	3.1406 7901	26
27	2.2212 8901	2.5315 6711	2.8833 6858	3.2820 0956	27
28	2.2879 2768	2.6201 7196	2.9987 0332	3.4296 9999	28
29	2.3565 6551	2.7118 7798	3.1186 5145	3.5840 3649	29
30	2.4272 6247	2.8067 9370	3.2433 9751	3.7453 1813	30
31	2.5000 8035	2.9050 3148	3.3731 3341	3.9138 5745	31
32	2.5750 8276	3.0067 0759	3.5080 5875	4.0899 8104	32
33	2.6523 3524	3.1119 4235	3.6483 8110	4.2740 3018	33
34	2.7319 0530	3.2208 6033	3.7943 1634	4.4663 6154	34
35	2.8138 6245	3.3335 9045	3.9460 8899	4.6673 4781	35
36	2.8982 7833	3.4502 6611	4.1039 3255	4.8773 7846	36
37	2.9852 2668	3.5710 2543	4.2680 8986	5.0968 6049	37
38	3.0747 8348	3.6960 1132	4.4388 1345	5.3262 1921	38
39	3.1670 2698	3.8253 7171	4.6163 6599	5.5658 9908	39
40	3.2620 3779	3.9592 5972	4.8010 2063	5.8163 6454	40
41	3.3598 9893	4.0978 3381	4.9930 6145	6.0781 0094	41
42	3.4606 9589	4.2412 5799	5.1927 8391	6.3516 1548	42
43	3.5645 1677	4.3897 0202	5.4004 9527	6.6374 3818	43
44	3.6714 5227	4.5433 4160	5.6165 1508	6.9361 2290	44
45	3.7815 9584	4.7023 5855	5.8411 7568	7.2482 4843	45
46	3.8950 4372	4.8669 4110	6.0748 2271	7.5744 1961	46
47	4.0118 9503	5.0372 8404	6.3178 1562	7.9152 6849	47
48	4.1322 5188	5.2135 8898	6.5705 2824	8.2714 5557	48
49	4.2562 1944	5.3960 6459	6.8333 4937	8.6436 7107	49
50	4.3839 0602	5.5849 2686	7.1066 8335	9.0326 3627	50

n	3%	3½%	4%	4½%	n
51	4.5154 2320	5.7803 9930	7.3909 5068	9.4391 0490	51
52	4.6508 8590	5.9827 1327	7.6865 8871	9.8638 6463	52
53	4.7904 1247	6.1921 0824	7.9940 5226	10.3077 3853	53
54	4.9341 2485	6.4088 3202	8.3138 1435	10.7715 8677	54
55	5.0821 4859	6.6331 4114	8.6463 6692	11.2563 0817	55
56	5.2346 1305	6.8653 0108	8.9922 2160	11.7628 4204	56
57	5.3916 5144	7.1055 8662	9.3519 1046	12.2921 6993	57
58	5.5534 0098	7.3542 8215	9.7259 8688	12.8453 1758	58
59	5.7200 0301	7.6116 8203	10.1150 2635	13.4233 5687	59
60	5.8916 0310	7.8780 9090	10.5196 2741	14.0274 0793	60
61	6.0683 5120	8.1538 2408	10.9404 1250	14.6586 4129	61
62	6.2504 0173	8.4392 0793	11.3780 2900	15.3182 8014	62
63	6.4379 1379	8.7345 8020	11.8331 5016	16.0076 0275	63
64	6.6310 5120	9.0402 9051	12.3064 7617	16.7279 4487	64
65	6.8299 8273	9.3567 0068	12.7987 3522	17.4807 0239	65
66	7.0348 8222	9.6841 8520	13.3106 8463	18.2673 3400	66
67	7.2459 2868	10.0231 3168	13.8431 1201	19.0893 6403	67
68	7.4633 0654	10.3739 4129	14.3968 3649	19.9483 8541	68
69	7.6872 0574	10.7370 2924	14.9727 0995	20.8460 6276	69
70	7.9178 2191	11.1128 2526	15.5716 1835	21.7841 3558	70
71	8.1553 5657	11.5017 7414	16.1944 8308	22.7644 2168	71
72	8.4000 1727	11.9043 3624	16.8422 6241	23.7888 2066	72
73	8.6520 1778	12.3209 8801	17.5159 5290	24.8593 1759	73
74	8.9115 7832	12.7522 2259	18.2165 9102	25.9779 8688	74
75	9.1789 2567	13.1985 5038	18.9452 5466	27.1469 9629	75
76	9.4542 9344	13.6604 9964	19.7030 6485	28.3686 1112	76
77	9.7379 2224	14.1386 1713	20.4911 8744	29.6451 9862	77
78	10.0300 5991	14.6334 6873	21.3108 3494	30.9792 3256	78
79	10.3309 6171	15.1456 4013	22.1632 6834	32.3732 9802	79
80	10.6408 9056	15.6757 3754	23.0497 9907	33.8300 9643	80
81	10.9601 1727	16.2243 8835	23.9717 9103	35.3524 5077	81
82	11.2889 2079	16.7922 4195	24.9306 6267	36.9433 1106	82
83	11.6275 8842	17.3799 7041	25.9278 8918	38.6057 6006	83
84	11.9764 1607	17.9882 6938	26.9650 0475	40.3430 1926	84
85	12.3357 0855	18.6178 5881	28.0436 0494	42.1584 5513	85
86	12.7057 7981	19.2694 8387	29.1653 4914	44.0555 8561	86
37	13.0869 5320	19.9439 1580	30.3319 6310	46.0380 8696	87
88	13.4795 6180	20.6419 5285	31.5452 4163	48.1098 0087	88
89	13.8839 4865	21.3644 2120	32.8070 5129	50.2747 4191	89
90	14.3004 6711	22.1121 7595	34.1193 3334	52.5371 0530	90
91	14.7294 8112	22.8861 0210	35.4841 0668	54.9012 7503	91
92	15.1713 6556	23.6871 1568	36.9034 7094	57.3718 3241	92
93	15.6265 0652	24.5161 6473	38.3796 0978	59.9535 6487	93
94	16.0953 0172	25.3742 3049	39.9147 9417	62.6514 7529	94
95	16.5781 6077	26.2623 2856	41.5113 8594	65.4707 9168	95
96	17.0755 0559	27.1815 1006	43.1718 4138	68.4169 7730	96
97	17.5877 7076	28.1328 6291	44.8987 1503	71.4957 4128	97
98	18.1154 0388	29.1175 1311	46.6946 6363	74.7130 4964	98
99	18.6588 6600	30.1366 2607	48.5624 5018	78.0751 3687	99
100	19.2186 3198	31.1914 0798	50.5049 4818	81.5885 1803	100

n	5%	5½%	6%	6½%	n
1	1.0500 0000	1.0550 0000	1.0600 0000	1.0650 0000	1
2	1.1025 0000	1.1130 2500	1.1236 0000	1.1342 2500	2
3	1.1576 2500	1.1742 4138	1.1910 1600	1.2079 4963	3
4	1.2155 0625	1.2388 2465	1.2624 7696	1.2864 6635	4
5	1.2762 8156	1.3069 6001	1.3382 2558	1.3700 8666	5
6	1.3400 9564	1.3788 4281	1.4185 1911	1.4591 4230	6
7	1.4071 0042	1.4546 7916	1.5036 3026	1.5539 8655	7
8	1.4774 5544	1.5346 8651	1.5938 4807	1.6549 9567	8
9	1.5513 2822	1.6190 9427	1.6894 7896	1.7625 7039	9
10	1.6288 9463	1.7081 4446	1.7908 4770	1.8771 3747	10
11	1.7103 3936	1.8020 9240	1.8982 9856	1.9991 5140	11
12	1.7958 5633	1.9012 0749	2.0121 9647	2.1290 9624	12
13	1.8856 4914	2.0057 7390	2.1329 2826	2.2674 8750	13
14	1.9799 3160	2.1160 9146	2.2609 0396	2.4148 7418	14
15	2.0789 2818	2.2324 7649	2.3965 5819	2.5718 4101	15
16	2.1828 7459	2.3552 6270	2.5403 5168	2.7390 1067	16
17	2.2920 1832	2.4848 0215	2.6927 7279	2.9170 4637	17
18	2.4066 1923	2.6214 6627	2.8543 3915	3.1066 5438	18
19	2.5269 5020	2.7656 4691	3.0255 9950	3.3085 8691	19
20	2.6532 9771	2.9177 5749	3.2071 3547	3.5236 4506	20
21	2.7859 6259	3.0782 3415	3.3995 6360	3.7526 8199	21
22	2.9252 6072	3.2475 3703	3.6035 3742	3.9966 0632	22
23	3.0715 2376	3.4261 5157	3.8197 4966	4.2563 8573	23
24	3.2250 9994	3.6145 8990	4.0489 3464	4.5330 5081	24
25	3.3863 5494	3.8133 9235	4.2918 7072	4.8276 9911	25
26	3.5556 7269	4.0231 2893	4.5493 8296	5.1414 9955	26
27	3.7334 5632	4.2444 0102	4.8223 4594	5.4756 9702	27
28	3.9201 2914	4.4778 4307	5.1116 8670	5.8316 1733	28
29	4.1161 3560	4.7241 2444	5.4183 8790	6.2106 7245	29
30	4.3219 4238	4.9839 5129	5.7434 9117	6.6143 6616	30
31	4.5380 3949	5.2580 6861	6.0881 0064	7.0442 9996	31
32	4.7649 4147	5.5472 6238	6.4533 8668	7.5021 7946	32
33	5.0031 8854	5.8523 6181	6.8405 8988	7.9898 2113	33
34	5.2533 4797	6.1742 4171	7.2510 2528	8.5091 5950	34
35	5.5160 1537	6.5138 2501	7.6860 8679	9.0622 5487	35
36	5.7918 1614	6.8720 8538	8.1472 5200	9.6513 0143	36
37	6.0814 0694	7.2500 5008	8.6360 8712	10.2786 3603	37
38	6.3854 7729	7.6488 0283	9.1542 5235	10.9467 4737	38
39	6.7047 5115	8.0694 8699	9.7035 0749	11.6582 8595	39
40	7.0399 8871	8.5133 0877	10.2857 1794	12.4160 7453	40
41	7.3919 8815	8.9815 4076	10.9028 6101	13.2231 1938	41
42	7.7615 8756	9.4755 2550	11.5570 3267	14.0826 2214	42
43	8.1496 6693	9.9966 7940	12.2504 5463	14.9979 9258	43
44	8.5571 5028	10.5464 9677	12.9854 8191	15.9728 6209	44
45	8.9850 0779	11.1265 5409	13.7646 1083	17.0110 9813	45
46	9.4342 5818	11.7385 1456	14.5904 8748	18.1168 1951	46
47	9.9059 7109	12.3841 3287	15.4659 1673	19.2944 1278	47
48	10.4012 6965	13.0652 6017	16.3938 7173	20.5485 4961	48
49	10.9213 3313	13.7838 4948	17.3775 0403	21.8842 0533	49
50	11.4673 9979	14.5419 6120	18.4201 5427	23.3066 7868	50

n	5%	5½%	6%	6½%	n
51	12.0407 6978	15.3417 6907	19.5253 6353	24.8216 1279	51
52	12.6428 0826	16.1855 6637	20.6968 8534	26.4350 1762	52
53	13.2749 4868	17.0757 7252	21.9386 9846	28.1532 9377	53
54	13.9386 9611	18.0149 4001	23.2550 2037	29.9832 5786	54
55	14.6356 3092	19.0057 6171	24.6503 2159	31.9321 6963	55
56	15.3674 1246	20.0510 7860	26.1293 4089	34.0077 6065	56
57	16.1357 8309	21.1538 8793	27.6971 0134	36.2182 6509	57
58	16.9425 7224	22.3173 5176	29.3589 2742	38.5724 5233	58
59	17.7897 0085	23.5448 0611	31.1204 6307	41.0796 6173	59
60	18.6791 8589	24.8397 7045	32.9876 9085	43.7498 3974	60
61	19.6131 4519	26.2059 5782	34.9669 5230	46.5935 7932	61
62	20.5938 0245	27.6472 8550	37.0649 6944	49.6221 6198	62
63	21.6234 9257	29.1678 8620	39.2888 6761	52.8476 0251	63
64	22.7046 6720	30.7721 1994	41.6461 9967	56.2826 9667	64
65	23.8399 0056	32.4645 8654	44.1449 7165	59.9410 7195	65
66	25.0318 9559	34.2501 3880	46.7936 6994	63.8372 4163	66
67	26.2834 9037	36.1338 9643	49.6012 9014	67.9866 6234	67
68	27.5976 6488	38.1212 6074	52.5773 6755	72.4057 9539	68
69	28.9775 4813	40.2179 3008	55.7320 0960	77.1121 7209	69
70	30.4264 2554	42.4299 1623	59.0759 3018	82.1244 6327	70
71	31.9477 4681	44.7635 6163	62.6204 8599	87.4625 5339	71
72	33.5451 3415	47.2255 5751	66.3777 1515	93.1476 1936	72
73	35.2223 9086	49.8229 6318	70.3603 7806	99.2022 1461	73
74	36.9835 1040	52.5632 2615	74.5820 0074	105.6503 5856	74
75	38.8326 8592	55.4542 0359	79.0569 2079	112.5176 3187	75
76	40.7743 2022	58.5041 8479	83.8003 3603	119.8312 7794	76
77	42.8130 3623	61.7219 1495	88.8283 5620	127.6203 1101	77
78	44.9536 8804	65.1166 2027	94.1580 5757	135.9156 3122	78
79	47.2013 7244	68.6980 3439	99.8075 4102	144.7501 4725	79
80	49.5614 4107	72.4764 2628	105.7959 9348	154.1589 0683	80
81	52.0395 1312	76.4626 2973	112.1437 5309	164.1792 3577	81
82	54.6414 8878	80.6680 7436	118.8723 7828	174.8508 8609	82
83	57.3735 6322	85.1048 1845	126.0047 2097	186.2161 9369	83
84	60.2422 4138	89.7855 8347	133.5650 0423	198.3202 4628	84
85	63.2543 5344	94.7237 9056	141.5789 0449	211.2110 6229	85
86	66.4170 7112	99.9335 9904	150.0736 3875	224.9397 8134	86
87	69.7379 2467	105.4299 4698	159.0780 5708	239.5608 6712	87
88	73.2248 2091	111.2285 9407	168.6227 4050	255.1323 2349	88
89	76.8860 6195	117.3461 6674	178.7401 0493	271.7159 2451	89
90	80.7303 6505	123.8002 0591	189.4645 1123	289.3774 5961	90
91	84.7668 8330	130.6092 1724	200.8323 8190	308.1869 9448	91
92	89.0052 2747	137.7927 2419	212.8823 2482	328.2191 4912	92
93	93.4554 8884	145.3713 2402	225.6552 6431	349.5533 9382	93
94	98.1282 6328	153.3667 4684	239.1945 8017	372.2743 6441	94
95	103.0346 7645	161.8019 1791	253.5462 5498	396.4721 9810	95
96	108.1864 1027	170.7010 2340	268.7590 3028	422.2428 9098	96
97	113.5957 3078	180.0895 7969	284.8845 7209	449.6886 7889	97
98	119.2755 1732	189.9945 0657	301.9776 4642	478.9184 4302	98
99	125.2392 9319	200.4442 0443	320.0963 0520	510.0481 4181	99
100	131.5012 5785	211.4686 3567	339.3020 8351	543.2012 7103	100

by dividing the interest rate (which is usually an annual one) by the number of interest periods in that rate period.

To apply Table 11 in solving a compound interest problem, find the compound amount of $6,150.00 at 5% interest compounded quarterly for 4 years.

Now by Formula (13-2), $i = \dfrac{r}{m} = \dfrac{.05}{4} = .0125 = 1\frac{1}{4}\%$. (The interest rate per period is expressed here as a percent because rates in Table 11 are stated in percent.)

Then from Table 11, Page 256, the compound amount to which $1.00 accumulates in $4 \times 4 = 16$ periods at a periodic rate of $1\frac{1}{4}\%$ is $1.21988155. Therefore the amount to which $6,150.00 will accumulate is ($6,150.00) (1.21988155) = $7,502.26.

As another example of the use of Table 11 in solving a compound interest problem, find the compound interest on $3,750.00 at 4% interest compounded monthly for 6 years.

By Formula (13-2), $i = \dfrac{r}{m} = \dfrac{.04}{12} = .0033 = \frac{1}{3}\%$. Then from Table 11, Page 248, the compound amount to which $1.00 accumulates in $12 \times 6 = 72$ periods at a periodic rate of $\frac{1}{3}\%$ is $1.27074188. Therefore the amount to which $3,750.00 will accumulate is ($3,750.00)(1.27074188) = $4,765.28.

Then by Formula (13-3) $I = S - P =$

$$\$4,765.28 - \$3,750.00 = \$1,015.28 \text{ interest.}$$

Compound Interest for Fractional Periods

The foregoing examples, both those computed by formula and those solved by Table 11 were for integral values of n. However, fractional, or more commonly mixed number values of n are often encountered, because even in multiple-period calculations, the first or last period may be fractional.

In applying the first method, by formula and logarithms, fractional or mixed number values of n cause no difficulty. In using the tables, however, interpolation is necessary, as is shown by the following example. Find the compound interest on $4,860.00 at the annual rate of 3% compounded quarterly on April 1, 1952 and subsequent quarter dates, if the period covered is from February 1, 1952 to December 31, 1955.

In this period there are $15\frac{2}{3}$ periods, taking February 1–April 1, 1952 as $\frac{2}{3}$ period. The periodic rate $i = \dfrac{3\%}{4} = \frac{3}{4}\%$. Now find in Table 11 the compound amount of $1.00 at $\frac{3}{4}\%$ for 16 periods and for 15 periods, and proceed with the steps shown:

Compound amount of $1.00 at compound interest for 16 periods at $\frac{3}{4}\%$ $1.12699211
Compound amount of $1.00 at compound interest for 15 periods at $\frac{3}{4}\%$ 1.11860259

Increment in compound amount of $1.00, 16th period at $\frac{3}{4}\%$........ $ .00838952
Fraction of period ($\frac{2}{3}$) × increment for that period ($.00838952)....   .00559302
Compound amount of $1.00 at compound interest for 15 periods at $\frac{3}{4}\%$ 1.11860259
Compound amount of $1.00 at compound interest for $15\frac{2}{3}$ periods...   1.12419561
Principal.. $4,860.00
Amount to which principal will accumulate..................... $5,463.59
Compound interest = $5,463.59 − 4,860.00 = $603.59

To avoid the necessity for interpolating to find the interest for the fraction of a period, another method (the so-called practical method) is often used. The basis of the practical method is to compute the interest for the fractional period at the simple interest rate. This method gives values differing very slightly from those obtained by the exact method. Thus, the practical method would be applied in above problem, as follows:

s (compound amount) of $1.00 (principal) for $15\frac{2}{3}$ periods at $\frac{3}{4}\%$ per period = s of $1.00 for 15 periods at $\frac{3}{4}\%$ + simple interest on $1.00 for the fractional period.

From Table 11, s of $1.00 for 15 periods at $\frac{3}{4}\%$ is $1.11860259.

Since the rate is 3% per year = $\frac{3}{4}\%$ per quarter, the simple interest for 2 months is $\frac{2}{3}$ of $\frac{3}{4}\% = \frac{1}{2}\%$.

Therefore s on $1.00 for $15\frac{2}{3}$ periods at $3\% = ($1.11860259 + (.005) = $1.12360259

And S for $4,860.00 = (4,860.00) × (1.12360259) = $5,460.71

Interest = $5,460.71 − $4,860.00 = $600.71.

Note that simple interest calculations for use for fractional periods, such as that above, can be made, as in earlier chapters, by use of Table 9. This method saves time when the fractional period is in days, instead of months, as in the calculation above.

Computing Effective Interest Rates

When interest is compounded during a period, the amount of interest is greater than that which would be earned in that period at simple interest. The simple interest rate which would yield the same amount of interest as that by compounding is called the effective interest rate. Since it is almost always computed on an annual basis, the term "effective rate" is used synonymously with "effective annual rate," and is treated here on that basis.

By Formula (13-2), $i = \dfrac{r}{m}$, where r is thus the interest rate per year (which is called the nominal interest rate), m is the number of periods per year that interest is compounded, and i is therefore the interest rate per period.

By Formula (13-1), $S = P(1 + i)^n$, where S is the compound amount of principal P at periodic rate i for n periods, then for 1 year

$$S = P(1 + i)^m$$

where m is the number of times compounded per year.

But by Formula (11-1), the simple interest I is Prn, where r is the annual (nominal) interest rate and n is the number of years.

Or, where n is 1, $I = Pr$

And by Formula (11-2)

$$S = P + I \text{ (the total sum at simple interest for one year)}$$

Therefore $S = P + Pr = P(1 + r)$

Now equate this simple interest formula to that for compound interest, using r_{eff} to denote the effective simple interest rate.

$$P(1 + r_{\text{eff}}) = P(1 + i)^m$$

So $1 + r_{\text{eff}} = (1 + i)^m$

$$r_{\text{eff}} = (1 + i)^m - 1 \tag{13-5}$$

To apply Formula (13-5), find the effective (annual) interest rate corresponding to a nominal rate of 3% compounded quarterly.

By Formula (13-2) $i = \dfrac{r}{m}$,

Substituting $i = \dfrac{.03}{4} = .0075$

Then substituting in Formula (13-5)

$$r_{\text{eff}} = (1 + .0075)^4 - 1$$
$$= 1.03034 - 1 = .03034 = 3.034\%.$$

Computing Other Quantities Than Interest or Total Amount by Compound Interest Formula and by Tables

The general compound interest formula, Formula (13-1) was $S = P(1 + i)^n = P\left(1 + \dfrac{r}{m}\right)^n$. It has been applied both directly and through the use of tables to the calculation of compound amount and interest. The same relationship can be used to compute time, rate, or principal both by formula or tables, as is shown by the following examples.

The sum of $5,000.00 is invested at 5% interest under a plan whereby the interest is compounded semi-annually. How long will it take for the compound amount to reach $8,000.00?

By Formulas (13-2) and (13-4)

$$\log S = \log P + n \log \left(1 + \frac{r}{m}\right)$$

Therefore, $\log S - \log P = n \log \left(1 + \frac{r}{m}\right)$

And $n = \dfrac{\log S - \log P}{\log \left(1 + \dfrac{r}{m}\right)}$ (13-6)

To apply Formula (13-6) to the solution of the above problem, substitute the values given, which are that S is \$8,000.00, P is \$5,000.00, r is $5\% = .05$, and m is 2.

Substituting values given,

$$n = \frac{\log (8,000.00) - \log (5,000.00)}{\log (1 + .05/2)}$$

From Table 6-1, Chapter 6 and rules for characteristics

$$\log 8,000.00 = 3.90309$$
$$\log 5,000.00 = 3.69897$$
$$\log 1.025 \quad = \quad .010724$$

Therefore

$$n = \frac{3.90309 - 3.69897}{.010724} = \frac{.20412}{.010724} = 19.034 \text{ semi-annual periods}$$

$$= 9.517 \text{ years.}$$

(Note that "about $9\frac{1}{2}$ years" is a more realistic answer, since the interest is payable semi-annually and the last small increment earned during the .017 years over the $9\frac{1}{2}$ would not be credited until the next six-month interest date.)

To solve this problem by Table 11, first find the necessary compound amount per dollar of principal. In other words, for \$5,000.00 to become \$8,000.00, each dollar of principal must produce an amount of $\dfrac{\$8,000.00}{\$5,000.00} = \$1.60$.

Then turn to Table 11, Page 258, and run down the $2\frac{1}{2}\%$ column (for 5% annual rate compounded semi-annually) until the values closest to \$1.60 are found. They are \$1.59865019 for 19 periods, and \$1.63861644 for 20 periods.

To interpolate,

Amount after 20 periods	\$1.63861644
Amount after 19 periods	1.59865019
Difference	\$ .03996625

Then   Amount sought $1.60000000
        Amount after 19 periods   1.59865019
        Difference $ .00134981

The part period over 19 is $\dfrac{.00134981}{.03996625}$ = .034 period

So the time is 19.034 periods = 9.517 years.

The methods of computing rate by formula and tables are illustrated by the following example.

What interest rate must be sought on a principal of $2,000.00 to yield a total sum of $3,000.00 in ten years, if interest is compounded quarterly?

Again starting from Formulas (13-2) and (13-4)

$$\log S = \log P + n \log \left(1 + \frac{r}{m}\right)$$

Therefore $\log S - \log P = n \log \left(1 + \frac{r}{m}\right)$

And $\dfrac{\log S - \log P}{n} = \log \left(1 + \frac{r}{m}\right)$

or $\log \left(1 + \frac{r}{m}\right) = \dfrac{\log S - \log P}{n}$ (13-7)

Substituting values given

$$\log \left(1 + \frac{r}{m}\right) = \frac{\log \$3,000.00 - \log \$2,000.00}{10 \times 4}$$

From Table 3, and rule for characteristics

$\log 3,000.00 = 3.477121$

$\log 2,000.00 = 3.301030$

Therefore $\log \left(1 + \frac{r}{4}\right) = \dfrac{3.477121 - 3.301030}{40}$

So $\log \left(1 + \frac{r}{4}\right) = .0044023$

Therefore $\left(1 + \frac{r}{4}\right) =$ antilog .0044023 = 1.01018

Then $\dfrac{r}{4} = .01018$

And $r = 4 \times .01018 = .04072 = 4.072\%$

To solve this problem by Table 11, first find the necessary compound amount per dollar of principal. In other words, for $2,000.00

to become \$3,000.00, each dollar of principal must produce an amount of

$$\frac{\$3,000.00}{\$2,000.00} = \$1.50.$$

Then turn to Table 11, and run across the $n = 40$ line (for 4 periods per year in ten years) until the figures closest to \$1.50 are found. They are found in the column for 1%, where the value of $n = 40$ is \$1.48886373, and the column for $1\frac{1}{8}\%$, where the value for $n = 40$ is 1.56437687.

Then interpolate between these values as follows:

$$
\begin{array}{lr}
n = 40; i = 1\frac{1}{8}\% & \$1.56437687 \\
n = 40; i = 1\% & \underline{1.48886373} \\
\text{Difference} & \$ \ .07551314 \\
\\
\text{Value sought} & \$1.50000000 \\
n = 40; i = 1\% & \underline{1.48886373} \\
\text{Difference} & \$ \ .01113627
\end{array}
$$

The percentage to be added is $(.125\%) \, \dfrac{.01113627}{.07551314} = .018\%$

Therefore $\dfrac{r}{4} = 1\% + .018\% = 1.018\%$

and $r = 4.072\%$

The calculation of the principal that will yield a required amount at compound interest is often necessary in various business activities. For that reason it is discussed at length in the next section.

Computing Principal (Present Value) at Compound Interest by Formula

As was explained in the concluding section of Chapter 11, the principal which produces a given amount in a given time at interest, is also called the present value of that sum. In Chapter 11, the calculation was made for simple interest, which applies to most short term transactions. For longer periods, compound interest is commonly the basis of the computation.

The first method for computing principal (present value) from compound amount is by formula and logarithms.

From Formulas (13-1) and (13-2),

$$S = P \left(1 + \frac{r}{m} \right)^n$$

Therefore $P = \dfrac{S}{\left(1 + \dfrac{r}{m} \right)^n} = \dfrac{S}{(1 + i)^n}$ \hfill (13-8)

An example to illustrate the use of this formula is: A sum of \$5,000.00 is payable in 5 years. What is its present value at 4% interest compounded semi-annually?

Here S is \$5,000.00; r is .04; m is 2; and n, the number of interest periods, is $2 \times 5 = 10$.

Substituting

$$P = \frac{\$5,000.00}{\left(1 + \frac{.04}{2}\right)^{10}} = \frac{\$5,000.00}{(1.02)^{10}}$$

To carry out this computation by logarithms, rewrite the above equation as

$$\log P = \log (\$5,000.00) - 10 \log 1.02$$

From Table 3 Chapter 6, $\log 1.02 = .00860$
Then $10 \log 1.02 = .08600$
From Table 3 Chapter 6, $\log (5,000.00) = 3.69897$
Then $\log P = 3.69897 - .08600 = 3.61297$
Then from Table 3, $P = \$4,101.76$

Another problem, which illustrates one application of present value computations at compound interest, is the following:

What sum should be deposited in a savings bank, which pays 3% interest and compounds quarterly, to yield a sum to pay an obligation of \$3,650.00 which becomes due in 6 years? (This problem assumes no changes in savings-bank interest rate during the period.)

By Formula (13-8) $$P = \frac{S}{\left(1 + \frac{r}{m}\right)^{n}}$$

where S is \$3,650.00, r is .03, m is 4, and n is $6 \times 4 = 24$.

Substituting $P = \dfrac{\$3,650.00}{(1 + .0075)^{24}}$

which by taking logarithms of both sides becomes

$$\log P = \log 3,650.00 - 24 (\log 1.0075)$$

From Table 3, Chapter 6, and rule for characteristics

$$\log 3,650.00 = 3.562293$$
And $\log 1.0075 = .003245$, so that $24 \log 1.0075 = \underline{\quad.07788\quad}$
Therefore $\log 3,650 - 24 \log 1.0075 \qquad = 3.484413$

Then $P = $ antilog $3.484413 \qquad\qquad\quad = \$3.050.80$

Computing Present Value at Compound Interest by Table 11

Problems in present value may be solved by the use of Table 11. That table gives, as was stated earlier in this chapter, the amount of \$1.00 at compound interest for various rates and numbers of periods; in other words, the value of S for a value of P of $1.00 (this value of S being denoted by s). If, therefore, the given value of S (the compound amount) is *divided* by the figure in Table 11 for the correct number of periods n, and correct periodic rate, i, the result is the present value P.

Thus, to solve by Table 11 the problem just solved by formula, find in that Table 11 the compound amounts of a principal of $1.00 compounded quarterly for 6 years at 3%, that is, for $6 \times 4 = 24$ periods (value of n); the value of i being $\dfrac{3\%}{4} = \tfrac{3}{4}\%$.

The value in Table 11 of s for $n = 24$ and $i = \tfrac{3}{4}\%$ is 1.19641353. Then since this is the value of s for $P = 1.00$, the value of P for S amounting to $3650.00 is $\dfrac{\$3650.00}{1.19641353} = \$3050.78$.

(Note the discrepancy of $.02 between this value and that found by formula and logarithms. Differences in the sixth significant figure are to be expected in results of various methods of making compound interest calculations with logarithms, due to the fact that the table of logarithms used here (Table 3) gives mantissas to six significant figures (and numbers to four significant figures).

The computation of present value by Table 11 is open to the objection that it requires division by a nine-place number, a somewhat protracted computation if a computer is not available. For that reason, and because present value calculations arise frequently in business mathematics, tables are used giving figures for the present value per $1.00 of compound amount, so that the present value for any compound amount can be found by multiplication.

Computing Present Value at Compound Interest by Table 12

The relationship used in calculating a present value table follows from Formula (13-8)

$$P = \frac{S}{(1 + i)^n},$$

where P is the present value of a compound amount S at a periodic rate i for n periods.

Then for a compound amount of $1.00, the present value, denoted by v, is given by the relationship

$$v = \frac{1}{(1 + i)^n} = (1 + i)^{-n} \qquad (13\text{-}9)$$

(See Chapter 4 for a discussion of negative exponents.)

Since v is the present value for a compound amount of $1.00, the present value of any other compound amount can be found by multiplying it by the value of v for that value of i and n.

The values of v are given in Table 12. It gives the present value per $1.00 of compound amount for interest periods numbering from 1 to 150, for periodic rates from $\frac{1}{4}\%$ to $1\frac{1}{8}\%$, and for interest periods numbering from 1 to 100, for periodic rates from $1\frac{1}{4}\%$ to $6\frac{1}{2}\%$.

The use of Table 12 is readily illustrated by its application in solving the problem that has already been computed by formula and by Table 11, namely, the present value of the compound amount of $3,650.00 at 3% per 6 years, compounded quarterly.

Reference to Page 279 of this Table using the column for $\frac{3}{4}\%$ and the line $n = 24(4 \times 6)$ shows a present value of $.83583140. Then ($3050.78) $\times$ (.83583140) is $3050.78461, which rounds off to $3050.78.

Another advantage of using Table 12 for present value is that the more complex calculations are easier to carry out by means of separate tables for compound amount and present value. An example of such a relatively more complex calculation is the following:

What is the present value of an investment of $7,000.00, due in 6 years with 6% interest compounded annually, if the value of money is taken as 4%?

To solve this problem, find from Table 11, the compound amount of $1.00 compounded for six periods at 6% per period. That value is $1.41851911. Then the compound amount of $7,000.00 is ($7,000.00) (1.41851911) = $9,929.63377, which rounds off to $9,929.63. Now compute the present value of $9,929.63 at 4% from Table 12. On Page 286 of that Table, the present value of $1.00 compounded for six periods at 4% per period is $0.79031453. Therefore the present value of $9,929.63 is ($9,929.63)(0.79031453) = $7,847.53.

Another example of this type is:

A debt of $4,000.00 at 6% interest compounded semi-annually and due in full in 10 years is discounted at $6\frac{1}{2}\%$. What is the amount paid for the debt, i.e., what is its present value?

From Table 11, the compound amount of $1.00 with interest for 20 periods at 3% each is found to be $1.80611123. Therefore the compound amount of $4,000.00 is ($4,000.00)(1.80611123) = $7,224.44. Then from Table 12, Page 288, the present value is found of $1.00 discounted for 10 periods at $6\frac{1}{2}\%$ (in discounting, compounding is assumed to be annual, unless otherwise stated). This present value is $0.53272604. Therefore the discounted value (i.e. present value) is ($7,224.44)(0.53272604) = $3,848.65. Note that the present value of this debt is less than its principal, due to the higher discount rate than interest rate.

n	$\frac{1}{4}\%$	$\frac{7}{24}\%$	$\frac{1}{3}\%$	$\frac{5}{12}\%$	n
1	0.9975 0623	0.9970 9182	0.9966 7774	0.9958 5062	1
2	0.9950 1869	0.9941 9209	0.9933 6652	0.9917 1846	2
3	0.9925 3734	0.9913 0079	0.9900 6630	0.9876 0345	3
4	0.9900 6219	0.9884 1791	0.9867 7704	0.9835 0551	4
5	0.9875 9321	0.9855 4341	0.9834 9871	0.9794 2457	5
6	0.9851 3038	0.9826 7726	0.9802 3127	0.9753 6057	6
7	0.9826 7370	0.9798 1946	0.9769 7469	0.9713 1343	7
8	0.9802 2314	0.9769 6996	0.9737 2893	0.9672 8308	8
9	0.9777 7869	0.9741 2875	0.9704 9395	0.9632 6946	9
10	0.9753 4034	0.9712 9580	0.9672 6972	0.9592 7249	10
11	0.9729 0807	0.9684 7110	0.9640 5620	0.9552 9211	11
12	0.9704 8187	0.9656 5460	0.9608 5335	0.9513 2824	12
13	0.9680 6171	0.9628 4630	0.9576 6115	0.9473 8082	13
14	0.9656 4759	0.9600 4617	0.9544 7955	0.9434 4978	14
15	0.9632 3949	0.9572 5418	0.9513 0852	0.9395 3505	15
16	0.9608 3740	0.9544 7030	0.9481 4803	0.9356 3656	16
17	0.9584 4130	0.9516 9453	0.9449 9803	0.9317 5425	17
18	0.9560 5117	0.9489 2682	0.9418 5851	0.9278 8805	18
19	0.9536 6700	0.9461 6717	0.9387 2941	0.9240 3789	19
20	0.9512 8878	0.9434 1554	0.9356 1071	0.9202 0371	20
21	0.9489 1649	0.9406 7191	0.9325 0236	0.9163 8544	21
22	0.9465 5011	0.9379 3627	0.9294 0435	0.9125 8301	22
23	0.9441 8964	0.9352 0857	0.9263 1663	0.9087 9636	23
24	0.9418 3505	0.9324 8881	0.9232 3916	0.9050 2542	24
25	0.9394 8634	0.9297 7696	0.9201 7192	0.9012 7012	25
26	0.9371 4348	0.9270 7300	0.9171 1487	0.8975 3041	26
27	0.9348 0646	0.9243 7690	0.9140 6798	0.8938 0622	27
28	0.9324 7527	0.9216 8864	0.9110 3121	0.8900 9748	28
29	0.9301 4990	0.9190 0820	0.9080 0453	0.8864 0413	29
30	0.9278 3032	0.9163 3556	0.9049 8790	0.8827 2610	30
31	0.9255 1653	0.9136 7068	0.9019 8130	0.8790 6334	31
32	0.9232 0851	0.9110 1356	0.8989 8468	0.8754 1577	32
33	0.9209 0624	0.9083 6416	0.8959 9802	0.8717 8334	33
34	0.9186 0972	0.9057 2247	0.8930 2128	0.8681 6599	34
35	0.9163 1892	0.9030 8847	0.8900 5444	0.8645 6364	35
36	0.9140 3384	0.9004 6212	0.8870 9745	0.8609 7624	36
37	0.9117 5445	0.8978 4341	0.8841 5028	0.8574 0372	37
38	0.9094 8075	0.8952 3231	0.8812 1290	0.8538 4603	38
39	0.9072 1272	0.8926 2881	0.8782 8528	0.8503 0310	39
40	0.9049 5034	0.8900 3288	0.8753 6739	0.8467 7487	40
41	0.9026 9361	0.8874 4450	0.8724 5920	0.8432 6128	41
42	0.9004 4250	0.8848 6365	0.8695 6066	0.8397 6227	42
43	0.8981 9701	0.8822 9030	0.8666 7175	0.8362 7778	43
44	0.8959 5712	0.8797 2444	0.8637 9245	0.8328 0775	44
45	0.8937 2281	0.8771 6604	0.8609 2270	0.8293 5211	45
46	0.8914 9407	0.8746 1508	0.8580 6249	0.8259 1082	46
47	0.8892 7090	0.8720 7153	0.8552 1179	0.8224 8380	47
48	0.8870 5326	0.8695 3539	0.8523 7055	0.8190 7100	48
49	0.8848 4116	0.8670 0662	0.8495 3876	0.8156 7237	49
50	0.8826 3457	0.8644 8520	0.8467 1637	0.8122 8784	50

n	$\frac{1}{4}\%$	$\frac{7}{24}\%$	$\frac{1}{3}\%$	$\frac{5}{12}\%$	n
51	0.8804 3349	0.8619 7112	0.8439 0336	0.8089 1735	51
52	0.8782 3790	0.8594 6435	0.8410 9969	0.8055 6084	52
53	0.8760 4778	0.8569 6487	0.8383 0534	0.8022 1827	53
54	0.8738 6312	0.8544 7266	0.8355 2027	0.7988 8956	54
55	0.8716 8391	0.8519 8769	0.8327 4446	0.7955 7467	55
56	0.8695 1013	0.8495 0995	0.8299 7787	0.7922 7353	56
57	0.8673 4178	0.8470 3942	0.8272 2047	0.7889 8608	57
58	0.8651 7883	0.8445 7608	0.8244 7222	0.7857 1228	58
59	0.8630 2128	0.8421 1989	0.8217 3311	0.7824 5207	59
60	0.8608 6911	0.8396 7085	0.8190 0310	0.7792 0538	60
61	0.8587 2230	0.8372 2893	0.8162 8216	0.7759 7216	61
62	0.8565 8085	0.8347 9412	0.8135 7026	0.7727 5236	62
63	0.8544 4474	0.8323 6638	0.8108 6737	0.7695 4591	63
64	0.8523 1395	0.8299 4571	0.8081 7346	0.7663 5278	64
65	0.8501 8848	0.8275 3207	0.8054 8850	0.7631 7289	65
66	0.8480 6831	0.8251 2545	0.8028 1246	0.7600 0620	66
67	0.8459 5343	0.8227 2584	0.8001 4531	0.7568 5265	67
68	0.8438 4382	0.8203 3320	0.7974 8702	0.7537 1218	68
69	0.8417 3947	0.8179 4752	0.7948 3756	0.7505 8474	69
70	0.8396 4037	0.8155 6878	0.7921 9690	0.7474 7028	70
71	0.8375 4650	0.8131 9695	0.7895 6502	0.7443 6874	71
72	0.8354 5786	0.8108 3202	0.7869 4188	0.7412 8008	72
73	0.8333 7442	0.8084 7397	0.7843 2745	0.7382 0423	73
74	0.8312 9618	0.8061 2278	0.7817 2171	0.7351 4114	74
75	0.8292 2312	0.8037 7843	0.7791 2463	0.7320 9076	75
76	0.8271 5523	0.8014 4089	0.7765 3618	0.7290 5304	76
77	0.8250 9250	0.7991 1015	0.7739 5632	0.7260 2792	77
78	0.8230 3491	0.7967 8619	0.7713 8504	0.7230 1536	78
79	0.8209 8246	0.7944 6899	0.7688 2230	0.7200 1529	79
80	0.8189 3512	0.7921 5853	0.7662 6807	0.7170 2768	80
81	0.8168 9289	0.7898 5479	0.7637 2233	0.7140 5246	81
82	0.8148 5575	0.7875 5774	0.7611 8505	0.7110 8959	82
83	0.8128 2369	0.7852 6738	0.7586 5619	0.7081 3901	83
84	0.8107 9670	0.7829 8368	0.7561 3574	0.7052 0067	84
85	0.8087 7476	0.7807 0662	0.7536 2366	0.7022 7453	85
86	0.8067 5787	0.7784 3618	0.7511 1993	0.6993 6052	86
87	0.8047 4600	0.7761 7234	0.7486 2451	0.6964 5861	87
88	0.8027 3915	0.7739 1509	0.7461 3739	0.6935 6874	88
89	0.8007 3731	0.7716 6440	0.7436 5853	0.6906 9086	89
90	0.7987 4046	0.7694 2026	0.7411 8790	0.6878 2493	90
91	0.7967 4859	0.7671 8264	0.7387 2548	0.6849 7088	91
92	0.7947 6168	0.7649 5153	0.7362 7125	0.6821 2868	92
93	0.7927 7973	0.7627 2691	0.7338 2516	0.6792 9827	93
94	0.7908 0273	0.7605 0876	0.7313 8720	0.6764 7960	94
95	0.7888 3065	0.7582 9706	0.7289 5735	0.6736 7263	95
96	0.7868 6349	0.7560 9179	0.7265 3556	0.6708 7731	96
97	0.7849 0124	0.7538 9294	0.7241 2182	0.6680 9359	97
98	0.7829 4388	0.7517 0048	0.7217 1610	0.6653 2141	98
99	0.7809 9140	0.7495 1439	0.7193 1837	0.6625 6074	99
100	0.7790 4379	0.7473 3467	0.7169 2861	0.6598 1153	100

n	$\frac{1}{4}\%$	$\frac{7}{24}\%$	$\frac{1}{3}\%$	$\frac{5}{12}\%$	n
101	0.7771 0104	0.7451 6128	0.7145 4681	0.6570 7372	101
102	0.7751 6313	0.7429 9421	0.7121 7290	0.6543 4727	102
104	0.7732 3006	0.7408 3345	0.7098 0688	0.6516 3214	103
104	0.7713 0180	0.7386 7897	0.7074 4872	0.6489 2827	104
105	0.7693 7836	0.7365 3075	0.7050 9839	0.6462 3562	105
106	0.7674 5971	0.7343 8879	0.7027 5587	0.6435 5415	106
107	0.7655 4584	0.7322 5305	0.7004 2114	0.6408 8380	107
108	0.7636 3675	0.7301 2352	0.6980 9416	0.6382 2453	108
109	0.7617 3242	0.7280 0019	0.6957 7491	0.6355 7630	109
110	0.7598 3284	0.7258 8303	0.6934 6336	0.6329 3905	110
111	0.7579 3799	0.7237 7203	0.6911 5950	0.6303 1275	111
112	0.7560 4787	0.7216 6716	0.6888 6329	0.6276 9734	112
113	0.7541 6247	0.7195 6842	0.6865 7470	0.6250 9279	113
114	0.7522 8176	0.7174 7578	0.6842 9372	0.6224 9904	114
115	0.7504 0575	0.7153 8923	0.6820 2032	0.6199 1606	115
116	0.7485 3441	0.7133 0875	0.6797 5448	0.6173 4379	116
117	0.7466 6774	0.7112 3431	0.6774 9616	0.6147 8220	117
118	0.7448 0573	0.7091 6591	0.6752 4534	0.6122 3123	118
119	0.7429 4836	0.7071 0353	0.6730 0200	0.6096 9086	119
120	0.7410 9562	0.7050 4714	0.6707 6611	0.6071 6102	120
121	0.7392 4750	0.7029 9673	0.6685 3765	0.6046 4168	121
122	0.7374 0399	0.7009 5229	0.6663 1660	0.6021 3279	122
123	0.7355 6508	0.6989 1379	0.6641 0292	0.5996 3431	123
124	0.7337 3075	0.6968 8122	0.6618 9660	0.5971 4620	124
125	0.7319 0100	0.6948 5456	0.6596 9761	0.5946 6842	125
126	0.7300 7581	0.6928 3379	0.6575 0592	0.5922 0091	126
127	0.7282 5517	0.6908 1890	0.6553 2152	0.5897 4365	127
128	0.7264 3907	0.6888 0988	0.6531 4437	0.5872 9658	128
129	0.7246 2750	0.6868 0669	0.6509 7445	0.5848 5966	129
130	0.7228 2045	0.6848 0933	0.6488 1175	0.5824 3286	130
131	0.7210 1791	0.6828 1778	0.6466 5623	0.5800 1613	131
132	0.7192 1986	0.6808 3202	0.6445 0787	0.5776 0942	132
133	0.7174 2629	0.6788 5203	0.6423 6665	0.5752 1270	133
134	0.7156 3720	0.6768 7780	0.6402 3254	0.5728 2593	134
135	0.7138 5257	0.6749 0932	0.6381 0552	0.5704 4906	135
136	0.7120 7239	0.6729 4656	0.6359 8557	0.5680 8205	136
137	0.7102 9664	0.6709 8950	0.6338 7266	0.5657 2486	137
138	0.7085 2533	0.6690 3814	0.6317 6677	0.5633 7745	138
139	0.7067 5843	0.6670 9246	0.6296 6788	0.5610 3979	139
140	0.7049 9595	0.6651 5243	0.6275 7596	0.5587 1182	140
141	0.7032 3785	0.6632 1804	0.6254 9099	0.5563 9351	141
142	0.7014 8414	0.6612 8928	0.6234 1295	0.5540 8483	142
143	0.6997 3480	0.6593 6613	0.6213 4181	0.5517 8572	143
144	0.6979 8983	0.6574 4857	0.6192 7755	0.5494 9615	144
145	0.6962 4921	0.6555 3659	0.6172 2015	0.5472 1609	145
146	0.6945 1292	0.6536 3017	0.6151 6958	0.5449 4548	146
147	0.6927 8097	0.6517 2929	0.6131 2583	0.5426 8429	147
148	0.6910 5334	0.6498 3394	0.6110 8887	0.5404 3249	148
149	0.6893 3001	0.6479 4410	0.6090 5867	0 5381 9003	149
150	0.6876 1098	0.6460 5976	0.6070 3522	0.5359 5688	150

TABLE 12—PRESENT VALUE OF COMPOUND AMOUNT OF $1.00. PRINCIPAL WHICH
WILL ACCUMULATE TO 1 IN n PERIODS IF INTEREST IS COMPOUNDED AT i PER
PERIOD (Cont.)

n	$\frac{1}{2}\%$	$\frac{7}{12}\%$	$\frac{5}{8}\%$	$\frac{2}{3}\%$	n
1	0.9950 2488	0.9942 0050	0.9937 8882	0.9933 7748	1
2	0.9900 7450	0.9884 3463	0.9876 1622	0.9867 9882	2
3	0.9851 4876	0.9827 0220	0.9814 8196	0.9802 6373	3
4	0.9802 4752	0.9770 0302	0.9753 8580	0.9737 7192	4
5	0.9753 7067	0.9713 3688	0.9693 2750	0.9673 2310	5
6	0.9705 1808	0.9657 0361	0.9633 0683	0.9609 1699	6
7	0.9656 8963	0.9601 0301	0.9573 2356	0.9545 5330	7
8	0.9608 8520	0.9545 3489	0.9513 7745	0.9482 3175	8
9	0.9561 0468	0.9489 9907	0.9454 6827	0.9419 5207	9
10	0.9513 4794	0.9434 9534	0.9395 9580	0.9357 1398	10
11	0.9466 1489	0.9380 2354	0.9337 5980	0.9295 1720	11
12	0.9419 0534	0.9325 8347	0.9279 6005	0.9233 6145	12
13	0.9372 1924	0.9271 7495	0.9221 9632	0.9172 4648	13
14	0.9325 5646	0.9217 9780	0.9164 6840	0.9111 7200	14
15	0.9279 1688	0.9164 5183	0.9107 7604	0.9051 3775	15
16	0.9233 0037	0.9111 3686	0.9051 1905	0.8991 4346	16
17	0.9187 0684	0.9058 5272	0.8994 9719	0.8931 8886	17
18	0.9141 3616	0.9005 9923	0.8939 1025	0.8872 7371	18
19	0.9095 8822	0.8953 7620	0.8883 5802	0.8813 9772	19
20	0.9050 6290	0.8901 8346	0.8828 4027	0.8755 6065	20
21	0.9005 6010	0.8850 2084	0.8773 5679	0.8697 6224	21
22	0.8960 7971	0.8798 8816	0.8719 0736	0.8640 0222	22
23	0.8916 2160	0.8747 8525	0.8664 9179	0.8582 8035	23
24	0.8871 8567	0.8697 1193	0.8611 0985	0.8525 9638	24
25	0.8827 7181	0.8646 6803	0.8557 6135	0.8469 5004	25
26	0.8783 7991	0.8596 5339	0.8504 4606	0.8413 4110	26
27	0.8740 0986	0.8546 6782	0.8451 6378	0.8357 6931	27
28	0.8696 6155	0.8497 1118	0.8399 1432	0.8302 3441	28
29	0.8653 3488	0.8447 8327	0.8346 9746	0.8247 3617	29
30	0.8610 2973	0.8398 8395	0.8295 1300	0.8192 7434	30
31	0.8567 4600	0.8350 1304	0.8243 6075	0.8138 4868	31
32	0.8524 8358	0.8301 7038	0.8192 4050	0.8084 5896	32
33	0.8482 4237	0.8253 5581	0.8141 5205	0.8031 0492	33
34	0.8440 2226	0.8205 6915	0.8090 9520	0.7977 8635	34
35	0.8398 2314	0.8158 1026	0.8040 6976	0.7925 0299	35
36	0.8356 4492	0.8110 7897	0.7990 7554	0.7872 5463	36
37	0.8314 8748	0.8063 7511	0.7941 1234	0.7820 4102	37
38	0.8273 5073	0.8016 9854	0.7891 7997	0.7768 6194	38
39	0.8232 3455	0.7970 4908	0.7842 7823	0.7717 1716	39
40	0.8191 3886	0.7924 2660	0.7794 0693	0.7666 0645	40
41	0.8150 6354	0.7878 3092	0.7745 6590	0.7615 2959	41
42	0.8110 0850	0.7832 6189	0.7697 5493	0.7564 8635	42
43	0.8069 7363	0.7787 1936	0.7649 7384	0.7514 7650	43
44	0.8029 5884	0.7742 0317	0.7602 2245	0.7464 9984	44
45	0.7989 6402	0.7697 1318	0.7555 0057	0.7415 5613	45
46	0.7949 8907	0.7652 4923	0.7508 0802	0.7366 4516	46
47	0.7910 3390	0.7608 1116	0.7461 4462	0.7317 6672	47
48	0.7870 9841	0.7563 9884	0.7415 1018	0.7269 2058	48
49	0.7831 8250	0.7520 1210	0.7369 0453	0.7221 0654	49
50	0.7792 8607	0.7476 5080	0.7323 2748	0.7173 2437	50

n	$\frac{1}{2}\%$	$\frac{7}{12}\%$	$\frac{5}{8}\%$	$\frac{2}{3}\%$	n
51	0.7754 0902	0.7433 1480	0.7277 7886	0.7125 7388	51
52	0.7715 5127	0.7390 0394	0.7232 5849	0.7078 5485	52
53	0.7677 1270	0.7347 1809	0.7187 6620	0.7031 6707	53
54	0.7638 9324	0.7304 5709	0.7143 0182	0.6985 1033	54
55	0.7600 9277	0.7262 2080	0.7098 6516	0.6938 8444	55
56	0.7563 1122	0.7220 0908	0.7054 5606	0.6892 8918	56
57	0.7525 4847	0.7178 2179	0.7010 7434	0.6847 2435	57
58	0.7488 0445	0.7136 5878	0.6967 1985	0.6801 8975	58
59	0.7450 7906	0.7095 1991	0.6923 9239	0.6756 8518	59
60	0.7413 7220	0.7054 0505	0.6880 9182	0.6712 1044	60
61	0.7376 8378	0.7013 1405	0.6838 1796	0.6667 6534	61
62	0.7340 1371	0.6972 4678	0.6795 7064	0.6623 4968	62
63	0.7303 6190	0.6932 0310	0.6753 4970	0.6579 6326	63
64	0.7267 2826	0.6891 8286	0.6711 5499	0.6536 0588	64
65	0.7231 1269	0.6851 8594	0.6669 8632	0.6492 7737	65
66	0.7195 1512	0.6812 1221	0.6628 4355	0.6449 7752	66
67	0.7159 3544	0.6772 6151	0.6587 2651	0.6407 0614	67
68	0.7123 7357	0.6733 3373	0.6546 3504	0.6364 6306	68
69	0.7088 2943	0.6694 2873	0.6505 6898	0.6322 4807	69
70	0.7053 0291	0.6655 4638	0.6465 2818	0.6280 6100	70
71	0.7017 9394	0.6616 8654	0.6425 1248	0.6239 0165	71
72	0.6983 0243	0.6578 4909	0.6385 2172	0.6197 6985	72
73	0.6948 2829	0.6540 3389	0.6345 5574	0.6156 6541	73
74	0.6913 7143	0.6502 4082	0.6306 1440	0.6115 8816	74
75	0.6879 3177	0.6464 6975	0.6266 9754	0.6075 3791	75
76	0.6845 0923	0.6427 2054	0.6228 0501	0.6035 1448	76
77	0.6811 0371	0.6389 9308	0.6189 3666	0.5995 1769	77
78	0.6777 1513	0.6352 8724	0.6150 9233	0.5955 4738	78
79	0.6743 4342	0.6316 0289	0.6112 7188	0.5916 0336	79
80	0.6709 8847	0.6279 3991	0.6074 7516	0.5876 8545	80
81	0.6676 5022	0.6242 9817	0.6037 0203	0.5837 9350	81
82	0.6643 2858	0.6206 7755	0.5999 5232	0.5799 2732	82
83	0.6610 2346	0.6170 7793	0.5962 2591	0.5760 8674	83
84	0.6577 3479	0.6134 9919	0.5925 2264	0.5722 7159	84
85	0.6544 6248	0.6099 4120	0.5888 4238	0.5684 8171	85
86	0.6512 0644	0.6064 0384	0.5851 8497	0.5647 1693	86
87	0.6479 6661	0.6028 8700	0.5815 5028	0.5609 7709	87
88	0.6447 4290	0.5993 9056	0.5779 3817	0.5572 6201	88
89	0.6415 3522	0.5959 1439	0.5743 4849	0.5535 7153	89
90	0.6383 4350	0.5924 5838	0.5707 8111	0.5499 0549	90
91	0.6351 6766	0.5890 2242	0.5672 3589	0.5462 6374	91
92	0.6320 0763	0.5856 0638	0.5637 1268	0.5426 4610	92
93	0.6288 6331	0.5822 1015	0.5602 1136	0.5390 5241	93
94	0.6257 3464	0.5788 3363	0.5567 3179	0.5354 8253	94
95	0.6226 2153	0.5754 7668	0.5532 7383	0.5319 3629	95
96	0.6195 2391	0.5721 3920	0.5498 3734	0.5284 1353	96
97	0.6164 4170	0.5688 2108	0.5464 2220	0.5249 1410	97
98	0.6133 7483	0.5655 2220	0.5430 2828	0.5214 3785	98
99	0.6103 2321	0.5622 4245	0.5396 5543	0.5179 8462	99
100	0.6072 8678	0.5589 8172	0.5363 0353	0.5145 5426	100

n	$\frac{1}{2}\%$	$\frac{7}{12}\%$	$\frac{5}{8}\%$	$\frac{2}{3}\%$	n
101	0.6042 6545	0.5557 3991	0.5329 7246	0.5111 4660	101
102	0.6012 5915	0.5525 1689	0.5296 6207	0.5077 6152	102
103	0.5982 6781	0.5493 1257	0.5263 7225	0.5043 9886	103
104	0.5952 9136	0.5461 2683	0.5231 0285	0.5010 5847	104
105	0.5923 2971	0.5429 5957	0.5198 5377	0.4977 4020	105
106	0.5893 8279	0.5398 1067	0.5166 2486	0.4944 4391	106
107	0.5864 5054	0.5366 8004	0.5134 1601	0.4911 6945	107
108	0.5835 3288	0.5335 6756	0.5102 2709	0.4879 1667	108
109	0.5806 2973	0.5304 7313	0.5070 5798	0.4846 8543	109
110	0.5777 4102	0.5273 9665	0.5039 0855	0.4814 7559	110
111	0.5748 6669	0.5243 3801	0.5007 7868	0.4782 8701	111
112	0.5720 0666	0.5212 9711	0.4976 6826	0.4751 1955	112
113	0.5691 6085	0.5182 7385	0.4945 7715	0.4719 7306	113
114	0.5663 2921	0.5152 6812	0.4915 0524	0.4688 4741	114
115	0.5635 1165	0.5122 7982	0.4884 5242	0.4657 4246	115
116	0.5607 0811	0.5093 0885	0.4854 1855	0.4626 5808	116
117	0.5579 1852	0.5063 5512	0.4824 0353	0.4595 9411	117
118	0.5551 4280	0.5034 1851	0.4794 0723	0.4565 5044	118
119	0.5523 8090	0.5004 9893	0.4764 2955	0.4535 2693	119
120	0.5496 3273	0.4975 9629	0.4734 7036	0.4505 2344	120
121	0.5468 9824	0.4947 1047	0.4705 2955	0.4475 3984	121
122	0.5441 7736	0.4918 4140	0.4676 0700	0.4445 7600	122
123	0.5414 7001	0.4889 8896	0.4647 0261	0.4416 3179	123
124	0.5387 7612	0.4861 5307	0.4618 1626	0.4387 0708	124
125	0.5360 9565	0.4833 3363	0.4589 4784	0.4358 0173	125
126	0.5334 2850	0.4805 3053	0.4560 9723	0.4329 1563	126
127	0.5307 7463	0.4777 4369	0.4532 6433	0.4300 4864	127
128	0.5281 3396	0.4749 7302	0.4504 4902	0.4272 0063	128
129	0.5255 0643	0.4722 1841	0.4476 5120	0.4243 7149	129
130	0.5228 9197	0.4694 7978	0.4448 7076	0.4215 6108	130
131	0.5202 9052	0.4667 5703	0.4421 0759	0.4187 6929	131
132	0.5177 0201	0.4640 5007	0.4393 6158	0.4159 9598	132
133	0.5151 2637	0.4613 5881	0.4366 3262	0.4132 4104	133
134	0.5125 6356	0.4586 8316	0.4339 2062	0.4105 0434	134
135	0.5100 1349	0.4560 2303	0.4312 2546	0.4077 8577	135
136	0.5074 7611	0.4533 7832	0.4285 4704	0.4050 8520	136
137	0.5049 5135	0.4507 4895	0.4258 8526	0.4024 0252	137
138	0.5024 3916	0.4481 3483	0.4232 4001	0.3997 3760	138
139	0.4999 3946	0.4455 3587	0.4206 1119	0.3970 9033	139
140	0.4974 5220	0.4429 5198	0.4179 9870	0.3944 6059	140
141	0.4949 7731	0.4403 8308	0.4154 0243	0.3918 4827	141
142	0.4925 1474	0.4378 2908	0.4128 2229	0.3892 5325	142
143	0.4900 6442	0.4352 8989	0.4102 5818	0.3866 7541	143
144	0.4876 2628	0.4327 6542	0.4077 0999	0.3841 1465	144
145	0.4852 0028	0.4302 5560	0.4051 7763	0.3815 7084	145
146	0.4827 8635	0.4277 6033	0.4026 6100	0.3790 4389	146
147	0.4803 8443	0.4252 7953	0.4001 6000	0.3765 3366	147
148	0.4779 9446	0.4228 1312	0.3976 7453	0.3740 4006	148
149	0.4756 1637	0.4203 6102	0.3952 0451	0.3715 6297	159
150	0.4732 5012	0.4179 2313	0.3927 4982	0.3691 0229	150

n	$\frac{3}{4}\%$	$\frac{7}{8}\%$	1%	$1\frac{1}{8}\%$	n
1	0.9925 5583	0.9913 2590	0.9900 9901	0.9888 7515	1
2	0.9851 6708	0.9827 2704	0.9802 9605	0.9778 7407	2
3	0.9778 3333	0.9742 0276	0.9705 9015	0.9669 9537	3
4	0.9705 5417	0.9657 5243	0.9609 8034	0.9562 3770	4
5	0.9633 2920	0.9573 7539	0.9514 6569	0.9455 9970	5
6	0.9561 5802	0.9490 7102	0.9420 4524	0.9350 8005	6
7	0.9490 4022	0.9408 3868	0.9327 1805	0.9246 7743	7
8	0.941 7540	0.9326 7775	0.9234 8322	0.9143 9054	8
9	0.9349 6318	0.9245 8761	0.9143 3982	0.9042 1808	9
10	0.9280 0315	0.9165 6765	0.9052 8695	0.8941 5881	10
11	0.9210 9494	0.9086 1724	0.8963 2372	0.8842 1142	11
12	0.9142 3815	0.9007 3581	0.8874 4923	0.8743 7470	12
13	0.9074 3241	0.8929 2273	0.8786 6260	0.8646 4742	13
14	0.9006 7733	0.8851 7743	0.8699 6297	0.8550 2835	14
15	0.8939 7254	0.8774 9931	0.8613 4947	0.8455 1629	15
16	0.8873 1766	0.8698 8779	0.8528 2126	0.8361 1005	16
17	0.8807 1231	0.8623 4230	0.8443 7749	0.8268 0846	17
18	0.8741 5614	0.8548 6225	0.8360 1731	0.8176 1034	18
19	0.8676 4878	0.8474 4709	0.8277 3992	0.8085 1455	19
20	0.8611 8985	0.8400 9624	0.8195 4447	0.7995 1995	20
21	0.8547 7901	0.8328 0917	0.8114 3017	0.7906 2542	21
22	0.8484 1589	0.8255 8530	0.8033 9621	0.7818 2983	22
23	0.8421 0014	0.8184 2409	0.7954 4179	0.7731 3210	23
24	0.8358 3140	0.8113 2499	0.7875 6613	0.7645 3112	24
25	0.8296 0933	0.8042 8748	0.7797 6844	0.7560 2583	25
26	0.8234 3358	0.7973 1101	0.7720 4796	0.7476 1516	26
27	0.8173 0380	0.7903 9505	0.7644 0392	0.7392 9806	27
28	0.8112 1966	0.7835 3908	0.7568 3557	0.7310 7348	28
29	0.8051 8080	0.7767 4258	0.7493 4215	0.7229 4040	29
30	0.7991 8690	0.7700 0504	0.7419 2292	0.7148 9780	30
31	0.7932 3762	0.7633 2594	0.7345 7715	0.7069 4467	31
32	0.7873 3262	0.7567 0477	0.7273 0411	0.6990 8002	32
33	0.7814 7158	0.7501 4104	0.7201 0307	0.6913 0287	33
34	0.7756 5418	0.7436 3424	0.7129 7334	0.6836 1223	34
35	0.7698 8008	0.7371 8388	0.7059 1420	0.6760 0715	35
36	0.7641 4896	0.7307 8947	0.6989 2495	0.6684 8667	36
37	0.7584 6051	0.7244 5053	0.6920 0490	0.6610 4986	37
38	0.7528 1440	0.7181 6657	0.6851 5337	0.6536 9578	38
39	0.7472 1032	0.7119 3712	0.6783 6967	0.6464 2352	39
40	0.7416 4796	0.7057 6171	0.6716 5314	0.6392 3216	40
41	0.7361 2701	0.6996 3986	0.6650 0311	0.6321 2080	41
42	0.7306 4716	0.6935 7111	0.6584 1892	0.6250 8855	42
43	0.7252 0809	0.6875 5500	0.6518 9992	0.6181 3454	43
44	0.7198 0952	0.6815 9108	0.6454 4546	0.6112 5789	44
45	0.7144 5114	0.6756 7889	0.6390 5492	0.6044 5774	45
46	0.7091 3264	0.6698 1798	0.6327 2764	0.5977 3324	46
47	0.7038 5374	0.6640 0792	0.6264 6301	0.5910 8355	47
48	0.6986 1414	0.6582 4824	0.6202 6041	0.5845 0784	48
49	0.6934 1353	0.6525 3853	0.6141 1921	0.5780 0528	49
50	0.6882 5165	0.6468 7835	0.6080 3882	0.5715 7506	50

n	$\frac{3}{4}\%$	$\frac{7}{8}\%$	1%	$1\frac{1}{8}\%$	n
51	0.6831 2819	0.6412 6726	0.6020 1864	0.5652 1637	51
52	0.6780 4286	0.6357 0484	0.5960 5806	0.5589 2843	52
53	0.6729 9540	0.6301 9067	0.5901 5649	0.5527 1044	53
54	0.6679 8551	0.6247 2433	0.5843 1336	0.5465 6162	54
55	0.6630 1291	0.6193 0541	0.5785 2808	0.5404 8120	55
56	0.6580 7733	0.6139 3349	0.5728 0008	0.5344 6843	56
57	0.6531 7849	0.6086 0817	0.5671 2879	0.5285 2256	57
58	0.6483 1612	0.6033 2904	0.5615 1365	0.5226 4282	58
59	0.6434 8995	0.5980 9571	0.5559 5411	0.5168 2850	59
60	0.6386 9970	0.5929 0776	0.5504 4962	0.5110 7887	60
61	0.6339 4511	0.5877 6482	0.5449 9962	0.5053 9319	61
62	0.6292 2592	0.5826 6649	0.5396 0358	0.4997 7077	62
63	0.6245 4185	0.5776 1238	0.5342 6097	0.4942 1090	63
64	0.6198 9266	0.5726 0211	0.5289 7126	0.4887 1288	64
65	0.6152 7807	0.5676 3530	0.5237 3392	0.4832 7602	65
66	0.6106 9784	0.5627 1158	0.5185 4844	0.4778 9965	66
67	0.6061 5170	0.5578 3056	0.5134 1429	0.4725 8309	67
68	0.6016 3940	0.5529 9188	0.5083 3099	0.4673 2568	68
69	0.5971 6070	0.5481 9517	0.5032 9801	0.4621 2675	69
70	0.5927 1533	0.5434 4007	0.4983 1486	0.4569 8566	70
71	0.5883 0306	0.5387 2622	0.4933 8105	0.4519 0177	71
72	0.5839 2363	0.5340 5325	0.4884 9609	0.4468 7443	72
73	0.5795 7681	0.5294 2082	0.4836 5949	0.4419 0302	73
74	0.5752 6234	0.5248 2857	0.4788 7078	0.4369 8692	74
75	0.5709 7999	0.5202 7615	0.4741 2949	0.4321 2551	75
76	0.5667 2952	0.5157 6322	0.4694 3514	0.4273 1818	76
77	0.5625 1069	0.5112 8944	0.4647 8726	0.4225 6433	77
78	0.5583 2326	0.5068 5447	0.4601 8541	0.4178 6337	78
79	0.5541 6701	0.5024 5796	0.4556 2912	0.4132 1470	79
80	0.5500 4170	0.4980 9959	0.4511 1794	0.4086 1775	80
81	0.5459 4710	0.4937 7902	0.4466 5142	0.4040 7194	81
82	0.5418 8297	0.4894 9593	0.4422 2913	0.3995 7670	82
83	0.5378 4911	0.4852 4999	0.4378 5063	0.3951 3148	83
84	0.5338 4527	0.4810 4089	0.4335 1547	0.3907 3570	84
85	0.5298 7123	0.4768 6829	0.4292 2324	0.3863 8882	85
86	0.5259 2678	0.4727 3188	0.4249 7350	0.3820 9031	86
87	0.5220 1169	0.4686 3136	0.4207 6585	0.3778 3961	87
88	0.5181 2575	0.4645 6640	0.4165 9985	0.3736 3621	88
89	0.5142 6873	0.4605 3671	0.4124 7510	0.3694 7956	89
90	0.5104 4043	0.4565 4197	0.4083 9119	0.3653 6916	90
91	0.5066 4063	0.4525 8187	0.4043 4771	0.3613 0448	91
92	0.5028 6911	0.4486 5613	0.4003 4427	0.3572 8503	92
93	0.4991 2567	0.4447 6444	0.3963 8046	0.3533 1029	93
94	0.4954 1009	0.4409 0651	0.3924 5590	0.3493 7976	94
95	0.4917 2217	0.4370 8204	0.3885 7020	0.3454 9297	95
96	0.4880 6171	0.4332 9075	0.3847 2297	0.3416 4941	96
97	0.4844 2850	0.4295 3234	0.3809 1383	0.3378 4861	97
98	0.4808 2233	0.4258 0654	0.3771 4241	0.3340 9010	98
99	0.4772 4301	0.4221 1305	0.3734 0832	0.3303 7340	99
100	0.4736 9033	0.4184 5159	0.3697 1121	0.3266 9805	100

n	$\frac{3}{4}\%$	$\frac{7}{8}\%$	1%	$1\frac{1}{8}\%$	n
101	0.4701 6410	0.4148 2190	0.3660 5071	0.3230 6358	101
102	0.4666 6412	0.4112 2370	0.3624 2644	0.3194 6955	102
103	0.4631 9019	0.4076 5670	0.3588 3806	0.3159 1550	103
104	0.4597 4213	0.4041 2064	0.3552 8521	0.3124 0099	104
105	0.4563 1973	0.4006 1526	0.3517 6753	0.3089 2558	105
106	0.4529 2281	0.3971 4028	0.3482 8469	0.3054 8883	106
107	0.4495 5117	0.3936 9545	0.3448 3632	0.3020 9031	107
108	0.4462 0464	0.3902 8049	0.3414 2210	0.2987 2960	108
109	0.4428 8302	0.3868 9516	0.3380 4168	0.2954 0628	109
110	0.4395 8612	0.3835 3919	0.3346 9474	0.2921 1993	110
111	0.4363 1377	0.3802 1233	0.3213 8093	0.2888 7014	111
112	0.4330 6577	0.3769 1433	0.3280 9993	0.2856 5651	112
113	0.4298 4196	0.3736 4494	0.3248 5141	0.2824 7862	113
114	0.4266 4124	0.3704 0391	0.3216 3506	0.2793 3609	114
115	0.4234 6615	0.3671 9099	0.3184 5056	0.2762 2852	115
116	0.4203 1379	0.3640 0593	0.3152 9758	0.2731 5552	116
117	0.4171 8491	0.3608 4851	0.3121 7582	0.2701 1671	117
118	0.4140 7931	0.3577 1847	0.3090 8497	0.2671 1170	118
119	0.4109 9683	0.3546 1559	0.3060 2473	0.2641 4013	119
120	0.4079 3730	0.3515 3961	0.3029 9478	0.2612 0161	120
121	0.4049 0055	0.3484 9032	0.2999 9483	0.2582 9578	121
122	0.4018 8640	0.3454 6748	0.2970 2459	0.2554 2228	122
123	0.3988 9469	0.3424 7086	0.2940 8375	0.2525 8075	123
124	0.3959 2525	0.3395 0024	0.2911 7203	0.2497 7082	124
125	0.3929 7792	0.3365 5538	0.2882 8914	0.2469 9216	125
126	0.3900 5252	0.3336 3606	0.2854 3479	0.2442 4441	126
127	0.3871 4891	0.3307 4207	0.2826 0870	0.2415 2723	127
128	0.3842 6691	0.3278 7318	0.2798 1060	0.2388 4028	128
129	0.3814 0636	0.3250 2917	0.2770 4019	0.2361 8322	129
130	0.3785 6711	0.3222 0984	0.2742 9722	0.2335 5572	130
131	0.3757 4899	0.3194 1496	0.2715 8141	0.2309 5744	131
132	0.3729 5185	0.3166 4432	0.2688 9248	0.2283 8808	132
133	0.3701 7553	0.3138 9771	0.2662 3018	0.2258 4730	133
134	0.3674 1988	0.3111 7493	0.2635 9424	0.2233 3478	134
135	0.3646 8475	0.3084 7577	0.2609 8439	0.2208 5021	135
136	0.3619 6997	0.3058 0002	0.2584 0039	0.2183 9329	136
137	0.3592 7541	0.3031 4748	0.2558 4197	0.2159 6370	137
138	0.3566 0090	0.3005 1795	0.2533 0888	0.2135 6114	138
139	0.3539 4630	0.2979 1122	0.2508 0087	0.2111 8530	139
140	0.3513 1147	0.2953 2711	0.2483 1770	0.2088 3590	140
141	0.3486 9625	0.2927 6541	0.2458 5911	0.2065 1263	141
142	0.3461 0049	0.2902 2594	0.2434 2486	0.2042 1521	142
143	0.3435 2406	0.2877 0849	0.2410 1471	0.2019 4335	143
144	0.3409 6681	0.2852 1288	0.2386 2843	0.1996 9676	144
145	0.3384 2860	0.2827 3891	0.2362 6577	0.1974 7516	145
146	0.3359 0928	0.2802 8640	0.2339 2650	0.1952 7828	146
147	0.3334 0871	0.2778 5517	0.2316 1040	0.1931 6584	147
148	0.3309 2676	0.2754 4503	0.2293 1723	0.1909 5757	148
149	0.3284 6329	0.2730 5579	0.2270 4676	0.1888 3320	149
150	0.3260 1815	0.2706 8728	0.2247 9877	0.1867 3245	150

n	$1\frac{1}{4}\%$	$1\frac{3}{8}\%$	$1\frac{1}{2}\%$	$1\frac{3}{4}\%$	n
1	0.9876 5432	0.9864 3650	0.9852 2167	0.9828 0098	1
2	0.9754 6106	0.9730 5696	0.9706 6175	0.9658 9777	2
3	0.9634 1833	0.9598 5890	0.9563 1699	0.9492 8528	3
4	0.9515 2428	0.9468 3986	0.9421 8423	0.9329 5851	4
5	0.9397 7706	0.9339 9739	0.9282 6033	0.9169 1254	5
6	0.9281 7488	0.9213 2912	0.9145 4219	0.9011 4254	6
7	0.9167 1593	0.9088 3267	0.9010 2679	0.8856 4378	7
8	0.9053 9845	0.8965 0571	0.8877 1112	0.8704 1157	8
9	0.8942 2069	0.8843 4596	0.8745 9224	0.8554 4135	9
10	0.8831 8093	0.8723 5113	0.8616 6723	0.8407 2860	10
11	0.8722 7746	0.8605 1899	0.8489 3323	0.8262 6889	11
12	0.8615 0860	0.8488 4734	0.8363 8742	0.8120 5788	12
13	0.8508 7269	0.8373 3400	0.8240 2702	0.7980 9128	13
14	0.8403 6809	0.8259 7682	0.8118 4928	0.7843 6490	14
15	0.8299 9318	0.8147 7368	0.7998 5150	0.7708 7459	15
16	0.8197 4635	0.8037 2250	0.7880 3104	0.7576 1631	16
17	0.8096 2602	0.7928 2120	0.7763 8526	0.7445 8605	17
18	0.7996 3064	0.7820 6777	0.7649 1159	0.7317 7990	18
19	0.7897 5866	0.7714 6020	0.7536 0747	0.7191 9401	19
20	0.7800 0855	0.7609 9649	0.7424 7042	0.7068 2458	20
21	0.7703 7881	0.7506 7472	0.7314 9795	0.6946 6789	21
22	0.7608 6796	0.7404 9294	0.7206 8763	0.6827 2028	22
23	0.7514 7453	0.7304 4926	0.7100 3708	0.6709 7817	23
24	0.7421 9707	0.7205 4181	0.6995 4392	0.6594 3800	24
25	0.7330 3414	0.7107 6874	0.6892 0583	0.6480 9632	25
26	0.7239 8434	0.7011 2823	0.6790 2052	0.6369 4970	26
27	0.7150 4626	0.6916 1847	0.6689 8574	0.6259 9479	27
28	0.7062 1853	0.6822 3771	0.6590 9925	0.6152 2829	28
29	0.6974 9978	0.6729 8417	0.6493 5887	0.6046 4697	29
30	0.6888 8867	0.6638 5615	0.6397 6243	0.5942 4764	30
31	0.6803 8387	0.6548 5194	0.6303 0781	0.5840 2716	31
32	0.6719 8407	0.6459 6985	0.6209 9292	0.5739 8247	32
33	0.6636 8797	0.6372 0824	0.6118 1568	0.5641 1053	33
34	0.6554 9429	0.6285 6546	0.6027 7407	0.5544 0839	34
35	0.6474 0177	0.6200 3991	0.5938 6608	0.5448 7311	35
36	0.6394 0916	0.6116 3000	0.5850 8974	0.5355 0183	36
37	0.6315 1522	0.6033 3416	0.5764 4309	0.5262 9172	37
38	0.6237 1873	0.5951 5083	0.5679 2423	0.5172 4002	38
39	0.6160 1850	0.5870 7850	0.5595 3126	0.5083 4400	39
40	0.6084 1334	0.5791 1566	0.5512 6232	0.4996 0098	40
41	0.6009 0206	0.5712 6083	0.5431 1559	0.4910 0834	41
42	0.5934 8352	0.5635 1253	0.5350 8925	0.4825 6348	42
43	0.5861 5656	0.5558 6933	0.5271 8153	0.4742 6386	43
44	0.5789 2006	0.5483 2979	0.5193 9067	0.4661 0699	44
45	0.5717 7290	0.5408 9252	0.5117 1494	0.4580 9040	45
46	0.5647 1397	0.5335 5612	0.5041 5265	0.4502 1170	46
47	0.5577 4219	0.5263 1923	0.4967 0212	0.4424 6850	47
48	0.5508 5649	0.5191 8050	0.4893 6170	0.4348 5848	48
49	0.5440 5579	0.5121 3860	0.4821 2975	0.4273 7934	49
50	0.5373 3905	0.5051 9220	0.4750 0468	0.4200 2883	50

n	$1\frac{1}{4}\%$	$1\frac{3}{8}\%$	$1\frac{1}{2}\%$	$1\frac{3}{4}\%$	n
51	0.5307 0524	0.4983 4003	0.4679 8491	0.4128 0475	51
52	0.5241 5332	0.4915 8079	0.4610 6887	0.4057 0492	52
53	0.5176 8229	0.4849 1323	0.4542 5505	0.3987 2719	53
54	0.5112 9115	0.4783 3611	0.4475 4192	0.3918 6947	54
55	0.5049 7892	0.4718 4820	0.4409 2800	0.3851 2970	55
56	0.4987 4461	0.4654 4829	0.4344 1182	0.3785 0585	56
57	0.4925 8727	0.4591 3518	0.4279 9194	0.3719 9592	57
58	0.4865 0594	0.4529 0770	0.4216 6694	0.3655 9796	58
59	0.4804 9970	0.4467 6468	0.4154 3541	0.3593 1003	59
60	0.4745 6760	0.4407 0499	0.4092 9597	0.3531 3025	60
61	0.4687 0874	0.4347 2749	0.4032 4726	0.3470 5676	61
62	0.4629 2222	0.4288 3106	0.3972 8794	0.3410 8772	62
63	0.4572 0713	0.4230 1461	0.3914 1669	0.3352 2135	63
64	0.4515 6259	0.4172 7705	0.3856 3221	0.3294 5587	64
65	0.4459 8775	0.4116 1731	0.3799 3321	0.3237 8956	65
66	0.4404 8173	0.4060 3434	0.3743 1843	0.3182 2069	66
67	0.4350 4368	0.4005 2709	0.3687 8663	0.3127 4761	67
68	0.4296 7277	0.3950 9454	0.3633 3658	0.3073 6866	68
69	0.4243 6817	0.3897 3568	0.3579 6708	0.3020 8222	69
70	0.4191 2905	0.3844 4949	0.3526 7692	0.2968 8670	70
71	0.4139 5462	0.3792 3501	0.3474 6495	0.2917 8054	71
72	0.4088 4407	0.3740 9126	0.3423 3000	0.2867 6221	72
73	0.4037 9661	0.3690 1727	0.3372 7093	0.2818 3018	73
74	0.3988 1147	0.3640 1210	0.3322 8663	0.2769 8298	74
75	0.3938 8787	0.3590 7483	0.3273 7599	0.2722 1914	75
76	0.3890 2506	0.3542 0451	0.3225 3793	0.2675 3724	76
77	0.3842 2228	0.3494 0026	0.3177 7136	0.2629 3586	77
78	0.3794 7879	0.3446 6117	0.3130 7523	0.2584 1362	78
79	0.3747 9387	0.3399 8636	0.3084 4850	0.2539 6916	79
80	0.3701 6679	0.3353 7495	0.3038 9015	0.2496 0114	80
81	0.3655 9683	0.3308 2609	0.2993 9916	0.2453 0825	81
82	0.3610 8329	0.3263 3893	0.2949 7454	0.2410 8919	82
83	0.3566 2547	0.3219 1263	0.2906 1531	0.2369 4269	83
84	0.3522 2268	0.3175 4637	0.2863 2050	0.2328 6751	84
85	0.3478 7426	0.3132 3933	0.2820 8917	0.2288 6242	85
86	0.3435 7951	0.3089 9071	0.2779 2036	0.2249 2621	86
87	0.3393 3779	0.3047 9971	0.2738 1316	0.2210 5770	87
88	0.3351 4843	0.3006 6556	0.2697 6666	0.2172 5572	88
89	0.3310 1080	0.2965 8748	0.2657 7997	0.2135 1914	89
90	0.3269 2425	0.2925 6472	0.2618 5218	0.2098 4682	90
91	0.3228 8814	0.2885 9652	0.2579 8245	0.2062 3766	91
92	0.3189 0187	0.2846 8214	0.2541 6990	0.2026 9057	92
93	0.3149 6481	0.2808 2085	0.2504 1369	0.1992 0450	93
94	0.3110 7636	0.2770 1194	0.2467 1300	0.1957 7837	94
95	0.3072 3591	0.2732 5468	0.2430 6699	0.1924 1118	95
96	0.3034 4287	0.2695 4839	0.2394 7487	0.1891 0190	96
97	0.2996 9666	0.2658 9237	0.2359 3583	0.1858 4953	97
98	0.2959 9670	0.2622 8594	0.2324 4909	0.1826 5310	98
99	0.2923 4242	0.2587 2843	0.2290 1389	0.1795 1165	99
100	0.2887 3326	0.2552 1916	0.2256 2944	0.1764 2422	100

n	2%	2¼%	2½%	2¾%	n
1	0.9803 9216	0.9779 9511	0.9756 0976	0.9732 3601	1
2	0.9611 6878	0.9564 7444	0.9518 1440	0.9471 8833	2
3	0.9423 2233	0.9354 2732	0.9285 9941	0.9218 3779	3
4	0.9238 4543	0.9148 4335	0.9059 5064	0.8971 6573	4
5	0.9057 3081	0.8947 1232	0.8838 5429	0.8731 5400	5
6	0.8879 7138	0.8750 2427	0.8622 9687	0.8497 8491	6
7	0.8705 6018	0.8557 6946	0.8412 6524	0.8270 4128	7
8	0.8534 9037	0.8369 3835	0.8207 4657	0.8049 0635	8
9	0.8367 5527	0.8185 2161	0.8007 2836	0.7833 6385	9
10	0.8203 4830	0.8005 1013	0.7811 9840	0.7623 9791	10
11	0.8042 6304	0.7828 9499	0.7621 4478	0.7419 9310	11
12	0.7884 9318	0.7656 6748	0.7435 5589	0.7221 3440	12
13	0.7730 3253	0.7488 1905	0.7254 2038	0.7028 0720	13
14	0.7578 7502	0.7323 4137	0.7077 2720	0.6839 9728	14
15	0.7430 1473	0.7162 2628	0.6904 6556	0.6656 9078	15
16	0.7284 4581	0.7004 6580	0.6736 2493	0.6478 7424	16
17	0.7141 6256	0.6850 5212	0.6571 9506	0.6305 3454	17
18	0.7001 5937	0.6699 7763	0.6411 6591	0.6136 5892	18
19	0.6864 3076	0.6552 3484	0.6255 2772	0.5972 3496	19
20	0.6729 7133	0.6408 1647	0.6102 7094	0.5812 5057	20
21	0.6597 7582	0.6267 1538	0.5953 8629	0.5656 9398	21
22	0.6468 3904	0.6129 2457	0.5808 6467	0.5505 5375	22
23	0.6341 5592	0.5994 3724	0.5666 9724	0.5358 1874	23
24	0.6217 2149	0.5862 4668	0.5528 7535	0.5214 7809	24
25	0.6095 3087	0.5733 4639	0.5393 9059	0.5075 2126	25
26	0.5975 7928	0.5607 2997	0.5262 3472	0.4939 3796	26
27	0.5858 6204	0.5483 9117	0.5133 9973	0.4807 1821	27
28	0.5743 7455	0.5363 2388	0.5008 7778	0.4678 5227	28
29	0.5631 1231	0.5245 2213	0.4886 6125	0.4553 3068	29
30	0.5520 7089	0.5129 8008	0.4767 4269	0.4431 4421	30
31	0.5412 4597	0.5016 9201	0.4651 1481	0.4312 8391	31
32	0.5306 3330	0.4906 5233	0.4537 7055	0.4197 4103	32
33	0.5202 2873	0.4798 5558	0.4427 0298	0.4085 0708	33
34	0.5100 2817	0.4692 9641	0.4319 0534	0.3975 7380	34
35	0.5000 2761	0.4589 6960	0.4213 7107	0.3869 3314	35
36	0.4902 2315	0.4488 7002	0.4110 9372	0.3765 7727	36
37	0.4806 1093	0.4389 9268	0.4010 6705	0.3664 9856	37
38	0.4711 8719	0.4293 3270	0.3912 8492	0.3566 8959	38
39	0.4619 4822	0.4198 8528	0.3817 4139	0.3471 4316	39
40	0.4528 9042	0.4106 4575	0.3724 3062	0.3378 5222	40
41	0.4440 1021	0.4016 0954	0.3633 4695	0.3288 0995	41
42	0.4353 0413	0.3927 7216	0.3544 8483	0.3200 0968	42
43	0.4267 6875	0.3841 2925	0.3458 3886	0.3114 4495	43
44	0.4184 0074	0.3756 7653	0.3374 0376	0.3031 0944	44
45	0.4101 9680	0.3674 0981	0.3291 7440	0.2949 9702	45
46	0.4021 5373	0.3593 2500	0.3211 4576	0.2871 0172	46
47	0.3942 6836	0.3514 1809	0.3133 1294	0.2794 1773	47
48	0.3865 3761	0.3436 8518	0.3056 7116	0.2719 3940	48
49	0.3789 5844	0.3361 2242	0.2982 1576	0.2646 6122	49
50	0.3715 2788	0.3287 2608	0.2909 4221	0.2575 7783	50

n	2%	$2\frac{1}{4}\%$	$2\frac{1}{2}\%$	$2\frac{3}{4}\%$	n
51	0.3642 4302	0.3214 9250	0.2838 4606	0.2506 8402	51
52	0.3571 0100	0.3144 1810	0.2769 2298	0.2439 7471	52
53	0.3500 9902	0.3074 9936	0.2701 6876	0.2374 4497	53
54	0.3432 3433	0.3007 3287	0.2635 7928	0.2310 9000	54
55	0.3365 0425	0.2941 1528	0.2571 5052	0.2249 0511	55
56	0.3299 0613	0.2876 4330	0.2508 7855	0.2188 8575	56
57	0.3234 3738	0.2813 1374	0.2447 5956	0.2130 2749	57
58	0.3170 9547	0.2751 2347	0.2387 8982	0.2073 2603	58
59	0.3108 7791	0.2690 6940	0.2329 6568	0.2017 7716	59
60	0.3047 8227	0.2631 4856	0.2272 8359	0.1963 7679	60
61	0.2988 0614	0.2573 5801	0.2217 4009	0.1911 2097	61
62	0.2929 4720	0.2516 9487	0.2163 3179	0.1860 0581	62
63	0.2872 0314	0.2461 5635	0.2110 5541	0.1810 2755	63
64	0.2815 7170	0.2407 3971	0.2059 0771	0.1761 8253	64
65	0.2760 5069	0.2354 4226	0.2008 8557	0.1714 6718	65
66	0.2706 3793	0.2302 6138	0.1959 8593	0.1668 7804	66
67	0.2653 3130	0.2251 9450	0.1912 0578	0.1624 1172	67
68	0.2601 2873	0.2202 3912	0.1865 4223	0.1580 6493	68
69	0.2550 2817	0.2153 9278	0.1819 9241	0.1538 3448	69
70	0.2500 2761	0.2106 5309	0.1775 5358	0.1497 1726	70
71	0.2451 2511	0.2060 1769	0.1732 2300	0.1457 1023	71
72	0.2403 1874	0.2014 8429	0.1689 9805	0.1418 1044	72
73	0.2356 0661	0.1970 5065	0.1648 7615	0.1380 1503	73
74	0.2309 8687	0.1927 1458	0.1608 5478	0.1343 2119	74
75	0.2264 5771	0.1884 7391	0.1569 3149	0.1307 2622	75
76	0.2220 1737	0.1843 2657	0.1531 0389	0.1272 2747	76
77	0.2176 6408	0.1802 7048	0.1493 6965	0.1238 2235	77
78	0.2133 9616	0.1763 0365	0.1457 2649	0.1205 0837	78
79	0.2092 1192	0.1724 2411	0.1421 7218	0.1172 8309	79
80	0.2051 0973	0.1686 2993	0.1387 0457	0.1141 4412	80
81	0.2010 8797	0.1649 1925	0.1353 2153	0.1110 8917	81
82	0.1971 4507	0.1612 9022	0.1320 2101	0.1081 1598	82
83	0.1932 7948	0.1577 4105	0.1288 0098	0.1052 2237	83
84	0.1894 8968	0.1542 6997	0.1256 5949	0.1024 0620	84
85	0.1857 7420	0.1508 7528	0.1225 9463	0.0996 6540	85
86	0.1821 3157	0.1475 5528	0.1196 0452	0.0969 9795	86
87	0.1785 6036	0.1443 0835	0.1166 8733	0.0944 0190	87
88	0.1750 5918	0.1411 3286	0.1138 4130	0.0918 7533	88
89	0.1716 2665	0.1380 2724	0.1110 6468	0.0894 1638	89
90	0.1682 6142	0.1349 8997	0.1083 5579	0.0870 2324	90
91	0.1649 6217	0.1320 1953	0.1057 1296	0.0846 9415	91
92	0.1617 2762	0.1291 1445	0.1031 3460	0.0824 2740	92
93	0.1585 5649	0.1262 7331	0.1006 1912	0.0802 2131	93
94	0.1554 4754	0.1234 9468	0.0981 6500	0.0780 7427	94
95	0.1523 9955	0.1207 7719	0.0957 7073	0.0759 8469	95
96	0.1494 1132	0.1181 1950	0.0934 3486	0.0739 5104	96
97	0.1464 8169	0.1155 2029	0.0911 5596	0.0719 7181	97
98	0.1436 0950	0.1129 7828	0.0889 3264	0.0700 4556	98
99	0.1407 9363	0.1104 9221	0.0867 6355	0.0681 7086	99
100	0.1380 3297	0.1080 6084	0.0846 4737	0.0663 4634	100

n	3%	3½%	4%	4½%	n
1	0.9708 7379	0.9661 8357	0.9615 3846	0.9569 3780	1
2	0.9425 9591	0.9335 1070	0.9245 5621	0.9157 2995	2
3	0.9151 4166	0.9019 4271	0.8889 9636	0.8762 9660	3
4	0.8884 8705	0.8714 4223	0.8548 0419	0.8385 6134	4
5	0.8626 0878	0.8419 7317	0.8219 2711	0.8024 5105	5
6	0.8374 8426	0.8135 0064	0.7903 1453	0.7678 9574	6
7	0.8130 9151	0.7859 9096	0.7599 1781	0.7348 2846	7
8	0.7894 0923	0.7594 1156	0.7306 9021	0.7031 8513	8
9	0.7664 1673	0.7337 3097	0.7025 8674	0.6729 0443	9
10	0.7440 9391	0.7089 1881	0.6755 6417	0.6439 2768	10
11	0.7224 2128	0.6849 4571	0.6495 8093	0.6161 9874	11
12	0.7013 7988	0.6617 8330	0.6245 9705	0.5896 6386	12
13	0.6809 5134	0.6394 0415	0.6005 7409	0.5642 7164	13
14	0.6611 1781	0.6177 8179	0.5774 7508	0.5399 7286	14
15	0.6418 6195	0.5968 9062	0.5552 6450	0.5167 2044	15
16	0.6231 6694	0.5767 0591	0.5339 0818	0.4944 6932	16
17	0.6050 1645	0.5572 0378	0.5133 7325	0.4731 7639	17
18	0.5873 9461	0.5383 6114	0.4936 2812	0.4528 0037	18
19	0.5702 8603	0.5201 5569	0.4746 4242	0.4333 0179	19
20	0.5536 7575	0.5025 6588	0.4563 8695	0.4146 4286	20
21	0.5375 4928	0.4855 7090	0.4388 3360	0.3967 8743	21
22	0.5218 9250	0.4691 5063	0.4219 5539	0.3797 0089	22
23	0.5066 9175	0.4532 8563	0.4057 2633	0.3633 5013	23
24	0.4919 3374	0.4379 5713	0.3901 2147	0.3477 0347	24
25	0.4776 0557	0.4231 4699	0.3751 1680	0.3327 3060	25
26	0.4636 9473	0.4088 3767	0.3606 8923	0.3184 0248	26
27	0.4501 8906	0.3950 1224	0.3468 1657	0.3046 9137	27
28	0.4370 7675	0.3816 5434	0.3334 7747	0.2915 7069	28
29	0.4243 4636	0.3687 4815	0.3206 5141	0.2790 1502	29
30	0.4119 8676	0.3562 7841	0.3083 1867	0.2670 0002	30
31	0.3999 8715	0.3442 3035	0.2964 6026	0.2555 0241	31
32	0.3883 3703	0.3325 8971	0.2850 5794	0.2444 9991	32
33	0.3770 2625	0.3213 4271	0.2740 9417	0.2339 7121	33
34	0.3660 4490	0.3104 7605	0.2635 5209	0.2238 9589	34
35	0.3553 8340	0.2999 7686	0.2534 1547	0.2142 5444	35
36	0.3450 3243	0.2898 3272	0.2436 6872	0.2050 2317	36
37	0.3349 8294	0.2800 3161	0.2342 9685	0.1961 9921	37
38	0.3252 2615	0.2705 6194	0.2252 8543	0.1877 5044	38
39	0.3157 5355	0.2614 1250	0.2166 2061	0.1796 6549	39
40	0.3065 5684	0.2525 7247	0.2082 8904	0.1719 2870	40
41	0.2976 2800	0.2440 3137	0.2002 7793	0.1645 2507	41
42	0.2889 5922	0.2357 7910	0.1925 7493	0.1574 4026	42
43	0.2805 4294	0.2278 0590	0.1851 6820	0.1506 6054	43
44	0.2723 7178	0.2201 0231	0.1780 4635	0.1441 7276	44
45	0.2644 3862	0.2126 5924	0.1711 9841	0.1379 6437	45
46	0.2567 3653	0.2054 6787	0.1646 1386	0.1320 2332	46
47	0.2492 5876	0.1985 1968	0.1582 8256	0.1263 3810	47
48	0.2419 9880	0.1918 0645	0.1521 9476	0.1208 9771	48
49	0.2349 5029	0.1853 2024	0.1463 4112	0.1156 9158	49
50	0.2281 0708	0.1790 5337	0.1407 1262	0.1107 0965	50

n	3%	3½%	4%	4½%	n
51	0.2214 6318	0.1729 9843	0.1353 0059	0.1059 4225	51
52	0.2150 1280	0.1671 4824	0.1300 9672	0.1013 8014	52
53	0.2087 5029	0.1614 9589	0.1250 9300	0.0970 1449	53
54	0.2026 7019	0.1560 3467	0.1202 8173	0.0928 3683	54
55	0.1967 6717	0.1507 5814	0.1156 5551	0.0888 3907	55
56	0.1910 3609	0.1456 6004	0.1112 0722	0.0850 1347	56
57	0.1854 7193	0.1407 3433	0.1069 3002	0.0813 5260	57
58	0.1800 6984	0.1359 7520	0.1028 1733	0.0778 4938	58
59	0.1748 2508	0.1313 7701	0.0988 6282	0.0744 9701	59
60	0.1697 3309	0.1269 3431	0.0950 6040	0.0712 8901	60
61	0.1647 8941	0.1226 4184	0.0914 0423	0.0682 1915	61
62	0.1599 8972	0.1184 9453	0.0878 8868	0.0652 8148	62
63	0.1553 2982	0.1144 8747	0.0845 0835	0.0624 7032	63
64	0.1508 0565	0.1106 1591	0.0812 5803	0.0597 8021	64
65	0.1464 1325	0.1068 7528	0.0781 3272	0.0572 0594	65
66	0.1421 4879	0.1032 6114	0.0751 2762	0.0547 4253	66
67	0.1380 0853	0.0997 6922	0.0722 3809	0.0523 8519	67
68	0.1339 8887	0.0963 9538	0.0694 5970	0.0501 2937	68
69	0.1300 8628	0.0931 3563	0.0667 8818	0.0479 7069	69
70	0.1262 9736	0.0899 8612	0.0642 1940	0.0459 0497	70
71	0.1226 1880	0.0869 4311	0.0617 4942	0.0439 2820	71
72	0.1190 4737	0.0840 0300	0.0593 7445	0.0420 3655	72
73	0.1155 7998	0.0811 6232	0.0570 9081	0.0402 2637	73
74	0.1122 1357	0.0784 1770	0.0548 9501	0.0384 9413	74
75	0.1089 4521	0.0757 6590	0.0527 8367	0.0368 3649	75
76	0.1057 7205	0.0732 0376	0.0507 5353	0.0352 5023	76
77	0.1026 9131	0.0707 2827	0.0488 0147	0.0337 3228	77
78	0.0997 0030	0.0683 3650	0.0469 2449	0.0322 7969	78
79	0.0967 9641	0.0660 2560	0.0451 1970	0.0308 8965	79
80	0.0939 7710	0.0637 9285	0.0433 8433	0.0295 5948	80
81	0.0912 3990	0.0616 3561	0.0417 1570	0.0282 8658	81
82	0.0885 8243	0.0595 5131	0.0401 1125	0.0270 6850	82
83	0.0860 0236	0.0575 3750	0.0385 6851	0.0259 0287	83
84	0.0834 9743	0.0555 9178	0.0370 8510	0.0247 8744	84
85	0.0810 6547	0.0537 1187	0.0356 5875	0.0237 2003	85
86	0.0787 0434	0.0518 9553	0.0342 8726	0.0226 9860	86
87	0.0764 1198	0.0501 4060	0.0329 6852	0.0217 2115	87
88	0.0741 8639	0.0484 4503	0.0317 0050	0.0207 8579	88
89	0.0720 2562	0.0468 0679	0.0304 8125	0.0198 9070	89
90	0.0699 2779	0.0452 2395	0.0293 0890	0.0190 3417	90
91	0.0678 9105	0.0436 9464	0.0281 8163	0.0182 1451	91
92	0.0659 1364	0.0422 1704	0.0270 9772	0.0174 3016	92
93	0.0639 9383	0.0407 8941	0.0260 5550	0.0166 7958	93
94	0.0621 2993	0.0394 1006	0.0250 5337	0.0159 6132	94
95	0.0603 2032	0.0380 7735	0.0240 8978	0.0152 7399	95
96	0.0585 6342	0.0367 8971	0.0231 6325	0.0146 1626	96
97	0.0568 5769	0.0355 4562	0.0222 7235	0.0139 8685	97
98	0.0552 0164	0.0343 4359	0.0214 1572	0.0133 8454	98
99	0.0535 9383	0.0331 8221	0.0205 9204	0.0128 0817	99
100	0.0520 3284	0.0320 6011	0.0198 0004	0.0122 5663	100

n	5%	5½%	6%	6½%	
1	0.9523 8095	0.9478 6730	0.9433 9623	0.9389 6714	1
2	0.9070 2948	0.8984 5242	0.8899 9644	0.8816 5928	2
3	0.8638 3760	0.8516 1366	0.8396 1928	0.8278 4909	3
4	0.8227 0247	0.8072 1674	0.7920 9366	0.7773 2309	4
5	0.7835 2617	0.7651 3435	0.7472 5817	0.7298 8084	5
6	0.7462 1540	0.7252 4583	0.7049 6054	0.6853 3412	6
7	0.7106 8133	0.6874 3681	0.6650 5711	0.6435 0621	7
8	0.6768 3936	0.6515 9887	0.6274 1237	0.6042 3119	8
9	0.6446 0892	0.6176 2926	0.5918 9846	0.5673 5323	9
10	0.6139 1325	0.5854 3058	0.5583 9478	0.5327 2604	10
11	0.5846 7929	0.5549 1050	0.5267 8753	0.5002 1224	11
12	0.5568 3742	0.5259 8152	0.4969 6936	0.4696 8285	12
13	0.5303 2135	0.4985 6068	0.4688 3902	0.4410 1676	13
14	0.5050 6795	0.4725 6937	0.4423 0096	0.4141 0025	14
15	0.4810 1710	0.4479 3305	0.4172 6506	0.3888 2652	15
16	0.4581 1152	0.4245 8109	0.3936 4628	0.3650 9533	16
17	0.4362 9669	0.4024 4653	0.3713 6442	0.3428 1251	17
18	0.4155 2065	0.3814 6590	0.3503 4379	0.3218 8969	18
19	0.3957 3396	0.3615 7906	0.3305 1301	0.3022 4384	19
20	0.3768 8948	0.3427 2896	0.3118 0473	0.2837 9703	20
21	0.3589 4236	0.3248 6158	0.2941 5540	0.2664 7608	21
22	0.3418 4987	0.3079 2567	0.2775 0510	0.2502 1228	22
23	0.3255 7131	0.2918 7267	0.2617 9726	0.2349 4111	23
24	0.3100 6791	0.2766 5656	0.2469 7855	0.2206 0198	24
25	0.2953 0277	0.2622 3370	0.2329 9863	0.2071 3801	25
26	0.2812 4073	0.2485 6275	0.2198 1003	0.1944 9579	26
27	0.2678 4832	0.2356 0450	0.2073 6795	0.1826 2515	27
28	0.2550 9364	0.2233 2181	0.1956 3014	0.1714 7902	28
29	0.2429 4632	0.2116 7944	0.1845 5674	0.1610 1316	29
30	0.2313 7745	0.2006 4402	0.1741 1013	0.1511 8607	30
31	0.2203 5947	0.1901 8390	0.1642 5484	0.1419 5875	31
32	0.2098 6617	0.1802 6910	0.1549 5740	0.1332 9460	32
33	0.1998 7254	0.1708 7119	0.1461 8622	0.1251 5925	33
34	0.1903 5480	0.1619 6321	0.1379 1153	0.1175 2042	34
35	0.1812 9029	0.1535 1963	0.1301 0522	0.1103 4781	35
36	0.1726 5741	0.1455 1624	0.1227 4077	0.1036 1297	36
37	0.1644 3563	0.1379 3008	0.1157 9318	0.0972 8917	37
38	0.1566 0536	0.1307 3941	0.1092 3885	0.0913 5134	38
39	0.1491 4797	0.1239 2362	0.1030 5552	0.0857 7590	39
40	0.1420 4568	0.1174 6314	0.0972 2219	0.0805 4075	40
41	0.1352 8160	0.1113 3947	0.0917 1905	0.0756 2512	41
42	0.1288 3962	0.1055 3504	0.0865 2740	0.0710 0950	42
43	0.1227 0440	0.1000 3322	0.0816 2962	0.0666 7559	43
44	0.1168 6133	0.0948 1822	0.0770 0908	0.0626 0619	44
45	0.1112 9651	0.0898 7509	0.0726 5007	0.0587 8515	45
46	0.1059 9668	0.0851 8965	0.0685 3781	0.0551 9733	46
47	0.1009 4921	0.0807 4849	0.0646 5831	0.0518 2848	47
48	0.0961 4211	0.0765 3885	0.0609 9840	0.0486 6524	48
49	0.0915 6391	0.0725 4867	0.0575 4566	0.0456 9506	49
50	0.0872 0373	0.0687 6652	0.0542 8836	0.0429 0616	50

n	5%	$5\frac{1}{2}\%$	6%	$6\frac{1}{2}\%$	n
51	0.0830 5117	0.0651 8153	0.0512 1544	0.0402 8747	51
52	0.0790 9635	0.0617 8344	0.0483 1645	0.0378 2861	52
53	0.0753 2986	0.0585 6250	0.0455 8156	0.0355 1982	53
54	0.0717 4272	0.0555 0948	0.0430 0147	0.0333 5195	54
55	0.0683 2640	0.0526 1562	0.0405 6742	0.0313 1638	55
56	0.0650 7276	0.0498 7263	0.0382 7115	0.0294 0505	56
57	0.0619 7406	0.0472 7263	0.0361 0486	0.0276 1038	57
58	0.0590 2291	0.0448 0818	0.0340 6119	0.0259 2524	58
59	0.0562 1230	0.0424 7221	0.0321 3320	0.0243 4295	59
60	0.0535 3552	0.0402 5802	0.0303 1434	0.0228 5723	60
61	0.0509 8621	0.0381 5926	0.0285 9843	0.0214 6218	61
62	0.0485 5830	0.0361 6992	0.0269 7965	0.0201 5229	62
63	0.0462 4600	0.0342 8428	0.0254 5250	0.0189 2233	63
64	0.0440 4381	0.0324 9695	0.0240 1179	0.0177 6745	64
65	0.0419 4648	0.0308 0279	0.0226 5264	0.0166 8305	65
66	0.0399 4903	0.0291 9696	0.0213 7041	0.0156 6484	66
67	0.0380 4670	0.0276 7485	0.0201 6077	0.0147 0877	67
68	0.0362 3495	0.0262 3208	0.0190 1959	0.0138 1105	68
69	0.0345 0948	0.0248 6453	0.0179 4301	0.0129 6812	69
70	0.0328 6617	0.0235 6828	0.0169 2737	0.0121 7664	70
71	0.0313 0111	0.0223 3960	0.0159 6921	0.0114 3346	71
72	0.0298 1058	0.0211 7498	0.0150 6530	0.0107 3565	72
73	0.0283 9103	0.0200 7107	0.0142 1254	0.0100 8042	73
74	0.0270 3908	0.0190 2471	0.0134 0806	0.0094 6518	74
75	0.0257 5150	0.0180 3290	0.0126 4911	0.0088 8750	75
76	0.0245 2524	0.0170 9279	0.0119 3313	0.0083 4507	76
77	0.0233 5737	0.0162 0170	0.0112 5767	0.0078 3574	77
78	0.0222 4512	0.0153 5706	0.0106 2044	0.0073 5751	78
79	0.0211 8582	0.0145 5646	0.0100 1928	0.0069 0846	79
80	0.0201 7698	0.0137 9759	0.0094 5215	0.0064 8681	80
81	0.0192 1617	0.0130 7828	0.0089 1713	0.0060 9090	81
82	0.0183 0111	0.0123 9648	0.0084 1238	0.0057 1916	82
83	0.0174 2963	0.0117 5022	0.0079 3621	0.0053 7010	83
84	0.0165 9965	0.0111 3765	0.0074 8699	0.0050 4235	84
85	0.0158 0919	0.0105 5701	0.0070 6320	0.0047 3460	85
86	0.0150 5637	0.0100 0664	0.0066 6340	0.0044 4563	86
87	0.0143 3940	0.0094 8497	0.0062 8622	0.0041 7430	87
88	0.0136 5657	0.0089 9049	0.0059 3040	0.0039 1953	88
89	0.0130 0626	0.0085 2180	0.0055 9472	0.0036 8031	89
90	0.0123 8691	0.0080 7753	0.0052 7803	0.0034 5569	90
91	0.0117 9706	0.0076 5643	0.0049 7928	0.0032 4478	91
92	0.0112 3530	0.0072 5728	0.0046 9743	0.0030 4674	92
93	0.0107 0028	0.0068 7894	0.0044 3154	0.0028 6079	93
94	0.0101 9074	0.0065 2032	0.0041 8070	0.0026 8619	94
95	0.0097 0547	0.0061 8040	0.0039 4405	0.0025 2224	95
96	0.0092 4331	0.0058 5820	0.0037 2081	0.0023 6831	96
97	0.0088 0315	0.0055 5279	0.0035 1019	0.0022 2376	97
98	0.0083 8395	0.0052 6331	0.0033 1150	0.0020 8804	98
99	0.0079 8471	0.0049 8892	0.0031 2406	0.0019 6060	99
100	0.0076 0449	0.0047 2883	0.0029 4723	0.0018 4094	100

Equation of Value

Just as the equation of value is used at simple interest to equate short-term debts, so it is used, at compound interest, to equate long-term debts. An example is the following:

Two debts, one of $2,000.00 due in 3 years at 4% interest and the other of $3,000.00 due in 7 years at 5% interest, are to be discharged by a payment of $2,500.00 in 2 years and the balance in 5 years. At an interest rate of 6%, what is the amount of the final payment?

As was done in setting up the equation of value at simple interest, choose the due date of the last debt, 7 years from present, as the focal date and x as the amount of the last payment.

Then the amount of the first debt on its due date (3 years away) is its principal, $2,000.00, plus compound interest for 3 years at 4%. From Table 11, the amount of $1.00 compounded annually at 4% for 3 years (annual compounding is assumed in problems when not otherwise stated) is $1.124864. Therefore the amount of the $2,000.00 in three years at 4% is ($2,000.00)(1.124864) = $2,249.73.

And, the amount due on the first debt on its focal date $7 - 3 = 4$ years from due date is its amount at maturity ($2,249.73) plus compound interest at 6% for 4 years. From Table 11, the amount of $1.00 compounded 4 times at 6% is $1.26247696. Therefore the amount of $2,249.73 compounded is ($2,249.73)(1.26247696) = $2,840.23.

The amount of the second debt on its due date (7 years away) is its principal $3,000.00, plus compound interest for 7 years at 5%. From Table 11, the amount of $1.00 compounded annually at 5% for 7 years is 1.40710042. Therefore the amount of the $3,000.00 for 7 years at 5% is ($3,000.00)(1.40710042) = $4,221.30.

And, the amount of the second debt on its focal date is the same as its maturity value, because the focal date is the due date.

The payment of $2,500.00 is to be made in two years, and therefore it earns compound interest at the given rate of 6% for $7 - 2 = 5$ years. From Table 11, the amount of $1.00 at 6% compounded annually for 5 years is $1.33822558. Therefore the amount of $2,500.00 on the focal date is ($2,500.00)(1.33822558) = $3,345.57. Then the equation of value becomes $2,840.23 + $4,221.30 = 3.345.57 + (last payment plus interest to focal date).

Therefore last payment plus interest = $3,715.96.

Now the last payment is to be made in $7 - 5 = 2$ years from focal date. Therefore its amount on the focal date = its principal plus interest compounded annually for 2 years at 6%. By Table 11, the amount of $1.00 at 6% interest compounded for two periods at 6% is $1.1236.

Then letting x = last payment,

$$(1.1236)x = \$3,715.96$$

Therefore $x = \dfrac{\$3,715.96}{1.1236} = \$3,307.19$, last payment.

Another type of problem using the equation of value is to find the equated date—that is, the date on which a number of debts may be satisfied by a single payment. This method for simple interest problems was explained in Chapter 11. For compound interest problems it is illustrated by the following problem:

Find the date on which a debt of \$4,000 due in 2 years at 4% interest, and a debt of \$3,500.00 due in 6 years at 5% interest, may be settled by a single payment of \$7,800.00 at an interest rate of 6%.

Here again the due date of the last debt due may conveniently be chosen as the focal date.

Then the amount of the first debt on its due date (2 years away) is its principal \$4,000.00, plus compound interest for 2 years at 4%. From Table 11, the amount of \$1.00 compounded annually at 4% for 2 years is \$1.0816. Therefore the amount of \$4,000.00 in 2 years at 4% is (\$4,000.00) (1.0816) = \$4,326.40.

And the amount due on the first debt on the focal date $(6 - 2 = 4$ years from due date) is its amount at maturity, \$4,326.40, plus compound interest at 6% for 4 years. From Table 11, the amount of \$1.00 compounded 4 times at 6% is \$1.26247696. Therefore the amount of \$4,326.40 so compounded is (\$4,326.40)(1.26247696) = \$5,461.98.

The amount of the second debt at its due date (6 years away) is its principal \$3,500.00, plus compound interest for 6 years at 5%. From Table 11, the amount of \$1.00 compounded annually at 5% for 6 years is \$1.34009564. Therefore, the amount of the \$3,500.00 debt at 5% for 6 years is (\$3,500.00)(1.34009564) = \$4,690.33.

And, the amount of the second debt on its focal date is the same as its maturity value, because its due date was taken as the focal date.

The amount of the single payment on the focal date = Principal + interest = (\$7,800.00) (Amount of \$1.00 compounded annually at 6% for time x)

Here x is the time in years from date of payment (equated date) being sought, to focal date.

The equation of value is then \$5,461.98 + \$4,690.33 = (\$7,800.00) × (Amount of \$1.00 compounded annually at 6% from equated date to focal date.)

Therefore amount of \$1.00 compounded annually at 6% from equated date to focal date $= \dfrac{\$10,152.31}{\$7,800.00} = \$1.3016$.

Now $s = (1 + i)^n$,

So $1.3016 = (1 + .06)^x$

where x is time in years from equated date to focal date.

Taking logarithms of both sides

$$\log 1.3016 = x \log (1.06)$$

or $$x = \frac{\log 1.3016}{\log 1.06}$$

Finding logs by Table 3, $x = \dfrac{.114467}{.025306} = 4.52$ years

x is therefore about $4\frac{1}{2}$ years from focal date.

Therefore the equated date for the $7,800.00 payment is $4\frac{1}{2}$ years before the focal date, or $1\frac{1}{2}$ years after the starting date.

Chapter 14

ANNUITIES

An annuity is a series of payments made at equal intervals of time. Annuity calculations enter into a very large number of business situations, as is evident at once from a brief consideration of the subject. Thus, an individual or institution may purchase an annuity in the sense that he pays a sum of money (which is called the present value of the annuity) with the understanding that he receives a payment (the rent of the annuity) at regular intervals for a period of time, and may or may not receive a partial or total repayment of his initial payment at the end of the period. Thus, it is seen that any bond or other fixed income obligation is an annuity, with the provision that in most instances (as will be seen in Chapter 18) bonds are "redeemable" at a stipulated amount, at the end of the period, that is, an agreed sum is returned to the bond holder then. Therefore, many calculations concerning bonds use annuity methods. As another example, a borrower or purchaser on an instalment plan is in effect selling an annuity to the seller or lender, and the computation of the required payments is made by annuity methods. As a final example, there is the calculation of the amount of money which a parent must deposit in a bank account, at a known rate of interest, in order to accumulate a sufficient fund for the education of his children when they are ready to attend college.

As a consequence of this great variety of applications of annuity mathematics, there are many kinds of annuities to be treated in this chapter. Contingent annuities depend for their number of payments upon an uncertain future event. Examples of contingent annuities are those pensions which cease partly or entirely on the death of the pensioner, and life insurance policies on which the payments by the insured are made during his lifetime.

Annuities certain are definite not only as to the number of payments but also as to the length of the periods at which they are made. Perpetuities continue forever; therefore the number of payments is unlimited, but the payment periods are definite.

Annuities certain can be subclassified into ordinary annuities, in which the payments are made at the end of each payment period, and annuities due, in which the payments are made at the beginning of each period. Unless otherwise stated the payment periods begin at the start of the term of the annuity, and continue to its end. However, there are also deferred annuities, which are annuities certain in which the payments do not begin (i.e. are deferred) for a stipulated number of payment periods, which constitute the interval of deferment. Deferred annuities, while usually ordinary annuities, are sometimes annuities due, in which the first payment is made at the end of the interval of deferment.

Another basis of classification of annuities is into simple annuities, in which the interest periods are the same as the payment periods, and general annuities in which the interest periods are not the same as the payment periods.

In this book, simple annuities are treated first, covering in order the simple case of ordinary annuities, annuities due and deferred annuities. Then perpetuities are treated, and finally the general case of these various annuities. The advantage of this method, which is standard in business mathematics, is that the formulas and tables developed for the simple case of ordinary annuities are readily modified for application to the other annuities. Moreover, these formulas are also modified for the computation of the general case of annuities.

A few terms that apply to annuities must be defined. The amount (or total amount) is the value of the annuity at the end of its term, (i.e., at the end of its final payment period or rent period). The periodic payment (or rent) is the annuity payment. The present value of an ordinary annuity or annuity due is its value at the beginning of the initial payment period (rent period). The present value of a deferred annuity is its value at the beginning of the interval of deferment. The interest period is the interval at which interest is compounded, while the payment period (or rent period) is the interval at which payments are made. For the simple case of annuities, the interest period and payment period are the same; for the general case, they are not. The interest rate is given as an annual rate; where the interest periods are not annual, the corresponding interest rate is designated as the interest rate per period or the periodic rate. The number of periods designates the total number of periods in the term of the annuity, unless explicitly stated otherwise.

Ordinary Annuity—Computation of Amount by Formula

The computations on the ordinary annuity follow directly the methods given in Chapter 13 on Compound Interest, since as defined above, an ordinary annuity consists of a definite number of payments made at the ends of equal intervals of time. Therefore, the amount (which is the total sum or final value) of an ordinary annuity at the end of its term (time from the beginning of first rent period to end of the last) can be found by computing the total amount of each payment at compound interest, and then adding total amounts of all the payments.

To illustrate an ordinary annuity, consider this question: What will an amount of $200.00 deposited in a federal savings and loan bank at the end of each year for 3 years, and earning 4% interest compounded annually, amount to in 3 years?

Note that this computation is that of an ordinary annuity, with a rent of $200.00, a rent period of one year, and a term of three years.

Since the first deposit would draw interest for 2 years, its amount at the end of the term would be ($200.00)$(1 + .04)^2$. Since the second deposit would draw interest for 1 year, its amount at the end of the term would be ($200.00)$(1 + .04)$, while since the last deposit (made at the end of the third year), would draw no interest, its amount at the end of the term would be $200.00. Therefore, the total amount of this ordinary annuity would be ($200.00)$(1.04)^2$ + ($200.00)$(1.04)$ + $200.00. The computations can be made by multiplication, or by Table 11, which gives the total amount of $1.00 compounded for two periods at 4% as $1.0816. Substituting this value for $(1.04)^2$ above, we have,

Total amount of annuity = ($200.00)(1.0816) + ($200.00)(1.04)
$$+ \$200.00 = \$216.32 + \$208.00 + \$200.00 = \$624.32.$$

If the term of this annuity has been 4 years instead of 3, then its total amount would have been,

$$(\$200.00)(1.04)^3 + (\$200.00)(1.04)^2 + (\$200.00)(1.04) + \$200.00.$$

And if its term had been 5 years, its total amount would have been,

$$(\$200.00)(1.04)^4 + (\$200.00)(1.04)^3 + (\$200.00)(1.04)^2$$
$$+ (\$200.00)(1.04) + \$200.00.$$

From this series of values of the total sum for an increasing number of periods, the general formula can readily be induced:

$$S_n = R(1 + i)^{n-1} + R(1 + i)^{n-2} + R(1+ i)^{n-3} \cdots R(1 + i) + R,$$

where S_n is the amount of the annuity, R is its rent, n is its number of periods, and i is the interest rate per period. Note that in this calculation, the number of rent periods is assumed equal to the number of interest periods, as is the case for all simple annuities.

Now rewrite the above expression by reversing the order of terms,

$$S_n = R + R(1 + i) \cdots R(1 + i)^{n-3} + R(1 + i)^{n-2} + R(1 + i)^{n-1}$$

Note that in this expression, each term is obtained from the preceding term by multiplying by $(1 + i)$, and that, therefore, the entire expression is a geometric progression, of which the sum is given by Formula (7-11) as

$$S = \frac{f(r^n - 1)}{r - 1}$$

where f is the first term, r is the ratio of consecutive terms and n is the number of terms.

The corresponding quantities in the expression derived for S_n are R as the first term, $(1 + i)$ as the ratio of consecutive terms, and n as the number of terms. Substituting these values,

$$S_n = \frac{R[(1 + i)^n - 1]}{(1 + i) - 1} = \frac{R[(1 + i)^n - 1]}{i} \qquad (14\text{-}1)$$

To apply Formula (14-1), find the amount of an annuity of $300.00 payable at the end of each year for 20 years, at an interest rate of 5% compounded annually.

Here the rent R is $300.00, the interest rate i is 5% = .05, and the number of periods n is 20.

Substituting, $\qquad S_n = \dfrac{\$300.00[(1 + .05)^{20} - 1]}{.05}$

This computation is made conveniently by logarithms, as explained in Chapter 6.

By Table 3, log 1.05　 = .021189

　　　　　　　　　　　　　　$\dfrac{20}{}$

Therefore, log $(1.05)^{20}$ = .42378

By Table 3, antilog .42378 = $(1.05)^{20}$ = 2.65325
Subtract $\qquad\qquad\qquad\qquad\qquad\quad \dfrac{1}{}$

$\qquad\qquad\qquad\qquad (1.05)^{20} - 1 = 1.65325$

Then $\dfrac{(1.05)^{20} - 1}{.05} = \dfrac{1.65325}{.05} = 33.065$

Then $S_n = \$300.00 \dfrac{(1.05)^{20} - 1}{.05}$

$\qquad\quad = (\$300.00)(33.065) = \$9.919.50$

As another example of the application of the Formula (14-1), solve the problem:

A periodic payment of $275.00 is made into a fund for 9 years at the end of each semi-annual period. If interest is computed at 4%, compounded semi-annually, what is the amount of the fund at the end of its term?

Here the rent R is \$275.00, the rate (per period) is $\frac{4\%}{2} = 2\%$ or .02, and the number of periods is $2 \times 9 = 18$.

Substituting in Formula (14-1) for the amount of an annuity,

$$S_n = \frac{\$275.00[(1 + .02)^{18} - 1]}{.02}$$

Then to compute by logarithms,

By Table 3, log 1.02 = .008600

$$\underline{18}$$

Therefore log $(1.02)^{18} = .154800$

By Table 3, antilog .154800 = $(1.02)^{18}$ = 1.42824

Subtract $\underline{\phantom{(1.02)^{18} = }1.}$

$(1.02)^{18} - 1 = .42824$

Then $S_n = \$275.00 \dfrac{(1.02)^{18} - 1}{.02} = \$275.00 \dfrac{.42824}{.02}$

$= (\$275.00)(21.412) = \$5,888.30$

Ordinary Annuity—Computation of Amount by Tables

Note that the Formula (14-1) for S_n, the amount of an annuity, includes as a factor the rent (periodic payment), expressed in dollars. Therefore, the product of other factors is the amount of the annuity for a periodic payment of \$1.00. This is a useful figure for the construction of tables, since it can be computed for various periods and interest rates per period, and tabulated against them. It is denoted by the symbol $s_{\overline{n}|i}$, and is given by the relationships:

$$S_n = R s_{\overline{n}|i} = R \frac{(1 + i)^n - 1}{i} \qquad (14\text{-}2)$$

or $\qquad s_{\overline{n}|i} = \dfrac{(1 + i)^n - 1}{i}$

Values of $s_{\overline{n}|i}$, the amount of an annuity having a rent (periodic payment) of \$1.00, are given in Table 13, Pages 298 to 314, for various numbers of periods and interest rates per period. The use of this table is illustrated by the example: A state deposits \$750.00 at the end of each quarter in a fund bearing interest at $4\frac{1}{2}\%$ compounded quarterly. What is the amount of the fund after 10 years?

Now the number of periods is $4 \times 10 = 40$, and the interest rate per period is $\dfrac{4\frac{1}{2}\%}{4} = 1\frac{1}{8}\%$. The amount of \$1.00 paid for 40 periods at $1\frac{1}{8}\%$ is found from Table 13, as \$50.16683248. Therefore the amount of \$750.00 is $(\$750.00)(50.16683248) = \$37,625.12$.

n	$\frac{1}{4}\%$	$\frac{7}{24}\%$	$\frac{1}{3}\%$	$\frac{5}{12}\%$	n
1	1.0000 0000	1.0000 0000	1.0000 0000	1.0000 0000	1
2	2.0025 0000	2.0029 1667	2.0033 3333	2.0041 6667	2
3	3.0075 0625	3.0087 5851	3.0100 1111	3.0125 1736	3
4	4.0150 2502	4.0175 3405	4.0200 4448	4.0250 6952	4
5	5.0250 6258	5.0292 5186	5.0334 4463	5.0418 4064	5
6	6.0376 2523	6.0439 2051	6.0502 2278	6.0628 4831	6
7	7.0527 1930	7.0615 4861	7.0703 9019	7.0881 1018	7
8	8.0703 5110	8.0821 4480	8.0939 5816	8.1176 4397	8
9	9.0905 2697	9.1057 1772	9.1209 3802	9.1514 6749	9
10	10.1132 5329	10.1322 7606	10.1513 4114	10.1895 9860	10
11	11.1385 3642	11.1618 2853	11.1851 7895	11.2320 5526	11
12	12.1663 8277	12.1943 8387	12.2224 6288	12.2788 5549	12
13	13.1967 9872	13.2299 5082	13.2632 0442	13.3300 1739	13
14	14.2297 9072	14.2685 3818	14.3074 1510	14.3855 5913	14
15	15.2653 6520	15.3101 5475	15.3551 0648	15.4454 9896	15
16	16.3035 2861	16.3548 0936	16.4062 9017	16.5098 5520	16
17	17.3442 8743	17.4025 1089	17.4609 7781	17.5786 4627	17
18	18.3876 4815	18.4532 6822	18.5191 8107	18.6518 9063	18
19	19.4336 1727	19.5070 9025	19.5809 1167	19.7296 0684	19
20	20.4822 0131	20.5639 8593	20.6461 8137	20.8118 1353	20
21	21.5334 0682	21.6239 6422	21.7150 0198	21.8985 2942	21
22	22.5872 4033	22.6870 3412	22.7873 8532	22.9897 7330	22
23	23.6437 0843	23.7532 0463	23.8633 4327	24.0855 6402	23
24	24.7028 1770	24.8224 8481	24.9428 8775	25.1859 2054	24
25	25.7645 7475	25.8948 8373	26.0260 3071	26.2908 6187	25
26	26.8289 8619	26.9704 1047	27.1127 8414	27.4004 0713	26
27	27.8960 5865	28.0490 7417	28.2031 6009	28.5145 7549	27
28	28.9657 9880	29.1308 8397	29.2971 7062	29.6333 8622	28
29	30.0382 1330	30.2158 4904	30.3948 2786	30.7568 5867	29
30	31.1133 0883	31.3039 7860	31.4961 4395	31.8850 1224	30
31	32.1910 9210	32.3952 8188	32.6011 3110	33.0178 6646	31
32	33.2715 6983	33.4897 6811	33.7098 0154	34.1554 4090	32
33	34.3547 4876	34.5874 4660	34.8221 6754	35.2977 5524	33
34	35.4406 3563	35.6883 2666	35.9382 4143	36.4448 2922	34
35	36.5292 3722	36.7924 1761	37.0580 3557	37.5966 8268	35
36	37.6205 6031	37.8997 2883	38.1815 6236	38.7533 3552	36
37	38.7146 1171	39.0102 6970	39.3088 3423	39.9148 0775	37
38	39.8113 9824	40.1240 4966	40.4398 6368	41.0811 1945	38
39	40.9109 2673	41.2410 7813	41.5746 6322	42.2522 9078	39
40	42.0132 0405	42.3613 6461	42.7132 4543	43.4283 4199	40
41	43.1182 3706	43.4849 1859	43.8556 2292	44.6092 9342	41
42	44.2260 3265	44.6117 4961	45.0018 0833	45.7951 6548	42
43	45.3365 9774	45.7418 6721	46.1518 1436	46.9859 7866	43
44	46.4499 3923	46.8752 8099	47.3056 5374	48.1817 5358	44
45	47.5660 6408	48.0120 0056	48.4633 3925	49.3825 1088	45
46	48.6849 7924	49.1520 3556	49.6248 8371	50.5882 7134	46
47	49.8066 9169	50.2953 9566	50.7902 9999	51.7990 5581	47
48	50.9312 0842	51.4420 9057	51.9596 0099	53.0148 8521	48
49	52.0585 3644	52.5921 3000	53.1327 9966	54.2357 8056	49
50	53.1886 8278	53.7455 2371	54.3099 0899	55.4617 6298	50

n	$\frac{1}{4}\%$	$\frac{7}{24}\%$	$\frac{1}{3}\%$	$\frac{5}{12}\%$	n
51	54.3216 5449	54.9022 8149	55.4909 4202	56.6928 5366	51
52	55.4574 5862	56.0624 1314	56.6759 1183	57.9290 7388	52
53	56.5961 0227	57.2259 2851	57.8648 3154	59.1704 4503	53
54	57.7375 9252	58.3928 3747	59.0577 1431	60.4169 8855	54
55	58.8819 3650	59.5631 4991	60.2545 7336	61.6687 2600	55
56	60.0291 4135	60.7368 7577	61.4554 2194	62.9256 7902	56
57	61.1792 1420	61.9140 2499	62.6602 7334	64.1878 6935	57
58	62.3321 6223	63.0946 0756	63.8691 4092	65.4553 1881	58
59	63.4879 9264	64.2786 3350	65.0820 3806	66.7280 4930	59
60	64.6467 1262	65.4661 1285	66.2989 7818	68.0060 8284	60
61	65.8083 2940	66.6570 5568	67.5199 7478	69.2894 4152	61
62	66.9728 5023	67.8514 7209	68.7450 4136	70.5781 4753	62
63	68.1402 8235	69.0493 7222	69.9741 9150	71.8722 2314	63
64	69.3106 3306	70.2507 6622	71.2074 3880	73.1716 9074	64
65	70.4839 0964	71.4556 6429	72.4447 9693	74.4765 7278	65
66	71.6601 1942	72.6640 7664	73.6862 7959	75.7868 9184	66
67	72.8392 6971	73.8760 1353	74.9319 0052	77.1026 7055	67
68	74.0213 6789	75.0914 8524	76.1816 7352	78.4239 3168	68
69	75.2064 2131	76.3105 0207	77.4356 1243	79.7506 9806	69
70	76.3944 3736	77.5330 7437	78.6937 3114	81.0829 9264	70
71	77.5854 2345	78.7592 1250	79.9560 4358	82.4208 3844	71
72	78.7793 8701	79.9889 2687	81.2225 6372	83.7642 5860	72
73	79.9763 3548	81.2222 2791	82.4933 0560	85.1132 7634	73
74	81.1762 7632	82.4591 2607	83.7682 8329	86.4679 1500	74
75	82.3792 1701	83.6996 3186	85.0475 1090	87.8281 9797	75
76	83.5851 6505	84.9437 5578	86.3310 0260	89.1941 4880	76
77	84.7941 2797	86.1915 0840	87.6187 7261	90.5657 9109	77
78	86.0061 1329	87.4429 0030	88.9108 3519	91.9431 4855	78
79	87.2211 2857	88.6979 4209	90.2072 0464	93.3262 4500	79
80	88.4391 8139	89.9566 4443	91.5078 9532	94.7151 0436	80
81	89.6602 7934	91.2190 1797	92.8129 2164	96.1097 5062	81
82	90.8844 3004	92.4850 7344	94.1122 9804	97.5102 0792	82
83	92.1116 4112	93.7548 2157	95.4360 3904	98.9165 0045	83
84	93.3419 2022	95.0282 7313	96.7541 5917	100.3286 5254	84
85	94.5752 7502	96.3054 3893	98.0766 7303	101.7466 8859	85
86	95.8117 1321	97.5863 2980	99.4035 9527	103.1706 3312	86
87	97.0512 4249	98.8709 5659	100.7349 4059	104.6005 1076	87
88	98.2938 7060	100.1593 3021	102.0707 2373	106.0363 4622	88
89	99.5396 0527	101.4514 6159	103.4109 5947	107.4781 6433	89
90	100.7884 5429	102.7473 6169	104.7556 6267	108.9259 9002	90
91	102.0404 2542	104.0470 4149	106.1048 4821	110.3798 4831	91
92	103.2955 2649	105.3505 1203	107.4585 3104	111.8397 6434	92
93	104.5537 6530	106.6577 8436	108.8167 2614	113.3057 6336	93
94	105.8151 4972	107.9688 6956	110.1794 4856	114.7778 7071	94
95	107.0796 8759	109.2837 7877	111.5467 1339	116.2561 1184	95
96	108.3473 8681	110.6025 2312	112.9185 3577	117.7405 1230	96
97	109.6182 5528	111.9251 1381	114.2949 3089	119.2310 9777	97
98	110.8923 0091	113.2515 6206	115.6759 1399	120.7278 9401	98
99	112.1695 3167	114.5818 7912	117.0615 0037	122.2309 2690	99
100	113.4499 5550	115.9160 7626	118.4517 0537	123.7402 2243	100

n	$\frac{1}{4}\%$	$\frac{7}{24}\%$	$\frac{1}{3}\%$	$\frac{5}{12}\%$	n
101	114.7335 8038	117.2541 6482	119.8465 4439	125.2558 0669	101
102	116.0204 1434	118.5961 5613	121.2460 3287	126.7777 0589	102
103	117.3104 6537	119.9420 6159	122.6501 8632	128.3059 4633	103
104	118.6037 4153	121.2918 9260	124.0590 2027	129.8405 5444	104
105	119.9002 5089	122.6456 6062	125.4725 5034	131.3815 5675	105
106	121.2000 0152	124.0033 7713	126.8907 9217	132.9289 7990	106
107	122.5030 0152	125.3650 5365	128.3137 6148	134.4828 5065	107
108	123.8092 5902	126.7307 0172	129.7414 7402	136.0431 9586	108
109	125.1187 8217	128.1003 3294	131.1739 4560	137.6100 4251	109
110	126.4315 7913	129.4739 5891	132.6111 9208	139.1834 1769	110
111	127.7476 5807	130.8515 9129	134.0532 2939	140.7633 4860	111
112	129.0670 2722	132.2332 4176	135.5000 7349	142.3498 6255	112
113	130.3896 9479	133.6189 2205	136.9517 4040	143.9429 8698	113
114	131.7156 6902	135.0086 4391	138.4082 4620	145.5427 4942	114
115	133.0449 5820	136.4024 1912	139.8696 0702	147.1491 7754	115
116	134.3775 7059	137.8002 5951	141.3358 3905	148.7622 9912	116
117	135.7135 1452	139.2021 7693	142.8069 5851	150.3821 4203	117
118	137.0527 9830	140.6081 8328	144.2829 8170	152.0087 3429	118
119	138.3954 3030	142.0182 9048	145.7639 2498	153.6421 0401	119
120	139.7414 1888	143.4325 1049	147.2498 0477	155.2822 7945	120
121	141.0907 7242	144.8508 5532	148.7406 3745	156.9292 8895	121
122	142.4434 9935	146.2733 3698	150.2364 3958	158.5831 6098	122
123	143.7996 0810	147.6999 6754	151.7372 2771	160.2439 2415	123
124	145.1591 0712	149.1307 5912	153.2430 1847	161.9116 0717	124
125	146.5220 0489	150.5657 2383	154.7538 2853	163.5862 3887	125
126	147.8883 0990	152.0048 7386	156.2696 7463	165.2678 4819	126
127	149.2580 3068	153.4482 2141	157.7905 7354	166.9564 6423	127
128	150.6311 7575	154.8957 7872	159.3165 4212	168.6521 1616	128
129	152.0077 5369	156.3475 5807	160.8475 9726	170.3548 3331	129
130	153.3877 7308	157.8035 7178	162.3837 5592	172.0646 4512	130
131	154.7712 4251	159.2638 3220	163.9250 3510	173.7815 8114	131
132	156.1581 7062	160.7283 5171	165.4714 5189	175.5056 7106	132
133	157.5485 6604	162.1971 4274	167.0230 2339	177.2369 4469	133
134	158.9424 3746	163.6702 1774	168.5797 6680	178.9754 3196	134
135	160.3397 9355	165.1475 8920	170.1416 9936	180.7211 6293	135
136	161.7406 4304	166.6292 6967	171.7088 3836	182.4741 6777	136
137	163.1449 9464	168.1152 7171	173.2812 0115	184.2344 7681	137
138	164.5528 5713	169.6056 0792	174.8588 0516	186.0021 2046	138
139	165.9642 3927	171.1002 9094	176.4416 6784	187.7771 2929	139
140	167.3791 4987	172.5993 3346	178.0298 0673	189.5595 3400	140
141	168.7975 9775	174.1027 4818	179.6232 3942	191.3493 6539	141
142	170.2195 9174	175.6105 4786	181.2219 8355	193.1466 5441	142
143	171.6451 4072	177.1227 4529	182.8260 5683	194.9514 3214	143
144	173.0742 5357	178.6393 5330	184.4354 7702	196.7637 2977	144
145	174.5069 3921	180.1603 8475	186.0502 6194	198.5835 7865	145
146	175.9432 0655	181.6858 5254	187.6704 2948	200.4110 1023	146
147	177.3830 6457	183.2157 6961	189.2959 9758	202.2460 5610	147
148	178.8265 2223	184.7501 4893	190.9269 8424	204.0887 4800	148
149	180.2735 8854	186.2890 0353	192.5634 0752	205.9391 1779	149
150	181.7242 7251	187.8323 4646	194.2052 8554	207.7971 9744	150

n	$\frac{1}{2}\%$	$\frac{7}{12}\%$	$\frac{5}{8}\%$	$\frac{2}{3}\%$	n
1	1.0000 0000	1.0000 0000	1.0000 0000	1.0000 0000	1
2	2.0050 0000	2.0058 3333	2.0062 5000	2.0066 6667	2
3	3.0150 2500	3.0175 3403	3.1087 8906	3.0200 4444	3
4	4.0301 0013	4.0351 3631	4.0376 5649	4.0401 7807	4
5	5.0502 5063	5.0586 7460	5.0628 9185	5.0671 1259	5
6	6.0755 0188	6.0881 8354	6.0945 3492	6.1008 9335	6
7	7.1058 7939	7.1236 9794	7.1326 2576	7.1415 6597	7
8	8.1414 0879	8.1652 5284	8.1772 0468	8.1891 7641	8
9	9.1821 1583	9.2128 8349	9.2283 1220	9.2437 7092	9
10	10.2280 2641	10.2666 2531	10.2859 8916	10.3053 9606	10
11	11.2791 6654	11.3265 1396	11.3502 7659	11.3740 9870	11
12	12.3355 6237	12.3925 8529	12.4212 1582	12.4499 2602	12
13	13.3972 4018	13.4648 7537	13.4988 4842	13.5329 2553	13
14	14.4642 2639	14.5434 2048	14.5832 1622	14.6231 4503	14
15	15.5365 4752	15.6282 5710	15.6743 6132	15.7206 3266	15
16	16.6142 3026	16.7194 2193	16.7723 2608	16.8254 3688	16
17	17.6973 0141	17.8169 5189	17.8771 5312	17.9376 0646	17
18	18.7857 8791	18.9208 8411	18.9888 8532	19.0571 9051	18
19	19.8797 1685	20.0312 5593	20.1075 6586	20.1842 3844	19
20	20.9791 1544	21.1481 0493	21.2332 3814	21.3188 0003	20
21	22.0840 1101	22.2714 6887	22.3659 4588	22.4609 2536	21
22	23.1944 3107	23.4013 8577	23.5057 3304	23.6106 6487	22
23	24.3104 0322	24.5378 9386	24.6526 4387	24.7680 6930	23
24	25.4319 5524	25.6810 3157	25.8067 2290	25.9331 8976	24
25	26.5591 1502	26.8308 3759	26.9680 1492	27.1060 7769	25
26	27.6919 1059	27.9873 5081	28.1365 6501	28.2867 8488	26
27	28.8303 7015	29.1506 1035	29.3124 1854	29.4753 6344	27
28	29.9745 2200	30.3206 5558	30.4956 2116	30.6718 6586	28
29	31.1243 9461	31.4975 2607	31.6862 1879	31.8763 4497	29
30	32.2800 1658	32.6812 6164	32.8842 5766	33.0888 5394	30
31	33.4414 1666	33.8719 0233	34.0897 8427	34.3094 4630	31
32	34.6086 2375	35.0694 8843	35.3028 4542	35.5381 7594	32
33	35.7816 6686	36.2740 6045	36.5234 8820	36.7750 9711	33
34	36.9605 7520	37.4856 5913	37.7517 6000	38.0202 6443	34
35	38.1453 7807	38.7043 2548	38.9877 0850	39.2737 3286	35
36	39.3361 0496	39.9301 0071	40.2313 8168	40.5355 5774	36
37	40.5327 8549	41.1630 2630	41.4828 2782	41.8057 9479	37
38	41.7354 4942	42.4031 4395	42.7420 9549	43.0845 0009	38
39	42.9441 2666	43.6504 9562	44.0092 3359	44.3717 3009	39
40	44.1588 4730	44.9051 2352	45.2842 9130	45.6675 4163	40
41	45.3796 4153	46.1670 7007	46.5673 1812	46.9719 9191	41
42	46.6065 3974	47.4363 7798	47.8583 6386	48.2851 3852	42
43	47.8395 7244	48.7130 9018	49.1574 7863	49.6070 3944	43
44	49.0787 7030	49.9972 4988	50.4647 1287	50.9377 5304	44
45	50.3241 6415	51.2889 0050	51.7801 1733	52.2773 3806	45
46	51.5757 8497	52.5880 8575	53.1037 4306	53.6258 5365	46
47	52.8336 6390	53.8948 4959	54.4356 4146	54.9833 5934	47
48	54.0978 3222	55.2092 3621	55.7758 6421	56.3499 1507	48
49	55.3683 2138	56.5312 9009	57.1244 6337	57.7255 8117	49
50	56.6451 6299	57.8610 5595	58.4814 9126	59.1104 1837	50

n	$\frac{1}{2}\%$	$\frac{7}{12}\%$	$\frac{5}{8}\%$	$\frac{2}{3}\%$	n
51	57.9283 8880	59.1985 7877	59.8470 0058	60.5044 8783	51
52	59.2180 3075	60.5439 0381	61.2210 4434	61.9078 5108	52
53	60.5141 2090	61.8970 7659	62.6036 7586	63.3205 7009	53
54	61.8166 9150	63.2581 4287	63.9949 4884	64.7427 0722	54
55	63.1257 7496	64.6271 4870	65.3949 1727	66.1743 2527	55
56	64.4414 0384	66.0041 4040	66.8036 3550	67.6154 8744	56
57	65.7636 1086	67.3891 6455	68.2211 5822	69.0662 5736	57
58	67.0924 2891	68.7822 6801	69.6475 4046	70.5266 9907	58
59	68.4278 9105	70.1834 9791	71.0828 3759	71.9968 7706	59
60	69.7700 3051	71.5929 0165	72.5271 0532	73.4768 5625	60
61	71.1188 8066	73.0105 2691	73.9803 9973	74.9667 0195	61
62	72.4744 7507	74.4364 2165	75.4427 7723	76.4664 7997	62
63	73.8368 4744	75.8706 3411	76.9142 9459	77.9762 5650	63
64	75.2060 3168	77.3132 1281	78.3950 0893	79.4960 9821	64
65	76.5820 6184	78.7642 0655	79.8849 7774	81.0260 7220	65
66	77.9649 7215	80.2236 6442	81.3842 5885	82.5662 4601	66
67	79.3547 9701	81.6916 3579	82.8929 1046	84.1166 8765	67
68	80.7515 7099	83.1681 7034	84.4109 9115	85.6774 6557	68
69	82.1553 2885	84.6533 1800	85.9385 5985	87.2486 4867	69
70	83.5661 0549	86.1471 2902	87.4756 7585	88.8303 0633	70
71	84.9839 3602	87.6496 5394	89.0223 9882	90.4225 0837	71
72	86.4088 5570	89.1609 4359	90.5787 8882	92.0253 2510	72
73	87.8408 9998	90.6810 4909	92.1449 0625	93.6388 2726	73
74	89.2801 0448	92.2100 2188	93.7208 1191	95.2630 8611	74
75	90.7265 0500	93.7479 1367	95.3065 6698	96.8981 7335	75
76	92.1801 3752	95.2947 7650	96.9022 3303	98.5441 6118	76
77	93.6410 3821	96.8506 6270	98.5078 7198	100.2011 2225	77
78	95.1092 4340	98.4156 2490	100.1235 4618	101.8691 2973	78
79	96.5847 8962	99.9897 1604	101.7493 1835	103.5482 5726	79
80	98.0677 1357	101.5729 8938	103.3852 5159	105.2385 7898	80
81	99.5580 5214	103.1654 9849	105.0314 0941	106.9401 6950	81
82	101.0558 4240	104.7672 9723	106.6878 5572	108.6531 0397	82
83	102.5611 2161	106.3784 3980	108.3546 5482	110.3774 5799	83
84	104.0739 2722	107.9989 8070	110.0318 7141	112.1133 0771	84
85	105.5942 9685	109.6289 7475	111.7195 7061	113.8607 2977	85
86	107.1222 6834	111.2684 7710	113.4178 1792	115.6198 0130	86
87	108.6578 7968	112.9175 4322	115.1266 7928	117.3905 9997	87
88	110.2011 6908	114.5762 2889	116.8462 2103	119.1732 0397	88
89	111.7521 7492	116.2445 9022	118.5765 0991	120.9676 9200	89
90	113.3109 3580	117.9226 8367	120.3176 1310	122.7741 4328	90
91	114.8774 9048	119.6105 6599	122.0695 9818	124.5926 3757	91
92	116.4518 7793	121.3082 9429	123.8325 3317	126.4232 5515	92
93	118.0341 3732	123.0159 2601	125.6064 8650	128.2660 7685	93
94	119.6243 0800	124.7335 1891	127.3915 2704	130.1211 8403	94
95	121.2224 2954	126.4611 3110	129.1877 2408	131.9886 5859	95
96	122.8285 4169	128.1988 2103	130.9951 4736	133.8685 8298	96
97	124.4426 8440	129.9466 4749	132.8138 6703	135.7610 4020	97
98	126.0648 9782	131.7046 6960	134.6439 5370	137.6661 1380	98
99	127.6952 2231	133.4729 4684	136.4854 7841	139.5838 8790	99
100	129.3336 9842	135.2515 3903	138.3385 1265	141.5144 4715	100

n	$\frac{1}{2}\%$	$\frac{7}{12}\%$	$\frac{5}{8}\%$	$\frac{2}{3}\%$	n
101	130.9803 6692	137.0405 0634	140.2031 2836	143.4578 7680	101
102	132.6352 6875	138.8399 0929	142.0793 9791	145.4142 6264	102
103	134.2984 4509	140.6498 0876	143.9673 9414	147.3836 9106	103
104	135.9699 3732	142.4702 6598	145.8671 9036	149.3662 4900	104
105	137.6497 8701	144.3013 4253	147.7788 6030	151.3620 2399	105
106	139.3380 3594	146.1431 0036	149.7024 7817	153.3711 0415	106
107	141.0347 2612	147.9956 0178	151.6381 1866	155.3935 7818	107
108	142.7398 9975	149.8589 0946	153.5858 5690	157.4295 3537	108
109	144.4535 9925	151.7330 8643	155.5457 6851	159.4790 6560	109
110	146.1758 6725	153.6181 9610	157.5179 2956	161.5422 5937	110
111	147.9067 4658	155.5143 0225	159.5024 1662	163.6192 0777	111
112	149.6462 8032	157.4214 6901	161.4993 0673	165.7100 0249	112
113	151.3945 1172	159.3397 6091	163.5086 7739	167.8147 3584	113
114	153.1514 8428	161.2692 4285	165.5306 0663	169.9335 0074	114
115	154.9172 4170	163.2099 8010	167.5651 7292	172.0663 9075	115
116	156.6918 2791	165.1620 3832	169.6124 5525	174.2135 0002	116
117	158.4752 8704	167.1254 8354	171.6725 3310	176.3749 2335	117
118	160.2676 6348	169.1003 8219	173.7454 8643	178.5507 5618	118
119	162.0690 0180	171.0868 0109	175.8313 9572	180.7410 9455	119
120	163.8793 4681	173.0848 0743	177.9303 4194	182.9460 3518	120
121	165.6987 4354	175.0944 6881	180.0424 0658	185.1656 7542	121
122	167.5272 3726	177.1158 5321	182.1676 7162	187.4001 1325	122
123	169.3648 7344	179.1490 2902	184.3062 1957	189.6494 4734	123
124	171.2116 9781	181.1940 6502	186.4581 3344	191.9137 7699	124
125	173.0677 5630	183.2510 3040	188.6234 9677	194.1932 0217	125
126	174.9330 9508	185.3199 9474	190.8023 9363	196.4878 2352	126
127	176.8077 6056	187.4010 2805	192.9949 0859	198.7977 4234	127
128	178.6917 9936	189.4942 0071	195.2011 2677	201.1230 6062	128
129	180.5852 5836	191.5995 8355	197.4211 3381	203.4638 8103	129
130	182.4881 8465	193.7172 4778	199.6550 1589	205.8203 0690	130
131	184.4006 2557	195.8472 6506	201.9028 5974	208.1924 4228	131
132	186.3226 2870	197.9897 0744	204.1647 5262	210.5803 9189	132
133	188.2542 4184	200.1446 4740	206.4407 8232	212.9842 6117	133
134	190.1955 1305	202.3121 5785	208.7310 3721	215.4041 5625	134
135	192.1464 9062	204.4923 1210	211.0356 0619	217.8401 8396	135
136	194.1072 2307	206.6851 8392	213.3545 7873	220.2924 5185	136
137	196.0777 5919	208.8908 4749	215.6880 4485	222.7610 6820	137
138	198.0581 4798	211.1093 7744	218.0360 9513	225.2461 4198	138
139	200.0484 3872	213.3408 4881	220.3988 2072	227.7477 8293	139
140	202.0486 8092	215.5853 3709	222.7763 1335	230.2661 0148	140
141	204.0589 2432	217.8429 1822	225.1686 6531	232.8012 0883	141
142	206.0792 1894	220.1136 6858	227.5759 6947	235.3532 1688	142
143	208.1096 1504	222.3976 6498	229.9983 1928	237.9222 3833	143
144	210.1501 6311	224.6949 8469	232.4358 0878	240.5083 8659	144
145	212.2009 1393	227.0057 0544	234.8885 3258	243.1117 7583	145
146	214.2619 1850	229.3299 0538	237.3565 8591	245.7325 2100	146
147	216.3332 2809	231.6676 6317	239.8400 6457	248.3707 3781	147
148	218.4148 9423	234.0190 5787	242.3390 6497	251.0265 4273	148
149	220.5069 6870	236.3841 6904	244.8536 8413	253.7000 5301	149
150	222.6095 0354	238.7630 7669	247.3840 1966	256.3913 8670	150

TABLE 13—AMOUNT OF AN ORDINARY ANNUITY OF *n* PAYMENTS OF 1 EACH, IMMEDIATELY AFTER THE LAST PAYMENT, IF INTEREST IS COMPOUNDED AT *i* PER PERIOD (Cont.)

n	¾%	⅞%	1%	1⅛%	*n*
1	1.0000 0000	1.0000 0000	1.0000 0000	1.0000 0000	1
2	2.0075 0000	2.0087 5000	2.0100 0000	2.0112 5000	2
3	3.0225 5625	3.0263 2656	3.0301 0000	3.0338 7656	3
4	4.0452 2542	4.0528 0692	4.0604 0100	4.0680 0767	4
5	5.0755 6461	5.0882 6898	5.1010 0501	5.1137 7276	5
6	6.1136 3135	6.1327 9133	6.1520 1506	6.1713 0270	6
7	7.1594 8358	7.1864 5326	7.2135 3521	7.2407 2986	7
8	8.2131 7971	8.2493 3472	8.2856 7056	8.3221 8807	8
9	9.2747 7856	9.3215 1640	9.3685 2727	9.4158 1269	9
10	10.3443 3940	10.4030 7967	10.4622 1254	10.5217 4058	10
11	11.4219 2194	11.4941 0662	11.5668 3467	11.6401 1016	11
12	12.5075 8636	12.5946 8005	12.6825 0301	12.7710 6140	12
13	13.6013 9325	13.7048 8350	13.8093 2804	13.9147 3584	13
14	14.7034 0370	14.8248 0123	14.9474 2132	15.0712 7662	14
15	15.8136 7923	15.9545 1824	16.0968 9554	16.2408 2848	15
16	16.9322 8183	17.0941 2028	17.2578 6449	17.4235 3780	16
17	18.0592 7394	18.2436 9383	18.4304 4314	18.6195 5260	17
18	19.1947 1849	19.4033 2615	19.6147 4757	19.8290 2257	18
19	20.3386 7888	20.5731 0526	20.8108 9504	21.0520 9907	19
20	21.4912 1897	21.7531 1993	22.0190 0399	22.2889 3519	20
21	22.6524 0312	22.9434 5973	23.2391 9403	23.5396 8571	21
22	23.8222 9614	24.1442 1500	24.4715 8598	24.8045 0717	22
23	25.0009 6336	25.3554 7688	25.7163 0183	26.0835 5788	23
24	26.1884 7059	26.5773 3730	26.9734 6485	27.3769 9790	24
25	27.3848 8412	27.8098 8900	28.2431 9950	28.6849 8913	25
26	28.5902 7075	29.0532 2553	29.5256 3150	30.0076 9526	26
27	29.8046 9778	30.3074 4126	30.8208 8781	31.3452 8183	27
28	31.0282 3301	31.5726 3137	32.1290 9669	32.6979 1625	28
29	32.2609 4476	32.8488 9189	33.4503 8766	34.0657 6781	29
30	33.5029 0184	34.1363 1970	34.7848 9153	35.4490 0769	30
31	34.7541 7361	35.4350 1249	36.1327 4045	36.8478 0903	31
32	36.0148 2991	36.7450 6885	37.4940 6785	38.2623 4688	32
33	37.2849 4113	38.0665 8820	38.8690 0853	39.6927 9829	33
34	38.5645 7819	39.3996 7085	40.2576 9862	41.1393 4227	34
35	39.8538 1253	40.7444 1797	41.6602 7560	42.6021 5987	35
36	41.1527 1612	42.1009 3163	43.0768 7836	44.0814 3417	36
37	42.4613 6149	43.4693 1478	44.5076 4714	45.5773 5030	37
38	43.7798 2170	44.8496 7128	45.9527 2361	47.0900 9549	38
39	45.1081 7037	46.2421 0591	47.4122 5085	48.6198 5906	39
40	46.4464 8164	47.6467 2433	48.8863 7336	50.1668 3248	40
41	47.7948 3026	49.0636 3317	50.3752 3709	51.7312 0934	41
42	49.1532 9148	50.4929 3996	51.8789 8946	53.3131 8545	42
43	50.5219 4117	51.9347 5319	53.3977 7936	54.9129 5879	43
44	51.9008 5573	53.3891 8228	54.9317 5715	56.5307 2957	44
45	53.2901 1215	54.8563 3762	56.4810 7472	58.1667 0028	45
46	54.6897 8799	56.3363 3058	58.0458 8547	59.8210 7566	46
47	56.0999 6140	57.8292 7347	59.6263 4432	61.4940 6276	47
48	57.5207 1111	59.3352 7961	61.2226 0777	63.1858 7097	48
49	58.9521 1644	60.8544 6331	62.8348 3385	64.8967 1201	49
50	60.3942 5732	62.3869 3986	64.4631 8218	66.6268 0002	50

304

n	¾%	⅞%	1%	1⅛%	n
51	61.8472 1424	63.9328 2559	66.1078 1401	68.3763 5152	51
52	63.3110 6835	65.4922 3781	67.7688 9215	70.1455 8548	52
53	64.7859 0136	67.0652 9489	69.4465 8107	71.9347 2332	53
54	66.2717 9562	68.6521 1622	71.1410 4688	73.7439 8895	54
55	67.7688 3409	70.2528 2224	72.8524 5735	75.5736 0883	55
56	69.2771 0035	71.8675 3443	74.5809 8192	77.4238 1193	56
57	70.7966 7860	73.4963 7536	76.3267 9174	79.2948 2981	57
58	72.3276 5369	75.1394 6864	78.0900 5966	81.1868 9665	58
59	73.8701 1109	76.7969 3900	79.8709 6025	83.1002 4923	59
60	75.4241 3693	78.4689 1221	81.6696 6986	85.0351 2704	60
61	76.9898 1795	80.1555 1519	83.4863 6655	86.9917 7222	61
62	78.5672 4159	81.8568 7595	85.3212 3022	88.9704 2966	62
63	80.1564 9590	83.5731 2362	87.1744 4252	90.9713 4699	63
64	81.7576 6962	85.3043 8845	89.0461 8695	92.9947 7464	64
65	83.3708 5214	87.0508 0185	90.9366 4882	95.0409 6586	65
66	84.9961 3353	88.8124 9636	92.8460 1531	97.1101 7672	66
67	86.6336 0453	90.5896 0571	94.7744 7546	99.2026 6621	67
68	88.2833 5657	92.3822 6476	96.7222 2021	101.3186 9621	68
69	89.9454 8174	94.1906 0957	98.6894 4242	103.4585 3154	69
70	91.6200 7285	96.0147 7741	100.6763 3684	105.6224 4002	70
71	93.3072 2340	97.8549 0671	102.6831 0021	107.8106 9247	71
72	95.0070 2758	99.7111 3714	104.7099 3121	110.0235 6276	72
73	96.7195 8028	101.5836 0959	106.7570 3052	112.2613 2784	73
74	98.4449 7714	103.4724 6618	108.8246 0083	114.5242 6778	74
75	100.1833 1446	105.3778 5025	110.9128 4684	116.8126 6579	75
76	101.9346 8932	107.2999 0644	113.0219 7530	119.1268 0828	76
77	103.6991 9949	109.2387 8063	115.1521 9506	121.4669 8487	77
78	105.4769 4349	111.1946 1996	117.3037 1701	123.8334 8845	78
79	107.2680 2056	113.1675 7288	119.4767 5418	126.2266 1520	79
80	109.0725 3072	115.1577 8914	121.6715 2172	128.6466 6462	80
81	110.8905 7470	117.1654 1980	123.8882 3694	131.0939 3960	81
82	112.7222 5401	119.1906 1722	126.1271 1931	133.5687 4642	82
83	114.5676 7091	121.2335 3512	128.3883 9050	136.0713 9481	83
84	116.4269 2845	123.2943 2855	130.6722 7440	138.6021 9801	84
85	118.3001 3041	125.3731 5393	132.9789 9715	141.1614 7273	85
86	120.1873 8139	127.4701 6903	135.3087 8712	143.7495 3930	86
87	122.0887 8675	129.5855 3301	137.6618 7499	146.3667 2162	87
88	124.0044 5265	131.7194 0642	140.0384 9374	149.0133 4724	88
89	125.9344 8604	133.8719 5123	142.4388 7868	151.6897 4739	89
90	127.8789 9469	136.0433 3080	144.8632 6746	154.3962 5705	90
91	129.8380 8715	138.2337 0994	147.3119 0014	157.1332 1494	91
92	131.8118 7280	140.4432 5491	149.7850 1914	159.9009 6361	92
93	133.8004 6185	142.6721 3339	152.2828 6933	162.6998 4945	93
94	135.8039 6531	144.9205 1455	154.8056 9803	165.5302 2276	94
95	137.8224 9505	147.1885 6906	157.3537 5501	168.3924 3776	95
96	139.8561 6377	149.4764 6903	159.9272 9256	171.2868 5269	96
97	141.9050 8499	151.7843 8813	162.5265 6548	174.2138 2978	97
98	143.9693 7313	154.1125 0153	165.1518 3114	177.1737 3537	98
99	146.0491 4343	156.4609 8592	167.8033 4945	180.1669 3989	99
100	148.1445 1201	158.8300 1955	170.4813 8294	183.1938 1796	100

n	$\frac{3}{4}\%$	$\frac{7}{8}\%$	1%	$1\frac{1}{8}\%$	n
101	150.2555 9585	161 2197 8222	173.1861 9677	186.2547 4842	101
102	152.3825 1281	163.6304 5532	175.9180 5874	189.3501 1434	102
103	154.5253 8166	166.0622 2180	178.6772 3933	192.4803 0312	103
104	156.6843 2202	168.5122 6624	181.4640 1172	195.6457 0653	104
105	158.8594 5444	170.9897 7482	184.2786 5184	198.8467 2073	105
106	161.0509 0035	173.4859 3535	187.1214 3836	202.0837 4634	106
107	163.2587 8210	176.0039 3728	189.9926 5274	205.3571 8849	107
108	165.4832 2296	178.5439 7174	192.8925 7927	208.6674 5686	108
109	167.7243 4714	181.1062 3149	195.8215 0506	212.0149 6575	109
110	169.9822 7974	183.6909 1101	198.7797 2011	215.4001 3411	110
111	172.2571 4684	186.2982 0648	201.7675 1731	218.8233 8562	111
112	174.5490 7544	188.9283 1579	204.7851 9248	222.2851 4871	112
113	176.8581 9351	191.5814 3855	207.8330 4441	225.7858 5663	113
114	179.1846 2996	194.2577 7614	210.9113 7485	229.3259 4752	114
115	181.5285 1468	196.9575 3168	214.0204 8860	232.9058 6443	115
116	183.8899 7854	199.6809 1009	217.1606 9349	236.5260 5540	116
117	186.2691 5338	202.4281 1805	220.3323 0042	240.1869 7352	117
118	188.6661 7203	205.1993 6408	223.5356 2343	243.8890 7698	118
119	191.0811 6832	207.9948 5852	226.7709 7966	247.6328 2909	119
120	193.5142 7708	210.8148 1353	230.0386 8946	251.4186 9842	120
121	195.9656 3416	213.6594 4315	233.3390 7635	255.2471 5878	121
122	198.4353 7642	216.5289 6328	236.6724 6712	259.1186 8931	122
123	200.9236 4174	219.4235 9170	240.0391 9179	263.0337 7457	123
124	203.4305 6905	222.3435 4813	243.4395 8370	266.9929 0453	124
125	205.9562 9832	225.2890 5418	246.8739 7954	270.9965 7471	125
126	208.5009 7056	228.2603 3340	250.3427 1934	275.0452 8617	126
127	211.0647 2784	231.2576 1132	253.8461 4653	279.1395 4564	127
128	213.6477 1330	234.2811 1542	257.3846 0800	283.2798 6553	128
129	216.2500 7115	237.3310 7518	260.9584 5408	287.4667 6402	129
130	218.8719 4668	240.4077 2209	264.5680 3862	291.7007 6511	130
131	221.5134 8628	243.5112 8965	268.2137 1900	295.9823 9872	131
132	224.1748 3743	246.6420 1344	271.8958 5619	300.3122 0071	132
133	226.8561 4871	249.8001 3106	275.6148 1475	304.6907 1296	133
134	229.5575 6982	252.9858 8220	279.3709 6290	309.1184 8349	134
135	232.2792 5160	256.1995 0867	283.1646 7253	313.5960 6643	135
136	235.0213 4598	259.4412 5437	286.9963 1926	318.1240 2217	136
137	237.7840 0608	262.7113 6535	290.8662 8245	322.7029 1742	137
138	240.5673 8612	266.0100 8980	294.7749 4527	327.3333 2524	138
139	243.3716 4152	269.3376 7808	298.7226 9473	332.0158 2515	139
140	246.1969 2883	272.6943 8276	302.7099 2167	336.7510 0318	140
141	249.0434 0580	276.0804 5861	306.7370 2089	341.5394 5197	141
142	251.9112 3134	279.4961 6263	310.8043 9110	346.3817 7081	142
143	254.8005 6558	282.9417 5405	314.9124 3501	351.2785 6573	143
144	257.7115 6982	286.4174 9440	319.0615 5936	356.2304 4959	144
145	260.6444 0659	289.9236 4747	323.2521 7495	361.2380 4215	145
146	263.5992 3964	293.4604 7939	327.4846 9670	366.3019 7012	146
147	266.5762 3394	297.0282 5858	331.7595 4367	371.4228 6729	147
148	269.5755 5569	300.6272 5585	336.0771 3911	376.6013 7454	148
149	272.5973 7236	304.2577 4433	340.4379 1050	381.8381 4001	149
150	275.6418 5265	307.9199 9960	344.8422 8960	387.1338 1908	150

n	$1\frac{1}{4}\%$	$1\frac{3}{8}\%$	$1\frac{1}{2}\%$	$1\frac{3}{4}\%$	n
1	1.0000 0000	1.0000 0000	1.0000 0000	1.0000 0000	1
2	2.0125 0000	2.0137 5000	2.0150 0000	2.0175 0000	2
3	3.0376 5625	3.0414 3906	3.0452 2500	3.0528 0625	3
4	4.0756 2695	4.0832 5885	4.0909 0338	4.1062 3036	4
5	5.1265 7229	5.1394 0366	5.1522 6693	5.1780 8938	5
6	6.1906 5444	6.2100 7046	6.2295 5093	6.2687 0596	6
7	7.2680 3762	7.2954 5893	7.3229 9419	7.3784 0831	7
8	8.3588 8809	8.3957 7149	8.4328 3911	8.5075 3045	8
9	9.4633 7420	9.5112 1335	9.5593 3169	9.6564 1224	9
10	10.5816 6637	10.6419 9253	10.7027 2167	10.8253 9945	10
11	11.7139 3720	11.7883 1993	11.8632 6249	12.0148 4394	11
12	12.8603 6142	12.9504 0933	13.0412 1143	13.2251 0371	12
13	14.0211 1594	14.1284 7745	14.2368 2960	14.4565 4303	13
14	15.1963 7988	15.3227 4402	15.4503 8205	15.7095 3253	14
15	16.3863 3463	16.5334 3175	16.6821 3778	16.9844 4935	15
16	17.5911 6382	17.7607 6644	17.9323 6984	18.2816 7721	16
17	18.8110 5336	19.0049 7697	19.2013 5539	19.6016 0656	17
18	20.0461 9153	20.2662 9541	20.4893 7572	20.9446 3468	18
19	21.2967 6893	21.5449 5697	21.7967 1636	22.3111 6578	19
20	22.5629 7854	22.8412 0013	23.1236 6710	23.7016 1119	20
21	23.8450 1577	24.1552 6663	24.4705 2211	25.1163 8938	21
22	25.1430 7847	25.4874 0155	25.8375 7994	26.5559 2620	22
23	26.4573 6695	26.8378 5332	27.2251 4364	28.0206 5490	23
24	27.7880 8403	28.2068 7380	28.6335 2080	29.5110 1637	24
25	29.1354 3508	29.5947 1832	30.0630 2361	31.0274 5915	25
26	30.4996 2802	31.0016 4569	31.5139 6896	32.5704 3969	26
27	31.8808 7337	32.4279 1832	32.9866 7850	34.1404 2238	27
28	33.2793 8429	33.8738 0220	34.4814 7867	35.7378 7977	28
29	34.6953 7659	35.3395 6698	35.9987 0085	37.3632 9267	29
30	36.1290 6880	36.8254 8602	37.5386 8137	39.0171 5029	30
31	37.5806 8216	38.3318 3646	39.1017 6159	40.6999 5042	31
32	39.0504 4069	39.8588 9921	40.6882 8801	42.4121 9955	32
33	40.5385 7120	41.4069 5907	42.2986 1233	44.1544 1305	33
34	42.0453 0334	42.9763 0476	43.9330 9152	45.9271 1527	34
35	43.5708 6963	44.5672 2895	45.5920 8789	47.7308 3979	35
36	45.1155 0550	46.1800 2835	47.2759 6921	49.5661 2949	36
37	46.6794 4932	47.8150 0374	48.9851 0874	51.4335 3675	37
38	48.2926 4243	49.4724 6004	50.7198 8538	53.3336 2365	38
39	49.8862 2921	51.1527 0636	52.4806 8366	55.2669 6206	39
40	51.4895 5708	52.8560 5608	54.2678 9391	57.2341 3390	40
41	53.1331 7654	54.5828 2685	56.0819 1232	59.2357 3124	41
42	54.7973 4125	56.3333 4072	57.9231 4100	61.2723 5654	42
43	56.4823 0801	58.1079 2415	59.7919 8812	63.3446 2278	43
44	58.1883 3687	59.9069 0811	61.6888 6794	65.4531 5367	44
45	59.9156 9108	61.7306 2810	63.6142 0096	67.5985 8386	45
46	61.6646 3721	63.5794 2423	65.5684 1398	69.7815 5908	46
47	63.4354 4518	65.4536 4131	67.5519 4018	72.0027 3637	47
48	65.2283 8824	67.3536 2888	69.5652 1929	74.2627 8425	48
49	67.0437 4310	69.2797 4128	71.6086 9758	76.5623 8298	49
50	68.8817 8989	71.2323 3772	73.6828 2804	78.9022 2468	50

n	$1\frac{1}{4}\%$	$1\frac{3}{8}\%$	$1\frac{1}{2}\%$	$1\frac{3}{4}\%$	n
51	70.7428 1226	73.2117 8237	75.7880 7046	81.2830 1361	51
52	72.6270 9741	75.2184 4437	77.9248 9152	83.7054 6635	52
53	74.5349 3613	77.2526 9798	80.0937 6489	86.1703 1201	53
54	76.4666 2283	79.3149 2258	82.2951 7136	88.6782 9247	54
55	78.4224 5562	81.4055 0277	84.5295 9893	91.2301 6259	55
56	80.4027 3631	83.5248 2843	86.7975 4292	93.8266 9043	56
57	82.4077 7052	85.6732 9482	89.0995 0606	96.4686 5752	57
58	84.4378 6765	87.8513 0262	91.4359 9865	99.1568 5902	58
59	86.4933 4099	90.0592 5804	93.8075 3863	101.8921 0405	59
60	88.5745 0776	92.2975 7283	96.2146 5171	104.6752 1588	60
61	90.6816 8910	94.5666 6446	98.6578 7149	107.5070 3215	61
62	92.8152 1022	96.8669 5610	101.1377 3956	110.3884 0522	62
63	94.9754 0034	99.1988 7674	103.6548 0565	113.3202 0231	63
64	97.1625 9285	101.5628 6130	106.2096 2774	116.3033 0585	64
65	99.3771 2526	103.9593 5064	108.8027 7215	119.3386 1370	65
66	101.6193 3933	106.3887 9171	111.4348 1374	122.4270 3944	66
67	103.8895 8107	108.8516 3760	114.1063 3594	125.5695 1263	67
68	106.1882 0083	111.3483 4761	116.8179 3098	128.7669 7910	68
69	108.5155 5334	113.8793 8739	119.5701 9995	132.0204 0124	69
70	110.8719 9776	116.4452 2897	122.3637 5295	135.3307 5826	70
71	113.2578 9773	119.0463 5087	125.1992 0924	138.6990 4653	71
72	115.6736 2145	121.6832 3819	128.0771 9738	142.1262 7984	72
73	118.1195 4172	124.3563 8272	130.9983 5534	145.6134 8974	73
74	120.5960 3599	127.0662 8298	133.9633 3067	149.1617 2581	74
75	123.1034 8644	129.8134 4437	136.9727 8063	152.7720 5601	75
76	125.6422 8002	132.5983 7923	140.0273 7234	156.4455 6699	76
77	128.2128 0852	135.4216 0695	143.1277 8292	160.1833 6441	77
78	130.8154 6863	138.2836 5404	146.2746 9967	163.9865 7329	78
79	133.4506 6199	141.1850 5429	149.4688 2016	167.8563 3832	79
80	136.1187 9526	144.1263 4878	152.7108 5247	171.7938 2424	80
81	138.8202 8020	147.1080 8608	156.0015 1525	175.8002 1617	81
82	141.5555 3370	150.1308 2226	159.3415 3798	179.8767 1995	82
83	144.3249 7787	153.1951 2107	162.7316 6105	184.0245 6255	83
84	147.1290 4010	156.3015 5398	166.1726 3597	188.2449 9239	84
85	149.9681 5310	159.4507 0035	169.6652 2551	192.5392 7976	85
86	152.8427 5501	162.6431 4748	173.2102 0389	196.9087 1716	86
87	155.7532 8945	165.8794 9076	176.8083 5695	201.3546 1971	87
88	158.7002 0557	169.1603 3375	180.4604 8230	205.8783 2555	88
89	161.6839 5814	172.4862 8834	184.1673 8954	210.4811 9625	89
90	164.7050 0762	175.8579 7481	187.9299 0038	215.1646 1718	90
91	167.7638 2021	179.2760 2196	191.7488 4889	219.9299 9798	91
92	170.8608 6796	182.7410 6726	195.6250 8162	224.7787 7295	92
93	173.9966 2881	186.2537 5694	199.5594 5784	229.7124 0148	93
94	177.1715 8667	189.8147 4610	203.5528 4971	234.7323 6850	94
95	180.3862 3151	193.4246 9886	207.6061 4246	239.8401 8495	95
96	183.6410 5940	197.0842 8847	211.7202 3459	245.0373 8819	96
97	186.9365 7264	200.7941 9743	215.8960 3811	250.3255 4248	97
98	190.2732 7980	204.5551 1765	220.1344 7868	255.7062 3947	98
99	193.6516 9580	208.3677 5051	224.4364 9586	261.1810 9866	99
100	197.0723 4200	212.2328 0708	228.8030 4330	266.7517 6789	100

n	2%	$2\frac{1}{4}\%$	$2\frac{1}{2}\%$	$2\frac{3}{4}\%$	n
1	1.0000 0000	1.0000 0000	1.0000 0000	1.0000 0000	1
2	2.0200 0000	2.0225 0000	2.0250 0000	2.0275 0000	2
3	3.0604 0000	3.0680 0625	3.0756 2500	3.0832 5625	3
4	4.1216 0800	4.1370 3639	4.1525 1563	4.1680 4580	4
5	5.2040 4016	5.2301 1971	5.2563 2852	5.2826 6706	5
6	6.3081 2096	6 3477 9740	6.3877 3673	6.4279 4040	6
7	7.4342 8338	7.4906 2284	7.5474 3015	7.6047 0876	7
8	8.5829 6905	8.6591 6186	8.7361 1590	8.8138 3825	8
9	9.7546 2843	9.8539 9300	9.9545 1880	10.0562 1880	9
10	10.9497 2100	11.0757 0784	11.2033 8177	11.3327 6482	10
11	12.1687 1542	12.3249 1127	12.4834 6631	12.6444 1585	11
12	13.4120 8973	13.6022 2177	13.7955 5297	13.9921 3729	12
13	14.6803 3152	14.9082 7176	15.1404 4179	15.3769 2107	13
14	15.9739 3815	16.2437 0788	16.5189 5284	16.7997 8639	14
15	17.2934 1692	17.6091 9130	17.9319 2666	18.2617 8052	15
16	18.6392 8525	19.0053 9811	19.3802 2483	19.7639 7948	16
17	20.0120 7096	20.4330 1957	20.8647 3045	21.3074 8892	17
18	21.4123 1238	21.8927 6251	22.3863 4871	22.8934 4487	18
19	22.8405 5863	23.3853 4966	23.9460 0743	24.5230 1460	19
20	24.2973 6980	24.9115 2003	25.5446 5761	26.1973 9750	20
21	25.7833 1719	26.4720 2923	27.1832 7405	27.9178 2593	21
22	27.2989 8354	28.0676 4989	28.8628 5590	29.6855 6615	22
23	28.8449 6321	29.6991 7201	30.5844 2730	31.5019 1921	23
24	30.4218 6247	31.3674 0338	32.3490 3798	33.3682 2199	24
25	32.0302 9972	33.0731 6996	34.1577 6393	35.2858 4810	25
26	33.6709 0572	34.8173 1628	36.0117 0803	37.2562 0892	26
27	35.3443 2383	36.6007 0590	37.9120 0073	39.2807 5467	27
28	37.0512 1031	38.4242 2178	39.8598 0075	41.3609 7542	28
29	38.7922 3451	40.2887 6677	41.8562 9577	43.4984 0224	29
30	40.5680 7921	42.1952 6402	43.9027 0316	45.6946 0830	30
31	42.3794 4079	44.1446 5746	46.0002 7074	47.9512 1003	31
32	44.2270 2961	46.1379 1226	48.1502 7751	50.2698 6831	32
33	46.1115 7020	48.1760 1528	50.3540 3445	52.6522 8969	33
34	48.0338 0160	50.2599 7563	52.6128 8531	55.1002 2765	34
35	49.9944 7763	52.3908 2508	54.9282 0744	57.6154 8391	35
36	51.9943 6719	54.5696 1864	57.3014 1263	60.1999 0972	36
37	54.0342 5453	56.7974 3506	59.7339 4794	62.8554 0724	37
38	56.1149 3962	59.0753 7735	62.2272 9664	65.5839 3094	38
39	58.2372 3841	61.4045 7334	64.7829 7906	68.3874 8904	39
40	60.4019 8318	63.7861 7624	67.4025 5354	71.2681 4499	40
41	62.6100 2284	66.2213 6521	70.0876 1737	74.2280 1898	41
42	64.8622 2330	68.7113 4592	72.8398 0781	77.2692 8950	42
43	67.1594 6777	71.2573 5121	75.6608 0300	80.3941 9496	43
44	69.5026 5712	73.8606 4161	78.5523 2308	83.6050 3532	44
45	71.8927 1027	76.5225 0605	81.5161 3116	86.9041 7379	45
46	74.3305 6447	79.2442 6243	84.5540 3443	90.2940 3857	46
47	76.8171 7576	82.0272 5834	87.6678 8530	93.7771 2463	47
48	79.3535 1927	84.8728 7165	90.8595 8243	97.3559 9556	48
49	81.9405 8966	87.7825 1126	94.1310 7199	101.0332 8544	49
50	84.5794 0145	90.7576 1776	97.4843 4879	104.8117 0079	50

n	2%	$2\frac{1}{4}\%$	$2\frac{1}{2}\%$	$2\frac{3}{4}\%$	n
51	87.2709 8948	93.7996 6416	100.9214 5751	108.6940 2256	51
52	90.0164 0927	96.9101 5661	104.4444 9395	112.6831 0818	52
53	92.8167 3746	100.0906 3513	108.0556 0629	116.7818 9365	53
54	95.6730 7221	103.3426 7442	111.7569 9645	120.9933 9573	54
55	98.5865 3365	106.6678 8460	115.5509 2136	125.3207 1411	55
56	101.5582 6432	110.0679 1200	119.4396 9440	129.7670 3375	56
57	104.5894 2961	113.5444 4002	123.4256 8676	134.3356 2718	57
58	107.6812 1820	117.0991 8992	127.5113 2893	139.0298 5692	58
59	110.8348 4257	120.7339 2169	131.6991 1215	143.8531 7799	59
60	114.0515 3942	124.4504 3493	135.9915 8995	148.8091 4038	60
61	117.3325 7021	128.2505 6972	140.3913 7970	153.9013 9174	61
62	120.6792 2161	132.1362 0754	144.9011 6419	159.1336 8002	62
63	124.0928 0604	136.1092 7221	149.5236 9330	164.5098 5622	63
64	127.5746 6216	140.1717 3083	154.2617 8563	170.0338 7726	64
65	131.1261 5541	144.3255 9477	159.1183 3027	175.7098 0889	65
66	134.7486 7852	148.5729 2066	164.0962 8853	181.5418 2863	66
67	138.4436 5209	152.9158 1137	169.1986 9574	187.5342 2892	67
68	142.2125 2513	157.3564 1713	174.4286 6314	193.6914 2021	68
69	146.0567 7563	161.8969 3651	179.7893 7971	200.0179 3427	69
70	149.9779 1114	166.5396 1758	185.2841 1421	206.5184 2746	70
71	153.9774 6937	171.2867 5898	190.9162 1706	213.1976 8422	71
72	158.0570 1875	176.1407 1106	196.6891 2249	220.0606 2054	72
73	162.2181 5913	181.1038 7705	202.6063 5055	227.1122 8760	73
74	166.4625 2231	186.1787 1429	208.6715 0931	234.3578 7551	74
75	170.7917 7276	191.3677 3536	214.8882 9705	241.8027 1709	75
76	175.2076 0821	196.6735 0941	221.2605 0447	249.4522 9181	76
77	179.7117 6038	202.0986 6337	227.7920 1709	257.3122 2983	77
78	184.3059 9558	207.6458 8329	234.4868 1751	265.3883 1615	78
79	188.9921 1549	213.3179 1567	241.3489 8795	273.6864 9485	79
80	193.7719 5780	219.1175 6877	248.3827 1265	282.2128 7345	80
81	198.6473 9696	225.0477 1407	255.5922 8047	290.9737 2747	81
82	203.6203 4490	231.1112 8763	262.9820 8748	299.9755 0498	82
83	208.6927 5180	237.3112 9160	270.5566 3966	309.2248 3137	83
84	213.8666 0683	243.6507 9567	278.3205 5566	318.7285 1423	84
85	219.1439 3897	250.1329 3857	286.2785 6955	328.4935 4837	85
86	224.5268 1775	256.7609 2969	294.4355 3379	338.5271 2095	86
87	230.0173 5411	263.5380 5060	302.7964 2213	348.8366 1678	87
88	235.6177 0119	270.4676 5674	311.3663 3268	359.4296 2374	88
89	241.3300 5521	277.5531 7902	320.1504 9100	370.3139 3839	89
90	247.1566 5632	284.7981 2555	329.1542 5328	381.4975 7170	90
91	253.0997 8944	292.2060 8337	338.3831 0961	392.9887 5492	91
92	259.1617 8523	299.7807 2025	347.8426 8735	404.7959 4568	92
93	265.3450 2094	307.5257 8645	357.5387 5453	416.9278 3418	93
94	271.6519 2135	315.4451 1665	367.4772 2339	429.3933 4962	94
95	278.0849 5978	323.5426 3177	377.6641 5398	442.2016 6674	95
96	284.6466 5898	331.8223 4099	388.1057 5783	455.3622 1257	96
97	291.3395 9216	340.2883 4366	398.8084 0177	468.8846 7342	97
98	298.1663 8400	348.9448 3139	409.7786 1182	482.7790 0194	98
99	305.1297 1168	357.7960 9010	421.0230 7711	497.0554 2449	99
100	312.2323 0591	366.8465 0213	432.5486 5404	511.7244 4867	100

Table 13—Amount of an Ordinary Annuity of n Payments of 1 Each, Immediately After the Last Payment, if Interest is Compounded at i per Period
(Cont.)

n	3%	$3\frac{1}{2}\%$	4%	$4\frac{1}{2}\%$	n
1	1.0000 0000	1.0000 0000	1.0000 0000	1.0000 0000	1
2	2.0300 0000	2.0350 0000	2.0400 0000	2.0450 0000	2
3	3.0909 0000	3.1062 2500	3.1216 0000	3.1370 2500	3
4	4.1836 2700	4.2149 4288	4.2464 6400	4.2781 9113	4
5	5.3091 3581	5.3624 6588	5.4163 2256	5.4707 0973	5
6	6.4684 0988	6.5501 5218	6.6329 7546	6.7168 9166	6
7	7.6624 6218	7.7794 0751	7.8982 9448	8.0191 5179	7
8	8.8923 3605	9.0516 8677	9.2142 2626	9.3800 1362	8
9	10.1591 0613	10.3684 9581	10.5827 9531	10.8021 1423	9
10	11.4638 7931	11.7313 9316	12.0061 0712	12.2882 0937	10
11	12.8077 9569	13.1419 9192	13.4863 5141	13.8411 7879	11
12	14.1920 2956	14.6019 6164	15.0258 0546	15.4640 3184	12
13	15.6177 9045	16.1130 3030	16.6268 3768	17.1599 1327	13
14	17.0863 2416	17.6769 8636	18.2919 1119	18.9321 0937	14
15	18.5989 1389	19.2956 8088	20.0235 8764	20.7840 5429	15
16	20.1568 8130	20.9710 2971	21.8245 3114	22.7193 3673	16
17	21.7615 8774	22.7050 1575	23.6975 1239	24.7417 0689	17
18	23.4144 3537	24.4996 9130	25.6454 1288	26.8550 8370	18
19	25.1168 6844	26.3571 8050	27.6712 2940	29.0635 6246	19
20	26.8703 7449	28.2796 8181	29.7780 7858	31.3714 2277	20
21	28.6764 8572	30.2694 7068	31.9692 0172	33.7831 3680	21
22	30.5367 8030	32.3289 0215	34.2479 6979	36.3033 7795	22
23	32.4528 8370	34.4604 1373	36.6178 8858	38.9370 2996	23
24	34.4264 7022	36.6665 2821	39.0826 0412	41.6891 9631	24
25	36.4592 6432	38.9498 5669	41.6459 0829	44.5652 1015	25
26	38.5530 4225	41.3131 0168	44.3117 4462	47.5706 4460	26
27	40.7096 3352	43.7590 6024	47.0842 1440	50.7113 2361	27
28	42.9309 2252	46.2906 2734	49.9675 8298	53.9933 3317	28
29	45.2188 5020	48.9107 9930	52.9662 8630	57.4230 3316	29
30	47.5754 1571	51.6226 7728	56.0849 3775	61.0070 6966	30
31	50.0026 7818	54.4294 7098	59.3283 3526	64.7523 8779	31
32	52.5027 5852	57.3345 0247	62.7014 6867	68.6662 4524	32
33	55.0778 4128	60.3412 1005	66.2095 2742	72.7562 2628	33
34	57.7301 7652	63.4531 5240	69.8579 0851	77.0302 5646	34
35	60.4620 8181	66.6740 1274	73.6522 2486	81.4966 1800	35
36	63.2759 4427	70.0076 0318	77.5983 1385	86.1639 6581	36
37	66.1742 2259	73.4578 6930	81.7022 4640	91.0413 4427	37
38	69.1594 4927	77.0288 9472	85.9703 3626	96.1382 0476	38
39	72.2342 3275	80.7249 0604	90.4091 4971	101.4644 2398	39
40	75.4012 5973	84.5502 7775	95.0255 1570	107.0303 2306	40
41	78.6632 9753	88.5095 3747	99.8265 3633	112.8466 8760	41
42	82.0231 9645	92.6073 7128	104.8195 9778	118.9247 8854	42
43	85.4838 9234	96.8486 2928	110.0123 8169	125.2764 0402	43
44	89.0484 0911	101.2383 3130	115.4128 7696	131.9138 4220	44
45	92.7198 6139	105.7816 7290	121.0293 9204	138.8499 6510	45
46	96.5014 5723	110.4840 3145	126.8705 6772	146.0982 1353	46
47	100.3965 0095	115.3509 7255	132.9453 9043	153.6726 3314	47
48	104.4083 9598	120.3882 5659	139.2632 0604	161.5879 0163	48
49	108.5406 4785	125.6018 4557	145.8337 3429	169.8593 5720	49
50	112.7968 6729	130.9979 1016	152.6670 8366	178.5030 2828	50

n	3%	$3\frac{1}{2}$%	4%	$4\frac{1}{2}$%	n
51	117.1807 7331	136.5828 3702	159.7737 6700	187.5356 6455	51
52	121.6961 9651	142.3632 3631	167.1647 1768	196.9747 6946	52
53	126.3470 8240	148.3459 4958	174.8513 0639	206.8386 3408	53
54	131.1374 9488	154.5380 5782	182.8453 5865	217.1463 7262	54
55	136.0716 1972	160.9468 8984	191.1591 7299	227.9179 5938	55
56	141.1537 6831	167.5800 3099	199.8055 3991	239.1742 6756	56
57	146.3883 8136	174.4453 3207	208.7977 6151	250.9371 0960	57
58	151.7800 3280	181.5509 1869	218.1496 7197	263.2292 7953	58
59	157.3334 3379	188.9052 0085	227.8756 5885	276.0745 9711	59
60	163.0534 3680	196.5168 8288	237.9906 8520	289.4979 5398	60
61	168.9450 3991	204.3949 7378	248.5103 1261	303.5253 6190	61
62	175.0133 9110	212.5487 9786	259.4507 2511	318.1840 0319	62
63	181.2637 9284	220.9880 0579	270.8287 5412	333.5022 8333	63
64	187.7017 0662	229.7225 8599	282.6619 0428	349.5098 8608	64
65	194.3327 5782	238.7628 7650	294.9683 8045	366.2378 3096	65
66	201.1627 4055	248.1195 7718	307.7671 1567	383.7185 3335	66
67	208.1976 2277	257.8037 6238	321.0778 0030	401.9858 6735	67
68	215.4435 5145	267.8268 9406	334.9209 1231	421.0752 3138	68
69	222.9068 5800	278.2008 3535	349.3177 4880	441.0236 1679	69
70	230.5940 6374	288.9378 6459	364.2904 5876	461.8696 7955	70
71	238.5118 8565	300.0506 8985	379.8620 7711	483.6538 1513	71
72	246.6672 4222	311.5524 6400	396.0565 6019	506.4182 3681	72
73	255.0672 5949	323.4568 0024	412.8988 2260	530.2070 5747	73
74	263.7192 7727	335.7777 8824	430.4147 7550	555.0663 7505	74
75	272.6308 5559	348.5300 1083	448.6313 6652	581.0443 6193	75
76	281.8097 8126	361.7285 6121	467.5766 2118	608.1913 5822	76
77	291.2640 7469	375.3890 6085	487.2796 8603	636.5599 6934	77
78	301.0019 9693	389.5276 7798	507.7708 7347	666.2051 6796	78
79	311.0320 5684	404.1611 4671	529.0817 0841	697.1844 0052	79
80	321.3630 1855	419.3067 8685	551.2449 7675	729.5576 9854	80
81	332.0039 0910	434.9825 2439	574.2947 7582	763.3877 9497	81
82	342.9640 2638	451.2069 1274	598.2665 6685	798.7402 4575	82
83	354.2529 4717	467.9991 5469	623.1972 2952	835.6835 5680	83
84	365.8805 3558	485.3791 2510	649.1251 1870	874.2893 1686	84
85	377.8569 5165	503.3673 9448	676.0901 2345	914.6323 3612	85
86	390.1926 6020	521.9852 5329	704.1337 2839	956.7907 9125	86
87	402.8984 4001	541.2547 3715	733.2990 7753	1000.8463 7685	87
88	415.9853 9321	561.1986 5295	763.6310 4063	1046.8844 6381	88
89	429.4649 5500	581.8406 0581	795.1762 8225	1094.9942 6468	89
90	443.3489 0365	603.2050 2701	827.9833 3354	1145.2690 0659	90
91	457.6493 7076	625.3172 0295	862.1026 6688	1197.8061 1189	91
92	472.3788 5189	648.2033 0506	897.5867 7356	1252.7073 8692	92
93	487.5502 1744	671.8904 2073	934.4902 4450	1310.0792 1933	93
94	503.1767 2397	696.4065 8546	972.8698 5428	1370.0327 8420	94
95	519.2720 2569	721.7808 1595	1012.7846 4845	1432.6842 5949	95
96	535.8501 8645	748.0431 4451	1054.2960 3439	1498.1550 5117	96
97	552.9256 9205	775.2246 5457	1097.4678 7577	1566.5720 2847	97
98	570.5134 6281	803.3575 1748	1142.3665 9080	1638.0677 6976	98
99	588.6288 6669	832.4750 3059	1189.0612 5443	1712.7808 1939	99
100	607.2877 3270	862.6116 5666	1237.6237 0461	1790.8559 5627	100

n	5%	$5\frac{1}{2}\%$	6%	$6\frac{1}{2}\%$	n
1	1.0000 0000	1.0000 0000	1.0000 0000	1.0000 0000	1
2	2.0500 0000	2.0550 0000	2.0600 0000	2.0650 0000	2
3	3.1525 0000	3.1680 2500	3.1836 0000	3.1992 2500	3
4	4.3101 2500	4.3422 6638	4.3746 1600	4.4071 7463	4
5	5.5256 3125	5.5810 9103	5.6370 9296	5.6936 4098	5
6	6.8019 1281	6.8880 5103	6.9753 1854	7.0637 2764	6
7	8.1420 0845	8.2668 9384	8.3938 3765	8.5228 6994	7
8	9.5491 0888	9.7215 7300	9.8974 6791	10.0768 5648	8
9	11.0265 6432	11.2562 5951	11.4913 1598	11.7318 5215	9
10	12.5778 9254	12.8753 5379	13.1807 9494	13.4944 2254	10
11	14.2067 8716	14.5834 9825	14.9716 4264	15.3715 6001	11
12	15.9171 2652	16.3855 9065	16.8699 4120	17.3707 1141	12
13	17.7129 8285	18.2867 9814	18.8821 3767	19.4998 0765	13
14	19.5986 3199	20.2925 7203	21.0150 6593	21.7672 9515	14
15	21.5785 6359	22.4086 6350	23.2759 6988	24.1821 6933	15
16	23.6574 9177	24.6411 3999	25.6725 2808	26.7540 1034	16
17	25.8403 6636	26.9964 0269	28.2128 7976	29.4930 2101	17
18	28.1323 8467	29.4812 0483	30.9056 5255	32.4100 6738	18
19	30.5390 0391	32.1026 7110	33.7599 9170	35.5167 2176	19
20	33.0659 5410	34.8683 1801	36.7855 9120	38.8253 0867	20
21	35.7192 5181	37.7860 7550	39.9927 2668	42.3489 5373	21
22	38.5052 1440	40.8643 0965	43.3922 9028	46.1016 3573	22
23	41.4304 7512	44.1118 4669	46.9958 2769	50.0982 4205	23
24	44.5019 9887	47.5379 9825	50.8155 7735	54.3546 2778	24
25	47.7270 9882	51.1525 8816	54.8645 1200	58.8876 7859	25
26	51.1134 5376	54.9659 8051	59.1563 8272	63.7153 7769	26
27	54.6691 2645	58.9891 0943	63.7057 6568	68.8568 7725	27
28	58.4025 8277	63.2335 1045	68.5281 1162	74.3325 7427	28
29	62.3227 1191	67.7113 5353	73.6397 9832	80.1641 9159	29
30	66.4388 4750	72.4354 7797	79.0581 8622	86.3748 6405	30
31	70.7607 8988	77.4194 2926	84.8016 7739	92.9892 3021	31
32	75.2988 2937	82.6774 9787	90.8897 7803	100.0335 3017	32
33	80.0637 7084	88.2247 6025	97.3431 6471	107.5357 0963	33
34	85.0669 5938	94.0771 2207	104.1837 5460	115.5255 3076	34
35	90.3203 0735	100.2513 6378	111.4347 7987	124.0346 9026	35
36	95.8363 2272	106.7651 8879	119.1208 6666	133.0969 4513	36
37	101.6281 3886	113.6372 7417	127.2681 1866	142.7482 4656	37
38	107.7095 4580	120.8873 2425	135.9042 0578	153.0268 8259	38
39	114.0950 2309	128.5361 2708	145.0584 5813	163.9736 2995	39
40	120.7997 7424	136.6056 1407	154.7619 6562	175.6319 1590	40
41	127.8397 6295	145.1189 2285	165.0476 8356	188.0479 9044	41
42	135.2317 5110	154.1004 6360	175.9505 4457	201.2711 0981	42
43	142.9933 3866	163.5759 8910	187.5075 7724	215.3537 3195	43
44	151.1430 0559	173.5726 6850	199.7580 3188	230.3517 2453	44
45	159.7001 5587	184.1191 6527	212.7435 1379	246.3245 8662	45
46	168.6851 6366	195.2457 1936	226.5081 2462	263.3356 8475	46
47	178.1194 2185	206.9842 3392	241.0986 1210	281.4525 0426	47
48	188.0253 9294	219.3683 6679	256.5645 2882	300.7469 1704	48
49	198.4266 6259	232.4336 2696	272.9584 0055	321.2954 6665	49
50	209.3479 9572	246.2174 7645	290.3359 0458	343.1796 7198	50

n	5%	5½%	6%	6½%	n
51	220.8153 9550	260.7594 3765	308.7560 5886	366.4863 5066	51
52	232.8561 6528	276.1012 0672	328.2814 2239	391.3079 6345	52
53	245.4989 7354	292.2867 7309	348.9783 0773	417.7429 8108	53
54	258.7739 2222	309.3625 4561	370.9170 0620	445.8962 7485	54
55	272.7126 1833	327.3774 8562	394.1720 2657	475.8795 3271	55
56	287.3482 4924	346.3832 4733	418.8223 4816	507.8117 0234	56
57	302.7156 6171	366.4343 2593	444.9516 8905	541.8194 6299	57
58	318.8514 4479	387.5882 1386	472.6487 9040	578.0377 2808	58
59	335.7940 1703	409.9055 6562	502.0077 1782	616.6101 8041	59
60	353.5837 1788	433.4503 7173	533.1281 8089	657.6898 4214	60
61	372.2629 0378	458.2901 4217	566.1158 7174	701.4396 8187	61
62	391.8760 4897	484.4960 9999	601.0828 2405	748.0332 6120	62
63	412.4698 5141	512.1433 8549	638.1477 9349	797.6554 2317	63
64	434.0933 4398	541.3112 7170	677.4366 6110	850.5030 2568	64
65	456.7980 1118	572.0833 9164	719.0828 6076	906.7857 2235	65
66	480.6379 1174	604.5479 7818	763.2278 3241	966.7267 9430	66
67	505.6698 0733	638.7981 1698	810.0215 0236	1030.5640 3593	67
68	531.9532 9770	674.9320 1341	859.6227 9250	1098.5506 9827	68
69	559.5509 6258	713.0532 7415	912.2001 6005	1170.9564 9365	69
70	588.5285 1071	753.2712 0423	967.9321 6965	1248.0686 6574	70
71	618.9549 3625	795.7011 2046	1027.0080 9983	1330.1931 2901	71
72	650.9026 8306	840.4646 8209	1089.6285 8582	1417.6556 8240	72
73	684.4478 1721	887.6902 3960	1156.0063 0097	1510.8033 0176	73
74	719.6702 0807	937.5132 0278	1226.3666 7903	1610.0055 1637	74
75	756.6537 1848	990.0764 2893	1300.9486 7977	1715.6558 7493	75
76	795.4864 0440	1045.5306 3252	1380.0056 0055	1828.1735 0681	76
77	836.2607 2462	1104.0348 1731	1463.8059 3659	1948.0047 8475	77
78	879.0737 6085	1165.7567 3226	1552.6342 9278	2075.6250 9576	78
79	924.0274 4889	1230.8733 5254	1646.7923 5035	2211.5407 2698	79
80	971.2288 2134	1299.5713 8693	1746.5998 9137	2356.2908 7423	80
81	1020.7902 6240	1372.0478 1321	1852.3958 8485	2510.4497 8106	81
82	1072.8297 7552	1448.5104 4294	1964.5396 3794	2674.6290 1683	82
83	1127.4712 6430	1529.1785 1730	2083.4120 1622	2849.4799 0292	83
84	1184.8448 2752	1614.2833 3575	2209.4167 3719	3035.6960 9661	84
85	1245.0870 6889	1704.0689 1921	2342.9817 4142	3234.0163 4289	85
86	1308.3414 2234	1798.7927 0977	2484.5606 4591	3445.2274 0518	86
87	1374.7584 9345	1898.7263 0881	2634.6342 8466	3670.1671 8652	87
88	1444.4964 1812	2004.1562 5579	2793.7123 4174	3909.7280 5364	88
89	1517.7212 3903	2115.3848 4986	2962.3350 8225	4164.8603 7713	89
90	1594.6073 0098	2232.7310 1660	3141.0751 8718	4436.5763 0164	90
91	1675.3376 6603	2356.5312 2252	3330.5396 9841	4725.9537 6125	91
92	1760.1045 4933	2487.1404 3976	3531.3720 8032	5034.1407 5573	92
93	1849.1097 7680	2624.9331 6394	3744.2544 0514	5362.3599 0485	93
94	1942.5652 6564	2770.3044 8796	3969.9096 6944	5711.9132 9867	94
95	2040.6935 2892	2923.6712 3480	4209.1042 4961	6084.1876 6308	95
96	2143.7282 0537	3085.4731 5271	4462.6505 0459	6480.6598 6118	96
97	2251.9146 1564	3256.1741 7611	4731.4095 3486	6902.9027 5216	97
98	2365.5103 4642	3436.2637 5580	5016.2941 0696	7352.5914 3105	98
99	2484.7858 6374	3626.2582 6237	5318.2717 5337	7831.5098 7406	99
100	2610.0251 5693	3826.7024 6680	5638.3680 5857	8341.5580 1588	100

Another problem solved by the use of Table 13 is: What is the amount of $500.00 at the end of 12 years paid at the end of semi-annual periods for 10 years, if interest is converted semi-annually at 5% for the 10 years, and if after ten years no further payments are made, but the interest continues to be compounded semi-annually at 5%?

Now the number of periods of the annuity is $2 \times 10 = 20$, and the interest rate per period is $\frac{5\%}{2} = 2\frac{1}{2}\%$. The amount of $1.00 paid for 20 periods at $2\frac{1}{2}\%$ is found from Table 13, as $25.54465761. Therefore the amount of a periodic payment of $500.00 is ($500.00)(25.54465761) = $12,772.33. This money now draws interest at 5% compounded semi-annually for 2 years. From Table 11, Chapter 13, a principal of $1.00 at $2\frac{1}{2}\%$ for 4 periods accumulates to an amount of $1.10381289. Therefore, the principal of $12.772.33 accumulates to ($12,772.33)(1.1038129) = $14,098.26. (Note that this problem involves both the amount of an annuity, and the amount of a principal accumulated at compound interest, and therefore the use of both Table 13 and Table 11 is necessary.

Ordinary Annuity—Computation of Present Value by Formula

The present value of an annuity is a sum of money which bears the same relation to the amount of annuity that the present value of an amount accumulated at compound interest bears to the amount. In other words, the present value of an ordinary annuity is the sum of the present values, at a time one period before the initial payment, of the periodic payments. Therefore, the present value of the annuity can be found by computing the present value of each payment at compound interest, at a time one period before the initial payment, and then adding the present values of all the payments.

As an example, find the present value of a series of $200.00 deposits made at the end of each year for 3 years in a fund that pays 4% interest compounded annually.

From Formula (13-7) Chapter 13, the present value of a sum at compound interest is,

$$P = \frac{S}{\left(1 + \dfrac{r}{m}\right)^n}$$

where P is present value, S is the sum, or compound amount, (in this case the periodic payment), r is the annual interest rate, m is the number of times compounded annually and n is the number of interest periods.

Since the first periodic payment is made at the end of 1 year, its present value is, $\dfrac{\$200.00}{\left(1 + \dfrac{.04}{1}\right)^1} = \dfrac{\$200.00}{1.04}$. Since the second periodic payment is made at the end of two years, its present value is $\dfrac{\$200.00}{\left(1 + \dfrac{.04}{1}\right)^2} = \dfrac{\$200.00.}{(1.04)^2}$

Since the third periodic payment is made at the end of 3 years, its present value is $\dfrac{\$200.00}{\left(1 + \dfrac{.04}{1}\right)^3} = \dfrac{\$200.00}{(1.04)^3}.$ Therefore the present value of this ordinary annuity is $\dfrac{\$200.00}{1.04} + \dfrac{\$200.00}{(1.04)^2} + \dfrac{\$200.00}{(1.04)^3}.$ The calculations can be made arithmetically, or by Table 12, Chapter 13, which gives the present value of $1.00 for 1 period at 4% as $.96153846; the present value of $1.00 for 2 periods at 4% as $.92455621; and the present value of $1.00 for 3 periods at 4% as $.88899636. Therefore the present value of the annuity is ($200.00)(.96153846) + ($200.00)(.92455621) + ($200.00)(.88899636) = $192.31 + $184.91 + $177.80 = $555.02. If the term of this annuity had been 4 years instead of 3, then its present value would have been,

$$\frac{\$200.00}{1.04} + \frac{\$200.00}{(1.04)^2} + \frac{\$200.00}{(1.04)^3} + \frac{\$200.00}{(1.04)^4}.$$

And if its term had been 5 years, then the present value of this annuity would have been,

$$\frac{\$200.00}{1.04} + \frac{\$200.00}{(1.04)^2} + \frac{\$200.00}{(1.04)^3} + \frac{\$200.00}{(1.04)^4} + \frac{\$200.00}{(1.04)^5}.$$

From this series of terms of the present value of an ordinary annuity for an increasing number of periods, one can induce the general formula,

$$P = \frac{R}{(1 + i)^1} + \frac{R}{(1 + i)^2} \cdots + \frac{R}{(1 + i)^{n-1}} + \frac{R}{(1 + i)^n}$$

where P is the present value of the annuity, R is its periodic payment, n is its number of periods, and i is the interest rate per period.

Note that in this expression, each term is obtained from the preceding term by multiplying by $\dfrac{1}{1 + i}$, and that therefore the entire expression is a geometric progression. However, by Formula (7-11) Chapter 7, the sum of a geometric progression was given as

$$S = \frac{f(r^n - 1)}{r - 1}$$

where f is the first term, r is the ratio of consecutive terms and n is the number of terms. The corresponding quantities in the expression derived for P are $\dfrac{R}{(1 + i)}$ as the first term, $\dfrac{1}{(1 + i)}$ as the ratio of consecutive terms, and n as the number of terms. Substituting these values,

$$P = \frac{\dfrac{R}{(1 + i)}\left[\dfrac{1}{(1 + i)^n} - 1\right]}{\dfrac{1}{1 + i} - 1}$$

Clear fractions in denominator, obtaining

$$P = \frac{\dfrac{R}{(1 + i)}\left[\dfrac{1}{(1 + i)^n} - 1\right]}{\dfrac{1 - 1 - i}{1 + i}}$$

Cancel $\dfrac{1}{1 + i}$ from numerator and denominator, obtaining,

$$P = \frac{R\left[\dfrac{1}{(1 + i)^n} - 1\right]}{-i}$$

Multiply numerator and denominator by -1 to give,

$$P = \frac{R\left[1 - \dfrac{1}{(1 + i)^n}\right]}{i}$$

This expression is usually written with $(1 + i)$ to a negative power, rather than to the reciprocal of a positive power (See Chapter 4 on Exponents), as,

$$P = \frac{R[1 - (1 + i)^{-n}]}{i} \tag{14-3}$$

To apply this formula, find the amount that must be paid, without profit to the seller (present value) for an annuity of a periodic payment of $300.00 to be made at the end of each year for 20 years at an interest rate of 5% compounded annually.

Here the periodic payment (rent) R is $300.00, the interest rate is 5% = .05, and the number of periods, n, is 20.

Substituting, $\quad P = \dfrac{\$300.00[1 - (1 + .05)^{-20}]}{.05}$

This computation is made conveniently by logarithms, as explained in Chapter 6.

By Table 3, Chapter 6, $\log 1.05 = \quad .021189$
$$\underline{ -20}$$
$$\log (1.05)^{-20} = \overline{-.42378}$$

Rewriting with positive mantissa, as explained in Chapter 6,

$$\log (1.05)^{-20} = \overline{1}.57622$$

By Table 3, Chapter 6, and rule for characteristics,

$$\text{antilog } \overline{1}.57622 = .376892$$

Then $\qquad\qquad 1 - .376892 \quad = .623108$

Then $P = \$300.00 \dfrac{.623105}{.05}$

$$= (\$300.00)(12.4622) = \$3,738.63$$

As another example of the application of Formula (14-3) for present value of an ordinary annuity, solve the problem:

A periodic payment of \$275.00 is made at the end of each semi-annual period into a fund for 9 years. If interest is computed at 4%, compounded semi-annually, what is the present value of the fund?

Here the periodic payment (rent) R is \$275.00, the rate per period is $\dfrac{4\%}{2} = 2\%$ or .02, and the number of periods is $2 \times 9 = 18$.

Substituting in the formula for the present value of an ordinary annuity,

$$P = (\$275.00) \frac{[1 - (1.02)^{-18}]}{.02}$$

Then to compute by logarithms

By Table 3, Chapter 6, log 1.02 = $\qquad$ .008600

$$\begin{array}{r} -18 \\ \hline \end{array}$$

$$\log (1.02)^{-18} \quad -.154800$$

Rewriting with positive mantissa, as explained in Chapter 6,

$$\log (1.02)^{-18} = \overline{1}.845200$$

By Table 3, Chapter 6, and rule for characteristics,

$$\text{antilog } \overline{1}.845200 = \quad .700164$$

Then $1 - .700154 = \quad .299836$

Then $P = \$275.00 \dfrac{.299836}{.02} = (\$275.00)(14.9918) = \$4122.75$

Ordinary Annuity—Computation of Present Value by Tables

Note that the formula for the present value of an annuity includes as a factor the rent (periodic payment) expressed in dollars. Therefore, the product of the other factors is the present value of the annuity for a periodic payment of \$1.00. This is a useful figure for the construction of tables, since it can be computed for various periods and interest rates per period, and tabulated against them. It is denoted by the symbol $a_{\overline{n}|i}$, and is given by the relationships:

$$P = Ra_{\overline{n}|i} = \frac{R\left[1 - (1 + i)^{-n}\right]}{i} \qquad (14\text{-}4)$$

or
$$a_{\overline{n}|i} = \frac{1 - (1 + i)^{-n}}{i}$$

Values of $a_{\overline{n}|i}$, the present value of an annuity having a rent (periodic payment) of \$1.00 are given in Table 14, Pages 320 to 336, for various numbers of periods and interest rates per period. The use of this table is illustrated by the example: A state deposits \$750.00 at the end of each quarter in a fund bearing interest at $4\frac{1}{2}\%$ interest compounded quarterly. What is the present value of the fund, if its term is 10 years?

The number of periods are $4 \times 10 = 40$, and the interest rate per period is $\frac{4\frac{1}{2}\%}{4} = 1\frac{1}{8}\%$. The present value of \$1.00 paid for 40 periods at $1\frac{1}{8}\%$ is found from Table 14, as \$32.06825260. Therefore the present value of \$750.00 is (\$750.00)(32.06825260) = \$24,051.19

Ordinary Annuity—Computation of Rent

Up to this point, the quantities calculated for ordinary annuities have been the amount and the present value, since the rent (periodic payment) the interest rate, and the number of payments and identical interest periods, have been known. There are, however, a number of business situations in which the unknown quantity is the rent (periodic payment).

In these situations, the known quantities may be either the interest rate, number of periods, and amount, or the interest rate, number of periods and present value. The methods of dealing with the latter situation will be discussed first.

To find the periodic payment when the interest rate per period, number of periods, and present value are known, the formula for amount, given on Page 296, is simply transposed, from the form

$$P = R\frac{1 - (1 + i)^{-n}}{i}$$

to
$$R = P\frac{i}{1 - (1 + i)^{-n}} \qquad (14\text{-}5)$$

To illustrate the use of this formula, solve the problem: What is the annual payment required to retire a non-interest-bearing debt of \$5,000.00 in 12 years, if the payments start at the end of the first year and bear 4% interest compounded annually.

Here the present value P is \$5,000.00, the interest rate i is $4\% = .04$, and the number of payments n is 12.

Substituting in the formula for R,

n	¼%	⁷⁄₂₄%	⅜%	⁵⁄₁₂%	*n*
1	0.9975 0623	0.9970 9182	0.9966 7774	0.9958 5062	1
2	1.9925 2492	1.9912 8390	1.9900 4426	1.9875 6908	2
3	2.9850 6227	2.9825 8470	2.9801 1056	2.9751 7253	3
4	3.9751 2446	3.9710 0260	3.9668 8760	3.9586 7804	4
5	4.9627 1766	4.9565 4601	4.9503 8631	4.9381 0261	5
6	5.9478 4804	5.9392 2327	5.9306 1759	5.9134 6318	6
7	6.9305 2174	6.9190 4273	6.9075 9228	6.8847 7661	7
8	7.9107 4487	7.8960 1269	7.8813 2121	7.8520 5969	8
9	8.8885 2357	8.8701 4144	8.8518 1516	8.8153 2915	9
10	9.8638 6391	9.8414 3725	9.8190 8487	9.7746 0164	10
11	10.8367 7198	10.8099 0834	10.7831 4107	10.7298 9374	11
12	11.8072 5384	11.7755 6295	11.7439 9442	11.6812 2198	12
13	12.7753 1555	12.7384 0915	12.7016 5557	12.6286 0280	13
14	13.7409 6314	13.6984 5542	13.6561 3512	13.5720 5257	14
15	14.7042 0264	14.6557 0959	14.6074 4364	14.5115 8762	15
16	15.6650 4004	15.6101 7990	15.5555 9167	15.4472 2418	16
17	16.6234 8133	16.5618 7442	16.5005 8970	16.3789 7843	17
18	17.5795 3250	17.5108 0125	17.4424 4821	17.3068 6648	18
19	18.5331 9950	18.4569 6842	18.3811 7762	18.2309 0438	19
20	19.4844 8828	19.4003 8396	19.3167 8832	19.1511 0809	20
21	20.4334 0477	20.3410 5587	20.2492 9069	20.0674 9352	21
22	21.3799 5488	21.2789 9213	21.1786 9504	20.9800 7653	22
23	22.3241 4452	22.2142 0071	22.1050 1167	21.8888 7289	23
24	23.2659 7957	23.1466 8952	23.0282 5083	22.7938 9831	24
25	24.2054 6591	24.0764 6648	23.9484 2275	23.6951 6843	25
26	25.1426 0939	25.0035 3949	24.8655 3763	24.5926 9884	26
27	26.0774 1585	25.9279 1639	25.7796 0561	25.4865 0506	27
28	27.0098 9112	26.8496 0503	26.6906 3682	26.3766 0254	28
29	27.9400 4102	27.7686 1324	27.5986 4135	27.2630 0668	29
30	28.8678 7134	28.6849 4879	28.5036 2925	28.1457 3278	30
31	29.7933 8787	29.5986 1947	29.4056 1055	29.0247 9612	31
32	30.7165 9638	30.5096 3303	30.3045 9523	29.9002 1189	32
33	31.6375 0262	31.4179 9720	31.2005 9325	30.7719 9524	33
34	32.5561 1234	32.3237 1967	32.0936 1454	31.6401 6122	34
35	33.4724 3126	33.2268 0814	32.9836 6898	32.5047 2486	35
36	34.3864 6510	34.1272 7025	33.8707 6642	33.3657 0109	36
37	35.2982 1955	35.0251 1366	34.7549 1670	34.2231 0481	37
38	36.2077 0030	35.9203 4597	35.6361 2960	35.0769 5084	38
39	37.1149 1302	36.8129 7478	36.5144 1488	35.9272 5394	39
40	38.0198 6336	37.7030 0767	37.3897 8228	36.7740 2881	40
41	38.9225 5697	38.5904 5217	38.2622 4147	37.6172 9009	41
42	39.8229 9947	39.4753 1582	39.1318 0213	38.4570 5236	42
43	40.7211 9648	40.3576 0612	39.9984 7388	39.2933 3013	43
44	41.6171 5359	41.2373 3056	40.8622 6633	40.1261 3788	44
45	42.5108 7640	42.1144 9659	41.7231 8903	40.9554 8999	45
46	43.4023 7047	42.9891 1167	42.5812 5153	41.7814 0081	46
47	44.2916 4137	43.8611 8320	43.4364 6332	42.6038 8461	47
48	45.1786 9463	44.7307 1859	44.2888 3387	43.4229 5562	48
49	46.0635 3580	45.5977 2521	45.1383 7263	44.2386 2799	49
50	46.9461 7037	46.4622 1042	45.9850 8900	45.0509 1582	50

n	$\frac{1}{4}\%$	$\frac{7}{24}\%$	$\frac{1}{3}\%$	$\frac{5}{12}\%$	n
51	47.8266 0386	47.3241 8154	46.8289 9236	45.8598 3317	51
52	48.7048 4176	48.1836 4589	47.6700 9205	46.6653 9401	52
53	49.5808 8953	49.0406 1076	48.5083 9739	47.4676 1228	53
54	50.4547 5265	49.8950 8341	49.3439 1767	48.2665 0184	54
55	51.3264 3656	50.7470 7110	50.1766 6213	49.0620 7651	55
56	52.1959 4669	51.5965 8106	51.0066 3999	49.8543 5003	56
57	53.0632 8847	52.4436 2048	51.8338 6046	50.6433 3612	57
58	53.9284 6730	53.2881 9656	52.6583 3268	51.4290 4840	58
59	54.7914 8858	54.1303 1645	53.4800 6580	52.2115 0046	59
60	55.6523 5769	54.9699 8730	54.2990 6890	52.9907 0584	60
61	56.5110 7999	55.8072 1623	55.1153 5106	53.7666 7800	61
62	57.3676 6083	56.6420 1035	55.9289 2133	54.5394 3035	62
63	58.2221 0557	57.4743 7673	56.7397 8870	55.3089 7627	63
64	59.0744 1952	58.3043 2244	57.5479 6216	56.0753 2905	64
65	59.9246 0800	59.1318 5451	58.3534 5065	56.8385 0194	65
66	60.7726 7631	59.9569 7996	59.1562 6311	57.5985 0814	66
67	61.6186 2974	60.7797 0580	59.9564 0842	58.3553 6078	67
68	62.4624 7355	61.6000 3900	60.7538 9543	59.1090 7296	68
69	63.3042 1302	62.4179 8652	61.5487 3299	59.8596 5770	69
70	64.1438 5339	63.2335 5529	62.3409 2989	60.6071 2798	70
71	64.9813 9989	64.0467 5224	63.1304 9490	61.3514 9672	71
72	65.8168 5774	64.8575 8427	63.9174 3678	62.0927 7680	72
73	66.6502 3216	65.6660 5824	64.7017 6423	62.8309 8103	73
74	67.4815 2834	66.4721 8103	65.4834 8595	63.5661 2216	74
75	68.3107 5146	67.2759 5945	66.2626 1058	64.2982 1292	75
76	69.1379 0670	68.0774 0035	67.0391 4676	65.0272 6596	76
77	69.9629 9920	68.8765 1050	67.8131 0308	65.7532 9388	77
78	70.7860 3411	69.6732 9670	68.5844 8812	66.4763 0924	78
79	71.6070 1657	70.4677 6569	69.3533 1042	67.1963 2453	79
80	72.4259 5169	71.2599 2422	70.1195 7849	67.9133 5221	80
81	73.2428 4458	72.0497 7901	70.8833 0082	68.6274 0467	81
82	74.0577 0033	72.8373 3675	71.6444 8587	69.3384 9426	82
83	74.8705 2402	73.6226 0413	72.4031 4206	70.0466 3326	83
84	75.6813 2072	74.4055 8781	73.1592 7780	70.7518 3393	84
85	76.4900 9548	75.1862 9442	73.9129 0146	71.4541 0846	85
86	77.2968 5335	75.9647 3060	74.6640 2139	72.1534 6898	86
87	78.1015 9935	76.7409 0294	75.4126 4591	72.8499 2759	87
88	78.9043 3850	77.5148 1803	76.1587 8329	73.5434 9633	88
89	79.7050 7581	78.2864 8243	76.9024 4182	74.2341 8720	89
90	80.5038 1627	79.0559 0268	77.6436 2972	74.9220 1212	90
91	81.3005 6486	79.8230 8532	78.3823 5520	75.6069 8300	91
92	82.0953 2654	80.5880 3685	79.1186 2645	76.2891 1168	92
93	82.8881 0628	81.3507 6377	79.8524 5161	76.9684 0995	93
94	83.6789 0900	82.1112 7253	80.5838 3882	77.6448 8955	94
95	84.4677 3966	82.8695 6959	81.3127 9616	78.3185 6218	95
96	85.2546 0315	83.6256 6138	82.0393 3172	78.9894 3950	96
97	86.0395 0439	84.3795 5432	82.7634 5354	79.6575 3308	97
98	86.8224 4827	85.1312 5480	83.4851 6964	80.3228 5450	98
99	87.6034 3967	85.8807 6919	84.2044 8802	80.9854 1524	99
100	88.3824 8346	86.6281 0386	84.9214 1663	81.6452 2677	100

n	$\frac{1}{4}\%$	$\frac{7}{24}\%$	$\frac{1}{3}\%$	$\frac{5}{12}\%$	n
101	89.1595 8450	87.3732 6514	85.6359 6344	82.3023 0049	101
102	89.9347 4763	88.1162 5935	86.3481 3635	82.9566 4777	102
103	90.7079 7768	88.8570 9280	87.0579 4323	83.6082 7991	103
104	91.4792 7948	89.5957 7177	87.7653 9195	84.2572 0818	104
105	92.2486 5784	90.3323 0252	88.4704 9034	84.9034 4381	105
106	93.0161 1755	91.0666 9131	89.1732 4621	85.5469 9795	106
107	93.7816 6339	91.7989 4436	89.8736 6735	86.1878 8175	107
108	94.5453 0014	92.5290 6788	90.5717 6150	86.8261 0628	108
109	95.3070 3256	93.2570 6806	91.2675 3641	87.4616 8258	109
110	96.0668 6539	93.9829 5109	91.9609 9977	88.0946 2163	110
111	96.8248 0338	94.7067 2312	92.6521 5927	88.7249 3437	111
112	97.5808 5126	95.4283 9028	93.3410 2255	89.3526 3171	112
113	98.3350 1372	96.1479 5870	94.0275 9726	89.9777 2450	113
114	99.0872 9548	96.8654 3448	94.7118 9098	90.6002 2354	114
115	99.8377 0123	97.5808 2372	95.3939 1131	91.2201 3959	115
116	100.5862 3564	98.2941 3246	96.0736 6578	91.8374 8338	116
117	101.3329 0338	99.0053 6678	96.7511 6194	92.4522 6558	117
118	102.0777 0911	99.7145 3269	97.4264 0727	93.0644 9681	118
119	102.8206 5747	100.4216 3621	98.0994 0927	93.6741 8767	119
120	103.5617 5308	101.1266 8335	98.7701 7538	94.2813 4869	120
121	104.3010 0058	101.8296 8009	99.4387 1304	94.8859 9036	121
122	105.0384 0457	102.5306 3237	100.1050 2964	95.4881 2315	122
123	105.7739 6965	103.2295 4616	100.7691 3256	96.0877 5747	123
124	106.5077 0040	103.9264 2738	101.4310 2916	96.6849 0367	124
125	107.2396 0139	104.6212 8194	102.0907 2677	97.2795 7209	125
126	107.9696 7720	105.3141 1573	102.7482 3269	97.8717 7301	126
127	108.6979 3237	106.0049 3464	103.4035 5420	98.4615 1666	127
128	109.4243 7144	106.6937 4451	104.0566 9857	99.0488 1324	128
129	110.1489 9894	107.3805 5120	104.7076 7303	99.6336 7290	129
130	110.8718 1939	108.0653 6053	105.3564 8478	100.2161 0576	130
131	111.5928 3730	108.7481 7831	106.0031 4101	100.7961 2189	131
132	112.3120 5716	109.4290 1032	106.6476 4888	101.3737 3131	132
133	113.0294 8345	110.1078 6235	107.2900 1552	101.9489 4401	133
134	113.7451 2065	110.7847 4016	107.9302 4806	102.5217 6994	134
135	114.4589 7321	111.4596 4947	108.5683 5358	103.0922 1899	135
136	115.1710 4560	112.1325 9603	109.2043 3915	103.6603 0104	136
137	115.8813 4224	112.8035 8553	109.8382 1181	104.2260 2590	137
138	116.5898 6758	113.4726 2368	110.4699 7859	104.7894 0335	138
139	117.2966 2601	114.1397 1613	111.0996 4646	105.3504 4314	139
140	118.0016 2196	114.8048 6856	111.7272 2242	105.9091 5496	140
141	118.7048 5981	115.4680 8660	112.3527 1341	106.4655 4847	141
142	119.4063 4395	116.1293 7588	112.9761 2636	107.0196 3330	142
143	120.1060 7875	116.7887 4201	113.5974 6817	107.5714 1902	143
144	120.8040 6858	117.4461 9058	114.2167 4572	108.1209 1517	144
145	121.5003 1778	118.1017 2717	114.8339 6586	108.6681 3126	145
146	122.1948 3071	118.7553 5734	115.4491 3545	109.2130 7674	146
147	122.8876 1168	119.4070 8663	116.0622 6128	109.7557 6103	147
148	123.5786 6502	120.0569 2057	116.6733 5015	110.2961 9353	148
149	124.2679 9503	120.7048 6467	117.2824 0882	110.8343 8356	149
150	124.9556 0601	121.3509 2444	117.8894 4404	111.3703 4044	150

n	$\tfrac{1}{2}\%$	$\tfrac{7}{12}\%$	$\tfrac{5}{8}\%$	$\tfrac{2}{3}\%$	n
1	0.9950 2488	0.9942 0050	0.9937 8882	0.9933 7748	1
2	1.9850 9938	1.9826 3513	1.9814 0504	1.9801 7631	2
3	2.9702 4814	2.9653 3733	2.9628 8699	2.9604 4004	3
4	3.9504 9566	3.9423 4034	3.9382 7279	3.9342 1196	4
5	4.9258 6633	4.9136 7723	4.9076 0029	4.9015 3506	5
6	5.8963 8441	5.8793 8084	5.8709 0712	5.8624 5205	6
7	6.8620 7404	6.8394 8385	6.8282 3068	6.8170 0535	7
8	7.8229 5924	7.7940 1875	7.7796 0813	7.7652 3710	8
9	8.7790 6392	8.7430 1781	8.7250 7640	8.7071 8917	9
10	9.7304 1186	9.6865 1315	9.6646 7220	9.6429 0315	10
11	10.6770 2673	10.6245 3669	10.5984 3200	10.5724 2035	11
12	11.6189 3207	11.5571 2016	11.5263 9205	11.4957 8180	12
13	12.5561 5131	12.4842 9511	12.4485 8837	12.4130 2828	13
14	13.4887 0777	13.4060 9291	13.3650 5676	13.3242 0028	14
15	14.4166 2465	14.3225 4473	14.2758 3281	14.2293 3802	15
16	15.3399 2502	15.2336 8160	15.1809 5186	15.1284 8148	16
17	16.2586 3186	16.1395 3432	16.0804 4905	16.0216 7035	17
18	17.1727 6802	17.0401 3354	16.9743 5931	16.9089 4405	18
19	18.0823 5624	17.9355 0974	17.8627 1733	17.7903 4177	19
20	18.9874 1915	18.8256 9320	18.7455 5759	18.6659 0242	20
21	19.8879 7925	19.7107 1404	19.6229 1438	19.5356 6466	21
22	20.7840 5896	20.5906 0220	20.4948 2174	20.3996 6688	22
23	21.6756 8055	21.4653 8745	21.3613 1353	21.2579 4723	23
24	22.5628 6622	22.3350 9938	22.2224 2338	22.1105 4361	24
25	23.4456 3803	23.1997 6741	23.0781 8473	22.9574 9365	25
26	24.3240 1794	24.0594 2079	23.9286 3079	23.7988 3475	26
27	25.1980 2780	24.9140 8862	24.7737 9457	24.6346 0406	27
28	26.0676 8936	25.7637 9979	25.6137 0889	25.4648 3847	28
29	26.9330 2423	26.6085 8307	26.4484 0635	26.2895 7464	29
30	27.7940 5397	27.4484 6702	27.2779 1935	27.1088 4898	30
31	28.6507 9997	28.2834 8006	28.1022 8010	27.9226 9766	31
32	29.5032 8355	29.1136 5044	28.9215 2060	28.7311 5662	32
33	30.3515 2592	29.9390 0625	29.7356 7265	29.5342 6154	33
34	31.1955 4818	30.7595 7540	30.5447 6785	30.3320 4789	34
35	32.0353 7132	31.5753 8566	31.3488 3761	31.1245 5088	35
36	32.8710 1624	32.3864 6463	32.1479 1315	31.9118 0551	36
37	33.7025 0372	33.1928 3974	32.9420 2550	32.6938 4653	37
38	34.5298 5445	33.9945 3828	33.7312 0546	33.4707 0848	38
39	35.3530 8900	34.7915 8736	34.5154 8369	34.2424 2564	39
40	36.1722 2786	35.5840 1396	35.2948 9062	35.0090 3209	40
41	36.9872 9141	36.3718 4487	36.0694 5652	35.7705 6168	41
42	37.7982 9991	37.1551 0676	36.8392 1145	36.5270 4803	42
43	38.6052 7354	37.9338 2612	37.6041 8529	37.2785 2453	43
44	39.4082 3238	38.7080 2929	38.3644 0774	38.0250 2437	44
45	40.2071 9640	39.4777 4248	39.1199 0831	38.7665 8050	45
46	41.0021 8547	40.2429 9170	39.8707 1634	39.5032 2566	46
47	41.7932 1937	41.0038 0287	40.6168 6096	40.2349 9238	47
48	42.5803 1778	41.7602 0170	41.3583 7114	40.9619 1296	48
49	43.3635 0028	42.5122 1380	42.0952 7566	41.6840 1949	49
50	44.1427 8635	43.2598 6460	42.8276 0314	42.4013 4387	50

n	$\frac{1}{2}\%$	$\frac{7}{12}\%$	$\frac{5}{8}\%$	$\frac{2}{3}\%$	n
51	44.9181 9537	44.0031 7940	43.5553 8201	43.1139 1775	51
52	45.6897 4664	44.7421 8335	44.2786 4050	43.8217 7260	52
53	46.4574 5934	45.4769 0144	44.9974 0671	44.5249 3967	53
54	47.2213 5258	46.2073 5853	45.7117 0853	45.2234 5000	54
55	47.9814 4535	46.9335 7933	46.4215 7370	45.9173 3444	55
56	48.7377 5657	47.6555 8841	47.1270 2976	46.6066 2362	56
57	49.4903 0505	48.3734 1020	47.8281 0410	47.2913 4796	57
58	50.2391 0950	49.0870 6898	48.5248 2396	47.9715 3771	58
59	50.9841 8855	49.7965 8889	49.2172 1636	48.6472 2289	59
60	51.7255 6075	50.5019 9394	49.9053 0818	49.3184 3334	60
61	52.4632 4453	51.2033 0800	50.5891 2614	49.9851 9868	61
62	53.1972 5824	51.9005 5478	51.2686 9679	50.6475 4835	62
63	53.9276 2014	52.5937 5787	51.9440 4650	51.3055 1161	63
64	54.6543 4839	53.2829 4073	52.6152 0149	51.9591 1749	64
65	55.3774 6109	53.9681 2668	53.2821 8781	52.6083 9486	65
66	56.0969 7621	54.6493 3888	53.9450 3137	53.2533 7238	66
67	56.8129 1165	55.3266 0040	54.6037 5788	53.8940 7852	67
68	57.5252 8522	55.9999 3413	55.2583 9293	54.5305 4158	68
69	58.2341 1465	56.6693 6287	55.9089 6191	55.1627 8965	69
70	58.9394 1756	57.3349 0925	56.5554 9010	55.7908 5064	70
71	59.6412 1151	57.9965 9579	57.1980 0258	56.4147 5229	71
72	60.3395 1394	58.6544 4488	57.8365 2431	57.0345 2215	72
73	61.0343 4222	59.3084 7877	58.4710 8006	57.6501 8756	73
74	61.7257 1366	59.9587 1959	59.1016 9447	58.2617 7572	74
75	62.4136 4543	60.6051 8934	59.7283 9201	58.8693 1363	75
76	63.0981 5466	61.2479 0988	60.3511 9703	59.4728 2811	76
77	63.7792 5836	61.8869 0297	60.9701 3370	60.0723 4581	77
78	64.4569 7350	62.5221 9021	61.5852 2604	60.6678 9319	78
79	65.1313 1691	63.1537 9310	62.1964 9792	61.2594 9654	79
80	65.8023 0538	63.7817 3301	62.8039 7309	61.8471 8200	80
81	66.4699 5561	64.4060 3118	63.4076 7512	62.4309 7549	81
82	67.1342 8419	65.0267 0874	64.0076 2745	63.0109 0281	82
83	67.7953 0765	65.6437 8667	64.6038 5337	63.5869 8954	83
84	68.4530 4244	66.2572 8585	65.1963 7602	64.1592 6114	84
85	69.1075 0491	66.8672 2705	65.7852 1840	64.7277 4285	85
86	69.7587 1135	67.4736 3089	66.3704 0338	65.2924 5979	86
87	70.4066 7796	68.0765 1789	66.9519 5367	65.8534 3687	87
88	71.0514 2086	68.6759 0845	67.5298 9185	66.4106 9888	88
89	71.6929 5608	69.2718 2283	68.1042 4034	66.9642 7041	89
90	72.3312 9958	69.8642 8121	68.6750 2146	67.5141 7590	90
91	72.9664 6725	70.4533 0363	69.2422 5735	68.0604 3964	91
92	73.5984 7487	71.0389 1001	69.8059 7004	68.6030 8574	92
93	74.2273 3818	71.6211 2017	70.3661 8141	69.1421 3815	93
94	74.8530 7282	72.1999 5379	70.9229 1320	69.6776 2068	94
95	75.4756 9434	72.7754 3047	71.4761 8703	70.2095 5696	95
96	76.0952 1825	73.3475 6967	72.0260 2438	70.7379 7049	96
97	76.7116 5995	73.9163 9075	72.5724 4658	71.2628 8460	97
98	77.3250 3478	74.4819 1294	73.1154 7487	71.7843 2245	98
99	77.9353 5799	75.0441 5539	73.6551 3030	72.3023 0707	99
100	78.5426 4477	75.6031 3712	74.1914 3384	72.8168 6132	100

n	$\frac{1}{2}\%$	$\frac{7}{12}\%$	$\frac{5}{8}\%$	$\frac{2}{3}\%$	n
101	79.1469 1021	76.1588 7702	74.7244 0630	73.3280 0792	101
102	79.7481 6937	76.7113 9392	75.2540 6838	73.8357 6944	102
103	80.3464 3718	77.2607 0648	75.7804 4062	74.3401 6830	103
104	80.9417 2854	77.8068 3331	76.3035 4348	74.8412 2677	104
105	81.5340 5825	78.3497 9288	76.8233 9724	75.3389 6697	105
106	82.1234 4104	78.8896 0355	77.3400 2210	75.8334 1088	106
107	82.7098 9158	79.4262 8359	77.8534 3812	76.3245 8032	107
108	83.2934 2446	79.9598 5115	78.3636 6521	76.8124 9699	108
109	83.8740 5419	80.4903 2428	78.8707 2319	77.2971 8242	109
110	84.4517 9522	81.0177 2093	79.3746 3174	77.7786 5801	110
111	85.0266 6191	81.5420 5895	79.8754 1043	78.2569 4503	111
112	85.5986 6856	82.0633 5606	80.3730 7868	78.7320 6458	112
113	86.1678 2942	82.5816 2991	80.8676 5583	79.2040 3764	113
114	86.7341 5862	83.0968 9803	81.3591 6108	79.6728 8505	114
115	87.2976 7027	83.6091 7785	81.8476 1349	80.1386 2751	115
116	87.8583 7838	84.1184 8671	82.3330 3204	80.6012 8559	116
117	88.4162 9690	84.6248 4182	82.8154 3557	81.0608 7970	117
118	88.9714 3970	85.1282 6033	83.2948 4280	81.5174 3015	118
119	89.5238 2059	85.6287 5926	83.7712 7235	81.9709 5708	119
120	90.0734 5333	86.1263 5554	84.2447 4271	82.4214 8052	120
121	90.6203 5157	86.6210 6602	84.7152 7226	82.8690 2036	121
122	91.1645 2892	87.1129 0742	85.1828 7926	83.3135 9636	122
123	91.7059 9893	87.6018 9638	85.6475 8188	83.7552 2815	123
124	92.2447 7505	88.0880 4946	86.1093 9814	84.1939 3523	124
125	92.7808 7070	88.5713 8308	86.5683 4597	84.6297 3696	125
126	93.3142 9920	89.0519 1361	87.0244 4320	85.0626 5259	126
127	93.8450 7384	89.5296 5731	87.4777 0753	85.4927 0122	127
128	94.3732 0780	90.0046 3032	87.9281 5655	85.9199 0185	128
129	94.8987 1422	90.4768 4873	88.3758 0776	86.3442 7334	129
130	95.4216 0619	90.9463 2851	88.8206 7852	86.7658 3442	130
131	95.9418 9671	91.4130 8554	89.2627 8610	87.1846 0371	131
132	96.4595 9872	91.8771 3561	89.7021 4768	87.6005 9969	132
133	96.9747 2509	92.3384 9442	90.1387 8030	88.0138 4072	133
134	97.4872 8865	92.7971 7758	90.5727 0092	88.4243 4507	134
135	97.9973 0214	93.2532 0060	91.0039 2638	88.8321 3084	135
136	98.5047 7825	93.7065 7892	91.4324 7342	89.2372 1604	136
137	99.0097 2960	94.1573 2787	91.8583 5868	89.6396 1856	137
138	99.5121 6875	94.6054 6270	92.2815 9869	90.0393 5616	138
139	100.0121 0821	95.0509 9857	92.7022 0988	90.4364 4649	139
140	100.5095 6041	95.4939 5056	93.1202 0857	90.8309 0709	140
141	101.0045 3772	95.9343 3364	93.5356 1100	91.2227 5536	141
142	101.4970 5246	96.3721 6272	93.9484 3330	91.6120 0861	142
143	101.9871 1688	96.8074 5261	94.3586 9148	91.9986 8402	143
144	102.4747 4316	97.2402 1804	94.7664 0147	92.3827 9867	144
145	102.9599 4344	97.6704 7364	95.1715 7910	92.7643 6952	145
146	103.4427 2979	98.0982 3397	95.5742 4010	93.1434 1340	146
147	103.9231 1422	98.5235 1350	95.9744 0010	93.5199 4706	147
148	104.4011 0868	98.9463 2663	96.3720 7463	93.8939 8712	148
149	104.8767 2505	99.3666 8765	96.7672 7913	94.2655 5010	149
150	105.3499 7518	99.7846 1078	97.1600 2895	94.6346 5239	150

n	$\frac{3}{4}\%$	$\frac{7}{8}\%$	1%	$1\frac{1}{8}\%$	n
1	0.9925 5583	0.9913 2590	0.9900 9901	0.9888 7515	1
2	1.9777 2291	1.9740 5294	1.9703 9506	1.9667 4923	2
3	2.9555 5624	2.9482 5570	2.9409 8521	2.9337 4460	3
4	3.9261 1041	3.9140 0813	3.9019 6555	3.8899 8230	4
5	4.8894 3961	4.8713 8352	4.8534 3124	4.8355 8200	5
6	5.8455 9763	5.8204 5454	5.7954 7647	5.7706 6205	6
7	6.7946 3785	6.7612 9323	6.7281 9453	6.6953 3948	7
8	7.7366 1325	7.6939 7098	7.6516 7775	7.6097 3002	8
9	8.6715 7642	8.6185 5859	8.5660 1758	8.5139 4810	9
10	9.5995 7958	9.5351 2624	9.4713 0453	9.4081 0690	10
11	10.5206 7452	10.4437 4348	10.3676 2825	10.2923 1832	11
12	11.4349 1267	11.3444 7929	11.2550 7747	11.1666 9302	12
13	12.3423 4508	12.2374 0202	12.1337 4007	12.0313 4044	13
14	13.2430 2242	13.1225 7945	13.0037 0304	12.8863 6880	14
15	14.1369 9495	14.0000 7876	13.8650 5252	13.7318 8509	15
16	15.0243 1261	14.8699 6656	14.7178 7378	14.5679 9514	16
17	15.9050 2492	15.7323 0885	15.5622 5127	15.3948 0360	17
18	16.7791 8107	16.5871 7111	16.3982 6858	16.2124 1395	18
19	17.6468 2984	17.4346 1820	17.2260 0850	17.0209 2850	19
20	18.5080 1969	18.2747 1445	18.0455 5297	17.8204 4845	20
21	19.3627 9870	19.1075 2361	18.8569 8313	18.6110 7387	21
22	20.2112 1459	19.9331 0891	19.6603 7934	19.3929 0371	22
23	21.0533 1473	20.7515 3300	20.4558 2113	20.1660 3580	23
24	21.8891 4614	21.5628 5799	21.2433 8726	20.9305 6693	24
25	22.7187 5547	22.3671 4547	22.0231 5570	21.6865 9276	25
26	23.5421 8905	23.1644 5647	22.7952 0366	22.4342 0792	26
27	24.3594 9286	23.9548 5152	23.5596 0759	23.1735 0598	27
28	25.1707 1251	24.7383 9060	24.3164 4316	23.9045 7946	28
29	25.9758 9331	25.5151 3319	25.0657 8530	24.6275 1986	29
30	26.7750 8021	26.2851 3823	25.8077 0822	25.3424 1766	30
31	27.5683 1783	27.0484 6417	26.5422 8537	26.0493 6233	31
32	28.3556 5045	27.8051 6894	27.2695 8947	26.7484 4236	32
33	29.1371 2203	28.5553 0998	27.9896 9255	27.4397 4522	33
34	29.9127 7621	29.2989 4422	28.7026 6589	28.1233 5745	34
35	30.6826 5629	30.0361 2809	29.4085 8009	28.7993 6460	35
36	31.4468 0525	30.7669 1757	30.1075 0504	29.4678 5127	36
37	32.2052 6576	31.4913 6810	30.7995 0994	30.1289 0114	37
38	32.9580 8016	32.2095 3467	31.4846 6330	30.7825 9692	38
39	33.7052 9048	32.9214 7179	32.1630 3298	31.4290 2044	39
40	34.4469 3844	33.6272 3350	32.8346 8611	32.0682 5260	40
41	35.1830 6545	34.3268 7335	33.4996 8922	32.7903 7340	41
42	35.9137 1260	35.0204 4446	34.1581 0814	33.3254 6195	42
43	36.6389 2070	35.7079 9947	34.8100 0806	33.9435 9649	43
44	37.3587 3022	36.3895 9055	35.4554 5352	34.5548 5438	44
45	38.0731 8136	37.0652 6944	36.0945 0844	35.1593 1212	45
46	38.7823 1401	37.7350 8743	36.7272 3608	35.7570 4536	46
47	39.4861 6774	38.3990 9535	37.3536 9909	36.3481 2891	47
48	40.1847 8189	39.0573 4359	37.9739 5949	36.9326 3674	48
49	40.8781 9542	39.7098 8212	38.5880 7871	37.5106 4202	49
50	41.5664 4707	40.3567 6047	39.1961 1753	38.0822 1708	50

Table 14—Present Value of an Ordinary Annuity of n Payments of 1 Each,
One Period Before the First Payment, if Interest is Compounded at i per
Period   (Cont.)

n	¾%	⅞%	1%	1⅛%	n
51	42.2495 7525	40.9980 2772	39.7981 3617	38.6474 3345	51
52	42.9276 1812	41.6337 3256	40.3941 9423	39.2063 6188	52
53	43.6006 1351	42.2639 2324	40.9843 5072	39.7590 7232	53
54	44.2685 9902	42.8886 4757	41.5686 6408	40.3056 3394	54
55	44.9316 1193	43.5079 5298	42.1471 9216	40.8461 1514	55
56	45.5896 8926	44.1218 8647	42.7199 9224	41.3805 8358	56
57	46.2428 6776	44.7304 9465	43.2871 2102	41.9091 0613	57
58	46.8911 8388	45.3338 2369	43.8486 3468	42.4317 4896	58
59	47.5346 7382	45.9319 1939	44.4045 8879	42.9485 7746	59
60	48.1733 7352	46.5248 2716	44.9550 3841	43.4596 5633	60
61	48.8073 1863	47.1125 9198	45.5000 3803	43.9650 4952	61
62	49.4365 4455	47.6952 5847	46.0396 4161	44.4648 2029	62
63	50.0610 8640	48.2728 7085	46.5739 0258	44.9590 3119	63
64	50.6809 7906	48.8454 7296	47.1028 7385	45.4477 4407	64
65	51.2962 5713	49.4131 0826	47.6266 0777	45.9310 2009	65
66	51.9069 5497	49.9758 1984	48.1451 5621	46.4089 1975	66
67	52.5131 0667	50.5336 5040	48.6585 7050	46.8815 0284	67
68	53.1147 4607	51.0866 4228	49.1669 0149	47.3488 2852	68
69	53.7119 0677	51.6348 3745	49.6701 9949	47.8109 5527	69
70	54.3046 2210	52.1782 7752	50.1685 1435	48.2679 4094	70
71	54.8929 2516	52.7170 0374	50.6618 9539	48.7198 4270	71
72	55.4768 4880	53.2510 5699	51.1503 9148	49.1667 1714	72
73	56.0564 2561	53.7804 7781	51.6340 5097	49.6086 2016	73
74	56.6316 8795	54.3053 0638	52.1129 2175	50.0456 0708	74
75	57.2026 6794	54.8255 8253	52.5870 5124	50.4777 3259	75
76	57.7693 9746	55.3413 4575	53.0564 8637	50.9050 5077	76
77	58.3319 0815	55.8526 3520	53.5212 7364	51.3276 1510	77
78	58.8902 3141	56.3594 8966	53.9814 5905	51.7454 7847	78
79	59.4443 9842	56.8619 4762	54.4370 8817	52.1586 9317	79
80	59.9944 4012	57.3600 4721	54.8882 0611	52.5673 1092	80
81	60.5403 8722	57.8538 2623	55.3348 5753	52.9713 8286	81
82	61.0822 7019	58.3433 2216	55.7770 8666	53.3709 5957	82
83	61.6201 1930	58.8285 7215	56.2149 3729	53.7660 9104	83
84	62.1539 6456	59.3096 1304	56.6484 5276	54.1568 2674	84
85	62.6838 3579	59.7864 8133	57.0776 7600	54.5432 1557	85
86	63.2097 6257	60.2592 1321	57.5026 4951	54.9253 0588	86
87	63.7317 7427	60.7278 4457	57.9234 1535	55.3031 4549	87
88	64.2499 0002	61.1924 1097	58.3400 1520	55.6767 8169	88
89	64.7641 6875	61.6529 4768	58.7524 9030	56.0462 6126	89
90	65.2746 0918	62.1094 8965	59.1608 8148	56.4116 3041	90
91	65.7812 4981	62.5620 7152	59.5652 2919	56.7729 3490	91
92	66.2841 1892	63.0107 2765	59.9655 7346	57.1302 1992	92
93	66.7832 4458	63.4554 9210	60.3619 5392	57.4835 3021	93
94	67.2786 5467	63.8963 9861	60.7544 0982	57.8329 0997	94
95	67.7703 7685	64.3334 8065	61.1429 8002	58.1784 0294	95
96	68.2584 3856	64.7667 7140	61.5277 0299	58.5200 5235	96
97	68.7428 6705	65.1963 0375	61.9086 1682	58.8579 0096	97
98	69.2236 8938	65.6221 1028	62.2857 5923	59.1919 9106	98
99	69.7009 3239	66.0442 2333	62.6591 6755	59.5223 6446	99
100	70.1746 2272	66.4626 7492	63.0288 7877	59.8490 6251	100

n	$\frac{3}{4}\%$	$\frac{7}{8}\%$	1%	$1\frac{1}{8}\%$	n
101	70.6447 8682	66.8774 9683	63.3949 2947	60.1721 2609	101
102	71.1114 5094	67.2887 2052	63.7573 5591	60.4915 9564	102
103	71.5746 4113	67.6963 7722	64.1161 9397	60.8075 1114	103
104	72.0343 8325	68.1004 9786	64.4714 7918	61.1199 1213	104
105	72.4907 0298	68.5011 1312	64.8232 4671	61.4288 3770	105
106	72.9436 2579	68.8982 5341	65.1715 3140	61.7343 2653	106
107	73.3931 7696	69.2919 4885	65.5163 6772	62.0364 1684	107
108	73.8393 8160	69.6822 2935	65.8577 8983	62.3351 4644	108
109	74.2822 6461	70.0691 2451	66.1958 3151	62.6305 5273	109
110	74.7218 5073	70.4526 6370	66.5305 2625	62.9226 7266	110
111	75.1581 6450	70.8328 7604	66.8619 0718	63.2115 4280	111
112	75.5912 3027	71.2097 9037	67.1900 0710	63.4971 9931	112
113	76.0210 7223	71.5834 3531	67.5148 5852	63.7796 7793	113
114	76.4477 1437	71.9538 3922	67.8364 9358	64.0590 1402	114
115	76.8711 8052	72.3210 3020	68.1549 4414	64.3352 4255	115
116	77.2914 9431	72.6850 3614	68.4702 4172	64.6083 9807	116
117	77.7086 7922	73.0458 8465	68.7824 1755	64.8785 1478	117
118	78.1227 5853	73.4036 0312	69.0915 0252	65.1456 2648	118
119	78.5337 5536	73.7582 1871	69.3975 2725	65.4097 6660	119
120	78.9416 9267	74.1097 5832	69.7005 2203	65.6709 6821	120
121	79.3465 9322	74.4582 4864	70.0005 1686	65.9292 6399	121
122	79.7484 7962	74.8037 1613	70.2975 4145	66.1846 8627	122
123	80.1473 7432	75.1461 8699	70.5916 2520	66.4372 6702	123
124	80.5432 9957	75.4856 8723	70.8827 9722	66.6870 3784	124
125	80.9362 7749	75.8222 4261	71.1710 8636	66.9340 3000	125
126	81.3263 3001	76.1558 7867	71.4565 2115	67.1782 7442	126
127	81.7134 7892	76.4866 2074	71.7391 2985	67.4198 0165	127
128	82.0977 4583	76.8144 9392	72.0189 4045	67.6586 4193	128
129	82.4791 5219	77.1395 2309	72.2959 8064	67.8948 2514	129
130	82.8577 1929	77.4617 3292	72.5702 7786	68.1283 8086	130
131	83.2334 6828	77.7811 4788	72.8418 5927	68.3593 3830	131
132	83.6064 2013	78.0977 9220	73.1107 5175	68.5877 2638	132
133	83.9765 9566	78.4116 8991	73.3769 8193	68.8135 7368	133
134	84.3440 1554	78.7228 6485	73.6405 7617	69.0369 0846	134
135	84.7087 0029	79.0313 4061	73.9015 6056	69.2577 5867	135
136	85.0706 7026	79.3371 4063	74.1599 6095	69.4761 5196	136
137	85.4299 4567	79.6402 8811	74.4158 0293	69.6921 1566	137
138	85.7865 4657	79.9408 0606	74.6691 1181	69.9056 7680	138
139	86.1404 9288	80.2387 1728	74.9199 1268	70.1168 6210	139
140	86.4918 0434	80.5340 4440	75.1682 3038	70.3256 9800	140
141	86.8405 0059	80.8268 0981	75.4140 8948	70.5322 1063	141
142	87.1866 0108	81.1170 3575	75.6575 1434	70.7364 2584	142
143	87.5301 2514	81.4047 4423	75.8985 2905	70.9383 6918	143
144	87.8710 9195	81.6899 5711	76.1371 5747	71.1380 6594	144
145	88.2095 2055	81.9726 9602	76.3734 2324	71.3355 4110	145
146	88.5454 2982	82.2529 8242	76.6073 4974	71.5308 1939	146
147	88.8788 3854	82.5308 3759	76.8389 6014	71.7239 2523	147
148	89.2097 6530	82.8062 8262	77.0682 7737	71.9148 8280	148
149	89.5382 2858	83.0793 3841	77.2953 2413	72.1037 1599	149
150	89.8642 4673	83.3500 2569	77.5201 2290	72.2904 4845	150

n	1¼%	1⅜%	1½%	1¾%	*n*
1	0.9876 5432	0.9864 3650	0.9852 2167	0.9828 0098	1
2	1.9631 1538	1.9594 9346	1.9558 8342	1.9486 9875	2
3	2.9265 3371	2.9193 5237	2.9122 0042	2.8979 8403	3
4	3.8780 5798	3.8661 9222	3.8543 8465	3.8309 4254	4
5	4.8178 3504	4.8001 8962	4.7826 4497	4.7478 5508	5
6	5.7460 0992	5.7215 1874	5.6971 8717	5.6489 9762	6
7	6.6627 2585	6.6303 5140	6.5982 1396	6.5346 4139	7
8	7.5681 2429	7.5268 5712	7.4859 2508	7.4050 5297	8
9	8.4623 4498	8.4112 0308	8.3605 1732	8.2604 9432	9
10	9.3455 2591	9.2835 5421	9.2221 8455	9.1012 2291	10
11	10.2178 0337	10.1440 7320	10.0711 1779	9.9274 9181	11
12	11.0793 1197	10.9929 2054	10.9075 0521	10.7395 4969	12
13	11.9301 8466	11.8302 5454	11.7315 3222	11.5376 4097	13
14	12.7705 5275	12.6562 3136	12.5433 8150	12.3220 0587	14
15	13.6005 4592	13.4710 0504	13.3432 3301	13.0928 8046	15
16	14.4202 9227	14.2747 2754	14.1312 6405	13.8504 9677	16
17	15.2299 1829	15.0675 4874	14.9076 4931	14.5950 8282	17
18	16.0295 4893	15.8496 1651	15.6725 6089	15.3268 6272	18
19	16.8193 0759	16.6210 7671	16.4261 6837	16.0460 5673	19
20	17.5993 1613	17.3820 7320	17.1686 3879	16.7528 8130	20
21	18.3696 9495	18.1327 4792	17.9001 3673	17.4475 4919	21
22	19.1305 6291	18.8732 4086	18.6208 2437	18.1302 6948	22
23	19.8820 3744	19.6036 9012	19.3308 6145	18.8012 4764	23
24	20.6242 3451	20.3242 3193	20.0304 0537	19.4606 8565	24
25	21.3572 6865	21.0350 0067	20.7196 1120	20.1087 8196	25
26	22.0812 5299	21.7361 2890	21.3986 3172	20.7457 3166	26
27	22.7962 9925	22.4277 4737	22.0676 1746	21.3717 2644	27
28	23.5025 1778	23.1099 8508	22.7267 1671	21.9869 5474	28
29	24.2000 1756	23.7829 6925	23.3760 7558	22.5916 0171	29
30	24.8889 0623	24.4468 2540	24.0158 3801	23.1858 4934	30
31	25.5692 9010	25.1016 7734	24.6461 4582	23.7698 7650	31
32	26.2412 7418	25.7476 4719	25.2671 3874	24.3438 5897	32
33	26.9049 6215	26.3848 5543	25.8789 5442	24.9079 6951	33
34	27.5604 5644	27.0134 2089	26.4817 2849	25.4623 7789	34
35	28.2078 5822	27.6334 6080	27.0755 9458	26.0072 5100	35
36	28.8472 6737	28.2450 9080	27.6606 8431	26.5427 5283	36
37	29.4787 8259	28.8484 2496	28.2371 2740	27.0690 4455	37
38	30.1025 0133	29.4435 7579	28.8050 5163	27.5862 8457	38
39	30.7185 1983	30.0306 5430	29.3645 8288	28.0946 2857	39
40	31.3269 3316	30.6097 6996	29.9158 4520	28.5942 2955	40
41	31.9278 3522	31.1810 3079	30.4589 6079	29.0852 3789	41
42	32.5213 1874	31.7445 4332	30.9940 5004	29.5678 0135	42
53	33.1074 7530	32.3004 1264	31.5212 3157	30.0420 6522	43
44	33.6863 9536	32.8487 4243	32.0406 2223	30.5081 7221	44
45	34.2581 6825	33.3896 3495	32.5523 3718	30.9662 6261	45
46	34.8228 8222	33.9231 9108	33.0564 8983	31.4164 7431	46
47	35.3806 2442	34.4495 1031	33.5531 9195	31.8589 4281	47
48	35.9314 8091	34.9686 9081	34.0425 5365	32.2938 0129	48
49	36.4755 3670	35.4808 2941	34.5246 8339	32.7211 8063	49
50	37.0128 7574	35.9860 2161	34.9996 8807	33.1412 0946	50

n	$1\tfrac{1}{4}\%$	$1\tfrac{3}{8}\%$	$1\tfrac{1}{2}\%$	$1\tfrac{3}{4}\%$	n
51	37.5435 8099	36.4843 6164	35.4676 7298	33.5540 1421	51
52	38.0677 3431	36.9759 4243	35.9287 4185	33.9597 1913	52
53	38.5854 1660	37.4608 5566	36.3829 9690	34.3584 4633	53
54	39.0967 0776	37.9391 9178	36.8305 3882	34.7503 1579	54
55	39.6016 8667	38.4110 3998	37.2714 6681	35.1354 4550	55
56	40.1004 3128	38.8764 8826	37.7058 7863	35.5139 5135	56
57	40.5930 1855	39.3356 2344	38.1338 7058	35.8859 4727	57
58	41.0795 2449	39.7885 3114	38.5555 3751	36.2515 4523	58
59	41.5600 2419	40.2352 9582	38.9709 7292	36.6108 5526	59
60	42.0345 9179	40.6760 0081	39.3802 6889	36.9639 8552	60
61	42.5033 0054	41.1107 2829	39.7835 1614	37.3110 4228	61
62	42.9662 2275	41.5395 5935	40.1808 0408	37.6521 3000	62
63	43.4234 2988	41.9625 7396	40.5722 2077	37.9873 5135	63
64	43.8749 9247	42.3798 5101	40.9578 5298	38.3168 0723	64
65	44.3209 8022	42.7914 6832	41.3377 8618	38.6405 9678	65
66	44.7614 6195	43.1975 0266	41.7121 0461	38.9588 1748	66
67	45.1965 0563	43.5980 2975	42.0808 9125	39.2715 6509	67
68	45.6261 7840	43.9931 2429	42.4442 2783	39.5789 3375	68
69	46.0505 4656	44.3828 5997	42.8021 9490	39.8810 1597	69
70	46.4696 7562	44.7673 0946	43.1548 7183	40.1779 0267	70
71	46.8836 3024	45.1465 4448	43.5023 3678	40.4696 8321	71
72	47.2924 7431	45.5206 3573	43.8446 6677	40.7564 4542	72
73	47.6962 7093	45.8896 5300	44.1819 3771	41.0382 7560	73
74	48.0950 8240	46.2536 6511	44.5142 2434	41.3152 5857	74
75	48.4889 7027	46.6127 3994	44.8416 0034	41.5874 7771	75
76	48.8779 9533	46.9669 4445	45.1641 3826	41.8550 1495	76
77	49.2622 1761	47.3163 4471	45.4819 0962	42.1179 5081	77
78	49.6416 9640	47.6610 0588	45.7949 8485	42.3763 6443	78
79	50.0164 9027	48.0009 9224	46.1034 3335	42.6303 3359	79
80	50.3866 5706	48.3363 6719	46.4073 2349	42.8799 3474	80
81	50.7522 5389	48.6671 9328	46.7067 2265	43.1252 4298	81
82	51.1133 3717	48.9935 3221	47.0016 9720	43.3663 3217	82
83	51.4699 6264	49.3154 4484	47.2923 1251	43.6032 7486	83
84	51.8221 8532	49.6329 9122	47.5786 3301	43.8361 4237	84
85	52.1700 5958	49.9462 3055	47.8607 2218	44.0650 0479	85
86	52.5136 3909	50.2552 2125	48.1386 4254	44.2899 3099	86
87	52.8529 7688	50.5600 2096	48.4124 5571	44.5109 8869	87
88	53.1881 2531	50.8606 8653	48.6822 2237	44.7282 4441	88
89	53.5191 3611	51.1572 7401	48.9480 0234	44.9417 6355	89
90	53.8460 6035	51.4498 3873	49.2098 5452	45.1516 1037	90
91	54.1689 4850	51.7384 3524	49.4678 3696	45.3578 4803	91
92	54.4878 5037	52.0231 1738	49.7220 0686	45.5605 3860	92
93	54.8028 1518	52.3039 3823	49.9724 2055	45.7597 4310	93
94	55.1138 9154	52.5809 5016	50.2191 3355	45.9555 2147	94
95	55.4211 2744	52.8542 0484	50.4622 0054	46.1479 3265	95
96	55.7245 7031	53.1237 5324	50.7016 7541	46.3370 3455	96
97	56.0242 6698	53.3896 4561	50.9376 1124	46.5228 8408	97
98	56.3202 6368	53.6519 3155	51.1700 6034	46.7055 3718	98
99	56.6126 0610	53.9106 5998	51.3990 7422	46.8850 4882	99
100	56.9013 3936	54.1658 7914	51.6247 0367	47.0614 7304	100

n	2%	$2\tfrac{1}{4}\%$	$2\tfrac{1}{2}\%$	$2\tfrac{3}{4}\%$	n
1	0.9803 9216	0.9779 9511	0.9756 0976	0.9732 3601	1
2	1.9415 6094	1.9344 6955	1.9274 2415	1.9204 2434	2
3	2.8838 8327	2.8698 9687	2.8560 2356	2.8422 6213	3
4	3.8077 2870	3.7847 4021	3.7619 7421	3.7394 2787	4
5	4.7134 5951	4.6794 5253	4.6458 2850	4.6125 8186	5
6	5.6014 3089	5.5544 7680	5.5081 2536	5.4623 6678	6
7	6.4719 9107	6.4102 4626	6.3493 9060	6.2894 0806	7
8	7.3254 8144	7.2471 8461	7.1701 3717	7.0943 1441	8
9	8.1622 3671	8.0657 0622	7.9708 6553	7.8776 7826	9
10	8.9825 8501	8.8662 1635	8.7520 6393	8.6400 7616	10
11	9.7868 4805	9.6491 1134	9.5142 0871	9.3820 6926	11
12	10.5753 4122	10.4147 7882	10.2577 6460	10.1042 0366	12
13	11.3483 7375	11.1635 9787	10.9831 8497	10.8070 1086	13
14	12.1062 4877	11.8959 3924	11.6909 1217	11.4910 0814	14
15	12.8492 6350	12.6121 6551	12.3813 7773	12.1566 9892	15
16	13.5777 0931	13.3126 3131	13.0550 0266	12.8045 7315	16
17	14.2918 7188	13.9976 8343	13.7121 9772	13.4351 0769	17
18	14.9920 3125	14.6676 6106	14.3533 6363	14.0487 6661	18
19	15.6784 6201	15.3228 9590	14.9788 9134	14.6460 0157	19
20	16.3514 3334	15.9637 1237	15.5891 6229	15.2272 5213	20
21	17.0112 0916	16.5904 2775	16.1845 4857	15.7929 4612	21
22	17.6580 4820	17.2033 5232	16.7654 1324	16.3434 9987	22
23	18.2922 0412	17.8027 8955	17.3321 1048	16.8793 1861	23
24	18.9139 2560	18.3890 3624	17.8849 8583	17.4007 9670	24
25	19.5234 5647	18.9623 8263	18.4243 7642	17.9083 1795	25
26	20.1210 3576	19.5231 1260	18.9506 1114	18.4022 5592	26
27	20.7068 9780	20.0715 0376	19.4640 1087	18.8829 7413	27
28	21.2812 7236	20.6078 2764	19.9648 8866	19.3508 2640	28
29	21.8443 8466	21.1323 4977	20.4535 4991	19.8061 5708	29
30	22.3964 5555	21.6453 2985	20.9302 9259	20.2493 0130	30
31	22.9377 0152	22.1470 2186	21.3954 0741	20.6805 8520	31
32	23.4683 3482	22.6376 7419	21.8491 7796	21.1003 2623	32
33	23.9885 6355	23.1175 2977	22.2918 8094	21.5088 3332	33
34	24.4985 9172	23.5863 2618	22.7237 8628	21.9064 0712	34
35	24.9986 1933	24.0457 9577	23.1451 5734	22.2933 4026	35
36	25.4888 4248	24.4946 6579	23.5562 5107	22.6699 1753	36
37	25.9694 5341	24.9336 5848	23.9573 1812	23.0364 1609	37
38	26.4406 4060	25.3629 9118	24.3486 0304	23.3931 0568	38
39	26.9025 8883	25.7828 7646	24.7303 4443	23.7402 4884	39
40	27.3554 7924	26.1935 2221	25.1027 7505	24.0781 0106	40
41	27.7994 8945	26.5951 3174	25.4661 2200	24.4069 1101	41
42	28.2347 9358	26.9879 0390	25.8206 0683	24.7269 2069	42
43	28.6615 6233	27.3720 3316	26.1664 4569	25.0383 6563	43
44	29.0799 6307	27.7477 0969	26.5038 4945	25.3414 7507	44
45	29.4901 5987	28.1151 1950	26.8330 2386	25.6364 7209	45
46	29.8923 1360	28.4744 4450	27.1541 6962	25.9235 7381	46
47	30.2865 8196	28.8258 6259	27.4674 8255	26.2029 9154	47
48	30.6731 1957	29.1695 4777	27.7731 5371	26.4749 3094	48
49	31.0520 7801	29.5056 7019	28.0713 6947	26.7395 9215	49
50	31.4236 0589	29.8343 9627	28.3623 1168	26.9971 6998	50

n	2%	2¼%	2½%	2¾%	n
51	31.7878 4892	30.1558 8877	28.6461 5774	27.2478 5400	51
52	32.1449 4992	30.4703 0687	28.9230 8072	27.4918 2871	52
53	32.4950 4894	30.7778 0623	29.1932 4948	27.7292 7368	53
54	32.8382 8327	31.0785 3910	29.4568 2876	27.9603 6368	54
55	33.1747 8752	31.3726 5438	29.7139 7928	28.1852 6879	55
56	33.5046 9365	31.6602 9768	29.9648 5784	28.4041 5454	56
57	33.8281 3103	31.9416 1142	30.2096 1740	28.6171 8203	57
58	34.1452 2650	32.2167 3489	30.4484 0722	28.8245 0806	58
59	34.4561 0441	32.4858 0429	30.6813 7290	29.0262 8522	59
60	34.7608 8668	32.7489 5285	30.9086 5649	29.2226 6201	60
61	35.0596 9282	33.0063 1086	31.1303 9657	29.4137 8298	61
62	35.3526 4002	33.2580 0573	31.3467 2836	29.5997 8879	62
63	35.6398 4316	33.5041 6208	31.5577 8377	29.7808 1634	63
64	35.9214 1486	33.7449 0179	31.7636 9148	29.9569 9887	64
65	36.1974 6555	33.9803 4405	31.9645 7705	30.1284 6605	65
66	36.4681 0348	34.2106 0543	32.1605 6298	30.2953 4409	66
67	36.7334 3478	34.4357 9993	32.3517 6876	30.4577 5581	67
68	36.9935 6351	34.6560 3905	32.5383 1099	30.6158 2074	68
69	37.2485 9168	34.8714 3183	32.7203 0340	30.7696 5522	69
70	37.4986 1929	35.0820 8492	32.8978 5698	30.9193 7247	70
71	37.7437 4441	35.2881 0261	33.0710 7998	31.0650 8270	71
72	37.9840 6314	35.4895 8691	33.2400 7803	31.2068 9314	72
73	38.2196 6975	35.6866 3756	33.4049 5417	31.3449 0816	73
74	38.4506 5662	35.8793 5214	33.5658 0895	31.4792 2936	74
75	38.6771 1433	36.0678 2605	33.7227 4044	31.6099 5558	75
76	38.8991 3170	36.2521 5262	33.8758 4433	31.7371 8304	76
77	39.1167 9578	36.4324 2310	34.0252 1398	31.8610 0540	77
78	39.3301 9194	36.6087 2675	34.1709 4047	31.9815 1377	78
79	39.5394 0386	36.7811 5085	34.3131 1265	32.0987 9685	79
80	39.7445 1359	36.9497 8079	34.4518 1722	32.2129 4098	80
81	39.9456 0156	37.1147 0004	34.5871 3875	32.3240 3015	81
82	40.1427 4663	37.2759 9026	34.7191 5976	32.4321 4613	82
83	40.3360 2611	37.4337 3130	34.8479 6074	32.5373 6850	83
84	40.5255 1579	37.5880 0127	34.9736 2023	32.6397 7469	84
85	40.7112 8999	37.7388 7655	35.0962 1486	32.7394 4009	85
86	40.8934 2156	37.8864 3183	35.2158 1938	32.8364 3804	86
87	41.0719 8192	38.0307 4018	35.3325 0671	32.9308 3994	87
88	41.2470 4110	38.1718 7304	35.4463 4801	33.0227 1527	88
89	41.4186 6774	38.3099 0028	35.5574 1269	33.1121 3165	89
90	41.5869 2916	38.4448 9025	35.6657 6848	33.1991 5489	90
91	41.7518 9133	38.5769 0978	35.7714 8144	33.2838 4905	91
92	41.9136 1895	38.7060 2423	35.8746 1604	33.3662 7644	92
93	42.0721 7545	38.8322 9754	35.9752 3516	33.4464 9776	93
94	42.2276 2299	38.9557 9221	36.0734 0016	33.5245 7202	94
95	42.3800 2254	39.0765 6940	36.1691 7089	33.6005 5671	95
96	42.5294 3386	39.1946 8890	36.2626 0574	33.6745 0775	96
97	42.6759 1555	39.3102 0920	36.3537 6170	33.7464 7956	97
98	42.8195 2505	39.4231 8748	36.4426 9434	33.8165 2512	98
99	42.9603 1867	39.5336 7968	36.5294 5790	33.8846 9598	99
100	43.0983 5164	39.6417 4052	36.6141 0526	33.9510 4232	100

n	3%	3½%	4%	4½%	n
1	0.9708 7379	0.9661 8357	0.9615 3846	0.9569 3780	1
2	1.9134 6970	1.8996 9428	1.8860 9467	1.8726 6775	2
3	2.8286 1135	2.8016 3698	2.7750 9103	2.7489 6435	3
4	3.7170 9840	3.6730 7921	3.6298 9522	3.5875 2570	4
5	4.5797 0719	4.5150 5238	4.4518 2233	4.3899 7674	5
6	5.4171 9144	5.3285 5302	5.2421 3686	5.1578 7248	6
7	6.2302 8296	6.1145 4398	6.0020 5467	5.8927 0094	7
8	7.0196 9219	6.8739 5554	6.7327 4487	6.5958 8607	8
9	7.7861 0892	7.6076 8651	7.4353 3161	7.2687 9050	9
10	8.5302 0284	8.3166 0532	8.1108 9578	7.9127 1818	10
11	9.2526 2411	9.0015 5104	8.7604 7671	8.5289 1692	11
12	9.9540 0399	9.6633 3433	9.3850 7376	9.1185 8078	12
13	10.6349 5533	10.3027 3849	9.9856 4785	9.6828 5242	13
14	11.2960 7314	10.9205 2028	10.5631 2293	10.2228 2528	14
15	11.9379 3509	11.5174 1090	11.1183 8743	10.7395 4573	15
16	12.5611 0203	12.0941 1681	11.6522 9561	11.2340 1505	16
17	13.1661 1847	12.6513 2059	12.1656 6885	11.7071 9143	17
18	13.7535 1308	13.1896 8173	12.6592 9697	12.1599 9180	18
19	14.3237 9911	13.7098 3742	13.1339 3940	12.5932 9359	19
20	14.8774 7486	14.2124 0330	13.5903 2634	13.0079 3645	20
21	15.4150 2414	14.6979 7420	14.0291 5995	13.4047 2388	21
22	15.9369 1664	15.1671 2484	14.4511 1533	13.7844 2476	22
23	16.4436 0839	15.6204 1047	14.8568 4167	14.1477 7489	23
24	16.9355 4212	16.0583 6760	15.2469 6314	14.4954 7837	24
25	17.4131 4769	16.4815 1459	15.6220 7994	14.8282 0896	25
26	17.8768 4242	16.8903 5226	15.9827 6918	15.1466 1145	26
27	18.3270 3147	17.2853 6451	16.3295 8575	15.4513 0282	27
28	18.7641 0823	17.6670 1885	16.6630 6322	15.7428 7351	28
29	19.1884 5459	18.0357 6700	16.9837 1463	16.0218 8853	29
30	19.6004 4135	18.3920 4541	17.2920 3330	16.2888 8854	30
31	20.0004 2849	18.7362 7576	17.5884 9356	16.5443 9095	31
32	20.3887 6553	19.0688 6547	17.8735 5150	16.7888 9086	32
33	20.7657 9178	19.3902 0818	18.1476 4567	17.0228 6207	33
34	21.1318 3668	19.7006 8423	18.4111 9776	17.2467 5796	34
35	21.4872 2007	20.0006 6110	18.6646 1323	17.4610 1240	35
36	21.8322 5250	20.2904 9381	18.9082 8195	17.6660 4058	36
37	22.1672 3544	20.5705 2542	19.1425 7880	17.8622 3979	37
38	22.4924 6159	20.8410 8736	19.3678 6423	18.0499 9023	38
39	22.8082 1513	21.1024 9987	19.5844 8484	18.2296 5572	39
40	23.1147 7197	21.3550 7234	19.7927 7388	18.4015 8442	40
41	23.4123 9997	21.5991 0371	19.9930 5181	18.5661 0949	41
42	23.7013 5920	21.8348 8281	20.1856 2674	18.7235 4975	42
43	23.9819 0213	22.0626 8870	20.3707 9494	18.8742 1029	43
44	24.2542 7392	22.2827 9102	20.5488 4129	19.0183 8305	44
45	24.5187 1254	22.4954 5026	20.7200 3970	19.1563 4742	45
46	24.7754 4907	22.7009 1813	20.8846 5356	19.2883 7074	46
47	25.0247 0783	22.8994 3780	21.0429 3612	19.4147 0884	47
48	25.2667 0664	23.0912 4425	21.1951 3088	19.5356 0654	48
49	25.5016 5693	23.2765 6450	21.3414 7200	19.6512 9813	49
50	25.7297 6401	23.4556 1787	21.4821 8462	19.7620 0778	50

n	3%	3½%	4%	4½%	n
51	25.9512 2719	23.6286 1630	21.6174 8521	19.8679 5003	51
52	26.1662 3999	23.7957 6454	21.7475 8193	19.9693 3017	52
53	26.3749 9028	23.9572 6043	21.8726 7493	20.0663 4466	53
54	26.5776 6047	24.1132 9510	21.9929 5667	20.1591 8149	54
55	26.7744 2764	24.2640 5323	22.1086 1218	20.2480 2057	55
56	26.9654 6373	24.4097 1327	22.2189 1940	20.3330 3404	56
57	27.1509 3566	24.5504 4760	22.3267 4943	20.4143 8664	57
58	27.3310 0549	24.6664 2281	22.4295 6676	20.4922 3602	58
59	27.5058 3058	24.8177 9981	22.5284 2957	20.5667 3303	59
60	27.6755 6367	24.9447 3412	22.6234 8997	20.6380 2204	60
61	27.8403 5307	25.0673 7596	22.7148 9421	20.7062 4118	61
62	28.0003 4279	25.1858 7049	22.8027 8289	20.7715 2266	62
63	28.1556 7261	25.3003 5796	22.8872 9124	20.8339 9298	63
64	28.3064 7826	25.4109 7388	22.9685 4927	20.8937 7319	64
65	28.4528 9152	25.5178 4916	23.0466 8199	20.9509 7913	65
66	28.5950 4031	25.6211 1030	23.1218 0961	21.0057 2165	66
67	28.7330 4884	25.7208 7951	23.1940 4770	21.0581 0684	67
68	28.8670 3771	25.8172 7489	23.2635 0740	21.1082 3621	68
69	28.9971 2399	25.9104 1052	23.3302 9558	21.1562 0690	69
70	29.1234 2135	26.0003 9664	23.3945 1498	21.2021 1187	70
71	29.2460 4015	26.0873 3975	23.4562 6440	21.2460 4007	71
72	29.3650 8752	26.1713 4275	23.5156 3885	21.2880 7662	72
73	29.4806 6750	26.2525 0508	23.5727 2966	21.3283 0298	73
74	29.5928 8106	26.3309 2278	23.6276 2468	21.3667 9711	74
75	29.7018 2628	26.4066 8868	23.6804 0834	21.4036 3360	75
76	29.8075 9833	26.4798 9244	23.7311 6187	21.4388 8383	76
77	29.9102 8964	26.5506 2072	23.7799 6333	21.4726 1611	77
78	30.0099 8994	26.6189 5721	23.8268 8782	21.5048 9579	78
79	30.1067 8635	26.6849 8281	23.8720 0752	21.5357 8545	79
80	30.2007 6345	26.7487 7567	23.9153 9185	21.5653 4493	80
81	30.2920 0335	26.8104 1127	23.9571 0754	21.5936 3151	81
82	30.3805 8577	26.8699 6258	23.9972 1879	21.6207 0001	82
83	30.4665 8813	26.9275 0008	24.0357 8730	21.6466 0288	83
84	30.5500 8556	26.9830 9186	24.0728 7240	21.6713 9032	84
85	30.6311 5103	27.0368 0373	24.1085 3116	21.6951 1035	85
86	30.7098 5537	27.0886 9926	24.1428 1842	21.7178 0895	86
87	30.7862 6735	27.1388 3986	24.1757 8694	21.7395 3009	87
88	30.8604 5374	27.1872 8489	24.2074 8745	21.7603 1588	88
89	30.9324 7936	27.2340 9168	24.2379 6870	21.7802 0658	89
90	31.0024 0714	27.2793 1564	24.2672 7759	21.7992 4075	90
91	31.0702 9820	27.3230 1028	24.2954 5923	21.8174 5526	91
92	31.1362 1184	27.3652 2732	24.3225 5695	21.8348 8542	92
93	31.2002 0567	27.4060 1673	24.3486 1245	21.8515 6499	93
94	31.2623 3560	27.4454 2680	24.3736 6582	21.8675 2631	94
95	31.3226 5592	27.4835 0415	24.3977 5559	21.8828 0030	95
96	31.3812 1934	27.5202 9387	24.4209 1884	21.8974 1655	96
97	31.4380 7703	27.5558 3948	24.4431 9119	21.9114 0340	97
98	31.4932 7867	27.5901 8308	24.4646 0692	21.9247 8794	98
99	31.5468 7250	27.6233 6529	24.4851 9896	21.9375 9612	99
100	31.5989 0534	27.6554 2540	24.5049 9900	21.9498 5274	100

n	5%	5½%	6%	6½%	n
1	0.9523 8095	0.9478 6730	0.9433 9623	0.9389 6714	1
2	1.8594 1043	1.8463 1971	1.8333 9267	1.8206 2642	2
3	2.7232 4803	2.6979 3338	2.6730 1195	2.6484 7551	3
4	3.5459 5050	3.5051 5012	3.4651 0561	3.4257 9860	4
5	4.3294 7667	4.2702 8448	4.2123 6379	4.1556 7944	5
6	5.0756 9206	4.9955 3031	4.9173 2433	4.8410 1356	6
7	5.7863 7340	5.6829 6712	5.5823 8144	5.4845 1977	7
8	6.4632 1276	6.3345 6599	6.2097 9381	6.0887 5096	8
9	7.1078 2168	6.9521 9525	6.8016 9227	6.6561 0419	9
10	7.7217 3493	7.5376 2583	7.3600 8705	7.1888 3022	10
11	8.3064 1422	8.0925 3633	7.8868 7458	7.6890 4246	11
12	8.8632 5164	8.6185 1785	8.3838 4394	8.1587 2532	12
13	9.3935 7299	9.1170 7853	8.8526 8296	8.5997 4208	13
14	9.8986 4094	9.5896 4790	9.2949 8393	9.0138 4233	14
15	10.3796 5804	10.0375 8094	9.7122 4899	9.4026 6885	15
16	10.8377 6956	10.4621 6203	10.1058 9527	9.7677 6418	16
17	11.2740 6625	10.8646 0856	10.4772 5969	10.1105 7670	17
18	11.6895 8690	11.2460 7447	10.8276 0348	10.4324 6638	18
19	12.0853 2086	11.6076 5352	11.1581 1649	10.7347 1022	19
20	12.4622 1034	11.9503 8249	11.4699 2122	11.0185 0725	20
21	12.8211 5271	12.2752 4406	11.7640 7662	11.2849 8333	21
22	13.1630 0258	12.5831 6973	12.0415 8172	11.5351 9562	22
23	13.4885 7388	12.8750 4240	12.3033 7898	11.7701 3673	23
24	13.7986 4179	13.1516 9895	12.5503 5753	11.9907 3871	24
25	14.0939 4457	13.4139 3266	12.7833 5616	12.1978 7672	25
26	14.3751 8530	13.6624 9541	13.0031 6619	12.3923 7251	26
27	14.6430 3362	13.8980 9991	13.2105 3414	12.5749 9766	27
28	14.8981 2726	14.1214 2172	13.4061 6428	12.7464 7668	28
29	15.1410 7358	14.3331 0116	13.5907 2102	12.9074 8984	29
30	15.3724 5103	14.5337 4517	13.7648 3115	13.0586 7591	30
31	15.5928 1050	14.7239 2907	13.9290 8599	13.2006 3465	31
32	15.8026 7667	14.9041 9817	14.0840 4339	13.3339 2925	32
33	16.0025 4921	15.0750 6936	14.2302 2961	13.4590 8850	33
34	16.1929 0401	15.2370 3257	14.3681 4114	13.5766 0892	34
35	16.3741 9429	15.3905 5220	14.4982 4636	13.6869 5673	35
36	16.5468 5171	15.5360 6843	14.6209 8713	13.7905 6970	36
37	16.7112 8734	15.6739 9851	14.7367 8031	13.8878 5887	37
38	16.8678 9271	15.8047 3793	14.8460 1916	13.9792 1021	38
39	17.0170 4067	15.9286 6154	14.9490 7468	14.0649 8611	39
40	17.1590 8635	16.0461 2469	15.0462 9687	14.1455 2687	40
41	17.2943 6796	16.1574 6416	15.1380 1592	14.2211 5199	41
42	17.4232 0758	16.2629 9920	15.2245 4332	14.2921 6149	42
43	17.5459 1198	16.3630 3242	15.3061 7294	14.3588 3708	43
44	17.6627 7331	16.4578 5063	15.3831 8202	14.4214 4327	44
45	17.7740 6982	16.5477 2572	15.4558 3209	14.4802 2842	45
46	17.8800 6650	16.6329 1537	15.5243 6990	14.5354 2575	46
47	17.9810 1571	16.7136 6386	15.5890 2821	14.5872 5422	47
48	18.0771 5782	16.7902 0271	15.6500 2661	14.6359 1946	48
49	18.1687 2173	16.8627 5139	15.7075 7227	14.6816 1451	49
50	18.2559 2546	16.9315 1790	15.7618 6064	14.7245 2067	50

n	5%	5½%	6%	6½%	n
51	18.3389 7663	16.9966 9943	15.8130 7607	14.7648 0814	51
52	18.4180 7298	17.0584 8287	15.8613 9252	14.8026 3675	52
53	18.4934 0284	17.1170 4538	15.9069 7408	14.8381 5658	53
54	18.5651 4556	17.1725 5486	15.9499 7554	14.8715 0852	54
55	18.6334 7196	17.2251 7048	15.9905 4297	14.9028 2490	55
56	18.6985 4473	17.2750 4311	16.0288 1412	14.9322 2996	56
57	18.7605 1879	17.3223 1575	16.0649 1898	14.9598 4033	57
58	18.8195 4170	17.3671 2393	16.0989 8017	14.9857 6557	58
59	18.8757 5400	17.4095 9614	16.1311 1337	15.0101 0852	59
60	18.9292 8952	17.4498 5416	16.1614 2771	15.0329 6574	60
61	18.9802 7574	17.4880 1343	16.1900 2614	15.0544 2793	61
62	19.0288 3404	17.5241 8334	16.2170 0579	15.0745 8021	62
63	19.0750 8003	17.5584 6762	16.2424 5829	15.0935 0255	63
64	19.1191 2384	17.5909 6457	16.2664 7009	15.1112 7000	64
65	19.1610 7033	17.6217 6737	16.2891 2272	15.1279 5305	65
66	19.2010 1936	17.6509 6433	16.3104 9314	15.1436 1789	66
67	19.2390 6606	17.6786 3917	16.3306 5390	15.1583 2666	67
68	19.2753 0101	17.7048 7125	16.3496 7349	15.1721 3770	68
69	19.3098 1048	17.7297 3579	16.3676 1650	15.1851 0583	69
70	19.3426 7665	17.7533 0406	16.3845 4387	15.1972 8247	70
71	19.3739 7776	17.7756 4366	16.4005 1308	15.2087 1593	71
72	19.4037 8834	17.7968 1864	16.4155 7838	15.2194 5158	72
73	19.4321 7937	17.8168 8970	16.4297 9093	15.2295 3200	73
74	19.4592 1845	17.8359 1441	16.4431 9899	15.2389 9718	74
75	19.4849 6995	17.8539 4731	16.4558 4810	15.2478 8468	75
76	19.5094 9519	17.8710 4010	16.4677 8123	15.2562 2974	76
77	19.5328 5257	17.8872 4180	16.4790 3889	15.2640 6549	77
78	19.5550 9763	17.9025 9887	16.4896 5933	15.2714 2299	78
79	19.5762 8351	17.9171 5532	16.4996 7862	15.2783 3145	79
80	19.5964 6048	17.9309 5291	16.5091 3077	15.2848 1826	80
81	19.6156 7665	17.9440 3120	16.5180 4790	15.2909 0917	81
82	19.6339 7776	17.9564 2768	16.5264 6028	15.2966 2832	82
83	19.6514 0739	17.9681 7789	16.5343 9649	15.3019 9843	83
84	19.6680 0704	17.9793 1554	16.5418 8348	15.3070 4078	84
85	19.6838 1623	17.9898 7255	16.5489 4668	15.3117 7538	85
86	19.6988 7260	17.9998 7919	16.5556 1008	15.3162 2101	86
87	19.7132 1200	18.0093 6416	16.5618 9630	15.3203 9531	87
88	19.7268 6857	18.0183 5466	16.5678 2670	15.3243 1485	88
89	19.7398 7483	18.0268 7645	16.5734 2141	15.3279 9516	89
90	19.7522 6174	18.0349 5398	16.5786 9944	15.3314 5086	90
91	19.7640 5880	18.0426 1041	16.5836 7872	15.3346 9564	91
92	19.7752 9410	18.0498 6769	16.5883 7615	15.3377 4239	92
93	19.7859 9438	18.0567 4662	16.5928 0769	15.3406 0318	93
94	19.7961 8512	18.0632 6694	16.5969 8839	15.3432 8937	94
95	19.8058 9059	18.0694 4734	16.6009 3244	15.3458 1161	95
96	19.8151 3390	18.0753 0553	16.6046 5325	15.3481 7992	96
97	19.8239 3705	18.0808 5833	16.6081 6344	15.3504 0368	97
98	19.8323 2100	18.0861 2164	16.6114 7494	15.3524 9172	98
99	19.8403 0571	18.0911 1055	16.6145 9900	15.3544 5232	99
100	19.8479 1020	18.0958 3939	16.6175 4623	15.3562 9326	100

$$R = (\$5,000.00) \frac{.04}{1 - (1 + .04)^{-12}}$$

Then to compute by logarithms

By Table 3, Chapter 6, log 1.04 =   .017033

$$\frac{-12}{\log (1.04)^{-12} = -.204396}$$

Rewriting with positive mantissa, as explained in Chapter 6,

$$\log (1.04)^{-12} = \bar{1}.795604$$

By Table 3, Chapter 6, and rules for characteristics,

$\bar{1}.795604$ is antilog   .624603

Then $1 - .624603$ $= .375397$

Then $R = \$5,000.00 \dfrac{.04}{.375397} = \$532.76$

The foregoing problem can also be solved by use of Table 14, which gives the present value of an annuity having a periodic payment of $1.00. That is, the table gives the value of $a_{\overline{n}|i}$. Formula (14-4) for present value is

$$P = Ra_{\overline{n}|i}$$

Therefore $R = \dfrac{P}{a_{\overline{n}|i}}$ (14-6)

In other words, the amount of the periodic payment can be found by dividing the present value of the annuity by the present value of the corresponding annuity having a periodic payment of $1.00 given in Table 14.

That value in Table 14, for an interest rate of 4% and 12 payments is 9.38507376. Therefore $R = \dfrac{\$5,000.00}{9.38507376} = \$532.76$

While this use of Table 14, to find the periodic payment of an ordinary annuity from the present value when the interest rate and number of payments are known, reduces the work to a single division, it is of advantage to have a table in which this computation can be made by multiplication. Multiplication is to be preferred because, as explained earlier in this book, it is a more rapid manual operation than division, and because many of the smaller office calculating machines are better adapted to multiplication than to division.

For this reason, Table 15, on Pages 339 to 355 has been included. It gives the values of

$$\frac{1}{a_{\overline{n}|i}} = \frac{i}{1 - (1 + i)^{-n}},$$ (14-7)

which is the periodic payment (rent) of an annuity having a present value of $1.00, tabulated for various interest rates per period and various periods.

To use it in solving the foregoing problem, which has already been solved by formula and by Table 14, look up in Table 15, the periodic rent of an annuity having a present value of $1.00, and an interest rate of 4% per period for 12 periods. The periodic rent found is $0.10655217. Therefore, the periodic rent of a corresponding annuity having a present value of ($5,000.00) is ($5,000.00)(.10655217) = $532.76.

Another example illustrating the use of Table 15 is:

A debt of $7,800.00 is to be paid in 15 years by equal payments at the end of each half year. If interest is at 6%, compounded semi-annually, what is the amount of the payments?

From Table 15, the rent of an annuity having a present value of $1.00, a number of periods $n = 2 \times 15 = 30$, and an interest rate i of $\frac{6\%}{2} = 3\%$, is $.05101926. Therefore the rent of the corresponding annuity having a present value of $7,800.00 is ($7,800.00)(.05101926) = $397.96.

The other important problem of finding the periodic payment on an ordinary annuity is when the interest rate per period, number of periods and amount are known. A formula may readily be set up by simply transposing Formula (14-1) for the amount,

$$S_n = \frac{R[(1 + i)^n - 1]}{i}$$

to
$$R = S_n \frac{i}{(1 + i)^n - 1} \tag{14-8}$$

To illustrate the use of this formula, solve the problem: What is the annual deposit which must be made by a parent in a bank account to accumulate a fund of $5,000.00 in 12 years, if his deposits start at the end of the first year, and bear 4% interest, compounded annually.

Here the amount S_n is $5,000.00, the interest rate i is $4\% = .04$, and the number of payments n is 12.

Substituting in the formula for R,

$$R = (\$5,000.00) \frac{.04}{(1.04)^{12} - 1}$$

Then to compute by logarithms,

By Table 3, Chapter 6, log 1.04 = .017033
$$\frac{12}{}$$
$$\log (1.04)^{12} = .204396$$

n	$\frac{1}{4}\%$	$\frac{7}{24}\%$	$\frac{1}{3}\%$	$\frac{5}{12}\%$	n
1	1.0025 0000	1.0029 1667	1.0033 3333	1.0041 6667	1
2	0.5018 7578	0.5021 8856	0.5025 0139	0.5031 2717	2
3	0.3350 0139	0.3352 7967	0.3355 5802	0.3361 1496	3
4	0.2515 6445	0.2518 2557	0.2520 8680	0.2526 0958	4
5	0.2015 0250	0.2017 5340	0.2020 0444	0.2025 0693	5
6	0.1681 2803	0.1683 7219	0.1686 1650	0.1691 0564	6
7	0.1442 8928	0.1445 2866	0.1447 6824	0.1452 4800	7
8	0.1264 1035	0.1266 4620	0.1268 8228	0.1273 5512	8
9	0.1125 0462	0.1127 3777	0.1129 7118	0.1134 3876	9
10	0.1013 8015	0.1016 1117	0.1018 4248	0.1023 0596	10
11	0.0922 7840	0.0925 0772	0.0927 3736	0.0931 9757	11
12	0.0846 9370	0.0849 2163	0.0851 4990	0.0856 0748	12
13	0.0782 7595	0.0785 0274	0.0787 2989	0.0791 8532	13
14	0.0727 7510	0.0730 0093	0.0732 2716	0.0736 8082	14
15	0.0680 0777	0.0682 3279	0.0684 5825	0.0689 1045	15
16	0.0638 3642	0.0640 6076	0.0642 8557	0.0647 3655	16
17	0.0601 5587	0.0603 7964	0.0606 0389	0.0610 5387	17
18	0.0568 8433	0.0571 0761	0.0573 3140	0.0577 8053	18
19	0.0539 5722	0.0541 8008	0.0544 0348	0.0548 5191	19
20	0.0513 2288	0.0515 4537	0.0517 6844	0.0522 1630	20
21	0.0489 3947	0.0491 6166	0.0493 8445	0.0498 3183	21
22	0.0467 7278	0.0469 9471	0.0472 1726	0.0476 6427	22
23	0.0447 9455	0.0450 1625	0.0452 3861	0.0456 8531	23
24	0.0429 8121	0.0432 0272	0.0434 2492	0.0438 7139	24
25	0.0413 1298	0.0415 3433	0.0417 5640	0.0422 0270	25
26	0.0397 7312	0.0399 9434	0.0402 1630	0.0406 6247	26
27	0.0383 4736	0.0385 6847	0.0387 9035	0.0392 3645	27
28	0.0370 2347	0.0372 4450	0.0374 6632	0.0379 1239	28
29	0.0357 9093	0.0360 1188	0.0362 3367	0.0366 7974	29
30	0.0346 4059	0.0348 6149	0.0350 8325	0.0355 2936	30
31	0.0335 6449	0.0337 8536	0.0340 0712	0.0344 5330	31
32	0.0325 5569	0.0327 7653	0.0329 9830	0.0334 4458	32
33	0.0316 0806	0.0318 2889	0.0320 5067	0.0324 9708	33
34	0.0307 1620	0.0309 3703	0.0311 5885	0.0316 0540	34
35	0.0298 7533	0.0300 9618	0.0303 1803	0.0307 6476	35
36	0.0290 8121	0.0293 0208	0.0295 2399	0.0299 7090	36
37	0.0283 3004	0.0285 5094	0.0287 7291	0.0292 2003	37
38	0.0276 1843	0.0278 3938	0.0280 6141	0.0285 0875	38
39	0.0269 4335	0.0271 6434	0.0273 8644	0.0278 3402	39
40	0.0263 0204	0.0265 2308	0.0267 4527	0.0271 9310	40
41	0.0256 9204	0.0259 1315	0.0261 3543	0.0263 8352	41
42	0.0251 1112	0.0253 3229	0.0255 5466	0.0260 0303	42
43	0.0245 5724	0.0247 7848	0.0250 0095	0.0254 4961	43
44	0.0240 2855	0.0242 4987	0.0244 7246	0.0249 2141	44
45	0.0235 2339	0.0237 4479	0.0239 6749	0.0244 1675	45
46	0.0230 4022	0.0232 6170	0.0234 8451	0.0239 3409	46
47	0.0225 7762	0.0227 9920	0.0230 2213	0.0234 7204	47
48	0.0221 3433	0.0223 5600	0.0225 7905	0.0230 2929	48
49	0.0217 0915	0.0219 3092	0.0221 5410	0.0226 0468	49
50	0.0213 0099	0.0215 2287	0.0217 4618	0.0221 9711	50

n	$\frac{1}{4}\%$	$\frac{7}{24}\%$	$\frac{1}{3}\%$	$\frac{5}{12}\%$	n
51	0.0209 0886	0.0211 3085	0.0213 5429	0.0218 0557	51
52	0.0205 3184	0.0207 5393	0.0209 7751	0.0214 2916	52
53	0.0201 6906	0.0203 9126	0.0206 1499	0.0210 6700	53
54	0.0198 1974	0.0200 4205	0.0202 6592	0.0207 1830	54
55	0.0194 8314	0.0197 0557	0.0199 2958	0.0203 8234	55
56	0.0191 5858	0.0193 8113	0.0196 0529	0.0200 5843	56
57	0.0188 4542	0.0190 6810	0.0192 9241	0.0197 4593	57
58	0.0185 4308	0.0187 6588	0.0189 9035	0.0194 4426	58
59	0.0182 5101	0.0184 7394	0.0186 9856	0.0191 5287	59
60	0.0179 6869	0.0181 9175	0.0184 1652	0.0188 7123	60
61	0.0176 9564	0.0179 1883	0.0181 4377	0.0185 9888	61
62	0.0174 3142	0.0176 5474	0.0178 7984	0.0183 3536	62
63	0.0171 7561	0.0173 9906	0.0176 2432	0.0180 8025	63
64	0.0169 2780	0.0171 5139	0.0173 7681	0.0178 3315	64
65	0.0166 8764	0.0169 1136	0.0171 3695	0.0175 9371	65
66	0.0164 5476	0.0166 7863	0.0169 0438	0.0173 6156	66
67	0.0162 2886	0.0164 5286	0.0166 7878	0.0171 3639	67
68	0.0160 0961	0.0162 3376	0.0164 5985	0.0169 1788	68
69	0.0157 9674	0.0160 2102	0.0162 4729	0.0167 0574	69
70	0.0155 8996	0.0158 1439	0.0160 4083	0.0164 9971	70
71	0.0153 8902	0.0156 1359	0.0158 4021	0.0162 9952	71
72	0.0151 9368	0.0154 1840	0.0156 4518	0.0161 0493	72
73	0.0150 0370	0.0152 2857	0.0154 5553	0.0159 1572	73
74	0.0148 1887	0.0150 4389	0.0152 7103	0.0157 3165	74
75	0.0146 3898	0.0148 6415	0.0150 9147	0.0155 5253	75
76	0.0144 6385	0.0146 8916	0.0149 1666	0.0153 7816	76
77	0.0142 9327	0.0145 1974	0.0147 4641	0.0152 0836	77
78	0.0141 2708	0.0143 5270	0.0145 8056	0.0150 4295	78
79	0.0139 6511	0.0141 9089	0.0144 1892	0.0148 8177	79
80	0.0138 0721	0.0140 3313	0.0142 6135	0.0147 2464	80
81	0.0136 5321	0.0138 7929	0.0141 0770	0.0145 7144	81
82	0.0135 0298	0.0137 2922	0.0139 5781	0.0144 2200	82
83	0.0133 5639	0.0135 8278	0.0138 1156	0.0142 7620	83
84	0.0132 1330	0.0134 3985	0.0136 6881	0.0141 3391	84
85	0.0130 7359	0.0133 0030	0.0135 2944	0.0139 9500	85
86	0.0129 3714	0.0131 6400	0.0133 9333	0.0138 5935	86
87	0.0128 0384	0.0130 3086	0.0132 6038	0.0137 2685	87
88	0.0126 7357	0.0129 0076	0.0131 3046	0.0135 9740	88
89	0.0125 4625	0.0127 7360	0.0130 0349	0.0134 7088	89
90	0.0124 2177	0.0126 4928	0.0128 7936	0.0133 4721	90
91	0.0123 0004	0.0125 2770	0.0127 5797	0.0132 2629	91
92	0.0121 8096	0.0124 0879	0.0126 3925	0.0131 0803	92
93	0.0120 6446	0.0122 9245	0.0125 2310	0.0129 9234	93
94	0.0119 5044	0.0121 7860	0.0124 0944	0.0128 7915	94
95	0.0118 3884	0.0120 6716	0.0122 9819	0.0127 6837	95
96	0.0117 2957	0.0119 5805	0.0121 8928	0.0126 5992	96
97	0.0116 2257	0.0118 5121	0.0120 8263	0.0125 5374	97
98	0.0115 1776	0.0117 4657	0.0119 7818	0.0124 4976	98
99	0.0114 1503	0.0116 4405	0.0118 7585	0.0123 4790	99
100	0.0113 1446	0.0115 4360	0.0117 7559	0.0122 4811	100

n	¾%	⁷⁄₂₄%	⅜%	⁵⁄₁₂%	n
101	0.0112 1584	0.0114 4515	0.0116 7734	0.0121 5033	101
102	0.0111 1917	0.0113 4864	0.0115 8103	0.0120 5449	102
103	0.0110 2439	0.0112 5403	0.0114 8660	0.0119 6054	103
104	0.0109 3144	0.0111 6124	0.0113 9401	0.0118 6842	104
105	0.0108 4027	0.0110 7024	0.0113 0320	0.0117 7809	105
106	0.0107 5083	0.0109 8096	0.0112 1413	0.0116 8948	106
107	0.0106 6307	0.0108 9337	0.0111 2673	0.0116 0256	107
108	0.0105 7694	0.0108 0741	0.0110 4097	0.0115 1727	108
109	0.0104 9241	0.0107 2305	0.0109 5680	0.0114 3358	109
110	0.0104 0942	0.0106 4023	0.0108 7417	0.0113 5143	110
111	0.0103 2793	0.0105 5891	0.0107 9306	0.0112 7079	111
112	0.0102 4791	0.0104 7906	0.0107 1340	0.0111 9161	112
113	0.0101 6932	0.0104 0064	0.0106 3518	0.0111 1386	113
114	0.0100 9211	0.0103 2360	0.0105 5834	0.0110 3750	114
115	0.0100 1625	0.0102 4792	0.0104 8285	0.0109 6249	115
116	0.0099 4172	0.0101 7355	0.0104 0868	0.0108 8880	116
117	0.0098 6846	0.0101 0046	0.0103 3579	0.0108 1639	117
118	0.0097 9646	0.0100 2863	0.0102 6416	0.0107 4524	118
119	0.0097 2567	0.0099 5801	0.0101 9374	0.0106 7530	119
120	0.0096 5608	0.0098 8859	0.0101 2451	0.0106 0655	120
121	0.0095 8764	0.0098 2032	0.0100 5645	0.0105 3896	121
122	0.0095 2033	0.0097 5318	0.0099 8951	0.0104 7251	122
123	0.0094 5412	0.0096 8715	0.0099 2367	0.0104 0715	123
124	0.0093 8899	0.0096 2219	0.0098 5892	0.0103 4288	124
125	0.0093 2491	0.0095 5828	0.0097 9521	0.0102 7965	125
126	0.0092 6186	0.0094 9540	0.0097 3253	0.0102 1745	126
127	0.0091 9981	0.0094 3352	0.0096 7085	0.0101 5625	127
128	0.0091 3873	0.0093 7262	0.0096 1015	0.0100 9603	128
129	0.0090 7861	0.0093 1267	0.0095 5040	0.0100 3677	129
130	0.0090 1942	0.0092 5366	0.0094 9159	0.0099 7844	130
131	0.0089 6115	0.0091 9556	0.0094 3368	0.0099 2102	131
132	0.0089 0376	0.0091 3834	0.0093 7667	0.0098 6449	132
133	0.0088 4725	0.0090 8200	0.0093 2053	0.0098 0883	133
134	0.0087 9159	0.0090 2651	0.0092 6524	0.0097 5403	134
135	0.0087 3675	0.0089 7186	0.0092 1079	0.0097 0005	135
136	0.0086 8274	0.0089 1801	0.0091 5715	0.0096 4689	136
137	0.0086 2952	0.0088 6497	0.0091 0430	0.0095 9453	137
138	0.0085 7707	0.0088 1270	0.0090 5223	0.0095 4295	138
139	0.0085 2539	0.0087 6119	0.0090 0093	0.0094 9213	139
140	0.0084 7446	0.0087 1043	0.0089 5037	0.0094 4205	140
141	0.0084 2425	0.0086 6040	0.0089 0054	0.0093 9271	141
142	0.0083 7476	0.0086 1109	0.0088 5143	0.0093 4408	142
143	0.0083 2597	0.0085 6247	0.0088 0301	0.0092 9615	143
144	0.0082 7787	0.0085 1454	0.0087 5528	0.0092 4890	144
145	0.0082 3043	0.0084 6728	0.0087 0822	0.0092 0233	145
146	0.0081 8365	0.0084 2067	0.0086 6182	0.0091 5641	146
147	0.0081 3752	0.0083 7471	0.0086 1607	0.0091 1114	147
148	0.0080 9201	0.0083 2938	0.0085 7094	0.0090 6650	148
149	0.0080 4712	0.0082 8467	0.0085 2643	0.0090 2247	149
150	0.0080 0284	0.0082 4056	0.0084 8252	0.0089 7905	150

n	$\frac{1}{2}\%$	$\frac{7}{12}\%$	$\frac{5}{8}\%$	$\frac{2}{3}\%$	n
1	1.0050 0000	1.0058 3333	1.0062 5000	1.0066 6667	1
2	0.5037 5312	0.5043 7924	0.5046 9237	0.5050 0554	2
3	0.3366 7221	0.3372 2976	0.3375 0865	0.3377 8762	3
4	0.2531 3279	0.2536 5644	0.2539 1842	0.2541 8051	4
5	0.2030 0997	0.2035 1357	0.2037 6558	0.2040 1772	5
6	0.1695 9546	0.1700 8594	0.1703 3143	0.1705 7709	6
7	0.1457 2854	0.1462 0986	0.1464 5082	0.1466 9198	7
8	0.1278 2886	0.1283 0351	0.1285 4118	0.1287 7907	8
9	0.1139 0736	0.1143 7698	0.1146 1218	0.1148 4763	9
10	0.1027 7057	0.1032 3632	0.1034 6963	0.1037 0321	10
11	0.0936 5903	0.0941 2175	0.0943 5358	0.0945 8572	11
12	0.0860 6643	0.0865 2675	0.0867 5742	0.0869 8843	12
13	0.0796 4224	0.0801 0064	0.0803 3039	0.0805 6052	13
14	0.0741 3609	0.0745 9295	0.0748 2198	0.0750 5141	14
15	0.0693 6436	0.0698 1999	0.0700 4845	0.0702 7734	15
16	0.0651 8937	0.0656 4401	0.0658 7202	0.0661 0049	16
17	0.0615 0579	0.0619 5966	0.0621 8732	0.0624 1546	17
18	0.0582 3173	0.0586 8499	0.0589 1239	0.0591 4030	18
19	0.0553 0253	0.0557 5532	0.0559 8252	0.0562 1027	19
20	0.0526 6645	0.0531 1889	0.0533 4597	0.0535 7362	20
21	0.0502 8163	0.0507 3383	0.0509 6083	0.0511 8843	21
22	0.0481 1380	0.0485 6585	0.0487 9281	0.0490 2041	22
23	0.0461 3465	0.0465 8663	0.0468 1360	0.0470 4123	23
24	0.0443 2061	0.0447 7258	0.0449 9959	0.0452 2729	24
25	0.0426 5186	0.0431 0388	0.0433 3096	0.0435 5876	25
26	0.0411 1163	0.0415 6376	0.0417 9094	0.0420 1886	26
27	0.0396 8565	0.0401 3793	0.0403 6523	0.0405 9331	27
28	0.0383 6167	0.0388 1415	0.0390 4159	0.0392 6983	28
29	0.0371 2914	0.0375 8186	0.0378 0946	0.0380 3789	29
30	0.0359 7892	0.0364 3191	0.0366 5969	0.0368 8832	30
31	0.0349 0304	0.0353 5633	0.0355 8430	0.0358 1316	31
32	0.0338 9453	0.0343 4815	0.0345 7633	0.0348 0542	32
33	0.0329 4727	0.0334 0124	0.0336 2964	0.0338 5898	33
34	0.0320 5586	0.0325 1020	0.0327 3883	0.0329 6843	34
35	0.0312 1550	0.0316 7024	0.0318 9911	0.0321 2898	35
36	0.0304 2194	0.0308 7710	0.0311 0622	0.0313 3637	36
37	0.0296 7139	0.0301 2698	0.0303 5636	0.0305 8680	37
38	0.0289 6045	0.0294 1649	0.0296 4614	0.0298 7687	38
39	0.0282 8607	0.0287 4258	0.0289 7250	0.0292 0354	39
40	0.0276 4552	0.0281 0251	0.0283 3271	0.0285 6406	40
41	0.0270 3631	0.0274 9379	0.0277 2429	0.0279 5595	41
42	0.0264 5622	0.0269 1420	0.0271 4499	0.0273 7697	42
43	0.0259 0320	0.0263 6170	0.0265 9278	0.0268 2509	43
44	0.0253 7541	0.0258 3443	0.0260 6583	0.0262 9847	44
45	0.0248 7117	0.0253 3073	0.0255 6243	0.0257 9541	45
46	0.0243 8894	0.0248 4905	0.0250 8106	0.0253 1439	46
47	0.0239 2733	0.0243 8798	0.0246 2032	0.0248 5399	47
48	0.0234 8503	0.0239 4624	0.0241 7890	0.0244 1292	48
49	0.0230 6087	0.0235 2265	0.0237 5563	0.0239 9001	49
50	0.0226 5376	0.0231 1611	0.0233 4943	0.0235 8416	50

n	$\frac{1}{2}\%$	$\frac{7}{12}\%$	$\frac{5}{8}\%$	$\frac{2}{3}\%$	n
51	0.0222 6269	0.0227 2563	0.0229 5928	0.0231 9437	51
52	0.0218 8675	0.0223 5027	0.0225 8425	0.0228 1971	52
53	0.0215 2507	0.0219 8919	0.0222 2350	0.0224 5932	53
54	0.0211 7686	0.0216 4157	0.0218 7623	0.0221 1242	54
55	0.0208 4139	0.0213 0671	0.0215 4171	0.0217 7827	55
56	0.0205 1797	0.0209 8390	0.0212 1925	0.0214 5618	56
57	0.0202 0598	0.0206 7251	0.0209 0821	0.0211 4552	57
58	0.0199 0481	0.0203 7196	0.0206 0801	0.0208 4569	58
59	0.0196 1392	0.0200 8170	0.0203 1809	0.0205 5616	59
60	0.0193 3280	0.0198 0120	0.0200 3795	0.0202 7639	60
61	0.0190 6096	0.0195 2999	0.0197 6709	0.0200 0592	61
62	0.0187 9796	0.0192 6762	0.0195 0508	0.0197 4429	62
63	0.0185 4337	0.0190 1366	0.0192 5148	0.0194 9108	63
64	0.0182 9681	0.0187 6773	0.0190 0591	0.0192 4590	64
65	0.0180 5789	0.0185 2946	0.0187 6800	0.0190 0837	65
66	0.0178 2627	0.0182 9848	0.0185 3739	0.0187 7815	66
67	0.0176 0163	0.0180 7449	0.0183 1376	0.0185 5491	67
68	0.0173 8366	0.0178 5716	0.0180 9680	0.0183 3835	68
69	0.0171 7206	0.0176 4622	0.0178 8622	0.0181 2816	69
70	0.0169 6657	0.0174 4138	0.0176 8175	0.0179 2409	70
71	0.0167 6693	0.0172 4239	0.0174 8313	0.0177 2586	71
72	0.0165 7289	0.0170 4901	0.0172 9011	0.0175 3324	72
73	0.0163 8422	0.0168 6100	0.0171 0247	0.0173 4600	73
74	0.0162 0070	0.0166 7814	0.0169 1999	0.0171 6391	74
75	0.0160 2214	0.0165 0024	0.0167 4246	0.0169 8678	75
76	0.0158 4832	0.0163 2709	0.0165 6968	0.0168 1440	76
77	0.0156 7908	0.0161 5851	0.0164 0147	0.0166 4659	77
78	0.0155 1423	0.0159 9432	0.0162 3766	0.0164 8318	78
79	0.0153 5360	0.0158 3436	0.0160 7808	0.0163 2400	79
80	0.0151 9704	0.0156 7847	0.0159 2256	0.0161 6889	80
81	0.0150 4439	0.0155 2650	0.0157 7096	0.0160 1769	81
82	0.0148 9552	0.0153 7830	0.0156 2314	0.0158 7027	82
83	0.0147 5028	0.0152 3373	0.0154 7895	0.0157 2649	83
84	0.0146 0855	0.0150 9268	0.0153 3828	0.0155 8621	84
85	0.0144 7021	0.0149 5501	0.0152 0098	0.0154 4933	85
86	0.0143 3513	0.0148 2060	0.0150 6696	0.0153 1570	86
87	0.0142 0320	0.0146 8935	0.0149 3608	0.0151 8524	87
88	0.0140 7431	0.0145 6115	0.0148 0826	0.0150 5781	88
89	0.0139 4837	0.0144 3588	0.0146 8337	0.0149 3334	89
90	0.0138 2527	0.0143 1347	0.0145 6134	0.0148 1170	90
91	0.0137 0493	0.0141 9380	0.0144 4205	0.0146 9282	91
92	0.0135 8724	0.0140 7679	0.0143 2542	0.0145 7660	92
93	0.0134 7213	0.0139 6236	0.0142 1137	0.0144 6296	93
94	0.0133 5950	0.0138 5042	0.0140 9982	0.0143 5181	94
95	0.0132 4930	0.0137 4090	0.0139 9067	0.0142 4308	95
96	0.0131 4143	0.0136 3372	0.0138 8387	0.0141 3668	96
97	0.0130 3583	0.0135 2880	0.0137 7933	0.0140 3255	97
98	0.0129 3242	0.0134 2608	0.0136 7700	0.0139 3062	98
99	0.0128 3115	0.0133 2549	0.0135 7679	0.0138 3082	99
100	0.0127 3194	0.0132 2696	0.0134 7865	0.0137 3308	100

n	$\frac{1}{2}\%$	$\frac{7}{12}\%$	$\frac{5}{8}\%$	$\frac{2}{3}\%$	n
101	0.0126 3473	0.0131 3045	0.0133 8251	0.0136 3735	101
102	0.0125 3947	0.0130 3587	0.0132 8832	0.0135 4357	102
103	0.0124 4611	0.0129 4319	0.0131 9602	0.0134 5168	103
104	0.0123 5457	0.0128 5234	0.0131 0555	0.0133 6162	104
105	0.0122 6481	0.0127 6238	0.0130 1687	0.0132 7334	105
106	0.0121 7679	0.0126 7594	0.0129 2992	0.0131 8680	106
107	0.0120 9045	0.0125 9029	0.0128 4465	0.0131 0194	107
108	0.0120 0575	0.0125 0628	0.0127 6102	0.0130 1871	108
109	0.0119 2264	0.0124 2385	0.0126 7897	0.0129 3708	109
110	0.0118 4107	0.0123 4298	0.0125 9848	0.0128 5700	110
111	0.0117 6102	0.0122 6361	0.0125 1950	0.0127 7842	111
112	0.0116 8242	0.0121 8571	0.0124 4198	0.0127 0131	112
113	0.0116 0526	0.0121 0923	0.0123 6588	0.0126 2562	113
114	0.0115 2948	0.0120 3414	0.0122 9118	0.0125 5132	114
115	0.0114 5506	0.0119 6041	0.0122 1783	0.0124 7838	115
116	0.0113 8195	0.0118 8799	0.0121 4579	0.0124 0675	116
117	0.0113 1013	0.0118 1686	0.0120 7504	0.0123 3641	117
118	0.0112 3956	0.0117 4698	0.0120 0555	0.0122 6732	118
119	0.0111 7021	0.0116 7832	0.0119 3727	0.0121 9944	119
120	0.0111 0205	0.0116 1085	0.0118 7018	0.0121 3276	120
121	0.0110 3505	0.0115 4454	0.0118 0425	0.0120 6724	121
122	0.0109 6918	0.0114 7936	0.0117 3945	0.0120 0284	122
123	0.0109 0441	0.0114 1528	0.0116 7575	0.0119 3955	123
124	0.0108 4072	0.0113 5228	0.0116 1314	0.0118 7734	124
125	0.0107 7808	0.0112 9033	0.0115 5157	0.0118 1618	125
126	0.0107 1647	0.0112 2940	0.0114 9102	0.0117 5604	126
127	0.0106 5586	0.0111 6948	0.0114 3148	0.0116 9690	127
128	0.0105 9623	0.0111 1054	0.0113 7292	0.0116 3875	128
129	0.0105 3755	0.0110 5255	0.0113 1531	0.0115 8154	129
130	0.0104 7981	0.0109 9550	0.0112 5864	0.0115 2527	130
131	0.0104 2298	0.0109 3935	0.0112 0288	0.0114 6992	131
132	0.0103 6704	0.0108 8410	0.0111 4800	0.0114 1545	132
133	0.0103 1197	0.0108 2972	0.0110 9400	0.0113 6185	133
134	0.0102 5775	0.0107 7619	0.0110 4086	0.0113 0910	134
135	0.0102 0436	0.0107 2349	0.0109 8854	0.0112 5719	135
136	0.0101 5179	0.0106 7161	0.0109 3703	0.0112 0609	136
137	0.0101 0002	0.0106 2052	0.0108 8633	0.0111 5578	137
138	0.0100 4902	0.0105 7021	0.0108 3640	0.0111 0625	138
139	0.0099 9879	0.0105 2067	0.0107 8723	0.0110 5749	139
140	0.0099 4930	0.0104 7187	0.0107 3881	0.0110 0947	140
141	0.0099 0055	0.0104 2380	0.0106 9111	0.0109 6218	141
142	0.0098 5250	0.0103 7644	0.0106 4414	0.0109 1560	142
143	0.0098 0516	0.0103 2978	0.0105 9786	0.0108 6972	143
144	0.0097 5850	0.0102 8381	0.0105 5226	0.0108 2453	144
145	0.0097 1252	0.0102 3851	0.0105 0734	0.0107 8000	145
146	0.0096 6719	0.0101 9386	0.0104 6307	0.0107 3613	146
147	0.0096 2250	0.0101 4986	0.0104 1944	0.0106 9291	147
148	0.0095 7844	0.0101 0649	0.0103 7645	0.0106 5031	148
149	0.0095 3500	0.0100 6373	0.0103 3407	0.0106 0833	149
150	0.0094 9217	0.0100 2159	0.0102 9230	0.0105 6695	150

n	$\frac{3}{4}\%$	$\frac{7}{8}\%$	1%	$1\frac{1}{8}\%$	n
1	1.0075 0000	1.0087 5000	1.0100 0000	1.0112 5000	1
2	0.5056 3200	0.5065 7203	0.5075 1244	0.5084 5323	2
3	0.3383 4579	0.3391·8361	0.3400 2211	0.3408 6130	3
4	0.2547 0501	0.2554 9257	0.2562 8109	0.2570 7058	4
5	0.2045 2242	0.2052 8049	0.2060 3980	0.2068 0034	5
6	0.1710 6891	0.1718 0789	0.1725 4837	0.1732 9034	6
7	0.1471 7488	0.1479 0070	0.1486 2828	0.1493 5762	7
8	0.1292 5552	0.1299 7190	0.1306 9029	0.1314 1071	8
9	0.1153 1929	0.1160 2868	0.1167 4037	0.1174 5432	9
10	0.1041 7123	0.1048 7538	0.1055 8208	0.1062 9131	10
11	0.0950 5094	0.0957 5111	0.0964 5408	0.0971 5984	11
12	0.0874 5148	0.0881 4860	0.0888 4879	0.0895 5203	12
13	0.0810 2188	0.0817 1669	0.0824 1482	0.0831 1626	13
14	0.0755 1146	0.0762 0453	0.0769 0117	0.0776 0138	14
15	0.0707 3639	0.0714 2817	0.0721 2378	0.0728 2321	15
16	0.0665 5879	0.0672 4965	0.0679 4460	0.0686 4363	16
17	0.0628 7321	0.0635 6346	0.0642 5806	0.0649 5698	17
18	0.0595 9766	0.0602 8756	0.0609 8205	0.0616 8113	18
19	0.0566 6740	0.0573 5715	0.0580 5175	0.0587 5120	19
20	0.0540 3063	0.0547 2042	0.0554 1532	0.0561 1531	20
21	0.0516 4543	0.0523 3541	0.0530 3075	0.0537 3145	21
22	0.0494 7748	0.0501 6779	0.0508 6371	0.0515 6525	22
23	0.0474 9846	0.0481 8921	0.0488 8584	0.0495 8833	23
24	0.0456 8474	0.0463 7604	0.0470 7347	0.0477 7701	24
25	0.0440 1650	0.0447 0843	0.0454 0675	0.0461 1144	25
26	0.0424 7693	0.0431 6959	0.0438 6888	0.0445 7479	26
27	0.0410 5176	0.0417 4520	0.0424 4553	0.0431 5273	27
28	0.0397 2871	0.0404 2300	0.0411 2444	0.0418 3299	28
29	0.0384 9723	0.0391 9243	0.0398 9502	0.0406 0498	29
30	0.0373 4816	0.0380 4431	0.0387 4811	0.0394 5953	30
31	0.0362 7352	0.0369 7068	0.0376 7573	0.0383 8866	31
32	0.0352 6634	0.0359 6454	0.0366 7089	0.0373 8535	32
33	0.0343 2048	0.0350 1976	0.0357 2744	0.0364 4349	33
34	0.0334 3053	0.0341 3092	0.0348 3997	0.0355 5763	34
35	0.0325 9170	0.0332 9324	0.0340 0368	0.0347 2299	35
36	0.0317 9973	0.0325 0244	0.0332 1431	0.0339 3529	36
37	0.0310 5082	0.0317 5473	0.0324 6805	0.0331 9072	37
38	0.0303 4157	0.0310 4671	0.0317 6150	0.0324 8589	38
39	0.0296 6893	0.0303 7531	0.0310 9160	0.0318 1773	39
40	0.0290 3016	0.0297 3780	0.0304 5560	0.0311 8349	40
41	0.0284 2276	0.0291 3169	0.0298 5102	0.0305 8069	41
42	0.0278 4452	0.0285 5475	0.0292 7563	0.0300 0709	42
43	0.0272 9338	0.0280 0493	0.0287 2737	0.0294 6064	43
44	0.0267 6751	0.0274 8039	0.0282 0441	0.0289 3949	44
45	0.0262 6521	0.0269 7943	0.0277 0505	0.0284 4197	45
46	0.0257 8495	0.0265 0053	0.0272 2775	0.0279 6652	46
47	0.0253 2532	0.0260 4228	0.0267 7111	0.0275 1173	47
48	0.0248 8504	0.0256 0338	0.0263 3384	0.0270 7632	48
49	0.0244 6292	0.0251 8265	0.0259 1474	0.0266 5910	49
50	0.0240 5787	0.0247 7900	0.0255 1273	0.0262 5898	50

n	$\frac{3}{4}\%$	$\frac{7}{8}\%$	1%	$1\frac{1}{8}\%$	n
51	0.0236 6888	0.0243 9142	0.0251 2680	0.0258 7494	51
52	0.0232 9503	0.0240 1899	0.0247 5603	0.0255 0606	52
53	0.0229 3546	0.0236 6084	0.0243 9956	0.0251 5149	53
54	0.0225 8938	0.0233 1619	0.0240 5658	0.0248 1043	54
55	0.0222 5605	0.0229 8430	0.0237 2637	0.0244 8213	55
56	0.0219 3478	0.0226 6449	0.0234 0823	0.0241 6592	56
57	0.0216 2496	0.0223 5611	0.0231 0156	0.0238 6116	57
58	0.0213 2597	0.0220 5858	0.0228 0573	0.0235 6726	58
59	0.0210 3727	0.0217 7135	0.0225 2020	0.0232 8366	59
60	0.0207 5836	0.0214 9390	0.0222 4445	0.0230 0985	60
61	0.0204 8873	0.0212 2575	0.0219 7800	0.0227 4534	61
62	0.0202 2795	0.0209 6644	0.0217 2041	0.0224 8969	62
63	0.0199 7560	0.0207 1557	0.0214 7125	0.0222 4247	63
64	0.0197 3127	0.0204 7273	0.0212 3013	0.0220 0329	64
65	0.0194 9460	0.0202 3754	0.0209 9667	0.0217 7178	65
66	0.0192 6524	0.0200 0968	0.0207 7052	0.0215 4758	66
67	0.0190 4286	0.0197 8879	0.0205 5136	0.0213 3037	67
68	0.0188 2716	0.0195 7459	0.0203 3888	0.0211 1985	68
69	0.0186 1785	0.0193 6677	0.0201 3280	0.0209 1571	69
70	0.0184 1464	0.0191 6506	0.0199 3282	0.0207 1769	70
71	0.0182 1728	0.0189 6921	0.0197 3870	0.0205 2552	71
72	0.0180 2554	0.0187 7897	0.0195 5019	0.0203 3896	72
73	0.0178 3917	0.0185 9411	0.0193 6706	0.0201 5779	73
74	0.0176 5796	0.0184 1441	0.0191 8910	0.0199 8177	74
75	0.0174 8170	0.0182 3966	0.0190 1609	0.0198 1072	75
76	0.0173 1020	0.0180 6967	0.0188 4784	0.0196 4442	76
77	0.0171 4328	0.0179 0426	0.0186 8416	0.0194 8269	77
78	0.0169 8074	0.0177 4324	0.0185 2488	0.0193 2536	78
79	0.0168 2244	0.0175 8645	0.0183 6984	0.0191 7226	79
80	0.0166 6821	0.0174 3374	0.0182 1885	0.0190 2323	80
81	0.0165 1790	0.0172 8494	0.0180 7180	0.0188 7812	81
82	0.0163 7136	0.0171 3992	0.0179 2851	0.0187 3678	82
83	0.0162 2847	0.0169 9854	0.0177 8886	0.0185 9908	83
84	0.0160 8908	0.0168 6067	0.0176 5273	0.0184 6489	84
85	0.0159 5308	0.0167 2619	0.0175 1998	0.0183 3409	85
86	0.0158 2034	0.0165 9497	0.0173 9050	0.0182 0654	86
87	0.0156 9076	0.0164 6691	0.0172 6417	0.0180 8215	87
88	0.0155 6423	0.0163 4190	0.0171 4089	0.0179 6081	88
89	0.0154 4064	0.0162 1982	0.0170 2056	0.0178 4240	89
90	0.0153 1989	0.0161 0060	0.0169 0306	0.0177 2684	90
91	0.0152 0190	0.0159 8413	0.0167 8832	0.0176 1403	91
92	0.0150 8657	0.0158 7031	0.0166 7624	0.0175 0387	92
93	0.0149 7382	0.0157 5908	0.0165 6673	0.0173 9629	93
94	0.0148 6356	0.0156 5033	0.0164 5971	0.0172 9119	94
95	0.0147 5571	0.0155 4401	0.0163 5511	0.0171 8851	95
96	0.0146 5020	0.0154 4002	0.0162 5284	0.0170 8816	96
97	0.0145 4696	0.0153 3829	0.0161 5284	0.0169 9007	97
98	0.0144 4592	0.0152 3877	0.0160 5503	0.0168 9418	98
99	0.0143 4701	0.0151 4137	0.0159 5936	0.0168 0041	99
100	0.0142 5017	0.0150 4604	0.0158 6574	0.0167 0870	100

n	$\frac{3}{4}\%$	$\frac{7}{8}\%$	1%	$1\frac{1}{8}\%$	n
101	0.0141 5533	0.0149 5271	0.0157 7413	0.0166 1899	101
102	0.0140 6243	0.0148 6133	0.0156 8446	0.0165 3122	102
103	0.0139 7143	0.0147 7184	0.0155 9668	0.0164 4534	103
104	0.0138 8226	0.0146 8418	0.0155 1073	0.0163 6128	104
105	0.0137 9487	0.0145 9830	0.0154 2656	0.0162 7900	105
106	0.0137 0922	0.0145 1415	0.0153 4412	0.0161 9844	106
107	0.0136 2524	0.0144 3169	0.0152 6336	0.0161 1956	107
108	0.0135 4291	0.0143 5086	0.0151 8423	0.0160 4231	108
109	0.0134 6217	0.0142 7162	0.0151 0669	0.0159 6665	109
110	0.0133 8296	0.0141 9393	0.0150 3069	0.0158 9252	110
111	0.0133 0527	0.0141 1774	0.0149 5620	0.0158 1990	111
112	0.0132 2905	0.0140 4301	0.0148 8317	0.0157 4873	112
113	0.0131 5425	0.0139 6971	0.0148 1156	0.0156 7898	113
114	0.0130 8084	0.0138 9780	0.0147 4133	0.0156 1061	114
115	0.0130 0878	0.0138 2724	0.0146 7245	0.0155 4358	115
116	0.0129 3803	0.0137 5799	0.0146 0488	0.0154 7786	116
117	0.0128 6857	0.0136 9003	0.0145 3860	0.0154 1342	117
118	0.0128 0037	0.0136 2331	0.0144 7356	0.0153 5022	118
119	0.0127 3338	0.0135 5781	0.0144 0973	0.0152 8824	119
120	0.0126 6758	0.0134 9350	0.0143 4709	0.0152 2743	120
121	0.0126 0294	0.0134 3034	0.0142 8561	0.0151 6777	121
122	0.0125 3942	0.0133 6832	0.0142 2525	0.0151 0924	122
123	0.0124 7702	0.0133 0740	0.0141 6599	0.0150 5179	123
124	0.0124 1568	0.0132 4754	0.0141 0780	0.0149 9542	124
125	0.0123 5540	0.0131 8874	0.0140 5065	0.0149 4008	125
126	0.0122 9614	0.0131 3096	0.0139 9452	0.0148 8576	126
127	0.0122 3788	0.0130 7418	0.0139 3939	0.0148 3244	127
128	0.0121 8060	0.0130 1838	0.0138 8524	0.0147 8008	128
129	0.0121 2428	0.0129 6352	0.0138 3203	0.0147 2866	129
130	0.0120 6888	0.0129 0960	0.0137 7975	0.0146 7817	130
131	0.0120 1440	0.0128 5659	0.0137 2837	0.0146 2858	131
132	0.0119 6080	0.0128 0446	0.0136 7788	0.0145 7987	132
133	0.0119 0808	0.0127 5320	0.0136 2825	0.0145 3202	133
134	0.0118 5621	0.0127 0279	0.0135 7947	0.0144 8501	134
135	0.0118 0516	0.0126 5321	0.0135 3151	0.0144 3882	135
136	0.0117 5493	0.0126 0444	0.0134 8437	0.0143 9343	136
137	0.0117 0550	0.0125 5646	0.0134 3801	0.0143 4883	137
138	0.0116 5684	0.0125 0926	0.0133 9242	0.0143 0499	138
139	0.0116 0894	0.0124 6281	0.0133 4759	0.0142 6190	139
140	0.0115 6179	0.0124 1711	0.0133 0349	0.0142 1955	140
141	0.0115 1536	0.0123 7213	0.0132 6012	0.0141 7792	141
142	0.0114 6965	0.0123 2787	0.0132 1746	0.0141 3699	142
143	0.0114 2464	0.0122 8430	0.0131 7549	0.0140 9674	143
144	0.0113 8031	0.0122 4141	0.0131 3419	0.0140 5717	144
145	0.0113 3664	0.0121 9918	0.0130 9356	0.0140 1826	145
146	0.0112 9364	0.0121 5761	0.0130 5358	0.0139 7999	146
147	0.0112 5127	0.0121 1668	0.0130 1423	0.0139 4235	147
148	0.0112 0953	0.0120 7638	0.0129 7551	0.0139 0533	148
149	0.0111 6841	0.0120 3669	0.0129 3739	0.0138 6891	149
150	0.0111 2790	0.0119 9760	0.0128 9988	0.0138 3309	150

n	$1\frac{1}{4}\%$	$1\frac{3}{8}\%$	$1\frac{1}{2}\%$	$1\frac{3}{4}\%$	n
1	1.0125 0000	1.0137 5000	1.0150 0000	1.0175 0000	1
2	0.5093 9441	0.5103 3597	0.5112 7792	0.5131 6295	2
3	0.3417 0117	0.3425 4173	0.3433 8296	0.3450 6746	3
4	0.2578 6102	0.2586 5243	0.2594 4478	0.2610 3237	4
5	0.2075 6211	0.2083 2510	0.2090 8932	0.2106 2142	5
6	0.1740 3381	0.1747 7877	0.1755 2521	0.1770 2256	6
7	0.1500 8872	0.1508 2157	0.1515 5616	0.1530 3059	7
8	0.1321 3314	0.1328 5758	0.1335 8402	0.1350 4292	8
9	0.1181 7055	0.1188 8906	0.1196 0982	0.1210 5813	9
10	0.1070 0307	0.1077 1737	0.1084 3418	0.1098 7534	10
11	0.0978 6839	0.0985 7973	0.0992 9384	0.1007 3038	11
12	0.0902 5831	0.0909 6764	0.0916 7999	0.0931 1377	12
13	0.0838 2100	0.0845 2903	0.0852 4036	0.0866 7283	13
14	0.0783 0515	0.0790 1246	0.0797 2332	0.0811 5562	14
15	0.0735 2646	0.0742 3351	0.0749 4436	0.0763 7739	15
16	0.0693 4672	0.0700 5388	0.0707 6508	0.0721 9958	16
17	0.0656 6023	0.0663 6780	0.0670 7966	0.0685 1623	17
18	0.0623 8479	0.0630 9301	0.0638 0578	0.0652 4492	18
19	0.0594 5548	0.0601 6457	0.0608 7847	0.0623 2061	19
20	0.0568 2039	0.0575 3054	0.0582 4574	0.0596 9122	20
21	0.0544 3748	0.0551 4884	0.0558 6550	0.0573 1464	21
22	0.0522 7238	0.0529 8507	0.0537 0331	0.0551 5638	22
23	0.0502 9666	0.0510 1080	0.0517 3075	0.0531 8796	23
24	0.0484 8665	0.0492 0235	0.0499 2410	0.0513 8565	24
25	0.0468 2247	0.0475 3981	0.0482 6345	0.0497 2952	25
26	0.0452 8729	0.0460 0635	0.0467 3196	0.0482 0269	26
27	0.0438 6677	0.0445 8763	0.0453 1527	0.0467 9079	27
28	0.0425 4863	0.0432 7134	0.0440 0108	0.0454 8151	28
29	0.0413 2228	0.0420 4639	0.0427 7878	0.0442 6424	29
30	0.0401 7854	0.0409 0511	0.0416 3919	0.0431 2975	30
31	0.0391 0942	0.0398 3798	0.0405 7430	0.0420 7005	31
32	0.0381 0791	0.0388 3850	0.0395 7710	0.0410 7812	32
33	0.0371 6786	0.0379 0053	0.0386 4144	0.0401 4779	33
34	0.0362 8387	0.0370 1864	0.0377 6189	0.0392 7363	34
35	0.0354 5111	0.0361 8801	0.0369 3363	0.0384 5082	35
36	0.0346 6533	0.0354 0438	0.0361 5240	0.0376 7507	36
37	0.0339 2270	0.0346 6394	0.0354 1437	0.0369 4257	37
38	0.0332 1983	0.0339 6327	0.0347 1613	0.0362 4990	38
39	0.0325 5365	0.0332 9931	0.0340 5463	0.0355 9399	39
40	0.0319 2141	0.0326 6931	0.0334 2710	0.0349 7209	40
41	0.0313 2063	0.0320 7078	0.0328 3106	0.0343 8170	41
42	0.0307 4906	0.0315 0148	0.0322 6426	0.0338 2057	42
43	0.0302 0466	0.0309 5936	0.0317 2465	0.0332 8666	43
44	0.0296 8557	9.0304 4257	0.0312 1038	0.0327 7810	44
45	0.0291 9012	0.0299 4941	0.0307 1976	0.0322 9321	45
46	0.0287 1675	0.0294 7836	0.0302 5125	0.0318 3043	46
47	0.0282 6406	0.0290 2799	0.0298 0342	0.0313 8836	47
48	0.0278 3075	0.0285 9701	0.0293 7500	0.0309 6569	48
49	0.0274 1563	0.0281 8424	0.0289 6478	0.0305 6124	49
50	0.0270 1763	0.0277 8857	0.0285 7168	0.0301 7391	50

n	1¼%	1⅜%	1½%	1¾%	*n*
51	0.0266 3571	0.0274 0900	0.0281 9469	0.0298 0269	51
52	0.0262 6897	0.0270 4461	0.0278 3287	0.0294 4665	52
53	0.0259 1653	0.0266 9453	0.0274 8537	0.0291 0492	53
54	0.0255 7760	0.0263 5797	0.0271 5138	0.0287 7672	54
55	0.0252 5145	0.0260 3418	0.0268 3018	0.0284 6129	55
56	0.0249 3739	0.0257 2249	0.0265 2106	0.0281 5795	56
57	0.0246 3478	0.0254 2225	0.0262 2341	0.0278 6606	57
58	0.0243 4303	0.0251 3287	0.0259 3661	0.0275 8503	58
59	0.0240 6158	0.0248 5380	0.0256 6012	0.0273 1430	59
60	0.0237 8993	0.0245 8452	0.0253 9343	0.0270 5336	60
61	0.0235 2758	0.0243 2455	0.0251 3604	0.0268 0172	61
62	0.0232 7410	0.0240 7344	0.0248 8751	0.0265 5892	62
63	0.0230 2904	0.0238 3076	0.0246 4741	0.0263 2455	63
64	0.0227 9203	0.0235 9612	0.0244 1534	0.0260 9821	64
65	0.0225 6268	0.0233 6914	0.0241 9094	0.0258 7952	65
66	0.0223 4065	0.0231 4949	0.0239 7386	0.0256 6813	66
67	0.0221 2560	0.0229 3682	0.0237 6376	0.0254 6372	67
68	0.0219 1724	0.0227 3082	0.0235 6033	0.0252 6596	68
69	0.0217 1527	0.0225 3122	0.0233 6329	0.0250 7459	69
70	0.0215 1941	0.0223 3773	0.0231 7235	0.0248 8930	70
71	0.0213 2941	0.0221 5009	0.0229 8727	0.0247 0985	71
72	0.0211 4501	0.0219 6806	0.0228 0779	0.0245 3600	72
73	0.0209 6600	0.0217 9140	0.0226 3368	0.0243 6750	73
74	0.0207 9215	0.0216 1991	0.0224 6473	0.0242 0413	74
75	0.0206 2325	0.0214 5336	0.0223 0072	0.0240 4570	75
76	0.0204 5910	0.0212 9157	0.0221 4146	0.0238 9200	76
77	0.0202 9953	0.0211 3435	0.0219 8676	0.0237 4284	77
78	0.0201 4435	0.0209 8151	0.0218 3645	0.0235 9806	78
79	0.0199 9341	0.0208 3290	0.0216 9036	0.0234 5748	79
80	0.0198 4652	0.0206 8836	0.0215 4832	0.0233 2093	80
81	0.0197 0356	0.0205 4772	0.0214 1019	0.0231 8828	81
82	0.0195 6437	0.0204 1086	0.0212 7583	0.0230 5936	82
83	0.0194 2881	0.0202 7762	0.0211 4509	0.0229 3406	83
84	0.0192 9675	0.0201 4789	0.0210 1784	0.0228 1223	84
85	0.0191 6808	0.0200 2153	0.0208 9396	0.0226 9375	85
86	0.0190 4267	0.0198 9843	0.0207 7333	0.0225 7850	86
87	0.0189 2041	0.0197 7847	0.0206 5584	0.0224 6636	87
88	0.0188 0119	0.0196 6155	0.0205 4138	0.0223 5724	88
89	0.0186 8490	0.0195 4756	0.0204 2984	0.0222 5102	89
90	0.0185 7146	0.0194 3641	0.0203 2113	0.0221 4760	90
91	0.0184 6076	0.0193 2799	0.0202 1516	0.0220 4690	91
92	0.0183 5271	0.0192 2222	0.0201 1182	0.0219 4882	92
93	0.0182 4724	0.0191 1902	0.0200 1104	0.0218 5327	93
94	0.0181 4425	0.0190 1829	0.0199 1273	0.0217 6017	94
95	0.0180 4366	0.0189 1997	0.0198 1681	0.0216 6944	95
96	0.0179 4540	0.0188 2397	0.0197 2321	0.0215 8101	96
97	0.0178 4941	0.0187 3022	0.0196 3186	0.0214 9480	97
98	0.0177 5560	0.0186 3866	0.0195 4268	0.0214 1074	98
99	0.0176 6391	0.0185 4921	0.0194 5560	0.0213 2876	99
100	0.0175 7428	0.0184 6181	0.0193 7057	0.0212 4880	100

n	2%	2¼%	2½%	2¾%	n
1	1.0200 0000	1.0225 0000	1.0250 0000	1.0275 0000	1
2	0.5150 4950	0.5169 3758	0.5188 2716	0.5207 1825	2
3	0.3467 5467	0.3484 4458	0.3501 3717	0.3518 3243	3
4	0.2626 2375	0.2642 1893	0.2658 1788	0.2674 2059	4
5	0.2121 5839	0.2137 0021	0.2152 4686	0.2167 9832	5
6	0.1785 2581	0.1800 3496	0.1815 4997	0.1830 7083	6
7	0.1545 1196	0.1560 0025	0.1574 9543	0.1589 9747	7
8	0.1365 0980	0.1379 8462	0.1394 6735	0.1409 5795	8
9	0.1225 1544	0.1239 8170	0.1254 5689	0.1269 4095	9
10	0.1113 2653	0.1127 8768	0.1142 5876	0.1157 3972	10
11	0.1021 7794	0.1036 3649	0.1051 0596	0.1065 8629	11
12	0.0945 5960	0.0960 1740	0.0974 8713	0.0989 6871	12
13	0.0881 1835	0.0895 7686	0.0910 4827	0.0925 3252	13
14	0.0826 0197	0.0840 6230	0.0855 3653	0.0870 2457	14
15	0.0778 2547	0.0792 8852	0.0807 6646	0.0822 5917	15
16	0.0736 5013	0.0751 1663	0.0765 9899	0.0780 9710	16
17	0.0699 6984	0.0714 4039	0.0729 2777	0.0744 3186	17
18	0.0667 0210	0.0681 7720	0.0696 7008	0.0711 8063	18
19	0.0637 8177	0.0652 6182	0.0667 6062	0.0682 7802	19
20	0.0611 5672	0.0626 4207	0.0641 4713	0.0656 7173	20
21	0.0587 8477	0.0602 7572	0.0617 8733	0.0633 1941	21
22	0.0566 3140	0.0581 2821	0.0596 4661	0.0611 8640	22
23	0.0546 6810	0.0561 7097	0.0576 9638	0.0592 4410	23
24	0.0528 7110	0.0543 8023	0.0559 1282	0.0574 6863	24
25	0.0512 2044	0.0527 3599	0.0542 7592	0.0558 3997	25
26	0.0496 9923	0.0512 2134	0.0527 6875	0.0543 4116	26
27	0.0482 9309	0.0498 2188	0.0513 7687	0.0529 5776	27
28	0.0469 8967	0.0485 2525	0.0500 8793	0.0516 7738	28
29	0.0457 7836	0.0473 2081	0.0488 9127	0.0504 8935	29
30	0.0446 4992	0.0461 9934	0.0477 7764	0.0493 8442	30
31	0.0435 9635	0.0451 5280	0.0467 3900	0.0483 5453	31
32	0.0426 1061	0.0441 7415	0.0457 6831	0.0473 9263	32
33	0.0416 8653	0.0432 5722	0.0448 5938	0.0464 9253	33
34	0.0408 1867	0.0423 9655	0.0440 0675	0.0456 4875	34
35	0.0400 0221	0.0415 8731	0.0432 0558	0.0448 5645	35
36	0.0392 3285	0.0408 2522	0.0424 5158	0.0441 1132	36
37	0.0385 0678	0.0401 0643	0.0417 4090	0.0434 0953	37
38	0.0378 2057	0.0394 2753	0.0410 7012	0.0427 4764	38
39	0.0371 7114	0.0387 8543	0.0404 3615	0.0421 2256	39
40	0.0365 5575	0.0381 7738	0.0398 3623	0.0415 3151	40
41	0.0359 7188	0.0376 0087	0.0392 6786	0.0409 7200	41
42	0.0354 1729	0.0370 5364	0.0387 2876	0.0404 4175	42
43	0.0348 8993	0.0365 3364	0.0382 1688	0.0399 3871	43
44	0.0343 8794	0.0360 3901	0.0377 3037	0.0394 6100	44
45	0.0339 0962	0.0355 6805	0.0372 6752	0.0390 0693	45
46	0.0334 5342	0.0351 1921	0.0368 2676	0.0385 7493	46
47	0.0330 1792	0.0346 9107	0.0364 0669	0.0381 6358	47
48	0.0326 0184	0.0342 8233	0.0360 0599	0.0377 7158	48
49	0.0322 0396	0.0338 9179	0.0356 2348	0.0373 9773	49
50	0.0318 2321	0.0335 1836	0.0352 5806	0.0370 4092	50

n	2%	$2\frac{1}{4}\%$	$2\frac{1}{2}\%$	$2\frac{3}{4}\%$	n
51	0.0314 5856	0.0331 6102	0.0349 0870	0.0367 0014	51
52	0.0311 0909	0.0328 1884	0.0345 7446	0.0363 7444	52
53	0.0307 7392	0.0324 9094	0.0342 5449	0.0360 6297	53
54	0.0304 5226	0.0321 7654	0.0339 4799	0.0357 6491	54
55	0.0301 4337	0.0318 7489	0.0336 5419	0.0354 7953	55
56	0.0298 4656	0.0315 8530	0.0333 7243	0.0352 0612	56
57	0.0295 6120	0.0313 0712	0.0331 0204	0.0349 4404	57
58	0.0292 8667	0.0310 3977	0.0328 4244	0.0346 9270	58
59	0.0290 2243	0.0307 8268	0.0325 9307	0.0344 5153	59
60	0.0287 6797	0.0305 3533	0.0323 5340	0.0342 2002	60
61	0.0285 2278	0.0302 9724	0.0321 2294	0.0339 9767	61
62	0.0282 8643	0.0300 6795	0.0319 0126	0.0337 8402	62
63	0.0280 5848	0.0298 4704	0.0316 8790	0.0335 7866	63
64	0.0278 3855	0.0296 3411	0.0314 8249	0.0333 8118	64
65	0.0276 2624	0.0294 2878	0.0312 8463	0.0331 9120	65
66	0.0274 2122	0.0292 3070	0.0310 9398	0.0330 0837	66
67	0.0272 2316	0.0290 3955	0.0309 1021	0.0328 3236	67
68	0.0270 3173	0.0288 5500	0.0307 3300	0.0326 6285	68
69	0.0268 4665	0.0286 7677	0.0305 6206	0.0324 9955	69
70	0.0266 6765	0.0285 0458	0.0303 9712	0.0323 4218	70
71	0.0264 9446	0.0283 3816	0.0302 3790	0.0321 9048	71
72	0.0263 2683	0.0281 7728	0.0300 8417	0.0320 4420	72
73	0.0261 6454	0.0280 2169	0.0299 3568	0.0319 0311	73
74	0.0260 0736	0.0278 7118	0.0297 9222	0.0317 6698	74
75	0.0258 5508	0.0277 2554	0.0296 5358	0.0316 3560	75
76	0.0257 0751	0.0275 8457	0.0295 1956	0.0315 0878	76
77	0.0255 6447	0.0274 4808	0.0293 8997	0.0313 8633	77
78	0.0254 2576	0.0273 1589	0.0292 6463	0.0312 6806	78
79	0.0252 9123	0.0271 8784	0.0291 4338	0.0311 5382	79
80	0.0251 6071	0.0270 6376	0.0290 2605	0.0310 4342	80
81	0.0250 3405	0.0269 4350	0.0289 1248	0.0309 3674	81
82	0.0249 1110	0.0268 2692	0.0288 0254	0.0308 3361	82
83	0.0247 9173	0.0267 1387	0.0286 9608	0.0307 3389	83
84	0.0246 7581	0.0266 0423	0.0285 9298	0.0306 3747	84
85	0.0245 6321	0.0264 9787	0.0284 9310	0.0305 4420	85
86	0.0244 5381	0.0263 9467	0.0283 9633	0.0304 5397	86
87	0.0243 4750	0.0262 9452	0.0283 0255	0.0303 6667	87
88	0.0242 4416	0.0261 9730	0.0282 1165	0.0302 8219	88
89	0.0241 4370	0.0261 0291	0.0281 2353	0.0302 0041	89
90	0.0240 4602	0.0260 1126	0.0280 3809	0.0301 2125	90
91	0.0239 5101	0.0259 2224	0.0279 5523	0.0300 4460	91
92	0.0238 5859	0.0258 3577	0.0278 7486	0.0299 7038	92
93	0.0237 6868	0.0257 5176	0.0277 9690	0.0298 9850	93
94	0.0236 8118	0.0256 7012	0.0277 2126	0.0298 2887	94
95	0.0235 9602	0.0255 9078	0.0276 4786	0.0297 6141	95
96	0.0235 1313	0.0255 1366	0.0275 7662	0.0296 9605	96
97	0.0234 3242	0.0254 3868	0.0275 0747	0.0296 3272	97
98	0.0233 5383	0.0253 6578	0.0274 4034	0.0295 7134	98
99	0.0232 7729	0.0252 9489	0.0273 7517	0.0295 1185	99
100	0.0232 0274	0.0252 2594	0.0273 1188	0.0294 5418	100

n	3%	$3\frac{1}{2}$%	4%	$4\frac{1}{2}$%	n
1	1.0300 0000	1.0350 0000	1.0400 0000	1.0450 0000	1
2	0.5226 1084	0.5264 0049	0.5301 9608	0.5339 9756	2
3	0.3535 3036	0.3569 3418	0.3603 4854	0.3637 7336	3
4	0.2690 2705	0.2722 5114	0.2754 9005	0.2787 4365	4
5	0.2183 5457	0.2214 8137	0.2246 2711	0.2277 9164	5
6	0.1845 9750	0.1876 6821	0.1907 6190	0.1938 7839	6
7	0.1605 0635	0.1635 4449	0.1666 0961	0.1697 0147	7
8	0.1424 5639	0.1454 7665	0.1485 2783	0.1516 0965	8
9	0.1284 3386	0.1314 4601	0.1344 9299	0.1375 7447	9
10	0.1172 3051	0.1202 4137	0.1232 9094	0.1263 7882	10
11	0.1080 7745	0.1110 9197	0.1141 4904	0.1172 4818	11
12	0.1004 6209	0.1034 8395	0.1065 5217	0.1096 6619	12
13	0.0940 2954	0.0970 6157	0.1001 4373	0.1032 7535	13
14	0.0885 2634	0.0915 7073	0.0946 6897	0.0978 2032	14
15	0.0837 6658	0.0868 2507	0.0899 4110	0.0931 1381	15
16	0.0796 1085	0.0826 8483	0.0858 2000	0.0890 1537	16
17	0.0759 5253	0.0790 4313	0.0821 9852	0.0854 1758	17
18	0.0727 0870	0.0758 1684	0.0789 9333	0.0822 3690	18
19	0.0698 1388	0.0729 4033	0.0761 3862	0.0794 0734	19
20	0.0672 1571	0.0703 6108	0.0735 8175	0.0768 7614	20
21	0.0648 7178	0.0680 3659	0.0712 8011	0.0746 0057	21
22	0.0627 4739	0.0659 3207	0.0691 9881	0.0725 4565	22
23	0.0608 1390	0.0640 1880	0.0673 0906	0.0706 8249	23
24	0.0590 4742	0.0622 7283	0.0655 8683	0.0689 8703	24
25	0.0574 2787	0.0606 7404	0.0640 1196	0.0674 3903	25
26	0.0559 3829	0.0592 0540	0.0625 6738	0.0650 2137	26
27	0.0545 6421	0.0578 5241	0.0612 3854	0.0647 1946	27
28	0.0532 9323	0.0566 0265	0.0600 1298	0.0635 2081	28
29	0.0521 1467	0.0554 4538	0.0588 7993	0.0624 1461	29
30	0.0510 1926	0.0543 7133	0.0578 3010	0.0613 9154	30
31	0.0499 9893	0.0533 7240	0.0568 5535	0.0604 4345	31
32	0.0490 4662	0.0524 4150	0.0559 4859	0.0595 6320	32
33	0.0481 5612	0.0515 7242	0.0551 0357	0.0587 4453	33
34	0.0473 2196	0.0507 5966	0.0543 1477	0.0579 8191	34
35	0.0465 3929	0.0499 9835	0.0535 7732	0.0572 7045	35
36	0.0458 0379	0.0492 8416	0.0528 8688	0.0566 0578	36
37	0.0451 1162	0.0486 1325	0.0522 3957	0.0559 8402	37
38	0.0444 5934	0.0479 8214	0.0516 3192	0.0554 0169	38
39	0.0438 4385	0.0473 8775	0.0510 6083	0.0548 5567	39
40	0.0432 6238	0.0468 2728	0.0505 2349	0.0543 4315	40
41	0.0427 1241	0.0462 9822	0.0500 1738	0.0538 6158	41
42	0.0421 9167	0.0457 9828	0.0495 4020	0.0534 0868	42
43	0.0416 9811	0.0453 2539	0.0490 8989	0.0529 8235	43
44	0.0412 2985	0.0448 7768	0.0486 6454	0.0525 8071	44
45	0.0407 8518	0.0444 5343	0.0482 6246	0.0522 0202	45
46	0.0403 6254	0.0440 5108	0.0478 8205	0.0518 4471	46
47	0.0099 6051	0.0436 6919	0.0475 2189	0.0515 0734	47
48	0.0395 7777	0.0433 0646	0.0471 8065	0.0511 8858	48
49	0.0392 1314	0.0429 6167	0.0468 5712	0.0508 8722	49
50	0.0388 6550	0.0426 3371	0.0465 5020	0.0506 0215	50

n	3%	3½%	4%	4½%	*n*
51	0.0385 3382	0.0423 2156	0.0462 5885	0.0503 3232	51
52	0.0382 1718	0.0420 2429	0.0459 8212	0.0500 7679	52
53	0.0379 1471	0.0417 4100	0.0457 1915	0.0498 3469	53
54	0.0376 2558	0.0414 7090	0.0454 6910	0.0496 0519	54
55	0.0373 4907	0.0412 1323	0.0452 3124	0.0493 8754	55
56	0.0370 8447	0.0409 6730	0.0450 0487	0.0491 8105	56
57	0.0368 3114	0.0407 3245	0.0447 8932	0.0489 8506	57
58	0.0365 8848	0.0405 0810	0.0445 8401	0.0487 9897	58
59	0.0363 5593	0.0402 9366	0.0443 8836	0.0486 2221	59
60	0.0361 3296	0.0400 8862	0.0442 0185	0.0484 5426	60
61	0.0359 1908	0.0398 9249	0.0440 2398	0.0482 9462	61
62	0.0357 1385	0.0397 0480	0.0438 5430	0.0481 4284	62
63	0.0355 1682	0.0395 2513	0.0436 9237	0.0479 9848	63
64	0.0353 2760	0.0393 5308	0.0435 3780	0.0478 6115	64
65	0.0351 4581	0.0391 8826	0.0433 9019	0.0477 3047	65
66	0.0349 7110	0.0390 3031	0.0432 4921	0.0476 0608	66
67	0.0348 0313	0.0388 7892	0.0431 1451	0.0474 8765	67
68	0.0346 4159	0.0387 3375	0.0429 8578	0.0473 7487	68
69	0.0344 8618	0.0385 9453	0.0428 6272	0.0472 6745	69
70	0.0343 3663	0.0384 6095	0.0427 4506	0.0471 6511	70
71	0.0341 9266	0.0383 3277	0.0426 3253	0.0470 6759	71
72	0.0340 5404	0.0382 0973	0.0425 2489	0.0469 7465	72
73	0.0339 2053	0.0380 9160	0.0424 2190	0.0468 8606	73
74	0.0337 9191	0.0379 7816	0.0423 2334	0.0468 0159	74
75	0.0336 6796	0.0378 6919	0.0422 2900	0.0467 2104	75
76	0.0335 4849	0.0377 6450	0.0421 3869	0.0466 4422	76
77	0.0334 3331	0.0376 6390	0.0420 5221	0.0465 7094	77
78	0.0333 2224	0.0375 6721	0.0419 6939	0.0465 0104	78
79	0.0332 1510	0.0374 7426	0.0418 9007	0.0464 3434	79
80	0.0331 1175	0.0373 8489	0.0418 1408	0.0463 7069	80
81	0.0330 1201	0.0372 9894	0.0417 4127	0.0463 0995	81
82	0.0329 1576	0.0372 1628	0.0416 7150	0.0462 5197	82
83	0.0328 2284	0.0371 3676	0.0416 0463	0.0461 9663	83
84	0.0327 3313	0.0370 6025	0.0415 4054	0.0461 4379	84
85	0.0326 4650	0.0369 8662	0.0414 7909	0.0460 9334	85
86	0.0325 6284	0.0369 1576	0.0414 2018	0.0460 4516	86
87	0.0324 8202	0.0368 4756	0.0413 6370	0.0459 9915	87
88	0.0324 0393	0.0367 8190	0.0413 0953	0.0459 5522	88
89	0.0323 2848	0.0367 1868	0.0412 5758	0.0459 1325	89
90	0.0322 5556	0.0366 5781	0.0412 0775	0.0458 7316	90
91	0.0321 8508	0.0365 9919	0.0411 5995	0.0458 3486	91
92	0.0321 1694	0.0365 4273	0.0411 1410	0.0457 9827	92
93	0.0320 5107	0.0364 8834	0.0410 7010	0.0457 6331	93
94	0.0319 8737	0.0364 3594	0.0410 2789	0.0457 2991	94
95	0.0319 2577	0.0363 8546	0.0409 8738	0.0456 9799	95
96	0.0318 6619	0.0363 3682	0.0409 4850	0.0456 6749	96
97	0.0318 0856	0.0362 8995	0.0409 1119	0.0456 3834	97
98	0.0317 5281	0.0362 4478	0.0408 7538	0.0456 1048	98
99	0.0316 9886	0.0362 0124	0.0408 4100	0.0455 8385	99
100	0.0316 4667	0.0361 5927	0.0408 0800	0.0455 5839	100

n	5%	5½%	6%	6½%	n
1	1.0500 0000	1.0550 0000	1.0600 0000	1.0650 0000	1
2	0.5378 0488	0.5416 1800	0.5454 3689	0.5492 6150	2
3	0.3672 0856	0.3706 5407	0.3741 0981	0.3775 7570	3
4	0.2820 1183	0.2852 9449	0.2885 9149	0.2919 0274	4
5	0.2309 7480	0.2341 7644	0.2373 9640	0.2406 3454	5
6	0.1970 1747	0.2001 7895	0.2033 6263	0.2065 6831	6
7	0.1728 1982	0.1759 6442	0.1791 3502	0.1823 3137	7
8	0.1547 2181	0.1578 6401	0.1610 3594	0.1642 3730	8
9	0.1406 9008	0.1438 3946	0.1470 2224	0.1502 3803	9
10	0.1295 0458	0.1326 6777	0.1358 6796	0.1391 0469	10
11	0.1203 8889	0.1235 7065	0.1267 9294	0.1300 5521	11
12	0.1128 2541	0.1160 2923	0.1192 7703	0.1225 6817	12
13	0.1064 5577	0.1096 8426	0.1129 6011	0.1162 8256	13
14	0.1010 2397	0.1042 7912	0.1075 8491	0.1109 4048	14
15	0.0963 4229	0.0996 2560	0.1029 6276	0.1063 5278	15
16	0.0922 6991	0.0955 8254	0.0989 5214	0.1023 7757	16
17	0.0886 9914	0.0920 4197	0.0954 4480	0.0989 0633	17
18	0.0855 4622	0.0889 1992	0.0923 5654	0.0958 5461	18
19	0.0827 4501	0.0861 5006	0.0896 2086	0.0931 5575	19
20	0.0802 4259	0.0836 7933	0.0871 8456	0.0907 5640	20
21	0.0779 9611	0.0814 6478	0.0850 0455	0.0886 1333	21
22	0.0759 7051	0.0794 7123	0.0830 4557	0.0866 9120	22
23	0.0741 3682	0.0776 6965	0.0812 7848	0.0849 6078	23
24	0.0724 7090	0.0760 3580	0.0796 7900	0.0833 9770	24
25	0.0709 5246	0.0745 4935	0.0782 2672	0.0819 8148	25
26	0.0695 6432	0.0731 9307	0.0769 0435	0.0806 9480	26
27	0.0682 9186	0.0719 5228	0.0756 9717	0.0795 2288	27
28	0.0671 2253	0.0708 1440	0.0745 9255	0.0784 5305	28
29	0.0660 4551	0.0697 6857	0.0735 7961	0.0774 7440	29
30	0.0650 5144	0.0688 0539	0.0726 4891	0.0765 7744	30
31	0.0641 3212	0.0679 1665	0.0717 9222	0.0757 5393	31
32	0.0632 8042	0.0670 9519	0.0710 0234	0.0749 9665	32
33	0.0624 9004	0.0663 3469	0.0702 7293	0.0742 9924	33
34	0.0617 5545	0.0656 2958	0.0695 9843	0.0736 5610	34
35	0.0610 7171	0.0649 7493	0.0689 7386	0.0730 6226	35
36	0.0604 3446	0.0643 6635	0.0683 9483	0.0725 1332	36
37	0.0598 3979	0.0637 9993	0.0678 5743	0.0720 0534	37
38	0.0592 8423	0.0632 7217	0.0673 5812	0.0715 3480	38
39	0.0587 6462	0.0627 7991	0.0668 9377	0.0710 9854	39
40	0.0582 7816	0.0623 2034	0.0664 6154	0.0706 9373	40
41	0.0578 2229	0.0618 9090	0.0660 5886	0.0703 1779	41
42	0.0573 9471	0.0614 8927	0.0656 8342	0.0699 6842	42
43	0.0569 9333	0.0611 1337	0.0653 3312	0.0696 4352	43
44	0.0566 1625	0.0607 6128	0.0650 0606	0.0693 4119	44
45	0.0562 6173	0.0604 3127	0.0647 0050	0.0690 5968	45
46	0.0559 2820	0.0601 2175	0.0644 1485	0.0687 9743	46
47	0.0556 1421	0.0598 3129	0.0641 4768	0.0685 5300	47
48	0.0553 1843	0.0595 5854	0.0638 9766	0.0683 2506	48
49	0.0550 3965	0.0593 0230	0.0636 6356	0.0681 1240	49
50	0.0547 7674	0.0590 6145	0.0634 4429	0.0679 1393	50

n	5%	5½%	6%	6½%	n
51	0.0545 2867	0.0588 3495	0.0632 3880	0.0677 2861	51
52	0.0542 9450	0.0586 2186	0.0630 4617	0.0675 5553	52
53	0.0540 7334	0.0584 2130	0.0628 6551	0.0673 9382	53
54	0.0538 6438	0.0582 3245	0.0626 9602	0.0672 4267	54
55	0.0536 6686	0.0580 5458	0.0625 3696	0.0671 0137	55
56	0.0534 8010	0.0578 8698	0.0623 8765	0.0669 6923	56
57	0.0533 0343	0.0577 2900	0.0622 4744	0.0668 4563	57
58	0.0531 3626	0.0575 8006	0.0621 1574	0.0667 2999	58
59	0.0529 7802	0.0574 3959	0.0619 9200	0.0666 2177	59
60	0.0528 2818	0.0573 0707	0.0618 7572	0.0665 2047	60
61	0.0526 8627	0.0571 8202	0.0617 6642	0.0664 2564	61
62	0.0525 5183	0.0570 6400	0.0616 6366	0.0663 3684	62
63	0.0524 2442	0.0569 5258	0.0615 6704	0.0662 5367	63
64	0.0523 0365	0.0568 4737	0.0614 7615	0.0661 7577	64
65	0.0521 8915	0.0567 4800	0.0613 9066	0.0661 0280	65
66	0.0520 8057	0.0566 5413	0.0613 1022	0.0660 3442	66
67	0.0519 7757	0.0565 6544	0.0612 3454	0.0659 7034	67
68	0.0518 7986	0.0564 8163	0.0611 6330	0.0659 1029	68
69	0.0517 8715	0.0564 0242	0.0610 9625	0.0658 5400	69
70	0.0516 9915	0.0563 2754	0.0610 3313	0.0658 0124	70
71	0.0516 1563	0.0562 5675	0.0609 7370	0.0657 5177	71
72	0.0515 3633	0.0561 8982	0.0609 1774	0.0657 0539	72
73	0.0514 6103	0.0561 2652	0.0608 6505	0.0656 6190	73
74	0.0513 8953	0.0560 6665	0.0608 1542	0.0656 2112	74
75	0.0513 2161	0.0560 1002	0.0607 6867	0.0655 8287	75
76	0.0512 5709	0.0559 5645	0.0607 2463	0.0655 4699	76
77	0.0511 9580	0.0559 0577	0.0606 8315	0.0655 1335	77
78	0.0511 3756	0.0558 5781	0.0606 4407	0.0654 8178	78
79	0.0510 8222	0.0558 1243	0.0606 0724	0.0654 5217	79
80	0.0510 2962	0.0557 6948	0.0605 7254	0.0654 2440	80
81	0.0509 7963	0.0557 2884	0.0605 3984	0.0653 9834	81
82	0.0509 3211	0.0556 9036	0.0605 0903	0.0653 7388	82
83	0.0508 8694	0.0556 5395	0.0604 7998	0.0653 5094	83
84	0.0508 4399	0.0556 1947	0.0604 5261	0.0653 2941	84
85	0.0508 0316	0.0555 8683	0.0604 2681	0.0653 0921	85
86	0.0507 6433	0.0555 5593	0.0604 0249	0.0652 9026	86
87	0.0507 2740	0.0555 2667	0.0603 7956	0.0652 7247	87
88	0.0506 9228	0.0554 9896	0.0603 5795	0.0652 5577	88
89	0.0506 5888	0.0554 7273	0.0603 3757	0.0652 4010	89
90	0.0506 2711	0.0554 4788	0.0603 1836	0.0652 2540	90
91	0.0505 9689	0.0554 2435	0.0603 0025	0.0652 1160	91
92	0.0505 6815	0.0554 0207	0.0602 8318	0.0651 9864	92
93	0.0505 4080	0.0553 8096	0.0602 6708	0.0651 8649	93
94	0.0505 1478	0.0553 6097	0.0602 5190	0.0651 7507	94
95	0.0504 9003	0.0553 4204	0.0602 3758	0.0651 6436	95
96	0.0504 6648	0.0553 2410	0.0602 2408	0.0651 5431	96
97	0.0504 4407	0.0553 0711	0.0602 1135	0.0651 4487	97
98	0.0504 2274	0.0552 9101	0.0601 9935	0.0651 3601	98
99	0.0504 0245	0.0552 7577	0.0601 8803	0.0651 2769	99
100	0.0503 8314	0.0552 6132	0.0601 7736	0.0651 1988	100

By Table 3, Chapter 6, and rules for characteristics,

$$.204396 \text{ is antilog} \quad 1.601035$$

Then $1.601035 - 1 \quad = .601035$

$$R = (\$5,000.00) \left(\frac{.04}{.601035} \right).$$

$$R = (\$5,000.00)(.0665519) = \$332.76.$$

The foregoing problem can also be solved by the use of Table 13, which gives the amount of an annuity having a periodic payment of $1.00. That is, the table gives the value of $s_{\overline{n}|i}$. But Formula (14-2) for amount of an annuity is,

$$S_n = R s_{\overline{n}|i}$$

Therefore $R = \dfrac{S_n}{s_{\overline{n}|i}}$ (14-9)

In other words, the amount of the periodic payment can be found by dividing the amount of the annuity by the amount of an annuity having a periodic interest rate of 4% and 12 payments of $1.00, which is $15.02580546 from Table 13.

Therefore $R = \dfrac{\$5,000.00}{15.02580546} = \$332.76.$

There is still a third method of finding the periodic payment of an annuity from the amount, interest rate per period and number of periods. That method has the advantage of avoiding division. Its basis is the use of Table 15, by the relationship between $\dfrac{1}{a_{\overline{n}|i}}$ and $\dfrac{1}{s_{\overline{n}|i}}$, which is found as follows:

Formula (14-7) is, $\dfrac{1}{a_{\overline{n}|i}} = \dfrac{i}{1 - (1 + i)^{-n}}$

Multiplying numerator and denominator by $(1 + i)^n$

$$\frac{1}{a_{\overline{n}|i}} = \frac{i(1 + i)^n}{(1 + i)^n - 1}$$

Formula (14-2) is, $\dfrac{1}{s_{\overline{n}|i}} = \dfrac{i}{(1 + i)^n - 1}$

Therefore $\dfrac{1}{a_{\overline{n}|i}} - \dfrac{1}{s_{\overline{n}|i}} = \dfrac{i(1 + i)^n}{(1 + i)^n - 1} - \dfrac{i}{(1 + i)^n - 1} = \dfrac{i(1 + i)^n - i}{(1 + i)^n - 1}$

Factoring numerator of fraction, and dividing it by denominator,

$$\frac{1}{a_{\overline{n}|i}} - \frac{1}{s_{\overline{n}|i}} = \frac{i[(1 + i)^n - 1]}{(1 + i)^n - 1} = i$$ (14-10)

Therefore to find $\dfrac{1}{s_{\overline{n}|i}}$ from $\dfrac{1}{a_{\overline{n}|i}}$, simply subtract i, the interest rate per period. Therefore, Table 15 which gives the periodic payment of an annuity having a present value of $1.00 can be used to find the periodic payment of an annuity having an amount of $1.00, simply by subtracting the interest rate per period.

The method is illustrated by its application to the example already solved by the other methods: To find the annual payment required to accumulate a fund of $5,000.00 in 12 years, if payments start at the end of the first year and bear 4% interest, compounded annually.

From Table 15, the periodic payment of an annuity of 12 periods at 4% with a present value of $1.00 is $.10655217 $= \dfrac{1}{a_{\overline{n}|i}}$

But from above relationship $\dfrac{1}{a_{\overline{n}|i}} = \dfrac{1}{a_{\overline{n}|i}} - i$, and since $i = .04$, then

$$\frac{1}{s_{\overline{n}|i}} = \$.10655217 - .04 = \$.06655217.$$

Therefore

$$R \text{ (periodic payment)} = S\,\frac{1}{s_{\overline{n}|i}} = (\$5,000.00)(.06655217) = \$332.76$$

Ordinary Annuity—Computation of Term

In cases where the known quantities are the periodic payment (rent), the interest per period and either the amount or the present value of an ordinary annuity, the term can be calculated. This calculation can be made by logarithms, by transposition of the formula,

$$S_n = \frac{R\,(1 + i)^n - 1}{i}$$

to

$$\frac{S_n i}{R} + 1 = (1 + i)^n$$

giving

$$n = \frac{\log\left(\dfrac{S_n i}{R} + 1\right)}{\log\,(1 + i)} \tag{14-11}$$

or if the present value is given instead of the amount, by transposing the formula,

$$P = \frac{R[1 - (1 + i)^{-n}]}{i}$$

to

$$\frac{R}{R - Pi} = (1 + i)^n$$

$$giving \qquad\qquad n = \frac{\log\left(\dfrac{R}{R - Pi}\right)}{\log(1 + i)} \qquad\qquad (14\text{-}12)$$

However, problems in finding the term are also solved by use of the tables, as is shown by the following examples:

How long will be required for an annuity of $200.00 per quarter, at 5% interest compounded quarterly, to amount to $10,000.00 if the $200.00 is paid at the end of each quarter?

By Formula (14-2), $\qquad S_n = Rs_{\overline{n}|i},$

where S_n is the amount of an ordinary annuity, R is its periodic payment, and $s_{\overline{n}|i}$ is the amount of an ordinary annuity having a periodic payment of $1.00. Substituting the given figures of $10,000.00 for S_n and $200.00 for R

$$\$10,000.00 = (\$200.00)s_{\overline{n}|i}.$$

Giving $s_{\overline{n}|i} = 50$.

Now since $i = \dfrac{5\%}{4} = 1\frac{1}{4}\%$, turn to Table 13, and run down the $1\frac{1}{4}\%$ column until the values of $s_{\overline{n}|i}$ just above and below 50 are found. They appear on Page 307, and are,

n	$s_{\overline{n}|i}$
40	51.48955708
39	49.88622921
Difference	1.60332787

Now the difference between $s_{\overline{n}|i} = 50$, and the lesser value above is,

n	$s_{\overline{n}|i}$
	50
39	49.88622921
Difference	.11377079

Therefore $n = 39\frac{1138}{16033} = 39.071$ periods.

Since these periods are quarters, the term of the annuity is $\dfrac{39.071}{4} = 9.768$ years.

Since, however, compound interest is not a linear function, and since fractional periods are often impractical to realize, the better answer is $9\frac{3}{4}+$ years.

An example of term computation in which the present value is given is the following:

How long will be required to retire a debt of $10,000.00 by paying

$200.00 at the end of each quarter if the debt bears 5% interest compounded quarterly?

Use Formula (14-4), $P = Ra_{\overline{n}|i}$

where P is the present value of an ordinary annuity, R is its periodic payment and $a_{\overline{n}|i}$ is the present value of an ordinary annuity per $1.00 periodic payment.

Substituting the given figures of $10,000.00 for P and $200.00 for R,

$$\$10,000.00 = (\$200.00)a_{\overline{n}|i}.$$

Giving $a_{\overline{n}|i} = 50$.

Since $i = \dfrac{5\%}{4} = 1\frac{1}{4}\%$, turn to Table 14, and run down the $1\frac{1}{4}\%$ column until the values of $a_{\overline{n}|i}$, just above and below 50 are found. They appear on Page 330, and are:

n	$a_{\overline{n}|i}$
79	50.01649027
78	49.64169640
Difference	.37479387

Now the difference between $a_{\overline{n}|i} = 50$ and the lesser value above is,

n	$a_{\overline{n}|i}$
	50
78	49.64169640
	.35830360

Therefore $n = 78\frac{358}{375}$, which is nearly 79. quarters, or $19\frac{3}{4}$ years.

Ordinary Annuities—Rate

Problems in ordinary annuities also arise in which the unknown quantity is the interest rate, given the periodic payment, term, and either the amount or the present value. These problems are also solved by interpolation in the tables, as is shown by the following examples.

What rate of interest compounded semi-annually must be obtained on an ordinary annuity of $500.00 paid semi-annually to yield an amount of $12,000.00 in ten years?

Use Formula (14-2). $S_n = Rs_{\overline{n}|i}$

where S_n is the amount of an ordinary annuity, R is its periodic payment, and $s_{\overline{n}|i}$ is the amount of an ordinary annuity having a periodic payment of $1.00. Substituting the given figures of $12,000.00 for S_n and $500.00 for R,

$$\$12,000.00 = (\$500.00)s_{\overline{n}|i}.$$

Giving $s_{\overline{n}|i} = 24$.

Now since $n = 2 \times 10 = 20$, turn to Table 13, and run across the line for $n = 20$ until the columns are reached having values of $s_{\overline{n}|i}$ just above and below 24. They appear on Page 307 and Page 309 and are,

	$1\frac{3}{4}\%$	2%
$n = 20$	23.70161119	24.29736980

Their difference is $24.29736980 - 23.70161119 = .59575861$.
The difference between the given value and the smaller tabulated value is $24. - 23.70161119 = .29838881$.

Therefore the interest rate per period

$$= 1\frac{3}{4}\% + (2\% - 1\frac{3}{4}\%) \left(\frac{.29838881}{.59575861}\right)$$

$$= 1\frac{3}{4}\% + (.25\%)(.500) = 1\frac{7}{8}\%$$

And the interest rate per year is about $2 \times 1\frac{7}{8}\%$, or about $3\frac{3}{4}\%$.

Another problem in finding interest rate, in which the present value, instead of the amount, is given, is:

An appliance is purchased for $200.00. If there is no down payment, and instalment payments are $20.00 at the end of each month for one year, what is the interest rate compounded monthly?

Use Formula (14-4), $P = Ra_{\overline{n}|i}$

where P is the present value of an ordinary annuity, R is its periodic payment, and $a_{\overline{n}|i}$ is the present value of an ordinary annuity having a periodic payment of $1.00.

Substituting the given figures of $200.00 for P and $20.00 for R,

$$\$200.00 = (\$20.00)a_{\overline{n}|i}.$$

Giving $a_{\overline{n}|i} = 10$.

Now since $n = 12 \times 1 = 12$, turn to Table 14, and run across the line for $n = 12$ until the columns are reached having values of $a_{\overline{n}|i}$ just above and below 10. They appear on Page 331 and Page 333, and are

	$2\frac{3}{4}\%$	3%
$n = 12$	10.10420366	9.95400399

Their difference is $10.10420366 - 9.95400399 = .15019967$.
The difference between the given value and the smaller tabulated value is $10. - 9.95400399 = .04599601$.

Therefore the interest rate per period

$$= 2\frac{3}{4}\% + (3\% - 2\frac{3}{4}\%) \left(\frac{.04599601}{.15019967}\right)$$

$$= 2.75\% + (.25)(.306) = 2.83\% \text{ per month.}$$

And the effective (equivalent) simple interest rate per year is $12 \times 2.83\%$ $= 33.96\%$.

Annuity Due

An annuity due differs from an ordinary annuity in that the payments are made at the beginnings of the payment periods instead of at their ends. Therefore the term of the annuity begins on the date of the first payment, and ends on payment period after the date of the last payment. There are various annuity due computations arising from prepaid business transactions, of which the rental of buildings or other real estate is among the most common.

Computations of annuities due, as well as certain other special types of annuities, may be made quite easily by suitable modification of the relations applying to ordinary annuities. This fact permits the application, to the calculations of annuities due, of the formulas and tables already derived and computed for ordinary annuities.

Thus, by Formula (14-1) the amount of an ordinary annuity was:

$$S_n = R \frac{(1+i)^n - 1}{i} = \frac{R[(1+i)^n - 1]}{i}$$

Now an ordinary annuity whose term is one period longer than an annuity due has the same payment dates, except for the last payment. Therefore, the amount of an annuity due is the amount of an ordinary annuity with one more period, less the last payment. For example, a five-year annual payment annuity due beginning January 1, 1954 would have payment dates on January 1 of 1954, 1955, 1956, 1957 and 1958. A six-year annual payment ordinary annuity beginning January 1, 1953 would have payment dates on January 1 of 1954, 1955, 1956, 1957, 1958, and 1959, and the terms of both annuities end on January 1, 1959. Therefore both annuities have the same payment dates and interest periods except for the last payment on the ordinary annuity. Since that payment occurs at the end of the term it draws no interest. So the amount of an annuity due is that of an ordinary annuity with one more period, less the periodic payment. Now Formula (14-2) for the amount of an ordinary annuity was $S_n = Rs_{\overline{n}|i}$. Therefore from the foregoing reasoning, the amount of an annuity due is

$$S_{due} = S_{n+1} - R = R(s_{\overline{n+1}|i} - 1) \tag{14-13}$$

As an example of the use of this formula, find the amount of an annuity due having a term of 8 years, a periodic payment of $800.00 at the beginning of each year, with interest at 5% compounded annually.

Here the number of periods of the annuity due is 8, so the number of periods of the corresponding ordinary annuity is 9. Then from Table 13, the amount of an ordinary annuity of 9 payments of $1.00 at 5% interest per period $= s_{\overline{9}|5} = \$11.026566432$.

Substituting in Formula (14-13),

$$S_{due} = R(s_{\overline{n+1}|t} - 1)$$

we have $S_{due} = (\$800.00)(s_{\overline{9}|1\frac{1}{4}\%} - 1)$

$$= (\$800.00)(10.02656)$$

$$= \$8,021.25.$$

As another example, find the amount in a trust fund account in which $500.00 is deposited on the first day of each quarter for 12 years, at 4% interest compounded quarterly.

Here the number of periods of the annuity due is $4 \times 12 = 48$, so the number of periods of the corresponding ordinary annuity is 49. From Table 13, the amount of an ordinary annuity of 49 payments of $1.00 at $\frac{4\%}{4} = 1\%$ per period $= s_{\overline{49}|1} = \$62.83483385$.

Substituting in Formula (14-13),

$$S_{due} = (\$500.00)(s_{\overline{49}|1\%} - 1)$$

$$= (\$500.00)(61.83483)$$

$$= \$30,917.42.$$

The present value of an annuity due is related to the present value of an ordinary annuity by analogous reasoning to that which established the relation between their amounts. That is, an annuity due whose term starts on the same date as an ordinary annuity of one plus period has the same payment dates, except for the additional payment on the annuity due at its beginning. Therefore, the present value of an annuity due is the same as that of an ordinary annuity with one less period, plus the first payment. For example, a five year, annual-payment annuity due beginning January 1, 1954 would have payment dates on January 1 of 1954, 1955, 1956, 1957 and 1958. A four-year, annual-payment ordinary annuity beginning January 1, 1954, would have payment dates on January 1 of 1955, 1956, 1957 and 1958. Therefore both annuities have the same payment dates except for the first payment on the annuity due. Since that payment occurs at the beginning of the term, it may simply be added to the present value of the ordinary annuity to yield the present value of the annuity due.

That is $P_{due} = P$ (for $n - 1$ periods) $+ R = R(a_{\overline{n-1}|t} + 1)$ (14-14)

As an example of the use of this formula, find the present value of an annuity due having a term of 8 years, a periodic payment of $800.00 at the beginning of each year, with interest at 5% compounded annually.

Here the number of periods of the annuity due is 8, so the number of periods of the corresponding ordinary annuity is 7. Then from Table 14, the present value of an ordinary annuity of 7 payments at 5% interest per period $= a_{\overline{7}|5} = \$5.78637340$.

Substituting in the formula,

$$P_{due} = R(a_{\overline{n-1}|i} + 1)$$
$$P_{due} = (\$800.00)(a_{\overline{7}|5} + 1)$$
$$P_{due} = (\$800.00)(5.78637340 + 1)$$
$$= (\$800.00)(6.78637) = \$5,429.10$$

As another example, find the present value of a trust fund account in which \$500.00 is deposited on the first day of each quarter for 12 years, at $4\frac{1}{2}\%$ interest compounded quarterly.

Here the number of periods of the annuity due is $4 \times 12 = 48$, so the number of periods of the corresponding ordinary annuity is 47. From Table 14, the present value of an ordinary annuity of 47 payments at $\frac{4\frac{1}{2}\%}{4} = 1\frac{1}{8}\%$ per period $= a_{\overline{47}|1} = \$36.34812891$.

Substituting in the formula,

$$P_{due} = R(a_{\overline{n-1}|i} + 1)$$
$$P_{due} = (\$500.00)(a_{\overline{47}|1\frac{1}{8}\%} + 1)$$
$$P_{due} = (\$500.00)(36.34812891 + 1)$$
$$= (\$500.00)(37.34813) = \$18,674.07.$$

Deferred Annuities

Deferred annuities do not begin until a future date. The length of time between their date of issue and the beginning of their term is the interval of deferment. The effect of the deferment upon their amount and present value depends on the other classification of the annuity, e.g. whether it is a deferred ordinary annuity or deferred annuity due.

A deferred ordinary annuity has a term which begins on a payment period before the first payment is due. Its amount is found by disregarding the period of deferment, and computing, using the number of periods in its term as the basis of calculation, as with a non-deferred ordinary annuity. However, its present value at the beginning of the interval of deferment is obviously different from the present value at the beginning of its term, which is the figure P given by formula and tables for ordinary annuities. To find its present value at the beginning of the interval of deferment (i.e. at its date of issue), recall that the present value of an ordinary annuity of n payments was defined as the sum of the present values of the individual payments. For example, the present value of an ordinary annuity of six consecutive payments is,

P (ordinary annuity of six payments) = P (first payment) +
P (second payment) + P (third payment) +
P (fourth payment) + P (fifth payment) +
P (sixth payment)

Similarly, P (ordinary annuity of three payments) = P (first payment) + P (second payment) + P (third payment).

Therefore P (ordinary annuity of three payments deferred for 3 payment periods) = P (fourth payment of ordinary annuity) + P (fifth payment of ordinary annuity) + P (sixth payment of ordinary annuity) = P (ordinary annuity of six payments) − P (ordinary annuity of three payments).

Thus
$$P_{def} = P_{\overline{m+n}|i} - P_{\overline{m}|i} \tag{14-15}$$

where P_{def} is the present value of a deferred ordinary annuity of n payments and deferment interval of m payment periods, $P_{\overline{m+n}|i}$ is the present value of an ordinary annuity of $m + n$ payments and $P_{\overline{n}|i}$ is the present value of an ordinary annuity of n payments.

By Formula (14-4) the present value of an ordinary annuity, $P = a_{\overline{n}|i}R$, the formula for the present value of a deferred ordinary annuity may be rewritten as

$$P_{def} = R(a_{\overline{m+n}|i} - a_{\overline{m}|i}). \tag{14-16}$$

The computation of the present value of a deferred ordinary annuity is illustrated by the following example: Find the amount and the present value of a deferred ordinary annuity having an interval of deferment of 2 years, and a term of four years, comprising 16 quarterly payments of $200.00 each, with interest compounded quarterly at 5%.

As explained above the amount is the same as that for an ordinary annuity of the same term.

Therefore
$$S_{def} = S_n = Rs_{\overline{n}|i}$$

Then $n = 4 \times 4 = 16$, and $i = \dfrac{5\%}{4} = 1\frac{1}{4}\%$.

From Table 13, the amount of an ordinary annuity having periodic payments of $1.00 for 16 periods at $1\frac{1}{4}\%$ per period = $s_{\overline{16}|1\frac{1}{4}}$ = $17.59116382. Substituting in formula above,

$$S_{def} = (\$200.00)(17.59116) = \$3,518.23$$

The present value is given by Formula (14-16),

$$P_{def} = R(a_{\overline{m+n}|i} - a_{\overline{m}|i})$$

where R is \$200.00, m is $2 \times 4 = 8$, n is $4 \times 4 = 16$ and i is $\dfrac{5\%}{4} = 1\frac{1}{4}\%$.

Substituting, $\qquad P_{def} = (\$200.00)(a_{\overline{24}|1\frac{1}{4}} - a_{\overline{8}|1\frac{1}{4}})$

From Table 14, $a_{\overline{24}|1\frac{1}{4}} = \$20.62423451$

and $\qquad\qquad a_{\overline{8}|1\frac{1}{4}} = \quad 7.56812429$

Therefore $P_{def} = (\$200.00)(20.62423451 - 7.56812429)$

$\qquad\qquad = (\$200.00)(13.05611022) = \$2,611.22.$

The formulas for the amount and present value of a deferred annuity due bear the same relation to those for an annuity due that those already developed for a deferred ordinary annuity bear to those for an ordinary annuity. That is, since the amount of an annuity due is $S_{due} = R(s_{\overline{n+1}|i} - 1)$ then the amount of a deferred annuity due is,

$$S_{def\text{-}due} = R(s_{\overline{n+1}|i} - 1) \tag{14-17}$$

where n is the number of payment periods in the term of the annuity, disregarding the number of periods m, in the interval of deferment.

Further, since the present value of an annuity due is $P_{due} = R(a_{\overline{n-1}|i} + 1)$, and the present value of a deferred ordinary annuity is $P_{def} = R(a_{\overline{m+n}|i} - a_{\overline{m}|i})$, then the present value of a deferred annuity due is

$$P_{def\text{-}due} = R(a_{\overline{m+n-1}|i} - a_{\overline{m-1}|i}) \tag{14-18}$$

where m is the number of payment periods in the interval of deferment, and n is the number of payment periods in the term of the annuity.

As an example of the use of these formulas, solve the problem: Find the amount and present value of a deferred annuity due having an interval of deferment of 2 years, and a term of 4 years comprising 16 quarterly payments of \$200.00 each, with interest compounded quarterly at 5%.

Using Formula (14-17) for the amount,

$$S_{def\text{-}due} = R(s_{\overline{n+1}|i} - 1),$$

where R is \$200.00, n is $4 \times 4 = 16$, and i is $\dfrac{5\%}{4} = 1\frac{1}{4}\%$.

Substituting, $\quad S_{def\text{-}due} = (\$200.00)(s_{\overline{16+1}|1\frac{1}{4}} - 1)$

$\qquad\qquad S_{def\text{-}due} = (\$200.00)(s_{\overline{17}|1\frac{1}{4}} - 1)$

From Table 13, $s_{\overline{17}|1\frac{1}{4}} = \$18.81105336$

Therefore $S_{def\text{-}due} = (\$200.00)(18.81105336 - 1)$

$\qquad\qquad = (\$200.00)(17.81105)$

$\qquad\qquad = \$3,562.21.$

The present value is given by Formula (14-18)

$$P_{def\text{-}due} = R(a_{\overline{m+n-1}|i} - a_{\overline{m-1}|i})$$

where R is \$200.00, n is $4 \times 4 = 16$, m is $2 \times 4 = 8$, and i is $\dfrac{5\%}{4} = 1\frac{1}{4}\%$.

Substituting,

$$P_{def\text{-}due} = (\$200.00)(a_{\overline{8+16-1}|1\frac{1}{4}} - a_{\overline{8-1}|1\frac{1}{4}})$$
$$= (\$200.00)(a_{\overline{23}|1\frac{1}{4}} - a_{\overline{7}|1\frac{1}{4}})$$

From Table 14, $a_{\overline{23}|1\frac{1}{4}} = \$19.88203744$

and $\qquad a_{\overline{7}|1\frac{1}{4}} = \$\ 6.66272585$

Therefore, $P_{def\text{-}due} = (\$200.00)(19.88203744 - 6.66272585)$
$$= (\$200.00)(13.21931) = \$2,643.86.$$

Perpetuities

A perpetuity is an annuity whose payments begin at a fixed date and continue forever. Therefore, the amount of a perpetuity has no meaning, since it would be indefinitely large. On the other hand the present value of a perpetuity enters into a number of calculations in applied business mathematics, since income from endowments, from some real estate, from preferred stock, etc., is treated as a perpetuity.

There are two types of perpetuities: the perpetuity in which the periods of payment and the interest period are the same, and the perpetuity in which they are different.

The present value of a perpetuity in which the period of payment is the same as the interest period is very easily expressed. Obviously the present value is a sum of money which, at the given interest rate per period, yields at simple interest, the periodic payment to be made. Expressed symbolically,

$$P_{per}i = R \quad \text{or} \quad P_{per} = \frac{R}{i}. \tag{14-19}$$

For example, find the present value of a perpetuity having a periodic payment of \$160.00 per half-year, with interest at 5%.

Here the interest rate per period is $\dfrac{5\%}{2} = 2\frac{1}{2}\%$. Therefore $\dfrac{R}{i} = \dfrac{\$160.00}{.025} = \$6,400.00$, which is P_{per}, the present value of the perpetuity.

The present value of a perpetuity in which the period of payment is different from the interest period can be found by computation of the rate of interest for the period of payment that is equivalent to the rate for the interest period. Then substitution of that equivalent rate for i in the formula $P_{per} = \dfrac{R}{i_{eq}}$ will yield the corresponding value of P_{per}.

For example, find the present value of a perpetuity having a periodic payment of $320.00 per year, with interest at 5% compounded semi-annually.

The compound amount of $1.00 for one year at 5% compounded semi-annually is (by Formula (13-1) Chapter 13), ($1.00 + .02½)² = $1.050625. Therefore, the compound interest on $1.00 for this period and rate is $1.050625 − $1.00 = $.050625. Therefore, the rate 5.0625% is the interest rate equivalent to 5% annually.

Substituting in above formula,

$$P_{per} = \frac{320.00}{.050625} = \$6,320.99,$$

the present value of the perpetuity.

The foregoing solution of a perpetuity can be expressed as a formula giving the present value for any perpetuity in which the payment period is a multiple of the interest period.   It is—

$$P_{per} = \frac{R}{(1+i)^n - 1} \tag{14-20}$$

where P_{per} is the present value of the perpetuity, R is its periodic payment, i is the interest rate per interest period, and n is the number of interest periods in a payment period.

Note also that the amount of $(1+i)^n$, the amount to which $1.00 will accumulate in n periods if interest is compounded at i per period is given in Table 11, Chapter 13.

To solve a problem by this formula and Table 11, find the present value of a perpetuity of $5,000.00 paid every two years at an interest rate of 4% compounded quarterly.

Here the number of interest periods in a payment period is 8, the interest rate per interest period is 1%, so from Table 11, Chapter 13, the compound amount per $1.00 of present value is $(1 + .01)^8 = 1.08285671$.

Substituting in above formula,

$$P_{per} = \frac{\$5,000.00}{1.08285671 - 1} = \frac{\$5,000.00}{.08285671} = \$60,345.15.$$

Capitalized Cost

The calculation of perpetuities has a direct application in regard to assets which it is desired to have forever.   In such cases, the total sum to acquire and retain the asset obviously includes its initial cost, plus an amount of money which yields interest sufficient both to maintain it for its useful life and to accumulate an amount sufficient to replace it at the end of its useful life.

In the practical use of capitalized cost figures, maintenance costs are often omitted, and the calculation is thus restricted to initial cost plus the perpetuity to yield at interest the amount for replacement plus the new reserve.

In other words, the present value of this perpetuity must be a sum which accumulates at compound interest to a total amount sufficient (1) to replace the asset at the end of its useful life, and (2) to leave a residue equal to that present value, so that the reaccumulation process can resume.

Let C be the cost of replacement, P_{per} be the present value of the required perpetuity, n the number of periods compounded, and i the periodic rate.

Then the total sum at the end of n periods is by Formula (13-1), $S = P(1 + i)^n$, which gives on substituting

$$S = P_{per}(1 + i)^n$$

But by above statement,

$$S = C + P_{per}.$$

Therefore $P_{per}(1 + i)^n = C + P_{per}$

Transposing $P_{per}[(1 + i)^n - 1] = C$

And $P_{per} = \dfrac{C}{(1 + i)^n - 1}$

But, Capitalized Cost = Initial Cost + Present Value of Perpetuity

Therefore Capitalized Cost = Initial Cost + $\dfrac{C}{(1 + i)^n - 1}$ \hfill (14-21)

For example, find the capitalized cost of a machine costing $8,000.00 which is to be replaced every 10 years at a cost of $10,000.00, if the fund draws interest at 4% compounded quarterly.

Substituting in Formula (14-21)

Capitalized Cost = $8,000.00 + $\dfrac{\$10,000.00}{(1 + .01)^{40} - 1}$

From Table 11, Chapter 13, $(1 + .01)^{40} = 1.48886373$
Therefore,

Capitalized Cost = $8,000.00 + $\dfrac{\$10,000.00}{1.48896373 - 1}$

$$= \$8,000.00 + \$20,451.42$$

$$= \$28,451.42$$

Annuities—The General Case

The treatment of annuities up to this point has been from the standpoint of the simple case, in which the rent period (payment period) was the same as the interest period. This case is, as may be seen from later chapters in this book, that most widely encountered in applications of annuity calculations to business situations. However, there are instances in which the rent period is not the same as the interest period. This requires a general method, and is treated in the remaining portion of this chapter.

The method of computation to be used for the general case is that of equivalent interest rates, which has already been introduced in finding the present value of a perpetuity in which the payment period is not the same as the interest period, and which is a generalized form of the effective interest rate. (See Formula (13-5) Chapter 13.) However, to find equivalent interest rates of annuities, it is useful to have formulas and tables for the value of the expression $(1 + i)^{1/p}$, where i is the interest rate expressed as a decimal, and p is the number of installments per interest period, so that $1/p$ is a fractional interest period. Since the expression $(1 + i)^{1/p}$ is identical in form and application with $(1 + i)^n$ (the amount of \$1.00 compounded at the interest rate per period for n integral periods which is tabulated in Table 11, Chapter 13), $(1 + i)^{1/p}$ is defined as the amount of \$1.00 for the fractional period $1/p$ compounded at the interest rate i per period. Values of $(1 + i)^{1/p}$ for some frequently-occurring fractional periods, are given in Table 16, on Pages 370 and 371. The value of $(1 + i)^{1/p}$ can also be computed by the formula

$$\log s_{\overline{1/p}|i} = \log (1 + i)^{1/p} = \frac{\log (1 + i)}{p} \qquad (14\text{-}21)$$

The equivalent interest rate of an annuity is generalized from the effective interest rate, which was defined in Chapter 13 as the simple interest rate equivalent to a given compound rate. Thus, when interest is compounded m periods per year at rate i per period, the effective interest rate by Formula (13-5) is

$$r_{eff} = (1 + i)^m - 1$$

A similar situation arises in annuities in which the payment period is not the same as the interest period, the method of solution being to find the rate per payment period equivalent to the given rate per interest period. Denoting the latter by i, and the former by i_{eq}, then

$$i_{eq} = (1 + i)^{k/k'} - 1, \qquad (14\text{-}22)$$

where k is the number of interest periods per year, and k' is the number of payment periods per year. If k is greater than k', then the ratio k/k' is integral, and the value of $(1 + i)^{k/k'}$ may be found in Table 11, Chapter 13; but if k is less than k', the ratio k/k' is fractional, and must be obtained from Table 16.

p	$\frac{1}{4}\%$	$\frac{7}{24}\%$	$\frac{1}{3}\%$	$\frac{5}{12}\%$	p
2	1.0012 4922	1.0014 5727	1.0016 6528	1.0020 8117	2
3	1.0008 3264	1.0009 7128	1.0011 0988	1.0013 8696	3
4	1.0006 2441	1.0007 2837	1.0008 3229	1.0010 4094	4
6	1.0004 1623	1.0004 8552	1.0005 5479	1.0006 9324	6
12	1.0002 0890	1.0002 4273	1.0002 7735	1.0003 4656	12
13	1.0001 9209	1.0002 2406	1.0002 5602	1.0003 1990	13
26	1.0000 9604	1.0001 1202	1.0001 2800	1.0001 5994	26
52	1.0000 4802	1.0000 5601	1.0000 6400	1.0000 7996	52
365	1.0000 0684	1.0000 0798	1.0000 0912	1.0000 1139	365
∞	1.0000 0000	1.0000 0000	1.0000 0000	1.0000 0000	∞

p	$\frac{1}{2}\%$	$\frac{7}{12}\%$	$\frac{5}{8}\%$	$\frac{2}{3}\%$	p
2	1.0024 9688	1.0029 1243	1.0031 2013	1.0033 2780	2
3	1.0016 6390	1.0019 4068	1.0020 7901	1.0022 1730	3
4	1.0012 4766	1.0014 5515	1.0015 5885	1.0016 6252	4
6	1.0008 3160	1.0009 6987	1.0010 3896	1.0011 0804	6
12	1.0004 1571	1.0004 8482	1.0005 1935	1.0005 5387	12
13	1.0003 8373	1.0004 4751	1.0004 7939	1.0005 1125	13
26	1.0001 9185	1.0002 2373	1.0002 3967	1.0002 5559	26
52	1.0000 9592	1.0001 1186	1.0001 1983	1.0001 2779	52
365	1.0000 1366	1.0000 1594	1.0000 1707	1.0000 1820	365
∞	1.0000 0000	1.0000 0000	1.0000 0000	1.0000 0000	∞

p	$\frac{3}{4}\%$	$\frac{7}{8}\%$	1%	$1\frac{1}{8}\%$	p
2	1.0037 4299	1.0043 6547	1.0049 8756	1.0056 0927	2
3	1.0024 9378	1.0029 0820	1.0033 2228	1.0037 3602	3
4	1.0018 6975	1.0021 8036	1.0024 9068	1.0028 0081	4
6	1.0012 4611	1.0014 5304	1.0016 5977	1.0018 6627	6
12	1.0006 2286	1.0007 2626	1.0008 2954	1.0009 3270	12
13	1.0005 7494	1.0006 7037	1.0007 6570	1.0008 6092	13
26	1.0002 8743	1.0003 3513	1.0003 8276	1.0004 3037	26
52	1.0001 4370	1.0001 6755	1.0001 9137	1.0002 1516	52
365	1.0000 2047	1.0000 2387	1.0000 2726	1.0000 3065	365
∞	1.0000 0000	1.0000 0000	1.0000 0000	1.0000 0000	∞

p	$1\frac{1}{4}\%$	$1\frac{3}{8}\%$	$1\frac{1}{2}\%$	$1\frac{3}{4}\%$	p
2	1.0062 3059	1.0068 5153	1.0074 7208	1.0087 1205	2
3	1.0041 4943	1.0045 6249	1.0049 7521	1.0057 9963	3
4	1.0031 1046	1.0034 1992	1.0037 2909	1.0043 4658	4
6	1.0020 7257	1.0022 7865	1.0024 8452	1.0028 9562	6
12	1.0010 3575	1.0011 3868	1.0012 4149	1.0014 4677	12
13	1.0009 5604	1.0010 5104	1.0011 4594	1.0013 3540	13
26	1.0004 7790	1.0005 2538	1.0005 7280	1.0006 6748	26
52	1.0002 3892	1.0002 6266	1.0002 8636	1.0003 3368	52
365	1.0000 3403	1.0000 3742	1.0000 4079	1.0000 4753	365
∞	1.0000 0000	1.0000 0000	1.0000 0000	1.0000 0000	∞

p	2%	$2\frac{1}{4}\%$	$2\frac{1}{2}\%$	$2\frac{3}{4}\%$	p
2	1.0099 5050	1.0111 8742	1.0124 2284	1.0136 5675	2
3	1.0066 2271	1.0074 4444	1.0082 6484	1.0090 8390	3
4	1.0049 6293	1.0055 7815	1.0061 9225	1.0068 0522	4
6	1.0033 0589	1.0037 1532	1.0041 2392	1.0045 3168	6
12	1.0016 5158	1.0018 5594	1.0020 5984	1.0022 6328	12
13	1.0015 2444	1.0017 1305	1.0019 0124	1.0020 8900	13
26	1.0007 6193	1.0008 5616	1.0009 5017	1.0010 4396	26
52	1.0003 8089	1.0004 2799	1.0004 7497	1.0005 2184	52
365	1.0000 5426	1.0000 6096	1.0000 6765	1.0000 7433	365
∞	1.0000 0000	1.0000 0000	1.0000 0000	1.0000 0000	∞

p	3%	$3\frac{1}{2}\%$	4%	$4\frac{1}{2}\%$	p
2	1.0148 8916	1.0173 4950	1.0198 0390	1.0222 5242	2
3	1.0099 0163	1.0115 3314	1.0131 5941	1.0147 8046	3
4	1.0074 1707	1.0086 3745	1.0098 5341	1.0110 6499	4
6	1.0049 3862	1.0057 5004	1.0065 5820	1.0073 6312	6
12	1.0024 6627	1.0028 7090	1.0032 7374	1.0036 7481	12
13	1.0022 7634	1.0026 4977	1.0030 2153	1.0033 9165	13
26	1.0011 3752	1.0013 2401	1.0015 0963	1.0016 9439	26
52	1.0005 6860	1.0006 6179	1.0007 5453	1.0008 4684	52
365	1.0000 8099	1.0000 9425	1.0001 0746	1.0001 2060	365
∞	1.0000 0000	1.0000 0000	1.0000 0000	1.0000 0000	∞

p	5%	$5\frac{1}{2}\%$	6%	$6\frac{1}{2}\%$	p
2	1.0246 9508	1.0271 3193	1.0295 6302	1.0319 8837	2
3	1.0163 9636	1.0180 0713	1.0196 1282	1.0212 1347	3
4	1.0122 7224	1.0134 7518	1.0146 7385	1.0158 6828	4
6	1.0081 6485	1.0089 6340	1.0097 5880	1.0105 5107	6
12	1.0040 7412	1.0044 7170	1.0048 6755	1.0052 6169	12
13	1.0037 6014	1.0041 2701	1.0044 9228	1.0048 5597	13
26	1.0018 7831	1.0020 6138	1.0022 4363	1.0024 2504	26
52	1.0009 3871	1.0010 3016	1.0011 2118	1.0012 1179	52
365	1.0001 3368	1.0001 4670	1.0001 5965	1.0001 7255	365
∞	1.0000 0000	1.0000 0000	1.0000 0000	1.0000 0000	∞

p	7%	$7\frac{1}{2}\%$	8%	$8\frac{1}{2}\%$	p
2	1.0344 0804	1.0368 2207	1.0392 3048	1.0416 3333	2
3	1.0228 0912	1.0243 9981	1.0259 8557	1.0275 6644	3
4	1.0170 5853	1.0182 4460	1.0194 2655	1.0206 0440	4
6	1.0113 4026	1.0121 2638	1.0129 0946	1.0136 8952	6
12	1.0056 5415	1.0060 4492	1.0064 3403	1.0068 2149	12
13	1.0052 1808	1.0055 7863	1.0059 3764	1.0062 9511	13
26	1.0026 0564	1.0027 8544	1.0029 6443	1.0031 4262	26
52	1.0013 0197	1.0013 9175	1.0014 8112	1.0015 7008	52
365	1.0001 8538	1.0001 9816	1.0002 1087	1.0002 2353	365
∞	1.0000 0000	1.0000 0000	1.0000 0000	1.0000 0000	∞

371

By use of Formula (14-22) Tables 11 and 16, and logarithms computations of the amounts, present values, periodic payments, etc. of general annuities may be made by the use of the formulas (but not the annuity tables) already derived for ordinary annuities, annuities due and deferred annuities, whichever corresponds to the given general annuity in term, number of payments, periodic payment and equivalent interest rate.

As an example, find the amount and present value of an annuity for which $1,000.00 is paid at the end of semi-annual periods for 5 years, if interest is compounded quarterly at 4% per year.

Here k, the number of interest periods per year, is 4; k', the number of payment periods per year is 2; and i, the rate per interest period, is $\frac{.04}{4}$ = .01. Substituting in Formula (14-22),

$$i_{eq} = (1 + .01)^{\frac{4}{2}} - 1 = (1.01)^2 - 1$$

From Table 11, Chapter 13, $(1.01)^2 = 1.0201$.

Therefore $i_{eq} = .0201$

Now, since the payments are made at the end of the periods, this is an ordinary annuity and its amount may be found by Formula (14-1)

$$S_n = R \frac{(1 + i)^n - 1}{i}$$

where R is the periodic payment ($1,000.00 in this problem); i is the interest rate per payment period (.0201 in this problem) and n is the number of payment periods (2 × 5 = 10 in this problem). Substituting these values,

$$S_n = (\$1,000.00) \frac{(1 + .0201)^{10} - 1}{.0201}$$

From Table 3, Chapter 6, log 1.0201 = .008643

Then log $(1.0201)^{10} = 10$ log 1.0201 = .08643

By Table 3, Chapter 6, $(1.0201)^{10}$ = antilog .08643 = 1.2202

Then $S_n = (\$1,000.00) \frac{1.2202 - 1}{.0201} = \$10,955.22$

Then to find the present value, use Formula (14-3) for the present value of an ordinary annuity

$$P = R \frac{1 - (1 + i)^{-n}}{i}$$

where R is the periodic payment ($1,000.00 in this problem); i is the interest rate per payment period (.0201 in this problem) and n is the number of payment periods ($2 \times 5 = 10$ in this problem). Substituting these values

$$P = (\$1,000.00) \frac{1 - (1.0201)^{-10}}{.0201}$$

From Table 3, Chapter 6, log $1.0201 = .008643$

Then log $(1.0201)^{-10} - 10$ log $(1.0201) = -.08643$

Rewriting with positive mantissa,

$$\log (1.0201)^{-10} = \bar{1}.91357$$

By Table 3, Chapter 6, $(1.0201)^{-10} = .81954$

Then $P = (\$1,000.00) \dfrac{1 - .81954}{.0201} = \$8,978.11$

Another example, that illustrates the case in which the number of payment periods exceeds the number of interest periods, is the following:

What is the amount and present value of an annuity in which $250.00 paid at the end of every two months for 12 years, if interest is compounded semi-annually at 5%?

By Formula (14-22) $\quad i_{eq} = (1 + i)^{k/k'} - 1$

where k, the number of interest periods per year, is 2, k', the number of payment periods per year, is 6, and i, the rate per interest period, is $\dfrac{.05}{2} = .025$. Substituting in Formula (14-22)

$$i_{eq} = (1 + .025)^{\frac{2}{6}} - 1.$$

In Table 16, $(1.025)^{\frac{1}{3}}$ is given under the figure $2\frac{1}{2}\%$, in line where p (at side of table) $= 3$ (because p is denominator of fractional exponent). This value of $(1.025)^{\frac{1}{3}}$ is 1.00826484.

Thus, $i_{eq} = .00826484$

Now, since the payments are made at the end of the periods, this is an ordinary annuity, and its amount may be found by Formula (14-1)

$$S_n = R \frac{(1 + i)^n - 1}{i}$$

where R is the periodic payment ($250.00 in this problem); i is the interest rate per payment period (.00826484 in this problem); and n is the number of payment periods ($6 \times 12 = 72$ in this problem). Substituting these values.

$$S_n = (\$250.00) \frac{(1 + .00826484)^{72} - 1}{.00826484}$$

From Table 3, Chapter 6, log 1.00826484 = .0035747

Then log $(1.00826484)^{72}$ = 72 log 1.00826484 = .257378

Then by Table 3, Chapter 6,

$$(1.00826484)^{72} = \text{antilog } .257378 = 1.80875$$

Then S_n = ($250.00) $\dfrac{1.80875 - 1}{.00826484}$ = $24,463.57

Then to find the present value, use Formula (14-3) for the present value of an ordinary annuity

$$P = R \frac{1 - (1 + i)^{-n}}{i}$$

where R is the periodic payment ($250.00 in this problem); i is the interest rate per payment period (.00826484 in this problem) and n is the number of payment periods ($6 \times 12 = 72$ in this problem). Substituting these values,

$$P = (\$250.00) \frac{1 - (1.00826484)^{-72}}{.00826484}$$

From Table 3, Chapter 6, log 1.00826484 = .0035747

Then log $(1.00826484)^{-72}$ = -72 log 1.00826484 = $-.257378$

Rewriting with positive mantissa,

$$\log (1.00826484)^{-72} = \bar{1}.742622$$

By Table 3, Chapter 6, $(1.00826484)^{-72}$ = antilog $\bar{1}.742622$ = .552869

Then P = ($250.00) $\dfrac{1 - .552869}{.00826484}$ = $13,525.10

As an example of the general case of an annuity due, solve the following problem:

What is the amount and present value of a fund in which $275.00 is deposited at the beginning of every quarter for 7 years, if interest is compounded annually at 6%?

By Formula (14-22),

$$i_{eq} = (1 + i)^{k/k'} - 1$$

where k, the number of interest periods per year, is 1; k' the number of payment periods per year is 4; and i, the rate per interest period, is 6%. Substituting in Formula (14-22)

$$i_{eq} = (1 + .06)^{\frac{1}{4}} - 1$$

In Table 16, $(1.06)^{\frac{1}{4}}$ is given under the figure 6% in the line where p (at side of table) = 4. This value of $(1.06)^{\frac{1}{4}}$ is 1.01467385.

Therefore i_{eq} = .01467385.

Now, since the payments are made at the beginning of the periods, this is an annuity due, and its amount may be found from Formulas (14-13) and (14-1)

$$S_{due} = S_{n+1} - R = R\left[\frac{(1+i)^{n+1} - 1}{i} - 1\right]$$

where R is the periodic payment (\$275.00 in this problem); i is the interest rate per period (.01467385 in this problem) and n is the number of payment periods ($4 \times 7 = 28$ in this problem). Substituting these values,

$$S_{due} = (\$275.00)\left[\frac{(1 + .01467385)^{29} - 1}{.01467385} - 1\right]$$

From Table 3, Chapter 6, log $1.01467385 = .0063265$
Then log $(1.01467385)^{29} = 29$ log $1.01467385 = .183485$
Then by Table 3, Chapter 6, $(1.01467385)^{29} =$ antilog $.1834685 = 1.52571$

$$\text{Then } S_{due} = (\$275.00)\left[\frac{1.5257 - 1}{.01467385} - 1\right]$$

$$= (\$275.00)[35.82563 - 1]$$

$$= \$9,577.05.$$

Then to find the present value, use Formulas (14-14) and (14-3)

$$P_{due} = R\left[\frac{1 - (1+i)^{1-n}}{i} + 1\right]$$

where R is the periodic payment (\$275.00 in this problem); i is the interest rate per payment period (.01467385 in this problem); and n is the number of payment periods ($4 \times 7 = 28$ in this problem). Substituting these values

$$P_{due} = (\$275.00)\left[\frac{1 - (1.01467385)^{-27}}{.01467385} + 1\right]$$

From Table 3, Chapter 6, log $1.01467385 = .0063265$
Then log $(1.0467385)^{-27} = -27$ log $1.01467385 = -.1708101$
Rewriting with positive mantissa, log $(1.01467385)^{-27} = \bar{1}.8291899$
By Table 3, Chapter 6, $(1.01467385)^{-27} =$ antilog $\bar{1}.8291899 = .674833$

$$\text{Then } P = (\$275.00)\left[\frac{1 - .674833}{.01467385} + 1\right]$$

$$= (\$275.00)\left[\frac{.325167}{.01467385} + 1\right]$$

$$= (\$275.00)(23.15962) = \$6,368.90.$$

Chapter 15

DEPRECIATION

Physical assets decrease in value by wear and exposure. Normal maintenance is necessary to prevent abnormally rapid depreciation, but even with normal maintenance, a time comes when the asset has reached the end of its useful life.

At that time, the asset may have a residual value, for example, a machine has at least the value represented by the weight of scrap metal it contains. Therefore, the residual value of an asset at the end of its useful life is called the scrap value. This scrap value enters into some of the methods of computing the depreciation charge, which is a periodic deduction from earnings to offset the capital loss incurred by the depreciation of the asset.

There are a number of methods of computing depreciation charges. The method used in a particular instance is often a matter of the practice of the particular business, or for the particular type of asset. The choice of a method is not necessarily a unilateral decision of the individual business or accountant; the policy of governmental taxing agencies must frequently be considered, in view of the close relationship between depreciation charges and earnings. It is the policy of the U. S. Government to permit the annual depreciation deduction to be computed in any manner that is consistent with recognized trade practices. Three methods were specifically listed in the 1954 code, and therefore these methods are discussed in this chapter. They are the straight-line method, the declining-balance method, and the sum of the years-digits method. There are, however, certain other general methods of computing depreciation charges, which are an integral part of business mathematics, and which are discussed later in this chapter.

Before discussing any of these methods, however, it is to be understood that their use in U. S. practice is subject to the general limitations upon permissible depreciation which are set forth in Publication 311 of the

U. S. Treasury Department of Internal Revenue, which is part of the 1954 Code of Federal Regulations. That publication sets forth general regulations on depreciation which stipulate the general character of property which may be depreciated, and the general rule that experience with similar equipment in the same industry be the basis for the assumed life of equipment. There is also, however, Internal Revenue Service Publication #173 of the U. S. Treasury Department which is called *Bulletin F*, and which gives information and tables of the average useful life of depreciable equipment. The data in this bulletin is arranged by industries, and varies greatly in the detail with which individual industries are treated. A few of the more important schedules are listed in Table 17, with the suggestion that the reader obtain *Bulletin F*, Internal Revenue Service Publication #173, from the Government Printing Office, if he seeks data on the average life of equipment used in industries not given here.

The Straight Line Method

The straight line method is one of the most simple methods of computing depreciation charges. It consists of dividing the total depreciation expense (which is initial cost of the asset minus its scrap value) by the number of periods of useful life. The quotient is depreciation expense per period, which by this method is the same for each period. For example, an asset having an initial cost of $1,100.00; a scrap value of $100.00; and a useful life of 10 years would have a depreciation expense of $\dfrac{\$1,100 - \$100}{10}$ = $100.00 per year. Since by this method this figure is the same for each year of the life, the book value (which is initial cost − depreciation fund) decreases at the same rate from year to year, and its graph is a straight line, which gives the name to the method.

As another example, find the annual depreciation charge of a machine costing $865.00, having a scrap value of $61.25 at the end of a probable life of 5 years. Also find the book value at the end of 3 years.

$$\text{Depreciation expense} = \$865 - 61.25 = \$803.75$$

$$\text{Depreciation charge per year} = \frac{803.75}{5} = \$160.75$$

$$\text{Depreciation fund after 3 years} = 3 \times 160.75 = \$482.25$$
$$\text{Book value after 3 years} = \$865.00 - \$482.25 = \$372.75$$

It is to be noted that the straight line method does not require the existence of a scrap value at the end of the period of depreciation, if the nature of the asset is such that its terminal value is then zero. In that case, the annual depreciation charge is the initial cost divided by the probable life in years. (*Continued on Page 402.*)

TABLE 17—AVERAGE USEFUL LIFE OF DEPRECIABLE EQUIPMENT

(From *Bulletin F, U. S. Internal Revenue Service Publication #173*)

AUTOMOBILE INDUSTRY

MANUFACTURING

The average life of the machinery varies from 15 to 20 years, and tools, dies, patterns, etc., generally have an average life of from 3 to 4 years. Most of the equipment used by automobile manufacturers is of standard metal and wood-working design, and items for this class of equipment can be taken from the list pertaining to fabricators of metal and wood.

ACCESSORIES

The remarks applying to the automobile manufacturing industry apply also to a considerable extent to the manufacturers of accessories. In general, however, the machinery has an over-all composite life of 15 years.

REPAIR SHOPS

The average composite life of machinery for automobile repair shops has been found to be approximately 10 years.

BAKERIES

In general, it has been found that the composite life of $12\frac{1}{2}$ years applies to cake bakeries, 14 years to bread bakeries, and 20 years to biscuit manufacturers. The item lives applicable to the baking industry are set forth in the following tabulation, some adjustment being needed, depending upon the type of bakery in which the assets are used:

Average useful life (years)

Ballers, dough	15	Slat apron bread	25
Beaters:		Spiral screw	25
Light	10	Cookers, doughnut	15
Heavy	15	Cookie machines, wire cut	17
Bins, flour storage:		Cooling equipment	20
Steel	33	Cooler and packer	15
Wood	25	Cracker cutting machines	15
Brakes, dough	15	Cracker peeling machines	15
Burners, gas or oil	15	Cracker machines	15
Cake machine, open saddle	20	Cutter—wafer	15
Case for shipping bread (inventory)	2	Cutting and panning machines	25
Cleaners, sack	15	Depositors—cake	15
Coating machines	20	Dies, rools, and cutters	10
Conveyors:		Dividers—dough:	
Belt	17	Hand	20
Chain and flight, cake	20	Power	12
Panning	20	Doughnut machines, automatic	15

TABLE 17—AVERAGE USEFUL LIFE OF DEPRECIABLE EQUIPMENT (CONT.)

Droppers:	
Cake............................ 15	
Cookie.......................... 20	
Dryers, special cookie............. 20	
Elevators, flour bucket, or pan and	
tray........................ 20	
Elongator........................ 20	
Embossing machine, biscuit....... 20	
Enrober.......................... 20	
Fans............................. 15	
Forming and stitching machines,	
carton..................... 15	
Fruitana machines................ 20	
Gluing machine................... 15	
Grinding machines................ 15	
Humidifiers...................... 15	
Ice boxes........................ 15	
Icing unit....................... 15	
Kettles—copper jacketed:	
Chocolate melting............. 25	
Marshmallow.................. 15	
Mixers:	
Cookie and cake, three spindle... 25	
Dough, fire barrel—	
High speed.................. 20	
Slow speed.................. 25	
Vertical dough, three and four	
speed:	
Light....................... 15	
Heavy...................... 20	
Molders:	
Dough....................... 12	
Roll......................... 12	
Ovens:	
Automatic or traveling.......... 17	
Band type................... 20	
Brick peel................... 20	
Portable peel................. 20	
Reel......................... 20	
Rotary...................... 15	
Stationary................... 25	
Packers......................... 15	
Pan greasers and cleaners........ 10	

Pans—baking.................... 6	
Paring machines................. 10	
Peeling machines................. 15	
Perforating machines............. 15	
Pie crimpers and trimmers........ 15	
Pie rolling machines.............. 15	
Pretzel cooking machines.......... 10	
Proofers........................ 15	
Pulverizers, sugar................ 20	
Reels, bolting.................... 15	
Refining machines, chocolate...... 20	
Refrigerating equipment. (See Ice	
manufacture and	
refrigeration.)	
Refrigerators.................... 15	
Roller, pie crust................. 15	
Rounding machine dough......... 15	
Rubbing and creaming machines... 20	
Sack cleaners.................... 15	
Sandwich machine............... 15	
Scales, automatic—Flour or water.. 15	
Sealer.......................... 15	
Sheeters........................ 15	
Sifters, flour, sugar, starch, etc..... 17	
Slicers, bread................... 12	
Spreader, sugar wafer............ 20	
Tables, sorting.................. 20	
Tanks:	
Galvanized iron............... 15	
Glass, enameled lined.......... 25	
Steel........................ 25	
Tempering and measuring....... 15	
Wood....................... 15	
Tape moistening machine........ 15	
Thermometers:	
Mercury column.............. 5	
Recording................... 10	
Topping machines............... 20	
Troughs, dough................. 25	
Trucks, bowl, bread or pan....... 20	
Wafer machines, automatic........ 20	
Wrapping machines............. 15	

BUILDINGS

The useful life of a building for business purposes depends to a large extent on the suitability of the structure to its use and location, its archi-

TABLE 17—AVERAGE USEFUL LIFE OF DEPRECIABLE EQUIPMENT (CONT.)

tectural quality, the rate of change in population, the shifting of land values, as well as the extent of maintenance and rehabilitations.

The extent to which the equipment of a building, such as heating, plumbing, electrical wiring and fixtures, elevators, and other improvements, must be replaced is an important factor in determining the over-all rate of depreciation to be applied to the building and its equipment. Such a rate contemplates that the cost of new equipment will be capitalized, and that the cost of the equipment replaced will be charged to the depreciation reserve. In instances, however, where it is not feasible to determine the cost of the old equipment, the cost of the new equipment may be charged to the depreciation reserve. Where this method of accounting is followed and in the absence of special circumstances, the composite rates of depreciation set forth in the table below are considered reasonable:

BUILDINGS—COMPOSITE RATE OF DEPRECIATION

| | Composite rate (percent) | | |
| | Type of construction | | |
	Good	Average	Cheap
Apartments............................	$2\frac{1}{2}$	$2\frac{1}{2}$	3
Banks................................	2	2	$2\frac{1}{2}$
Dwellings.............................	2	$2\frac{1}{2}$	3
Factories.............................	$2\frac{1}{4}$	$2\frac{1}{2}$	3
Farm buildings........................	2	2	$2\frac{1}{2}$
Garages..............................	2	$2\frac{1}{2}$	3
Grain elevators........................	$1\frac{1}{2}$	2	$2\frac{1}{2}$
Hotels...............................	$2\frac{1}{2}$	$2\frac{1}{2}$	3
Loft buildings.........................	2	2	3
Machine shops.........................	2	$2\frac{1}{2}$	3
Office buildings........................	2	$2\frac{1}{2}$	3
Stores...............................	2	2	$2\frac{1}{2}$
Theaters.............................	$2\frac{1}{2}$	3	$3\frac{1}{2}$
Warehouses...........................	$1\frac{1}{2}$	2	$2\frac{1}{2}$

Where, however, the building equipment is set up as a separate account for depreciation purposes, the above composite rates are not applicable and the appropriate rate should be determined by reference to the table of useful lives indicated below, which are considered reasonable for buildings of standard or sound construction:

TABLE 17—AVERAGE USEFUL LIFE OF DEPRECIABLE EQUIPMENT (CONT.)

Total life (years)

Apartments	50	Hotels	50
Banks	67	Loft buildings	67
Dwellings	60	Machine shops	60
Factories	50	Office buildings	67
Farm buildings	60	Stores	67
Garages	60	Theaters	50
Grain elevators	75	Warehouses	75

BUILDING EQUIPMENT

Average useful life (years)

Air conditioning:
Air conditioning systems—
  Large—over 20 tons.......... 20
  Medium—5 to 15 tons....... 15
  Small—under 5 tons.......... 10
Air washer. (*See* Dehumidifier.)
Compressors—
  Refrigerating............... 20
  Air for pneumatic controls.... 20
Condensers—
  Shell and tube.............. 20
  Double pipe................. 20
  Evaporation................. 15
Coolers, water—tank and coil or
  shell and tube............. 20
Dehumidifier.................. 10
Drums, purge or surge.......... 20
Fans......................... 15
Filters, air, oil, self-cleaning..... 20
  Dry cleanable.............. 10
Gauges....................... 15
Grilles and registers—
  Anemostats................. 20
  Grilles and registers—
    Wall type................ 20
    Ceiling................... 20
    Window units............. 15
  Placques.................... 20
Heaters—
  Boiler, oil burner and tank.... 20
  Booster heaters.............. 20
  Electric heaters.............. 15
  Finned tube heaters, steam
    water cleanable tube...... 20
  Preheaters and reheaters...... 20
  Water heaters, open or closed
    type.................. 20

Insulation—
  Cork, cold pipes and tanks.... 20
  Magnesia, hot pipes.......... 15
  Wool felt................... 20
  Asbestos.................... 15
Louvres and screens, fresh air—
  Copper.................... 25
  Steel...................... 15
Manometers................... 15
Motors—
  Synchronous and exciter set... 20
  Induction, indoor............ 20
  Induction, weatherproof for
    outdoor................. 20
Piping, refrigerant and other.... 20
Pumps—
  Chilled water................ 20
  Condenser water............. 20
  Condensate................. 20
  Dehumidifiers............... 22
  Evaporative condenser....... 15
  Sump...................... 25
  Well....................... 25
Receivers, refrigerant.......... 25
Regulators, suction or static
  pressure................... 5
Silica gel beds................ 15
Spray pond................... 15
Switchboard, electric panel...... 20
Thermometers, room type or re-
  cording................... 15
Tower, cooling................. 15
Valves—
  Relief...................... 20
  Automatic expansion and by-
    pass.................... 5

TABLE 17—AVERAGE USEFUL LIFE OF DEPRECIABLE EQUIPMENT (CONT.)

Solenoid	15	Plumbing:	
Water regulating	20	Faucets and flushing valves	15
Ammeters	15	Bath tubs, lavoratories, toilet	
Clocks	15	bowls, etc	25
Clocks, watchman	15	Pipes—	
Compressors, air and vacuum	20	Iron, cold-water	25
Electric clock systems:		Iron, hot-water or steam	20
Clocks, time	20	Valves—	
Conduits, fittings and wiring.		Iron body, water or steam	20
(See Lighting systems.)		Pumps:	
Motors and generators	20	Suction, pressure and sump	13
Switch equipment—		Roofs:	
Boxes.[1]		Asbestos	25
Switch parts	20	Asphalt and tar (prepared)	15
Elevators—		Galvanized iron—	
Freight	25	Light or cold dipped	15
Passenger	20	Heavy or hot dipped	20
Fire equipment:		Tar and gravel (5-ply)	20
Fire alarm systems	25	Tarred felt	10
Movable equipment	20	Starters, electric	20
Guards, machine	25	Switchboards, electric	25
Heaters, electric	10	Tanks and vats, water:	
Heaters, gas	15	Metal	25
Heating systems:		Wood	15
Boilers and furnaces	20	Telephone equipment:	
Burner equipment—		Wiring and fixtures	20
Gas	16	Tools, small, miscellaneous	5
Oil	10	Transformers	25
Radiators	25	Trucks, conveyance (within build-	
Lighting.systems:		ing)	10
Wiring	20	Trucks, lift	15
Fixtures	15	Voltmeters	15
Miscellaneous facilities:		Welfare equipment:	
Awnings	5	Athletic	10
Doors, louvre, ventilating	15	Cafeteria	10
Incinerators	14	Hospital and first aid	10
Screens, window	10	Police and fire	10
Shades	5	Wells and well pumps	25
Venetian blinds	8		

CHEMICALS

Estimated average lives for machinery and equipment, including power-generation facilities, for the various divisions of the chemical industries, are tabulated in detail for manufacturers of acids, alkalies, carbide and carbon products, electro-chemicals and soap:

TABLE 17—AVERAGE USEFUL LIFE OF DEPRECIABLE EQUIPMENT (CONT.)

	Years		*Years*
Acids	15	Chromium products	15
Atmospheric nitrogen	15	Coal-tar products	20
Alkaline products	22	Electro chemicals	17
Aniline dyes	20	Oxygen products	18
Carbide and carbon products	15	Pharmaceuticals	20
Carbonic gas products	16	Soap	20

Item lives are as follows:

ACIDS

Acetic:
Blow cases, cast-iron and copper   3
Columns, fractionating   8
Condensers—
Copper   10
Duriron   14
Lead   6
Motors   14
Pipes—
Aluminum   3
Glass   5
Acid—
Copper   10
Rubber   8
Water   10
Pots   17
Pumps, vacuum   7
Receivers, acid (stoneware)   14
Scrubbers (stoneware)   14
Receivers, acid, for product
(stoneware)   20
Stills—
Cast iron   12
Refining, copper   14
Refining, heating coil   3
Tanks, storage—
Steel   12
Wood   25
Muriatic:
Air lifts (hard rubber)   10
Cars, tank   10
Coolers   10
Elevators, bucket   10
Exhausters (rubber-lined)   8
Flues (earthenware)   10
Furnaces, Manheim   8
Furnaces, pot and muffle   10
Furnaces, retort   8

ACIDS—continued

Grinders and coolers, salt cake...   12
Motors   14
Pipes—
Acid (hard rubber)   7
Chemical ware   2
Oil   20
Water   4
Pots, condensing (earthenware)..   7
Pumps and blowcases—
Chemical ware-lined   3
Rubber-lined blowcase   5
Storage tanks (wooden, rubber
lined)   14
Tanks, sulphuric-acid storage
(steel)   20
Tourilles (silica)   10
Towers, absorbing   10
Nitric:
Blowers (stoneware)   5
Blowcases (earthenware)   2
Condensers (duriron)   12
Condensers, S bend (stoneware)..   2
Elevators and conveyors (screw)   10
Flues, gas (duriron)   8
Pans, niter cake (steel)   14
Pipes and fittings (earthenware,
duriron, lead)   2
Pumps, sulphuric (iron), centrif-
ugal   5
Receivers (stoneware)   5
Retorts, 24-hour service   3
Tanks (steel)   10
Towers, condensing   9
Sulphuric (chamber):
Air lifts, acid   10
Blowers, gas (lead)   17
Blowcases   10
Chambers   17

TABLE 17—AVERAGE USEFUL LIFE OF DEPRECIABLE EQUIPMENT (CONT.)

ACIDS—cont.

Coolers, acid (lead, coil), for salt water	10
Fans (cast-iron)	10
Pipes (lead)	10
Pots, niter	20
Pumps, acid	5
Tanks (steel), acid storage	20
Tanks, tower, acid distributing	8
Towers	20

Sulphuric (contact):

Air lifts	14
Blowcases (cast-iron and steel)	5
Blowers	20
Burners—	
Brimstone	10
Glens Falls	10
Other	15
Coke boxes	17
Combustion chambers, brimstone	10
Compressors, air	15
Contact mass, including plates and supports	17
Converters	14
Conveyors and elevators	10
Coolers—	
Drying acid	10
Gas	14
Gas, tower	10
Dust chambers (brick)	14
Filters, preliminary	11
Flues (iron)	13
Gauges, meters, pyrometers	14
Heaters, preliminary	14
Melters brimstone	10
Motors	17
Pipes, acid	10
Platinum, in catalyst	50
Pumps, acid (iron)	7
Pumps, acid (lead)	8
Separators	14
Sublimers, brimstone	10
Tanks—	
Roasted ore storage (steel)	20
Storage (lead)	20
Storage (steel)	17
Tank cars (steel)	12
Towers—	
Absorbing	9

ACIDS—cont.

Cooler, cold scrub	12
Dry	10
Oleum	10
Scrub	10
Transferrers	9

ALKALIES

Absorbers	30
Bins:	
Charging	30
Storage	25
Classifiers	20
Compressors:	
Chlorine dry gas	28
For carbon dioxide	25
Concentrating units (ammonium chloride)	12
Concentrating and evaporating units (for potassium carbonate)	20
Conveyors	20
Coolers, brine	20
Dryers:	
Salt (calcium chloride)	16
Steam (bicarbonate of soda)	20
Evaporators, caustic soda (cast iron, magnesia covered)	17
Feeder, lime	19
Filter wheel for causticizer	20
Flaker wheel with speed reducer	15
Furnaces (for calcining bicarbonate of soda into soda ash)	6
Kiln, lime	22
Pans, settler	20
Pots, cast iron	12
Pumps:	
Caustic soda (centrifugal type)	18
Chlorine dry gas	18
Receivers, vacuum	20
Recovery units	7
Retorts, cast iron	20
Scrubbers	35
Scrubbers, vacuum	20
Separators	20
Settling units (calcium chloride)	15
Slaker	21
Tanks:	
Ash storage	30
Bottom dissolver (caustic plant)	18

TABLE 17—AVERAGE USEFUL LIFE OF DEPRECIABLE EQUIPMENT (CONT.)

ALKALIES—cont.

Dissolver and mixer............ 30
Feeder, steel................... 33
Filter wheel causticizer......... 20
Lime.......................... 21
Mixing........................ 25
Mud........................... 33
Mud storage................... 30
Salt settling................... 20
Settling....................... 33
Storage....................... 30
Storage (weak caustic soda solution)............ 22
Thickener..................... 25
Towers........................ 25
Towers:
  Carbonating and precipitating... 33
  Distillation................... 33
  Washing (for chlorine gas)—
    Cast iron................... 20
    Stone...................... 22
Washers....................... 37

CARBIDE AND CARBON PRODUCTS

Absorbers...................... 10
Bagging machines............... 14
Barrels, tilting and tumbling...... 8
Breakers....................... 12
Briquetting machines............ 18
Buckets, charging............... 8
Cells, chlorine.................. 6
Charging machines.............. 12
Chlorinators................... 12
Coke quenchers................. 15
Columns....................... 8
Columns, ammonia.............. 6
Concentrators (hydraulic type).... 12
Condensers (closed type)......... 17
Containers, copper.............. 9
Coolers, after, fore, and inter...... 17
Coolers........................ 10
Crushers, gyratory, jaw and roll... 12
Digesters...................... 10
Dryers (rotary and tunnel types).. 25
Evaporators.................... 17
Fillers, bag.................... 14
Furnaces:
  Electric, carbide and metallurgical 20

CARBIDE AND CARBON PRODUCTS—cont.

Gas for heat treating, torching,
  and branding.............. 8
  Pre-heating and welding........ 12
Generators, acetylene............ 12
Grinders....................... 12
Holders, gas................... 25
Hydrators...................... 12
Hydrolyzers.................... 7
Incinerators................... 22
Kettles:
  Melting.................... 6
  Nitrating................... 6
  Reducing................... 6
  Salt....................... 6
  Steam jacketed.............. 6
Kilns:
  Calcinating................. 22
  Rotary..................... 22
  Vertical.................... 28
Ladles......................... 22
Mills.......................... 12
Mills, stamp................... 12
Mixers......................... 12
Ovens, coke................... 17
Oxygen manifolds............... 20
Pans:
  Melting.................... 6
  Nitrating................... 6
  Reducing................... 6
  Steam jacketed.............. 6
Pre-heater..................... 9
Precipitators................... 18
Press, filter................... 17
Pulverizers.................... 12
Purifiers...................... 18
Receivers, copper.............. 9
Retorts........................ 22
Saturators..................... 12
Screens........................ 12
Sifters........................ 12
Stills (closed type)............. 17
Thickeners.................... 17
Towers:
  Acid and reaction........... 5
  Cooling.................... 7

CARBONIC GAS PRODUCTS

Absorbers, gas.................. 16

TABLE 17—AVERAGE USEFUL LIFE OF DEPRECIABLE EQUIPMENT (CONT.)

CARBONIC GAS PRODUCTS—cont.

Compressors:

Air	22
Carbonic dry ice	6
Coolers, gas	15
Cylinders	25
Interchargers, heat	15
Liquefiers	14
Scrubbers, gas	16
Towers, purifier	15

ELECTRO CHEMICALS

Absorbers	20
Air washers	20
Blowers, noncorrosive fumes	25
Burners, phosphorus	10
Cells, electrolytic	15
Centrifugals	25
Compressors, air	25
Compressors (gas pumps)	15

Condensers:

Concrete construction	25
Steel, with tubes	20
Conveyors	20

Coolers:

Lead-lined	15
Rotary	20
Crystallizers	15
Digesters, lead-lined	15
Dishes, silica	10
Dissolvers, lead-lined	15
Drainers, lead-lined	15

Dryers:

Rotary tube	10
Vacuum	20
Drying pans, lead-lined	20
Dust collectors	15
Eggs, lead-lined	15

Elevators:

Bucket and belt	15
Screw conveyors	10

Evaporators:

Lead-lined	15
Steam	15
Evaporating pans, steam jacketed kettles	15
Fans	20
Filters	20

ELECTRO CHEMICALS—cont.

Filter presses:

Cast-iron plates	15
Steel leaves	20
Furnaces, electric	20

Heaters:

Electric, hot plate	15
Electric, hot water	12
Hoppers, sheet metal	15
Kilns, rotary	15
Meter, liquid measuring	10
Metering equipment, electric	25
Mills, grinding	20
Mixers	20
Motor	20
Motor generator sets	20
Pipe, silica	4

Piping:

Air, gas, steam, water	25
Corrosive matter	15

Pots:

Caustic	18
Ceramics	15
Furnace (cast-iron)	20
Melting (cast-iron)	15

Pumps:

Corrosive liquor	10
Water	20
Reactors, electrical	25
Regulators, temperature	10
Rotary converters	25
Scales	15
Scooper, bucket type	10
Speed reducers	12
Stills, lead	10
Stoker, to kiln	15

Tanks:

Aluminum	15
Cast-iron	25
Galvanized-iron	15
Hot water storage	15
Lead-lined	15
Steel or concrete lined	15
Wooden, lead-lined	15
Towers, steel	20
Transformers	25
Troughs, silica	4

TABLE 17—AVERAGE USEFUL LIFE OF DEPRECIABLE EQUIPMENT (CONT.)

OXYGEN

Columns	10
Compressors:	
Air	25
Nitrogen	20
Oxygen	20
Cylinders	25
Cylinder drying chambers	18
Cylinder testing apparatus	10
Dryers, oxygen	14
Engines, expansion	25
Holders, oxygen	25
Oxygen filling manifolds	12
Towers:	
Cooling	12
Decarbonizing (steel drum type)	16

SOAP

Absorber, heat	20
Acid egg	5
Air duct	25
Auto	5
Baling machine	20
Barrel and factory equipment:	
Boring machine	20
Crozer	15
Expander	20
Header	20
Hoop driver	15
Hoop remover	20
Jointer	20
Lathe	30
Leveling machine	20
Punch press	25
Riveter	15
Windlass	20
Barrel packer	20
Blowers:	
Roots	15
Centrifugal	15
Boilers	20
Box, picker	13
Breeching, boiler	20
Brush, air	10
Bunker room	15
Burners, oil	15
Can-filling machines	15
Can labeler	22

SOAP—cont.

Can-testing equipment	15
Cars, box	25
Carton-feeding machines	15
Carton-filling machines	15
Carton folders	15
Catchall—copper	10
Catchall—steel	10
Causticizer	20
Crystallizing machine	20
Coal-handling equipment	15
Compressor, air	20
Conveyors:	
Belt	15
Flight	20
Gravity	20
Screw	10
Copra mill equipment:	
Accumulator	25
Attrition mills	13
Cage press	20
Cake breaker	20
Cake former	25
Cake trimmer	20
Cooker	15
Cooler	20
Expeller	10
Hydraulic press	25
Hydraulic pump	20
Steel rolls	20
Crane, coal (locomotive)	25
Crusher, coal	15
Crutcher	15
Deaerater	20
Deodorizer	15
Drums	15
Dryer, catalyst	15
Dust collectors	15
Ejector	15
Electric, cells—gas equipment	13
Electric, welding equipment	20
Elevators:	
Bucket	20
Freight	25
Hydraulic	25
Exchanger, heat	20
Exchanger, multiwhirl	15
Fans	15

TABLE 17—AVERAGE USEFUL LIFE OF DEPRECIABLE EQUIPMENT (CONT.)

SOAP—cont.

Fat acid:
Mat, lead.................... 8
Pipe........................ 10
Pump....................... 4
Stills....................... 10
Tanks, copper............... 25
Tubs—lead-lined............. 8
Tufls—unlined.............. 7
Framer, box................... 20
Furnace—fat acid, fuel:
Oil fired.................... 8
Meprolene.................. 8
Selox...................... 8
Silicate.................... 5
Hardening machine.............. 20
Heater, feed water............. 20
Heating unit.................. 15
Hoist........................ 15
Hoop driver................... 15
Hose, fire.................... 5
Hose house.................... 15
Ice machines.................. 25
Kettles, refining.............. 25
Kettles, soap................. 25
Kiln, lime................... 25
Laboratory equipment........... 10
Laundry equipment............. 15
Locomotive................... 25
Machine shop:
Drill press................. 25
Forge...................... 22
Grinder.................... 20
Lathe...................... 25
Milling machine............. 20
Planer..................... 25
Pipe machine............... 20
Shaper..................... 20
Meters:
Electric.................... 25
Flow...................... 25
Gas....................... 25
Water..................... 30
Mixer........................ 12
Mixer, concrete............... 12
Nailing machines.............. 20
Pans, candle factory........... 20
Pans, granite................. 20
Perforator................... 20

SOAP—cont.

Pipes and fittings............... 20
Pits, unloading................. 30
Presses, filter.................. 25
Presses, hydraulic, cold.......... 25
Presses, hydraulic, hot........... 25
Printer, box................... 20
Pumps, centrifugal and rotary:
Brine...................... 20
Deep well.................. 25
Oil........................ 20
Soap...................... 15
Stock...................... 15
Vacuum.................... 20
Water..................... 25
Pumps, reciprocating:
Brine...................... 20
Fat acid................... 7
High pressure............... 20
Oil........................ 20
Soap...................... 15
Stock—glycerine............. 20
Stock—lye.................. 15
Stock—silicate.............. 15
Vacuum.................... 20
Water..................... 25
Reduction unit, gear............. 20
Refrigerators.................. 20
Regulator, feed water........... 20
Roaster....................... 10
Rolls, lard.................... 25
Saws, motor-driven............. 15
Scale:
Automatic.................. 10
Beam, portable.............. 15
Check weigher.............. 10
Tank...................... 25
Track...................... 25
Sealer:
Carbon—
Bottom.................. 20
Top.................... 20
Compression unit............ 20
Container.................. 20
Sewing machine................ 15
Shears, paper.................. 20
Soap:
Chip, dryer................. 15
Cooling rools............... 20

TABLE 17—AVERAGE USEFUL LIFE OF DEPRECIABLE EQUIPMENT (CONT.)

SOAP—cont.		SOAP—cont.	
Cutting machine	15	Lye	20
Frames—iron or aluminum	20	Silicate	20
Mills—pulverizing	20	U	20
Plodder	15	Water	20
Powder tower	15	Thermometer, recording	20
Rotary screen	15	Tower, cooling	15
Rolls—granite or steel	20	Tractors:	
Slabbing machine	20	Edison cell	7
Wrapping machine	15	Electric	10
Spraying equipment	10	Gasoline	8
Sprinkler system	25	Lead cell	3
Stacking device	15	Transmission machinery	15
Stacks, metal	25	Tubs (other than fat acid)	15
Stencil machine	20	Turbines	25
Stills, glycerine	15	Utensils, small	10
Stitching machine	15	Ventilating system	15
Stoker	15	Washer, air	20
Superheater	5	Wells:	
Switchboard	25	Deep	40
Tanks:		Hot	20
Bleacher	20	Wiring, power:	
Oil	25	Inside	25
Sludge	20	Outside	15
Stock—			
Glycerine	20		

CONSTRUCTION

Ordinarily, the physical property used by contractors in construction has relatively short lives, due to hard usage and, often, general lack of up-keep during rush jobs. Where a taxpayer maintains complete repair facilities, and equipment is kept in good condition or reconditioned after each job, lives are considerably longer than the average under such circumstances. In the absence of special circumstances the following lives are considered reasonable:

	Years
Buildings construction	10
Highway construction	6
Levee construction	10
Marine construction	20

The item lives applicable to the various construction facilities are as follows:

TABLE 17—AVERAGE USEFUL LIFE OF DEPRECIABLE EQUIPMENT (CONT.)

Average useful life (years)

Automobiles:

Light	2
Medium	3
Heavy	5

Backfillers, power:

Light	3
Medium	5
Heavy	6
Tractor	5

Barges:

Steel	30
Wood	25

Batcher plants:

All steel, demountable	10
Steel frame, wood bin	10
Stationary	14
Wood frame and wood bin	7
Batch, measuring devices	4
Benders, bar	5
Bending blocks	10

Bending machines:

Angle	15
Pipe	10
Rail	10

Bins:

Steel, concrete	6
Steel	12
Wood	8
Bin frames, steel	6
Blacksmith shop outfits, portable	4
Blocks, pulley, differential	6
Blowers, mechanical	10

Boats:

House	20
Motor	8

Boilers:

Upright	7
Locomotive	15
Stationary	20
Borers (wood) portable	3
Boring apparatus, test	10
Boxes, mortar and batch	3

Brakes:

Bending	10
Cornice (sheet metal)	22
Breakers, pavement, pneumatic	3

Buckets:

Cableway	6
Clamshell	6
Concrete	5
Elevator	5
Orange peel	6
Bail, pivot turnover	5
Scraper or drag line	6

Buggies:

Concrete	3
Timber	3

Bulldozers:

Gradebuilders	8
Tractor	4
Bunkers, stone portable, with screens	6
Burner equipment, gas and oil	12
Cables, wire	4
Cableways, cable only	3
Cableway carriage	5
Camping equipment	3
Capstans, electric	10

Cars:

Ballast spreader	10
Batch box, steel	5
Boarding and tool	20
Concrete	8
Derrick, bridge	10
Dump, steel	8
Dump, wood	6
Flat, steel	12
Flat, wood	10
Hand	10
Hopper	10
Scale	10
Skip hoist	10
Tank	20
Carts, concrete	3
Carts, tool (steel)	4
Cement gun machines	4

Chains:

Hawsers and lines	6
Power, transmission	5
Channelers, rock	6
Chipping and calking tools, pneumatic	3
Chutes, concrete, gravity	2
Clamps, column form	5
Cleaning machine for exterior of building, steam or stand	15

TABLE 17—AVERAGE USEFUL LIFE OF DEPRECIABLE EQUIPMENT (CONT.)

Compressors:
  Belt driven................... 10
  Electric, portable............. 8
  Gasoline, portable............. 6
  Motor-truck unit.............. 5
  Steam portable............... 6
Concrete machines, pneumatic..... 5
Concrete mixers:
  Electric...................... 5
  Gasoline, $3\frac{1}{2}$s, 5s, 7s............ 3
  Gasoline, 10s, 14s............. 4
  Gasoline, 21s, 28s............. 5
  Paving, gas................... 8
  Paving, steam................. 8
  Steam....................... 8
  Truck mounted............... 5
Controllers, motor.............. 12
Conveyors:
  Belt, elevating—
    Portable................... 3
    Stationary................. 6
  Bucket...................... 6
  Cable—
    Drag...................... 6
    Monorail.................. 15
  Chain, portable............... 6
  Portable..................... 5
  Scraper..................... 6
Cranes:
  Bridge and cantilever.......... 20
  Crawler—
    Electric—
      $2\frac{1}{2}$, 5 tons............... 5
      10, 15 tons.............. 7
      20 tons and over.......... 9
    Gas—
      $2\frac{1}{2}$, 5 tons............... 5
      10, 15 tons.............. 9
      20 tons and over.......... 12
      Locomotive gas........... 7
    Steam—
      $2\frac{1}{2}$, 5 tons............... 6
      10, 15 tons.............. 10
      20 tons and over.......... 12
      Locomotive............... 10
  Dock or wharf, traveling........ 20
  Dragline..................... 10
  Universal (gas, $2\frac{1}{2}$ to 5 ton),
    mounted on 10-ton truck.... 6

Craneways:
  Steel........................ 15
  Wood....................... 10
Crushers, rock:
  Portable..................... 8
  Stationary................... 10
Cutters:
  Bar, power................... 5
  Corrugated iron, hand.......... 10
Cutting and welding outfits, port-
    able...................... 4
Davits......................... 15
Derricks:
  Boat........................ 10
  Circle swing, hand............. 8
  Crab—
    Hand..................... 16
    Power.................... 10
  Guy—
    Steel..................... 12
    Wood.................... 8
  Stiffleg—
    Steel..................... 12
    Wood.................... 8
Diggers, clay, pneumatic......... 3
Drag lines:
  Electric—
    $\frac{1}{2}$, $\frac{3}{4}$ cubic yard.............. 6
    1, $1\frac{1}{4}$, and $1\frac{1}{2}$ cubic yards...... 8
    2 cubic yards and over........ 10
  Gasoline—
    $\frac{1}{2}$, $\frac{3}{4}$ cubic yard.............. 5
    1, $1\frac{1}{4}$, and $1\frac{1}{2}$ cubic yard...... 9
    2 cubic yards and over........ 12
  Steam—
    $\frac{1}{2}$, $\frac{3}{4}$ cubic yard.............. 6
    1, $1\frac{1}{4}$, and $1\frac{1}{2}$ cubic yards...... 10
    2 cubic yards and over........ 12
Dredges:
  Clamshell.................... 16
  Dipper...................... 8
  Hydraulic.................... 20
  Pipe........................ 10
Drill boats..................... 12
Drill points, well................ 5
Drills:
  Airdrifter.................... 3
  Electric or pneumatic, hand, for
    wood or metal............. 5

TABLE 17—AVERAGE USEFUL LIFE OF DEPRECIABLE EQUIPMENT (CONT.)

Hand, electric	3	Gas or oil	7
Rock, electric	3	Generator sets:	
Jackhammer	3	Steam engine	12
Steam	5	Turbine, headlight or floodlight	4
Traction, well	7	Gin poles (steel)	10
Tripod	7	Gradebuilders (bulldozers)	8
Tunnel carriage	5	Graders:	
Well	10	Blade, road—	
Drums for oil (steel)	10	7-, 8-foot blade	4
Elevators:		9-, 10-foot blade	5
Bucket, stationary	6	Over 10-foot blade	8
Cage (steel tower)	5	Elevating	8
Engines:		Form, subgrade planers	6
Blowing	12	Rooters, wheel	5
Fire	7	Grinders:	
Gas	10	Metal surface	15
Marine	20	Saw filers and setters	14
Oil	20	Surface, concrete	4
Plumbing	14	Hammers:	
Steam	11	Electric	3
Excavators:		Pneumatic riveting	3
Cableway, complete	4	Harness	4
Trench, gasoline—		Heaters, asphalt, tar, and pitch	
7-foot depth	6	kettles	4
12-foot depth	6	Helmets, gas and diving suits and	
18-foot depth	8	equipment	10
Trench, steam—		Hoists:	
7-foot depth	8	Air, electric, or steam	8
12-foot depth	8	Chain	6
18-foot depth	10	Electric monorail or post	5
Trench, vertical boom	5	Gas	6
Wheel or ladder type	5	Hand power	8
Extinguishers, fire	3	Slew—	
Fans, exhaust	15	Electric	8
Finishing machines	4	Steam	12
Floats, bridge (steel)	5	Holders on pneumatic	4
Forges, gas or oil burning	10	Horses	5
Forms:		Hose:	
Concrete (metal pans)	5	Fire, linen or rubber lined cotton	5
Concrete, supports, adjustable	4	Metal, flexible	10
Steel, for—		Oil	5
Pavements	4	Reel or cart	10
Pipes	3	Rubber, air, steam, or water	10
Roads	4	Inundators, batch	4
Tunnels and conduits	4	Inland craft:	
Walls	5	Graders, hydraulic	7
Furnaces, metal melting:		Quarter boats	10
Coal fired	10	Jacks:	
Electric	12	Hydraulic	8

TABLE 17—AVERAGE USEFUL LIFE OF DEPRECIABLE EQUIPMENT (CONT.)

Rail	25	Small	8
Ratchet	8	Hydraulic	5
Screw	5	Pneumatic	5
Steamboat, push and pull	3	Mowers, right of way	5
Jibs, steam	17	Mules	5
Jointers, bench, electric, steam, or		Pile drivers:	
gas	5	Barge	8
Ladder:		Railroad outfits	10
Rope, wood rungs	2	Steam, on skids	10
Steel	3	Track	12
Ladles, metal	7	Pile hammers, steam or air:	
Lathes:		Heavy	10
Metalworking	15	Light	4
Woodworking	17	Medium	5
Launches, gasoline	10	Pipe:	
Levee construction equipment:		Black or galvanized	4
Drag lines	8	Wood	5
Shovels	8	Wood and steel combination	6
Tower excavators	12	Pipe lines and fittings, for floating	
Life-saving equipment	10	dredges	10
Light plant	4	Pit and quarry plants	6
Lighters	22	Planers:	
Loaders, bucket:		Metalworking	15
Crawler	5	Woodworking	20
Portable	5	Plows:	
Stationary	6	Furrow	3
Locomotive battery	4	Rooter	6
Locomotives, industrial:		Pontoons	20
Diesel	10	Presses, drill	12
Electric	16	Pumping units:	
Gas—		Electric—	
Up to 10 tons	8	Centrifugal	6
10 to 20 tons	15	Diaphragm	6
Over 20 tons	20	Piston	6
Steam—		Gas—	
Up to 10 tons	8	Centrifugal	6
10 to 20 tons	18	Diaphragm	6
Over 20 tons	20	Highway contractor's pump	4
Locomotives, standard gauge	30	Piston	5
Magnets, lifting	15	Steam, centrifugal	10
Milling machines	15	Pumps:	
Mixers; portable mortar	3	Air lift	10
Less than $\frac{1}{3}$ cubic yard	6	Centrifugal	6
Over $\frac{1}{3}$ cubic yard	8	Humdinger	6
Caterpillar	8	Impulse	6
Motors:		Hydraulic	15
AC and DC—		Oil	10
Large	12	Steam piston unit	6
Medium	10	Testing for pipe lines	15

TABLE 17—AVERAGE USEFUL LIFE OF DEPRECIABLE EQUIPMENT (CONT.)

Punches, hydraulic	20	$\frac{1}{2}$, $\frac{3}{4}$ cubic yard	5
Punches for steel, power	15	1, $1\frac{1}{4}$, $1\frac{1}{2}$ cubic yards	6
Racks, storage, for pipe and steel:		2 cubic yards and over	8
Steel	20	Steam, crawler or wheel—	
Wood	15	$\frac{1}{2}$, $\frac{3}{4}$ cubic yard	7
Rails, steel	10	1, $1\frac{1}{4}$, $1\frac{1}{2}$ cubic yards	8
Razing equipment, for buildings	8	2 cubic yards and over	10
Reamers:		Railroad, steam	10
Electric	3	Tunnel	4
Pneumatic	3	Spouting plants, complete, concrete	4
Riveters, pneumatic	5	Spraying equipment, paint	12
Rollers:		Spreaders, stone:	
Concrete finishing (steel)	10	Hopper wagon	5
Road, gas	10	Steel box	5
Road, steam	10	Steamers, paddle wheel	30
Rolls, ridge	5	Switches:	
Rowboats	6	Portable	4
Sand-blast outfits	10	Stationary	5
Sawmills, portable	10	Tampers, backfill, pneumatic	3
Saws:		Tamping machines	10
Band, cut-off and rip, power	10	Tanks:	
Hand, electric and pneumatic	3	Gasoline, storage	6
Saws and woodworkers:		Relay	6
Steel frames	10	Water or air, storage (steel)	10
Wood frames	5	Water storage (wood)	14
Scales, large, track and wagon	20	Tarpaulins and tents	3
Scarifiers:		Threading and cutting machines,	
Attachments	4	pipe	10
Blocks, steerable	5	Ties:	
Drag, all steel	4	Steel	12
Grader type	4	Wood	6
Scows	25	Tongs, chain	4
Scows, dump	25	Towers:	
Scrapers:		Cableway—	
Blade, carryall	6	Steel	6
Fresno or Morman	2	Wood	3
Rotary	4	Steel boom with counterweights	5
Slip	2	Tracks, industrial, portable	6
Wheel	5	Tractors:	
Screens and bunkers, for gravel pits		Electric—	
only	5	3-ton	3
Screws, revolving	6	5-ton	5
Sharpeners, drill	8	10-ton	6
Shears, for steel, hand	10	20-ton	8
Shores, adjustable	4	Gas or steam—	
Shovel attachments, for cranes	6	3-ton	4
Shovels:		5-ton	6
Electric or gasoline, crawler or		10-ton	8
wheel—		20-ton	10

TABLE 17—AVERAGE USEFUL LIFE OF DEPRECIABLE EQUIPMENT (CONT.)

Trailers:
  Dump—
    Steel...................... 10
    Wood...................... 10
  Platform, wood............... 4
  Drop platform, heavy duty...... 5
Transformers, car............... 10
Trenching machines. (*See* Excavators.)
Trucks, auto:
  General purpose or dump—
    ⅓–⅔ cubic yard.............. 3
    1–1⅔ cubic yards............ 5
    2 cubic yards and over........ 8
Tugs, screw-propelled, steam or gas 25
Turntables, industrial railway..... 4
Vises........................... 5

Wagons:
  Dump—
    Steel...................... 6
    Wood...................... 6
  Farm—
    Heavy..................... 10
    Light...................... 10
  Road oilers, tank, steel......... 10
  Tank or sprinkler—
    Steel...................... 10
    Wood...................... 8
Washers, gravel................. 3
Welding outfits, acetylene or electric 10
Wheelbarrows.................. 2
Winches, electric and pneumatic... 10
Wire and cables:
  Electric...................... 6
  Flexible, steel armored......... 8

LAUNDRIES

The general composite life applicable to laundry machinery is 14 years. The item machinery used by laundries is listed below:

Average useful life (years)

Assembly wheel.................. 10
Bins:
  Metal....................... 30
  Wood....................... 20
Blocking machines, hat........... 20
Blowers......................... 15
Booths, marking (metal)......... 15
Brushing machines, blanket....... 15
Burners, gas or oil.............. 15
Cabinets, towel.................. 10
Carding machines................ 15
Chutes, metal................... 20
Clarifiers....................... 14
Cleaning machines:
  Dry-cleaning solvent.......... 15
  Rug......................... 12
Conveyors...................... 20
Cookers, starch................. 12
Dampeners...................... 15
Dryers.......................... 15
Dryrooms, conveyor type......... 15
Extractors...................... 15
Filtration systems............... 12

Fluters, electric................. 8
Glove machine................... 14
Hand irons:
  Electric...................... 6
  Gas......................... 10
Heaters, hot water.............. 20
Ironers......................... 15
Kettles, soap................... 25
Mangles, or flat work ironers...... 15
Marking machines............... 15
Molders, collar.................. 15
Pleating machines............... 12
Presses......................... 15
Pumps, steam................... 20
Purifiers........................ 14
Scales, platform................. 20
Sewing machines................. 15
Softeners, water................. 20
Spotting units................... 10
Starchers....................... 14
Stretchers, curtain............... 20
Tables.......................... 14

TABLE 17—AVERAGE USEFUL LIFE OF DEPRECIABLE EQUIPMENT (CONT.)

Tanks:		Tubs:	
Dry, copper	30	Granite	14
Hot water	25	Wood	8
Rug dye	12	Tumblers	15
Soap	14	Vacuum machines	15
Trays, identification	10	Washers:	
Trucks:		Brass	12
Canvas, fiber or wood	5	Monel metal	15
Galvanized	10	Wood	8
Monel metal	20		

MOTOR AND OTHER VEHICLES

Motor vehicles included in this classification are those used by commercial enterprises other than public utility and construction. Lives considered reasonable are indicated below:

	Years		Years
Automobiles:		Trucks:	
Passenger	5	Outside use—	
Salesman	3	Electric	10
Horse-drawn vehicles	8	Gas, light	4
Motorcycles	4	Medium	6
Tractors	6	Heavy	8
Trailers	6	Inside use	15

OFFICE EQUIPMENT

A composite life of about 15 years has been found applicable to office equipment. Where the equipment is segregated into groups, the following lives are recognized:

	Years
Safes	50
Furniture, fixtures, and filing cases	20
Mechanical equipment	8

Item lives are given in the following list:

Average useful life (years)

		Cases:	
Adding machines	10	Book	20
Addressing and mailing machines	15	Display	20
Billing machines	8	Chairs:	
Binders, loose-leaf	20	Bentwood	5
Blue-printing machines	15	Heavy	16
Bookkeeping machines	8	Check perforators	10
Cabinets and files	15	Check writers	8
Calculators	10	Cleaners, electric vacuum	6
Call system and annunciators	14		

TABLE 17—AVERAGE USEFUL LIFE OF DEPRECIABLE EQUIPMENT (CONT.)

Clocks:		Mirrors	20
Time	15	Money machines	10
Time-stamping	10	Numbering machines	10
Wall	20	Photographing machines	16
Coolers, water	10	Pneumatic-tube systems	20
Desks	20	Racks and stands	15
Dictation machines	6	Rugs, carpets, and mats	10
Duplicating machines	10	Safes and vaults	50
Fans, electric	10	Scales, counter and mail	10
Folding and sealing machines	10	Settees	13
Helmets, rescue	6	Shades, window	10
Hospital equipment	15	Signs, board	10
Lamps, desk and floor	10	Tables	15
Linoleum	8	Typewriter	5
Lockers	25	Wardrobes	20
Lunch-room equipment	15		

PRINTING AND PUBLISHING

The composite life applicable to the machinery of publishing companies and large jobbers is approximately 17 years. The general classification is as follows:

	Years
Printing department	20-25
Linotype department	17
Composing room	12
Assembling department	10
Photography department	10
Rotogravure department	17
Type	6

The estimated item lives are given in the following schedule:

Average useful life (years)

Addressing and mailing machines	15	Furnaces, melting	13
Balers, paper	17	Galleys (steel and brass)	5
Binder machines	15	Mill fixtures	10
Blowers	15	Molders, curved plate	15
Boxes, casting	10	Molds, casting, flat	15
Casting machines:		Plates, aluminum and zinc	10
Lead and rule	10	Pots, melting:	
Slug	15	Electric	10
Conveyors	20	Gas-fired	6
Cranes	20	Presses:	
Cutters	20	Hand	20
Cylinders, finishing	20	Power	25
Elevators, hydraulic	20	Rolling machines	15
Folders, rotary	20	Routers	10

TABLE 17—AVERAGE USEFUL LIFE OF DEPRECIABLE EQUIPMENT (CONT.)

Ruling machines	15	Stacking machines	15
Scales:		Stands, ingot	20
Platform	20	Stitchers	10
Platform, portable	15	Stones, lithographing	20
Scorchers:		Tables, steam	15
Gas-fired	3	Trimmers	15
Plate, electric	10	Type faces, metal	6
Shaving machines, plate	10	Typesetting machines	20

TEXTILES

The composite life for the machinery of concerns spinning and weaving cotton, wool, or silk is approximately 25 years, and for those engaged in knitting the same materials 15 years. Rayon manufacturing machinery composite life is approximately 16 years.

The following are the item lives considered reasonable for the manufacturing facilities used in the textile industry, exclusive of rayon:

Average useful life (years)

Aging machines	25	Cards	40
Agitators	25	Cleaning and scouring machine	25
Air compressor	25	Cloth turning machine	25
Atomizing machine	25	Coating machine	20
Back filling machine	25	Combers	25
Balling and winding machine	30	Compress press, cotton—hydraulic	
Banding machine	30	and mechanical	40
Beaming machine	25	Conditioning machine	20
Beating machine	30	Conewinding machine	20
Beetling machine—wool	30	Conveyor, seed—cotton gin	15
Bleaching machine	20	Copper rolls for printing machine	10
Blending or mixing machine	25	Copping machine	20
Blowers	20	Crabbing machine—worsted,	
Boarding machine—hosiery	15	woolen, and wool silk	30
Boilers	25	Creasing machine	25
Boil-off or degumming machine	20	Crocheting machine	15
Braiding machine	30	Cropping and shearing machine	30
Breaker—bale	30	Cutting and folding machine	30
Brushing machine	30	Decating machine	25
Buffing machine	25	Degumming or boil-off machine	20
Burring machine	25	Doubling machine	30
Button breaker machine	25	Double sole cutter	15
Banding machine for cotton bales	20	Downe spinning machine	15
Band cutting machine—cotton bales	20	Drawing-in and tying machine	25
Calendars:		Dry boxes	25
Plain	25	Drying machine:	
Moire—silk	25	Continuous type	25
Can dryer	25	Cylinder or can type	20
Carbonizing machine	20	Dust-collecting system	30

TABLE 17—AVERAGE USEFUL LIFE OF DEPRECIABLE EQUIPMENT (CONT.)

Dye equipment:
Dye beck.................... 15
Dye drum................... 20
Dye jiggers.................. 15
Dyeing machines—
  Warp..................... 15
  Reel...................... 15
Dye tanks, tubs, and vats—
  Ferrous metal.............. 20
  Nonferrous metal........... 15
  Wood..................... 10
Embroidering machine........... 15
Examining machine............. 20
Exhaust fans.................. 15
Extractor:
  Hydro..................... 15
  Horizontal roll............. 15
Eyelet machine................ 20
Facing machine................ 25
Fans, exhaust................. 15
Filters:
  Chemical................... 25
  Water—wood, gravity.......... 25
  Water—steel, pressure.......... 25
Fish line machine............... 30
Folding and cutting machine...... 30
Fringing machine.............. 20
Fulling machine............... 20
Garnet machine................ 40
Gassing machine............... 20
Gins, cotton.................. 30
Grinders for cards............. 20
Hankwinding machine.......... 25
Heads for jacquard looms........ 20
Humidifying heads............. 15
Humidifying system........... 25
Insert machine................ 20
Inspecting machine............ 20
Intermediate roving frame....... 25
Jacquard heads................ 20
Jigger-dye................... 15
Kettle, copper or steam jacket..... 20
Kettle, mixing................. 15
Kiers........................ 33
Kneading machine:
  Silk....................... 25
  Circular................... 15
  Flat...................... 15

Lacing machine for jacquard card
  patterns.................. 20
Lap machine.................. 30
Loom....................... 25
Looping machine.............. 15
Lustering machine............. 30
Mangle...................... 25
Measuring machine............. 25
Mercerizing machine........... 25
Mixing kettle................. 15
Mixing or blending machine....... 25
Moistening equipment.......... 25
Motors, electric............... 25
Mules, spinning frame........... 30
Napping machine.............. 25
Necktie machine............... 15
Opening machine.............. 25
Palming finishing machine........ 25
Picking machine............... 30
Pile-raising machine........... 25
Polishing machine............. 25
Pre-shrinking machine.......... 20
Press, balling—hydraulic or mechan-
  ical...................... 35
Print machine................. 30
Pump:
  Air....................... 25
  Chemical.................. 15
  Feed water................. 25
  Fire...................... 35
  Humidifying system.......... 25
Quetch...................... 25
Quilling machine.............. 20
Reel:
  Dyeing.................... 15
  Yarn..................... 25
Rolling machine............... 25
Rope machine................. 25
Roving frame—intermediate and
  finishing.................. 25
Rubbing machine.............. 25
Scales, platform.............. 20
Scouring and cleaning machine..... 25
Scutcher.................... 25
Seaming machine.............. 15
Sewing machine............... 15
Sewing machine—railway......... 25
Shears...................... 25
Shearing and shaving machine..... 30

TABLE 17—AVERAGE USEFUL LIFE OF DEPRECIABLE EQUIPMENT (CONT.)

Singeing machine	20	Silk	15
Skeining machine	25	Twist setting machine—silk	20
Slashing machine	25	Tiering or loading machine	15
Slubber	25	Tubing machine	25
Speeder—roving	25	Vacuum suction unit	25
Spinning frame:		Velour machine	25
Mule	30	Ventilating system	20
Ring	30	Warping machine	30
Spooling machine	25	Washing machine	20
Spool stamping machine	20		
Squeezing machine or mangle	25	WATER FILTRATION AND SOFTENING PLANT	
Starching equipment	25		
Steam engine	25	Concrete settling basin	40
Strippers, card:		Filter—water:	
Mechanical	15	Wood gravity	25
Vacuum	25	Steel pressure	25
Suction feeder—cotton gin	20	Pumps:	
Tables, inspection	20	Raw water	20
Tanks, tubs, and vats:		Chemical	15
Wood	20	Softener, water	25
Ferrous	20	Tank:	
Nonferrous	15	Steel	25
Teasel gig	20	Wood (acid salts)	20
Tenter frame	20	Waterproofing machine	20
Throwing machinery—silk	15	Waxing machine	20
Ticket machine	33	Winding machine	25
Twisting machine:		Wire stitching machine	20
Cotton	25	Wrapping machine	20

RAYON

The following group lives are considered reasonable at the present time:

Group life (years)

Air-conditioning machinery	17	Sewers	25
Buildings	25	Scientific instruments	12
Conveyor equipment	20	Shop equipment	15
Dam and lake	40	Smokestacks	40
Electrical equipment	25	Solution manufacturing equipment	25
Factory transportation equipment	12	Spinning machines	20
Factory utensils	15	Spool frames and racks	10
Finishing equipment	15	Spools	7
Guards and pans	15	Tanks and vats	15
Hand tools	5	Textile department accessories	12
Land improvements	25	Textile machinery	15
Maintenance machinery	25	Track scales	25
Piping, process	25	Village improvements	30
Piping—power and heating	25	Welfare equipment	10
Railroad siding	33		

TABLE 17—AVERAGE USEFUL LIFE OF DEPRECIABLE EQUIPMENT (CONT.)

The following item lives are considered reasonable for the facilities used in the manufacture of rayon under present conditions:

Average useful life (years)

Benches	20	Piping, chemical:	
Boilers and auxiliary equipment	20	Acid	15
Boxes	10	Nonacid	20
Aging	10	Piping water:	
Metal	15	Above ground	25
Buckets	10	Air and vacuum	40
Bunkers, coal and handling equipment	30	Boiler feed-water	25
		Condensate	25
Cars, spool	15	Sprinkler system	40
Chairs	15	Underground	40
Clocks	15	Piping, steam:	
Clocks, watchman	15	Exhaust	25
Compressors, air	25	High pressure	25
Coning machines	15	Plumbing shop equipment	25
Cranes	25	Pot spinning machines	20
Cranes, overhead	25	Presses and pumps, solution	25
Cupboards	20	Presses, filter, solution	25
Drums, sulphidizing, solution	25	Pumps:	
Drying equipment	15	Air	25
Elevators	20	Humidifying and ventilating	15
Extractors, finishing	15	Reclaiming equipment, chemical	20
Fences, steel (cyclone wire)	25	Reeling machines	25
Forges	25	Reels, extra	15
Frames and racks, spool	10	Refrigerating machinery	15
Generators	25	Rods, glass	10
Guards	25	Scales and small equipment, miscellaneous	10
Heating, room	20	Scales, track, large platform	25
Humidifying and ventilating machinery	15	Sewers:	
Instruments:		Sanitary and storm	33
Laboratory	10	Waste, for plant	15
Measuring	10	Waste, for village	33
Optical	15	Sewing machines	15
Recording	15	Shelves and racks	15
Knitting machines	15	Shredders, solution	25
Manometers	5	Skein spinning machines	20
Metal working machines	25	Spool spinning machines	20
Miscellaneous, apparatus, solution	25	Spools:	
Mixers, solution	25	Spinning	6
Monorail system, overhead	15	Textile	10
Motors and starters	20	Stacks, smoke, brick	40
Ovens, tempering	15	Stands, inspection skein	10
Pails	10	Stools	15
Pans, drip	10	Switchboards	20

TABLE 17—AVERAGE USEFUL LIFE OF DEPRECIABLE EQUIPMENT (CONT.)

Tables..........................	20	Turbines, steam..................	25
Tanks and vats:		Twisting machines..............	15
Receivers, air and storage.......	25	Village improvements:	
Spinning bath—		Lighting systems..............	25
Metal.....................	15	Roads........................	33
Wood.....................	8	Sewer, sanitary...............	33
Storage, acid (metal)...........	20	Sidewalks....................	33
Viscose processing—		Water system—	
Metal.....................	20	Above ground..............	25
Wood......................	10	Under ground..............	40
Water conditioning and soften-		Volt meters...................	15
ing—		Walkways, concrete.............	25
Metal.....................	25	Washing equipment:	
Wood......................	15	Skein........................	15
Telephone and signal system......	25	Spool and cake vacuum........	15
Thermometers..................	5	Welfare equipment:	
Tools, small, miscellaneous........	5	Athletic......................	10
Tracks:		Cafeteria.....................	10
Industrial and transfer..........	15	Hospital and first aid..........	10
Spur........................	33	Police and fire.................	10
Transformers...................	25	Wells and pumps................	25
Trucks:		Winding machines..............	15
Lift.........................	15	Wiring, light and power..........	25
Transportation...............	10	Wood working machines.........	25

However, by U. S. tax regulations if an asset is sold at the end of a depreciation period for more than the assumed scrap value, or if it is sold during the period for more than its current book value, the difference must be taken as a capital gain. On the other hand, failure to deduct the full amount of depreciation allowable each year does not prevent such amount from reducing the adjusted basis, nor does it entitle the taxpayer to a greater deduction in a subsequent year.

Declining-Balance Method

The declining-balance method is also designated by the more descriptive name of constant-percentage method. It is also referred to as a liberalized method, since it may be so applied as to give depreciation charges during the early years that exceed those calculated by the straight-line method. However, the extent of that excess is limited by U. S. Government regulations (generally to twice the depreciation charges for the first year calculated by the straight-line method). Also, the type of property to which the liberalized declining method may be applied is restricted; it cannot be applied to leases, patents and other intangible assets.

The basis of the declining-balance method is to depreciate the asset each year by a constant percentage of its book value.

This percentage may be assumed arbitrarily, or computed by the formula,

$$\text{Percentage Depreciation } d = 1 - \sqrt[n]{\frac{S.V.}{C}}, \qquad (15\text{-}1)$$

Where n is the period of depreciation in years, $S.V.$ is the Scrap Value and C is the original cost.

For example, an asset costing $4,000.00, on January 1, 1958 estimated to have a scrap value of $800.00 in ten years, would have an annual percentage depreciation:

$$d = 1 - \sqrt[10]{\frac{\$800.00}{\$4,000.00}} = 1 - \sqrt[10]{.2}$$

The figure $\sqrt[10]{.2}$ is evaluated by logarithms as follows:
By Table 3 and rule for characteristics,

$$\log .2 = \overline{1}.30103 = 9.30103 - 10$$

Then $\qquad \dfrac{\log .2}{10} = .930103 - 1 = \overline{1}.930103$

which by Table 3 is approximately .85.

So that $\qquad d = 1 - .85 = .15 = 15\%$

Then applying this annual depreciation rate, the asset would have the following depreciation charges and book values for the first 5 years:

Depreciation Rate 15%					
(Values of Asset costing $4,000.00 at Jan. 1 in various years)					
Year	1958	1959	1960	1961	1962
Book Value	$4,000.00	$3,400.00	$2,890.00	$2,456.50	$2,088.02
Depreciation Charge		600.00	510.00	433.50	368.48
Depreciation Fund		600.00	1,110.00	1,543.50	1,911.98

Since the asset was purchased on January 1, 1958, it has undergone one year's depreciation by January 1, 1959. The charge for this depreciation is 15% of its book value at the beginning of 1958, which is 15% of $4,000.00, the cost. Therefore, the new book value as of January 1, 1959 is book value at beginning of year minus the depreciation charge, which is $4,000.00 − $600.00 = $3,400.00, the $600.00 going into the depreciation fund.

On January 1, 1960, the depreciation charge for 1959 is 15% of $3,400.00 (book value at beginning of 1959) = $510.00. Then the new book value as of January 1, 1960 is that at beginning of year minus the depreciation charge, which is \$3,400.00 minus \$510.00 = \$2,890.00, the \$510.00 going into the depreciation fund.

Thus, for each year, the depreciation charge is found by multiplying the book value at the beginning of the year by the depreciation rate, while the book value at the end of the year is the book value at beginning of the year less the depreciation charge. The depreciation fund is the total of the depreciation charges.

The reason for totaling the depreciation charges from year to year to form the depreciation fund is because of a common practice in accounting that is illustrated fully in Chapter 18, where balance sheets are discussed. As explained there, machinery and other depreciable assets are often carried on the books and reported on the balance sheet at their initial cost, while the depreciation charges that have been made against these assets over the years are reported as a total "fund" or "reserve" which is subtracted from the initial cost to show the present value of the particular class of assets. It follows that a depreciation fund is merely a total of charges that have been made. It is thus not a "fund" at all in the ordinary everyday use of that term to denote a sum of money. The latter type of fund is called a sinking fund, and is treated in the last section of this chapter.

To derive general formulas, write these terms in symbols, using C for cost, BV for book value, D for depreciation charge, d for depreciation rate (decimal value), and ΣD (the Greek letter Σ, sigma, means "sum of") for depreciation fund.

Then at the end of one year:

Depreciation charge for the year $= D_1 = Cd$

Book value $= (BV)_1 = C - Cd = C(1 - d)$

Depreciation fund $= \sum^{1} D_i = D_1 = Cd$

Then at the end of the second year:

Depreciation charge for the second year $= D_2 = (BV)_1 d = C(1 - d)d$

Book value at end of second year $= (BV)_2 = (BV)_1 - D_2 = C(1 - d) - C(1 - d)d = C(1 - d)^2$

Depreciation Fund at end of second year $= \sum^{2} D_i = C - (BV)_2$

At the end of the third year;

Depreciation charge for the third year $= D_3 = (BV)_2 d = C(1 - d)^2 d$

Book Value at end of third year $= (BV)_3 = (BV)_2 - D_3 = C(1 - d)^2 - C(1 - d)^2 d = C(1 - d)^3$

Depreciation fund at end of third year $= \sum^{3} D_i = C - (BV)_3$

Then at the end of the nth year

Depreciation charge for the nth year $= D_n = C(1 - d)^{n-1}d$ (15-2)

Book value at end of nth year $= (BV)_n = C(1 - d)^n$ (15-3)

Depreciation fund at end of nth year $= \sum^{n} D_i = C - (BV)_n$ (15-4)

To apply these general formulas, solve the problem: An asset is purchased for \$8,000.00 on January 1, 1955. If it is depreciated by the declining-balance method at 14% annually, what is its book value on January 1, 1965, what is its depreciation fund on that date, and what is the depreciation charge from January 1, 1964 to January 1, 1965 (tenth year).

Then by the Formula (15-3)

$$(BV)_{10} = C(1 - d)^{10} = (\$8,000)(1 - .14)^{10}$$
$$= (\$8,000)(.86)^{10}$$

This computation is readily made by logarithms (see Chapter 6).

From Table 3, log .86 $= \bar{1}.934498$

$$\frac{10}{\bar{1}.344980}$$

From Table 3, log 8,000 $= 3.903090$

Then log .86 $+$ log 8,000 $= 3.248070$

From Table 3, 3.248070 is log \$1,770.39, which is the book value of the asset after depreciation at 14% for 10 years.

Then by Formula (15-4), depreciation fund $=$ cost $-$ book value $=$ \$8,000.00 $-$ \$1,770.39 $=$ \$6,229.61, and by Formula (15-2) the depreciation charge during the tenth year $= C(1 - d)^{n-1}d = (\$8,000.00)(1 - .14)^9(.14)$. This computation is readily made by logarithms, as was that of the book value above. There it was found that $1 - .14 = .86$ and that

$$\log .86 = \bar{1}.934498$$

$$\frac{9}{}$$

$$\log (.86)^9 = \bar{1}.410482$$

From Table 3, log .14 $= \bar{1}.146128$

and log 8,000 $\quad 3.903090$

So that log 8,000 $+$ log $(.86)^9$ $+$ log $(.14) = 2.459700$

From Table 6, antilog 2.459700 $=$ \$288.20, which is the depreciation during the tenth year.

Note that by the declining-balance method an asset depreciated at an annual rate of 14% had a book value after 10 years of \$1,770.39 or about 22% of its initial cost, whereas if the straight-line method had been used on the basis of a 10-year life and no scrap value, its first year depreciation would have been only 10% of the cost, but the book value would have been reduced to 0 in 10 years. Thus, the declining balance method gives more rapid initial depreciation, but slower depreciation later and never depreciates completely.

To compensate partly for this effect, the U. S. Government allows higher initial depreciation rates where the declining-balance method is used, extending up to twice the straight line rate, that is, an asset with an estimated life of ten years may be depreciated as much as 20% annually, under specified restrictions.

The advantage of using the accelerated declining-balance method, or other accelerated methods, is felt particularly in instances where depreciation is hastened by obsolescence. For example, the useful life of a machine may be terminated, not by wear to a point where maintenance becomes excessive, but by the introduction of new machines so much more efficient that the old machine can no longer operate competitively. In industries undergoing rapid development, therefore, methods of accelerated depreciation are highly advantageous.

It should be added here that the U. S. Tax Code of 1954 stated that the annual depreciation deduction could be increased by an allowance for extraordinary obsolescence, starting from the year in which it was reasonably certain that the property was affected by revolutionary inventions, abnormal growth, or radical economic changes, which cause its abandonment prior to the end of its normal useful life.

Sum of Years—Digits Method

This method is allowable, under U. S. Tax Regulations, for property similar to that for which the liberalized declining-balance method may be used.

In this method the depreciation in any year is found by multiplying the cost of the asset less its scrap value by a fraction, whose numerator is the number of the year in question (counting from date on which the asset is to be scrapped) and whose denominator is the values of all the years added together.

For example, an asset costing $6,000.00 purchased January 1, 1955, with a useful life of 6 years, and a scrap value of $460.00, would have:

The number 6 assigned to the first year of its life.
The number 5 assigned to the second year of its life.
The number 4 assigned to the third year of its life.
The number 3 assigned to the fourth year of its life.
The number 2 assigned to the fifth year of its life.
The number 1 assigned to the sixth and last year of its life.
The number 21 as the total of its year numbers.

Then the depreciation charge during the first year

$= \frac{6}{21}$ (Cost $-$ Scrap Value) $= \frac{6}{21}$ ($6,000.00 $-$ 460.) $= \frac{2}{7}$ ($5540.00)

$= \$1,582.86.$

The depreciation charge during the second year

$= \frac{5}{21}$ ($5,540.00) $= \$1,319.05.$

The depreciation charge during the third year

$= \frac{4}{21}$ ($5,540.00) $= \$1,055.23.$

The depreciation charge during the fourth year

$= \frac{3}{21}$ ($5,540.00) $= \$ 791.43.$

The depreciation charge during the fifth year

$= \frac{2}{21}$ ($5,540.00) $= \$ 527.62.$

The depreciation charge during the sixth and last year

$= \frac{1}{21}$ ($5,540.00) $= \$ 263.81.$

Note that the depreciation fund at the end of any period is found by adding the depreciation charges, and that the book value at the end of any period is the difference between initial cost and depreciation fund.

For example, the depreciation fund at the end of six years is

$$\begin{array}{r} \$1,582.86, D_1 \\ 1,319.05, D_2 \\ 1,055.23, D_3 \\ 791.43, D_4 \\ 527.62, D_5 \\ 263.81, D_6 \\ \hline \end{array}$$

Depreciation or fund at end of 6 years $= \sum_{}^{6} D_i = \$5,540.00$

which checks the difference between cost and scrap value, as it should, since the calculation above was made on the basis of a useful life of 6 years.

As another example, consider an asset having a cost of $350.00 and an estimated salvage value of $50.00 after a useful life of 5 years. What is its depreciation charge for each year after date of purchase, and its depreciation fund and book value at the end of each year?

Since its useful life is 5 years:

The number 5 is assigned to the first year of its life.
The number 4 is assigned to the second year of its life.
The number 3 is assigned to the third year of its life.
The number 2 is assigned to the fourth year of its life.
The number 1 is assigned to the fifth year of its life.
The number 15 is the total of its year numbers.

First year. Depreciation charge $= D_1 = \frac{5}{15}$ ($300.00) $= \$100.00.$

Depreciation fund at end of 1 year $= \sum_{}^{1} D_i = \$100.00.$ Then book value at end of 1 year $= \$350.00 - \$100.00 = \$250.00.$

Second year. Depreciation charge $= D_2 = \frac{4}{15}$ (300.00) $= \$80.00$.

Depreciation fund at end of 2 years $= \overset{2}{\sum} D_i = D_1 + D_2 = \$180.00$. Book value at end of two years $= \$350.00 - \$180.00 = \$170.00$.

Third year. Depreciation charge $= D_3 = \frac{3}{15}$ (300.00) $= \$60.00$.

Depreciation fund at end of 3 years $= \overset{3}{\sum} D_i = D_1 + D_2 + D_3 = \$240.00$. Book value at end of 3 years $= \$350.00 - \$240.00 = \$110.00$.

Fourth year. Depreciation charge $= D_4 = \frac{2}{15}$ (300.00) $= \$40.00$.

Depreciation fund at end of 4 years $= \overset{4}{\sum} D_i = D_1 + D_2 + D_3 + D_4 = \$280.00$. Book value at end of 4 years $= \$350.00 - \$280.00 = \$70.00$.

Fifth year. Depreciation charge $= D_5 = \frac{1}{15}$ (300.00) $= \$20.00$.

Depreciation fund at end of 5 years $= \overset{5}{\sum} D_i = D_1 + D_2 + D_3 + D_4 + D_5 = \$300.00$. Book value at end of 5 years $= \$350.00 - \$300.00 = \$50.00 =$ scrap value.

As stated earlier in this chapter the only methods specifically suggested in the U. S. Code are the straight-line method, the declining-balance method, and the sum of years—digits method. It is also stated, however, that any other consistent method may be used to determine the annual depreciation allowance for property similar to that for which the liberalized declining-balance method may be used, if the total allowances for the property, at the end of each year, do not exceed, during the first two-thirds of the useful life of the property, the total allowances which would result if the declining-balance method were used.

Unit of Production Methods

The basis of these unit of production methods, which apply most directly to machinery, is production. If a machine fabricates one article, or a limited number of kinds of articles, its output is most conveniently measured in terms of the number of articles produced. On the other hand, if the machine is used for working on a relatively small number of large articles, especially if several machines of the same type are so used, then the output is probably better measured in machine hours.

Whichever of these methods are used, they require the maintenance of records showing the number of hours for which the machine is operated daily, or the number of units which it produces daily, so that its annual output in machine hours or production units can be computed. There are also required estimates of the useful life of the machine in the same terms, that is, in terms of machine hours or units produced. In addition, of course, the initial cost and estimated salvage value of the machine are also required.

For example, a machine costing $6,000.00 has an estimated salvage value of $400.00, and an estimated production during its useful life of 70,000 units. What is its depreciation charge, depreciation fund and book value during its first four years of operation if its production is: First year, 10,000 units, second year, 6,000 units, third year, 8,000 units, fourth year, 7,000 units?

Then, *first year*; Depreciation charge $= D_1 = \left(\dfrac{10,000}{70,000}\right)$ ($6,000.00 $-$ $400.00) = $800.00; Depreciation fund $= \sum^{1} D_i = $800.00; Book value $=$ $6,000.00 $-$ $800.00 = $5,200.00.

Second year. Depreciation charge $= D_2 = \left(\dfrac{6,000}{70,000}\right)$ ($6,000.00 $-$ $400.00) = $480.00; Depreciation fund $= \sum^{2} D_i = D_1 + D_2 = $1,280.00. Book value $=$ $6,000.00 $-$ $1,280.00 = $4,720.00.

Third year. Depreciation charge $= D_3 = \left(\dfrac{8,000}{70,000}\right)$ ($6,000.00 $-$ $400.00) = $640.00; Depreciation fund $= \sum^{3} D_i = D_1 + D_2 + D_3 = $1,920.00. Book value $=$ $6,000.00 $-$ $1,920.00 = $4,080.00.

Fourth year. Depreciation charge $= D_4 = \left(\dfrac{7,000}{70,000}\right)$ ($6,000.00 $-$ $400.00) = $560.00; Depreciation fund $= \sum^{4} D_i = D_1 + D_2 + D_3 + D_4 = $2,480.00; Book value $=$ $6,000.00 $-$ $2,480.00 = $3,520.00.

Note that the general formula for depreciation charge, as is apparent from the foregoing examples, can be written as

$$D_i = \left(\frac{N_i}{N_T}\right) (C - S.V.), \qquad (15\text{-}5)$$

where D_i is the depreciation charge in any one year; N_i is the number of units produced in that year; N_T is the estimated total number of units produced during the useful life of the machine; and C and $S.V.$ are the initial cost of the machine and its estimated scrap value at the end of its useful life, respectively.

Note also that this formula can be rearranged in the form $D_i = N_i \left(\dfrac{C - S.V.}{N_T}\right)$, where the expression in parentheses has in its numerator,

$C - S.V.$, which is the total depreciation during the useful life of the machine, and in its denominator, N_T, the total number of units estimated to be produced during that life. This expression is, therefore, the depreciation charge per unit produced, and is one of the unit costs entering into the total cost of the article produced. In accounting systems in which unit costs are calculated, this depreciation unit cost is computed for use in determining the unit cost of the article produced, and is therefore available for depreciation calculations on the machine.

An example of the use of unit depreciation costs is given in the solution of the following problem: A machine costs $2,750.00, and has an estimated scrap value of $250.00. Its estimated total production is 40,000 units. If it produces 8,000 units during the first year of operation, 3,763 during the second year, 6,592 during the third year, and 4,278 during the fourth year, what is its depreciation charge for each of the four years, and its depreciation fund and book value at the end of each of them?

Here the total depreciation is (Cost − Estimated Scrap Value at end of useful life), which is $2,750.00 − $250.00 = $2,500.00. Then depreciation cost per unit produced $= \dfrac{\$2,500.00}{40,000} = \$.0625$.

Then for *first year*, depreciation charge $= D_1 = N_1 \times$ Unit depreciation charge $= (8,000)(\$.0625) = \$500.00$; Depreciation fund $= \sum\limits^{1} D_i = D_1 = \$500.00$; Book value $= \$2,750.00 - \$500.00 = \$2,250.00$.

Second year. Depreciation charge $= D_2 = N_2 \times$ Unit charge $= (3,763)(\$.0625) = \$235.19$; Depreciation fund $= \sum\limits^{2} D_i = D_1 + D_2 = \$735.19$; Book value $= \$2,750.00 - \$735.19 = \$2,014.81$.

Third year. Depreciation charge $= D_3 = N_3 \times$ Unit charge $= (6,592)(\$.0625) = \$412.00$; Depreciation fund $= \sum\limits^{3} D_i = D_1 + D_2 + D_3 = \$1,147.19$; Book value $= \$2,750.00 - \$1,147.19 = \$1,602.81$.

Fourth year. Depreciation charge $= D_4 = N_4 \times$ Unit charge $= (4,278)(\$.0625) = \$267.38$; Depreciation fund $= \sum\limits^{4} D_i = D_1 + D_2 + D_3 + D_4 = \$1,414.57$; Book value $= \$2,750.00 - \$1,414.57 = \$1,335.43$.

Depreciation calculations based upon machine hours are made in essentially the same way as those just described for the unit production basis. The annual depreciation charge can be computed by the relation $\left(\dfrac{N_i}{N_T}\right)(C - S.V.)$ where N_i is the number of hours the machine is operated in a given year, N_T is the estimated total number of hours which the machine can operate in its useful life, C is initial cost and $S.V.$ is estimated scrap value at the end of useful life. Also, the unit cost method can be used for machine-hour calculations of depreciation in the form, $N_i \left(\dfrac{C - S.V.}{N_T} \right)$ where N_i is again the number of hours the machine is operated in a given year, and the expression in parentheses is the depreciation charge per hour operated.

The machine hour method is illustrated by the following example:

A machine costs $3,600.00, and has an estimated scrap value of $450.00, and an estimated useful life of 16,000 working hours. If it is operated for 2,463 hours during its first year of service, 2,082 hours during its second year, 1,948 hours during its third year and 2,660 hours during its fourth year, what is the depreciation charge for each of the four years, and its depreciation fund and book value at the end of each of them?

Here the total depreciation is Cost − Estimated Value at end of useful life, which is $3,600.00 − $450.00 = $3,150.00. The depreciation cost per hour operated is $\dfrac{\$3,150.00}{16,000} = \$.196875$.

Then for *first year*, Depreciation charge = $D_1 = N_1 \times$ Unit charge = $(2,463)(\$.196875) = \$484.90$; Depreciation fund = $\sum\limits^{1} D_i = D_1 = \$484.90$; Book value = $3,600 − \$484.90 = \$3,115.10$.

Second year. Depreciation charge = $D_2 = N_2 \times$ Unit charge = $(2,082)(\$.196875) = \$409.89$; Depreciation fund = $\sum\limits^{2} D_i = D_1 + D_2 = \$894.79$; Book value = $\$3,600.00 − \$894.79 = \$2,705.21$.

Third year. Depreciation charge = $D_3 = N_3 \times$ Unit charge = $(1,948)(\$.196875) = \$383.51$; Depreciation fund = $\sum\limits^{3} D_i = D_1 + D_2 + D_3 = \$1,278.30$; Book value = $\$3,600.00 − \$1,278.30 = \$2,321.70$.

Fourth year. Depreciation charge = $D_4 = N_4 \times$ Unit charge = $(2,660)(\$.196875) = \$523.69$; Depreciation fund = $\sum\limits^{4} D_i = D_1 + D_2 + D_3 + D_4 = \$1,801.99$; Book value = $\$3,600.00 − \$1,801.99 = \$1,798.01$.

Sinking Fund Method

The depreciation calculations made up to this point have been based upon the general usage of the term depreciation. In other words, the depreciation charges have been treated from the point of view of deductions from earnings to offset the gradual loss of assets by depreciation, which indeed they are. However, if sums of money are segregated to constitute a sinking fund to replace the depreciated assets, a somewhat infrequent practice, then the depreciation charges can be reduced by the interest which they will earn from the date of deposit to the date of retirement of the depreciated asset. The actual amount of the sinking fund can be computed by the method for finding the value of the rent of an ordinary annuity, as explained in Chapter 14.

As an example of the application of this method, find the depreciation charge for each year, and the value of the sinking fund at the end of each year for a machine costing $865.00, having a scrap value of $61.25 at the end of a probable life of 5 years, if interest is credited at 4%.

The total depreciation cost for the 5 years, which is the sum the sinking fund must then total, is Cost − Scrap Value = $865.00 − $61.25 = $803.75.

Follow the third method given in Chapter 14 for finding the periodic payment of an annuity when the required amount is known. Turn to Table 15, Chapter 14, and find the periodic payment of an ordinary annuity of 5 payments at 4%, of which the present value is $1.00. The figure tabulated is 0.22462711. Therefore the periodic rent of such an annuity whose amount is $1.00 is .22462711 − .04 (the periodic rate) = .18462711. Then the periodic payment of such an annuity whose amount is $803.75 is ($803.75)(.18462711) = $148.39, which is the amount of the annual payment into the sinking fund for depreciation.

Then at the end of the first year, the depreciation sinking fund is $148.39.

At the end of the second year, the amount of the depreciation sinking fund is ($148.39)(1.04) + $148.39 = $154.32 + $148.39 = $302.71.

At the end of the third year, the amount of the depreciation sinking fund is ($302.71)(1.04) + $148.39 = $314.81 + $148.39 = $463.30.

At the end of the fourth year, the amount of the depreciation sinking fund is ($463.30)(1.04) + $148.39 = $481.82 + $148.39 = $630.21.

At the end of the fifth year, the amount of the depreciation sinking fund is ($630.21)(1.04) + $148.39 = $655.42 + $148.39 = $803.81, which is six cents greater (due the fractional cent rounding-off) than the required amount.

Note that the annual depreciation charges computed by this method resemble those by the straight-line method in that they do not change throughout the depreciation period. They differ, however, in that they are not only charges, but sums of money, and are therefore credited with interest, which reduces their amount. To gain an idea of the effect of this reduction, compare the annual charges on a $865.00 asset, with a scrap value of $61.25 and a life of 5 years. When this computation was made by the sinking fund method above, the annual depreciation charge and deposit was found to be $148.39, against an annual charge of $160.75 for the same asset when computed earlier in this chapter by the straight line method.

The figure of $148.39 was based upon a 4% interest rate on the sinking fund; higher rates would increase the difference, and lower rates would decrease it.

Interest on Investment Method

This method of computing depreciation charges includes interest, but does not accumulate cash, as did the sinking fund method, described above. Like the latter method, the interest on investment method applies particularly to internal business calculations, rather than to tax computations. For example, suppose that a business has installed certain machinery purely for auxiliary service economies. An example would be the purchase by a company not in the printing business of a printing press to do part or all of its own printing. Since the products of the business in question are in no way related to printing, the only justification for the printing press is the possible saving made by its use. In such cases, the accountant would tend to segregate the costs of the printing press, and to include among them, of course, the interest on its capital cost. One means of doing this is to add to each depreciation charge the interest on the initial cost. Thus, in the example of straight line depreciation, a machine costing $865.00, with a scrap value of $61.25 and a useful life of 5 years, was found to have depreciation charges of $160.75 per year. The interest on the initial cost at 4% is ($865.00)(.04) = $34.60 per year, making the depreciation charge by the interest on investment method, $160.75 + $34.60 = $195.35 per year, on the basis of a 4% interest charge.

Combination Methods

In recent years the United States Internal Revenue Service has been willing to accept in many instances a combination of the straight line and the double declining balance methods. This combination can best be illustrated by an example. Consider an asset with an accepted life of 10 years, costing $100. By the accepted method one would depreciate it by the straight line amount of $10 for the first year. In later years, he could choose whichever of these two methods gave the highest depreciation. Thus the second year one would use the $9.00 figure of the declining balance method multiplied by 2, which is $18, leaving a value of $72. Likewise, on the third year he would use twice the declining balance amount of $7.20, which is $14.40, leaving a balance of $57.60. Similarly, for the fourth year one would use a figure of $11.52, leaving a balance of $46.08. Then thereafter one could revert to the $10 annual basis of the straight line method, which gives greater deductions then than the double declining balance method.

Chapter 16

AMORTIZATION

In its common usage in business mathematics, the term amortization means the retirement of a debt by means of periodic payments. The methods of computation include interest calculations, and the manner in which these enter depends upon which of the two common methods of retirement are used. In the first method the payments are made directly to the creditor, and each payment includes interest from the date of the debt to the date of that payment. In the second method, the payments on principal are deposited in a fund, called a "sinking fund," which is reserved until the due date of the entire debt. In this second method, two interest rates are involved, the interest rate on the debt, and the interest rate on the sinking fund. The two methods are discussed in the foregoing order in this chapter.

Amortization of a Debt—Method I

In amortization calculations, it is customary, and extremely helpful, to prepare an amortization schedule showing the principal outstanding at the beginning of each payment period, the interest due on it at the end of each period and the payment made at the end of each period. The difference between the payment and the interest, which represents the amount by which the principal of the debt is reduced at the end of each period, may also be entered, or else the new value of the unpaid principal may be entered directly below its previous value, so that reduction of unpaid principal can readily be found from the difference.

As an example, prepare an amortization schedule for a debt of $10,000.00, payable semi-annually in 6 years at 4% interest compounded semi-annually.

Now the quantity to be found here is the periodic payment which will retire an amount of $10,000 in six years, at 2% interest payable at the end of 12 periods. This is, however, the periodic payment of an ordinary

414

annuity having 12 periods and an interest rate of 2% per period. Therefore, Formula (14-5) Chapter 14, applies,

$$R = P \frac{i}{1 - (1 + i)^{-n}}$$

Substituting, $\qquad R = (\$10,000.00) \dfrac{.02}{1 - (1.02)^{-12}}$

From Table 3, Chapter 6, log 1.02 = .008600

$$\underline{-12}$$

Then log $(1.02)^{-12}$ $\qquad -.103200$

Rewriting with positive mantissa, log $(1.02)^{-12} = \bar{1}.896800$
And by Table 3 $(1.02)^{-12} = $ antilog $\bar{1}.896800 = .788495$

Substituting, $R = (\$10,000.00) \left(\dfrac{.02}{1 - .788495} \right)$

$$= (\$10.000.00) \left(\frac{.02}{.211505} \right)$$

$$= \$945.60$$

The periodic payment can also be found by Table 15, Chapter 14, using the formula,

$$R = \frac{P}{a_{\overline{n}|i}}$$

Substituting, $\qquad R = (\$10,000.00) \left(\dfrac{1}{a_{\overline{12}|2}} \right)$

By Table 15, $\qquad \dfrac{1}{a_{\overline{12}|2}} = .09455960$

Therefore $R = \$945.60$.

From this figure, the amortization schedule is readily constructed, as follows:

First Period

Principal outstanding, \$10,000.00; plus Interest at 2%, \$200.00, = \$10,200.00; deducting \$945.60, leaves \$9,254.40, the outstanding principal for the next period.

Second Period

Principal outstanding, \$9,254.40; plus Interest at 2%, \$185.09, = \$9,439.49; deducting \$945.60, leaves \$8,493.89, the outstanding principal for the next period.

Third Period

Principal outstanding, \$8,493.89; plus Interest at 2%, \$169.88, = \$8,663.77; deducting \$945.60, leaves \$7,718.17, the outstanding principal for the next period.

Fourth Period

Principal outstanding, $7,718.17; plus Interest at 2%, $154.36, = $7,872.53; deducting $945.60, leaves $6,926.93, the outstanding principal for the next period.

Fifth Period

Principal outstanding, $6,926.93; plus Interest at 2%, $138.54, = $7,065.47; deducting $945.60, leaves $6,119.87, the outstanding principal for the next period.

Sixth Period

Principal outstanding, $6,119.87; plus Interest at 2%, $122.40, = $6,242.27; deducting $945.60, leaves $5,296.67, the outstanding principal for the next period.

Seventh Period

Principal outstanding, $5,296.67; plus Interest at 2%, $105.93, = $5,402.60; deducting $945.60, leaves $4,457.00, the outstanding principal for the next period.

Eighth Period

Principal outstanding, $4,457.00; plus Interest at 2%, $89.14, = $4,546.14; deducting $945.60, leaves $3,600.54, the outstanding principal for the next period.

Ninth Period

Principal outstanding, $3,600.54; plus Interest at 2%, $72.01, = $3,672.55; deducting $945.60, leaves $2,726.95, the outstanding principal for the next period.

Tenth Period

Principal outstanding, $2,726.95; plus Interest at 2%, $54.54, = $2,781.49; deducting $945.60, leaves $1,835.89, the outstanding principal for the next period.

Eleventh Period

Principal outstanding, $1,835.89; plus Interest at 2%, $36.72, = $1,872.61; deducting $945.60, leaves $927.01, the outstanding principal for the next period.

Twelfth Period

Principal outstanding, $927.01; plus Interest at 2%, $18.54, = $945.55; deducting $945.55, leaves 0, terminating the amortization of the debt.

(Note the difference of .05 between computed value of periodic payment and payment in last period. This difference, less than

$.005 per period, is due to the fact that payments are not made in fractions of cents, but are rounded off to the nearest cent.)

The amortization schedule is prepared by tabulating the foregoing figures:

AMORTIZATION SCHEDULE

Year	Period	Principal Outstanding	Interest	Periodic Payment
1	1	$10,000.00	$200.00	$945.60
	2	9,254.40	185.09	945.60
2	3	8,493.89	169.88	945.60
	4	7,718.17	154.36	945.60
3	5	6,926.93	138.54	945.60
	6	6,119.87	122.40	945.60
4	7	5,296.67	105.93	945.60
	8	4,457.00	89.14	945.60
5	9	3,600.54	72.01	945.60
	10	2,726.95	54.54	945.60
6	11	1,835.89	36.72	945.60
	12	927.01	18.54	945.55

Amortization of a Debt—Method II (Sinking Fund Method)

In this method of debt amortization, the principal outstanding remains unchanged until the end of the entire term, when it is retired by payment from the sinking fund. Therefore, the interest on the principal is the same for each interest period, being computed on the unchanged principal outstanding. Since this interest is paid to the creditor at the end of each interest period, it does not enter into the sinking fund calculations. The latter are concerned with the periodic payment to be made into the sinking fund to yield, at the rate of interest earned on the sinking fund, the amount necessary to retire the debt at the end of its term.

Take an example with the same figures as those in the example given under Method I, so that a comparison between the two methods is obtainable. That is, prepare a sinking fund schedule for a debt of $10,000.00 on which interest is payable semi-annually at 6% per year, and of which the principal is to be paid by a sinking fund earning 4% interest compounded semi-annually, and into which payments are made semi-annually.

Here the semi-annual interest payment to the creditor is 3% of $10,000.00 = $300.00 semi-annually for 6 years.

The semi-annual payment into the sinking fund is that payment which will, at 2% interest compounded semi-annually, yield a total amount of $10,000.00 in 6 years. This is, however, the periodic payment of a simple annuity having 12 periods and an interest rate of 2% per period.   Therefore, Formula (14-8), Chapter 14 applies,

$$R = S_n \frac{i}{(1 + i)^n - 1}$$

Substituting, $R = (\$10,000.00) \dfrac{.02}{(1.02)^{12} - 1}$

From Table 3, Chapter 6, log 1.02 =   .008600

Then log $(1.02)^{12}$ $\dfrac{12}{.103200}$

And $(1.02)^{12}$ = antilog .103200   = 1.26824

Substituting, $R = (\$10,000.00) \left(\dfrac{.02}{1.26824 - 1} \right)$

$$= (\$10,000.00) \left(\frac{.02}{.26824} \right)$$

$$= \$745.60$$

The periodic payment can also be found by Table 15, Chapter 14, using Formula (14-9),

$$R = \frac{S_n}{s_{\overline{n}|i}}$$

Substituting, $R = \dfrac{\$10,000.00}{s_{\overline{12}|2}}$

By Formula (14-10), Chapter 14,

$$\frac{1}{a_{\overline{n}|i}} - \frac{1}{s_{\overline{n}|i}} = i$$

Therefore, $\dfrac{1}{s_{\overline{12}|2}} = \dfrac{1}{a_{\overline{12}|2}} - .02$

By Table 15, $\dfrac{1}{a_{\overline{12}|2}} = .09455960$

Therefore, $\dfrac{1}{s_{\overline{12}|2}} = .09455960 - .02$

$$= .07455960$$

Substituting, $R = (\$10,000.00)(.0745596)$

$$= \$745.60$$

From this figure, the sinking fund schedule is readily constructed, as follows:

First Period

Amount of Sinking Fund (at Beginning of Period) 0; plus interest at 2%, 0 = 0, plus periodic payment, $745.60, = $745.60, the amount carried to the next period.

Second Period

Amount of Sinking Fund, $745.60; plus interest at 2%, $14.91, = $760.51; plus periodic payment, $745.60, = $1,506.11, the amount carried to the next period.

Third Period

Amount of Sinking Fund, $1,506.11; plus interest at 2%, $30.12, = $1,536.23; plus periodic payment, $745.60, = $2,281.83, the amount carried to the next period.

Fourth Period

Amount of Sinking Fund, $2,281.83; plus interest at 2%, $45.64, = $2,327.47; plus periodic payment, $745.60, = $3,073.07, the amount carried to the next period.

Fifth Period

Amount of Sinking Fund, $3,073.07; plus interest at 2%, $61.46, = $3,134.53; plus periodic payment, $745.60, = $3,880.13, the amount carried to the next period.

Sixth Period

Amount of Sinking Fund, $3,880.13; plus interest at 2%, $77.60, = $3,957.73; plus periodic payment, $745.60, = $4,703.33, the amount carried to the next period.

Seventh Period

Amount of Sinking Fund, $4,703.33; plus interest at 2%, $94.07, = $4,797.40; plus periodic payment, $745.60, = $5,543.00, the amount carried to the next period.

Eighth Period

Amount of Sinking Fund, $5,543.00; plus interest at 2%, $110.86, = $5,653.86; plus periodic payment, $745.60, = $6,399.46, the amount carried to the next period.

Ninth Period

Amount of Sinking Fund, $6,399.46; plus interest at 2%, $127.99, = $6,527.45; plus periodic payment, $745.60, = $7,273.05, the amount carried to the next period.

Tenth Period

Amount of Sinking Fund, $7,273.05; plus interest at 2%, $145.44, = $7,418.49; plus periodic payment, $745.60, = $8,164.09, the amount carried to the next period.

Eleventh Period

Amount of Sinking Fund, $8,164.09; plus interest at 2%, $163.28, = $8,327.37; plus periodic payment, $745.60, = $9,072.97, the amount carried to the next period.

Twelfth Period

Amount of Sinking Fund, $9,072.97; plus interest at 2%, $181.46, = $9,254.43; plus periodic payment, $745.60, = $10,000.03, the amount to retire the debt.

The sinking fund schedule is prepared by tabulating the foregoing figures:

SINKING FUND AMORTIZATION SCHEDULE

	Period	Amount of Sinking Fund (at Beginning of Period)	Interest	Periodic Payment
1	1	0	0	$745.60
	2	$ 745.60	$ 14.91	745.60
2	3	1,506.11	30.12	745.60
	4	2,281.83	45.64	745.60
3	5	3,073.07	61.46	745.60
	6	3,880.13	77.60	745.60
4	7	4,703.33	94.07	745.60
	8	5,543.00	110.86	745.60
5	9	6,399.46	127.99	745.60
	10	7,273.05	145.44	745.60
6	11	8,164.09	163.28	745.60
	12	9,072.97	181.46	745.60

12 (End) $10,000.03

This chapter has developed two amortization schedules at length, not only because of their wide use in retiring bond issues and other forms of business indebtedness but also because of their application to other business situations, such as mortgage payments. In Chapter 20, The Mathematics of Real Estate, amortization calculations are discussed further, and a detailed table is given.

Chapter 17

THE MATHEMATICS OF LIFE ANNUITIES
AND LIFE INSURANCE

The basic concept of insurance is that of the sharing of risk. For example, if the experience of a community of ten thousand homes is that the number destroyed by fire *averages* ten per year, then if each of the ten thousand home owners contributes annually $\frac{1}{1000}$ of the value of his home to a common fund, the amount in that fund will be sufficient to pay the annual losses. Of course, this example ignores several conditions that exist in an actual insurance operation, such as the interest on the money and the cost of operation. Moreover, it assumes a knowledge of the mathematics of probability which, while apparently simple in the above statement, requires more detailed treatment for its general application.

Elementary Mathematics of Probability

Since a knowledge of combinations and permutations is required in any mathematical treatment or probability, those topics are discussed briefly below.

Consider a group of 4 objects represented by the letters *a, b, c* and *d*. They can be combined into various sets, depending on the number in the sets. Thus, the different sets of two letters each that can be formed from the four letters *a, b, c* and *d*, are *ab, ac, ad, bc, bd* and *cd*, a total of six different combinations. A permutation differs from a combination in being an arrangement in a definite order. Thus, there are 2 permutations of the combination of *a* and *b*, namely *ab* and *ba*. Since the same statement applies to *a* and *c*, *a* and *d*, etc., it follows that the four letters *a, b, c* and *d* above, which had the six combinations given, have the twelve permutations: *ab, ba, ac, ca, ad, da, bc, cb, bd, db, cd* and *dc*.

The foregoing statement can be expressed in the form that the number of permutations of 4 things taken 2 at a time is 12. The symbolic representation commonly used is $P_2^4 = 12$. Now add one thing to the total number of objects and also add one thing to the number of them in each set, and determine by trial how many permutations can be formed, that is, add the letter e to a, b, c and d, and find the number of three letter permutations that can be formed from each of the original permutations. Thus, the first permutation ab gives the five new permutations, abc, abd, eab, aeb and abe. The same number of new permutations is obtained from each of the other two-letter permutations yielding the result that the number of permutations of 5 things taken 3 at a time is 5 times 12 (the number of permutations of 4 things taken 2 at a time). Thus $P_3^5 = 60$.

The foregoing operation can be summarized in the general statement that, if there are m ways of doing a certain thing, and if for each way of doing it, there are n ways of doing a second thing, then the number of ways of doing both together is $m \times n$. Further, if for each of the $m \times n$ ways of doing the two things together, a third can be done in p ways, then the number of ways in which the three things can be done is $m \times n \times p$.

By this rule, or by mathematical induction from the two permutations already computed (which is the same process) it is found that the number of permutations of n things taken r at a time is

$$P_r^n = n(n - 1)(n - 2) \cdots (n - r + 1). \tag{17-1}$$

Substituting 4 for n and 2 for r, gives as above $P_2^4 = 12$; substituting 5 and 3, gives $P_3^5 = 60$, substituting 6 and 4, gives $P_4^6 = 360$, etc.

If $r = n$, the formula for P_r^n becomes:

$$P_n^n = n(n - 1)(n - 2) \cdots (n - n + 1)$$

which is,

$$P_n^n = n(n - 1)(n - 2) \cdots 1 \tag{17-2}$$

This number obtained for P_n^n, which is the product of all the integers from 1 to n, is called factorial n, and is expressed by the symbol $n!$ It is important in many mathematical formulas, including the relationship between the number of permutations (of n things taken r at a time) and the corresponding number of combinations. For if r is two (that is, if the things are to be taken two at a time, then for every combination of a and b, there are $1 \times 2 = 2$ permutations, ab and ba; for every combination of a, b and c, there are $1 \times 2 \times 3 = 6$ permutations, abc, acb, bac, bca, cab and cba; for every combination of a, b, c and d, there are $1 \times 2 \times 3 \times 4 = 24$ permutations, $abcd$, $abdc$, $acbd$, $acdb$, $adbc$, $adcb$, $bacd$, $badc$, $bcad$, $bcda$, $bdac$, $bdca$, $cabd$, $cadb$, $cbad$, $cbda$, $cdab$, $cdba$, $dabc$, $dacb$, $dbac$, $dbca$, $dcab$, and $dcba$. Therefore, if things are taken r at a time, there are $r!$ times as many permutations as combinations. That is

$$P_r^n = r! \times C_r^n$$

where $C_r{}^n$ is the number of possible combinations of n things taken r at a time.

Transposing this formula, gives

$$C_r{}^n = \frac{P_r{}^n}{r!}$$

Then substituting the value for $P_r{}^n$ from Formula (17-1)

gives
$$C_r{}^n = \frac{n(n-1)(n-2)\,\cdots\,(n-r+1)}{(1)(2)\,\cdots\,(r)} \qquad (17\text{-}3)$$

which is the basic formula for the number of combinations of n things taken r at a time.

Substituting $n = 4$ and $r = 2$, gives $C_r{}^n = 6$;
substituting $n = 5$ and $r = 2$, gives $C_r{}^n = 10$;
substituting $n = 6$ and $r = 2$, gives $C_r{}^n = 15$;
substituting $n = 5$ and $r = 3$, gives $C_r{}^n = 10$, etc.

The theory of probability is based on the fundamental concept that if an occurrence can happen in x ways and fail to happen in y ways, then the probability that it will happen on any single occasion is $\dfrac{x}{x+y}$, and the probability that it will fail on any single is $\dfrac{y}{x+y}$. Thus if there are three red balls and two black balls the probability of success in obtaining a red ball on a single draw is $\dfrac{3}{3+2} = \dfrac{3}{5}$, and the probability of failure to obtain a red ball on a single draw is $\dfrac{2}{3+2} = \dfrac{2}{5}$.

The application of this fundamental concept depends upon an exact knowledge of the number of ways in which the occurrence can succeed and of the number in which it can fail. However, in the case of many events in the world, these numbers are not known definitely—that is, the number of ways in which a child aged 10 years can live to the age of fifty years, and the number of ways in which it can fail, are not definitely determinate. Therefore, a modified method of determining these ways must be adopted. Such a method is available in Bernoulli's Probability Theorem, which may be stated in the following form: If a sufficiently great number of trials is made (the number n), and the number of successes is s, then the probability of success in a single trial is $\dfrac{s}{n}$, and the probability of failure in a single trial is $\dfrac{n-s}{n}$.

To appreciate the importance of Bernoulli's Theorem, consider its application to the red and black balls in a box. If the number of each kind, and their sum were unknown, the Theorem asserts that if that total number were sufficiently large, and if in a sufficient number of trials, n, a number of successes, s, were obtained, then the probability of success in a single trial, p, would be $\frac{s}{n}$; and the probability of failure in a single trial would be $\frac{n-s}{n}$.

Note that the probability that a single trial will be either a success or a failure is $\frac{s}{n} + \frac{n-s}{n} = \frac{n}{n} = 1$. Since a single trial must be either a success or a failure, a probability of 1 is a certainty. If $s = 0$, then $p = \frac{0}{n} = 0$, and thus an impossibility has a probability of 0. Thus all probabilities lie between 1 and 0.

To extend the general principle of probability to various successions of events, one can project the above examples, which were concerned with success and failure, or with red balls and black balls, to more complex systems, such as a large box of red, black, green and yellow balls. Then if in a sufficient number of trials, n, there are drawn r red balls, b black balls, g green balls and y yellow balls, then the probability of drawing a ball of a given color in a single trial is

$$\frac{r}{n} \text{ for a red ball,}$$

$$\frac{b}{n} \text{ for a black ball,}$$

$$\frac{g}{n} \text{ for a green ball,}$$

$$\frac{y}{n} \text{ for a yellow ball.}$$

Furthermore, the probability of drawing either a red or a black ball is $\frac{r}{n} + \frac{b}{n}$; and the probability of drawing either a green or red or black ball is $\frac{g}{n} + \frac{r}{n} + \frac{b}{n}$.

The principle illustrated by this example may be stated in the form: the probability of the occurrence of mutually exclusive events is the sum of their individual probabilities.

Consider, however, the probability of drawing first a red ball and then a black ball. To return to the basic definition, the probability of success

Find Interest compounded semiannually on $1,006
over 20 years   4 0 Periods

Hartman

From _____ To _____ Date _____

Company _____   AM

                                                             PM

D-202

Message: Pres. Value 3145

original 10 0 6

Gain   21 3 9

Find 3.12 opposite 40
periods number 2¼% (2.95)
or 3% (3.26) = approx. 2.87%

$$
\begin{array}{r}
3.12 \\
1006\,\overline{)\,3145.} \\
\underline{3018} \\
1270\!\!\!\!\!\diagup\, \\
\underline{1006} \\
2640\!\!\!\!\!\diagup
\end{array}
$$

326
295
___
 31

2.95
275
___
287

is the ratio of the number of ways an event can succeed to the total number of ways in which it can succeed or fail. The number of ways in which the draw of a red ball can succeed is $\frac{r}{n}$. The next draw may produce a ball of any of the four colors; the chances that it will give a black ball, after the red ball, is the fraction $\frac{r}{n}$ represented by $\frac{b}{n}$. That is, the probability of drawing a red ball on one trial, and a black on the next, is $\frac{r}{n} \times \frac{b}{n}$ or $p_r \times p_b$, using p_r to represent the probability of drawing a red ball on one trial, and p_b to represent the probability of drawing a black ball on a single trial.

The rule expressed here is that the probability of occurrence of mutually dependent events is the product of their individual probabilities.

Mortality Table

The application of probability theory in insurance appears in the construction of a mortality table, and its use in solving problems in insurance. The basis of this table, which is Table 18, Pages 426, 427, 428, 429, is the data in the first and second columns (which are headed x and l_x) showing the number of males and females left alive at the end of each year out of a given number born. The number born is 9,983,614. The figure in this second column shows how many out of this number are still alive each year up to age 99 for males, and 102 for females. Thus, at the end of their 10th year, 9,837,940 females and 9,799,938 males out of 9,983,614 are still alive; at the end of their 20th year, 9,706,098 females and 9,656,344 males are still alive, etc.

The third column in this table, which is headed e_x, gives the number of deaths in each year out of the population group in the second l_x column. Therefore, the number in the third column is the difference between the second column figure on that line, and the figure on the next line. Thus the d_x (third column figure for the tenth year) is 11,956 males, which is l_x figure for the tenth year (9,799,938) minus the l_x figure for the eleventh year (9,787,982). Or expressing this relation in symbols, $d_x = l_x - l_{x+1}$, or by transposition,

$$l_x = l_{x+1} + d_x \qquad (17\text{-}4)$$

Now to return to the Bernoulli Probability Theorem, the probability of one of the group living through a given year is the ratio of the number living through that year, to the total of those living through it plus those dying during it, or in symbols

$$p_x = \frac{l_{x+1}}{l_{x+1} + d_x}$$

TABLE 18—MORTALITY TABLE AND COMMUTATION COLUMNS

1958 CSO—Age Last Birthday—$2\frac{1}{2}\%$

Age x M F		l_x	d_x	1000 q_x	D_x	N_x	S_x
0*		9 983 614	39 356	3.9421	10 909 364.6	319 718 650.2	9 412 753 183.7
0		9 983 614	39 356	3.9421	10 909 364.6	319 718 650.2	9 412 753 183.7
1		9 944 258	15 315	1.5401	10 549 863.3	308 809 285.6	9 057 707 193.7
2		9 928 943	13 703	1.3801	10 226 811.3	298 259 422.3	8 713 412 464.1
3		9 915 240	13 088	1.3200	9 915 240.0	288 032 611.0	8 379 565 420.6
4		9 902 152	12 526	1.2650	9 613 739.8	278 117 371.0	8 055 895 543.7
5		9 889 626	12 016	1.2150	9 321 921.0	268 503 631.2	7 742 140 906.8
6		9 877 610	11 557	1.1700	9 039 412.4	259 181 710.2	7 438 046 906.0
7		9 866 053	11 198	1.1350	8 765 860.3	250 142 297.8	7 143 365 993.6
8		9 854 855	10 989	1.1151	8 500 884.4	241 376 437.5	6 857 857 424.0
9		9 843 866	10 926	1.1099	8 244 082.8	232 875 553.1	6 581 287 011.4
10		9 832 940	10 964	1.1150	7 995 080.0	224 631 470.3	6 313 426 854.7
11		9 821 976	11 100	1.1301	7 753 558.5	216 636 390.3	6 054 055 032.8
12		9 810 876	11 331	1.1549	7 519 219.5	208 882 831.8	5 802 955 321.5
13		9 799 545	11 661	1.1900	7 291 781.8	201 363 612.3	5 559 916 963.3
14		9 787 884	12 088	1.2350	7 070 975.7	194 071 830.5	5 324 734 451.7
0*		9 964 600	44 138	4.4295	9 964 600.0	288 147 462.5	8 379 889 147.9
0		9 964 600	44 138	4.4295	9 964 600.0	288 147 462.5	8 379 889 147.9
1		9 920 462	16 270	1.6400	9 631 516.3	278 182 862.5	8 056 103 418.7
2		9 904 192	14 758	1.4901	9 335 650.9	268 551 346.0	7 742 282 289.5
3		9 889 434	14 142	1.4300	9 050 233.0	259 215 695.1	7 438 139 659.9
4		9 875 292	13 578	1.3749	8 774 069.1	250 165 462.1	7 143 423 982.9
5		9 861 714	13 067	1.3250	8 506 801.1	241 391 393.0	6 857 891 628.5
6		9 848 647	12 607	1.2801	8 248 086.8	232 884 591.9	6 581 305 801.2
7		9 836 040	12 246	1.2450	7 997 600.6	224 636 505.1	6 313 436 292.1
8		9 823 794	11 984	1.2199	7 754 993.7	216 638 904.5	6 054 059 240.5
9		9 811 810	11 872	1.2100	7 519 935.3	208 883 910.8	5 802 956 907.5
10		9 799 938	11 956	1.2200	7 292 074.2	201 363 975.5	5 559 917 419.7
11		9 787 982	12 186	1.2450	7 071 046.5	194 071 901.3	5 324 734 526.4
12	15	9 775 796	12 611	1.2900	6 856 546.6	187 000 854.8	5 097 207 329.0
13	16	9 763 185	13 229	1.3550	6 648 253.9	180 144 308.2	4 877 139 991.0
14	17	9 749 956	13 894	1.4250	6 445 869.6	173 496 054.3	4 664 341 503.7
15	18	9 736 062	14 604	1.5000	6 249 207.7	167 050 184.7	4 458 625 429.8
16	19	9 721 458	15 360	1.5800	6 058 091.2	160 800 977.0	4 259 809 665.0
17	20	9 706 098	16 063	1.6549	5 872 349.0	154 742 885.8	4 067 716 315.7
18	21	9 690 035	16 618	1.7150	5 691 874.3	148 870 536.8	3 882 171 536.3
19	22	9 673 417	17 073	1.7649	5 516 614.6	143 178 662.5	3 703 005 649.8
20	23	9 656 344	17 478	1.8100	5 346 483.5	137 662 047.9	3 530 052 636.8
21	24	9 638 866	17 783	1.8449	5 181 365.5	132 315 564.4	3 363 150 614.3
22	25	9 621 083	18 039	1.8749	5 021 171.1	127 134 198.9	3 202 141 577.9
23	26	9 603 044	18 246	1.9000	4 865 783.2	122 113 027.8	3 046 871 390.2
24	27	9 584 798	18 402	1.9199	4 715 085.5	117 247 244.6	2 897 189 749.7
25	28	9 566 396	18 607	1.9450	4 568 965.9	112 532 159.1	2 752 950 127.7
26	29	9 547 789	18 857	1.9750	4 427 259.4	107 963 193.2	2 614 009 704.2
27	30	9 528 932	19 152	2.0099	4 289 820.9	103 535 933.8	2 480 229 304.7
28	31	9 509 780	19 542	2.0549	4 156 503.7	99 246 112.9	2 351 473 283.3
29	32	9 490 238	19 976	2.1049	4 027 148.0	95 089 609.2	2 227 609 413.0
30	33	9 470 262	20 456	2.1600	3 901 622.6	91 062 461.2	2 108 508 780.2
31	34	9 449 806	20 978	2.2199	3 779 801.0	87 160 838.6	1 994 045 659.0
32	35	9 428 828	21 545	2.2850	3 661 563.1	83 381 037.6	1 884 097 416.0
33	36	9 407 283	22 201	2.3600	3 546 792.6	79 719 474.5	1 778 544 417.8
34	37	9 385 082	23 039	2.4549	3 435 361.4	76 172 681.9	1 677 269 944.1
35	38	9 362 043	24 107	2.5750	3 327 114.7	72 737 320.5	1 580 160 102.6
36	39	9 337 936	25 398	2.7199	3 221 890.7	69 410 205.8	1 487 103 728.1
37	40	9 312 538	27 052	2.9049	3 119 541.4	66 188 315.1	1 397 992 247.7
38	41	9 285 486	29 061	3.1297	3 019 882.9	63 068 773.7	1 312 719 534.1
39	42	9 256 425	31 377	3.3898	2 922 749.1	60 048 890.8	1 231 181 772.6
40	43	9 225 048	33 992	3.6848	2 828 001.6	57 126 141.7	1 153 277 281.7
41	44	9 191 056	36 808	4.0048	2 735 515.6	54 298 140.1	1 078 906 351.3
42	45	9 154 248	39 817	4.3496	2 645 204.4	51 562 624.5	1 007 971 111.2
43	46	9 114 431	43 061	4.7245	2 556 989.3	48 917 420.1	940 375 413.3
44	47	9 071 370	46 577	5.1345	2 470 785.2	46 360 430.8	876 024 757.4

1958 CSO—Age Last Birthday—2½%

Age x M	F	C_x	M_x	R_x	$D_x - M_x$	$10,000,000/D_x$
	0*	10 337.100	1 573 061.294	125 435 633.260	8 690 669.7	.930 1235
0		41 348.398	1 597 170.814	125 466 644.558	8 659 658.4	.930 1235
1		15 697.875	1 555 417.263	123 375 042.517	8 397 432.5	.957 1497
2		13 703.000	1 539 643.728	121 324 788.874	8 142 610.8	.982 5918
3		12 768.781	1 525 940.753	119 290 233.106	7 894 387.2	1.008 5485
4		11 922.427	1 513 233.920	117 269 380.338	7 652 552.1	1.035 1285
5		11 158.051	1 501 410.401	115 261 296.351	7 416 926.8	1.062 3506
6		10 470.072	1 490 430.592	113 265 134.791	7 187 339.3	1.090 2340
7		9 897.400	1 480 162.355	111 280 131.282	6 963 623.6	1.118 7989
8		9 475.780	1 470 502.929	109 305 597.845	6 745 619.9	1.148 0719
9		9 191.664	1 461 593.927	107 340 961.808	6 533 174.5	1.178 0874
10		8 998.665	1 452 415.899	105 385 801.551	6 326 142.0	1.208 8813
11		8 888.085	1 443 760.885	103 439 832.958	6 124 383.2	1.240 4865
12		8 851.759	1 435 253.664	101 502 863.030	5 927 764.8	1.272 9373
13		8 887.370	1 426 822.378	99 574 781.187	5 736 158.8	1.306 2694
14		8 988.104	1 418 398.150	97 655 551.103	5 549 442.0	1.340 5213
0*		10 765.366	1 547 865.113	119 365 893.250	7 929 509.0	1.003 5526
0		43 061.464	1 571 955.538	119 398 189.348	7 897 212.9	1.003 5526
1		15 486.020	1 529 103.157	117 330 802.239	7 654 174.0	1.033 2180
2		13 704.270	1 513 767.065	115 306 476.594	7 418 113.0	1.060 7882
3		12 811.954	1 500 261.452	113 297 636.969	7 188 187.2	1.088 9305
4		12 000.974	1 487 696.402	111 302 501.614	6 964 203.7	1.117 7522
5		11 267.633	1 476 293.927	109 320 178.213	6 745 995.8	1.147 2734
6		10 605.831	1 465 040.541	107 349 855.786	6 533 402.7	1.177 5155
7		10 050.862	1 454 789.868	105 390 800.992	6 326 269.6	1.208 5003
8		9 595.929	1 445 122.759	103 442 352.029	6 124 447.1	1.240 2570
9		9 274.387	1 435 938.048	101 503 953.928	5 927 792.3	1.272 8161
10		9 112.203	1 427 104.203	99 575 151.756	5 736 168.1	1.306 2170
11		9 060.972	1 418 466.929	97 655 623.971	5 549 443.8	1.340 5078
12	15	9 148.276	1 409 919.897	95 745 208.389	5 367 496.1	1.375 7333
13	16	9 362.523	1 401 332.378	93 843 853.779	5 190 207.1	1.411 9481
14	17	9 593.328	1 392 586.419	91 951 647.445	5 017 465.3	1.449 2104
15	18	9 837.618	1 383 668.423	90 068 803.634	4 849 165.0	1.487 5605
16	19	10 094.516	1 374 567.666	88 195 553.151	4 685 203.6	1.527 0401
17	20	10 299.048	1 365 274.674	86 332 140.286	4 525 481.4	1.567 6931
18	21	10 395.020	1 355 829.312	84 478 821.937	4 369 900.8	1.609 5491
19	22	10 419.156	1 346 362.209	82 635 802.636	4 218 366.2	1.652 6220
20	23	10 406.162	1 336 909.358	80 803 178.355	4 070 781.0	1.696 9326
21	24	10 329.516	1 327 514.012	78 980 973.230	3 927 049.7	1.742 5098
22	25	10 222.652	1 318 233.319	77 169 174.267	3 787 077.8	1.789 3738
23	26	10 087.764	1 309 093.108	75 367 704.820	3 650 771.7	1.837 5535
24	27	9 925.866	1 300 117.322	73 576 458.025	3 518 039.5	1.887 0778
25	28	9 791.649	1 291 328.368	71 795 298.994	3 388 790.8	1.937 9755
26	29	9 681.179	1 282 700.389	70 024 065.829	3 262 936.6	1.990 2961
27	30	9 592.811	1 274 211.185	68 262 624.313	3 140 390.8	2.044 0906
28	31	9 549.418	1 265 840.346	66 510 863.976	3 021 070.0	2.099 4124
29	32	9 523.412	1 257 547.719	64 768 696.450	2 904 893.5	2.156 3288
30	33	9 514.389	1 249 317.866	63 036 078.342	2 791 783.5	2.214 8992
31	34	9 519.199	1 241 135.787	61 312 983.646	2 681 664.5	2.275 1861
32	35	9 538.036	1 232 989.195	59 599 403.339	2 574 463.4	2.337 2544
33	36	9 588.730	1 224 866.125	57 895 342.231	2 470 109.1	2.401 1724
34	37	9 707.968	1 216 739.621	56 200 819.159	2 368 532.7	2.467 0239
35	38	9 910.236	1 208 551.933	54 515 884.817	2 269 667.7	2.534 9223
36	39	10 186.301	1 200 234.184	52 840 658.443	2 173 450.7	2.605 0033
37	40	10 585.040	1 191 726.373	51 175 342.305	2 079 822.3	2.677 4105
38	41	11 093.787	1 182 928.294	49 520 212.468	1 988 725.8	2.752 3411
39	42	11 685.756	1 173 752.197	47 875 667.671	1 900 109.5	2.830 0067
40	43	12 350.890	1 164 133.363	46 242 216.661	1 813 925.0	2.910 6232
41	44	13 047.878	1 154 016.435	44 620 451.407	1 730 127.8	2.994 4224
42	45	13 770.266	1 143 380.391	43 011 037.043	1 648 675.5	3.081 6242
43	46	14 528.943	1 132 210.002	41 414 670.557	1 569 528.2	3.172 4636
44	47	15 331.956	1 120 481.383	39 832 074.337	1 492 647.0	3.267 2112

427

TABLE 18—MORTALITY TABLE AND COMMUTATION COLUMNS (Cont.)

1958 CSO—Age Last Birthday—3%

Age M x	Age F	l_x	d_x	1000 q_x	D_x	N_x	S_x
45	48	9 024 793	50 443	5.5894	2 386 503.8	43 889 645.6	814 826 225.9
46	49	8 974 350	54 691	6.0941	2 304 043.5	41 503 141.8	756 688 408.7
47	50	8 919 659	59 352	6.6541	2 223 303.1	39 199 098.3	701 521 322.3
48	51	8 860 307	64 449	7.2739	2 144 183.7	36 975 795.2	649 236 310.4
49	52	8 795 858	70 003	7.9586	2 066 589.4	34 831 611.5	599 745 943.1
50	53	8 725 855	76 031	8.7133	1 990 429.3	32 765 022.1	552 963 916.1
51	54	8 649 824	82 459	9.5330	1 915 617.5	30 774 592.8	508 804 952.6
52	55	8 567 365	89 295	10.4227	1 842 093.1	28 858 975.3	467 184 708.6
53	56	8 478 070	96 584	11.3922	1 769 799.6	27 016 882.2	428 019 683.1
54	57	8 381 486	104 322	12.4467	1 698 677.4	25 247 082.6	391 227 157.8
55	58	8 277 164	112 578	13.6010	1 628 674.1	23 548 405.2	356 725 142.2
56	59	8 164 586	121 410	14.8703	1 559 730.6	21 919 731.1	324 432 312.6
57	60	8 043 176	130 816	16.2642	1 491 783.4	20 360 000.5	294 267 960.0
58	61	7 912 360	140 747	17.7882	1 424 777.4	18 868 217.1	266 151 926.9
59	62	7 771 613	151 211	19.4568	1 358 672.9	17 443 439.7	240 004 538.0
60	63	7 620 402	162 164	21.2802	1 293 434.4	16 084 766.8	215 746 540.1
61	64	7 458 238	173 504	23.2634	1 229 038.6	14 791 332.4	193 299 061.3
62	65	7 284 734	185 222	25.4260	1 165 482.6	13 562 293.8	172 583 574.8
63	66	7 099 512	197 284	27.7884	1 102 765.9	12 396 811.2	153 521 878.7
64	67	6 902 228	209 656	30.3751	1 040 895.0	11 294 045.3	136 036 102.1
65	68	6 692 572	222 332	33.2207	979 881.2	10 253 150.3	120 048 715.9
66	69	6 470 240	235 264	31.3609	919 736.8	9 273 269.1	105 482 551.7
67	70	6 234 976	248 306	39.8247	860 479.9	8 353 532.3	92 260 828.6
68	71	5 986 670	261 038	43.6032	802 147.1	7 493 052.4	80 307 181.5
69	72	5 725 632	272 833	47.6512	744 826.2	6 690 905.3	69 545 697.8
70	73	5 452 799	283 079	51.9144	688 674.1	5 946 079.1	59 900 980.9
71	74	5 169 720	291 248	56.3373	633 904.9	5 257 405.0	51 298 285.6
72	75	4 878 472	297 028	60.8855	580 769.3	4 623 500.1	43 663 754.3
73	76	4 581 444	300 591	65.6105	529 523.2	4 042 730.8	36 924 737.4
74	77	4 280 853	302 453	70.6525	480 369.8	3 513 207.6	31 010 172.8
75	78	3 978 400	303 012	76.1643	433 427.6	3 032 837.8	25 850 979.0
76	79	3 675 388	302 506	82.3059	388 753.3	2 599 410.2	21 380 380.9
77	80	3 372 882	300 912	89.2151	346 365.7	2 210 656.9	17 534 119.0
78	81	3 071 970	297 756	96.9267	306 276.3	1 864 291.2	14 250 573.3
79	82	2 774 214	292 266	105.3509	268 534.0	1 558 014.9	11 470 833.8
80	83	2 481 948	283 916	114.3924	233 246.3	1 289 480.9	9 138 761.7
81	84	2 198 032	272 442	123.9481	200 548.2	1 056 234.6	7 201 105.7
82	85	1 925 590	257 880	133.9226	170 573.4	855 686.4	5 607 707.2
83	86	1 667 710	240 646	144.2973	143 427.0	685 113.0	4 311 749.8
84	87	1 427 064	221 372	155.1241	119 156.2	541 686.0	3 270 010.7
85	88	1 205 692	200 709	166.4679	97 740.0	422 529.8	2 443 074.3
86	89	1 004 983	179 281	178.3921	79 096.5	324 789.8	1 795 462.0
87	90	825 702	157 726	191.0205	63 093.5	245 693.3	1 295 661.1
88	91	667 976	136 650	204.5732	49 554.7	182 599.8	916 060.7
89	92	531 326	116 556	219.3681	38 269.1	133 045.1	632 809.3
90	93	414 770	97 812	235.8223	29 003.9	94 776.0	425 601.2
91	94	316 958	80 646	254.4375	21 518.6	65 772.1	277 404.7
92	95	236 312	65 180	275.8218	15 576.2	44 253.5	174 150.9
93	96	171 132	51 454	300.6685	10 951.4	28 677.3	104 403.7
94	97	119 678	39 577	330.6957	7 435.6	17 725.9	59 028.4
95	98	80 101	29 689	370.6446	4 831.7	10 290.3	30 872.3
96	99	50 412	21 853	433.4881	2 952.3	5 458.6	14 464.4
97	100	28 559	15 686	549.2489	1 623.8	2 506.3	5 727.8
98	101	12 873	9 665	750.7962	710.6	882.5	1 701.4
99	102	3 208	3 208	1000.0000	171.9	171.9	278.3

1958 CSO—Age Last Birthday—3%

Age M	Age F	C_x	M_x	R_x	$D_x - M_x$	$10{,}000{,}000/D_x$
45	48	16 199.556	1 108 164.624	38 264 007.060	1 417 995.5	3.366 1751
46	49	17 135.398	1 095 214.124	36 711 271.739	1 345 538.7	3.469 7229
47	50	18 142.195	1 081 581.872	35 174 735.974	1 275 244.2	3.578 2725
48	51	19 219.708	1 067 218.785	33 655 335.607	1 207 082.1	3.692 2982
49	52	20 366.828	1 052 076.402	32 154 077.435	1 141 025.0	3.812 3362
50	53	21 581.100	1 036 818.268	30 672 038.971	1 077 047.9	3.938 9937
51	54	22 834.792	1 019 412.909	29 210 367.335	1 015 128.0	4.072 9573
52	55	24 124.719	1 001 506.816	27 770 276.799	955 244.5	4.214 9628
53	56	25 457.541	982 900.101	26 353 021.055	897 378.7	4.365 8405
54	57	26 826.547	963 325.408	24 959 890.030	841 512.5	4.526 5541
55	58	28 243.405	942 798.261	23 592 216.546	787 630.0	4.698 1950
56	59	29 716.258	921 291.805	22 251 369.519	735 715.9	4.882 0509
57	60	31 237.529	898 773.654	20 938 765.897	685 756.8	5.079 6381
58	61	32 789.221	875 217.634	19 655 878.533	637 741.2	5.292 7107
59	62	34 367.779	850 611.527	18 404 228.698	591 658.5	5.523 2778
60	63	35 958.260	824 946.023	17 185 368.084	547 499.5	5.773 6977
61	64	37 534.431	798 224.993	16 000 875.249	505 255.8	6.046 7155
62	65	39 092.105	770 464.253	14 852 340.674	464 919.4	6.345 5018
63	66	40 622.297	741 693.755	13 741 340.530	426 482.4	6.673 8281
64	67	42 116.865	711 942.209	12 669 432.491	389 936.3	7.036 1984
65	68	43 573.944	681 245.797	11 638 146.749	355 272.2	7.438 0350
66	69	44 983.837	649 641.565	10 648 977.872	322 481.1	7.885 9627
67	70	46 319.555	617 173.132	9 703 382.939	291 552.3	8.388 1119
68	71	47 506.937	583 902.887	8 802 771.843	262 475.3	8.954 4209
69	72	48 442.476	549 945.429	7 948 480.302	235 237.0	9.596 7300
70	73	49 035.794	515 487.344	7 141 695.698	209 821.9	10.328 8286
71	74	49 220.344	480 776.531	6 383 353.570	186 208.1	11.166 7663
72	75	48 972.833	446 104.224	5 674 047.236	164 366.3	12.129 2645
73	76	48 351.499	411 773.734	5 013 961.246	144 257.6	13.238 5313
74	77	47 464.400	378 043.347	4 402 848.089	125 834.0	14.522 3097
75	78	46 392.316	345 092.544	3 840 086.431	109 038.9	16.017 0113
76	79	45 185.215	313 042.339	3 324 789.173	93 811.3	17.770 9474
77	80	43 850.850	281 977.604	2 855 884.231	80 086.5	19.848 9022
78	81	42 332.620	251 976.592	2 432 164.504	67 798.5	22.338 0126
79	82	40 538.630	223 153.893	2 052 295.627	56 879.8	25.353 9346
80	83	38 419.948	195 688.563	1 714 759.370	47 259.9	29.048 0236
81	84	35 968.068	169 784.096	1 417 761.743	38 863.4	33.620 1016
82	85	33 215.197	145 650.526	1 159 184.064	31 608.7	39.336 2712
83	86	30 239.454	123 472.231	936 574.453	25 408.3	46.554 3496
84	87	27 139.018	103 378.916	747 180.039	20 169.1	55.764 9530
85	88	24 005.704	85 433.284	588 025.079	15 795.5	67.653 7804
86	89	20 919.821	69 636.618	456 009.137	12 190.3	83.194 3295
87	90	17 955.733	55 937.402	347 998.899	9 258.6	103.789 3491
88	91	15 176.989	44 236.279	260 908.482	6 908.6	131.504 0247
89	92	12 629.517	34 393.978	191 773.798	5 053.9	169.458 2082
90	93	10 339.996	26 243.475	137 816.103	3 614.5	222.505 5460
91	94	8 317.393	19 602.916	96 487.925	2 518.4	298.448 6638
92	95	6 558.354	14 287.245	65 499.743	1 701.1	410.308 5931
93	96	5 050.982	10 116.127	42 828.954	1 106.8	580.747 0730
94	97	3 790.318	6 919.294	26 716.519	686.7	851.194 2255
95	98	2 773.988	4 531.917	15 655.066	400.2	
96	99	1 992.031	2 793.308	8 383.931	213.1	
97	100	1 394.997	1 550.797	3 886.784	98.2	
98	101	838.570	1 110.119	1 381.668	34.7	
99	102	271.549	271.549	271.549	6.8	

429

But from Formula (17-4),

$$l_x = l_{x+1} + d_x$$

Substituting, $$p_x = \frac{l_{x+1}}{l_x} \qquad (17\text{-}5)$$

where p_x is the probability that a person x years old will live through one year. By similar reasoning, it can be shown that q_x the probability that a person aged x years will die during the year is

$$q_x = \frac{d_x}{l_x} \qquad (17\text{-}6)$$

Thus the probability that a man aged 80 will die during his 80th year is

$$q_{80} = \frac{d_{80}}{l_{80}} = \frac{283,916}{2,481,948} = .1143924,$$

as given in the fourth column of the table. (Note that this column gives $1000 \times q_x$. The figures in the table can be applied over longer periods than one year. Thus, the probability that a person aged x will survive n years is given by

$$_n p_x = \frac{l_{x+n}}{l_x} \qquad (17\text{-}7)$$

And the probability that he will not survive n years is found by recalling from the explanation of probability theory that the probability of two mutually exclusive events is their sum. Therefore the probability that the person will either *live* or *die* in n years from age x is $_n p_x + {}_n q_x$. But this sum is a certainty, therefore

$$_n p_x + {}_n q_x = 1$$

and $$_n q_x = 1 - {}_n p_x$$

Substituting from (17-7)

$$_n q_x = 1 - \frac{l_{x+n}}{l_x} \qquad (17\text{-}8)$$

Thus from the table, the probability that a woman aged 80 will die in 5 years is

$$_5 q_{80} = 1 - \frac{l_{85}}{l_{80}}$$

$$= 1 - \frac{1,925,590}{3,372,882}$$

$$= 1 - .57 = .43.$$

The other columns in the Commissioner's 1958 Standard Ordinary Mortality Table, on Pages 426, 427, 428, 429, are headed by the symbols D_x, N_x, S_x, C_x, M_x, R_x and $D_x - M_x$. These seven expressions are called the commutation symbols and the figures they represent play an important part in the calculations of various forms of annuities and life insurance. They appear in formulas for these various types of computations, and their meaning is explained throughout the following sections in connection with the derivation of those formulas. Before proceeding to the detailed discussion of the various types of life annuities and life insurance, the relationship between the other annuities already discussed in Chapter 14, and those entering into the calculations in this present chapter, which are called contingent annuities, must be clearly established.

Relationship Between the Contingent Annuities and Other Annuities

All types of life annuities and life insurance introduce the element of contingency in one form or another. Since the annuities that have been dealt with in Chapter 14 assume the existence of a definite term (with the possible exception of the perpetual annuity), annuity calculations in which that term is not definite but is contingent upon the occurrence of an event, require the introduction into the formula of modifying factors to take care of this contingency. For that purpose the concept of probability, and its specific application in the probability of living to a given age or for a given number of years, and the complementary probability of dying before a given age or during a given number of years, has already been discussed. To apply it in annuity mathematics, two new concepts are needed, that of mathematical expectation and that of the probability of receiving a payment in case an event occurs. Since the letter p has already been used to express the probability of occurrence of an event, add the letter S for the payment to be received in case the event occurs. Then, the mathematical expectation, which is usually symbolized by M, is equal to the product of that sum by its probability of occurrence, or in symbols

$$M = Sp. \tag{17-8a}$$

This formula can readily be used to find the mathematical expectation of various events by substituting in it for S the sum of money to be paid if the events occur and for p the values of the probabilities of their occurrence. For example, if the event is the payment by an insurance company of a whole life insurance policy before the insured reaches a given age, then the probability of his dying before that age can be obtained by substituting for P the corresponding value from Formula (17-8), which is

$$1 - \frac{l_{x+n}}{l_x}$$

where the values of l_{x+n} and l_x are obtained from Table 18, x being the present age of the insured and n the number of years in the future that is stipulated.

Just as this formula $M = Sp$ can be used for finding the mathematical expectation of an insured dying before a given age, so it can be used to determine the present value of a contingent payment. To be consistent with the usage of the letter P for the present value of an annuity in Chapter 14, that usage will be continued in this chapter, and P (or P_x) will be substituted for M in the formula $M = Sp$ whenever the calculation of a present value of a contingent payment is to be made by that formula.

For example, it was shown in Chapter 13 that the present value of a sum of money to be paid in n periods, with interest compounded at the rate i per period is, $P = Sv^n$. This present value was, of course, for the *certain* payment of the sum. Therefore the present value of the contingent payment would be obtained by multiplying the present value of the certain payment by the probability of the payment being made. Thus, to find the present value of a man now x years old, receiving a payment contingent upon his living n years, one would substitute the values Sv^n for S in the formula $M = Sp$ and $_np_x = \dfrac{l_{x+n}}{l_x}$ for p in that formula so as to obtain the formula

$$P_x = \frac{(Sv^n)(l_{x+n})}{l_x}. \tag{17-9}$$

Where P_x is the present value of the conditional payment of S dollars to a man now x years old on the condition that he live n years.

For example, the present value of a payment of \$200 to be made to a man now 20 years old on reaching age of 40 if money is compounded annually at $3\frac{1}{2}\%$ interest is given by:

$$P = \frac{(\$200)(.50256588)(9,225,048)}{(9,656,344)} = \$96.02$$

where \$200 is the amount of the payment to be received if the man lives 20 years, .50256588 is the value of v^{20} from Table 12 for 20 periods at $3\frac{1}{2}\%$ each, (9,225,048) is the value of l_{20+20} from Table 18 and (9,656,344) is the value of l_{20} from Table 18.

Note that in the foregoing example the quantity determined was the present value of a single future payment. In the life annuity and life insurance calculations to be made in the following sections, the values involved are more frequently those of annuities rather than single sums, but the principle of multiplying present values by probabilities to obtain contingent present values (mathematical expectations) is the same.

Life Annuities and Life Insurance Calculations—General

As has already been indicated, calculations of life annuities and insurance differ from other interest and annuity calculations in that they introduce a new factor, that of probability or contingency. In addition, there is another factor that enters into all actual policies or annuities. It is the share of the costs of operating the insurance company, and is called the loading of the policy. The periodic payment made by the insured is called the gross premium, because it consists of the loading plus the net premium, which takes account only of the mathematical expectation of payments by the company, and the interest earned on its funds.

The calculations in this chapter, unless specifically stated otherwise, deal with net premiums and net payments rather than gross premiums or payments, for two reasons. First, in any mathematical treatment the net figures must be computed; and second, because the net figures furnish the basis necessary for calculating the loadings on various types of policies issued by various companies. In comparing policies, or companies, due allowance must be made for differences in the added benefits which many life insurance policies provide, and especially for differences between companies in their dividend policies, because some companies have higher rates and higher dividends than others, and obviously both must be considered in finding the expenditures by the insured.

The calculation of the net premium involves certain assumptions, in addition to its disregard of the costs of operating the insurance company. These assumptions are that the mortality table used represents the actual annual death rates of the policy-holders, and that the interest rate earned by the company is known. Uniformity of calculations requires the use of an accepted mortality table, such as the Commissioner's 1958 Standard Ordinary Mortality Table, and the adoption of a uniform rate of interest earned on insurance funds, which is taken in that table as $2\frac{1}{2}\%$ per year, and used in computing the last four columns in that table (Table 18).

Whole Life Annuities

A whole life annuity consists of a number of periodic payments that depends upon the life of the annuitant, the payments ceasing upon his death. Just as in the case of the annuities certain discussed in Chapter 14, there are whole life ordinary annuities, on which the periodic payment is made at the beginning of each period, and whole life annuities due, on which the periodic payment is made at the end of each period. Moreover, either of these types may be deferred, so that there are deferred whole life ordinary annuities and deferred whole life annuities due.

The calculations of whole life annuities are commonly made upon the basis of annual payments, that is, for annual whole life annuities. Then an annual whole life ordinary annuity consists of a series of payments made at the end of each year for the life of the annuitant, and the formula to be derived is that for the present value of such an annuity. In other words, it is the amount that an annuitant x years old should pay to receive the payment at the end of his $x + 1$ year, and at the end of every year thereafter until he dies.

By Formula (17-9), derived earlier in this chapter, the present value of a contingent payment of dollars in n years to a person x years old was found to be

$$P_x = \frac{Sv^n l_{x+n}}{l_x}$$

To convert this formula into a form that can readily be used with tabulated figures, multiply both numerator and denominator by v^x, obtaining,

$$P_x = S \frac{v^x v^n l_{x+n}}{v^x l_x}$$

$$= S \frac{v^{x+n} l_{x+n}}{v^x l_x}$$

Now the product of a given power of v by a value of l for a corresponding year is denoted by the letter D, called a commutation symbol, and these values are tabulated in Table 18 on Pages 426 and 428.

Thus the present value of the payment T, payable in n years to a person aged x becomes

$$P_x = T \frac{D_{x+n}}{D_x} \qquad (17\text{-}10)$$

However, the person who buys a whole life annuity acquires the mathematical expectation of receiving a series of payments extending from an age of $x + 1$ years, indefinitely. Therefore the present value of the annuity is the sum of the present values of all the payments. To make this indefinite number definite, it is taken to the end of the table, that is, to the age of 99 for males, and 102 for females. (As is evident from the figures, the mathematical expectations at the greater ages become very small.) Therefore the present value of a whole life ordinary annuity of annual payments of R dollars each becomes

$$P_x = R \frac{D_{x+1}}{D_x} + R \frac{D_{x+2}}{D_x} \cdots R \frac{D_{99}}{D_x}$$

$$= R \frac{D_{x+1} + D_{x+2} \cdots D_{99}}{D_x}$$

To avoid the need for adding the values of D_{x+1}, $D_{x+2} \cdots D_{99}$, their sums are given in Table 18, in the column headed by the commutation symbol N_x. Thus, the present value of a whole life ordinary annuity of annual payments of R dollars becomes

$$P_x = R \frac{N_{x+1}}{D_x} \qquad (17\text{-}11)$$

To apply this formula, find the present value of an ordinary annuity of annual payments of $2,500.00 each for the life of a man now 35 years old.
From Table 18,

$$N_{36} \text{ is found to be } 69,410,205.8$$

and $\qquad D_{35}$ is found to be $\ \ 3,327,114.7$

Substituting in Formula (17-11)

$$P_x = (\$2,500.00) \ \frac{69,410,205.8}{3,327,114.7}$$

Thus $\qquad P_x = \$52,154.96$

A whole life annuity due differs from the whole life ordinary annuity, in that the payments are made at the beginning, instead of the end, of each payment period. The effect of the change is to make the year of the first payment the same as the age of the annuitant. Therefore the payments in the whole life annuity due are identical with those of the ordinary annuity, with one added payment at the start. (This method was used with annuities due certain, in Chapter 14.)

Therefore, the present value of a whole life annuity due of annual payments of R dollars each becomes, from Formula (17-11).

$$P_{x(due)} = R + R\frac{N_{x+1}}{D_x}$$

$$= R\left(1 + \frac{N_{x+1}}{D_x}\right)$$

$$= R\left(\frac{D_x + N_{x+1}}{D_x}\right)$$

However, since $N_{x+1} = D_{x+1} + D_{x+2} \cdots D_{99}$
and $N_x = D_x + D_{x+1} + D_{x+2} \cdots D_{99}$
Then $N_x = D_x + N_{x+1}$
Substituting in above formula

$$P_{x(due)} = R\frac{N_x}{D_x} \qquad\qquad (17\text{-}12)$$

To apply this formula, find the present value of an annuity of annual payments of $1,500.00 for the life of a woman 42 years old, if she receives the first payment at age 42.
From Table 18,

$$N_{42} \text{ is found to be } 60,048,890.8$$

and $\qquad D_{42}$ is found to be $\ \ 2,922,749.1$

Substituting in Formula (17-12)

$$P_{x(due)} = (\$1,500.00)\left(\frac{60,048,890.8}{2,922,749.1}\right)$$

$$= \$30,818.02$$

A whole life deferred ordinary annuity differs from a whole life ordinary annuity in that the annuitant receives no payments for a period of years.

Let x be his present age, and k the number of periods (years) of deferment. Then when the annuitant reaches the age of $x + k$ years, the deferred ordinary annuity will become an ordinary annuity and its present value, by Formula (17-11) will be

$$P_{x+k} = R\,\frac{N_{x+1+k}}{D_{x+k}}$$

To find the present value of this annuity at the age of x years, that is, k years earlier, substitute its present value $R\,\dfrac{N_{x+1+k}}{D_{x+k}}$ for T in Formula (17-10), which gives the present value of a single contingent payment of T dollars.

That is, by formula (17-10), $P_x = T\,\dfrac{D_{x+n}}{D_x}$, where n is the number of periods of deferment. Here k is the symbol used instead of n, and R instead of T, so Formula (17-10) becomes

$$P_x = R\,\frac{D_{x+k}}{D_x}$$

Then substituting for this value of P_x, the value found above for P_{x+k}, which was $R\,\dfrac{N_{x+1+k}}{D_{x+k}}$, there is obtained

$$_kP_x = \left(R\,\frac{N_{x+k+1}}{D_{x+k}}\right)\left(\frac{D_{x+k}}{D_x}\right)$$

Cancelling like terms,

$$_kP_x = R\,\frac{N_{x+k+1}}{D_x} \tag{17-13}$$

To apply this formula, find the present value of an annuity of annual payments of \$1,500.00, for a man 42 years old, if the payments start at the end of the seventeenth year following.

Here x is 42 and k is 17.

Then substituting in Formula (17-13),

$$_kP_x = (\$1,500.00)\,\frac{N_{60}}{D_{42}}$$

From Table 18,

$$N_{60} \text{ is found to be } 16,084,766.8$$

and D_{42} is found to be   2,645,204.4

Substituting, $_{17}P_{42} = (\$1,500.00) \dfrac{16,084,766.8}{2,645,204.4}$

Thus $_{17}P_{42} = \$9,121.09$

For most purposes of annuity calculation, the formula for the deferred whole life annuity due is unnecessary, since in most cases Formula (17-13) is adequate, unless the period of deferment, rather than the age at which payments begin, is stated.   However, it is convenient for use in calculations of this type.   The formula is derived in the same way as Formula (17-13), as follows:

By Formula (17-12), an annuity due, deferred for k years, will then have a present value, for a person now x years old, of

$$P_{x+k(due)} = R\left(\frac{N_{x+k}}{D_{x+k}}\right)$$

Then by Formula (17-10), the present value at x years of $P_{x+k(due)}$ is

$$_{k}P_{x(due)} = R\frac{N_{x+k}}{D_{x+k}}\frac{D_{x+k}}{D_x}$$

$$= R\frac{N_{x+k}}{D_x} \qquad (17\text{-}14)$$

To apply this formula, find the present value of an annuity due paying $1,200.00 annually for a woman 40 years old, if the period of deferment is 10 years.   Here x is 40 and k is 10.   Substituting in Formula (17-14)

$$_{k}P_{x(due)} = (\$1,200.00)\frac{N_{50}}{D_{40}}$$

From Table 18,

N_{50} is found to be 39,199,098.3

and D_{40} is found to be   3,119,541.4

Substituting

$$_{10}P_{50(due)} = (\$1,200.00)\frac{39,199,098.3}{3,119,541.4} = \$15,078.79$$

Temporary Life Annuities

Temporary life annuities are life annuities in which the payments continue only for a specified number of years, being terminated at the end of that time, or during it by the death of the annuitant.   They are issued in all four of the forms in which the whole life annuities are written, that is, as temporary life ordinary annuities, temporary life annuities due, deferred temporary life ordinary annuities, and deferred temporary life annuities due.

Fortunately, the formulas for their present values are easy to remember, because they are merely the difference between the value of the corresponding whole life annuity for the present age of the annuitant, and a whole life annuity deferred to the age he will be when the temporary annuity expires. The mathematical justification for this statement is seen from the derivation of Formula (17-11), where the commutation term N was shown to be the sum of the D terms, of which there was one for the mathematical expectation of each year of life of the annuitant.

By this difference method, the formulas for the present values of the temporary annuities can be written directly from Formulas (17-11), (17-12), (17-13) and (17-14) for the whole life annuities.

In temporary annuity calculations, let n be the number of years for which the temporary annuity continues.

Then since the present value of a whole life ordinary annuity is by Formula (17-11), $P_x = R \dfrac{N_{x+1}}{D_x}$, and that of a deferred ordinary annuity is by Formula (17-13), $_nP_x = R \dfrac{N_{x+n+1}}{D_x}$, the present value of a temporary life ordinary annuity is,

$$P_{x:n} = P_x - {_nP_x} = R\left(\frac{N_{x+1}}{D_x}\right) - R\left(\frac{N_{x+n+1}}{D_x}\right)$$

$$= R\left(\frac{N_{x+1}}{D_x} - \frac{N_{x+n+1}}{D_x}\right)$$

$$= R\frac{N_{x+1} - N_{x+n+1}}{D_x} \qquad (17\text{-}15)$$

Since the present value of a whole life annuity due is by Formula (17-12), $P_{x(due)} = R \dfrac{N_x}{D_x}$, and that of a whole life deferred annuity due is by Formula (17-14), $_nP_{x(due)} = R \dfrac{N_{x+n}}{D_x}$, then the present value of a temporary life annuity due is

$$P_{x:n(due)} = R\left(\frac{N_x}{D_x}\right) - R\left(\frac{N_{x+n}}{D_x}\right)$$

$$P_{x:n(due)} = R\frac{N_x - N_{x+n}}{D_x} \qquad (17\text{-}16)$$

Since the present value of a deferred whole life ordinary annuity is, by Formula (17-13), $_kP_x = R \dfrac{N_{x+k+1}}{D_x}$, then the present value of a deferred temporary life ordinary annuity is

$$_kP_{x:n} = R\left(\frac{N_{x+k+1}}{D_x}\right) - R\left(\frac{N_{x+k+n+1}}{D_x}\right)$$

$$= R\frac{N_{x+k+1} - N_{x+k+n+1}}{D_x} \tag{17-17}$$

Since the present value of a deferred whole life annuity due is by Formula (17-14), $_kP_{x(due)} = R\dfrac{N_{x+k}}{D_x}$, then the present value of a deferred temporary life annuity due is

$$_kP_{x:n(due)} = R\left(\frac{N_{x+k}}{D_x}\right) - R\left(\frac{N_{x+k+n}}{D_x}\right)$$

$$= R\frac{N_{x+k} - N_{x+k+n}}{D_x} \tag{17-18}$$

To illustrate the use of these four temporary life annuity formulas the following four calculations are given.

1. What is the present value of a temporary life annuity of $1,500.00 paid annually to a man aged 45 for 10 years, if the first payment is made at the end of the first year?

Since this is a temporary life ordinary annuity, Formula (17-15) applies,

$$P_{x:n} = R\frac{N_{x+1} - N_{x+n+1}}{D_x}$$

where R is $1,500.00, $x + 1$ is $45 + 1 = 46$, $x + n + 1$ is $45 + 10 + 1 = 56$, and $x = 45$.

Substituting $P_{45:10} = (\$1,500.00)\left(\dfrac{N_{46} - N_{56}}{D_{45}}\right)$

From Table 18,

N_{46} is found to be 41,503,141.8

N_{56} is found to be 21,919,731.1

and D_{45} is found to be   2,304,043.5

Therefore $P_{45:10} = (\$1,500.00)\left(\dfrac{41,503,141.8 - 21,919,731.1}{2,304,043.5}\right)$

$$= (\$1,500.00)\left(\frac{19,583,410.7}{2,304,043.5}\right)$$

$$= \$12,749.38.$$

2. What is the present value of a temporary life annuity of $1,500.00 paid annually to a woman aged 52 for 10 years, if the first payment is made at once (age 52)?

Since this is a temporary life annuity due, formula (17-16) applies,

$$P_{x:n(due)} = R\frac{N_x - N_{x+n}}{D_x}$$

where R is \$1,500.00, x is 52 and $x + n$ is 62.

Substituting $P_{52:10(due)} = (\$1,500.00)\left(\dfrac{N_{52} - N_{62}}{D_{52}}\right)$

From Table 18,

N_{52} is found to be 34,831,611.5

N_{62} is found to be 17,443,439.7

and D_{52} is found to be   2,066,589.4

Therefore $P_{52:10(due)} = (\$1,500.00)\left(\dfrac{34,831,611.5 - 17,443,439.7}{2,066,589.4}\right)$

$$= (\$1,500.00)\left(\frac{17,388,171.8}{2,066,589.4}\right)$$

$$= \$12,620.92$$

3. What is the present value of a deferred temporary life ordinary annuity of \$1,500.00 paid annually to a man aged 48 for 10 years, if the first payment is made at age 61?

Since this is a deferred temporary life ordinary annuity, Formula (17-17) applies

$$_kP_{x:n} = R\left(\frac{N_{x+k+1} - N_{x+k+n+1}}{D_x}\right)$$

where R is \$1,500.00, x is 48, n is 10, and k is $61 - 1 - x = 61 - 49 = 12$.

Substituting $_{12}P_{48:10} = (\$1,500.00)\left(\dfrac{N_{61} - N_{71}}{D_{48}}\right)$

From Table 18,

N_{61} is found to be 14,791,332.4

N_{71} is found to be   5,257,405.0

and D_{48} is found to be   2,144,183.7

Therefore $_{12}P_{48:10} = (\$1,500.00)\left(\dfrac{14,791,332.4 - 5,257,405.0}{2,144,183.7}\right)$

$$= (\$1,500.00)\left(\frac{9,533,927.4}{2,144,183.7}\right)$$

$$= \$6,667.52.$$

4. What is the present value of an annuity due of \$1,500.00 paid annually to a person aged 42 for 10 years, if the first payment is made at age 61?

To treat this as a deferred temporary life annuity due, Formula (17-18) applies

$$_kP_{x:n(due)} = R\left(\frac{N_{x+k} - N_{x+k+n}}{D_x}\right)$$

where R is $1,500.00, x is 42, n is 10, and k is $61 - 42 = 19$.

Substituting $_{19}P_{42:10(due)} = (\$1,500.00)\left(\frac{N_{61} - N_{71}}{D_{42}}\right)$

From Table 18,

N_{61} is found to be 18,868,217.1

N_{71} is found to be 7,493,052.4

and D_{42} is found to be 2,922,749.1

Therefore $_{19}P_{42:10(due)} = (\$1,500.00)\left(\dfrac{18,868,217.1 - 7,493,052.4}{2,922,749.1}\right)$

$$= (\$1,500.00)\left(\frac{11,375,164.7}{2,922,749.1}\right)$$

$$= \$5,837.91$$

Life Insurance

As stated in the earlier part of this chapter, the insurance .computations, like the annuity calculations just concluded, include no allowances for costs of the insurance company, because of differences between companies, not so much in their overall charges to the insured, as in methods of distributing those charges over the period of the policy.   Therefore, the premiums to be computed in the following sections are not gross premiums, but net premiums (gross premiums less the loading charges).   While net premiums are not the premiums actually paid, their computation is essential to any mathematical analysis, or even evaluation, of insurance.

While there are policies in which the entire payment by the insured is made in a single sum, most policies are "ordinary" policies in which the net premiums are not only net premiums but net annual premiums, that is, net premiums paid in a single payment at the beginning of each policy year, which is the standard basis of computing net premiums.   Most companies add the loading charge to the net annual premium to find the gross annual premium, which is that actually paid by the insured.   If he wishes to pay it throughout the year, instead of at the beginning, the practice is to add an interest charge for the entire year, and then divide by the number of annual payments.   Moreover, many companies compute this interest at higher rates for more frequent payments throughout the year, to cover their added costs of bookkeeping and collection.

Since the purpose of insurance policies, as well as annuities, is to protect the insured and his dependents against financial contingencies affecting his income, there are many forms of policies issued, varying both in the basis, the amount and the distribution of benefits and of premiums. Moreover, there are many combination policies, which include features of more than one of the basic types. For purposes of calculation, these basic types are treated here in three groups, whole life insurance, term insurance, and endowment insurance.

Whole Life Insurance

A whole life insurance policy provides for the payment of a benefit on the death of the insured. The formulas for calculating the cost to him of that insurance are derived by computing that cost as a single payment (single net premium), and then distributing it into the usual annual premiums. Let A_x denote the amount of the single net premium per \$1.00 of the benefit, where x is the age of the insured. Then out of a group of people of that age, the number d_x, (given in the third column of the mortality table) will die during the first year, d_{x+1} will die in the second year, d_{x+2} in the third, etc. The payments made by the insurance company per \$1.00 of benefit will be, therefore, d_x dollars the first year, d_{x+1}, the second, d_{x+2}, the third, and so on to d_{99}, at the end of the table. The present value of the sum of these payments at compound interest is

$$vd_x + v^2d_{x+1} + v^3d_{x+2} \cdots + v^{99-x+1}d_{99}$$

However, the number of people whose aggregate payments to the company must be equal to that present value are the number from which the values of d_x, d_{x+1} etc. were taken, that is, the number alive in the table at age x; this number being given in the second column, l_x, of the table. Therefore the payment to be made by each per \$1.00 of benefit at age x is the sum of the present values of the payments by the company, divided by l_x. Denoting by A_x this payment per dollar of benefit, we have

$$A_x = \frac{vd_x + v^2d_{x+1} + v^3d_{x+2} \cdots v^{99-x+1}d_{99}}{l_x}$$

To convert this expression into a form suitable for solution by the tabulated values, multiply both numerator and denominator by v^x, obtaining

$$A_x = \frac{v^{x+1}d_x + v^{x+2}d_{x+1} + v^{x+3}d_{x+2} \cdots v^{99+1}d_{99}}{v^x l_x}$$

Now in deriving Formula (17-10), $v^x d_x$ was denoted by the commutation symbol D_x, and the values of the latter are tabulated in the fourth column of Table 18. Therefore in the denominator of the expression above $v^x l_x$ is replaced by the symbol D_x, to represent the value of that product for a given value of x. Moreover, the values of the products $v^{x+1}d_x$, $v^{x+2}d_{x+1}$,

$v^{x+3}d_{x+2} \cdots v^{99+1}d_{99}$ can also be computed, and they are given in the sixth column of Table 18, and are represented by the commutation symbols $C_x C_{x+1} \cdots C_{99}$.

Thus, in terms of commutation symbols and the products they represent, the above formula becomes

$$A_x = \frac{C_x + C_{x+1} + C_{x+2} \cdots C_{99}}{D_x}$$

Finally, just as the values of the sums of the products $D_x + D_{x+1} + D_{x+2} \cdots D_{99}$ were tabulated in the fifth column of Table 18 and represented by the symbol N_x, so the values of the sums of the products $C_x + C_{x+1} + C_{x+2} \cdots C_{99}$ are tabulated in the seventh column of Table 18, and represented by the symbol M_x.

Using this notation the above formula becomes

$$A_x = \frac{M_x}{D_x}$$

where A_x is the single net premium per dollar of whole life insurance. Then for a total amount of life insurance, T, the net single premium would be

$$TA_x = T\frac{M_x}{D_x} \qquad (17\text{-}19)$$

For example, the single net premium, for a boy at age 15, for a whole life policy of $8,000.00,

$$TA_x = (\$8,000.00)\left(\frac{M_{15}}{D_{15}}\right)$$

From Table 18,

M_{15} is found to be 1,383,668.423

and $\qquad$ D_{15} is found to be 6,249,207.7

Therefore $\quad TA_x = (\$8,000.00)\left(\frac{1,383,668.423}{6,249,207.7}\right) = \$1,771.32$

To find the value of the annual net premium, as in an ordinary whole life policy, equate TA_x in Formula (17-19) to the sum of the present values of the expected future premium payments. These constitute a whole life annuity due, paid to the company by the insured, which has the present value, by Formula (17-12) of

$$R\frac{N_x}{D_x}$$

Thus $\qquad\qquad$ $R\dfrac{N_x}{D_x} = T\dfrac{M_x}{D_x}$

Transposing and cancelling,

$$R_x = T \frac{M_x}{N_x} \tag{17-20}$$

That is, the annual net premium on a whole life insurance policy is the product of the benefit by the ratio of M_x to N_x, using tabulated values from Table 18. It is well to recall again that Table 18 is based on an assumed death rate, as shown in columns 2 and 3, and an assumed interest rate of $2\frac{1}{2}\%$.

As an example of the use of Formula (17-20) find the annual net premium on a life insurance policy of $25,000.00 on a person aged 35.

Substituting in Formula (17-20)

$$R_x = (\$25,000.00) \left(\frac{M_{35}}{N_{35}} \right)$$

From Table 18,

$$M_{35} \text{ is found to be } 1,232,989.195$$

$$N_{35} \text{ is found to be } 83,381,037.6$$

Therefore $R_x = (\$25,000.00) \left(\dfrac{1,232,989.195}{83,381,037.6} \right) = \$369.69$

Whole Life Insurance—n-Payment Policy

A special form of the whole life policy is the n-payment life policy, which is fully paid by annual payments for a period of n years. In computing the value of each of the n premiums, equate the value of TA_x, which by Formula (17-19) was $T \dfrac{M_x}{D_x}$, to the present value of an n-payment temporary life annuity due, paid to the company by the insured. The present value of such an annuity, by Formula (17-16) is

$$R \frac{N_x - N_{x+n}}{D_x}$$

Thus,

$$R \frac{N_x - N_{x+n}}{D_x} = T \frac{M_x}{D_x}$$

Transposing and cancelling,

$$_n R_x = T \frac{M_x}{N_x - N_{x+n}} \tag{17-21}$$

As an example of the use of Formula (17-21), find the annual net premium for a $10,000 20-payment life insurance policy issued to a man at age 30.

Substituting in Formula (17-21).

$$_n R_x = (\$10,000.00) \frac{M_{30}}{N_{30} - N_{50}}$$

From Table 18,

M_{30} is found to be   1,249,317.866

N_{30} is found to be 91,062,461.2

and $\qquad$ N_{50} is found to be 32,765,022.1

Therefore

$$_nR_x = (\$10,000.00)\ \frac{1,249,317.866}{91,062,461.2 - 32,765,022.1}$$

$$= (\$10,000.00)\ \frac{1,249,317.866}{58,297,439.1}$$

$$= \$214.30$$

Term Insurance

A term life insurance policy provides for the payment of a benefit on the death of the insured only if it occurs in a specified number of years after the issuance of the policy.   In deriving the formula relating that benefit to the premiums, the latter will be taken, first, on the assumption of the payment a single net premium, as was done in deriving the formula for whole life insurance.

Let $A_{x:n}$ denote the amount of the single net premium per \$1.00 of benefit, where x is the age of the insured, and n is the term in years.   Then out of a group of people of age x, the number d_x, given in the third column of Table 18, will die in the first year, d_{x+1} will die in the second, etc., up to d_{x+n-1} the nth year.   The payments made by the insurance company will be, therefore, d_x dollars the first year, d_{x+1} dollars the second year, etc. up to d_{x+n-1} dollars the nth year.   The present value of the sum of these payments at compound interest is

$$vd_x + v^2d_{x+1} \cdots v^nd_{x+n-1}$$

However the number of people whose aggregate payments to the company must be equal to that present value are the number from which the values of d_x, $d_{x+1} \cdots d_{x+n-1}$ were taken, that is, the number alive at age x—this number being given in the second column, l_x, of Table 18.   Therefore the payment at age x to be made by each person per \$1.00 of benefit is the sum of the present values of the payments by the company, divided by l_x. Since this single net premium per person is to be denoted by $A_{x:n}$, we have

$$A_{x:n} = \frac{vd_x + v^2d_{x+1} \cdots v^nd_{x+n-1}}{l_x}$$

Multiplying numerator and denominator by v^x gives

$$A_{x:n} = \frac{v^{x+1}d_x + v^{x+2}d_{x+1} \cdots v^{x+n}d_{x+n-1}}{v^xl_x}$$

However, as explained in deriving the formula for whole life insurance, $v^{x+1}d_x$ is C_x, $v^{x+2}d_{x+1}$ is C_{x+1} etc. to $v^{x+n}d_{x+n-1}$ is C_{x+n-1}, and $v^x l_x$ is D_x, (the C and D terms symbolizing constant values for assumed death and interest rates tabulated in Table 18, so that

$$A_{x:n} = \frac{C_x + C_{x+1} \cdots C_{x+n-1}}{D_x}$$

Now $C_x + C_{x+1} \cdots C_{99} = M_x$ (a)

and $C_{x+n} + C_{x+n+1} \cdots C_{99} = M_{x+n}$ (b)

So subtracting (b) from (a)

$$C_x + C_{x+1} \cdots C_{x+n-1} = M_x - M_{x+n}$$

Substituting in above formula for $A_{x:n}$,

$$A_{x:n} = \frac{M_x - M_{x+n}}{D_x}$$

which gives the amount of a net single premium per $1.00 of term life insurance. Therefore the net single premium for a total amount, T, of term life insurance is

$$TA_{x:n} = T \frac{M_x - M_{x+n}}{D_x} \qquad (17\text{-}22)$$

As an example of the use of Formula (17-22), find the net single premium for $10,000 term insurance for a woman 30 years old, covering a term of 20 years.

Substituting in Formula (17-22)

$$TA_{x:n} = (\$10,000.00) \frac{M_{30} - M_{50}}{D_{30}}$$

From Table 18,

M_{30} is found to be 1,274,211.185

M_{50} is found to be 1,081,581.872

D_{30} is found to be 4,289,802.9

Therefore

$$TA_{x:n} = (\$10,000.00) \left(\frac{1{,}274{,}211.185 - 1{,}081{,}581.872}{4{,}289{,}802.9} \right)$$

$$= (\$10,000.00) \left(\frac{192{,}629.313}{4{,}289{,}820.9} \right)$$

$$= \$449.04$$

To find the value of the net annual premium, assuming that it is paid once a year for the n years of the term of the policy, or for the number of years that the insured lives, if that period is less than the term, equate $TA_{x:n}$

in Formula (17-22) to the sum of the present values of the expected annual payments. These constitute a temporary life annuity due which has the present value, by Formula (17-16), of

$$R \frac{N_x - N_{x+n}}{D_x}$$

Thus
$$R \frac{N_x - N_{x+n}}{D_x} = T \frac{M_n - M_{x+n}}{D_x}$$

Transposing and cancelling,

$$_nR_{x:n} = T \frac{M_x - M_{x+n}}{N_x - N_{x+n}} \tag{17-23}$$

the net annual premium on a term life policy. As an example of the use of Formula (17-23), find the amount of each of the 15 net annual premiums on a 15-year term life insurance policy for $12,500 on a man aged 40.

Substituting in Formula (17-23),

$$_nR_{x:n} = (\$12,500.00) \frac{M_{40} - M_{55}}{N_{40} - N_{55}}$$

From Table 18,

$$M_{40} \text{ is found to be } 1,164,133.363$$
$$M_{55} \text{ is found to be } 942,798.261$$
$$N_{40} \text{ is found to be } 57,126,141.7$$
$$N_{55} \text{ is found to be } 23,548,405.2$$

Therefore,

$$_nR_{x:n} = (\$12,500.00) \left(\frac{1,164,133.363 - 942,798.261}{57,126,141.7 - 23,548,405.2} \right)$$

$$= (\$12,500.00) \left(\frac{221,335.102}{33,577,736.5} \right) = \$82.40$$

Endowments

An endowment is a single payment annuity—that is, it is an agreement by a policy holder to make periodic payments for a stipulated term, for which the company pays a single sum, usually at the end of the term. On the other hand, endowment insurance also includes life insurance during the term of the endowment. The most direct derivation of the formula for the endowment (which is often called a "pure" endowment to distinguish it from endowment insurance) is as follows:

By Formula (17-10), the present value of the payment of T dollars after n years to a person aged x years is

$$P_x = T \frac{D_{x+n}}{D_x}$$

In return for the expectation of this payment, the endowment buyer agrees to pay the insurance company R dollars annually for n years, beginning at age x. This is a temporary life annuity due, and its present value to the insurance company is, by Formula (17-16),

$$P_{x:n(due)} = R \frac{N_x - N_{x+n}}{D_x}$$

Equating P_x and $P_{x:n(due)}$,

$$T \frac{D_{x+n}}{D_x} = R \frac{N_x - N_{x+n}}{D_x}$$

Gives

$$T(D_{x+n}) = R(N_x - N_{x+n})$$

hence

$$Re_{x:n} = T \frac{D_{x+n}}{N_x - N_{x+n}} \tag{17-24}$$

where $Re_{x:n}$ is the annual premium on an n-payment endowment having a period of n years, and a benefit of T dollars, issued to a person aged x.

As an example of the use of Formula (17-24), find the net annual premium on a 20-payment 20-year endowment of $5,000, issued to a person aged 30. Substituting in Formula (17-24)

$$Re_{x:n} = (\$5,000.00) \frac{D_{30+20}}{N_{30} - N_{30+20}}$$

From Table 18,

$$D_{50} \text{ is found to be} \quad 2,223,303.1$$
$$N_{30} \text{ is found to be} \quad 103,535,933.8$$
$$N_{50} \text{ is found to be} \quad 39,199,098.3$$

Therefore $Re_{x:n} = (\$5,000.00) \left(\dfrac{2,223,303.1}{103,535,933.8 - 39,199,098.3} \right)$

$$= (\$5,000.00) \left(\frac{2,223,303.1}{64,577,736.5} \right)$$

$$Re_{x:n} = \$172.14$$

Note that the comparatively small size of this premium is due to the fact that, in a "straight" or "pure" endowment, without life insurance provision, the insured receives nothing if he dies during the term. Therefore, the premium reflects, not only the interest on the funds, but also the funds accruing to the company from the paid-in premiums of those policy holders who die during the term. For this reason, while the rate is low, the "pure" endowment is not widely used.

Sometimes the number of annual payments for an endowment is not the same as the number of years in its term (i.e. until it is payable), but is less than that figure. In that case, the formula for the premium is derived as follows: From Formula (17-10), the present value of the payment of T dollars after n years to a person aged x years is:

$$P_x = T \frac{D_{x+n}}{D_x}$$

In return for this expectation of payment, the endowment buyer agrees to pay the insurance company R dollars annually for m years, beginning at age x. This is a temporary life annuity due, and its present value to the insurance company is, by Formula (17-16)

$$P_{x:m(due)} = R \frac{N_x - N_{x+m}}{D_x}$$

Equating P_x and $P_{x:m(due)}$

$$T \frac{D_{x+n}}{D_x} = R \frac{N_x - N_{x+m}}{D_x}$$

So, $$T(D_{x+n}) = R(N_x - N_{x+m})$$

which gives $$_mRe_{x:n} = T \frac{D_{x+n}}{N_x - N_{x+m}} \qquad (17\text{-}25)$$

where $_mRe_{x:n}$ is the annual premium on an m-payment endowment having a period of n years and a benefit of T dollars, issued to a person aged x years.

As an example of the use of Formula (17-25), find the net annual premium on a 10-payment, 20-year endowment of \$5,000.00, issued to a woman aged 30.

Substituting in Formula (17-25)

$$_mRe_{x:n} = (\$5,000.00) \frac{D_{30+20}}{N_{30} - N_{30+10}}$$

From Table 18,

$$D_{50} \text{ is found to be } 1,990,429.3$$
$$N_{30} \text{ is found to be } 91,062,461.2$$
$$N_{40} \text{ is found to be } 57,126,141.7$$

Therefore $_mRe_{x:n} = (\$5,000.00) \left(\frac{1,990,429.3}{91,062,461.2 - 57,126,141.7} \right)$

$$= (\$5,000.00) \left(\frac{1,990,429.3}{33,936,319.5} \right)$$

$$= \$293.26$$

Endowment Insurance

Since, as stated above, endowment insurance is a combination of an endowment, and a life insurance policy for the term of the endowment, the amount of the premium can be found by adding the premiums for the two.   That is, the net annual premium for an n-year, n-payment endowment of T dollars is given by Formula (17-24) as

$$Re_{x:n} = T \frac{D_{x+n}}{N_x - N_{x+n}}$$

And the net annual premium for an n-year term life insurance policy is given by Formula (17-23) as

$$_nR_{x:n} = T \frac{M_x - M_{x+n}}{N_x - N_{x+n}}$$

Therefore the net annual premium for an n-year n-payment endowment insurance policy is

$$Re\text{-}ins_{x:n} = Re_{x:n} + {_nR_{x:n}}$$

$$= T \frac{D_{x+n}}{N_x - N_{x+n}} + \frac{M_x - M_{x+n}}{N_x - N_{x+n}}$$

$$Re\text{-}ins_{x:n} = T \frac{D_{x+n} + M_x - M_{x+n}}{N_x - N_{x+n}} \qquad (17\text{-}26)$$

where $Re\text{-}ins_{x:n}$ is the annual premium on an endowment insurance policy having a period of n years and n payments, and a benefit of T dollars, issued to a person aged x.

Moreover, by reasoning analogous to that used in deriving the formula for an n-year, m-payment endowment, the formula for an n-year, m-payment endowment insurance policy becomes

$$_mRe\text{-}ins_{x:n} = \frac{D_{x+n} + M_x - M_{x+n}}{N_x - N_{x+m}} \qquad (17\text{-}27)$$

As an example of the use of Formula (17-26) find the net annual premium on a 20-payment, 20-year endowment insurance policy of \$5,000.00, issued to a woman aged 30.

Substituting in Formula (17-26)

$$Re\text{-}ins_{x:n} = (\$5,000.00) \frac{D_{30+20} + M_{30} - M_{30+20}}{N_{30} - N_{30+20}}$$

From Table 18,

$$D_{50} \text{ is found to be}\quad 2,223,303.1$$
$$M_{30} \text{ is found to be}\quad 1,274,211.185$$
$$M_{50} \text{ is found to be}\quad 1,081,581.872$$
$$N_{30} \text{ is found to be}\quad 103,535,933.8$$
$$N_{50} \text{ is found to be}\quad 39,199,098.3$$

Therefore

$$Re\text{-}ins_{x:n} = (\$5,000.00) \left(\frac{2,223,303.1 + 1,274,211.185 - 1,081,581.872}{103,535,933.8 - 39,199,098.3} \right)$$

$$= (\$5,000.00) \left(\frac{2,415,932.807}{64,336,835.5} \right) = \$187.75$$

As an example of the use of Formula (17-27), find the net annual premium on a 10-payment 20-year endowment insurance policy of $5,000.00, issued to a man of age 30.

Substituting in Formula (17-27)

$$_mRe\text{-}ins_{x:n} = (\$5,000.00)\,\frac{D_{30+20} + M_{30} - M_{30+20}}{N_{30} - N_{30+10}}$$

From Table 18,

$$D_{50} \text{ is found to be } 1,990,429.3$$
$$M_{30} \text{ is found to be } 1,249,317.866$$
$$M_{50} \text{ is found to be } 1,036,818.268$$
$$N_{30} \text{ is found to be } 91,062,461.2$$
$$N_{40} \text{ is found to be } 57,126,161.7$$

Therefore

$$_mRe\text{-}ins_{x:n} = (\$5,000.00)\left(\frac{1,990,429.3 + 1,249,317.866 - 1,036,108.268}{91,062,461.2 - 57,126,161.7}\right)$$

$$= (\$5,000.00)\left(\frac{2,203,638.898}{33,936,299.5}\right) = \$324.67$$

Policy Reserve

The nature of the policy reserve can be discovered by using Formula (17-20) to find the net annual premium on a whole life policy, and then by using Formula (17-23) to find the net annual premium on a term life policy for various terms of 1 year each at various ages. For example, calculation by those formulas of, first, the net annual premium on a whole life insurance policy beginning at age 40, and, second, the net annual premium on one-year term life insurance policies for ages 40-41, 50-51, 60-61 and 70-71, discloses at once that the premiums for the earlier annual terms are lower than the whole life premiums, while the premiums for the later annual terms are higher. This is a natural consequence of the larger proportion, and hence greater probability of deaths at the later ages. It means that the single net premium charged throughout the life of a whole life policy holder must be "greater than expectation," that is, greater than the one-year term rate, in the earlier years, to offset the "lower expectation," that is, lower than the one-year term rates in the later years. (Since they reflect directly the increasing probability of death with the years, these one year term premiums are called "natural" premiums, while the unchanging whole life premiums are called "level" premiums.)

In other words, the insurance company collects an excess of premiums paid in over benefits paid out in the earlier years of the whole life policyholders, which offsets the excess of benefits paid over premiums received in their later years. In accounting terms, this excess is called a reserve, and a major function of the insurance company is to invest and administer these reserve funds.

The reserve on any individual policy at the end of a policy year is called the terminal reserve on that policy for that year.   Thus, the reserve at the end of any given year, for example, the kth year that the policy has been in effect (for ordinary whole life policies the annual premium is paid at the start of the net policy year, that is, the $k + 1^{th}$ premium is not included in the kth year) is called the kth terminal reserve.

The terminal reserve on a policy is the basis for computing surrender value, subject of course, to cost deductions by the company.   The logical justification for this statement is the fact that by surrendering the policy the insured saves the company from the greater mortality probability of his later years, and is thus entitled to part of the excess of the "level" premiums over the "natural" premiums that accrued during his younger years.

Two methods are available to compute the terminal reserve on a life insurance policy, both of which give the same result.   The retrospective method "looks back" at the period the policy has been in existence, and computes the difference between the premiums received by the insurance company and the benefits paid.   The prospective method "looks ahead" into the future, and computes the difference between the benefits to be paid and the premiums to be received.

For the purposes of this book, the retrospective method is preferable, since it permits of the computation of policy reserves for all the types of insurance discussed here by means of a single formula.   That formula is

$$\text{Policy Reserve} = R \frac{(N_x - N_{x+n})}{D_{x+n}} - T \frac{(M_x - M_{x-n})}{D_{x+n}} \qquad (17\text{-}28)$$

where R is the net annual premium, x is the age of insured when policy was issued, n is the number of years it was in effect, and T is its face value. By substituting the correct value of R for the particular type of policy, the amount of the policy reserve can be computed.

As an example of the use of Formula (17-28) find the terminal reserve of an ordinary whole life insurance policy taken out by a man at age 25 after 15 years, the face value being $5,000.00.   First find the net annual premium using Formula (17-20),

$$R_x = T \frac{M_x}{N_x}$$

Substituting $R_x = (\$5,000.00) \dfrac{M_{25}}{N_{25}}$

$$= (\$5,000.00) \left(\frac{1,291,328.368}{112,532,159.2} \right)$$

$$= \$57.38$$

Then, substituting in Formula (17-28)

$$\text{Policy Reserve} = (\$73.00)\,\frac{(N_{25} - N_{25+15})}{D_{25+15}} - (\$5,000.00)\,\frac{(M_{25} - M_{25+15})}{D_{25+15}}$$

From Table 18,

N_{25} is found to be 112,532,519.2
N_{40} is found to be 57,126,141.7
D_{40} is found to be   2,828,001.6
M_{25} is found to be   1,291,328.368
M_{40} is found to be   1,164,133.363

Therefore

$$\text{Policy Reserve} = (\$73.00)\left(\frac{112,532,159.2 - 57,126,141.7}{2,828,001.6}\right)$$

$$- (\$5,000.00)\left(\frac{1,291,328.368 - 1,164,133.363}{2,828,001.6}\right)$$

$$\text{Policy Reserve} = (\$73.00)\left(\frac{55,406,017.5}{2,828,001.6}\right) - (\$5,000.00)\left(\frac{127,195.005}{2,828,001.6}\right)$$

$$= \$1,430.21 - \$224.89 = \$1,205.32$$

As an example of the application of Formula (17-28) to a term insurance policy which is surrendered before the end of the term, find the terminal reserve of a term life insurance policy taken out by a woman at age 30 for a term of 20 years in amount of $5,000.00, if the policy is surrendered after 12 years.

First find the net annual premium using Formula (17-23)

$$_nR_{x:n} = T\,\frac{M_x - M_{x+n}}{N_x - N_{x+n}}$$

Substituting values from this problem,

$$_nR_{x:n} = (\$5,000.00)\,\frac{M_{30} - M_{50}}{N_{30} - N_{50}}$$

From Table 18,

M_{30} is found to be   1,274,211.185
M_{50} is found to be   1,081,581.872
N_{30} is found to be 103,535,933.8
N_{50} is found to be 39,199,098.3

$$\text{Therefore }\,_nR_{x:n} = (\$5,000.00)\left(\frac{1,274,211.285 - 1,081,581.872}{103,535,933.8 - 39,199,098.3}\right)$$

$$= (\$5,000.00)\left(\frac{192,629.413}{64,336,835.5}\right)$$

$$= \$14.97$$

Then, substituting in Formula (17-28)

Policy Reserve $= (\$18.50) \dfrac{(N_{30} - N_{30+12})}{D_{30+12}} - (\$5,000.00) \dfrac{(M_{30} - M_{30+12})}{D_{30+12}}$

From Table 18,

N_{30} is found to be 103,535,933.8
N_{42} is found to be   60,048,890.8
D_{42} is found to be   2,922,749.1
M_{30} is found to be   1,274,211.185
M_{42} is found to be   1,173,752.197

Therefore,

Policy Reserve $= (\$18.50) \left(\dfrac{103,535,933.8 - 60,048,890.8}{2,922,211.185} \right)$

$\qquad\qquad - (\$5,000.00) \left(\dfrac{1,274,211.185 - 1,173,752.197}{2,922,211.185} \right)$

Policy Reserve $= (\$18.50) \left(\dfrac{43,487,043.0}{2,922,211.85} \right) - (\$5,000.00) \left(\dfrac{100,458.988}{2,922,211.185} \right)$

$\qquad = \$275.31 - \$171.89 = \$103.42$

Chapter 18

THE MATHEMATICS OF SECURITIES

Types of Securities

Securities may be considered to belong to two general classes—stocks and bonds. Stocks are shares of the ownership of an industrial business, railroad or other enterprise. Bonds are written promises to make interest payments at a specified rate on their face value at specified intervals until their redemption date, at which a specified sum, called the redemption price, must be paid. (The single exception to this definition of bonds is the special class of perpetual bonds, which are promises to pay interest forever. Perpetual bonds are represented by the consols of Great Britain and rentes of France.)

There are two general classes of stocks—common and preferred. The dividends on common stock depend upon earnings, and are voted by the directors in accordance with recent and anticipated earnings, the financial position of the business and similar considerations. The dividends on preferred stock are paid at a rate specified in the stock certificates, on their face (par) value. Their payment is also subject to the action of the directors, but must be made before dividends on common stock, for that period.

Special kinds of preferred stock are: Cumulative preferred stock, on which any deficits in the specified dividends are accumulated from period to period, and must be paid in full before dividends are paid on common stock; Prior preferred stock, which has dividend priority to another issue of preferred stock of the same enterprise, both issues having dividend priority to the common stock; Convertible preferred stock, which has the additional privilege of convertibility into common on a specified basis and commonly for a specified period.

There are many classes of bonds and various bases of classification. While most bonds carry a pledge of payment at a specified date and of a specified amount, the redemption date and redemption price, respectively,

455

however some bonds are subject to call at the demand of the bondholder, usually at specified dates before maturity. Serial bonds provide for redemption at a number of dates, instead of a single one. Annuity bonds provide for the repayment of both principal and interest, in equal installments at uniform periods.

Collateral trust bonds are secured by collateral deposited with a bank or other third party. Mortgage bonds are secured by real property or other physical assets. Equipment bonds are secured by equipment; this type of bond is usually issued by railroads to purchase rolling stock, on which it is secured. Refunding bonds are issued to raise money to be used, partly or entirely, to retire existing debts. Convertible bonds are exchangeable for other securities, usually common or preferred stock, in a specified ratio and usually for a specified period. Guaranteed bonds carry the additional pledge of payment by another party (besides the debtor).

Bond Terminology and Its Notation

The face value or par value of a bond is, as the term implies, the value as stated on the bond. The face value is the basis upon which dividends are computed. In this chapter, face value is denoted by the letter F.

The redemption price of a bond is the amount which is due to be paid at the maturity date, both the amount and the date being stated in the bond. (Except, of course, in the case of a perpetual bond.) Redemption price is denoted by the letter C.

The redemption date of a bond is the date on which the redemption price is payable.

The dividends on a bond are the periodic payments of interest. They differ from stock dividends in that bond interest payments are obligatory. The amount of a dividend payment is denoted by the letter R.

The dividend dates of a bond are the dates each year on which the dividends are payable.

The dividend rate or coupon rate on a bond is the interest rate on the face value.

The purchase price of a bond is the price paid for it by the purchaser. The purchase price is denoted by the letter P.

The premium on a bond is the excess, if any, of the purchase price over the redemption price. It is denoted by the letters Pr. Thus

$$Pr = P - C$$

The discount on a bond is the excess, if any, of the redemption price over the purchase price. It is denoted by the letter D. Thus

$$D = C - P$$

The yield rate on a bond is the interest rate received by the purchaser on his investment.

Calculating the Price for a Given Yield—Bond Purchased on Dividend Date

For many purposes, bonds are quoted on a yield basis, rather than a price basis. As a result of this practice, one of the most common determinations to be made in financial mathematics is that of the purchase price of a bond when its yield rate, redemption price, coupon or interest rate, and interest period and maturity date are known.

To derive a formula for this computation, the price of the bond is regarded as the present value of its redemption price plus the present value of all interest payments to be received up to the date of redemption. Obviously there are certain conditions under which this computation is greatly simplified, such as the use of the identical and coincident yield periods and interest periods, the assumption that the purchase is made at the beginning of an interest period, so that the purchaser receives each interest payment thereafter at the end of its period, and the assumption that he receives the redemption price on its pledged date.

From these assumptions, it follows that the present value of the redemption price on the date of purchase is its present value compounded at the yield rate for the number of interest periods, which is $C(1 + r)^{-n}$, where C is the redemption price, r is the yield rate per interest period, and n is the number of periods. It also follows that the present value of all the interest payments is the present value at the yield rate per period of an annuity of the amount of the interest paid for the number of interest periods, which is $Ra_{\overline{n}|r}$, where R is the amount of one interest payment, and $a_{\overline{n}|r}$ is the present value of an annuity of $1.00 paid for the number of periods, n, at the yield rate per period, r.

Adding these two terms gives the formula for the purchase price of the bond,

$$P = C(1 + r)^{-n} + Ra_{\overline{n}|r}. \tag{18-1}$$

To apply this formula, find the purchase price of a bond having a face (par) value of $1,000.00 redeemable at par and maturing in 12 years with interest at 5% payable annually, to yield 4% annually.

Here C, the redemption price, is $1,000.00; r, the yield rate, is 4%; n, the number of periods, is 12; and R, the interest payment, is $50.00.

Substituting in above formula,

$$P = (\$1,000.00)(1 + .04)^{-12} + (\$50.00)a_{\overline{12}|4}.$$

Then, from Table 12, Chapter 13, $(1 + .04)^{-12} = .62459705$, and from Table 14, Chapter 14, $a_{\overline{12}|4} = 9.38507376$.

Substituting, $P = (\$1,000.00)(.62459705) + (\$50.00)(9.38507376)$

$$= \$624.60 + \$469.25 = \$1,093.85$$

As another application of Formula (18-1), find the purchase price of a bond having a face (par) value of \$1,000.00; redeemable in 8 years at 110 (note that bonds are quoted in \$10.00 units and 32's thereof, so that this quotation of the redemption price means \$1,100.00), with interest at $4\frac{1}{2}\%$ payable semiannually, to yield $3\frac{1}{2}\%$ compounded semiannually.

Substituting in Formula (18-1),

$$P = (\$1,100.00)(1 + .0175)^{-16} + (\$22.50)a_{\overline{16}|.75}$$

Then from Table 12, Chapter 13, $(1 + .0175)^{-16} = .75761631$
and from Table 14, Chapter 14, $a_{\overline{16}|.75} = 13.85049677$

Substituting, $P = (\$1,100.00)(.75761631) + (\$22.50)(13.85049677)$

$$= \$833.38 + \$311.63 = \$1,145.01$$

Premium and Discount

In accordance with the definition given at the beginning of this chapter, the premium on a bond is the excess of its purchase price over its redemption price, or in symbols

$$Pr = P - C \qquad (18\text{-}2)$$

In the first example in this chapter, the \$1,000.00 bond redeemable at par, which was purchased for \$1,093.85, had a premium of \$1,093.85 − \$1,000.00 = \$93.85. Since on its redemption date, 12 years later, the purchaser would receive only \$1,000.00, he must set aside part of the interest payments to accumulate a fund to restore his original capital when the bond is redeemed—in other words, to amortize the premium. The periodic payments necessary to accumulate the amount of the premium are the difference between the interest payments received and the interest on the capital invested in the bond, the latter being, on any interest date, the purchase price less the total of the amortization fund at that date. (Note that this amortization fund is accumulated without interest on the fund itself in most bond amortization schedules, and that practice is followed here. However, if interest on the fund is to be credited, see Chapter 16 for amortization funds on which interest is earned.)

The amortization schedule for the bond whose purchase price was calculated in the first example of this chapter is given below—corresponding to its redemption price of \$1,000.00, yield rate of 4%; purchase price of \$1,093.85; premium of \$93.85; term of 12 years with interest at 5% payable annually (that is, \$50.00 payable annually).

AMORTIZATION SCHEDULE OF BOND PREMIUM

End of period	Book Value	Dividend	Interest on Book Value at Yield Rate	Amortization Payments (Dividends less Interest)
	$1,093.85			
1	1,087.60	$50.00	$43.75	$6.25
2	1,081.10	50.00	43.50	6.50
3	1,074.34	50.00	43.24	6.76
4	1,067.31	50.00	42.97	7.03
5	1,060.00	50.00	42.69	7.31
6	1,052.40	50.00	42.40	7.60
7	1,044.50	50.00	42.10	7.90
8	1,036.28	50.00	41.78	8.22
9	1,027.73	50.00	41.45	8.55
10	1,018.84	50.00	41.11	8.89
11	1,009.60	50.00	40.76	9.24
12	1,000.00	50.00	40.40	9.60

When the interest rate on a bond is less than the yield rate, the bond is purchased at a discount instead of a premium. Consider, for example, a bond having a face value of $1,000.00: redeemable in 5 years at 102 ($1,020.00), with coupons at 4% semiannually, and yielding 5%, compounded semiannually.

To find the price, Formula (18-1) is used

$P = C(1 + r)^{-n} + Ra_{\overline{n}|r}$ where C is $1,020.00; r is $2\frac{1}{2}\%$ semiannually, n is 10, and R is $20.00.

Substituting, $P = (\$1,020.00)(1 + .025)^{-10} + (\$20.00)a_{\overline{10}|2\frac{1}{2}}$

From Table 12, Chapter 13, $(1 + .025)^{-10} = .78119840$

From Table 14, Chapter 14, $a_{\overline{10}|2\frac{1}{2}} = 8.75206393$

Therefore $P = (\$1,020.00)(.7811984) + (\$20.00)(8.75206393)$
$= \$796.82 + \$175.04 = \$971.86$

In accordance with the definition given at the beginning of this chapter, the discount on a bond is the excess of its redemption price over its purchase price, or in symbols

$$D = C - P \qquad (18-3)$$

In this example, then

$$D = \$1,020.00 - \$981.86 = \$48.14$$

In the case of bonds bought at a discount, which therefore have a lower interest rate than yield rate, it is customary to set up an Accumulation Schedule of Bond Discount, wherein an amount of money equal to the difference between interest on the book value and the interest payments is credited in each period toward the discount. In other words, the discount is not taken as a single payment at maturity, but its payment is antici-pated, and credited to each period, and the credits are accumulated in an accumulation fund.

In this book, the policy is followed of not crediting interest on the accumulation fund of bond discount just as in the case of amortization fund of bond premium.

However, if this practice is to be followed, see Chapter 16 for informa-tion about interest-bearing amortization funds, which are computed in the same way as interest bearing accumulation funds.

The accumulation schedule for this bond is then as given below.

ACCUMULATION SCHEDULE OF BOND DISCOUNT

End of Period	Book Value	Dividend	Interest on Book Value at Yield Rate	Accumulation Amounts (Interest less Dividends)
	$ 971.86			
1	976.16	$20.00	$24.30	$4.30
2	980.56	20.00	24.40	4.40
3	984.07	20.00	24.51	4.51
4	989.70	20.00	24.63	4.63
5	994.45	20.00	24.75	4.75
6	999.31	20.00	24.86	4.86
7	1,004.28	20.00	24.97	4.97
8	1,009.37	20.00	25.09	5.09
9	1,014.58	20.00	25.21	5.21
10	1,020.00	20.00	25.42	5.42

Calculating the Price for a Given Yield—Bond Purchased on a Date Other Than Dividend Date

Since many of the purchases of bonds are made at dates other than their dividend dates, the calculation of their prices under these conditions arises frequently in financial mathematics. While there are several possible methods of computing the price of a bond between dividend dates from the price at a given dividend date, one method is widely used, because it is also the basis on which bonds are quoted. This method is based upon the calculation of ordinary simple interest (for exact time) from the pre-vious dividend date to the date of purchase, and the addition of that in-terest to the price computed at the dividend date, to arrive at the price actually paid for the bond.

As an example of the application of this method, find the price includ-ing interest paid for a $1,000.00 4% bond, with dividends payable semi-annually (Jan. 1 and July 1) redeemable at 104 on January 1, 1964, if purchased on February 5, 1959 to yield $3\frac{1}{2}\%$ compounded semiannually.

By Formula (18-1), the price at the preceding dividend date (January 1, 1959) is

$$P = C(1 + r)^{-n} + Ra_{\overline{n}|r}$$

where C is \$1,040.00, r is $1\frac{3}{4}\%$ semiannually, n is 10, and R is \$20.00.
Substituting, $P = (\$1,040.00)(1 + .0175)^{-10} + \$20.00a_{\overline{10}|\frac{3}{4}}$
From Table 12, Chapter 13, $(1 + .0175)^{-10} = .84072860$
From Table 14, Chapter 14, $a_{\overline{10}|\frac{3}{4}} = 9.10122291$
Substituting, $P = (\$1,040.00)(.8407286) + (\$20.00)(9.0122291)$
$$= \$874.36 + \$180.24 = \$1,054.60, \text{ the purchase price}$$
of the bond as of January 1, 1959.

From Chapter 12, the exact time from January 1 to February 5 is 35 days. The ordinary interest for this time, which is computed at the yield rate, is

$$(\$1,054.60)(.035)\left(\frac{35}{360}\right) = \$3.59$$

Therefore the price actually paid is the price at the dividend date plus simple interest to the date of purchase, which is

$$\$1,054.60 + \$3.59 = \$1,058.19$$

It was mentioned above that the computation of the price as of the dividend date is the price of bonds actually quoted. In other words, if the purchaser of this bond had asked for a quotation prior to purchase, he would have been quoted \$1,054.60 (plus interest) but he would have been charged \$1,058.19.

Calculating the Yield on a Bond from Its Purchase Price

For many purposes the approximate yield on a bond is all that is required; that is, the yield obtained by dividing the average income per period by the average investment, both averages being taken over the term to maturity. The average income per period is equal to the sum of all the dividends to be received, plus the discount or minus the premium, and divided by the number of periods. The average price is the average of the purchase price and the redemption price.

In symbols

$$\text{Average income} = \frac{nR + D}{2} \quad \text{or} \quad \frac{nR - P}{2}$$

The average income can be expressed in a single formula as follows

$$\text{Average income per period} = \frac{nR + (C - P)}{n} \qquad (18\text{-}4)$$

where n is the number of periods, R is the interest per period, C is the redemption price and P is the purchase price. If the bond is bought at a premium, then $(C - P)$ is negative.

Also, in symbols

$$\text{Average investment} = \frac{C + P}{2}$$

$$\text{Therefore, approximate yield} = \frac{\text{Aver. income}}{\text{Aver. investment}} = \frac{\dfrac{nR + (C - P)}{n}}{\dfrac{C + P}{2}}$$

$$(18\text{-}5)$$

As an example, find the approximate yield by this formula in the case of a \$1,000.00 5% bond, with coupons payable annually, that is redeemable at 103 in 16 years, and that is purchased at 98 (\$980.00).

Substituting in the above formula

$$\text{Approximate yield} = \frac{16(\$50.00) + (\$1,030.00 - \$980.00)}{\dfrac{16}{\dfrac{\$1,030.00 + \$980.00}{2}}}$$

$$= \frac{\dfrac{\$850.00}{16}}{\$1,005.00} = \frac{\$53.125}{\$1,005.00}$$

$$= 5.29\%$$

If a value closer to the true yield is desired, it may be obtained by interpolation in the table of present values of annuities, using values bracketing the approximate yield just found.

This is done by the following method:

Compute the yield by Formula (18-1) using the values of $a_{\overline{n}|r}$ in the tables that bracket the approximate value already found for r.

In this problem the approximate value of r, the yield rate, was found to be 5.29%. In Table 14, Chapter 14, the values given for r that bracket 5.29% are 5% and $5\frac{1}{2}$%. Substitute both these values in equation (18-1), solve for the two purchase prices, and use them to interpolate from the actual purchase price.

Using Formula (18-1)

$$P = C(1 + r^{-n}) + Ra_{\overline{n}|r},$$

Substitute from this problem the values of C as \$1,030.00, n as 16, R as \$50.00, and r as 5% (1) and then $5\frac{1}{2}$% (2) giving

(1) $P = (\$1,030.00)(1 + .05)^{-16} + (\$50.00)a_{\overline{16}5}$
    From Table 12, Chapter 13, $(1 + .05)^{-16} = .45811152$
    From Table 14, Chapter 14, $a_{\overline{16}5} = 10.83776956$
    Substituting, $P = (\$1,030.00)(.4581152) + (\$50.00)(10.83776956)$
        $= \$471.85 + \$541.89 = \$1,013.75$

(2) $P = (\$1,030.00)(1 + .055)^{-16} + (\$50.00)a_{\overline{16}5.5}$
    From Table 12, Chapter 13, $(1 + .055)^{-16} = .42458109$
    From Table 14, Chapter 14, $a_{\overline{16}5.5} = 10.46216203$
    Substituting, $P = (\$1,030.00)(.42458109) + (\$50.00)(10.46216203)$
        $= \$437.32 + \$523.18 = \$960.50$

Rewriting above results.

$$\begin{array}{lll} \text{Price to yield} & 5\% = & \$1,013.74 \\ \text{``\quad``\quad``} & 5\tfrac{1}{2}\% = & \underline{960.50} \\ & & \$53.24 \end{array}$$

Difference between purchase price and lower price above is $\$980.00 - \$960.50 = \$19.50$

Therefore, interpolated rate is

$$5\% + \tfrac{1}{2}\% \left(\frac{\$19.50}{\$53.24}\right) = 5.183\%$$

Evaluation of Securities—Intrinsic

As stated in the beginning of this chapter, a security represents a share of the ownership of a business, as in the case of a stock, or a promise to pay a specified sum at a future date with specified interest payments during the interval, as in the case of a bond. Therefore, the value of a stock is determined, to a very great extent, by the present condition and anticipated future development of the business it represents. Similarly, the value of a bond depends upon the present condition and anticipated future status of the debtor, which may be a business, a governmental unit, a governmental agency, etc. Therefore, one of the most important, if not the most important, steps to be taken in the evaluation of a security is the procurement of all information bearing in any way upon the financial status and future of the corporate entity it represents, and also upon the systematic appraisal of this information. These operations are the subject of this present section on the evaluation of securities, which has been characterized by the use of the word *internal* to distinguish them from another aspect of that evaluation.

Securities in the great majority of instances are fully negotiable. They are bought and sold in the open market. Therefore, their value as measured by their price is subject to fluctuations with supply and demand which may have the effect, temporarily at any rate, of producing fluctuations that do not correspond to changes in the present status or anticipated future development of the corporate entity represented. These supply and demand factors, and their general effect upon the price of securities are discussed in the next section, under the heading "Evaluation of Securities—Extrinsic."

To return to the intrinsic evaluation of securities, the first step is, as stated above, the procurement of information. There are many books and services which furnish detailed information about securities and the corporate entities issuing them. Representative publications of this type are *Moody's Manual of Investments, Standard-Poor's Bond Guide, Standard Statistics*, which publishes a service combining periodical summaries on the individual corporate entities with weekly reports of major developments affecting them, including their own financial statements and news releases as they appear.

The information which these publications present covers all factors pertinent to the financial condition of the corporation. They usually have a brief description of the type of business conducted, the geographical area occupied, such as the location of factories, the areas serviced by railroads, and even the trackage they possess and similar general information. There is also given a statement of the financial structure of the corporate entity, often listing the outstanding quantities of each class of security so as to furnish a basis for judging, in cases where more than one class of bonds or preferred stocks have been issued, which of them has priority in payment of dividends. There is also given a history of the changes in capital structure and of the earnings for a number of years past; in some cases the price ranges for past years are also stated. Most of these reporting services also give a rating of securities by letter, or by letter and number, and of course these reporting services will furnish, or include in their books, a full statement of the significance of these ratings.

One of the types of information which have been mentioned above is certainly among the most important. It consists of the most recent financial statements of the corporations, or frequently of their comparative financial statements for the two periods immediately preceding.

Therefore, knowledge of the interpretation of financial statements and of the major items they contain is essential in any analysis of the condition of a corporate enterprise.

Financial Statements and Their Interpretation

The nature and interpretation of financial statements clearly merits extended discussion, not only because it is fundamental to the evaluation of securities, but also because it has many other business applications. It is, moreover, extremely complex. This complexity is not due to complications intentionally introduced by the business enterprises issuing the statements, for many of them have adopted, especially in their periodic reports to stockholders, designations and arrangements of the items in their statements which are even more descriptive and easier to follow than those used in conventional accounting practice. Rather is the complexity due to the variations between different types of business, and other corporate entities, and to the inherent difficulty in summarizing in one or two pages the financial condition and operation of an entire enterprise.

For this reason many commercial investment bankers and better informed investors attach great importance to the experience and reputation of the accounting firm that certifies a financial statement. So many of the summary items and in fact, the operations or entities which they represent, require a considerable amount of judgment and experience in their evaluation.

There are two fundamental financial statements. The balance sheet summarizes the financial condition of a business at a specified date. The profit and loss statement summarizes the operation of a business over a specified period. Since the dates reported by the balance sheets are commonly at the beginning and end of the period of operation covered by the profit and loss statements, the latter show the effect of the operations during the period upon the financial condition of the business, and also the profit or loss resulting from those operations.

The name "balance sheet" originated from the fact that the figures shown on it proceed from the balances shown in various accounts kept on the books of the business. The types of accounts so used are (1) asset accounts, covering essentially what is owned; (2) liability accounts, covering essentially what is owed, and (3) capital accounts, the result of subtracting (2) from (1), showing the excess of assets over liabilities, constituting the owner's share of the business, which is its capital or net worth. If the liabilities exceed the assets the business has a deficit instead of a net worth.

In the ordinary arrangement of the balance sheet, the assets are shown on the left, and the liabilities and capital items on the right.

The assets are usually summarized under such major headings as cash, U. S. Government bonds and short term securities, notes receivable, accounts receivable, inventories (which may be finished merchandise or raw materials on hand) investments (a term usually applied to common stocks and long term securities), machinery and equipment, land and buildings, intangible assets, such as patents, licenses and copyrights, and miscellaneous assets, including prepaid expenses.

The liabilities are usually summarized under such headings as accounts payable, notes payable, bonds and mortgages owed, taxes and other charges that have accrued but are not yet payable, and reserves.

The capital or ownership items are usually summarized under the various preferred and common stocks and the surplus entries.

A simplified balance sheet which illustrates the arrangement of many of the items just discussed is the following:

Balance Sheet of XYZ Corporation

January 1, 1958

Assets:

Cash...		$ 125,285,261.
U. S. Government and Other Short-Term Securities at Cost, Approximately Market...............................		42,592,320.
Accounts Receivable...................................		62,113,120.
Notes Receivable......................................		27,381,451.
Inventory..		382,964,576.
Other Investments at Cost............................		21,665,723.
Machinery and Equipment.................	868,111,255.	
Less Depreciation Reserve...............	471,471,672.	
Net Value..		396,639,583.
Land and Buildings........................	425,942,500.	
Less Depreciation Reserve................	290,953,880.	
Net Value..		134,988,620.
Patents and Trademarks...............................		1.
Prepaid Expenses.....................................		19,714,876.
Total..		$1,213,455,531.

Liabilities:

Accounts Payable......................................	$ 88,528,519.
Notes Payable..	20,000,000.
Long Term Debt Due Within One Year..................	7,646,651.
Interest and Taxes Accrued...........................	22,369,476.
Reserves (Other than Depreciation on Machinery and Equipment)...	14,470,791.
Long Term Debt due after One Year.....................	323,186,724.
Total..	$ 476,202,161.

Capital:

Preferred Stock at Par Value...........................	$ 71,663,340.
Common Stock at Par Value...........................	171,897,262.
Surplus—Earnings Obtained in the Business...............	493,582,768.
Total..	$1,213,455,531.

The profit and loss statement shows the result of the operation of a business over a period. Since its most significant item is usually the net income, it is also called the Statement of Income, the Statement of Earnings and various similar names. To obtain this figure it summarizes the major categories of income and expense, and shows the disposition of the gross income. The following profit and loss statement illustrates these major items:

Profit and Loss Statement of XYZ Corporation
January 1, 1957–January 1, 1958

Sales...		$1,021,461,419.
Cost of Goods Sold:		
Costs of Production.......................	$736,449,014.	
Depreciation of Plant and Equipment.........	85,002,241.	
Total..		821,451,255.
Gross Profit.......................................		$ 200,010,164.
Selling and Administrative Expenses.......................		92,112,104.
Operating Profit...................................		$ 107,898,060.
Other Income......................................		9,046,951.
Gross Income......................................		$ 116,945,011.
Interest...................................	$ 12,168,940.	
Other Deductions...........................	1,372,815.	
Total..		13,541,755.
Net Income Before U. S. Taxes on Income.................		$ 103,403,256.
Net Income After Taxes..............................		74,623,256.
Preferred Dividends...........................	35,172,158.	
Common Dividends...........................	18,429,727.	
Total Dividends................................		53,601,885.
Addition to Surplus................................		$ 21,021,371.
Previous Surplus...................................		472,561,397.
Surplus, January 1, 1958..............................		$ 493,582,768.

As a first step in the evaluation of the financial statements of a company, the assets and liabilities listed in the balance sheet are each divided into two groups, current assets and fixed assets, and current liabilities and fixed liabilities. The distinction between current and fixed items is essentially in their rate of turnover, even though this may vary considerably with the nature of the business. Usually, cash, accounts receivable, notes receivable and inventory are classed as current assets, and machinery and equipment and land and buildings are classed as fixed assets. Securities are placed in either classification, depending upon their marketability and relation to the company. In the foregoing balance sheet, two entries were made for securities. The first item, "U. S. Government and Other Short-Term Securities" is a current asset; while the second "Other Investments" would consist of securities not readily marketable (in the quantity held), or which represent holdings in a subsidiary which would be sold only in event of a realignment of company policy.

The last item in the given balance sheet, "Patents and Trademarks" is considered to be so far from being current that it is often not even classed as a fixed asset, but in a third group called "Intangible Assets."

Note that the order of arrangement of asset entries in the balance sheet brings the current assets in the first group, ending in this particular case with "Inventory," and the fixed assets into the second group. The same arrangement is made of the fixed liabilities, where accounts payable, notes payable and long term debt due within a year are current liabilities, while reserves and long term debt are fixed liabilities. In accounting practice, the capital items are classed with liabilities, being called capital liabilities, even though they are not debts at all.

A common working rule for distinguishing between current and fixed liabilities is to class those payable in less than one year as current, as was done in the balance sheet cited.

The importance of the concept of current items is that it gives a measure of the liquidity of the capital of the business. The excess of current assets over current liabilities is called the working capital. The trend of the changes in working capital in successive statements is obviously one measure of the financial health of the business, since if the current liabilities become greater than the current assets, thus creating a working capital deficit, the business must raise new capital, or face the imminent danger of being unable to meet its obligations.

It should be recognized, however, that while a shrinking working capital is a real hazard to a business, and one that is too small restricts the potential and even the credit of a business, there are also unfavorable implications of too much working capital. It represents capital that is unused, or rather inefficiently used, and so reduces the return yielded on the capital investment. Moreover, it may indicate, especially if its trend is still upward, a decline in sales or other phases of business activity.

For this reason accountants tend to observe rather than the working capital (the difference between current assets and current liabilities), the *ratio* of current assets to current liabilities, which is called the current ratio. Insofar as one may attempt to generalize for all types of business, a 2-to-1 current ratio may be regarded as a sound working value, subject to the stability of its markets and the rate of obsolescence of its product, and subject also to favorable values of other business ratios discussed later in this section.

Another grouping of assets are the so-called "quick" assets, consisting only of those current assets which have a fixed dollar value. In other words, quick assets in the balance sheet cited are cash, U. S. Government and other short term securities, and accounts receivable, excluding inventory. The ratio of quick assets to current liabilities is used for various purposes, including credit decisions. Its desirable average value is less definitely established than that of the current ratio, although it probably should not fall below 1:1.

The foregoing discussion related to groups of balance sheet items, the ratios between them and the use of both in appraising the condition of a business. Equally important, of course, are the individual items on the balance sheet or the profit-and-loss statement.

While the determination of the value of such assets as cash or short term securities, raises few questions, the general method of valuation of assets requires a brief explanation. In the earlier days of accounting the basis of valuation was almost invariably the original cost, subject to deductions for depreciation, depletion, and other obvious adjustments. Even in earlier days, however, it was recognized that inventories and many securities were subject to more frequent and extensive changes in value than most other assets, and therefore the more conservative basis of evaluation was cost or market price, whichever was the lower. This protected the business against carrying volatile securities or inventories at an excessive figure, resulting from a decline in price between the date of their purchase and the date of the report.

In recent years, however, the trend of inventory prices has frequently been in the other direction, that is, prices have been rising. This has necessitated a modified method of charging off inventory as it is used in production. It is called the "last in first out" or LIFO method, and its effect is to keep the inventory figure in the balance sheet below *both* cost and market value. (The other method is called "first in first out," abbreviated as FIFO.) The LIFO method of accounting is still more conservative in its evaluation of inventory, in periods of rising prices, and hence of the net worth and earnings of a business, than the FIFO method, and is therefore of particular interest to businesses whose inventory constitutes a significant proportion of their total assets.

As in the case of current assets and current liabilities, or quick assets and current liabilities, inventory can also be judged by the ratio method. Here the important criterion is the dollar annual sales volume per dollar of inventory. The two items, must, of course, be measured on the same basis, that is, if the sales figure is used, then the inventory must be taken at, or calculated to, its selling price. If the annual cost of goods sold is used, then the inventory can be taken at cost. Obviously if the ratio is 1:1, then the annual volume of business is equal to the inventory, which is thus said to *turn* once a year. Therefore, the ratio is called the inventory turnover or the merchandise turnover. While this ratio is one of the most important of all the evaluating ratios, especially in merchandising, its optimum value varies so much with the type of business that it can only be used to advantage by comparison with similar figures from other businesses of the same type.

It should be emphasized that the ratio of sales to inventory, that is, the "turnover," cannot be used as the sole criterion of the operation of a business, particularly a merchandising business. For if too much value is placed upon turnover alone, it is easy to fall into other bad practices. For example, if a high merchandise turnover is obtained by reducing markup, as by cutting prices or offering expensive inducements to purchase, then the business may operate at a loss in spite of the relatively great sales volume. This condition is spoken of as "overtrading."

The primary question to be answered in the evaluation of accounts receivable is whether they will be paid, and paid promptly. Conservative accounting practice is to set up a reserve, often called a bad debt reserve, for the expected losses on accounts receivable, the amount depending on experience with the creditors, or even with the various classes of creditors. Various methods have been developed for evaluating accounts receivable, either directly by "age analysis" of the accounts, or indirectly, as by the ratio method. The ratio method of appraising accounts receivable is based on the ratio of accounts receivable to net sales. This ratio gives, as well as can be done by a single computation, a measure of the promptness of the customers in settling their accounts and the extent to which the accounts are past due. If it is extremely high, it gives warning of the possibility of high "bad debt" losses, or at any rate, that the receivables are not as liquid as they should be. The use of this ratio is complicated in businesses which sell both for cash and on credit, since to be a true criterion of the receivables it should be applied, of course, only to the credit sales. It is especially important to businesses having a large volume of small credit accounts.

The item of notes receivable can be evaluated by the same method as that used for accounts receivable. The parallel is especially close because of the fact that those businesses having large numbers of notes receivable, such as heavy equipment dealers, use notes in much the same way as accounts receivable are used in other types of business.

The items on the current liability side of the balance sheet are also of use in the evaluation of a business. Thus, the accounts payable are a measure of the promptness of payment by the business. The measuring ratio here is that of accounts receivable to purchases. If the figure for purchases can be obtained from an annual profit-and-loss statement, then a ratio of 1:12 or lower indicates that accounts are being settled monthly, and if the ratio is 1.20 or lower it indicates that probably cash discounts are being taken.

Notes payable may be used profitably as a means of taking cash discounts, since bank discount rates are lower than cash discounts. Therefore, relatively high notes payable figures are not an adverse indication when coupled with low ratios of accounts payable to purchases. The only final criterion of the notes payable item is the purpose for which the notes are used, and, of course, the channels through which they are given.

The evaluation of the fixed assets and liabilities is essentially more difficult than that of current items. Consider the appraisal of such fixed assets as machinery and equipment. Their evaluation at original cost is clearly unrealistic for such long-lived assets. This suggests the use of replacement value, or replacement value less depreciation. This method has been discussed very widely, and many "pros" and "cons" advanced by accountants. One of the most serious objections is that the earnings of any operating business are the major determining factor of the market value of the business as a whole. Therefore, its market value has no direct relation to either its cost or its replacement value less depreciation. So neither basis furnishes an accurate means of evaluation unless a large value is placed upon intangibles. That is, since the value of the business on an earnings basis far exceeds its physical valuation, the use of the physical appraisals alone would require the placing of a high value on patents, trademarks, good will or other intangibles.

However, conservative accounting practice tends to eliminate intangibles from the balance sheet where they appear, if at all, at a value of $1.00. This practice is not so general as to make departures from it suspicious *per se*, but they invite careful scrutiny of the other items.

In most of the larger businesses, especially those of complex capital structure, the proportions of that structure are of fundamental importance. What is the relationship between borrowed capital and equity capital? For obviously a disproportionately great amount of borrowed capital threatens the business with bankruptcy during periods of reduced activity or decreased profits. This situation resulted, in the case of a number of utilities and railroads, in defaults on bonds and recapitalization. To provide a balance sheet guard against it various ratios have been devised.

The first such ratio is that of bonded debt to net worth, for which maximum limits of 1:2 have been suggested for railroads (that is, the net worth should be at least twice the debt), with somewhat higher indebtedness being permitted to public utilities. Another ratio often used is that of working capital to bonded debt, which is applied particularly to merchandising and manufacturing businesses, and for which a 1:1 ratio is considered the minimum for full security.

The first two major items in the profit and loss statement provide what is probably the most significant indication of the trend of a business, particularly of a manufacturing or merchandising enterprise. They are particularly useful if there are available comparative statements from past years. For the difference between them is the gross profit, which is used to pay all the other charges, and then to provide earnings. The trend of gross profit from year to year, or the trend of the ratio of sales to cost of goods sold, is far more significant than the trend of sales alone, which may be obtained at decreasing profit due to increasing cost of the product.

A factor that should often be added to the analysis of sales and cost of goods sold is the selling expense, which in the statement given in this section was combined with administrative expense. This last grouping is used on many statements, but for any type of business in which the selling expense is relatively large, that figure and its trend should be checked, along with the trend of sales and cost of goods sold. In fact, these three figures are used to compute a most important ratio, the operating ratio. It is the ratio of the sum of the cost of goods sold and the operating expense to the sales. The operating expense includes the administrative expense as well as the sales expense, so that the first term of the operating ratio includes all major charges except those for capital. However, if the administrative expense is relatively stable, its omission will often make the above ratio more sensitive to changes in the business. In applying the operating ratio, note that the lower it is, the better it is, from the standpoint of earnings. Above all else, a low operating ratio gives greater insurance against adverse factors. This is particularly true in a new business, or a business drawing much of its profit from a new product of such nature that competition can be expected, sooner or later, to curtail sales.

Another important criterion of the financial condition of a business is the adequacy of its reserves. At one time the rate of depreciation, or more particularly, the method of calculating depreciation, was less flexible and more restricted. Today the more extensive use that is permitted by tax authorities of accelerated methods of depreciating machinery and equipment, makes possible the establishment of more nearly adequate reserves, especially in view of the steadily accelerating rate of technological progress, which often causes more rapid obsolescence than can be provided for by depreciation reserves alone. Under these circumstances, inadequate reserves for depreciation raise doubts of the soundness of management.

The figure of earnings before taxes has a significant relationship to bonds and preferred stocks, that is, to all the fixed income securities in the capital structure. Earlier in this section, it was explained that the relationship between net worth and bonded debt, or that between working capital and bonded debt, was useful in assessing the soundness of the business (and hence of its bonds). Clearly the relation of earnings before interest and taxes to the interest payments due on the bonds is equally important. This is the figure used as a basis of the "number of times" earned, a figure used so frequently in evaluating a particular bond issue. When companies have outstanding more than one issue, this figure may be computed for each issue in order of priority, the amount of earnings available for each successive issue being decreased by the sum required to pay the charges on the previous issue or issues. A similar figure may be computed for preferred stocks, using the earnings after income taxes to compute the amount earned per preferred share. In interpreting this figure, be sure to consider the number of preferred shares outstanding, because for small issues the earnings per share may be large for a relatively small amount of net earnings.

A related ratio used primarily for common stocks is the price-earnings ratio, that is, the market price divided by the annual earnings. This ratio obviously reflects, not only the present earnings of the business, but its future prospects, its dividends, and many other factors. One of the most important of these is the demand for that particular security. The influence of this factor is discussed fully in the next section.

The Evaluation of Securities—Extrinsic

As stated at the beginning of the preceding section, the market price of securities is established, like that of any other entity that is bought and sold freely, by supply and demand. The demand for a particular security is determined to a great extent, of course, by the accounting facts and values of that individual security, and of the corporate entity it represents. Therefore the direct appraisal of these facts and values was discussed in the preceding section of this chapter. There remains to be discussed those factors entering into supply and demand which are largely independent of the accounting situation, and which act, sometimes together with those facts and figures, sometimes even in spite of them, to determine its market price at a given time or over a given period.

One of the most potent, and certainly the most general of these factors is the supply of money. If money is in ample supply, the price of a security, or of anything bought and sold on an open market *may be* expected to be higher than if money is "tight." Moreover, if the supply of money, specifically of a particular currency, is increasing or decreasing, then prices of securities in terms of that currency, *may be* expected to increase or decrease. The words "may be" in the foregoing statements have been italicized to make clear the fact that changing money supply does not, in itself, change prices, but does so only to the extent that it changes the supply and demand relationship. Therefore a changing money supply may have widely varying effects upon the prices of different entities, such as different types of securities. The character of some of these differences can be understood from a consideration of certain of the mechanisms by which a changing money supply affects the supply and demand for securities.

First of all, a changing money supply may change the amount of currency in circulation, and consequently change the cash reserves of many purchasers of securities, thus changing the effective supply or demand. Second, a changing money supply may change the available supply of credit funds, and/or change the interest rates at which they are available, thus changing the effective supply or demand for securities by those who purchase on credit. (This effect has been limited, at least to some extent, by the policy of changing the margin requirements on loans on securities.) The third of the effects of a changing money supply to be considered here is essentially psychological, though none the less real, and is best expressed by the phrases "flight from inflation" and "flight from deflation." Since many prospective purchasers wish to anticipate the effect upon security prices of a changing money supply, they tend to buy securities, particularly equity securities, during periods when an increase in the money supply is anticipated or in progress, and to sell, or refrain from buying, when a decrease in the money supply is anticipated or in progress. The effect of this psychological buying or selling is marked by its differing effects upon different types of securities.

During periods when there is expectation of deflation, whether due to contracting money supply, declining business activity or other reasons, the fixed-income securities, especially the higher-grade bonds, are more attractive to purchasers than the common stocks, whose return depends upon profitable business operation. Therefore, the supply and demand situation of the former is better, and even if they undergo a decline in price, it is likely to be relatively less than that of the equity-type securities.

On the other hand, during periods when there is expectation of inflation, whether due to increasing money supply, expanding business activity or other reasons, the equity securities, offering as they do the possibility of enhancement in value of the equities they represent, or increased dividend return with increased earnings, are more attractive to purchasers than the bonds and other fixed-return securities. Therefore, the supply and demand situation of the former is better and they tend to increase in price, while the bonds increase at a slower rate, or may even remain essentially unchanged or decline. This action is clearly illustrated by the accompanying diagram (Figure 18-1), which shows the ratio of stock prices to bond prices over the period 1920-1958, during which this ratio often changed more rapidly than either the stock prices or the bond prices alone.

From the foregoing discussion, it is apparent that the prices of securities are the result of the interplay of supply and demand which reflects, not

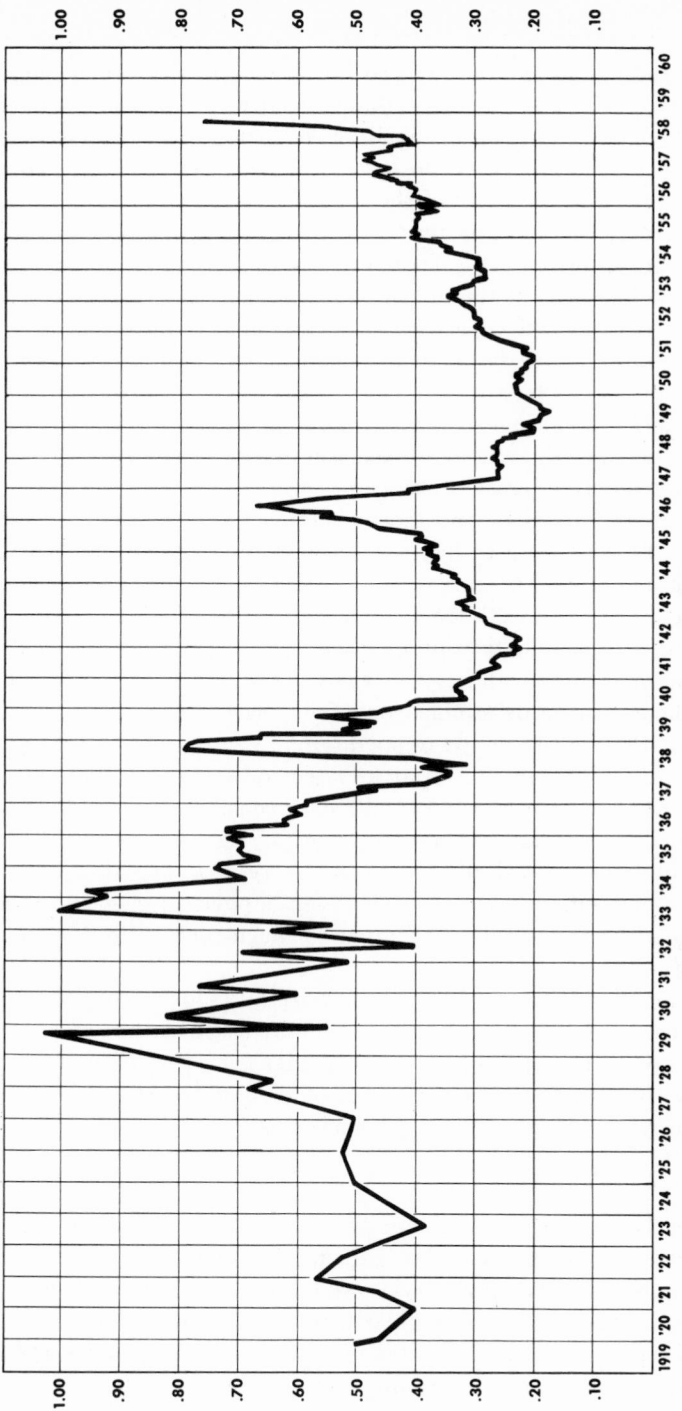

Figure 18-1. Graph showing ratio of yield on 15 representative high grade corporate bonds to earnings yield on 50 representative high grade common stocks, by years.

475

only their individual values, but also the volume of the money supply of the country. It is also apparent that the latter is not the only general cause of changes in supply or demand for securities, which as stated above, are also affected by changes in the level of business activity in the country. Moreover, brief consideration of the situation shows that major variables other than these two, such as agricultural activity, governmental expenditures, etc., must play a part. Therefore any effort to measure, let alone to forecast, the influence of these general conditions upon the general trend of security prices, must cope with three problems: recognition of all the general variables which have an independent effect upon the trend, the choice of statistics which measure fairly the changes in those variables, and the combination of all the statistics into a correctly-weighted formula. Such statistics include, among others, the money in circulation and gold stock figures reported by the Federal Reserve System (both of which may be regarded as indices of the money supply), the railroad carloadings figures, the Federal Reserve figures for commercial agricultural loans, the check clearings, and other statistics, all of which may be regarded as indices of the level of business activity and agricultural production.

Difficult as this statistical problem appears, it has been attacked by a number of investment advisory services. The degree of correlation of their methods can be determined only by a systematic analysis of their results over their entire period of operation.

It is only fair to say that in at least several instances, these methods have obtained fair or even good results over considerable periods of time. Obviously, no more can be expected from any method for extrapolation into the future on the basis of the past and present, an operation which has resulted in some serious misconceptions even in physical science, where the variables can be measured and limited so much more definitely than in economics.

The same limitation applies to the famous Dow-Jones Theory, which is discussed here, not because it is superior to any other method of extrapolation into the future, for in fact its record is far from perfect, and it is considered by some to be outmoded. It does require discussion, however, if only because its averages are still in general use.

The Dow-Jones Theory

Charles H. Dow was a financial writer and reporter whose activities extended over the last two decades of the nineteenth century. He founded the Dow-Jones financial news service, and appears to have been a pioneer in the use of stock price averages, particularly in the selection of a limited number of representative stocks as the basis for compiling an average price that would have interpretive meaning and use. There is, however, reason to believe that the use of these averages in which he was primarily interested was as an indicator of business trends, and not of the trend of stock prices. The reason for this divergence between Dow's purposes and the Dow Theory as it has developed is because it was extended and modified into its present form by other writers who succeeded him.

The basic principle of the Dow Theory is that it assumes the existence of certain trends in the direction of change of the price of stocks generally (in spite of the independent action of the prices of a minority of securities which, for reasons specific to them, may move "against the trend"). As a corollary to this principle, the Dow Theory also assumes that recognition of the direction of these trends is facilitated by recording or charting, not the average price of all stocks, but rather the average price of certain representative issues.

The "justification" for this assumption is the view that these representative issues, being chosen from the more actively-traded stocks, respond more quickly to changes in the supply and demand equilibrium than does the average price of all stocks, which is likely to respond more slowly to such changes. However, it cannot be too strongly emphasized that the Dow Theory, and every other theory for the extrapolation of present economic trends into the future, cannot be "justified" in a mathematical or statistical sense. Their only measure of validity is the test of use, or rather, of successful application in the past.

The stocks selected as the basis of Dow-Jones computations are divided into three groups, Industrials, Rails and Utilities, which are combined into these three separate averages, which are reported in the newspapers. The individual issues making up these averages have been changed over the years to keep the results representative and up to date. The stocks currently used in calculating these averages are given in Table 19 on page 478.

Of these three averages, only two—the Industrial Average and the Rail Average, enter into the Dow Theory. Their use involves the further assumption that the change over a period of time in the average prices of stocks exhibits definite trends, which may be identified as primary, secondary and tertiary. Primary trends are broad movements, either up or down which usually last for a period of one to several years. The primary trend at a given time, if it is up or in the direction of increasing stock prices, constitutes a bull market; while if it is down or in the direction of decreasing stock prices, it constitutes a bear market. These primary trends are not continuous in the same direction, but are interrupted by secondary trends, in which the average prices of stocks move in a direction opposite to that of the prevailing primary trends, usually lasting from 1 to 4 months, and representing reversals in price of stock averages amounting to, usually, $\frac{1}{3}$ to $\frac{2}{3}$ of the gain made by the primary trend since the last secondary.

TABLE 19

The Thirty Stocks Used in the Dow-Jones Industrial Averages:

Allied Chemical Company
American Can Company
American Smelting & Refining Company
American Telephone & Telegraph
  Company
American Tobacco Company
Bethlehem Steel Corporation
Chrysler Corporation
Corn Products Refining Company
E. I. du Pont de Nemours Company
Eastman Kodak Company
General Electric Company
General Foods Corporation
General Motors Corporation
Goodyear Tire & Rubber Company
International Harvester Company

International Nickel Company
International Paper
Johns Manville Corporation
National Distillers Company
National Steel Company
Procter & Gamble Company
Sears Roebuck Company
Standard Oil of California
Standard Oil of New Jersey
Texas Company
Union Carbide Company
United Aircraft Company
U. S. Steel Corporation
Westinghouse Electric Company
F. W. Woolworth Company

The Twenty Stocks Used in the Dow-Jones Rail Averages:

Atchison, Topeka and Santa Fe Railroad
Atlantic Coast Line Railroad
Baltimore & Ohio Railroad
Canadian Pacific Railroad
Chesapeake & Ohio Railroad
Chicago Rock Island & Pacific Railroad
Delaware & Hudson Railroad
Erie Railroad
Great Northern Railway
Illinois Central Railroad
Kansas City Southern Railroad

Louisville & Nashville Railroad
New York Central Railroad
New York, Chicago & St. Louis Railroad
New York, New Haven & Hartford
  Railroad
Norfolk & Western Railroad
Pennsylvania Railroad
Southern Pacific Railroad
Southern Railway
Union Pacific Railroad

The Fifteen Stocks Used in the Dow-Jones Utility Averages:

American Electric Power & Light
  Company
Cleveland Electric Illumination Company
Columbus Gas System
Consolidated Edison Company
Commonwealth Edison Company
Consolidated Natural Gas Company
Detroit Edison Company
Houston Light & Power Company

Niagara Mohawk Power Company
Pacific Gas & Electric Company
Panhandle Electric Power and Light
  Company
Peoples Gas Company
Philadelphia Electric Company
Public Service Electric & Gas Company
Southern California Edison Company

Finally, these secondary trends are themselves interrupted by minor trends, which usually last from a few days to a few weeks and during which average stock prices move in a direction opposite to that of the prevailing secondary trend.

The Dow Theory is directed primarily to the recognition of the boundaries of primary trends. To do this it makes use of two of the averages of the prices of representative stocks, as mentioned earlier in this chapter, the Dow-Jones Industrial Average, and the Dow-Jones Rail Average. Its application of these averages rests upon the following assumption: the prevailing primary trend is assumed to continue until the secondary trends of *both* Industrial and Rail Averages have signaled a reversal of the primary trend. This happens in a bull market (advancing primary trend) only when a secondary reaction has produced lower prices in *both* Industrial and Rail Averages than the preceding reaction. This reversal of the primary bull trend would be further confirmed if, when the secondary decline was over, the resumed upward trend in *both* averages would fail to reach the level attained at the beginning of the secondary reaction. An example of this sort is seen in the summer of 1950 on the accompanying charts of the Dow-Jones Industrial and Rail Averages (Figures 18-2 and 18-3). However useful they may be for this purpose, the Dow-Jones averages are always subject to the criticism that their limited number of stocks may not be representative of the market as a whole. For that reason a number of averages have been developed based upon a larger number of securities, such averages including Standard and Poor's and that of the New York Stock Exchange, which is based upon all the securities traded there.

By strictly analogous reasoning, the reaching of new lows on intermediate reactions by both Industrial and Rail Averages would signal the start or the continuation of a primary bear trend—as would the failure of both averages to reach new highs on subsequent recoveries. An example of a bear market signal is the penetration by both Industrial and Rail Averages of previous lows in early 1957, signaling the short bear market which may have reached its lows in December of 1957, provided the Rail Averages confirm the favorable action in 1958 of the Industrials.

Careful analysis of these two examples and of these charts of the Industrial and Rail Averages discloses obvious limitations to the Dow Theory.

Obviously, one might inquire first of all as to the limitations on the validity of its conclusions, as stated in the two foregoing paragraphs. That is, one might ask whether every change in the primary trend has been signaled by successively higher or lower maximum or minimum points reached by secondary trends of *both* Industrial and Rail Averages. Conversely, one might ask whether such signals have always been followed by primary trend changes. These questions are difficult to answer conclusively—so much so that there is considerable difference of opinion among market statisticians. One of the reasons for this disagreement is the non-quantitative nature of the definitions of primary, secondary and minor trends, whence the mapping of the charts of price averages into such trends cannot be done systematically or rigorously. Another source of difficulty is the fact that the price averages often remain in a relatively narrow range for a period of weeks or even months, and that such horizontal movements have occurred at the conclusion of primary bull or bear trends, or merely

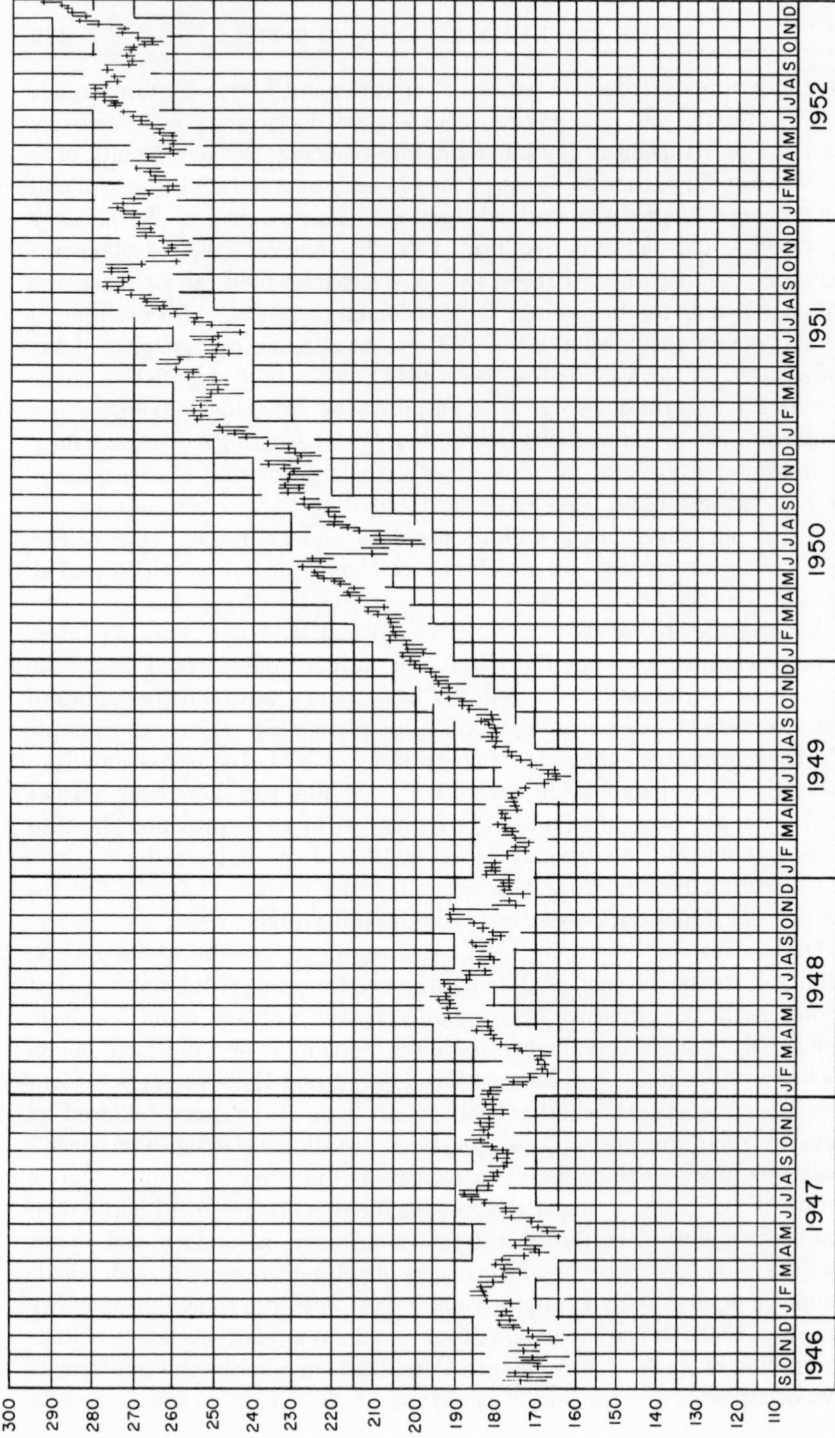

Figure 18-2. Graph showing monthly range and close of the Dow-Jones Industrial Average from September, 1946 to December, 1952.

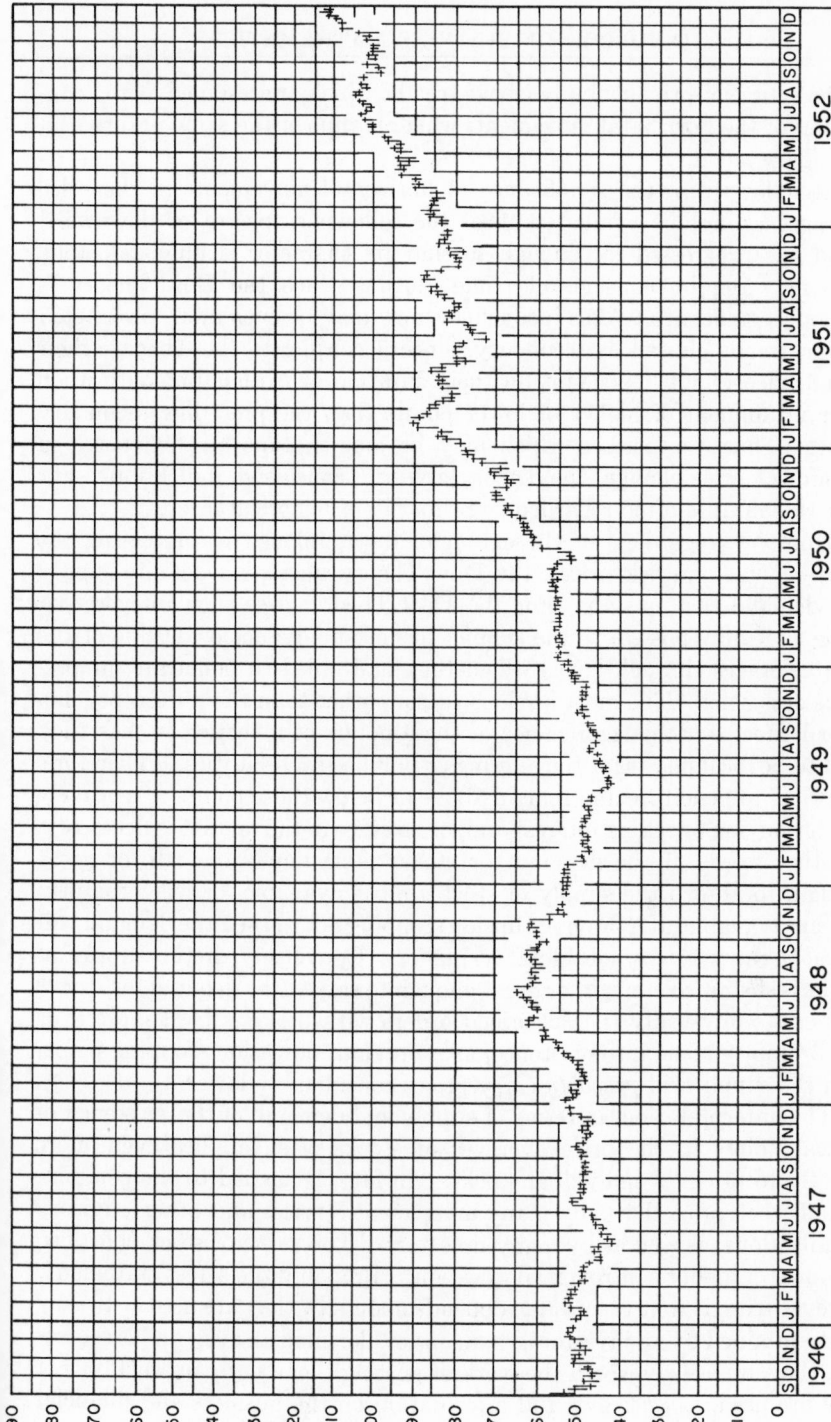

190
180
170
160
150
140
130
120
110
100
90
80
70
60
50
40
30
20
10
0

| 1946 | 1947 | 1948 | 1949 | 1950 | 1951 | 1952 |
| S O N D | J F M A M J J A S O N D | J F M A M J J A S O N D | J F M A M J J A S O N D | J F M A M J J A S O N D | J F M A M J J A S O N D | J F M A M J J A S O N D |

Figure 18-3. Graph showing monthly range and close of Dow-Jones Rail Average from September, 1946 to December, 1952.

481

in the course of primary bull or bear trends, which are resumed at the conclusion of the horizontal movement, which is thus of the same nature as a secondary trend.

It follows that the significance of horizontal movements in the price averages cannot be evaluated until the following upward or downward trend has progressed far enough so that its character is unmistakeable. This may require considerable time, during which the Dow Theory is without significance. This inconclusiveness may be even more protracted during trends classed as secondary, since according to the Theory, their significance is not dependent on their duration or extent, but only upon their attainment of higher or lower points than the preceding secondary trend. Thus, for periods which may be long in time and extensive in amount of price change, the Theory gives no conclusive indication. For that reason, it is often regarded as primarily of historical interest.

However, regardless of the extent of its usefulness in forecasting the future course of stock prices, the Dow Theory suggests a definite supply and demand relationship. For the Dow Theory owes such interpretive value as it may possess to the significance of an advance or decline of the price averages through levels which they had failed to penetrate on previous occasions. The most obvious reason, other than the purely psychological effect, for the significance of these points of inflection is that they tend to be focal points for the offering or purchase of securities. Therefore, for prices to penetrate and remain above or below those points, a relatively greater buying or selling interest and/or activity in the market is necessary. In other words, if the demand for stocks is sustained enough, or great enough, to absorb the supply of stock that is available, or will promptly become available, at a previous upside stopping point, then the demand will *probably* carry prices considerably higher. Conversely, if the supply of stocks is sustained enough, or great enough to satisfy the demand for stocks that exists physically (i.e. as priced orders with brokers, banks, etc.), or will promptly come into existence, at a previous downside stopping point, then the supply will *probably* carry prices considerably lower.

This interpretation, in terms of supply and demand, of the existence of critical points in the price averages of stocks often applies even more directly to prices of individual stocks. In fact, it has led to the compilation of stock price charts by many investment services and other advisory organizations, as well as by many investors. The value of stock charts is, of course, a highly controversial question. Probably the safest statement, however trite, is that their value depends upon how they are used. If they are maintained by an investor as a means of "keeping an eye" on his securities, they are clearly worth the work of posting them, daily or weekly. If they are used, *together with* full information on the business and financial status of the companies they represent, as part of an independently advised investment program that is diversified for the needs of the individual investor, they may well add the important factor of supply and demand evaluation. It is the use of charts as a means of trading in the stock market, especially without business and financial data on the companies represented, and without responsible advice, that is the least desirable, and presents serious hazards, often a great probability of loss, arising from the inherent difficulty in interpreting charts.

To illustrate the nature of that difficulty, as well as the use of charts in indicating the supply-and-demand relationship three of the formations identified by chartists are discussed below.

Figure 18-4 shows the daily price range (vertical lines) of a stock plotted for a period of months. The portion of the chart enclosed in the ruled lines constitutes what chartists call an ascending triangle. It is characterized by successive higher minimum points at which the decline in price of the stock stops on successive declines, while on the intervening advances the price of the stock reaches essentially the same level. Then the ascending triangle is formed by connecting the successively higher stopping points of the declines, and the successively identical prices reached on the advances. This chart acquires forecasting significance, in the eyes of chartists, when and only when, the price of the stock "breaks out" of the upper (flat) side of the triangle on greatly increased volume, as it did during the two days marked by the letter "A" on the chart. This advance through a previous resistance point on greatly increased volume is considered to be the result of demand overcoming supply, indicating a relatively strong demand that is likely to produce a basic uptrend for some time.

The descending triangle chart formation is directly opposed, in its graphical form and its forecasting implications, to the ascending triangle. Figure 18-5 shows a representative descending triangle. It is characterized by successively lower maximum prices reached on successive advances, and essentially the same minimum prices reached on the intervening declines, culminating in a "break-out" through the base of the triangle on greatly increased volume, which occurred at point "B" on the chart. This decline through a previous resistance point on greatly increased volume is considered to be the effect of supply overcoming demand, indicating a relatively great supply that is likely to produce a basic downtrend for some time to come.

The third type of triangle recognized by chartists is neither ascending nor descending. On the contrary, it is characterized by successively higher minimum prices on reactions and successively lower maximum prices on the intervening advances. Thus the two lines drawn to connect the maxima and the minima form a triangle whose altitude is horizontal or

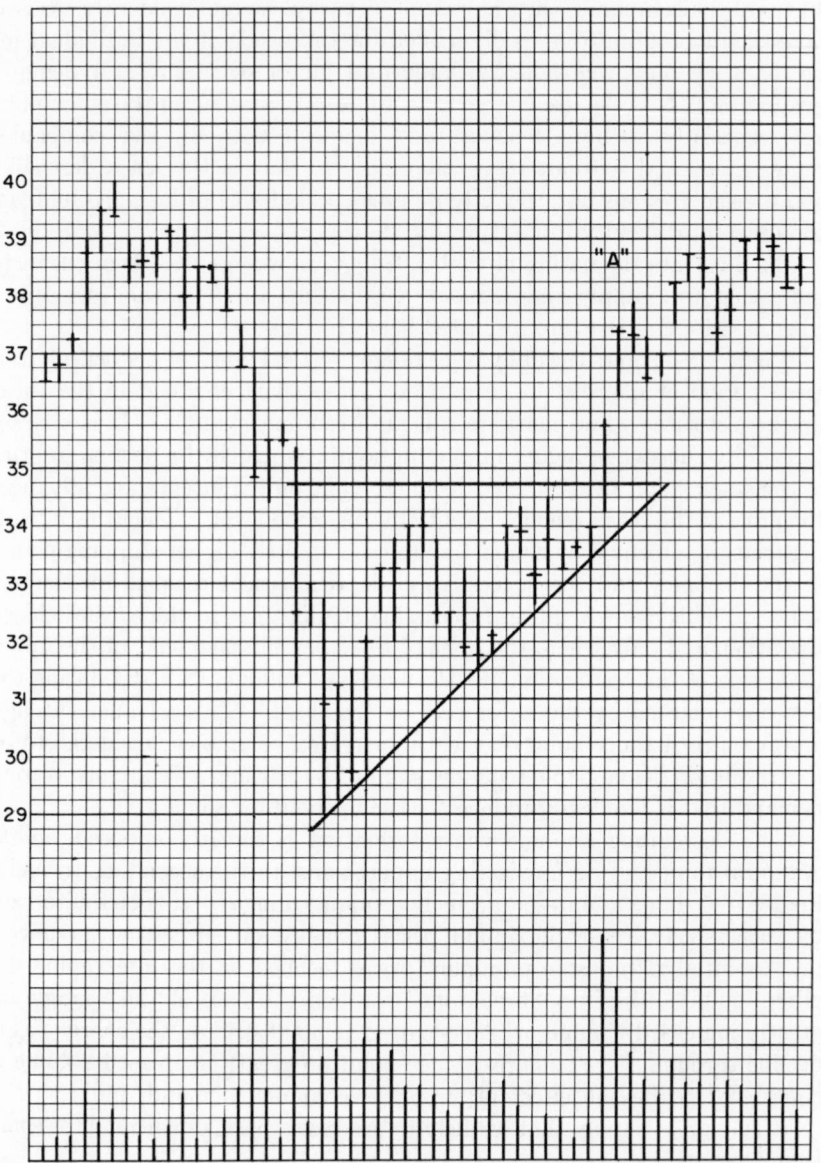

Figure 18-4.   Chart showing "ascending triangle" formation in price movement of
a stock.   Upper lines show daily price range and closing price (horizontal mark);
lower lines show daily sales volume.

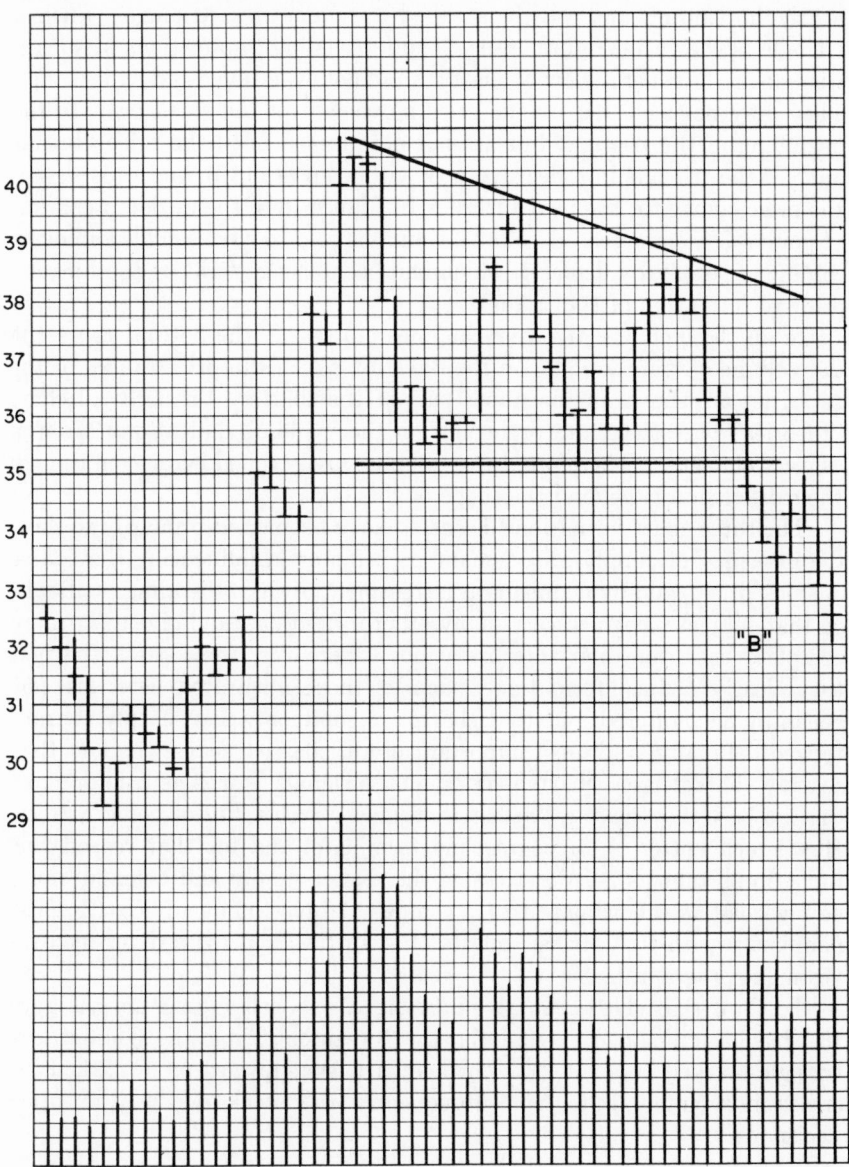

Figure 18-5. Chart showing "descending triangle" formation in price movement of a stock. Upper lines show daily price range and closing price (horizontal mark); lower lines show daily sales volume.

nearly horizontal, and which is called a symmetrical triangle. Such a triangle is shown in Figure 18-6. The forecasting implications of such a triangle, in the general view of chartists, are not even suggested by its shape. They may be suggested by the price movement of the stock prior to the beginning of the triangle, but are not determined until the price "breaks out" of the triangle in a decisive way, either up or down, and thus signals the price course for the near future. In Figure 18-6, the upside break out at point "C", on increased volume, would be said to have signaled an overcoming of supply by demand, which had been "suggested" by the uptrend prior to formation of the triangle.

In all these charts, the vertical lines plotted at the bottom represent the volume of transactions, on the days for which the price ranges of the securities are shown in the upper part of the charts. Virtually all chart "theories" base their interpretations on the "volume indications" as well as price changes. Therefore, these volumes are graphed here, even though their discussion is beyond the scope of this book.

The three chart formations discussed have been cited primarily to show the interplay of supply and demand as a factor in influencing the course of stock prices, and by no means as a treatment of chart "reading." Books on that subject recognize very many other formations, and give a far more complete basis for their interpretation. Moreover, they stress the fact that clearly defined formations, such as those illustrated here, are not generally encountered, but that charts are commonly less sharply characterized. Finally, and most important of all, chartists stress the fact that sharply characterized charts may give false signals as well as true ones, so that at best they have a "better than even" *probability* of being correct. How much better is, of course, indeterminate, and for that reason this topic, important as it is in stressing the role of supply and demand, must be regarded as subordinate to (1) competent investment advice, (2) close familiarity with the intrinsic merits of securities, and (3) a diversified investment program.

To show that charts can give false signals as well as true ones, Figure 18-7 has been included. Note that the "break out" from the symmetrical triangle marked at point "D" on the chart, was upward on a marked increase in volume, but that subsequently the stock declined in price decisively.

Figure 18-6. Chart showing "symmetrical triangle" formation in price movement
of a stock. Upper lines show daily price range and closing price (horizontal mark);
lower lines show daily sales volume.

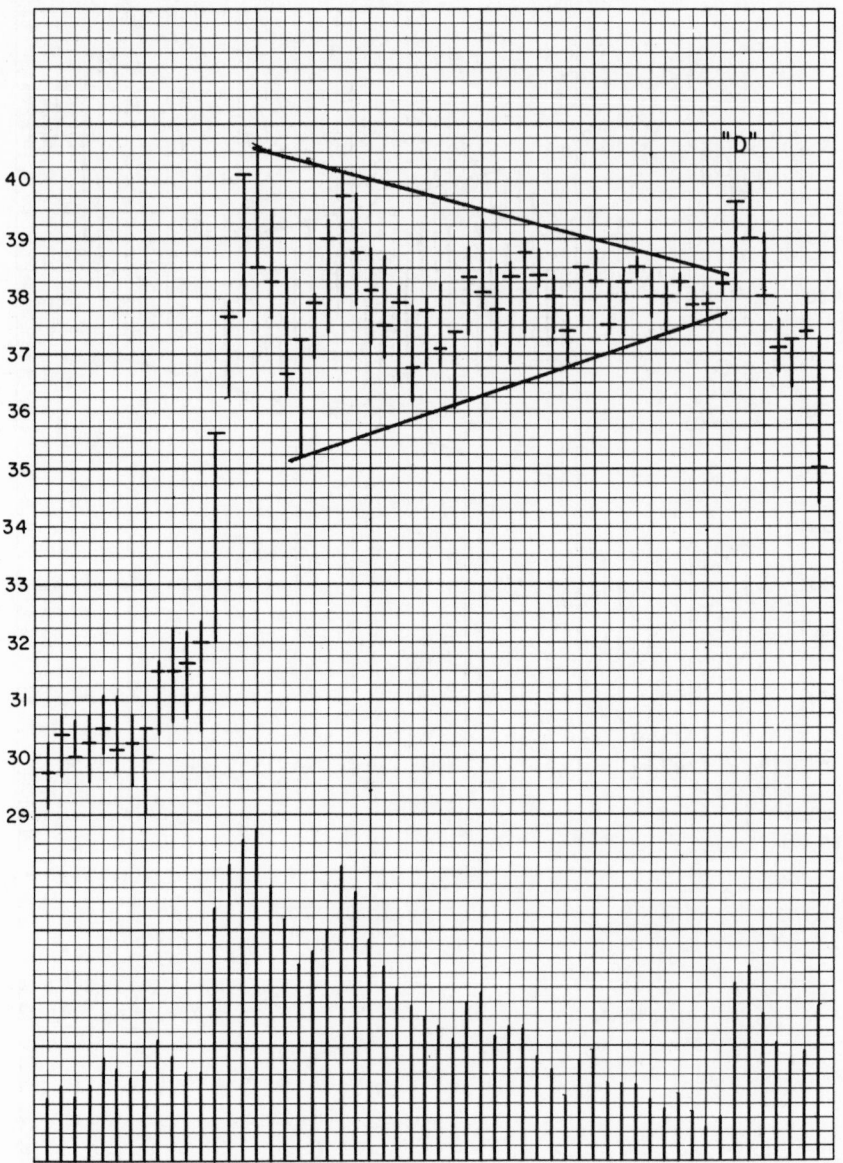

Figure 18-7. Chart showing "symmetrical triangle with false breakout" formation in price movement of a stock. Upper lines show daily price range and closing price (horizontal mark); lower lines show daily sales volume.

Chapter 19

INSTALMENT LOANS

Instalment loans are loans that are arranged for repayment in a number of payments, usually at regular periods. In this respect they differ from loans of the type discussed in Chapters 11 and 12, for while the latter may be discharged by more than one payment, and while definite methods exist for computing the application of such payments, they are not usually arranged at the time the loan is obtained.

There are other important differences between instalment loans and those other loans, differences which have gone far to make possible the great expansion in consumer credit which has played so significant a part in our national economy. Instalment loans are granted upon a much broader security basis. While the single-payment loans are usually secured by negotiable bonds or stocks of market value greater than the amount of the loan, by the credit of an established business or upon an equally secure basis, instalment loans are granted upon such security as automobiles, merchandise and even the wages of the borrower. While such collateral can be repossessed or levied upon, the costs and losses involved can well constitute a large proportion of the loan. Moreover, a lending organization operating in a community would naturally wish to minimize as much as possible the need for taking such action. It is therefore required to make credit investigations to a greater extent than required for the one-payment loans, which are often based upon established credit relations. Then there is always the greater office costs of collection and bookkeeping for a number of payments instead of a single one. All of these added costs must be borne by the interest return on loans of relatively small average size.

In consequence of this situation, the rate of interest charged on an instalment loan is more of the nature of a cost rate than an interest rate. This fact is recognized in the state laws, which establish different statutory limitations on interest rates—the legal and contract rate being much lower than the rates established for various classes of small loans. The higher rates granted on the latter make the granting of small loans economically possible, and hence obtainable from regular lending institutions that operate legally.

These statutory limitations by states on loans of all types have been summarized in the report "Rate Sections in Collateral Statutes" by Dr. M. R. Neifeld, Vice President of the Beneficial Finance System, with whose kind permission this report is reprinted below.

RATE SECTIONS IN COLLATERAL STATUTES

(As of October, 1958)

Preliminary Legend

1. *Loan and Investment Companies.* Statute authorizes a term loan which may be secured by an investment certificate or the like. Such investment certificate may be fully paid or may be purchased on the instalment basis.
2. *Instalment Loans.* Statute permits the making of loans and receiving payments in instalments.
3. *Retail Sales Finance.* General sales finance statute. It may have in some states (like Connecticut) a provision relating to motor vehicles, in which case, there is no separate reference to a Motor Vehicle Sales Finance Statute.
4. *Motor Vehicle Sales Finance.* Statute deals with the retail sales finance of motor vehicles. Statutes refer to classes of cars by model years.

Abbreviations and Definitions

Important abbreviations and definitions used in this report are as follows:

Acq. chg.	means "acquisition charge," or "acquisition cost." Also referred to as Min. chg.
Aggregated	A term used in the statutes of some of the southern states. The scheduled amount of each instalment is obtained by adding the amount of interest, computed as a per cent per annum, to the principal and dividing the total by the number of instalments.
Chg.	means "charge."
D.B.	means "on declining balances."
Del. chg: 5% or $5	means delinquency charge computed at 5% of delinquent instalment, but cannot exceed $5.
Del. chg: 5¢/$1, Max. $15	means delinquency charge is 5¢ per $1 of the instalment. Maximum charge: $15.
Disclosure	statute requires contract disclose certain information pertaining to transaction, but statute does not set maximum charges.
Ext. chg.	means "extension charge," or "refinance charges."
Fee: $1/$50	means an investigation or initial fee or service fee of $1 for each $50 of loan, or fraction thereof, all being taken or reserved at time of making the loan.
Int.	means "interest."
Inv.	means "investigation."
ISC.	means "Instalment Sales Contract."
Max.	means "maximum."

Min...................... means "minimum."
Mo...................... means "monthly" or "month."
No...................... means "number."
N. C...................... means "New Cars."
N. & U. C.................. means "New and Used Cars."
U. C...................... means "Used Cars."
O. U. C.................... means "Other Used Cars."
p.a...................... means "per annum."
Rule of 78ths.............. means sum-of-the-digits method of computing refunds.
Refund is that portion of the total charge as the total of the balances prepaid bears to the total of all balances in the contract.
RP...................... means "real property." (real estate)
x...................... all references to interest have been converted to per cent per annum, unless otherwise stated.
xx...................... means constitutional provision re interest.
*...................... means rate fixed by Department of Financial Institutions.
5¢/$1..................... The 1st figure is the amount permitted to be charged on the second figure.
6%/8%.................... The first figure refers to the legal rate of interest, the second to the contract rate. Legal rate is the statutory rate in absence of contract. Contract rate is maximum rate which may be reserved by contract.

Rate Sections in Collateral Statutes

	Legal and Contract Rate of Interest	Other Statutes	
ALABAMA..........	6%/8%	Instalment Loans........	6% p.a. aggregated.
ALASKA............	6%/8%	Instalment Loans........	$6/$100 discount. Ceiling: $3,500. 36 mos. max. Del. chg: 5¢/$1 after 15 days. Max: $15 for all defaults. Refund: Rule of 78ths. No refund if less than $5.
ARIZONA..........	6%/8%	Instalment Loans........	$8/$100 p.a. add-on, $1,000 or less / $6/$100 p.a. add-on, $1,000 to $3,500 ∫ Step Rate, Ceiling $3,500, Refund: Rule of 78ths. No refund if less than $1.
		Instalment Loans........	Industrial Bank Act 10% discount. Ceiling: $1,000. Refund: Unearned discount. Min: $3.00 if prepaid.
ARKANSAS^xx	6%/10%	Loan & Investment Cos...	Industrial Loan Institutions Statute No rate mentioned. No ceiling. Del. chg: 5¢/$1, or fraction.
CALIFORNIA^xx	7%/10%	Instalment Loans........	Industrial Loan Law. 2 1/2%–2%–5/6% @ $100–$300. No Ceiling. If insurance is taken, 2%–5/6% @ $300. No Ceiling. 24 mos. max. May deduct charges in advance, subject to refund if prepaid.

Legal and Contract Rate of Interest	Other Statutes	
	Motor Vehicle Sales Finance	1% of unpaid balance times no. of mos. Min. chg: $25 Del. chg: interest by contract. Refund: Rule of 78ths, after deducting acq. chg. $25.
COLORADO .... 6%/no limit	Instalment Loans	Industrial banks. 10% p.a. discount Fee: $1/$25. Max: $10 Del. chg: 1 1/2% per mo. Min: 25¢ Refund: Rule of 78ths. Instalment Loans: 2% per mo. (secured loans in excess of $1,500 only.)
	Motor Vehicle Sales Finance	Disclosure Del. Chg: 5% or $5. Refund: Rule of 78ths after deducting acq. chg. of $15. and insurance cost.
CONNECTICUT .... 6%/12% 12% not applicable to banks or trust companies on loans over $500.	Instalment Loans	Industrial Banks 6% discount. 36 mos. max. (360 mos. RP.) Fee: $1/$50. Max: $10.
	Retail Sales Finance	Disclosure. Ceiling: $5,000
		N. C., current model $7/$100
		U. C., model not more than 2 yrs. old $9/$100
		U. C., model more than 2, but not more than 4 yrs. $12/$100
		U. C., model yr. more than 4 yrs. $14/$100
		But U. C. more than 4 yrs. old; if principal balance $300 or less: $15/$100
		Min. chg: $15. Ext. chg: 12% p.a. on D. B. Del. chg: 5% or $5. Refund: Rule of 78ths, after deducting acq. chg. $15.
		Savings Banks: Ceiling: $2,000-Rate 1% per mo. unpaid balance.
DELAWARE .... 6%/6% DISTRICT OF COLUMBIA 6%/8%	Motor Vehicle Sales Finance	Disclosure. Rules of Commissioners of D. C. Bank & Trust Company Instalment Loans: Ceiling: $5,000, 6% Discount May require deposits.
FLORIDA .... 6%/10% (Corporations may contract for 15% p.a. Interest)	Instalment Loans	Florida Consumer Finance Law. $10/$100 add-on, of which $2 is inv. fee. Deferment chgs. provided Ceiling: $600. 24 mos. max. Mo. fee: 20¢/$25. Max: $2.40
	Loan & Investment Cos...	Morris Plan Bank. 8% Discount, plus 2% fee taken in advance. Del. chg: 5¢/$1.00
	Motor Vehicle Sales Finance	Ceiling: $7,500
		N. C., current model $8/$100
		N. & U. C. model less than 2 yrs. old $11/$100
		U. C. 2 to 4 yrs. $15/$100
		O. U. C. $17/$100
		Min. chg: $25

(continued)

	Legal and Contract Rate of Interest	Other Statutes	

Del. chg: 5% or $5
Ext. chg: $5 plus 1% per mo. simple int. on D. B.
Refund: Rule of 78ths, after deducting acq. chg. $25.

GEORGIA.......... 7%/8%   Instalment Loans........ 6% aggregated.

HAWAII............ 6%/1% per mo.   Instalment Loans........ Banks, same as Industrial Loan Act.

The Industrial Loan Act.

Max. discount: 4 yrs.
12% for first 18 mos.
9% for next 12 mos.
6% for next 12 mos.
3% for next 6 mos.
On ISC: $15 min. on contracts $100 or more
Del. fee: 12% p.a. on default instalment.
Deferment chgs. provided as per original contract.
$10 transfer of equity under ISC or chattel mortgage.
Refund: Unearned interest-contract rate on prepaid principal after deducting min. chg. $15.

Retail Sales Finance..... Same as Instalment Loans.
Del. chg: 5% or $5.

IDAHO............. 6%/8%
In lieu of int., a min. of $2.50   Instalment Loans........ Banks, S & L

Finance Commission supervised Corporations except Credit Unions, and S/L Licensees.
Ceiling: $1,000, 6% discount
Del. chg: 4% not in excess of $4.
Cannot be secured by R. P.

Retail Sales Finance..... Disclosure

ILLINOIS........... 5%/7%   Retail Sales Finance..... Retail Instalment Sales Act

Disclosure
Del. chg: 5% or $5.
Refund: Rule of 78ths, after deducting acq. chg. $10.

INDIANA.......... 6%/8%   Instalment Loans........ Industrial Loan and Investment Act.

Chgs.* may be precomputed. (R. P. 240 mos. max.)
Instalment Loan Act.
8% discount. Del. fee:*
Refund:* Min. chg.*

Retail Sales Finance..... Retail Instalment Sales Act.
Ceiling: $5,000.
Rate and Del. chg:* Refund:*

IOWA.............. 5%/7%   Loan & Investment Cos... Loan Corporations (Morris Plan)
On loans of $300 or more, it is usurious to chg. more than 2% per mo., but this is not an authorization to chg. more than 7% p.a.   7%. Reporting Statute only.

Motor Vehicle Sales Finance.............. Contract may be written in dollars.
N. C., current model yr.   1 1/4% per mo. simple int. on D. B.
N. & U. C., model yr. less than 2 yrs. old.   1 3/4% per mo. simple int. on D. B.
U. C., 2 to 4 yrs.   2 1/4% per mo. simple int. on D. B.
O. U. C.   2 1/4% per mo. simple int. on D. B. plus $1 mo. chg. not more than $12.

(continued)

	Legal and Contract Rate of Interest	Other Statutes	

KANSAS............ 6%/10%

Instalment Loans.......

Min: $25
Ext. chg: 1% per mo. simple int. on D. B.
Refund: Rule of 78ths, after deducting
acq. chg. $25
(Only those specially exempted from
licensing requirements of small loan
statutes).
8% Discount. Ceiling: $2,000.
30 mos. max. If int. less than $1.50, may
charge $1.50.
Refund: Rule of 78ths.

Retail Sales Finance.....

Motor Vehicles
N. C., current model $7/$100
N. & U. C., less than 2 yrs.
old $10/$100
O. U. C., more than 2 yrs. old $13/$100
Other Goods—services that
part of principal balance
.01–$300 $12/$100
300.01–1,000   9/$100
Over $1,000.01   8/$100
Min: $15. Del. chg: $5/$2.50
Ext. Refund as if prepaid and recompute
according to present classification.
Deferment: Rule of 78ths basis.
Refund: Rule of 78ths

KENTUCKY........ 6%/6%
Bank min: $1.00

Loan & Investment Cos...

Ceiling $5,000.
6% discount on portion up to $2,000,
plus fee $1/$50 on portion in excess
of $2,000.
3 yrs. 32 days max.
5% discount plus del. fee: 5¢/$1 or $5.
Banks, Trust Companies

Instalment loans, same as loan and investment companies.

Motor Vehicle Sales
Finance..............

Ceiling $5,000
N. C. & U. C., current model $9/$100
N. & U. C., less than 2 yrs. old $13/$100
O. U. C. $15/$100
Del. chg: 5% or $5.
Ext. chg: $5, plus 1% per mo. simple int.
on D. B.
Refund: Rule of 78ths, after deducting
acq. chg. $25.

LOUISIANA........ 5%/8%

No limit if in writing and "discounted"
and if interest not more than 8% after
maturity.

Motor Vehicles Sales
Finance..............

Motor Vehicle Sales Finance Act
(Effective January 1, 1959)
Applies to motor vehicles with cash sales
price of $7,500 or less.
N. C., current model   1 1/4% per mo.
N. or U. C., not more
than 2 yrs. old   1 3/4% per mo.
U. C., 2 to 4 yrs. old   2 1/4% per mo.
O. U. C., more than
4 yrs. old   2 1/4% per mo.,
plus $1 per mo.
Max: $12.
Min: $25.
Del. chg: 5% or $5
Refund: Rule of 78ths after deducting
acq. chg. $25

(continued)

	Legal and Contract Rate of Interest	Other Statutes	
MAINE.............	6%/no limit		Refinance: Refund, reclassify and recompute according to present model year.
		Loan & Investment Cos...	Industrial Banks or Morris Plan. 12% discount.
			24 mos. max.
			Inv. fee: $1/$50. Max: $5.
		Motor Vehicle Sales Finance..............	N. C., current model $7/$100
			N. & U. C., model yr. less
			than 3 yrs. old. $11/$100
			O. U. C. $13/$100
			Min: $25
			Ext. chg: $5 plus 1% per mo.
			Del. chg: 5% of instalment or 6% p.a. of unpaid balance.
			Refund: Rule of 78ths, after deducting acq. chg. $25.
MARYLAND.......	6%/6%	Instalment Loans........	Maryland Industrial Finance Law.
			6% discount, or 1/2% per mo. for no. of mos.
			Ceiling: $1,500. Del. chg: 5¢/$1.
			Inv. fee:
			$500 or less: $4 min., or 1/25 of loan.
			Over $500: $20 min., or 1/50 of loan.
			Refund: Rule of 78ths or int. divided by no. of mos. under original contract multiplied by no. of mos. anticipated.
		Retail Sales Finance.....	Retail Instalment Sales Act and Finance Companies and Investigation Act
			Disclosure. Ceiling: $2,000
			Del. chg: 5% or $5.
			Motor Vehicles
			N. C. $9/$100
			U. C., model yr. less than
			2 yrs. old $12/$100
			O. U. C. $15/$100
			Ext. chg: 15% simple int. Previous instalment may be refunded.
			Refund: Either Rule of 78ths, or Pro Rata.
MASSACHUSETTS..	6%/no limit		Tender Act: A right to prepay with int. at 18% p.a., plus $5.00.
			Ceiling $1,000
			Small loans by licensees exempted.
		Loan & Investment Cos...	Morris or similar plan companies.
			Less than $500, 12% discount.
			More than $500, 9% discount.
		Retail Sales Finance.....	Disclosure.
			Refund: Rule of 78ths, after deducting acq. chg. Motor Vehicles (other than those subject to motor vehicle sales finance statute)—$12.50
			Other goods—$5.00
		Motor Vehicle Sales Finance..............	Retail Instalment Sales of Motor Vehicles
			N. & U. C., model year of year of sale or prior $8/$100
			N. & U. C., not in above and not more than 2 yrs. old $10/$100
			O. U. C. $12/$100
			Del. chg: $5 or 5%
			Refund: Rule of 78ths, after deducting acq. chg. of $12.50
			Ext. chgs:

(continued)

	Legal and Contract Rate of Interest	Other Statutes
		Refund and recompute as in original contract.
MICHIGAN.........	5%/7%	Instalment Loans........ Industrial Bank 7% discount. 36 mos. max. Inv. fee: $1/$50, Max: $15.
		Motor Vehicle Sales Finance.............. N. & U. C., not more than 1 yr.

Motor Vehicle Sales
Finance.............. N. & U. C., not more than 1 yr.
  prior to sale yr. $6/$100
N. & U. C., more than 1 yr. but
  not more than 2 yrs. old $9/$100
N. & O. U. C., more than 2 yrs.
  old $12/$100
Min. chg: $15.
Del. chg: 2% per mo. (deemed full month
 after 10 days)
Refund: Rule of 78ths, subject to $15.
 min.
Ext. chgs:
 Less than 1 yr. old 1% per mo.
 1 to 2 yrs. old   1 1/2% per mo.
 Over 2 yrs. old   2% per mo.,
  or refund and recompute as if new
  contra

MINNESOTA....... 6%/8% Bank Instalment Loans

6% discount, Ceiling $3,000.
Max. 36 mos., Min. $3.

Loan & Investment Cos... Industrial Loan and Thrift Company

8% discount. 24 mos., max.
Inv. fee: $1/$50. Max. $10.
 If over $500, additional 1% on excess
  over $500, but not in excess of $15
  total.
 If less than $50., Max: $1.
Del. chg: 5¢/$1 aggregate not to exceed $5
 If less than $50, aggregate not to ex-
  ceed 50¢
Refund: Rule of 78ths. Chart furnished
 by commissioner.

Motor Vehicle Sales
Finance.............. Motor Vehicle Retail Instalment Sales Act

N. & U. C., not more
 than 1 yr. prior to
 yr. of sale $8/$100 p.a.
N. & U. C., 2 or 3 yrs. $11/$100 p.a.
O. U. C. $13/$100 p.a.
       plus flat chg.
       $3 for each sale.
Refinance chg: $5, plus 1% per mo. simple
 int. on D. B.
Del. chg: 5% or $5.
Refund: Rule of 78ths, after deducting
 acq. chg. $15.

MISSISSIPPI....... 6%/8% Instalment Loans........ Instalment Loans. 5% aggregated.
Usury is charged in ex-   Personal Property and Wage Loans. 10%
cess of 10%   Inv. fee: $ .01–$ 5 $ .50 max.
            5.01–$10 .70 max.
           10.01–$20 1.00 max.
           20.01–$35 1.50 max.
           35.01–$60 2.00 max.
           Over $60 6% of amount of
                loan.

Motor Vehicle Sales
Finance.............. Ceiling $7,500
 N. C., current model $7/$100
 N. & U. C., not more than
  2 yrs. old $10/$100

(continued)

	Legal and Contract Rate of Interest	Other Statutes	

| | | | U. C., more than 2 yrs., not more than 4 yrs. old $13/$100 |

U. C., more than 2 yrs., not
  more than 4 yrs. old $13/$100
O. U. C. $15/$100
Min: $25, Del. chg: 5%/$5
Refund: Rule of 78ths after deducting $10.
Ext. chg:
  N. C., current model 1% per mo.
  N. & U. C., not more
    than 2 yrs. old   1 1/2% per mo.
  U. C., more than
    2 yrs., not more
    than 4 yrs. old   2% per mo.
  O. U. C.   2 1/2% per mo.
Refund or recompute as if new contract.

MISSOURI.......... 6%/8%   Instalment Loans........ $400 or less: $15/$100 for 12 mos. instalments, or 2.218% per mo.
Refund: Recompute or under a modified Rule of 78ths.
On portion over $400, 8% p.a.

MONTANA......... 6%/10%   Loan & Investment Cos... Morris Plan Co. 6% discount.
12 mos. max.
Inv. fee: $1/$50

NEBRASKA........ 6%/9%   Instalment Loans........ Industrial Loan and Investment Company.
36 mos. max.
Rate: On that portion
  $ .01–$1,000   18% p.a. simple int. D. B.
  $1,000.01–$3,000 12% p.a. simple int. D. B.
  Over $3,000   9% p.a. simple int. D. B.
May be precomputed.
Del. at monthly per cent.
Refund: Pro Rata

Motor Vehicle Sales
  Finance............. Disclosure

NEVADA........... 7%/12%   Motor Vehicle Sales
  Finance............. 1% of unpaid balance times no. of mos., or $25 min.
Del. int. by contract.
Refund: Rule of 78ths, after deducting $25 acq. chg.

NEW HAMPSHIRE 6%/no limit

NEW JERSEY...... 6%/6%   Bank Instalment Loans
Ceiling: $2,500. 6% Discount according to formula.

Retail Sales Finance ..... Retail Instalment Sales Act
Ceiling: $3,000
Del. chg: 5% or $5.
Ext. chg: $5 plus 10% p.a. on D. B.
Refund: Rule of 78ths, after deducting acq. chg. $10.

NEW MEXICO..... 6%/10% or 12% if no collateral, min. of $2.

NEW YORK........ 6%/6%   Bank Instalment Loans
$6/$100 discount. Ceiling $5,000.
Max. 25 mos. if $1,200 or less.
37 mos. max. over $1,200, not in excess of $5,000.
37 mos. max. for R. P. improvement, min. $10

(continued)

Legal and
Contract
Rate of
Interest   Other Statutes

Del. chg: 5¢/$1, max. $5 or an aggregate
of 2% of loan, but not in excess of $25.
Refund: Rule of 78ths, subject to $10
min. chg.

Loan & Investment Cos...   Industrial Banks

$6/$100 discount.   Ceiling $5,000.
25 mos. max., if less than $1,200.
37 mos. if more than $1,200 or if R. P.
Min. chg: $10.
Fee: $1/$50 up to $250.   Max: $5.
More than $250: $5 plus 1% of excess
above $250.   Max: $20.
Del. chg: 5¢/$1.   Max: $5 per instalment.
Total Max: 2% or $25.
Refund: Pro-rata as of following date,
subject to $10 min. chg.

Retail Sales Finance.....   Retail Instalment Sales Act

(All Goods Act)   Unpaid principal balance
$500 $10/$100 p.a.
Unpaid principal balance
over $500   8/$100 p.a.
Revolving credit: on that amount not in
excess of $500—1 1/2% per mo.
More than $500—1% per mo.
Min: 70¢ per mo. or on schedule of fixed
amounts as above less differential of
not more than $5.
Deferment chg: 1% per mo. simple int.
on D. B.
Min. $12.   If maturity less than 8 mos:
Min. $10
Refinance or Ext. chg: not to exceed 1%
D. B. min. $1 or refund and recompute.
Del. chg: 5% or $5.
Refund: Rule of 78ths
Merchandise certificate refund: pro-rata.

Motor Vehicle Sales
Finance..............   N. C., current model $7/$100
N. & U. C., not more than
2 yrs. old $10/$100
O. U. C. $13/$100
Insurance premium $7/$100
Del. chg: 5% or $5.
Ext. or Refinance chg: service fee not to
exceed $5, plus total additional chg.
not to exceed 1% per mo.
Refund: Rule of 78ths, after deducting
acq. chg. $15
Refinance chg: 1% per mo. or refund and
charge as per contract on unpaid
balance.

NORTH CAROLINA 6%/6%   Instalment Loans........   Industrial Banks

6% discount.
Step fee: $ .01–$ 50. $2.50
50.01– 250. $1/$50
250.01 and over $5 plus
$1/$250 for excess over $250.
Additional $5 if R. P.

Motor Vehicle Sales
Finance.............   Disclosure
Retail Sales Finance.....   Disclosure in written agreement.

NORTH DAKOTA.. 4%/7%   Retail Sales Finance.....   Retail Instalment Sales Act

New Article current model: $7/$100
New or Used not more than
2 yrs. old: $10/$100

(continued)

	Legal and Contract Rate of Interest	Other Statutes	

| | | | Other: $13/$100 |

Del. chg: 5% or $5
Refinance chg: $5, plus 1% per mo. simple int. on D. B.
Refund: Rule of 78ths, after deducting acq. chg. $15.

OHIO.............. 6%/8%   Retail Sales Finance .....   Retail Instalment Sales Act

$8/$100. Mo. chg: 50¢/first $50., plus 25¢/$50. Max: $1.75 per mo.
Not applicable where charges do not exceed $15.
Del. chg: 5¢/$1. Max: $3 or 8% p.a.
Refund: Rule of 78ths, after deducting acq. chg. $10.

OKLAHOMA**...... 6%/10%   Loan & Investment Cos...   By court decision (10% discount, for 1 yr. For longer term: add-on plus common law fees)

OREGON.......... 6%/10%   Bank Instalment Loans

10% p.a. or in lieu of int. on that part of loan not exceeding $500.—$8/$100. 10% above.
Refund: Rule of 78ths, subject to min. chg. of $3.

Loan & Investment Cos...   Industrial Loan Company

10% discount. 18 mos. max. if no security. 24 mos. if loan is secured by chattel mortgage.
Fee: $ .01–$100 $3
       100.01 and over   3%
Del. chg: (Ext.) 5¢/$1 per wk. Max: 4 weeks.

Motor Vehicle Sales
Finance ....   N. C., model yr. less than
                              1 yr. old $8/$100.
                          N. & U. C., not more than
                              2 yrs. old $10/$100
                          O. U. C. $12/$100
                          Min. chg: $25
                          Del. chg: 5% or $5.
                          Ext. chg: $5 plus 1% per mo. simple int. on D. B.
                          Refund: Rule of 78ths, after deducting acq. chg. $15.

PENNSYLVANIA... 6%/6%   Instalment Loans........   Consumer Discount Company Act

6% discount. Ceiling: $2,000.
Fee: $1/$50. Max: $15.
Min. chg: (where contract payable in one year)
    If less than $25: $3.
      More than $25: $6
      Max: 3 yrs.
Del. or Ext. chg: 1 1/2% per mo., Min: 25¢
Refund: Rule of 78ths

Motor Vehicle Sales
Finance ....   N. C.   6% p.a.
                          U. C., not more than
                              2 yrs. old   9% p.a.
                          O. U. C.   12% p.a.
                          Min. chg: $10.
                          Refinance chg:
                              N. C.   1% per mo.
                              U. C., not more than
                                  2 yrs. old   1 1/2% per mo.

(continued)

	Legal and Contract Rate of Interest	Other Statutes	
			O. U. C. 2% per mo., or recompute as originally computed after making adjustments for insurance, default chgs., etc. Del. chg: 2% per mo. Refund: Rule of 78ths, subject to min. chg.
PUERTO RICO.....	6%/9%/8%		On loans of $3,000 or less the max. rate is 9%. On portion over $3,000, the max. is 8%.
RHODE ISLAND...	6%/30%		The 30% rate applies only on loans over $50. On loans of less than $50, the rate is 5% per mo. for the first six months and 2 1/2% per mo. thereafter including all charges.
		Loan & Investment Cos...	Loan and Investment Companies Act 6% (8% R. P.) discount. Ceiling: $10,000. 24 mos. max. (but 300 mos. R. P.) Inv. fee: $1/$50 (5% in R. P.). If less than $50: $1. Del. chg: 5¢/$1. Max: 10 successive defaults, but not in excess of one full instalment.
SOUTH CAROLINA (Banks, brokers, authorized corps. may charge $1)	6%/7%	Instalment Loans........	Industrial Banks. 1 1/2% per mo. Ceiling: $200 Min. loan: $10. Instalment Loans. 7% discount. Ceiling: $1,000 Min. loan: $10. Min. term: 6 mos.
SOUTH DAKOTA...	6%/8%	Instalment Loans........	8% add-on to $1,000. 6% add-on over $1,000. Min. $3. Ceiling $3,000. 36 mos. max. Del. chg: 5% per instalment or 6% p.a., whichever is greater. Refund: Pro-rate, subject to min.
		Motor Vehicle Sales Finance..............	Motor Vehicle Retail Instalment Sales Act N. C., current model 1 1/4% per mo. N. or U. C., not more than 2 yrs. old 1 1/2% per mo. O. U. C. 2 1/4% per mo. Min. $20 Del. chg: 5% or $5. Refinance chg: $5, plus rate as per contract. Refund: Rule of 78ths, after deducting acq. chg: $15.
TENNESSEE[xx]......	6%/6%	Loan & Investment Cos...	Industrial Loan and Thrift Company 6% discount. 36 mos. max. Fee: $4/$100. Del. chg: 5¢/$1.
TEXAS[xx]............	6%/10%	Loan & Investment Cos...	10% discount Fee: $1/$50. Max. total chgs: 3 1/2% of face amount of loan, limitation on certain chgs. Del. chg: 10% p.a.
		Motor Vehicle Sales Finance..............	Disclosure.
UTAH..............	6%/10%		On loans of $100 or less, $1 may be taken as int. for the first month and 10% p.a. thereafter. Contracts may provide for a 4% service chg.

(continued)

Legal and Contract Rate of Interest	Other Statutes	

Instalment Loans......... **Industrial Loan Company**
Rate (add-on):
$ .01–$2,000   1% per mo.
2,000.01–$5,000   3/4 of 1% per mo.
Ceiling: $5,000.   37 mos. max.
Fee: on loans less than $100: $2
more than $100: 2%. $20 max.
Refund: by regulation of bank commissioner (commerical practices)
Instalment Loans
7% discount, but not to yield over 14% p.a.
Ceiling: $5,000.   63 mos. max.
Refund: by regulation of bank commissioner (commercial practices)

Retail Sales Finance...... **Retail Instalment Sales Act**
1% unpaid balance times no. of mos.
Ceiling: $7,500
Del. chg: int. by contract.
Refund: 7% of Rule of 78ths, after deducting $15 on motor vehicles, $5 on others.

VERMONT......... 6%/6%

VIRGINIA.......... 6%/6%   Instalment Loans....... **Instalment Loans (Banks)**
Ceiling $1,000, 6% discount.
2% fee, $1 min.
Industrial Loan Association
6% discount.   120 mos. max.
Inv. fee: 2% Min. total chg: $1.
Del. fee: per by-laws, but not in excess of 10%.

Motor Vehicle Sales Finance.............. Disclosure
Retail Sales Finance..... Disclosure

WASHINGTON..... 6%/12%   Loan & Investment Cos... **Industrial Loan Company**
10% discount.   24 mos. max.
Fee: on loans under $100: $2
$100 or more: 2%
Mo. fee: 50¢ per mo.
Del. fee: 5¢/$1

WEST VIRGINIA... 6%/6%
(min. of $1.)   Instalment Loans........ **Industrial Loan Companies**
6% discount.   24 mos. max.   (Board of Directors may extend max. time)
Fee: $1/$50, plus actual expenses except credit examination and drawing papers.
Del. fee: 5¢/$1.

WISCONSIN........ 5%/10%   Instalment Loans........ **Instalment Loans (banks)**
Bank commission rules may permit a max. service chg. not in excess of $1 for each 90-day period or fraction, in addition to int. on loans not in excess of $1,000.
Secured Loans
10% add-on.   Fee: 4% p.a. for 1 yr.
Refund: Pro-rata.
Discount Loans
8% discount to $300
7% discount over $300
Ceiling: $2,000.   30 1/2 mos. max.
Inv. fee: 2%.   Max: $20.
Del. chg: 1% if more than 10 days, additional 1% for each additional 20-day period.
Refund: Rule of 78ths

(continued)

Legal and Contract Rate of Interest	Other Statutes	
	Motor Vehicle Sales Finance..............	N. C. $7/$100
		U. C., model yr. less than 2 yrs. old $9/$100
		U. C., 2 to 5 yrs. old $12/$100
		U. C., over 5 yrs. old $15/$100
		Min. chg: $15.
		Del. chg: regulated by bank commissioner.
		Refund: regulated by bank commissioner.
WYOMING......... 7%/10%		Bank loans of less than $200, service chg: $1 plus 10% p.a. single payment loan, 90 days or less.
	Instalment Loans........	Banks, Trust Companies, and Finance Companies
		8% discount. Ceiling: $1,000.
		Min: 50¢ for each instalment in lieu of int. if int. is less than $3. May require periodic deposits also.

CANADA

Legal and Contract Rate of Interest	Other Statutes	
5%/agreed upon by parties, unless otherwise provided for by an Act of Parliament of Canada.	Loan Companies Act.....	Applies to every loan company incorporated by special Act of Parliament.
ALBERTA....................	Retail Sales Finance.....	Applicable to amounts in excess of $100. Disclosure.
MANITOBA....................	Special statute..........	Relates to sales of farm machinery sales of $50 or more.
NEW BRUNSWICK............	Retail Sales Finance.....	15% down payment, max. 24 mos. Seller must deliver copy of contract to buyer within 20 days. Does not apply to similar goods as in Quebec act and such other goods prescribed by Order of the Governor-in-Council.
NOVA SCOTIA.................	Instalment Payment Contracts Act........	Requires licensing of sales finance companies, prohibits certain provisions in any conditional sales contract. Disclosure.
QUEBEC......................	Instalment Loans........	Instalment Sales Act
		3/4 of 1% per mo. for duration of term on total deferred payments.
		Applicable to sales of $800 or less, except: on agricultural implements, marine and fishing equipment, machines, instruments and furnishings, professional, commercial and industrial purposes, books of a religious, scientific, professional or educational character, artificial limbs, stationary engines, motor tractors, automobiles and other mechanically-driven vehicles.
		Downpayment at least 15%. If deferred payments total less than $50, max. 6 mos. If deferred payments total less than $100, max. 12 months. If deferred payments total less than $300, max. 18 mos. All other cases, max. 24 mos.

(continued)

Legal and Contract Rate of Interest	Other Statutes	Similar monthly charge may be made on past due payment. Refund: pro-rata.
SASKATCHEWAN..............	Conditional Sales Contract Statute......	Disclosure.

Instalment Loan Calculations—Actuarial Yield Method

Instalment loan calculations by the actuarial yield method are concerned with the computation of rate of charge (i.e. rate of interest), amount of charge (i.e. amount of interest), the time to maturity, the present value or the amount, by annuity formulas. Since an instalment loan is an annuity, this method yields answers correct to about the number of significant figures given in the annuity tables used. However, since actuarial tables are often not available, especially to many borrowers, other methods have been developed which give results correct within a few parts per hundred of the actuarial result. Thus, while the actuarial method is given first in the necessarily limited treatment of the subject in this book, the results obtained from the use of a working formula by a lending agency may well give results differing from it to a minor degree.

The use of the annuity tables to solve problems in instalment computations follows the methods established in Chapter 14. For example, those methods give the amount of required monthly payment directly, as is clear from the solution of the following problem: Find the monthly payment required to pay a debt of $200.00 in ten monthly payments at charge rate of $2\frac{1}{4}\%$ on the unpaid balance.

Here the problem is to find the periodic payment of an annuity having a present value of $200.00, 10 payment periods, and a rate of $2\frac{1}{4}\%$.

By Formula (14-14), Chapter 14, $P = Ra_{\overline{n}|i}$, where P is the present value of an annuity, $a_{\overline{n}|i}$ is its present value per $1.00 of periodic payment, and R is its periodic payment. In this problem, P is $200.00, n is 10 and i is $2\frac{1}{4}\%$.

Substituting $200.00 = Ra_{\overline{10}|2\frac{1}{4}}$
From Table 14, Chapter 14, $a_{\overline{10}|2\frac{1}{4}} = 8.86621635$

Therefore $R = \dfrac{\$200.00}{8.86621635} = \dfrac{200.00}{8.8662} = \$22.56$

The problem of finding the charge rate (interest rate) is illustrated by the following problem: Find the monthly rate on a loan of $250.00, for which the borrower agrees to pay $282.00 in 12 equal monthly instalments.

Here the problem is that of finding the rate for an annuity having a present value of $250.00, a periodic payment of $\dfrac{\$282}{12} = \$23.50$, payable for 12 periods.

By Formula (14-14), Chapter 14, $P = Ra_{\overline{n}|i}$, where P is \$250.00, R is \$23.50, and n is 12.

Substituting \$250.00 = \$23.50 $a_{\overline{12}|i}$

Therefore $a_{\overline{12}|i} = \dfrac{250.00}{23.50} = 10.63829790$

Now, in Table 14, Chapter 14, $a_{\overline{12}|1\frac{3}{4}} = 10.73954969$
And in Table 14, Chapter 14, $a_{\overline{12}|2} = \underline{10.57534122}$
$\qquad\qquad$ Difference $\qquad$ .16420847

Also, the value found above for $a_{\overline{12}|i} = 10.63829790$
And the Table 14 value of $a_{\overline{12}|2} = \underline{10.57534122}$
$\qquad\qquad$ Difference $\qquad$ .06295668

Therefore $i = 1.75\% + \left(\dfrac{1}{4}\right)\left(\dfrac{.06295668}{.16420847}\right) = 1.75\% + \left(\dfrac{1}{4}\right)\left(\dfrac{.063}{.164}\right)\% =$
1.85% monthly.

The method of finding the number of payments on an instalment debt is illustrated in the solution of the problem: How many payments are required to pay \$150.00 at a monthly charge rate of $2\frac{1}{2}\%$ at \$15.00 per month?

By Formula (14-14), Chapter 14, $P = Ra_{\overline{n}|i}$ and here P is \$150.00, R is \$15.00 and i is $2\frac{1}{2}\%$.

Substituting $\qquad\qquad$ \$150.00 = \$15.00 $a_{\overline{n}|2\frac{1}{2}}$
Therefore $a_{\overline{n}|2\frac{1}{2}} = 10$.

From Table 14, Chapter 14, $a_{\overline{12}|2\frac{1}{2}} = 10.25776460$
From Table 14, Chapter 14, $a_{\overline{11}|2\frac{1}{2}} = \underline{\;9.51420871}$
$\qquad\qquad$ Difference $\qquad$ .74355589

Also, value found above for $a_{\overline{n}|2\frac{1}{2}} \quad = 10$.
Subtracting Table 14 value for $a_{\overline{11}|2\frac{1}{2}} = \underline{\;9.51420871}$
$\qquad\qquad\qquad\qquad\qquad\qquad$ .48579129

Therefore $n = 11 + \dfrac{.48579129}{.74355589}$

$\qquad = 11 + \frac{4859}{7436} = 11.66$ payments, that is, a total of 11 payments of \$15.00, plus a fractional payment of \$9.80.

Amortization Schedules for Instalment Loans

Amortization schedules are used extensively in the instalment loan business. They are constructed in the same way as explained in Chapter 16, and serve a number of purposes, not the least of which is the checking of the computations. As an example of the method to be followed, consider the following loan and amortization schedule:

R. Jones borrows \$220.00 to be repaid at $2\frac{1}{2}\%$ per month for 12 months. Find the payments, and construct the amortization schedule.

Here, as before $P = Ra_{\overline{n}i}$

Substituting $\$220.00 = Ra_{12\frac{1}{2}i}$

From Table 14, Chapter 14, $a_{12\frac{1}{2}i} = 10.25776460$. Therefore, $R =$
$$\frac{\$220.00}{10.25776460} = \frac{220.00}{10.2578} = \$21.45$$

The amortization schedule is constructed as follows: In the last column, above the first line, enter the amount borrowed. In the first column enter the numbers of the periods at the end of which payments are to be made. In the second column, enter the payments to be made in each period. Now fill out each line by computing interest on the unpaid balance (column 7), which is entered in the third column "Credit Charge per Month" and added to the preceding item in the fourth column. Then

AMORTIZATION SCHEDULE

Loan of \$220.00   Payments \$21.45 per month for 12 Months
Rate $2\frac{1}{2}\%$ Monthly

(1)	(2)	(3)	(4)	(5)	(6)	(7)
						Unpaid
	Monthly	Credit Charge		Reduction of Principal		Principal
Period	Payment	Per Month	Cumulative	Monthly	Cumulative	Balance
						\$220.00
1	\$21.45	\$5.50	\$ 5.50	\$15.95	\$ 15.95	205.05
2	21.45	5.10	10.60	16.35	32.30	187.70
3	21.45	4.69	15.29	16.76	49.06	170.94
4	21.45	4.28	19.57	17.17	66.23	153.77
5	21.45	3.84	23.41	17.61	83.84	136.16
6	21.45	3.40	26.81	18.05	101.89	118.11
7	21.45	2.95	29.76	18.50	120.39	99.61
8	21.45	2.49	32.25	18.96	139.35	80.65
9	21.45	2.02	34.27	19.43	158.78	61.22
10	21.45	1.53	35.80	19.92	178.70	41.30
11	21.45	1.03	36.83	20.42	199.12	20.88
12	21.45	.57	37.40	20.88	220.00	
Total	\$257.40	\$37.40		\$220.00		

The rules for using this Amortization Schedule as a check are:

Rule I.   Total of Column (2) = Total of Column (3) + Total of Column (5)

Rule II.   Total of Column (5) = Last entry in Column (6) = Original debt.

Rule III. Last entry in Column (5) = Last entry in Column (7).

compute the "Reduction in Principal—Monthly" which is the difference between the entries in Columns (2) and (3), and which is entered in Column (5); added to the preceding entry in Column (6); and subtracted from the preceding entry in Column (7).

Thus, to start the Schedule, enter $220.00 above the first line Column (7). Then enter the period numbers in the first Column (1-12), and the corresponding payments ($21.45 per period) in Column (2). Then compute the first month's interest ($220.00 $\times$ .025) = $5.50, enter it in Column (3), and add it to the preceding entry in Column (4), i.e. $5.50 + 0 = $5.50. Then compute the "Reduction in Principal—Monthly" by subtracting the entry in Column (3) from that in Column (2), ($21.45 − $5.50 = $15.95), enter it in Column (5), add it to the preceding entry in Column (6), i.e. $15.95 + 0 = $15.95; and subtract it from the preceding entry in Column (7), i.e., $220.00 − $15.95 = $204.05. Proceed similarly to fill out the balance of the Schedule.

Approximate Methods

As stated earlier in this chapter, a number of approximate methods of making instalment loan computations are in use where the actuarial method just described is not used because the annuity tables are unavailable, or their use is considered too complex. Where large aggregate sums are involved, or where precise yield figures are required, the actuarial method is necessary. However, where its great accuracy is not required, the other methods are used. They differ in their ways of distributing the carrying charge, and thus give different cost rates. Note that cost rate comparisons should specify both the method of computation and the time period to which the rate refers, since many banks and investment houses use the annual rates, obtained from monthly rates by multiplying by 12, for purposes of comparison.

Before discussing the approximate methods, there are two terms used in instalment computations that require explanation. The equivalent balance or equivalent principal is the single principal that is equivalent in investment value (interest return) to the successive periodic balances of an instalment loan. Thus the sum of $200.00 repaid in four months can be considered as separable into a $50.00 loan for four months, a $100.00 loan for three months, a $150.00 loan for two months and a $200.00 dollar loan for one month, the equivalent of a single $1,000.00 loan for one month, obtained by multiplying each balance by the time it is outstanding. This result is called the "action of the principal" or simply the "action."

The Maximum Yield or Interest at End Method is based on the theory of applying the payments made by the debtor first to repayment of the principal of the loan, and only after it is completely repaid are further instalments applied to payment of the credit charges. Its Amortization Schedule is easy to prepare because the periodic payments are applied entirely to reduce principal until it is paid in full.

The Minimum Yield Method is based on the theory that the credit costs are paid first, and that payments are applied to principal only after these costs have been satisfied. Like that of the maximum yield method, the Amortization Schedule of the minimum yield method is easy to prepare because the periodic payments are first applied to credit costs, and then to repayment of the principal of the loan.

Both the Maximum and Minimum Yield Methods are contrary to the fundamental concept of a true rate, that the charge is applied to the entire transaction, and not to any particular period or periods. This objection has considerable weight from the standpoint of the instalment loan business itself, which naturally prefers methods which distribute earnings more uniformly in relation to income and expenses, and which also prefers methods yielding rate figures closer to the actuarial values.

This result is obtained by the use of the Constant Ratio Method, which distributes the charges according to the number of payments. That is, the total charge is divided by the number of payments, and the quotient is credited each month. Therefore, the amount credited to principal each month is also uniform, being the difference between the amount of the monthly payment and the credit for charges. Due to its ease of calculation, the Constant Ratio Method is used extensively, especially because its results are sufficiently close to the actuarial values for all purposes but those requiring the most accurate calculations. It also facilitates calculation of charge rates when payments are irregular, as in the case of a "balloon" note, which has a larger final payment, or a "drop" note, which has a smaller final payment, or even of an instalment loan with payments deferred.

The Direct Ratio Method gives yield figures that are the closest to the actuarial values of all four approximate methods discussed. It is, moreover, much more readily computed by formula. For these reasons it is widely used as an adequate substitute for the actuarial method, even by banking institutions as a means of distributing income from instalment loans. It is also suitable for making refunds, and under the name, the "78s Method," is widely used for that purpose.

The basis of the Direct Ratio Method is the concept of instalment-months. If a loan is to be paid in 5 instalments, then it may be considered that 5 instalments are outstanding for the first month, 4 for the second, 3 for the third, 2 for the fourth, and 1 for the fifth. The total number of instalment-months involved is the sum of arithmetic progression 5,4,3,2,1, which by the Formula (7-5) of Chapter 7, is 15. The Direct Ratio Method distributes the charge for credit according to these debt balances, that is, $\frac{5}{15}$ of it to the first month, $\frac{4}{15}$ to the second, $\frac{3}{15}$ to the third, $\frac{2}{15}$ to the fourth and $\frac{1}{15}$ to the fifth.

Since the method is based upon arithmetical progression, it is also called the Sum of the Digits Method. The name "78s Method" arises from the fact that charges on loans payable monthly for twelve months are distributed according to sequence $\frac{12}{78}$, $\frac{11}{78}$, $\frac{10}{78}$, $\frac{9}{78}$, $\frac{8}{78}$, $\frac{7}{78}$, $\frac{6}{78}$, $\frac{5}{78}$, $\frac{4}{78}$, $\frac{3}{78}$, $\frac{2}{78}$, and $\frac{1}{78}$, since the sum of the arithmetical progression 12, 11 ... 2, 1, is 78. Since the sum of the digits is 78 only in the case of 12-payment loans, the name "78s Method" can be misinterpreted, and the name Direct Ratio or Sum of the Digits Method is preferred.

A method has been developed for deriving formulas for finding i, the monthly interest rate, by these various methods. This method was developed at length in an article by H. E. Stelson, *The Rate of Interest in Instalment Payment Plans* which appeared in the American Mathematical Monthly, **60**, 326-329 (1953). Formulas for computing the differences between the rates computed by these methods and the actuarial rate are also given in the book "Mathematics of Finance" by H. E. Stelson, D. Van Nostrand Company, Inc., Princeton, New Jersey (1957). This method is based upon the use of a single unifying postulate. Since the value of different obligations can be compared only if they are accumulated or discounted to the same date, that assumption makes use of a focal date or comparison date, and equates the value of the debt on that date to the value of the payments. The assumption is that for all payments made before that date, the accumulation factor $(1 + ni)$ be used, while for all payments after the focal date, the discount factor $(1 - ni)$ be used.

Let B be the amount of the loan, I, the total charge, R, the periodic payment, n, the number of payments, and i the interest rate per period.

Then to derive the Maximum Yield or Interest at End (or Merchant's Rule) Formula by this assumption, the focal date is taken at the end of the instalment term, i.e., at n periods, giving $(B + ni) = R[1 + (n - 1)i] + R[1 + (n - 2)i] \cdots + R(1 + i) + R$.

Solving this equation for i gives

$$i_{max} = \frac{2I}{n(B + R - I)} = \frac{2I}{B(n + 1) - I(n - 1)} \qquad (19\text{-}1)$$

where i_{max} is the interest rate per period as computed by the Maximum Yield Method.

To derive the Minimum Yield Formula by this assumption, the focal date is taken at the beginning of the instalment term, i.e., thus giving

$$B(1 + ni) = R[1 - (n - 1)i] + R[1 - (n - 2)i] \cdots + R(1 - i) + R.$$

Solving this equation for i gives

$$i_{min} = \frac{2I}{B(n+1) + I(n-1)} \tag{19-2}$$

where i_{min} is the interest rate per period as computed by the Minimum Yield Method, *provided that* the charge is equal to or less than one payment. Obviously this formula will not apply if it is greater. However, a formula can be derived for that case also but is not included in this book. For detailed methods of making instalment computations and, in fact, all calculations related to instalment accounting, the reader is referred to *Neifeld's Guide to Instalment Computations* by M. R. Neifeld, Mack Publishing Company, Easton, Pa., (1953).

To obtain the Constant Ratio Formula, the focal date is taken at the average time, i.e., at $\frac{(n+1)}{2}$ periods, giving

$$i_c = \frac{2I}{B(n+1)} \tag{19-3}$$

where i_c is the interest per period as computed by the Constant Ratio Formula.

As stated above the Direct Ratio Method assumes that the total interest charge is distributed to each instalment in proportion to the outstanding balance at that time. To derive a formula for the interest rate by this method, the average time for the entire loan is computed. Since the principal outstanding for the first period is B, that for the second period is $B - \frac{B}{n}$ etc., the formula for the average time becomes

$$n_{av} = \frac{B \cdot 1 + \left(B - \frac{B}{n}\right) \cdot 2 + \left(B - \frac{2B}{n}\right) \cdot 3 \cdots \left[B - \frac{(n-1)B}{n}\right] \cdot n}{B + \left(B - \frac{B}{n}\right) + \left(B - \frac{2B}{n}\right) \cdots \left[B - \frac{(n-1)B}{n}\right]}$$

$$= \frac{n+2}{3}$$

Placing the focal date at $\frac{(n+2)}{3}$, and using the same derivation as that for i_{max}, i_{min}, and i_c, the following formula is obtained for the interest per period by the direct ratio method.

$$i_D = \frac{6I}{3B(n+1) + I(n-1)} \tag{19-4}$$

where i_D is the interest rate by the Direct Ratio Method. Its error, i.e., difference from the compound interest rate, can be shown to be

$$i - i_D \frac{(n-1)(n+2)i^3}{36} \tag{19-5}$$

Formula (19-4) for i_D above assumes that all payments are equal. However, many instalment payments have an irregular last payment. By the method of derivation already used, the formula for the Direct Ratio Formula can be modified to

$$i_{D\text{-}ir} = \frac{2I}{n(B + Z) + \left(\dfrac{I}{3}\right)(n - 4)} \tag{19-6}$$

where $i_{D\text{-}ir}$ is the interest rate per period by the Direct Ratio Method, and Z is the last irregular payment.

Since all four of the approximate methods cited have some extent of use, although the Direct Ratio Method is the closest to the true, or actuarial value, it is of interest to compute the interest rate on an instalment loan by all four methods. Let us compute the rate on a loan of $360, that is to be paid in 12 monthly instalments of $32.25.

The total charge is (12)($32.25) − $360. = $27.00. Now substituting these values in Formula (19-1) for i_{max} which is

$$i_{max} = \frac{2I}{B(n + 1) - I(n - 1)},$$

we have

$$i_{max} = \frac{2(\$27.00)}{(\$360.00)(12 + 1) - (\$27.00)(12 - 1)}$$

$$= \frac{\$54.00}{(\$4,680.00) - (\$297.00)} = \frac{\$54.00}{\$4,383.00}$$

$$= 1.232\% \text{ monthly or } 14.784\% \text{ annually.}$$

Substituting the above values in Formula (19-2) for i_{min} which is

$$i_{min} = \frac{2I}{B(n + 1) + I(n - 1)}$$

we have

$$i_{min} = \frac{2(\$27.00)}{(\$360.00)(12 + 1) + (\$27.00)(12 - 1)}$$

$$= \frac{\$54.00}{(\$4,680.00) + (\$297.00)} = \frac{\$54.00}{\$4,977.00}$$

$$= 1.085\% \text{ monthly or } 13.020\% \text{ annually.}$$

Substituting the values in this problem in Formula (19-3) for i_c which is

$$i_c = \frac{2I}{B(n + 1)}$$

we have

$$i_c = \frac{2(\$27.00)}{(\$360.00)(12 + 1)} = \frac{\$54.00}{\$4,680.00}$$

$$= 1.154\% \text{ monthly or } 13.848\% \text{ annually.}$$

Substituting the above values from the problem in Formula (19-4) for i_D which is

$$i_D = \frac{6I}{3B(n + 1) + I(n - 1)}$$

we have

$$i_D = \frac{6(\$27.00)}{3(\$360.00)(12 + 1) + \$27.00(12 - 1)}$$

$$= \frac{\$162.00}{\$14,040.00 + \$297.00} = \frac{\$162.00}{\$14,337.00}$$

$$= 1.1300\% \text{ monthly or } 13.560\% \text{ annually.}$$

To compare the interest rates yielded by these approximate methods, with the accurate value obtained by the actuarial method we use Formula (14-14) for the present value of an annuity, to calculate i by the actuarial method.

$$P = Ra_{\overline{n}|i}$$

and obtain values of $a_{\overline{n}|i}$ from Table 14, Chapter 14.

Substituting

$$\$360.00 = (\$32.25)a_{\overline{12}|i}$$

$$a_{\overline{12}|i} = \frac{360.00}{32.25} = 11.16279070$$

From Table 14, Chapter 14, $a_{\overline{12}|1\frac{1}{8}} = 11.16669302$
From Table 14, Chapter 14, $a_{\overline{12}|1\frac{1}{4}} = \underline{11.07931197}$
                   Difference   .08738105

Repeating $a_{\overline{12}|1\frac{1}{8}}$ $= 11.16669302$
Value found above, $a_{\overline{12}|i} = \underline{11.16279070}$
         Difference   .00390232

Therefore $i = 1\frac{1}{8}\% + \frac{0039}{0874}(.125) = 1.1306\%$ monthly or 13.5672% annually.

Recapitulating these values the following comparative results are obtained:

Interest by Maximum Yield Method:
        1.232% monthly; 14.784% annually.
Interest by Minimum Yield Method:
        1.085% monthly; 13.020% annually.

Interest by Constant Ratio Method:
1.154% monthly; 13.848% annually.
Interest by Direct Ratio Method:
1.1300% monthly; 13.560% annually.
Interest by Actuarial Method:
1.1306% monthly; 13.5672% annually.

It appears from the foregoing table that the Direct Ratio Method, of all the four approximate methods discussed here, yields results that are closest to the actuarial figures, and for that reason the Direct Ratio Method is used in two representative problems to follow.

Compute the interest rate, by the Direct Ratio method, on a motor cycle that is sold for $720.00 cash, or a down payment of $240.00 and ten monthly payments of $53.50.

Treat the difference between the cash price and the down payment as the amount of an instalment loan, which is thus $720.00 − $240.00 = $480.00.   The total payments are 10 × $53.50 = $535.00.   Therefore the charge is $535.00 − $480.00 = $55.00.

Substituting in Formula (19-4) for i_D

$$i_D = \frac{6I}{3B(n+1) + I(n-1)}$$

$$= \frac{(6)(\$55.00)}{3(\$480.00)(10+1) + (\$55.00)(10-1)}$$

$$= \frac{\$330.00}{\$15,840 + \$495.}$$

$$= \frac{\$330.00}{\$16,335} = 2.02\% \text{ monthly, or } 24.24\% \text{ annually.}$$

A refrigerator costing $265.00 is bought for a down payment of $5.00 and 12 monthly instalments of $17.75 each.   Find the interest rate by the Direct Ratio method.

The outstanding balance is $265.00 − $5.00 = $260.00.   Substituting in Formula (19-4)

$$I_D = \frac{6I}{3B(n+1) + I(n-1)}$$

$$= \frac{6(\$17.75)}{3(\$260.00)(12+1) + \$17.75(12-1)}$$

$$= \frac{\$106.50}{\$8,580.00 + \$195.25}$$

$$= \frac{\$106.50}{\$8,775.75} = 1.214\% \text{ monthly or } 14.57\% \text{ annually.}$$

As an example of a problem with an irregular payment, find the interest rate on a radio set which is priced for cash at \$620.00, but is sold on credit for \$20.00 down and payment over a period of 2 years, there being 23 monthly payments of \$30.00, and a final payment of \$15.00.

The total amount is 23(\$30.00) + \$15.00 = \$705.00. Therefore the charge is \$705.00 − \$600.00 = \$105.00.

Direct Ratio Formula (19-6) derived for one irregular payment was

$$i_{d\text{-}tr} = \frac{2I}{n(B + Z) + \dfrac{I}{3}(n - 4)}$$

Substituting

$$i_{d\text{-}tr} = \frac{2(\$105.00)}{24(\$600.00 + \$15.00) + \dfrac{\$105}{3}(24 - 4)}$$

$$= \frac{\$210.00}{\$14,760.00 + \$700.00}$$

$$= \frac{\$210.00}{\$15,460.00} = 1.358\% \text{ monthly or } 16.30\% \text{ annually.}$$

Refunds on Anticipated Payments of Instalment Loans

One of the most common methods of determining the refunds to be given on instalment loans for repayment in advance of some of the instalments is the Direct Ratio Method. It provides a relatively simple means of making this calculation, since its charge distribution is based on action, expressed in instalment months. If there were n payment periods in the original loan as arranged, then the action of the payments is

$$R(1 + 2 \cdots + n - 1 + n)$$

as explained earlier in this chapter.

Using Formula (7-5), Chapter 7, for an arithmetical progression,

$$S = \frac{n(f + l)}{2}$$

the total of the above progression is $R\,\dfrac{n(1 + n)}{2}$ and the action per dollar is simply $\dfrac{n(n + 1)}{2}$.

If the number of periods anticipated is n', then their action per dollar is $\dfrac{n'(n' + 1)}{2}$. Therefore the fraction of the charge due for refund is, by this method,

$$\frac{\dfrac{n'(n'+1)}{2}}{\dfrac{n(n+1)}{2}} = \frac{n'(n'+1)}{n(n+1)} \tag{19-7}$$

Conversely, the fraction of the charge retained by the lender is $1 - \dfrac{n'(n'+1)}{n(n+1)}$.

As an example of the use of this method, find the refund by the direct ratio method due a borrower who owes a charge of \$26.80 on an instalment loan payable in 14 monthly payments, if he pays it off at the end of eleven months.

Substituting in above formula,

$$\text{Fraction of Charge Refunded} = \frac{3(3+1)}{14(14+1)} = \frac{12}{210} = 5.714\%.$$

5,714% of \$26.80 = \$1.53.

Note from the foregoing problem that the total charge and the number of periods of the loan and those anticipated is all the information that is necessary to calculate the amount of the rebate.

For convenience, a table of values of the refund fraction $\dfrac{n'(n'+1)}{n(n+1)}$ is given below for anticipating any number of payments in 12-payment instalment loans (Table 20). If loans run for longer periods, the factors can be found by calculation from Formula (19-7).

Another method of rebating instalment loans for anticipated payments is required by certain authorities, such as the Pennsylvania Banking Department for finance companies operating under the Personal Consumer Discount Act. The method is to compute the interest on the full instalments whose payment is anticipated at the original contract rate, which is obtained by dividing the charge by the principal.

As an example of this method a loan of \$300 for one year which carries a charge of \$21 and is payable in 12 monthly instalments of \$26.75 each, on which the borrower anticipates four payments would be computed as follows: contract rate = $\dfrac{\$21}{\$300} = 7\%$. The total amount of the unpaid instalments is 4 × \$26.75 = \$107.00. The interest on \$107.00 at 7% per year, for four months, is \$2.50, which is the amount of rebate to be made to the borrower.

Other methods of refund are based upon the Merchant's Rule which is discussed in Chapter 11. One of these methods applies the Sum of Digits as is exemplified by the following problem: Find the amount of rebate on a loan of \$300 on which the total charges are \$21.00, the loan being payable

TABLE 20—TABLE OF REFUND FACTORS FOR COMPUTING REFUNDS OF UNEARNED DISCOUNT BY THE DIRECT RATIO METHOD (RULE OF 78THS)

Repayment in full at end of	2 Months	3 Months	4 Months	5 Months	6 Months	7 Months	8 Months	9 Months	10 Months	11 Months	12 Months	Repayment in full at end of
1 Month	.33333	.50000	.60000	.66667	.71429	.75000	.77778	.80000	.81818	.83333	.84615	1 Month
2 Months	--	.16667	.30000	.40000	.47619	.53571	.58333	.62222	.65455	.68182	.70513	2 Months
3 Months		--	.10000	.20000	.28571	.35714	.41667	.46667	.50909	.54545	.57692	3 Months
4 Months			--	.06667	.14286	.21429	.27778	.33333	.38182	.42424	.46154	4 Months
5 Months				--	.04762	.10714	.16667	.22222	.27273	.31818	.35897	5 Months
6 Months					--	.03571	.08333	.13333	.18182	.22727	.26923	6 Months
7 Months						--	.02778	.06667	.10909	.15152	.19231	7 Months
8 Months							--	.02222	.05455	.09091	.12821	8 Months
9 Months								--	.01818	.04545	.07692	9 Months
10 Months									--	.01515	.03846	10 Months
11 Months										--	.01282	11 Months
12 Months											--	12 Months

in 12 monthly instalments of $26.75, and on which the borrower anticipates four payments.

The rate of interest is $\dfrac{\$21}{\$300} = 7\%$ per year. This rate is equal to $\tfrac{7}{12}\%$ per month. The number of payment periods anticipated is, by the Rule of Digits, $4 + 3 + 2 + 1 = 10$. Therefore the rebate is $(\$26.75) \times \tfrac{7}{12}\% \times 10 = \$1.56$. From the foregoing problem the general formula for this particular Merchant's Rule method of refund may be written as:

$$\text{Refund} = Ri\,\frac{n'(n' + 1)}{2}. \tag{19-8}$$

As an application of this formula find the amount of refund on a loan of $240, carrying charges of $16, and payable in 10 monthly instalments of $25.60 each, if the borrower anticipates three payments. For substitution in the above formula, R is \$25.60, i is $\dfrac{\$16}{(\$240)(\frac{10}{12})} = 8\%$ annually, or $\tfrac{2}{3}\%$ monthly, and n' is 3, giving amount of rebate $= (\$25.60)(\tfrac{2}{3}\%)\dfrac{3(3 + 1)}{2} = (\$.07067) \times 6 = \$.42$, rebate.

Chapter 20

THE MATHEMATICS OF REAL ESTATE

For the purposes of this chapter, real estate problems, and the mathematical methods for their solution, may be divided into two broad categories, reflecting the viewpoints of (1) those whose interest is from the standpoint of ownership of their own home, and (2), those whose interest is primarily in real estate as a source of income. While obviously these two groups overlap to a considerable extent, and both are interested, to a greater or lesser degree, in all phases of real estate calculations, the arrangement of the topics in the chapter is given in the sequence indicated to facilitate its use for purposes of reference.

Mortgage Calculations

The mortgage constitutes the greatest cash expenditure by those purchasing homes on deferred payments. Therefore, the computation of the amount of those payments, and their distribution between principal and interest, merits first place in this treatment.

At one time mortgages did not carry provisions for payment of principal at stipulated periods and in stipulated amounts (i.e. they had no provision for amortization). Therefore, their proportion of the value of the property was restricted to a figure that was safely in excess of the depreciated value of the property at the end of the term of the mortgage. Other older mortgages provided for periodic payments on principal in amounts unvarying throughout the term of the mortgage. Such mortgages had the disadvantage that the totals of their payments of principal and interest were highest at the beginning of the term, decreasing throughout it as the principal was paid off. Thus, the home buyer was faced with the higher payments in the earlier years of home ownership, when presumably his income, from wages at any rate, was lower.

While these unvarying-payment-on-principal mortgages are still used to some extent, especially as short term mortgages, they present no diffi-

culties in computation. At the end of each period, the simple interest on
the unpaid outstanding principal is computed and paid, along with the
stipulated payment for reduction of principal. The latter is subtracted
from the outstanding principal to determine the amount of principal that
will be outstanding for the next period. The following schedule shows
the calculations for a mortgage of this type.

INTEREST AND PRINCIPAL PAYMENTS
ON 10-YEAR MORTGAGE FOR $3,000.00

Interest 6% per Annum Compounded Annually
Principal Payments of $300.00 Annually

Year	Outstanding Principal	Interest Payment	Principal Payment
1	$3,000.00	$180.00	$300.00
2	2,700.00	162.00	300.00
3	2,400.00	144.00	300.00
4	2,100.00	126.00	300.00
5	1,800.00	108.00	300.00
6	1,500.00	90.00	300.00
7	1,200.00	72.00	300.00
8	900.00	54.00	300.00
9	600.00	36.00	300.00
10	300.00	18.00	300.00

To meet the disadvantage of mortgages with constant principal payments, most home-purchase mortgages today are based on the principle
of equalizing the amount of the periodic payments to cover both interest
and amortization of principal. The system of monthly payments is now
very common, the interest being compounded monthly at $\frac{1}{12}$th of the
annual rate, and the constant monthly payment being computed, (1) to
amortize the mortgage in a stipulated number of years, or (2) to constitute
a stipulated percentage of the initial principal of the mortgage, or other
stipulated amount.

Whichever of these bases is adapted, the mathematical relationship is
that of an ordinary annuity, of which the initial principal is the present
value. Now by Formula (14-4), Chapter 14, the present value of an
ordinary annuity is

$$P = Ra_{\overline{n}|i}$$

where P is the present value, R is the monthly payment, and $a_{\overline{n}|i}$ is the
present value per $1.00 payment given in Table 14.

As an example of this calculation find the monthly payment required to amortize a mortgage of $14,500 in 10 years, with interest at 6%, compounded monthly.

Here $n = 12 \times 10 = 120$ monthly periods

$$i = \tfrac{6}{12} = \tfrac{1}{2}\% \text{ per month.}$$

Substituting in above formula

$$\$14,500 = Ra_{\overline{120}|\frac{1}{2}}$$

From Table 14, $a_{\overline{120}|\frac{1}{2}} = 90.07345333$

Then $R = \dfrac{\$14,500.00}{90.07345333} = \$160.98$

To find the number of payments required for a stipulated monthly payment, e.g. 1% of the initial principal of a mortgage for $14,500.00 at 6% interest compounded monthly:

1% of $14,500.00 = $145.00, the monthly payment.

Then using Formula (14-4), $P = Ra_{\overline{n}|i}$, $\$14,500.00 = (\$145.00)(a_{\overline{n}|\frac{1}{2}})$, so that $100 = a_{\overline{n}|\frac{1}{2}}$.

Now refer to Table 14, Chapter 14, and run down the column for the interest rate of $\frac{1}{2}\%$, to find the value of $a_{\overline{n}|}$ closest below 100. It is 99.51216875, and has a corresponding value in the n column of $n = 138$. Then the present value of 138 payments of $145.00, is $(\$145.00)(a_{\overline{138}|\frac{1}{2}})$ which is $(\$145.00)(99.51216875) = \$14,429.26$. Therefore the last payment has a present value of $\$14,500.00 - \$14,429.26 = \$70.74$. Now, the amount to which this present value will accumulate in 139 periods at $\frac{1}{2}\%$ interest per period, is by Formula (13-1) Chapter 13,

$$S = P(1 + i)^n$$

or $\qquad S = (70.74)(1 + .005)^{139}$

By Table 11 $(1.005)^{139} = 2.00024219$ or $S = (\$70.74)(2.00024219) = \$141.50$. Therefore the mortgage can be amortized by 138 monthly payments of $145.00, and another payment of $141.50.

It is to be noted that the annuity and compound interest tables in this book extend only as far as 150 (or 100) monthly payments. This is ample for the problems encountered in all the chapters of this book, with the exception of this present one. While most mortgages on homes at the present time are amortized over periods of 20, 25 or 30 years, some extend as far as 40 years—which, on a monthly payment basis, would require interest and annuity tables extending to 480 monthly payments. Rather than burden this book with these by adding so many pages, a method for calculating monthly payments by formula is used. The formula used is

Formula 14-5, Chapter 14, for the rent (periodic payment) of an ordinary annuity, which is

$$R = P \frac{i}{1 - (1 + i)^{-n}}$$

where R is the periodic payment, P, the present value, i, the interest rate per period, and n, the number of periods.

To apply this formula, find the amount of the equal monthly payments to amortize a mortgage of \$19.000 in 25 years at 6% per annum interest. Now 6% per annum is $\frac{1}{2}$% per month $= i$, while $n = 12 \times 25 = 300$.

Substituting, $R = (\$19.000) \dfrac{.005}{1 - (1.005)^{-300}}$

From Table 3, Chapter 6, log $1.005 = .002166$
Then, log $(1.005)^{-300} = (-300 \times .002166) = -.6498 = \overline{1}.3502$
From Table 3, Chapter 6, $\overline{1}.3502 =$ antilog $.223975$

Thus $R = (\$19,000) \dfrac{.005}{1 - .223975} = (\$19.000) \dfrac{.005}{.776025} = \$122.42$

In addition to this formula method of computing long-term mortgage payments, and the annuity-table method already discussed, there is also a direct-reading tabular method. For this, see Table 21, which is an amortization table giving the amounts of the constant payments necessary to liquidate a loan of \$1,000.00 in equal payments from 0 to 40 years at various interest rates.

As an example of the use of this table, let us find the monthly payment necessary to liquidate a mortgage of \$12,750, in 25 years at 5% interest.

Find 25 years in Column I of the table, and move across the 25 year row until reaching the Column headed 5%. The figure there, that is, for 25 years and 5%, is \$5.85, the required monthly payment for \$1.000.00. Then the payment for \$12,750.00 is $(12.75)(\$5.85) = \$74.58\frac{3}{4}$.

By using Table 21 in the reverse of the above order, the number of payments for a given mortgage amount can be found. For example, find the number of payments necessary to amortize a mortgage of \$21,500.00 at 5% by payments of \$150.00 per month.

\$150.00 monthly on \$21.500.00 is equivalent to $\dfrac{\$150.00}{21.5}$

$$= \$6.98 \text{ per } \$1000.00.$$

Now run down the 5% column in Table 21 until the figure \$6.98 is reached, and then find the corresponding term of the loan, in Columns 1, 2 and 3. It is 18 years 3 months or 219 monthly payments.

TABLE 21—AMORTIZATION TABLE.

Monthly installments necessary to liquidate a loan in equal payments from 1 to 40 years at the specified interest rate

Term of loan		Number of payments	Monthly installment per thousand dollars including interest—						
Years	Months		At 3¾%	At 4%	At 4¼%	At 4½%	At 4¾%	At 5%	At 5¼%
40	0	480	$4.03	$4.18	$4.34	$4.50	$4.66	$4.83	$4.99
39	11	479	4.03	4.19	4.34	4.50	4.67	4.83	5.00
39	10	478	4.04	4.19	4.35	4.51	4.67	4.83	5.00
39	9	477	4.04	4.20	4.35	4.51	4.67	4.84	5.00
39	8	476	4.04	4.20	4.36	4.51	4.68	4.84	5.01
39	7	475	4.05	4.20	4.36	4.52	4.68	4.84	5.01
39	6	474	4.05	4.21	4.36	4.52	4.68	4.85	5.01
39	5	473	4.06	4.21	4.37	4.52	4.69	4.85	5.02
39	4	472	4.06	4.21	4.37	4.53	4.69	4.85	5.02
39	3	471	4.06	4.22	4.37	4.53	4.69	4.86	5.02
39	2	470	4.07	4.22	4.38	4.53	4.70	4.86	5.03
39	1	469	4.07	4.22	4.38	4.54	4.70	4.86	5.03
39	0	468	4.07	4.23	4.38	4.54	4.70	4.87	5.03
38	11	467	4.08	4.23	4.39	4.55	4.71	4.87	5.03
38	10	466	4.08	4.24	4.39	4.55	4.71	4.87	5.04
38	9	465	4.09	4.24	4.39	4.55	4.71	4.88	5.04
38	8	464	4.09	4.24	4.40	4.56	4.72	4.88	5.04
38	7	463	4.09	4.25	4.40	4.56	4.72	4.88	5.05
38	6	462	4.10	4.25	4.41	4.56	4.72	4.89	5.05
38	5	461	4.10	4.25	4.41	4.57	4.73	4.89	5.05
38	4	460	4.11	4.26	4.41	4.57	4.73	4.89	5.06
38	3	459	4.11	4.26	4.42	4.57	4.73	4.90	5.06
38	2	458	4.11	4.27	4.42	4.58	4.74	4.90	5.07
38	1	457	4.12	4.27	4.43	4.58	4.74	4.90	5.07
38	0	456	4.12	4.27	4.43	4.59	4.75	4.91	5.07
37	11	455	4.13	4.28	4.43	4.59	4.75	4.91	5.08
37	10	454	4.13	4.28	4.44	4.59	4.75	4.92	5.08
37	9	453	4.13	4.29	4.44	4.60	4.76	4.92	5.08
37	8	452	4.14	4.29	4.44	4.60	4.76	4.92	5.09
37	7	451	4.14	4.29	4.45	4.61	4.76	4.93	5.09
37	6	450	4.15	4.30	4.45	4.61	4.77	4.93	5.09
37	5	449	4.15	4.30	4.46	4.61	4.77	4.93	5.10
37	4	448	4.16	4.31	4.46	4.62	4.78	4.94	5.10
37	3	447	4.16	4.31	4.47	4.62	4.78	4.94	5.10
37	2	446	4.16	4.32	4.47	4.63	4.78	4.94	5.11
37	1	445	4.17	4.32	4.47	4.63	4.79	4.95	5.11
37	0	444	4.17	4.32	4.48	4.63	4.79	4.95	5.12
36	11	443	4.18	4.33	4.48	4.64	4.80	4.96	5.12
36	10	442	4.18	4.33	4.49	4.64	4.80	4.96	5.12
36	9	441	4.19	4.34	4.49	4.65	4.80	4.96	5.13
36	8	440	4.19	4.34	4.49	4.65	4.81	4.97	5.13
36	7	439	4.19	4.35	4.50	4.65	4.81	4.97	5.13
36	6	438	4.20	4.35	4.50	4.66	4.82	4.98	5.14
36	5	437	4.20	4.35	4.51	4.66	4.82	4.98	5.14
36	4	436	4.21	4.36	4.51	4.67	4.82	4.98	5.15
36	3	435	4.21	4.36	4.52	4.67	4.83	4.99	5.15
36	2	434	4.22	4.37	4.52	4.68	4.83	4.99	5.15
36	1	433	4.22	4.37	4.52	4.68	4.84	5.00	5.16
36	0	432	4.23	4.38	4.53	4.68	4.84	5.00	5.16
35	11	431	4.23	4.38	4.53	4.69	4.85	5.00	5.17
35	10	430	4.24	4.39	4.54	4.69	4.85	5.01	5.17
35	9	429	4.24	4.39	4.54	4.70	4.85	5.01	5.17
35	8	428	4.25	4.39	4.55	4.70	4.86	5.02	5.18
35	7	427	4.25	4.40	4.55	4.71	4.86	5.02	5.18
35	6	426	4.25	4.40	4.56	4.71	4.87	5.03	5.19
35	5	425	4.26	4.41	4.56	4.71	4.87	5.03	5.19
35	4	424	4.26	4.41	4.57	4.72	4.88	5.03	5.20
35	3	423	4.27	4.42	4.57	4.72	4.88	5.04	5.20
35	2	422	4.27	4.42	4.57	4.73	4.88	5.04	5.20
35	1	421	4.28	4.43	4.58	4.73	4.89	5.05	5.21

TABLE 21—AMORTIZATION TABLE (Cont.)

Monthly installments necessary to liquidate a loan in equal payments from 1 to 40 years at the specified interest rate

Term of loan		Number of payments	Monthly installment per thousand dollars including interest—						
Years	Months		At 3¾%	At 4%	At 4¼%	At 4½%	At 4¾%	At 5%	At 5¼%
35	0	420	4.28	4.43	4.58	4.74	4.89	5.05	$5.21
34	11	419	4.29	4.44	4.59	4.74	4.90	5.06	5.22
34	10	418	4.29	4.44	4.59	4.75	4.90	5.06	5.22
34	9	417	4.30	4.45	4.60	4.75	4.91	5.07	5.23
34	8	416	4.30	4.45	4.60	4.76	4.91	5.07	5.23
34	7	415	4.31	4.46	4.61	4.76	4.92	5.07	5.23
34	6	414	4.31	4.46	4.61	4.77	4.92	5.08	5.24
34	5	413	4.32	4.47	4.62	4.77	4.93	5.08	5.24
34	4	412	4.32	4.47	4.62	4.78	4.93	5.09	5.25
34	3	411	4.33	4.48	4.63	4.78	4.94	5.09	5.25
34	2	410	4.33	4.48	4.63	4.79	4.94	5.10	5.26
34	1	409	4.34	4.49	4.64	4.79	4.95	5.10	5.26
34	0	408	4.35	4.49	4.64	4.80	4.95	5.11	5.27
33	11	407	4.35	4.50	4.65	4.80	4.95	5.11	5.27
33	10	406	4.36	4.50	4.65	4.81	4.96	5.12	5.28
33	9	405	4.36	4.51	4.66	4.81	4.96	5.12	5.28
33	8	404	4.37	4.51	4.66	4.82	4.97	5.13	5.29
33	7	403	4.37	4.52	4.67	4.82	4.97	5.13	5.29
33	6	402	4.38	4.52	4.67	4.83	4.98	5.14	5.29
33	5	401	4.38	4.53	4.68	4.83	4.98	5.14	5.30
33	4	400	4.39	4.54	4.68	4.84	4.99	5.15	5.30
33	3	399	4.39	4.54	4.69	4.84	5.00	5.15	5.31
33	2	398	4.40	4.55	4.70	4.85	5.00	5.16	5.31
33	1	397	4.40	4.55	4.70	4.85	5.01	5.16	5.32
33	0	396	4.41	4.56	4.71	4.86	5.01	5.17	5.32
32	11	395	4.42	4.56	4.71	4.86	5.02	5.17	5.33
32	10	394	4.42	4.57	4.72	4.87	5.02	5.18	5.33
32	9	393	4.43	4.57	4.72	4.87	5.03	5.18	5.34
32	8	392	4.43	4.58	4.73	4.88	5.03	5.19	5.34
32	7	391	4.44	4.59	4.73	4.88	5.04	5.19	5.35
32	6	390	4.44	4.59	4.74	4.89	5.04	5.20	5.35
32	5	389	4.45	4.60	4.74	4.90	5.05	5.20	5.36
32	4	388	4.46	4.60	4.75	4.90	5.05	5.21	5.37
32	3	387	4.46	4.61	4.76	4.91	5.06	5.21	5.37
32	2	386	4.47	4.61	4.76	4.91	5.06	5.22	5.38
32	1	385	4.47	4.62	4.77	4.92	5.07	5.22	5.38
32	0	384	4.48	4.63	4.77	4.92	5.08	5.23	5.39
31	11	383	4.49	4.63	4.78	4.93	5.08	5.24	5.39
31	10	382	4.49	4.64	4.79	4.94	5.09	5.24	5.40
31	9	381	4.50	4.64	4.79	4.94	5.09	5.25	5.40
31	8	380	4.50	4.65	4.80	4.95	5.10	5.25	5.41
31	7	379	4.51	4.66	4.80	4.95	5.10	5.26	5.41
31	6	378	4.52	4.66	4.81	4.96	5.11	5.26	5.42
31	5	377	4.52	4.67	4.82	4.96	5.12	5.27	5.43
31	4	376	4.53	4.67	4.82	4.97	5.12	5.28	5.43
31	3	375	4.54	4.68	4.83	4.98	5.13	5.28	5.44
31	2	374	4.54	4.69	4.83	4.98	5.13	5.29	5.44
31	1	373	4.55	4.69	4.84	4.99	5.14	5.29	5.45
31	0	372	4.56	4.70	4.85	4.99	5.15	5.30	5.45
30	11	371	4.56	4.71	4.85	5.00	5.15	5.30	5.46
30	10	370	4.57	4.71	4.86	5.01	5.16	5.31	5.47
30	9	369	4.58	4.72	4.87	5.01	5.16	5.32	5.47
30	8	368	4.58	4.73	4.87	5.02	5.17	5.32	5.48
30	7	367	4.59	4.73	4.88	5.03	5.18	5.33	5.48
30	6	366	4.60	4.74	4.88	5.03	5.18	5.34	5.49
30	5	365	4.60	4.75	4.89	5.04	5.19	5.34	5.50
30	4	364	4.61	4.75	4.90	5.05	5.20	5.35	5.50
30	3	363	4.62	4.76	4.90	5.05	5.20	5.35	5.51
30	2	362	4.62	4.77	4.91	5.06	5.21	5.36	5.51
30	1	361	4.63	4.77	4.92	5.07	5.21	5.37	5.52

TABLE 21—AMORTIZATION TABLE (Cont.)

Monthly installments necessary to liquidate a loan in equal payments from 1 to 40 years at the specified interest rate

Term of loan		Number of payments	Monthly installment per thousand dollars including interest—						
Years	Months		At 3¾%	At 4%	At 4¼%	At 4½%	At 4¾%	At 5%	At 5¼%
30	0	360	$4.64	$4.78	$4.92	$5.07	$5.22	$5.37	$5.53
29	11	359	4.64	4.79	4.93	5.08	5.23	5.38	5.53
29	10	358	4.65	4.79	4.94	5.09	5.23	5.39	5.54
29	9	357	4.66	4.80	4.94	5.09	5.24	5.39	5.55
29	8	356	4.66	4.81	4.95	5.10	5.25	5.40	5.55
29	7	355	4.67	4.81	4.96	5.11	5.25	5.41	5.56
29	6	354	4.68	4.82	4.97	5.11	5.26	5.41	5.57
29	5	353	4.69	4.83	4.97	5.12	5.27	5.42	5.57
29	4	352	4.69	4.84	4.98	5.13	5.28	5.43	5.58
29	3	351	4.70	4.84	4.99	5.13	5.28	5.43	5.59
29	2	350	4.71	4.85	4.99	5.14	5.29	5.44	5.59
29	1	349	4.72	4.86	5.00	5.15	5.30	5.45	5.60
29	0	348	4.72	4.86	5.01	5.15	5.30	5.45	5.61
28	11	347	4.73	4.87	5.02	5.16	5.31	5.46	5.61
28	10	346	4.74	4.88	5.02	5.17	5.32	5.47	5.62
28	9	345	4.75	4.89	5.03	5.18	5.32	5.47	5.63
28	8	344	4.75	4.89	5.04	5.18	5.33	5.48	5.63
28	7	343	4.76	4.90	5.05	5.19	5.34	5.49	5.64
28	6	342	4.77	4.91	5.05	5.20	5.35	5.50	5.65
28	5	341	4.78	4.92	5.06	5.21	5.35	5.50	5.66
28	4	340	4.78	4.93	5.07	5.21	5.36	5.51	5.66
28	3	339	4.79	4.93	5.08	5.22	5.37	5.52	5.67
28	2	338	4.80	4.94	5.08	5.23	5.38	5.53	5.68
28	1	337	4.81	4.95	5.09	5.24	5.38	5.53	5.69
28	0	336	4.82	4.96	5.10	5.24	5.39	5.54	5.69
27	11	335	4.82	4.97	5.11	5.25	5.40	5.55	5.70
27	10	334	4.83	4.97	5.12	5.26	5.41	5.56	5.71
27	9	333	4.84	4.98	5.12	5.27	5.42	5.56	5.71
27	8	332	4.85	4.99	5.13	5.28	5.42	5.57	5.72
27	7	331	4.86	5.00	5.14	5.28	5.43	5.58	5.73
27	6	330	4.87	5.01	5.15	5.29	5.44	5.59	5.74
27	5	329	4.87	5.01	5.16	5.30	5.45	5.59	5.75
27	4	328	4.88	5.02	5.16	5.31	5.45	5.60	5.75
27	3	327	4.89	5.03	5.17	5.32	5.46	5.61	5.76
27	2	326	4.90	5.04	5.18	5.33	5.47	5.62	5.77
27	1	325	4.91	5.05	5.19	5.33	5.48	5.63	5.78
27	0	324	4.92	5.06	5.20	5.34	5.49	5.64	5.78
26	11	323	4.93	5.07	5.21	5.35	5.50	5.64	5.79
26	10	322	4.94	5.07	5.22	5.36	5.50	5.65	5.80
26	9	321	4.94	5.08	5.22	5.37	5.51	5.66	5.81
26	8	320	4.95	5.09	5.23	5.38	5.52	5.67	5.82
26	7	319	4.96	5.10	5.24	5.39	5.53	5.68	5.83
26	6	318	4.97	5.11	5.25	5.39	5.54	5.69	5.83
26	5	317	4.98	5.12	5.26	5.40	5.55	5.69	5.84
26	4	316	4.99	5.13	5.27	5.41	5.56	5.70	5.85
26	3	315	5.00	5.14	5.28	5.42	5.57	5.71	5.86
26	2	314	5.01	5.15	5.29	5.43	5.57	5.72	5.87
26	1	313	5.02	5.16	5.30	5.44	5.58	5.73	5.88
26	0	312	5.03	5.17	5.31	5.45	5.59	5.74	5.89
25	11	311	5.04	5.17	5.32	5.46	5.60	5.75	5.90
25	10	310	5.05	5.18	5.32	5.47	5.61	5.76	5.90
25	9	309	5.06	5.19	5.33	5.48	5.62	5.77	5.91
25	8	308	5.07	5.20	5.34	5.49	5.63	5.77	5.92
25	7	307	5.08	5.21	5.35	5.49	5.64	5.78	5.93
25	6	306	5.09	5.22	5.36	5.50	5.65	5.79	5.94
25	5	305	5.10	5.23	5.37	5.51	5.66	5.80	5.95
25	4	304	5.11	5.24	5.38	5.52	5.67	5.81	5.96
25	3	303	5.12	5.25	5.39	5.53	5.68	5.82	5.97
25	2	302	5.13	5.26	5.40	5.54	5.69	5.83	5.98
25	1	301	5.14	5.27	5.41	5.55	5.70	5.84	5.99

523

Table 21—Amortization Table (Cont.)

Monthly installments necessary to liquidate a loan in equal payments from 1 to 40 years at the specified interest rate

Term of loan		Number of payments	Monthly installment per thousand dollars including interest—						
Years	Months		At 3¾%	At 4%	At 4¼%	At 4½%	At 4¾%	At 5%	At 5¼%
25	0	300	$5.15	$5.28	$5.42	$5.56	$5.71	$5.85	$6.00
24	11	299	5.16	5.29	5.43	5.57	5.72	5.86	6.01
24	10	298	5.17	5.30	5.44	5.58	5.73	5.87	6.02
24	9	297	5.18	5.31	5.45	5.59	5.74	5.88	6.03
24	8	296	5.19	5.32	5.46	5.60	5.75	5.89	6.04
24	7	295	5.20	5.34	5.47	5.61	5.76	5.90	6.05
24	6	294	5.21	5.35	5.48	5.62	5.77	5.91	6.06
24	5	293	5.22	5.36	5.50	5.64	5.78	5.92	6.07
24	4	292	5.23	5.37	5.51	5.65	5.79	5.93	6.08
24	3	291	5.24	5.38	5.52	5.66	5.80	5.94	6.09
24	2	290	5.25	5.39	5.53	5.67	5.81	5.95	6.10
24	1	289	5.26	5.40	5.54	5.68	5.82	5.96	6.11
24	0	288	5.28	5.41	5.55	5.69	5.83	5.97	6.12
23	11	287	5.29	5.42	5.56	5.70	5.84	5.98	6.13
23	10	286	5.30	5.43	5.57	5.71	5.85	6.00	6.14
23	9	285	5.31	5.45	5.58	5.72	5.86	6.01	6.15
23	8	284	5.32	5.46	5.59	5.73	5.87	6.02	6.16
23	7	283	5.33	5.47	5.61	5.75	5.89	6.03	6.17
23	6	282	5.35	5.48	5.62	5.76	5.90	6.04	6.18
23	5	281	5.36	5.49	5.63	5.77	5.91	6.05	6.20
23	4	280	5.37	5.50	5.64	5.78	5.92	6.06	6.21
23	3	279	5.38	5.52	5.65	5.79	5.93	6.07	6.22
23	2	278	5.39	5.53	5.66	5.80	5.94	6.09	6.23
23	1	277	5.41	5.54	5.68	5.82	5.96	6.10	6.24
23	0	276	5.42	5.55	5.69	5.83	5.97	6.11	6.25
22	11	275	5.43	5.56	5.70	5.84	5.98	6.12	6.26
22	10	274	5.44	5.58	5.71	5.85	5.99	6.13	6.28
22	9	273	5.46	5.59	5.73	5.86	6.00	6.14	6.29
22	8	272	5.47	5.60	5.74	5.88	6.02	6.16	6.30
22	7	271	5.48	5.62	5.75	5.89	6.03	6.17	6.31
22	6	270	5.49	5.63	5.76	5.90	6.04	6.18	6.32
22	5	269	5.51	5.64	5.78	5.91	6.05	6.19	6.34
22	4	268	5.52	5.65	5.79	5.93	6.07	6.21	6.35
22	3	267	5.53	5.67	5.80	5.94	6.08	6.22	6.36
22	2	266	5.55	5.68	5.82	5.95	6.09	6.23	6.37
22	1	265	5.56	5.69	5.83	5.97	6.10	6.24	6.39
22	0	264	5.57	5.71	5.84	5.98	6.12	6.26	6.40
21	11	263	5.59	5.72	5.86	5.99	6.13	6.27	6.41
21	10	262	5.60	5.73	5.87	6.01	6.14	6.28	6.43
21	9	261	5.61	5.75	5.88	6.02	6.16	6.30	6.44
21	8	260	5.63	5.76	5.90	6.03	6.17	6.31	6.45
21	7	259	5.64	5.78	5.91	6.05	6.18	6.32	6.47
21	6	258	5.66	5.79	5.92	6.06	6.20	6.34	6.48
21	5	257	5.67	5.80	5.94	6.07	6.21	6.35	6.49
21	4	256	5.69	5.82	5.95	6.09	6.23	6.37	6.51
21	3	255	5.70	5.83	5.97	6.10	6.24	6.38	6.52
21	2	254	5.71	5.85	5.98	6.12	6.25	6.39	6.53
21	1	253	5.73	5.86	6.00	6.13	6.27	6.41	6.55
21	0	252	5.74	5.88	6.01	6.15	6.28	6.42	6.56
20	11	251	5.76	5.89	6.03	6.16	6.30	6.44	6.58
20	10	250	5.77	5.91	6.04	6.18	6.31	6.45	6.59
20	9	249	5.79	5.92	6.06	6.19	6.33	6.47	6.61
20	8	248	5.81	5.94	6.07	6.21	6.34	6.48	6.62
20	7	247	5.82	5.95	6.09	6.22	6.36	6.50	6.64
20	6	246	5.84	5.97	6.10	6.24	6.37	6.51	6.65
20	5	245	5.85	5.98	6.12	6.25	6.39	6.53	6.67
20	4	244	5.87	6.00	6.13	6.27	6.40	6.54	6.68
20	3	243	5.88	6.02	6.15	6.28	6.42	6.56	6.70
20	2	242	5.90	6.03	6.16	6.30	6.44	6.57	6.71
20	1	241	5.92	6.05	6.18	6.32	6.45	6.59	6.73

524

TABLE 21—AMORTIZATION TABLE (Cont.)

Monthly installments necessary to liquidate a loan in equal payments from 1 to 40 years at the specified interest rate

Term of loan		Number of payments	Monthly installment per thousand dollars including interest—						
Years	Months		At 3¾%	At 4%	At 4¼%	At 4½%	At 4¾%	At 5%	At 5¼%
20	0	240	5.93	6.06	6.20	6.33	6.47	6.60	$6.74
19	11	239	5.95	6.08	6.21	6.35	6.48	6.62	6.76
19	10	238	5.97	6.10	6.23	6.36	6.50	6.64	6.78
19	9	237	5.98	6.11	6.25	6.38	6.52	6.65	6.79
19	8	236	6.00	6.13	6.26	6.40	6.53	6.67	6.81
19	7	235	6.02	6.15	6.28	6.41	6.55	6.69	6.82
19	6	234	6.04	6.17	6.30	6.43	6.57	6.70	6.84
19	5	233	6.05	6.18	6.32	6.45	6.58	6.72	6.86
19	4	232	6.07	6.20	6.33	6.47	6.60	6.74	6.88
19	3	231	6.09	6.22	6.35	6.48	6.62	6.75	6.89
19	2	230	6.11	6.24	6.37	6.50	6.64	6.77	6.91
19	1	229	6.13	6.26	6.39	6.52	6.65	6.79	6.93
19	0	228	6.14	6.27	6.40	6.54	6.67	6.81	6.95
18	11	227	6.16	6.29	6.42	6.56	6.69	6.83	6.96
18	10	226	6.18	6.31	6.44	6.57	6.71	6.84	6.98
18	9	225	6.20	6.33	6.46	6.59	6.73	6.86	7.00
18	8	224	6.22	6.35	6.48	6.61	6.75	6.88	7.02
18	7	223	6.24	6.37	6.50	6.63	6.76	6.90	7.04
18	6	222	6.26	6.39	6.52	6.65	6.78	6.92	7.05
18	5	221	6.28	6.41	6.54	6.67	6.80	6.94	7.07
18	4	220	6.30	6.43	6.56	6.69	6.82	6.96	7.09
18	3	219	6.32	6.45	6.58	6.71	6.84	6.98	7.11
18	2	218	6.34	6.47	6.60	6.73	6.86	7.00	7.13
18	1	217	6.36	6.49	6.62	6.75	6.88	7.02	7.15
18	0	216	6.38	6.51	6.64	6.77	6.90	7.04	7.17
17	11	215	6.40	6.53	6.66	6.79	6.92	7.06	7.19
17	10	214	6.42	6.55	6.68	6.81	6.94	7.08	7.21
17	9	213	6.44	6.57	6.70	6.83	6.96	7.10	7.23
17	8	212	6.46	6.59	6.72	6.85	6.98	7.12	7.25
17	7	211	6.48	6.61	6.74	6.87	7.00	7.14	7.27
17	6	210	6.51	6.63	6.76	6.89	7.03	7.16	7.29
17	5	209	6.53	6.66	6.79	6.92	7.05	7.18	7.32
17	4	208	6.55	6.68	6.81	6.94	7.07	7.20	7.34
17	3	207	6.57	6.70	6.83	6.96	7.09	7.22	7.36
17	2	206	6.60	6.72	6.85	6.98	7.11	7.25	7.38
17	1	205	6.62	6.75	6.87	7.00	7.14	7.27	7.40
17	0	204	6.64	6.77	6.90	7.03	7.16	7.29	7.43
16	11	203	6.67	6.79	6.92	7.05	7.18	7.31	7.45
16	10	202	6.69	6.82	6.94	7.07	7.20	7.34	7.47
16	9	201	6.71	6.84	6.97	7.10	7.23	7.36	7.49
16	8	200	6.74	6.86	6.99	7.12	7.25	7.38	7.52
16	7	199	6.76	6.89	7.02	7.15	7.28	7.41	7.54
16	6	198	6.79	6.91	7.04	7.17	7.30	7.43	7.57
16	5	197	6.81	6.94	7.06	7.19	7.32	7.46	7.59
16	4	196	6.84	6.96	7.09	7.22	7.35	7.48	7.61
16	3	195	6.86	6.99	7.11	7.24	7.37	7.51	7.64
16	2	194	6.89	7.01	7.14	7.27	7.40	7.53	7.66
16	1	193	6.91	7.04	7.17	7.29	7.42	7.56	7.69
16	0	192	6.94	7.06	7.19	7.32	7.45	7.58	7.71
15	11	191	6.97	7.09	7.22	7.35	7.48	7.61	7.74
15	10	190	6.99	7.12	7.25	7.37	7.50	7.63	7.77
15	9	189	7.02	7.15	7.27	7.40	7.53	7.66	7.79
15	8	188	7.05	7.17	7.30	7.43	7.56	7.69	7.82
15	7	187	7.07	7.20	7.33	7.45	7.58	7.71	7.85
15	6	186	7.10	7.23	7.35	7.48	7.61	7.74	7.87
15	5	185	7.13	7.26	7.38	7.51	7.64	7.77	7.90
15	4	184	7.16	7.28	7.41	7.54	7.67	7.80	7.93
15	3	183	7.19	7.31	7.44	7.57	7.70	7.83	7.96
15	2	182	7.22	7.34	7.47	7.60	7.72	7.85	7.99
15	1	181	7.25	7.37	7.50	7.63	7.75	7.88	8.01

TABLE 21—AMORTIZATION TABLE (Cont.)

Monthly installments necessary to liquidate a loan in equal payments from 1 to 40 years at the specified interest rate

Term of loan		Number of payments	Monthly installment per thousand dollars including interest—						
Years	Months		At 3¾%	At 4%	At 4¼%	At 4½%	At 4¾%	At 5%	At 5¼%
15	0	180	7.28	7.40	7.53	7.65	7.78	7.91	$8.04
14	11	179	7.31	7.43	7.56	7.68	7.81	7.94	8.07
14	10	178	7.34	7.46	7.59	7.72	7.84	7.97	8.10
14	9	177	7.37	7.49	7.62	7.75	7.87	8.00	8.13
14	8	176	7.40	7.52	7.65	7.78	7.90	8.03	8.16
14	7	175	7.43	7.56	7.68	7.81	7.94	8.06	8.20
14	6	174	7.46	7.59	7.71	7.84	7.97	8.10	8.23
14	5	173	7.50	7.62	7.75	7.87	8.00	8.13	8.26
14	4	172	7.53	7.65	7.78	7.90	8.03	8.16	8.29
14	3	171	7.56	7.69	7.81	7.94	8.06	8.19	8.32
14	2	170	7.60	7.72	7.84	7.97	8.10	8.23	8.36
14	1	169	7.63	7.75	7.88	8.00	8.13	8.26	8.39
14	0	168	7.67	7.79	7.91	8.04	8.17	8.29	8.42
13	11	167	7.70	7.82	7.95	8.07	8.20	8.33	8.46
13	10	166	7.74	7.86	7.98	8.11	8.23	8.36	8.49
13	9	165	7.77	7.89	8.02	8.14	8.27	8.40	8.53
13	8	164	7.81	7.93	8.05	8.18	8.31	8.43	8.56
13	7	163	7.84	7.97	8.09	8.22	8.34	8.47	8.60
13	6	162	7.88	8.00	8.13	8.25	8.38	8.51	8.63
13	5	161	7.92	8.04	8.17	8.29	8.42	8.54	8.67
13	4	160	7.96	8.08	8.20	8.33	8.45	8.58	8.71
13	3	159	8.00	8.12	8.24	8.37	8.49	8.62	8.75
13	2	158	8.03	8.16	8.28	8.40	8.53	8.66	8.78
13	1	157	8.07	8.20	8.32	8.44	8.57	8.70	8.82
13	0	156	8.11	8.24	8.36	8.48	8.61	8.74	8.86
12	11	155	8.15	8.28	8.40	8.52	8.65	8.78	8.90
12	10	154	8.20	8.32	8.44	8.56	8.69	8.82	8.94
12	9	153	8.24	8.36	8.48	8.61	8.73	8.86	8.98
12	8	152	8.28	8.40	8.52	8.65	8.77	8.90	9.03
12	7	151	8.32	8.44	8.57	8.69	8.82	8.94	9.07
12	6	150	8.37	8.49	8.61	8.73	8.86	8.98	9.11
12	5	149	8.41	8.53	8.65	8.78	8.90	9.03	9.15
12	4	148	8.45	8.58	8.70	8.82	8.95	9.07	9.20
12	3	147	8.50	8.62	8.74	8.87	8.99	9.12	9.24
12	2	146	8.55	8.67	8.79	8.91	9.04	9.16	9.29
12	1	145	8.59	8.71	8.84	8.96	9.08	9.21	9.33
12	0	144	8.64	8.76	8.88	9.01	9.13	9.25	9.38
11	11	143	8.69	8.81	8.93	9.05	9.18	9.30	9.43
11	10	142	8.74	8.86	8.98	9.10	9.22	9.35	9.47
11	9	141	8.78	8.91	9.03	9.15	9.27	9.40	9.52
11	8	140	8.83	8.96	9.08	9.20	9.32	9.45	9.57
11	7	139	8.89	9.01	9.13	9.25	9.37	9.50	9.62
11	6	138	8.94	9.06	9.18	9.30	9.42	9.55	9.67
11	5	137	8.99	9.11	9.23	9.35	9.48	9.60	9.72
11	4	136	9.04	9.16	9.28	9.41	9.53	9.65	9.78
11	3	135	9.10	9.22	9.34	9.46	9.58	9.71	9.83
11	2	134	9.15	9.27	9.39	9.51	9.64	9.76	9.88
11	1	133	9.21	9.33	9.45	9.57	9.69	9.81	9.94
11	0	132	9.26	9.38	9.50	9.62	9.75	9.87	9.99
10	11	131	9.32	9.44	9.56	9.68	9.80	9.93	10.05
10	10	130	9.38	9.50	9.62	9.74	9.86	9.98	10.11
10	9	129	9.44	9.56	9.68	9.80	9.92	10.04	10.17
10	8	128	9.50	9.62	9.74	9.86	9.98	10.10	10.22
10	7	127	9.56	9.68	9.80	9.92	10.04	10.16	10.28
10	6	126	9.62	9.74	9.86	9.98	10.10	10.22	10.35
10	5	125	9.68	9.80	9.92	10.04	10.16	10.28	10.41
10	4	124	9.75	9.86	9.98	10.10	10.23	10.35	10.47
10	3	123	9.81	9.93	10.05	10.17	10.29	10.41	10.54
10	2	122	9.88	9.99	10.11	10.23	10.36	10.48	10.60
10	1	121	9.94	10.06	10.18	10.30	10.42	10.54	10.67

TABLE 21—AMORTIZATION TABLE (Cont.)

Monthly installments necessary to liquidate a loan in equal payments from 1 to 40 years at the specified interest rate

Term of loan		Number of payments	Monthly installment per thousand dollars including interest—						
Years	Months		At 3¾%	At 4%	At 4¼%	At 4½%	At 4¾%	At 5%	At 5¼%
10	0	120	10.01	10.13	10.25	10.37	10.49	10.61	$10.73
9	11	119	10.08	10.20	10.32	10.44	10.56	10.68	10.80
9	10	118	10.15	10.27	10.39	10.51	10.63	10.75	10.87
9	9	117	10.22	10.34	10.46	10.58	10.70	10.82	10.94
9	8	116	10.30	10.41	10.53	10.65	10.77	10.89	11.02
9	7	115	10.37	10.49	10.61	10.73	10.85	10.97	11.09
9	6	114	10.45	10.56	10.68	10.80	10.92	11.04	11.16
9	5	113	10.52	10.64	10.76	10.88	11.00	11.12	11.24
9	4	112	10.60	10.72	10.84	10.96	11.08	11.20	11.32
9	3	111	10.68	10.80	10.92	11.04	11.16	11.28	11.40
9	2	110	10.76	10.88	11.00	11.12	11.24	11.36	11.48
9	1	109	10.84	10.96	11.08	11.20	11.32	11.44	11.56
9	0	108	10.93	11.05	11.16	11.28	11.40	11.52	11.64
8	11	107	11.01	11.13	11.25	11.37	11.49	11.61	11.73
8	10	106	11.10	11.22	11.34	11.46	11.57	11.69	11.82
8	9	105	11.19	11.31	11.43	11.54	11.66	11.78	11.90
8	8	104	11.28	11.40	11.52	11.63	11.75	11.87	11.99
8	7	103	11.37	11.49	11.61	11.73	11.85	11.97	12.09
8	6	102	11.47	11.59	11.70	11.82	11.94	12.06	12.18
8	5	101	11.57	11.68	11.80	11.92	12.04	12.16	12.28
8	4	100	11.66	11.78	11.90	12.02	12.13	12.25	12.37
8	3	99	11.76	11.88	12.00	12.12	12.23	12.35	12.47
8	2	98	11.87	11.98	12.10	12.22	12.34	12.45	12.57
8	1	97	11.97	12.09	12.20	12.32	12.44	12.56	12.68
8	0	96	12.08	12.19	12.31	12.43	12.55	12.66	12.78
7	11	95	12.19	12.30	12.42	12.54	12.65	12.77	12.89
7	10	94	12.30	12.41	12.53	12.65	12.77	12.88	13.00
7	9	93	12.41	12.53	12.64	12.76	12.88	13.00	13.12
7	8	92	12.53	12.64	12.76	12.88	12.99	13.11	13.23
7	7	91	12.65	12.76	12.88	13.00	13.11	13.23	13.35
7	6	90	12.77	12.88	13.00	13.12	13.23	13.35	13.47
7	5	89	12.89	13.01	13.12	13.24	13.36	13.48	13.59
7	4	88	13.02	13.14	13.25	13.37	13.48	13.60	13.72
7	3	87	13.15	13.27	13.38	13.50	13.61	13.73	13.85
7	2	86	13.28	13.40	13.51	13.63	13.75	13.86	13.98
7	1	85	13.42	13.53	13.65	13.77	13.88	14.00	14.12
7	0	84	13.56	13.67	13.79	13.91	14.02	14.14	14.26
6	11	83	13.70	13.82	13.93	14.05	14.16	14.28	14.40
6	10	82	13.85	13.96	14.08	14.19	14.31	14.43	14.54
6	9	81	14.00	14.11	14.23	14.34	14.46	14.58	14.69
6	8	80	14.15	14.27	14.38	14.50	14.61	14.73	14.85
6	7	79	14.31	14.42	14.54	14.65	14.77	14.89	15.00
6	6	78	14.47	14.59	14.70	14.82	14.93	15.05	15.16
6	5	77	14.64	14.75	14.87	14.98	15.10	15.21	15.33
6	4	76	14.81	14.92	15.04	15.15	15.27	15.38	15.50
6	3	75	14.98	15.10	15.21	15.33	15.44	15.56	15.67
6	2	74	15.16	15.28	15.39	15.51	15.62	15.74	15.85
6	1	73	15.35	15.46	15.57	15.69	15.80	15.92	16.04
6	0	72	15.54	15.65	15.76	15.88	15.99	16.11	16.23
5	11	71	15.73	15.85	15.96	16.07	16.19	16.30	16.42
5	10	70	15.93	16.05	16.16	16.27	16.39	16.50	16.62
5	9	69	16.14	16.25	16.37	16.48	16.60	16.71	16.83
5	8	68	16.35	16.46	16.58	16.69	16.81	16.92	17.04
5	7	67	16.57	16.68	16.80	16.91	17.03	17.14	17.26
5	6	66	16.80	16.91	17.02	17.14	17.25	17.37	17.48
5	5	65	17.03	17.14	17.26	17.37	17.48	17.60	17.71
5	4	64	17.27	17.38	17.50	17.61	17.72	17.84	17.95
5	3	63	17.52	17.63	17.74	17.86	17.97	18.09	18.20
5	2	62	17.77	17.88	18.00	18.11	18.23	18.34	18.46
5	1	61	18.04	18.15	18.26	18.38	18.49	18.60	18.72

TABLE 21—AMORTIZATION TABLE (Cont.)

Monthly installments necessary to liquidate a loan in equal payments from 1 to 40 years at the specified interest rate

Term of loan		Number of payments	Monthly installment per thousand dollars including interest—						
Years	Months		At 3¾%	At 4%	At 4¼%	At 4½%	At 4¾%	At 5%	At 5¼%
5	0	60	18. 31	18. 42	18. 53	18. 65	18. 76	18. 88	$18.99
4	11	59	18. 59	18. 70	18. 82	18. 93	19. 04	19. 16	19.27
4	10	58	18. 88	19. 00	19. 11	19. 22	19. 34	19. 45	19.56
4	9	57	19. 19	19. 30	19. 41	19. 52	19. 64	19. 75	19.87
4	8	56	19. 50	19. 61	19. 72	19. 84	19. 95	20. 06	20.18
4	7	55	19. 82	19. 93	20. 05	20. 16	20. 27	20. 39	20.50
4	6	54	20. 16	20. 27	20. 38	20. 50	20. 61	20. 72	20.84
4	5	53	20. 51	20. 62	20. 73	20. 85	20. 96	21. 07	21.19
4	4	52	20. 87	20. 98	21. 09	21. 21	21. 32	21. 43	21.55
4	3	51	21. 25	21. 36	21. 47	21. 58	21. 70	21. 81	21.92
4	2	50	21. 64	21. 75	21. 86	21. 98	22. 09	22. 20	22.32
4	1	49	22. 05	22. 16	22. 27	22. 38	22. 50	22. 61	22.72
4	0	48	22. 47	22. 58	22. 70	22. 81	22. 92	23. 03	23.15
3	11	47	22. 92	23. 03	23. 14	23. 25	23. 36	23. 48	23.59
3	10	46	23. 38	23. 49	23. 60	23. 71	23. 83	23. 94	24.05
3	9	45	23. 86	23. 97	24. 08	24. 20	24. 31	24. 42	24.53
3	8	44	24. 37	24. 48	24. 59	24. 70	24. 81	24. 93	25.04
3	7	43	24. 89	25. 01	25. 12	25. 23	25. 34	25. 45	25.57
3	6	42	25. 45	25. 56	25. 67	25. 78	25. 90	26. 01	26.12
3	5	41	26. 03	26. 14	26. 25	26. 36	26. 48	26. 59	26.70
3	4	40	26. 64	26. 75	26. 86	26. 97	27. 09	27. 20	27.31
3	3	39	27. 28	27. 39	27. 50	27. 61	27. 73	27. 84	27.95
3	2	38	27. 96	28. 07	28. 18	28. 29	28. 40	28. 51	28.63
3	1	37	28. 67	28. 78	28. 89	29. 00	29. 11	29. 23	29.34
3	0	36	29. 42	29. 53	29. 64	29. 75	29. 86	29. 98	30.09
2	11	35	30. 21	30. 32	30. 43	30. 55	30. 66	30. 77	30.88
2	10	34	31. 05	31. 16	31. 28	31. 39	31. 50	31. 61	31.72
2	9	33	31. 94	32. 06	32. 17	32. 28	32. 39	32. 50	32.61
2	8	32	32. 89	33. 00	33. 11	33. 23	33. 34	33. 45	33.56
2	7	31	33. 90	34. 01	34. 12	34. 23	34. 35	34. 46	34.57
2	6	30	34. 98	35. 09	35. 20	35. 31	35. 42	35. 53	35.65
2	5	29	36. 13	36. 24	36. 35	36. 46	36. 57	36. 68	36.80
2	4	28	37. 36	37. 47	37. 58	37. 69	37. 81	37. 92	38.03
2	3	27	38. 68	38. 80	38. 91	39. 02	39. 13	39. 24	39.35
2	2	26	40. 11	40. 22	40. 33	40. 44	40. 56	40. 67	40.78
2	1	25	41. 65	41. 76	41. 87	41. 98	42. 10	42. 21	42.32
2	0	24	43. 32	43. 43	43. 54	43. 65	43. 76	43. 88	43.99
1	11	23	45. 13	45. 24	45. 36	45. 47	45. 58	45. 69	45.80
1	10	22	47. 11	47. 22	47. 33	47. 45	47. 56	47. 67	47.78
1	9	21	49. 28	49. 39	49. 50	49. 61	49. 72	49. 84	49.95
1	8	20	51. 66	51. 77	51. 89	52. 00	52. 11	52. 22	52.33
1	7	19	54. 30	54. 41	54. 52	54. 63	54. 74	54. 86	54.97
1	6	18	57. 22	57. 34	57. 45	57. 56	57. 67	57. 79	57.90
1	5	17	60. 50	60. 61	60. 72	60. 83	60. 95	61. 06	61.17
1	4	16	64. 18	64. 29	64. 40	64. 52	64. 63	64. 74	64.85
1	3	15	68. 35	68. 46	68. 58	68. 69	68. 80	68. 92	69.03
1	2	14	73. 12	73. 23	73. 35	73. 46	73. 57	73. 69	73.80
1	1	13	78. 62	78. 73	78. 85	78. 96	79. 08	79. 19	79.30
1	0	12	85. 04	85. 15	85. 27	85. 38	85. 50	85. 61	85.73

Cash Expenditures of Home Ownership

The purpose of this section is to list the cash expenditures required in the normal course of home ownership, where the home is subject to a mortgage that is to be amortized. This list provides the home owner, or more particularly, the prospective home owner, with a means of checking, and often of determining, the various items, both of capital and expense, which make up the total cash requirement of home ownership.

I. *Payments of Interest, and Amortization of Mortgage.* The preceding section gives methods for computing these figures, or else the single figure that is their sum.

II. *Insurance.* In many tabulations of home costs, the insurance figure is restricted to the insurable risks of damage to, or destruction of the house, as by fire, wind, and similar agencies. However, many home owners today carry other types of insurance, such as liability insurance against personal injury. While one may question whether all the cost of such comprehensive insurance should be considered to be a cost of home ownership, it is nevertheless a cash expenditure to be made. While the cost of insurance varies widely with the construction of the house, the availability of fire fighting agencies and facilities and many other factors, it generally is $\frac{1}{2}$-1% of the value or original cost of the home.

III. *Repairs.* The item of repairs constitutes the most difficult cash expenditure to estimate or even to define. As is explained in the following section, repairs do not properly include expenditures necessary to prevent obsolescence of major items of equipment, but only those necessary to avoid excessive depreciation. Thus, to replace an outmoded furnace is not a repair, in the sense that it is an unavoidable cost, but to replace a worn out furnace, or one that has deteriorated to the extent that its fuel cost is excessive, is a repair that the home owner may be obliged to make. For houses that are not "old" or badly depreciated, repair costs may be expected to be $\frac{1}{2}$-1$\frac{1}{2}$% of the value or original cost of the house.

IV. *Heat, Light and Power.* The item of heating depends, not only on the geographical location of the home, but also upon its condition and the efficiency of its heating system, as well upon the fuel used and its unit cost. While the heating cost may be negligible in the far South (except for hot water and cooking), there may be an offsetting expense for air conditioning. Lighting and power are items that are included here only as reminders, since they are rarely furnished in rented quarters, and therefore are not to be considered as expenditures attributable to home ownership.

V. *Taxes.* Taxes are, of course, the most variable charge of all. It is fortunate, therefore, that they can be determined before buying a home, in the great majority of instances, by application to the local government.

Cost of Home Ownership

The costs of home ownership differ in many ways from the cash expenditures, as outlined in the preceding section. The greatest difference, in dollar amount, is usually in the items of amortization and interest, since the former is not a cost at all, while the interest cost usually exceeds the interest cash payment.

I. *Interest.* The interest cost of a home should obviously include (1) the interest actually paid on the mortgage, and (2) the interest on the owner's equity, less any depreciation that has been taken. (1) The interest paid on the mortgage can be determined, in cases where a single payment is computed for the sum of interest and principal payment, by constructing an amortization schedule as explained in Chapter 16. (The interest for the first period is computed on the initial principal of the mortgage, the difference between the periodic payment and that interest is the amount to be subtracted from the initial principal to give the principal at the beginning of the second period, etc.). An example of a mortgage loan amortization schedule is given in Table 22. This differs from many such schedules in that it carries the mortgage insurance premium in its second column of figures. In this chapter, however, mortgage insurance is considered to be included in the mortgage interest payments, in contrast with the FHA practice.

The sum of the original down payment, plus the total reduction to the given date in the principal of the mortgage, is the owners equity; in other words, it is the original cost less the balance of principal due on the mortgage. This equity, less the depreciation to date, is the theoretical amount which the owner could obtain by selling the house. The interest on this sum, at a fair rate for this type of investment, is a proper cost of home ownership, and should be added to the interest paid on the mortgage to obtain the total interest cost to the owner.

Note that in the preceding paragraph, mention was made of the fair rate of interest on an investment in a home. Further discussion of this rate is given in the concluding section of this chapter, "Appraisal of Real Estate." Furthermore, the assumption that the theoretical amount which the owner could obtain by selling the house is his equity less depreciation, implies that any change in market value other than that due to depreciation, such as that due to inflation or deflation, is to be regarded as a capital gain or loss on the investment, and should not enter into depreciation calculations.

II. *Depreciation.* There are more ways than one of defining depreciation, and more methods than one of computing it after it has been defined. As is shown later in this chapter, in the replacement cost method of valu-

TABLE 22

Payment No.	Mortgage Insurance Premium 1/2%	Payment to Interest 4-1/2%	Payment to Principal	Total Periodic Payment	Balance Due
	$49.28				$10,000.00
1	3.97	$37.50	$25.80	$67.27	9,974.20
2	3.97	37.40	25.90	67.27	9,948.30
3	3.97	37.31	25.99	67.27	9,922.31
4	3.97	37.21	26.09	67.27	9,896.22
5	3.97	37.11	26.19	67.27	9,870.03
6	3.97	37.01	26.29	67.27	9,843.74
7	3.97	36.91	26.39	67.27	9,817.35
8	3.97	36.82	26.48	67.27	9,790.87
9	3.97	36.72	26.58	67.27	9,764.29
10	3.97	36.62	26.68	67.27	9,737.61
11	3.97	36.52	26.78	67.27	9,710.83
12	3.97	36.42	26.88	67.27	9,683.95
	47.64	443.55	316.05	807.24	
13	3.83	36.31	26.99	67.13	9,656.96
14	3.83	36.21	27.09	67.13	9,629.87
15	3.83	36.11	27.19	67.13	9,602.68
16	3.83	36.01	27.29	67.13	9,575.39
17	3.83	35.91	27.39	67.13	9,548.00
18	3.83	35.81	27.49	67.13	9,520.51
19	3.83	35.70	27.60	67.13	9,492.91
20	3.83	35.60	27.70	67.13	9,465.21
21	3.83	35.49	27.81	67.13	9,437.40
22	3.83	35.39	27.91	67.13	9,409.49
23	3.83	35.29	28.01	67.13	9,381.48
24	3.83	35.18	28.12	67.13	9,353.36
	45.96	429.01	330.59	805.56	
25	3.69	35.08	28.22	66.99	9,325.14
26	3.69	34.97	28.33	66.99	9,296.81
27	3.69	34.86	28.44	66.99	9.268.37
28	3.69	34.76	28.54	66.99	9,239.83
29	3.69	34.65	28.65	66.99	9,211.18
30	3.69	34.54	28.76	66.99	9,182.42
31	3.69	34.43	28.87	66.99	9.153.55
32	3.69	34.33	28.97	66.99	9,124.58
33	3.69	34.22	29.08	66.99	9,095.50
34	3.69	34.11	29.19	66.99	9,066.31
35	3.69	34.00	29.30	66.99	9,037.01
36	3.69	33.89	29.41	66.99	9,007.60
	44.28	413.84	345.76	803.88	

TABLE 22 (Cont.)

Payment No.	Mortgage Insurance Premium 1/2%	Payment to Interest 4-1/2%	Payment to Principal	Total Periodic Payment	Balance Due
37	$3.53	$33.78	$29.52	$66.83	$8,978.08
38	3.53	33.67	29.63	66.83	8,948.45
39	3.53	33.56	29.74	66.83	8,918.71
40	3.53	33.45	29.85	66.83	8,888.86
41	3.53	33.33	29.97	66.83	8,858.89
42	3.53	33.22	30.08	66.83	8,828.81
43	3.53	33.11	30.19	66.83	8,798.62
44	3.53	32.99	30.31	66.83	8,768.31
45	3.53	32.88	30.42	66.83	8,737.89
46	3.53	32.77	30.53	66.83	8,707.36
47	3.53	32.65	30.65	66.83	8,676.71
48	3.53	32.54	30.76	66.83	8,645.95
	42.36	397.95	361.65	801.96	
49	3.37	32.42	30.88	66.67	8,615.07
50	3.37	32.31	30.99	66.67	8,584.08
51	3.37	32.19	31.11	66.67	8,552.97
52	3.37	32.07	31.23	66.67	8,521.74
53	3.37	31.96	31.34	66.67	8,490.40
54	3.37	31.84	31.46	66.67	8,458.94
55	3.37	31.72	31.58	66.67	8,427.36
56	3.37	31.60	31.70	66.67	8,395.66
57	3.37	31.48	31.82	66.67	8,363.84
58	3.37	31.36	31.94	66.67	8,331.90
59	3.37	31.24	32.06	66.67	8,299.84
60	3.37	31.12	32.18	66.67	8,267.66
	40.44	381.31	378.29	800.04	
61	3.20	31.00	32.30	66.50	8,235.36
62	3.20	30.88	32.42	66.50	8,202.94
63	3.20	30.76	32.54	66.50	8,170.40
64	3.20	30.64	32.66	66.50	8,137.74
65	3.20	30.52	32.78	66.50	8,104.96
66	3.20	30.39	32.91	66.50	8,072.05
67	3.20	30.27	33.03	66.50	8,039.02
68	3.20	30.15	33.15	66.50	8,005.87
69	3.20	30.02	33.28	66.50	7,972.59
70	3.20	29.90	33.40	66.50	7,939.19
71	3.20	29.77	33.53	66.50	7,905.66
72	3.20	29.65	33.65	66.50	7,872.01
	38.40	362.95	395.65	798.00	

TABLE 22 (Cont.)

Payment No.	Mortgage Insurance Premium 1/2%	Payment to Interest 4-1/2%	Payment to Principal	Total Periodic Payment	Balance Due
73	$3.03	$29.52	$33.78	$66.33	$7,838.23
74	3.03	29.39	33.91	66.33	7,804.32
75	3.03	29.27	34.03	66.33	7,770.29
76	3.03	29.14	34.16	66.33	7,736.13
77	3.03	29.01	34.29	66.33	7,701.84
78	3.03	28.88	34.42	66.33	7,667.42
79	3.03	28.75	34.55	66.33	7,632.87
80	3.03	28.62	34.68	66.33	7,598.19
81	3.03	28.49	34.81	66.33	7,563.38
82	3.03	28.36	34.94	66.33	7,528.44
83	3.03	28.23	35.07	66.33	7,493.37
84	3.03	28.10	35.20	66.33	7,458.17
	36.36	345.76	413.84	795.96	
85	2.84	27.97	35.33	66.14	7,422.84
86	2.84	27.84	35.46	66.14	7,387.38
87	2.84	27.70	35.60	66.14	7,351.78
88	2.84	27.57	35.73	66.14	7,316.05
89	2.84	27.44	35.86	55.14	7,280.19
90	2.84	27.30	36.00	66.14	7,244.19
91	2.84	27.17	36.13	66.14	7,208.06
92	2.84	27.03	36.27	66.14	7,171.79
93	2.84	26.89	36.41	66.14	7,135.38
94	2.84	26.76	36.54	66.14	7,098.84
95	2.84	26.62	36.68	66.14	7,062.16
96	2.84	26.48	36.82	66.14	7,025.34
	34.08	326.77	432.83	793.68	
97	2.65	26.35	36.95	65.95	6,988.39
98	2.65	26.21	37.09	65.95	6,951.30
99	2.65	26.07	37.23	65.95	6,914.07
100	2.65	25.93	37.37	65.95	6,876.70
101	2.65	25.79	37.51	65.95	6,839.19
102	2.65	25.65	37.65	65.95	6,801.54
103	2.65	25.51	37.79	65.95	6,763.75
104	2.65	25.36	37.94	65.95	6,725.81
105	2.65	25.22	38.08	65.95	6,687.73
106	2.65	25.08	38.22	65.95	6,649.51
107	2.65	24.94	38.36	65.95	6,611.15
108	2.65	24.79	38.51	65.95	6,572.64
	31.80	306.90	452.70	791.40	

TABLE 22 (Cont.)

Payment No.	Mortgage Insurance Premium 1/2%	Payment to Interest 4-1/2%	Payment to Principal	Total Periodic Payment	Balance Due
109	$2.45	$24.65	$38.65	$65.75	$6,533.99
110	2.45	24.50	38.80	65.75	6,495.19
111	2.45	24.36	38.94	65.75	6,456.25
112	2.45	24.21	39.09	65.75	6,417.16
113	2.45	24.06	39.24	65.75	6,377.92
114	2.45	23.92	39.38	65.75	6,338.54
115	2.45	23.77	39.53	65.75	6,299.01
116	2.45	23.62	39.68	65.75	6,259.33
117	2.45	23.47	39.83	65.75	6,219.50
118	2.45	23.32	39.98	65.75	6,179.52
119	2.45	23.17	40.13	65.75	6,139.39
120	2.45	23.02	40.28	65.75	6,099.11
	29.40	286.07	473.53	789.00	
121	2.24	22.87	40.43	65.54	6,058.68
122	2.24	22.72	40.58	65.54	6,018.10
123	2.24	22.57	40.73	65.54	5,977.37
124	2.24	22.42	40.88	65.54	5,936.49
125	2.24	22.26	41.04	65.54	5,895.45
126	2.24	22.11	41.19	65.54	5,854.26
127	2.24	21.95	41.35	65.54	5,812.91
128	2.24	21.80	41.50	65.54	5,771.41
129	2.24	21.64	41.66	65.54	5,729.75
130	2.24	21.49	41.81	65.54	5,687.94
131	2.24	21.33	41.97	65.54	5,645.97
132	2.24	21.17	42.13	65.54	5,603.84
	26.88	264.33	495.27	786.48	
133	2.02	21.01	42.29	65.32	5,561.55
134	2.02	20.86	42.44	65.32	5,519.11
135	2.02	20.70	42.60	65.32	5,476.51
136	2.02	20.54	42.76	65.32	5,433.75
137	2.02	20.38	42.92	65.32	5,390.83
138	2.02	20.22	43.08	65.32	5,347.75
139	2.02	20.05	43.25	65.32	5,304.50
140	2.02	19.89	43.41	65.32	5,261.09
141	2.02	19.73	43.57	65.32	5,217.52
142	2.02	19.57	43.73	65.32	5,173.79
143	2.02	19.40	43.90	65.32	5,129.89
144	2.02	19.24	44.06	65.32	5,085.83
	24.24	241.59	518.01	783.84	

TABLE 22 (Cont.)

Payment No.	Mortgage Insurance Premium 1/2%	Payment to Interest 4-1/2%	Payment to Principal	Total Periodic Payment	Balance Due
145	$1.79	$19.07	$44.23	$65.09	$5,041.60
146	1.79	18.91	44.39	65.09	4,997.21
147	1.79	18.74	44.56	65.09	4,952.65
148	1.79	18.57	44.73	65.09	4,907.92
149	1.79	18.40	44.90	65.09	4,863.02
150	1.79	18.24	45.06	65.09	4,817.96
151	1.79	18.07	45.23	65.09	4,772.73
152	1.79	17.90	45.40	65.09	4,727.33
153	1.79	17.73	45.57	65.09	4,681.76
154	1.79	17.56	45.74	65.09	4,636.02
155	1.79	17.39	45.91	65.09	4,590.11
156	1.79	17.21	46.09	65.09	4,544.02
	21.48	217.79	541.81	781.08	
157	1.55	17.04	46.26	64.85	4,497.76
158	1.55	16.87	46.43	64.85	4,451.33
159	1.55	16.69	46.61	64.85	4,404.72
160	1.55	16.52	46.78	64.85	4,357.94
161	1.55	16.34	46.96	64.85	4,310.98
162	1.55	16.17	47.13	64.85	4,263.85
163	1.55	15.99	47.31	64.85	4,216.54
164	1.55	15.81	47.49	64.85	4,169.05
165	1.55	15.63	47.67	64.85	4,121.38
166	1.55	15.46	47.84	64.85	4,073.54
167	1.55	15.28	48.02	64.85	4,025.52
168	1.55	15.10	48.20	64.85	3,977.32
	18.60	192.90	566.70	778.20	
169	1.29	14.91	48.39	64.59	3,928.93
170	1.29	14.73	48.57	64.59	3,880.36
171	1.29	14.55	48.75	64.59	3,831.61
172	1.29	14.37	48.93	64.59	3,782.68
173	1.29	14.19	49.11	64.59	3,733.57
174	1.29	14.00	49.30	64.59	3,684.27
175	1.29	13.82	49.48	64.59	3,634.79
176	1.29	13.63	49.67	64.59	3,585.12
177	1.29	13.44	49.86	64.59	3,535.26
178	1.29	13.26	50.04	64.59	3,485.22
179	1.29	13.07	50.23	64.59	3,434.99
180	1.29	12.88	50.42	64.59	3,384.57
	15.48	166.85	592.75	775.08	

TABLE 22 (Cont.)

Payment No.	Mortgage Insurance Premium 1/2%	Payment to Interest 4-1/2%	Payment to Principal	Total Periodic Payment	Balance Due
181	$1.03	$12.69	$50.61	$64.33	$3,333.96
182	1.03	12.50	50.80	64.33	3,283.16
183	1.03	12.31	50.99	64.33	3,232.17
184	1.03	12.12	51.18	64.33	3,180.99
185	1.03	11.93	51.37	64.33	3,129.62
186	1.03	11.74	51.56	64.33	3,078.06
187	1.03	11.54	51.76	64.33	3,026.30
188	1.03	11.35	51.95	64.33	2,974.35
189	1.03	11.15	52.15	64.33	2,922.20
190	1.03	10.96	52.34	64.33	2,869.86
191	1.03	10.76	52.54	64.33	2,817.32
192	1.03	10.56	52.74	64.33	2,764.58
	12.36	139.61	619.99	771.96	
193	.75	10.37	52.93	64.05	2,711.65
194	.75	10.17	53.13	64.05	2,658.52
195	.75	9.97	53.33	64.05	2,605.19
196	.75	9.77	53.53	64.05	2,551.66
197	.75	9.57	53.73	64.05	2,497.93
198	.75	9.37	53.93	64.05	2,444.00
199	.75	9.17	54.13	64.05	2,389.87
200	.75	8.96	54.34	64.05	2,335.53
201	.75	8.76	54.54	64.05	2,280.99
202	.75	8.55	54.75	64.05	2,226.24
203	.75	8.35	54.95	64.05	2,171.29
204	.75	8.14	55.16	64.05	2,116.13
	9.00	111.15	648.45	768.60	
205	.47	7.94	55.36	63.77	2,060.77
206	.47	7.73	55.57	63.77	2,005.20
207	.47	7.52	55.78	63.77	1,949.42
208	.47	7.31	55.99	63.77	1,893.43
209	.47	7.10	56.20	63.77	1,837.23
210	.47	6.89	56.41	63.77	1,780.82
211	.47	6.68	56.62	63.77	1,724.20
212	.47	6.47	56.83	63.77	1,667.37
213	.47	6.25	57.05	63.77	1,610.32
214	.47	6.04	57.26	63.77	1,553.06
215	.47	5.82	57.48	63.77	1,495.58
216	.47	5.61	57.69	63.77	1,437.89
	5.64	81.36	678.24	765.24	

TABLE 22 (Cont.)

Payment No.	Mortgage Insurance Premium 1/2%	Payment to Interest 4-1/2%	Payment to Principal	Total Periodic Payment	Balance Due
217	$ .16	$ 5.39	$57.91	$63.46	$1,379.98
218	.16	5.17	58.13	63.46	1,321.85
219	.16	4.96	58.34	63.46	1,263.51
220	.16	4.74	58.56	63.46	1,204.95
221	.16	4.52	58.78	63.46	1,146.17
222	.16	4.30	59.00	63.46	1,087.17
223	.16	4.08	59.22	63.46	1,027.95
224	.16	3.85	59.45	63.46	968.50
225	.16	3.63	59.67	63.46	908.83
226	.16	3.41	59.89	63.46	848.94
227	.16	3.18	60.12	63.46	788.82
228	.16	2.96	60.34	63.46	728.48
	1.92	50.19	709.41	761.52	
229		2.73	60.57	63.30	667.91
230		2.50	60.80	63.30	607.11
231		2.28	61.02	63.30	546.09
232		2.05	61.25	63.30	484.84
233		1.82	61.48	63.30	423.36
234		1.59	61.71	63.30	361.65
235		1.36	61.94	63.30	299.71
236		1.12	62.18	63.30	237.53
237		.89	62.41	63.30	175.12
238		.66	62.64	63.30	112.48
239		.42	62.88	63.30	49.60
240		.19	49.60	49.79	
		17.61	728.48	746.09	

ation, depreciation is based on the difference in value between a new building equivalent to the old one and to the old one itself. In the capitalization of income method, the basis of depreciation is amortization of the original investment.

The basis suggested for used by the home owner is the assumption that the value of the home in 40 years will be only the present land value. The latter can be determined, in many cases, from recent local selling prices, with sufficient accuracy to serve as a basis for depreciation calculations. However, if values are required more in accord with other modern appraisal methods, they can be determined by the methods given in the last section of this chapter.

For computing the annual depreciation from the original cost and residual value, several of the methods explained in Chapter 15 are currently in use. Two of them are recommended for use by the home owner—the straight line method and the declining balance method.

As pointed out in Chapter 15, the straight line method charges the same amount of depreciation every year. For example, on a home costing $15,000, with an estimated residual value (land value) of $2,000.00, depreciated over 40 years, the annual depreciation charge would be $\dfrac{\$15,000 - \$2,000.00}{40} = \$325.00$ per year.

The declining-balance (constant-ratio) method depreciates more rapidly during the early years, and more slowly later; the percentage depreciation per year being constant.

By Formula (15-1), Chapter 15 this percentage is

$$d = 1 - \sqrt[n]{\frac{S.V.}{C}}$$

Substituting, $d = 1 - \sqrt[40]{\dfrac{\$2,000.00}{\$15,000.00}} = 1 - \sqrt[40]{0.1333}$

From Table 6, log .1333 = $\bar{1}$.124928

Adding 40, log .1333   = 39.124928 − 40

Dividing by 40, log $\sqrt[40]{.1333}$ = .978123 − 1 = $\bar{1}$.978123

Then $\sqrt[40]{.1333}$ = antilog $\bar{1}$.978123 = .959

Therefore, $d = 1 - .959 = .041$.

Therefore, the depreciation charge is:

        First Year   4.1% of $15,000.00 = $615.00

        Second Year   4.1% of $14,385.00 = $589.79

        Third Year   4.1% of $13,795.21 = $565.60, etc.

III. *Insurance.* The costs of home insurance are, of course directly chargeable to the costs of home ownership. However, liability policies and other costs that would be incurred whether the home was owned or rented should not be included.

IV. *Heat, Light and Power.* The only sound rule in arriving at realistic costs of home ownership is to include only such of these costs as would be not paid by the tenant of rented premises. Since the practice varies markedly from one region or community to another, the distribution of heat, light and power costs must be made upon an individual basis.

V. *Taxes.* Taxes are, of course, directly chargeable to home ownership. Note, however, that some communities bill their personal property taxes and real estate taxes on the same form. The former is not, of course, a cost of home ownership, and should be deducted in such cost computations.

Appraisal of Real Estate

There are three basic methods of appraising real estate in use today: capitalization of income, replacement cost and market comparison. The first of these is concerned with future income, usually as discounted to present value. The second would appear to be the easiest to determine definitely, but its practical application requires, as is explained later, various assumptions and modifications; especially as U. S. Government policies have tended for some years toward a rejection of market value as the primary basis of valuation. The market comparison method is also easy to apply if the necessary data is available, but even then has basic objections. The present view that is most generally accepted is that all three approaches should be correlated in making an appraisal, with due regard to the one most suitable for the particular property, and to the specialized concepts of value that often enter a particular situation. Therefore, the three methods are discussed in the order in which they are stated above, after a preliminary discussion of the influence of national, regional and local conditions upon a particular real property. For over the long periods with which the real estate appraiser has to do, valuations are subject to many types and causes of change. These changes may be brought about, not only by variations in the circumstances of the property itself, but also by changes occurring on an international, national, regional or community level.

International, National, Regional and Local Conditions

Of these broad-gauge influences, the first two may properly be dismissed from the present discussion, even though their effect may be very great indeed. For the forecasting of such influences as, for example, inflation (at the national level) of currency or credit is a problem for an economist (or possibly a soothsayer!!) rather than a real estate appraiser. The latter is properly concerned, however, with the effect of regional and community changes, which are often designated, with particular emphasis upon the latter, as the economic base or economic background of real estate appraisal.

Partly because rural land incomes are less influenced by regional and community considerations, most economic base studies have been concerned with urban areas. One approach to evaluation of their future starts by the classification of cities on the basis of their major economic function or functions. On this basis, five recognized urban types are manufacturing cities, commercial cities, educational cities (i.e. those having an education institution as their most important activity), political cities (i.e. those state capitals, county seats and other places where political administration is the most important employment) and resort cities. This type of analysis leads to a method of forecasting the future of real estate in terms of the predicted growth of the dominant enterprise, or in the case of manufacturing cities, on the growth of the industry to which its dominant enterprise belongs.

An extension of the foregoing method to cities in general is made by determining the number of people in each of these various types of enterprises, and then determining the growth potential of each separately, in order to arrive at a total figure for the city as a whole. From this point of view, manufacturing enterprises which distribute the bulk of their product non-locally, and mining or other extractive industries which do the same either directly or indirectly, are considered to make the greatest contribution per employee to the growth potential of the community. These activities are given, on the FHA Economic Background Rating Form, a factor of 2 by which to multiply the number of employees engaged in them, in order to take into account the contribution of such employment to service activities. On the other hand, the employment in service activities that are limited to the local community has a lower growth potential. Intermediate between the two are various activities which, while not directly productional, draw outside revenue into the community. These are variously designated and evaluated, and make a corresponding contribution to community growth potential.

There are, of course many other means of analyzing the economic base of a community. Studies that have been made by the Federal Reserve Bank of San Francisco compare the national distribution of employment in various categories with that in a particular region, and from these past and present statistics, endeavor to predict the trend in the region from that in the nation.

Whichever methods are used, the effect of regional and industry conditions upon urban growth or decline cannot be disregarded in any well-founded projection of real estate values. They certainly require consideration along with the neighborhood conditions.

By neighborhood conditions is meant the tendency of real estate in various neighborhoods to fluctuate in value independently of the overall potential of the city as a whole. Some analysts have endeavored to forecast such charges geometrically by postulating certain preferred directions of urban expansion. Others have tried to forecast neighborhood changes on assumptions as to the extent of the effects of adjoining neighborhoods, and the rate at which they make themselves felt. Probably the best plan is to analyze a particular neighborhood by appraising its good and bad points for its present and possible future use—considering the quality of locations, buildings, transportation, schools (for residential areas), etc. From this present condition, future trends can often be anticipated.

Capitalization of Income Method

A simple and direct method of capitalizing income which has been long in use is that of gross rent factors or gross rent multipliers. Simply multiply the gross rent of the property by a factor that is determined for similar property, in similar situations, and in the same community. From the number of qualifying phrases used, it is easy to see why this method has limited applicability. Some efforts have been made to refine this method, by setting up indices for various criteria of real estate investment and using them to obtain a single value, but the gross rent factors so obtained are considered to be of limited usefulness. Therefore, appraisers have developed a capitalization of **net** income method.

This method consists essentially of computing the present value of the income to be earned over the years to come. However, while this calculation is straightforward, once the future earnings have been forecast, that operation is often difficult. Leaving aside for the moment those properties which are not producing income at the time of appraisal, there is still the need for estimating the changes that may occur in income over future years. These changes may be due, as has already been explained, to changes in larger entities of which the property is a part. It now remains to discuss the property itself, from the capitalization of income standpoint.

The mathematics of this method of appraising real estate is that explained in Chapter 14 for the calculation of the present value of an annuity. In this case the rent, or periodic payment of the annuity is the income from the property, and its present value per dollar of rent is found from Table 14.

The practical application of this method of appraisal requires an estimation of (1) the useful life of the property; (2) the future income expected from the property for each year of its useful life; (3) the interest rate at which this income should be capitalized, and (4) the terminal value at the end of the useful life.

As explained in the discussion of depreciation earlier in this chapter, the limiting conditions on the useful life of a building are variously affected by factors of physical depreciation and obsolescence. From the standpoint of income (which as used here, is *net* income), this means that the life of the building ends when its gross rent is so decreased by obsolescence, or its maintenance expense so increased by physical depreciation, that its net income is inadequate even as return on its terminal value. From this point of view, the useful life of a home was arbitrarily set at 40 years, a figure which would, of course, vary considerably with the community, type of construction and similar factors.

The difficulty of estimation of the income from property over its useful life is evident from the criticisms of existing methods that have appeared in reviews of past results. The method of Frederick M. Babcock was the use of four premises for projecting income. In the first premise, the future income was projected in equal annual instalments, while in his other three premises, each year's income was expected to be less than that of the preceding year. The rate of decrease was uniform (straight-line) in his fourth premise, while in his second premise it started more slowly, but accelerated toward the end of the useful life. The rate of decrease in his third premise was roughly intermediate between that of the second and fourth premises.

Obviously much of the success of an appraiser in using such a multiple-choice method of forecasting income depends upon his judgment in choosing the premise best suited to the property under consideration. The same statement can be made about the tables in *The Appraisal of Real Estate*, by the American Institute of Real Estate Appraisers (Chicago, 1952). Moreover, in the case of buildings containing relatively large numbers of leased units, the percentage of occupancy is also a basis for income projection, to provide allowances for the possibility of partial vacancy.

The interest rate at which the income is to be capitalized has a relatively very great effect upon the value so determined, as is evident from the fact that capitalized value varies inversely as the interest rate, so the use of a 9% rate instead of 8% would reduce the value for that income to $\frac{8}{9}$ of its value on an 8% basis.

One way of capitalizing income is the band of investment method. The total investment in the property is divided into bands of various grades of investments—such as first mortgage, second mortgage and equity.

By allotting income on the portions of the value which would be covered by mortgages at the current interest rates on similar properties, the remainder of the income can be used to capitalize the equity, and if it is a good investment, at a rate higher than that used for the second mortgage.

A different method, but one using a somewhat analogous process, is the summation method, which arrives at the interest rate by a process of summation of rates. In the form used by the FHA, this sum consists of separate interest rate percentages for five elements of value: (1) Safety of Principal, having ratings varying from $2\frac{1}{2}\%$ to $3\frac{1}{2}\%$; (2) Certainty of Return, having ratings varying from 1% to 2%; (3) Regularity of Return, with ratings from $\frac{3}{4}\%$ to $1\frac{3}{4}\%$; (4) Liquidity, with ratings from $\frac{1}{2}\%$ to $1\frac{1}{2}\%$; and (5) Burden of Management, with ratings from $\frac{1}{4}\%$ to $1\frac{1}{4}\%$. By choosing a figure from each of these five ranges, using higher figures for poorer evaluations, and then adding the figures, one can obtain a total interest rate at which the income should be capitalized.

Another way of arriving at a composite rate is the application of the comparison method originally proposed by Schmutz. While the comparison method may be merely an assumption of similar income rates for similar properties, Schmutz used weighting factors for a number of criteria, including the five mentioned above, in order to arrive at a total percentage (less than 100%), which represented the departure of the true capitalization from ideality, the latter being taken as the actual or current rate.

The last consideration in the capitalization of income method is the terminal value at the end of useful life. This refers, as, in fact, do many of the preceding terms, to building appraisement. Since the life of a building ends with its demolition, this factor becomes the land value, as it will be at that time. Since this value is difficult to appraise at such a distance in time, even with the aid of the regional and urban studies discussed earlier in this chapter, some appraisers take it at its present value, so that their results are at least comparable. Still others separate building values and land values throughout the entire analysis. This last method is associated with the residual methods of capitalizing real estate income, which are clearly beyond the scope of this chapter. There is an excellent discussion of them in *Real Estate Appraisal*, by Paul F. Wendt (Henry Holt & Co., 1956).

Replacement Cost Method

In view of the number of factors entering into the capitalization of income method, the apparent simplicity of the replacement cost method might well seem to make it preferable. Indeed, this is true in certain applications, especially those in which the appraisals are most likely to be subjected to review or attack, such as those by governmental agencies and insurance companies. Nevertheless, the method is subject to difficulties, both the theoretical problem of reconciling cost with value, and a number of practical questions involved directly in its application.

To apply the replacement cost method, a decision must be made as to the extent to which the depreciation and obsolescence of the property should enter the calculations. Various of the methods given earlier in this chapter and in Chapter 15 are used for calculating depreciation. Before depreciation deductions are applied, however, the appraiser must determine the replacement cost of the property.

Three fundamental methods are in use for making this determination. While their names and details vary somewhat in different sources, their description in the *FHA Underwriting Manual* is representative. It characterizes them as the In-Place Unit Method, the Integrated Square-Foot Method and the Repeat Case Method.

The In-Place Unit Method divides the structure into its component parts, uses prices per unit area or unit volume to determine the cost of each, and then adds these costs to obtain a subtotal cost of the structure. This subtotal is then increased by allowances for the on-site improvements, such as detached garages and other detached buildings, walks and driveways. This gives a net total cost figure, which is increased by allowances for (1) builder's overhead and profit; (2) effect of locality upon cost; (3) effect of quality upon cost; (4) cost of architectural services. The final result is the replacement cost by a new building, which is subject, as stated above, to depreciation deductions.

The Integrated Square-Foot Method is, as the name indicates, an elaboration of the square-foot method. In the latter a unit cost per square foot is multiplied by the area, a method which applies, even approximately, only under essentially "identical" conditions. As modified into the FHA Integrated Method, it involves, first of all, the calculation of the square-foot area of the building, and its multiplication by a factor chosen from the FHA *Cost Data Handbook* for similar buildings. This gives, after specified adjustments, a modified basic cost of the building. This figure corresponds to the subtotal cost of the structure in the In-Place Unit Method already described, and from that point on the calculations are identical with those of that method.

The Repeat Case Method of the FHA follows the same steps as the Integrated Square Food Method, with the exception of the initial determination of the basic cost of the building, which is found by direct comparison with similar basic structures, and modified by gross deductions to allow for its variations from them. Wherever applicable, this method is preferable, since it is shorter than the Integrated Square Foot Method.

From the point of view of their usefulness to the appraiser as measures of value, there is little reason for preferring any one of the three foregoing methods to another. All are subject to the inherent disadvantage of the replacement cost method in that it does not measure the utility value, and hence, in the eyes of many economists, does not measure value at all.

The Market Comparison Method

The foregoing objection, at least theoretically, cannot be made to the market comparison method. This method is ideal from the standpoint of classical economics, which regards the market price as the resultant of supply and demand, under competitive conditions in a free market.

The qualifications in the preceding sentence, however, give some indication of the practical difficulties in the way of correlating market price and a fair appraisal. Obviously circumstances may exist for a particular property, in which demand is virtually nonexistent, and hence there is no "free market." Moreover, in times of a local or national recession or depression, this may be true for many properties. Moreover, even if "adequate" demand is present, so that property is selling steadily, there is the problem that the method involves comparison of the property being appraised with the other properties that have sold recently. Therefore, the application of the market comparison method has required the development and evaluation of factors for comparing properties. Two procedures of this sort are well-known for their application to one-family residences. They both consist of the establishment of multiplying factors to relate the market price of the particular property to that of a property that has been sold. In one procedure one set of factors is used, while in the other there are separate factors for the property and the location. In the table given in the *FHA Underwriting Manual*, the property factors are visual appeal, natural light and ventilation, structural quality, resistance to the elements and to use, suitability of mechanical equipment, and adjustments for nonconformity; while the location factors are protection against inharmonious land uses, physical and social attractiveness, adequacy of civic, social and educational centers, adequacy of transportation, sufficiency of utilities and services, level of taxes and assessments, and relative marketability. Each of these factors is assigned a number of rating grades, with a stipulated number of credits for each. The credits are added to obtain totals for property and location, which are then combined into a single rating.

Modifications of the foregoing are applied even more effectively to the appraisal of vacant land for building purposes. Frederick M. Babcock recognized three such methods of land appraisal. His building method was the most elaborate, since it involved the calculation of income obtainable by erecting a building upon the land, and required the preparation of building plans sufficiently detailed to permit the computation of a rent roll. His least complicated method, the so-called "chunk method," was a direct comparison of the particular property with others sold recently, with the use of multiplying factors to adjust for differences. His third method also used multiplying factors, but was based on the relative areas of the properties, and was therefore called the "square-foot method."

Another method of land appraisal, that is widely used, is the unit foot method, described at length in *The Appraisal of Real Estate*, American Institute of Real Estate Appraisers, Chicago (1951). This method takes into consideration, in addition to other factors, the front footage to area ratio of the property. To avoid mathematical calculations, market value adjustments are tabulated in "Depth and Width" Tables, so that the correct adjustment for a property of given dimensions can be found in the tables.

In conclusion, it can be stated that the real estate appraiser must be prepared to apply all three of the methods of property appraisal. While in many circumstances, some of which are indicated in the foregoing discussion, one of the methods should have the greatest weight, in general he must form a judgment based upon them all.

Chapter 21

THE ROLE OF MACHINES
IN BUSINESS COMPUTATIONS

Business Information Systems

For purposes of analysis, the information system of any business may be said to perform three fundamental functions—information processing, information documentation and information storage.   The first of these, information processing, obviously includes business computations.   Therefore, the use of machines for carrying out business computations, and especially the evaluation of various types and combinations of such machines, can be discussed comprehensively only from the standpoint of their relationship to the business information system as a whole.

To generalize that system adequately, its character and functions must be interpreted broadly.   The information flowing into it from outside includes all communications which play a part in the three fundamental functions, irrespective of the channels through which they are received.   These communications include orders for goods or services; payments or other messages pertaining to accounts receivable; invoices, statements and other communications pertaining to accounts payable; payments on notes, dividends received, tax bills and similar communications pertaining to all the other accounts of the business; and, finally, market reports, economic surveys and all other information pertaining to the control of the business.

As these incoming communications pass into the information system of the business they are variously processed, documented and stored, depending upon their nature.   For example, the incoming orders, or more exactly, the facts from the incoming orders, undergo, in one sequence or another, a series of processing operations which may include credit checking, inventory checking, pricing, discounting and computation; a series of documentation operations which may include the preparation of invoices, shipping instructions, account records, inventory records, and sales records;

547

and finally, a series of storage operations which may include the transfer of the incoming information, as well as the information produced by processing it, to storage. This medium of this transfer can be documents produced in the second function, or any other means for transferring intelligence—manual, mechanical, electrical or electronic.

Particular emphasis should be placed upon this transfer activity, because it enters, directly or indirectly, into so many of the others. Thus, the activities of credit checking and inventory checking mentioned above as entering into the processing of orders, require intra-business communication between the storage and processing functions, just as the maintenance of accounting records requires intra-business communication between the processing and/or documentation functions and the storage function. Thus the transfer of intelligence within the business is a major activity, as important as any of the other three functions, and treated separately whenever convenient for purposes of analysis.

The example cited above of incoming invoices, and the operations to which they give rise, is representative, in complexity at any rate, of the other types of incoming information. There are, in addition, other kinds of activities arising in the information system of a business which are initiated, not by incoming information, but within the business itself. Examples that readily occur to mind are the preparation of statements of accounts receivable, to be sent to customers; the preparation of payments of accounts payable, to be sent to creditors, and the preparation of payroll vouchers, reports and payments, to be paid, not only to the employees of the business, but to governmental units, insurance companies, banks, unions, etc. These internally-initiated activities of the information system involve all three of the basic functions—storage (i.e., recall from storage) processing and documentation. In this respect they are quite similar to still another class of internally-initiated activities, the summaries and reports.

Summaries and reports produced by the information system of a business enter into both its external relations and its internal control. The former use may be exemplified by summaries of sales required by governmental units for products on which sales taxes are paid; and by the balance sheets and income statements prepared for governmental departments and stockholders. The latter are also important to the managers of a business for use in internal control, but obviously many additional reports and summaries are necessary for that purpose. Their number, scope and frequency will obviously increase with increasing rate of change in general economic conditions, whether positive or negative, with the amount of fluctuation in the industry represented by the business, and with changes in the competitive nature, price structure, sales potential and market distribution of the products of the business, as well as with many other variables.

In short, the wider and faster the changes in conditions affecting a business, the greater is the amount of information needed by management for its effective control, and the shorter is the permissible delay in obtaining it. Both these requirements increase the work load of the information system. For any business the amount of that work load is the total of that from all these various operations, both those that are "routine", and those that are essential to managerial control. And it is the size of this work load that determines the type and character of the mechanization that is most efficient for the particular business; in other words, that will perform *all* of its activities at minimum cost.

This optimum mechanization of the information system of the business determines the methods and machines used in information documentation, information storage, and first and foremost, in information processing, of which mathematical computation is a major component. Thus, the types, sizes and distribution of computational machinery are determined, not merely by their efficiency in performing given calculations, but by their integration into the entire information system of the business. Often this process goes even further, resulting in the integration of two, or all three, of the basic functions in one machine. For example, the invoicing operation may be performed, not by the use of separate machines for computation and preparation of the invoice, but by a single machine that combines these two activities, thus integrating the processing and documentation functions into a single machine. The great digital computers can readily be used, with auxiliary equipment, to combine all three functions of processing, storage and documentation.

For this reason the choice of machines for performing business calculations must be made with due regard to their ability to perform or participate in other information processing operations, as well as information documentation, transmission and storage. The storage or memory function possessed to some degree by practically all computational machines. However, there are great differences in the storage capacity of these machines, as well as in their degree of integration of the computing and storage sections, as is apparent from the descriptions below.

Computational Machine Types

On the basis of storage capacity, computational machines may be divided into four groups. The machines of the first group are characterized by limited storage capacity. Numbers and instructions must be fed into the machine as it operates or immediately before. The desk-type calculating machines are included in this group.

The second group consists of machines having large storage capacity for numbers, but not for instructions. Most of these machines are of the multiple-component type. The punched card accounting system is an outstanding member of this group, since its number-capacity may be extended indefinitely by addition of cards, but its operations are limited to those of the machine through which they are passed.

The third group consists of machines having large storage capacity for instructions, but not for numbers. Machines of this type are more common in engineering applications rather than in business information systems. They are designed to apply a wide range of computational sequences to a limited group of numbers. They are used extensively in control systems, such as those of machine tools and guided missiles. The load-distributing calculator for an electrical power system, mentioned in Chapter 22, is a computational machine of this group.

The machines of the fourth group have large storage capacity for both numbers and instructions. They are often designated by the shorter word "computer" and that usage is followed in this chapter. They include all the general-purpose "giant" machines, although smaller models have been developed more recently.

In this chapter, the four groups are discussed in the above order, with the necessary digressions to treat the compound and special purpose machines in the various groups—that is, the machines which combine other functions with those of computation, often to enable them to perform more efficiently a specific operation, such as billing or bookkeeping.

A useful basis of classification of the computational machines of limited storage capacity for both numbers and instructions is from the standpoint of the number of registers that they contain. A register is a set of parts which can represent and store a group of numbers or other symbols. Upon this basis of classification, the simplest calculating machines are the single-register types which are discussed first. (The number of registers in a machine is not commonly the number visible, as may be seen from the detailed discussions.) Moreover, the classification to be followed here is that of functional registers, that is, register action which defines the manner in which the machines calculate. There are, however, especially for accounting purposes, machines with a multiplicity of registers that perform the same function. They are discussed later in this chapter.

Single Functional-Register Machines

The single-register machines are the most limited in their applications. They consist primarily of key-activated adding machines (called "add-on" machines by dealers) of the full keyboard type. The keys are arranged in a number of columns of nine keys each, the keys in each column being numbered from 9 at the top to 1 on the bottom key (0 is usually omitted because only the keys that are depressed add). The number of these columns of keys varies from as few as 6 to as many as 14 or more, and determines the magnitude of the largest number which can be entered into the register on one operation. Thus the largest number which can be entered into the register with a single use of the keys in each column on a 6-column machine is 999999, while the 14-column machine can enter the number 99999999999999. The numbers are written here without commas or decimal points, because registers in the simpler machines make no such distinction. However, the keys are usually colored differently, generally with the two columns at the right in one color, with each group of three columns to the left of them in a new color, for convenience in computation with American money, or other decimal currencies.

Adding machines with a single functional-register are necessarily made with "live" keyboards, as stated above—that is, with keys which add into the register when they are depressed, without requiring the use of any handle (for mechanically operated machines) or motor bar (for electrically operated machines). This arrangement saves time, provided that the operator is sufficiently skilled, and provided that the job permits concentration upon the single task of computation. Otherwise, the time spent in correcting errors may more than offset the time saved in operating the handle or motor bar; and two functional-register machines are preferable. Some special single functional-machines have a two-position keyboard, in which depressing a key slightly, to the primary position, indexes the amount which that key represents, while depressing the key fully, to the secondary position, acts as a motor bar; the entire amount indexed then prints and adds.

The single register, key-activated (add on) machines are used far less commonly now that most of the continuous work is done on electrically-powered, rather than lever-operated machines. For the latter nullify much of the speed advantage of the skilled operator of an add-on machine. Moreover, two-register or multi-register machines are obtainable with an add-on button, so that they can be used both for key-actuated and key-setting operation.

On one-register (and some two-register) adding machines multiplication can be performed only by repeated addition—however, with practice this operation can be done rapidly. To perform it, choose the greater of the two numbers as the multiplicand, and the smaller as the multiplier. For example, the number 4623 is multiplied by 38 by placing the fingers on the keys 4623 in the four columns at the right side of the keyboard and depressing them 8 times. Then move each finger to the key one column to the left and depress these keys 3 times.

Division is performed on an adding machine of this type (or even on some of the calculating and special machines that do not have direct division) by multiplying the dividend by the reciprocal of the divisor. For this purpose a table of reciprocals is required, as given in this book for the numbers from 2 to 999 in Table 1, Chapter 1, and tables extending to larger numbers may be purchased. For example, to divide $46.23 by 38, look up the reciprocal of 38 in the table, and use as many significant figures as the calculation requires. By inspection, this is three or four figures to give accuracy to the nearest penny. In Table 1, the decimal value of $\frac{1}{38}$ is given as 0.0263158, which to four significant figures is 0.02632. Then use the method of multiplication given above for one-register machines to multiply 4623 by 2632. The result is 12167736. Since by inspection $\frac{$46.23}{38}$ is a three-figure sum of dollars and cents, the result is $1.22, to the nearest penny.

Subtraction is performed on one functional-register machines by adding the complement (the difference between the number to be subtracted and the next higher power of 10) and then subtracting that power from the result. For example, to subtract from the number 8603 the number 4528, find the complement of 4528, which is $10,000 - 4528 = 5472$. Now add on the machine 8603 and 5472, obtaining 14,075—then subtract 10,000, obtaining 4075 as the required difference.

Two Functional-Register Machines

The two functional-register machines include a number of widely-used types, including both full-keyboard and ten-key varieties. They are usually key-set machines, as distinguished from the key-responsive machines that have only one register. They are also called adding-listing machines, because many, if not most models, produce printed records, on tape or otherwise, of the numbers added and their totals and subtotals. The two registers are called the setting register and the adding register.

In the full-keyboard types, the setting register is a full keyboard of a number of columns of keys numbered from 1 to 9. When the keys are depressed, they remain in that position, unless released by an error-clearing key, until they are added into the adding register. This is accomplished by movement of a lever, in the manually-operated types, or by movement of a key or bar, called the motor bar, in the electric types. Moreover, in those models designed for printing, the number on the keyboard is printed as well as added into the adding register. Many such machines have a "non-add" key for printing without adding. Other keys are: the sub-total key, which causes the total in the adding register to print without clearing; the total key, which causes the total in the adding register to print and clear; and on many models, the subtract key, which causes the number on the keyboard to be subtracted from the total in the adding register, and to print with a minus sign; and finally, the repeat key, which causes the keys depressed to remain in that position after being added and printed. This repeat key is necessary because the depressed keys themselves are automatically raised from their depressed position when the motor bar is pressed, thus clearing the adding register for the next operation.

Figure 21-1. NCR Model 77 HS Lever Operated Adding Machine. (Courtesy *National Cash Register Company*).

On this full-keyboard, two-register machine subtraction is usually performed directly by use of the subtract key. Multiplication is done by repeated addition, using the repeat key, and resetting the number on the keyboard anew for each power of 10 in the multiplier. Division is done by repeated subtraction, by first entering the dividend at the left side of the keyboard and transferring it to the adding register. Then the divisor is repeatedly subtracted, by setting it on the keyboard, using the repeat and subtract keys, and resetting it for each successively lower power of 10 in the quotient. On this machine, as on all one- and two-register machines, the operator must keep track of the multiplier or the quotient, in multiplication and division respectively.

The ten-key type of machine has only ten numbered keys, nine numbered from 1 to 9, and a tenth key or bar numbered 0. These keys are "live", that is, they return to normal position after being depressed, but the number produced by depressing them remains in the setting register, and is visible through an opening in the case of the machine. To set this

Figure 21-2. Burroughs 10-Key Adding Machine. (Courtesy *Burroughs Corporation*).

number, the keys corresponding to its digits are depressed in order, starting from the left, and depressing the "0" key for all significant 0's in the number. This last procedure differs from that followed with the full keyboard machine, where 0's need not be set. In all other respects save one, the operating features (i.e., control levers or keys) are the same. That one exception is the manner of showing the totals in the registers of the ten-key machines.

Some two functional-register ten-key machines have only the setting register total visible. The total in the adding register can always be learned by printing it by use of the sub-total or total keys.   Such ten-key machines are competitive with the corresponding full keyboard two functional-register machines; they perform the four operations of arithmetic in essentially the same way; and the choice between them is a larger matter of specific requirements.

There are, however, two functional-register ten-key machines which have an auxiliary keyboard for multiplication and addition.   Such machines are better called calculating machines because that term, as used

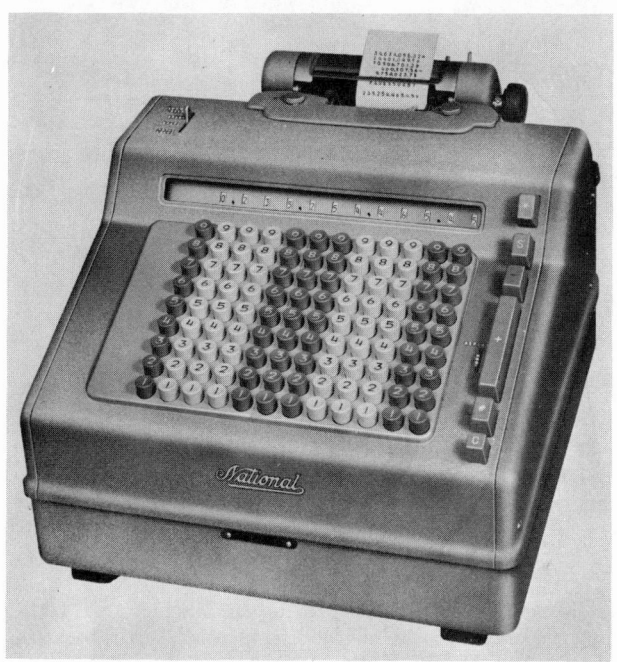

Figure 21-3.   NCR 211 EN Electric Adding Machine.   (Courtesy *National Cash Register Company*).

today, connotes the direct performance by a machine of operations beyond addition and subtraction.

To multiply with these machines, the multiplicand is introduced into the setting register by use of the keys as described above.   Then the digits of the multiplier are set on the auxiliary keyboard, in order of their ascending powers of ten (i.e., 843 would be set in the order 3, 4, 8).   After all the multiplier digits have been entered, the total in the adding register is printed, thus obtaining the product of the two numbers.   Moreover, the multiplier is printed at the same time.

Division is performed by first entering the dividend into the setting register, adding enough 0's to move it to the left side, then transferring it to the adding register by use of the add key or bar. Then the divisor is entered in the setting register and moved to the left side by the same process. Finally, the divide key is depressed, which initiates the process of division that continues by repeated subtraction until all the elements

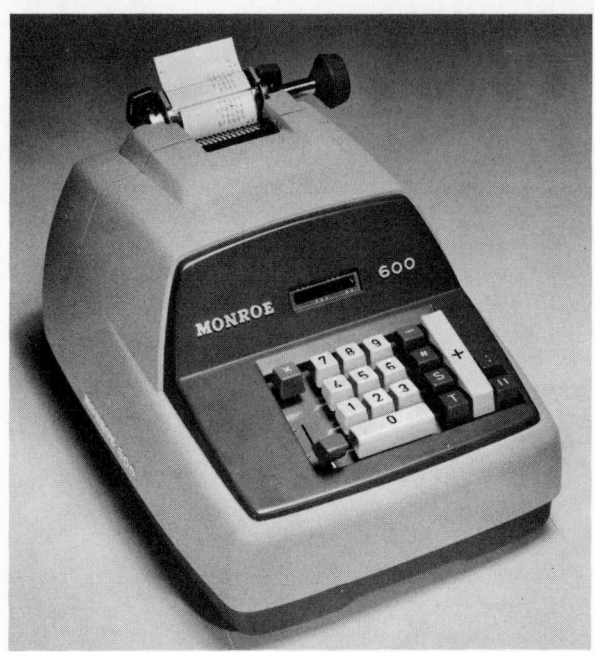

Figure 21-4. Monroe 10-Key Electrical Adding Machine. In addition to functions shown by the keys, this machine has an automatic credit balance. (Courtesy *Monroe Calculating Machine Company, Inc.*).

in the machine have been engaged. Then the operation of the machine stops, and the quotient and remainder are automatically printed.

Three Functional-Register Machines

The machine just discussed which while having only two registers, perform multiplication and division directly, obviously anticipates the three functional-register machines which have a multiplier register in addition to their setting and adding registers. (In such machines, the adding register is better called a product register.)

Machines of this type usually have their product and multiplier registers in a moveable carriage at the top of the machine, with the setting register below and either of full keyboard or ten-key type.   The carriage is moved mechanically by a manual device, or electrically by a button which can shift it either to right or left.   When all the way to the left, its two registers have their right-hand ends aligned with the right-hand of the scale.   Then a number in the setting register is moved unchanged into the product register by operating the add control or lever.   At the same time that this transfer is made, the digit 1 appears in the right-hand dial of the multiplier

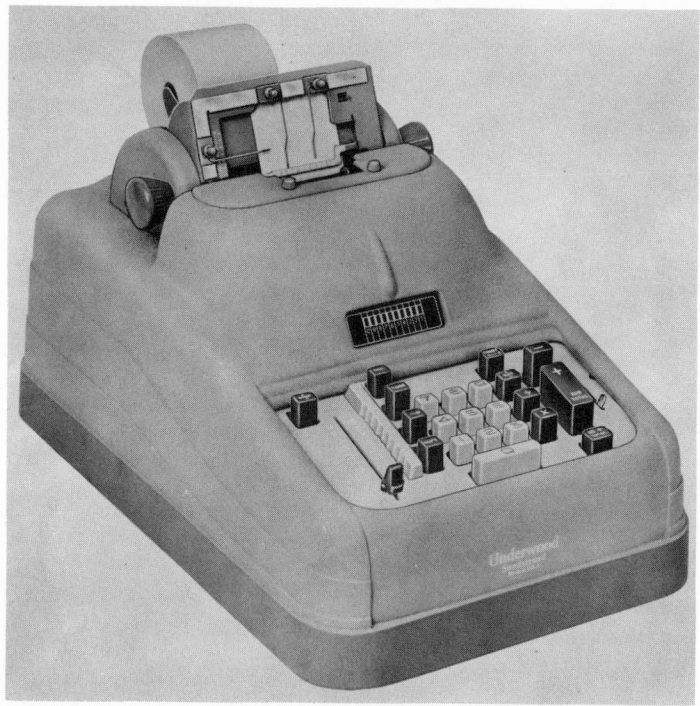

Figure 21-5.   Underwood Sundstrand Printing Calculator with "touch multiplier and automatic division."   (Courtesy *Underwood Corporation*).

register, to show a multiplication of the number in the setting register by 1 to give the same number in the product register.   By depressing the repeat key, this process can be repeated as often as desired—either by cranking a manual machine or by holding down the add key of an electric machine. If it is held too long, so that the units dial of the multiplier register shows, for example, 9 when multiplication by 8 is wanted, the additional amount is removed by use of the subtract key.   Then to multiply by a number in the 10's column, the carriage is moved, manually or by use of the control button, one place to the right and the multiplicand added, by the add button, into the product register, a number of times corresponding to the digit in the tens place in the multiplier. In the same way, this process is continued until all digits in the multiplier have been used, when the product is read from, or printed from, the product register.

Division is performed by setting the dividend on the setting register, transferring it to the product register when placed in its farthest position to the right, and then setting the divisor on the setting register in the correct relative position. The operation of division is carried out by repeated

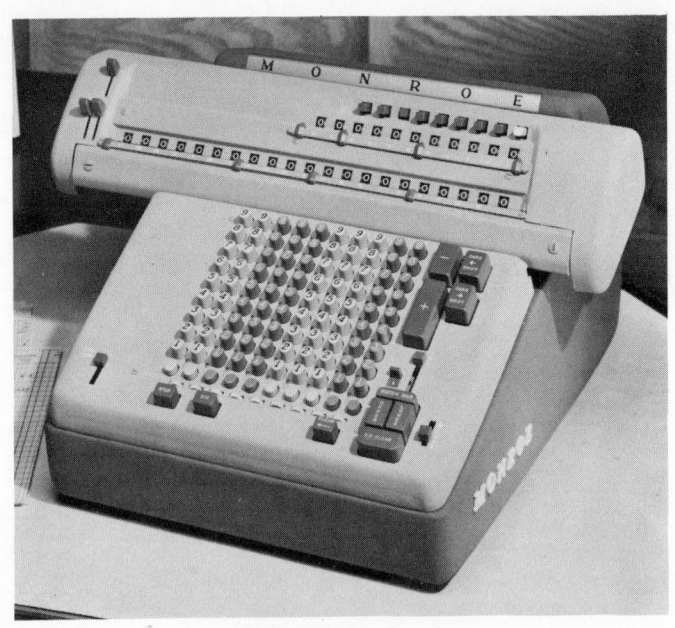

Figure 21-6. Monroe Calculator Model 4N4. A fully automatic dividing machine with carryover dials for short-cut multiplication, having such added features as automatic decimals and automatic clearance. (Courtesy *Monroe Calculating Machine Company, Inc.*).

subtraction in each decimal place of the quotient, followed each time by a movement of the carriage one place to the left. In some machines there is means for automatic division by depressing a divide key or keys. Machines of this type are arranged so that the carriage is shifted automatically one place to the left after each digit in the quotient is determined. While these machines are designed to stop when the last place in the multiplier register is reached, showing in the register the quotient, and in the product register, the remainder, certain incorrect settings cause the division process to keep going. Therefore, means are provided to stop the division in emergencies.   Of course, machines of the three functional-register type are also available with an auxiliary keyboard for multiplication, such as was described for the special two-functional register machines discussed in the 1st section.   These keys are usually arranged so that they automatically shift the carriage one place to the right after the particular key has effected the correct number of repetitions of the multiplicand (setting register) in the product register.

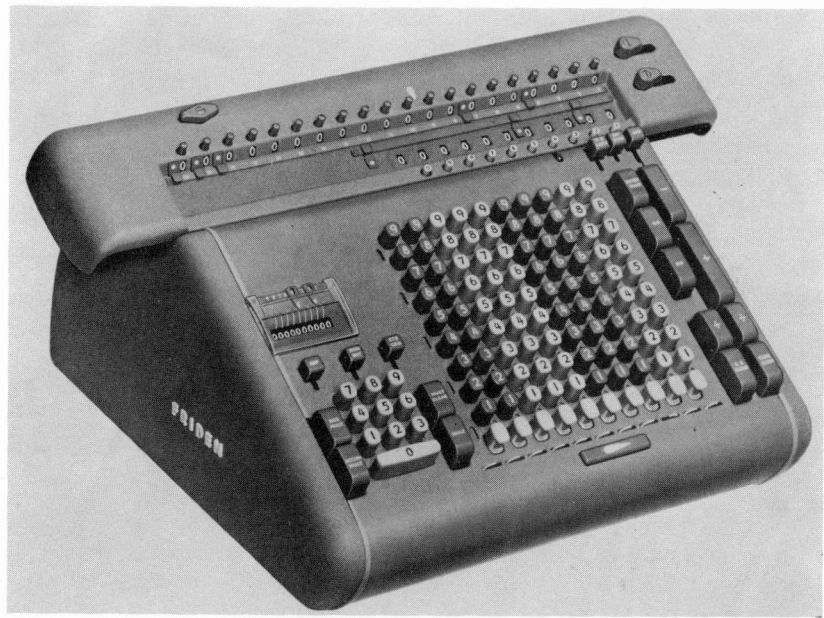

Figure 21-7.   Friden Automatic Calculator with Operating Multiplier Keyboard and Control Keys.   It provides automatic multiplication, dial clearance, carriage positioning and decimal point, as well as many other features.   (Courtesy *Friden, Inc.*).

Four Functional-Register Machines

The three functional-register machine of the type discussed at the end of the previous paragraph accomplishes, in effect, some of the results achieved by the four functional-register machines.   In machines of the latter type there is, in addition to the usual setting register, product register and multiplier register, also a control register, on which the multiplier is set, and can be read.   The operation of the four functional-register machines is most clearly evident from the type having two keyboards. The regular keyboard controls the setting register the same way as that on the three functional-register machines, and the product register and multiplier register are mounted on a moveable carriage and function in the same way. The control register has a ten-key keyboard of its own, which is used to set the control register. Once this is done, simply depressing the multiplication control key completes the multiplication, the product being found in the product register, and the multiplier, for purposes of check, now appearing in the multiplier register. However, there are a number of types of these four functional-register machines which do not use a separate keyboard to set the control register, but simply transfer the multiplier to it from the regular keyboard by means of a special key. Division in these machines usually does not differ from that in the three functional-element machines, being effected by entering the dividend in the product register, the divisor in the setting register, and depressing the division control key.

Duplicate Register Machines

In the early part of this chapter, it was explained that the number of functional registers was quite different from the number of registers in an

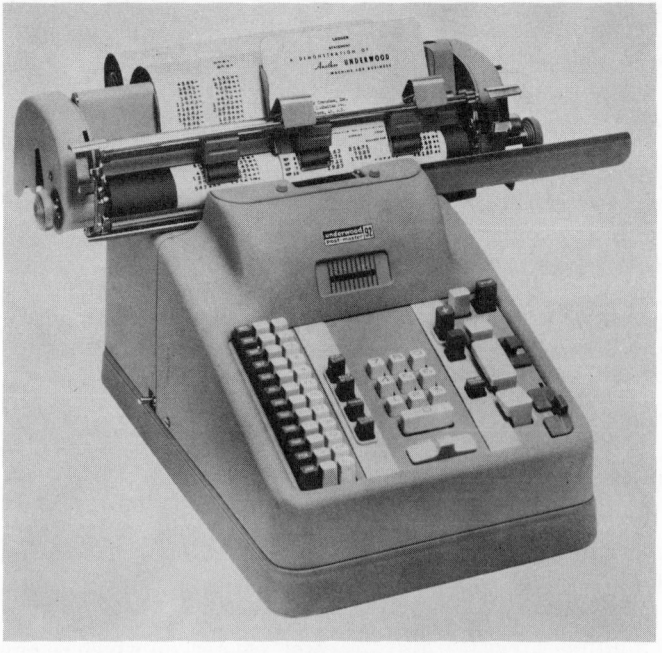

Figure 21-8. Underwood "Post-Master 92." An accounts receivable posting machine with two registers. Among its features are the date keyboard, automatic carriage return, automatic debit and credit balances and means for programming computing operations. (Courtesy *Underwood Corporation*).

adding or calculating machine. This is due to the development of machines, especially for business calculations, that have duplicate registers. That is, these machines have more than one setting, product, multiplier or control register. Such machines usually have greater storage capacity. This is shown by the fact that the registers most frequently duplicated are the adding (or product) registers.

One ten-key adding machine, for example, has duplex adding registers, and therefore permits the separate listing, sub-totaling and totaling of any two items likely to occur together, such as tax and amount, or cost and selling price, or the calculation of individual net pay (including the subtraction of deductions) while carrying the total payroll on the duplicate register. Nor are these extra registers limited in number to one of a kind; some machines, especially those used in accounting, have several, so that they can carry running totals of all the columns which they print on the particular record.

This duplication of registers is a most significant aspect of the development of calculating machines. It shows clearly an increasing trend toward their specialization for the job to be done, under the pressure of the present-day increasing volume of transactions and cost of operation of the business

Figure 21-9. NCR Class 31 General Purpose Bookkeeping Machine. (Courtesy *National Cash Register Company*).

information system.   While at one time the same machines were used by all departments of a business, today business machines are increasingly specialized, except possibly in the case of the large computers, for the immediate job to be done.   This development is shown clearly by some of the specialized business machines discussed below, which integrate with their numerical registers, not only duplicate registers, but also electric typewriters and many other devices.

Specialized Business Calculators

In addition to having duplicated registers, accounting machines have means for providing a greater or less degree of programming.   This pro-

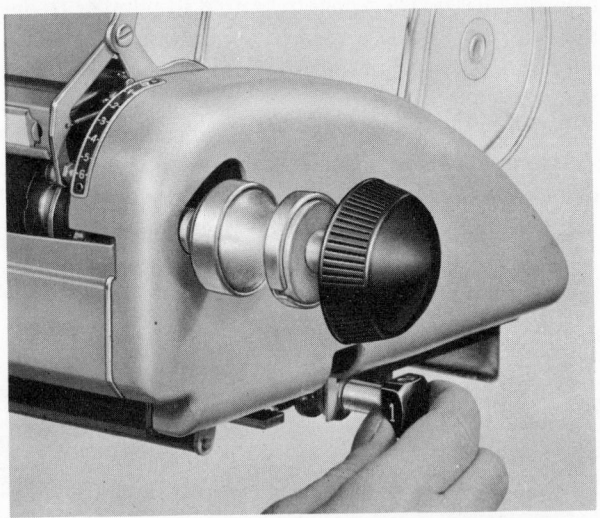

Figure 21-10.   Program Selector Knob for turning Burroughs Sensimatic Accounting Machine from one program to another.   (Courtesy *Burroughs Corporation*).

gramming is of particular interest, because it anticipates that to be encountered in the great computers.   In the smaller, mechanical-electrical machines the programming is accomplished by program bars, which run the length of the machine, and carry metal parts, cams, gears, and pinions which engage with elements of the calculator, at pre-determined positions of the carriage, to perform certain calculations or transfers.   For example, a payroll accounting machine can be programmed to compute and print the amount of the Withholding Tax Deduction, at a pre-determined position of the carriage, and from a total wage figure in a previous column. At another position, this machine can be programmed to add the deductions in previous columns, and at still another, to subtract the total deductions from the wages, and print the net wages.

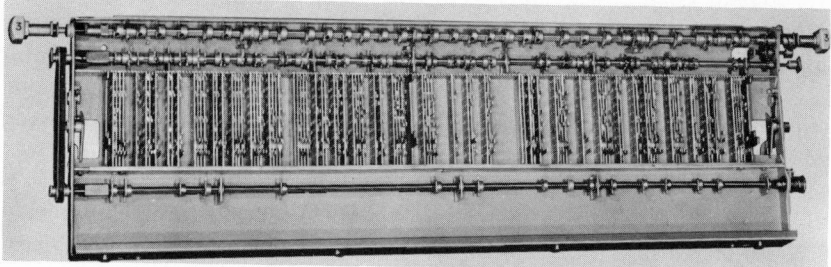

Figure 21-11. Programmed Sensing Unit for Burroughs Sensimatic Accounting
Machine. (Courtesy *Burroughs Corporation*).

These program bars can, of course, be changed to fit various accounting
needs in the same machine.   In fact, they can even be constructed to vary
their program in the same machine.   The Burroughs Company, for
example, offers as part of one of its accounting machines a program rod
controlled by a four-sided knob, which can be turned to four numbered
positions, providing four different programs for bank accounting.   As
described in a publication of the Burroughs Company, Schedule No. 1 is
for posting "Checking Account Ledgers or Statements, Savings Interest
or Deposit Proof"; Schedule No. 2, for posting "Savings, Mortgage Loan,

Figure 21-12.   One of the series of Burroughs Sensimatic Accounting Machines.
Its automatic programming mechanism is shown in Figures 21-10 and 21-11.
(Courtesy *Burroughs Corporation*).

Instalment Loan, Asset-Expense, and Liability-Income Ledgers"; Schedule No. 3 for posting "Commercial Loan Ledgers, with a special position for listing income numbers and amounts"; Schedule No. 4, for posting "automatic printing of proof totals of all applications—Deposit Proof; Checking Account Ledger and Statement Posting and Savings, Instalment Loan, Mortgage Loan, Commercial Loan, and General Ledger Posting", as well as to "transfer checking account balances".

As indicated earlier in this discussion, some accounting machines have electric typewriters integrated with their adding or calculating machines.

Figure 21-13.   The Friden Computyper, an automatic writing-calculating machine. It combines the features of a typewriter with those of a calculating machine. (Courtesy *Friden, Inc.*).

Such machines are not limited to the preparation of large single forms, but on the contrary are used extensively for preparing, or making entries upon, several documents at once.   This permits the programming of the entries that are to be made in more than one place, such as journal, ledger and statement, so that such entries are typed only once, and the transfer is made without possibility of human error, as well as at a saving of time. Such combination possibilities, cited as examples of the use of one of its accounting machines by Remington-Rand are (1) Sales to Statement, Sales Journal and Accounts Receivable Ledger; (2) Cash Receipts, to Cash Journal, Accounts Receivable Ledger, Statement, and Bank Deposit;

(3) Purchases to Purchase Journal, Voucher-Check, and Check; (3A) Disbursements to Voucher-Check and Check to Disbursements Journal; and (4) Payrolls to Payroll Journal, Individual Wage Record, Employees Statement and Check.

Multiple Component Information Systems

As the work load on the information system of a business increases or as one of the basic processes of computation, documentation and storage becomes disproportionate to the others in volume or complexity, a point is reached to which the most efficient mechanization requires a group of machines working in series, rather than individual machines assigned to the various departments of the business that are concerned with information. Since the multiple component systems subdivide the information functions, they are extremely flexible in their adaptability to the relative demands of the functions. For example, some businesses, such as insurance companies, have huge information storage requirements. The multiple component system permits more efficient expansion of this single function than would be possible with the single machine methods hitherto described.

However, the single machine calculators, accounting machines and other equipment may well have a prominent place in a multiple component information system. For example, some companies, including the Monroe Calculating Machine Company and the National Cash Register Company, have developed data processing, adding, computing and accounting machines, which perform all the operations already described for the corresponding machines without the data processing feature, and in addition are provided with equipment that simultaneously and automatically punches on tape or cards the results obtained, or selected figures from them. In other words, systems of this type not only print results in numbers or letters on paper tapes or forms, but at the same time they automatically punch on tape or cards records of the same data, or selected portions of it.

It is obvious that these punched-card and punched-tape systems, in which information is recorded by punching variously spaced holes, add a new dimension to the storage capacity and storage efficiency of the information system of a business. Rolls of tape and banks of cards require a minimum of storage space, and their cost of filing is far below that of individual records. They have the further advantage that information stored in punched holes on tape or cards can readily be transmitted over a distance, either by transfer of the tape and cards themselves, or by direct telegraphic transmission through the agency of suitable "reading" devices. This readiness of transmission of information by the use of punched cards or tape illustrates its basic role in the communication of information, which in the case of these multiple machine systems is a process equal in importance to the other three basic processes of processing, documentation and storage.

As their name indicates, the multiple-machine systems require the use of a number of machines. While obviously all of the types of these machines are not required in every system, their various functions are best understood from a brief description of each type.

As indicated above, the starting point of a punched card or punched tape system is the card punch itself. The card punch may be a simple

Figure 21-14. Friden Model C Computyper. This machine is designed to produce a punched tape automatically, to function as a calculating machine, and also for automatic operation from selected punched tapes or cards. (Courtesy *Friden, Inc.*).

manually-operated device, of the ten-key variety; it may be a component or machine electrically connected to a standard computing machine, as described above; or it may be an electronic card punch operated by an electric typewriter keyboard. Modern types of these machines feed, position and move the tape or card automatically so that the operator is concerned only with the typing function.

Duplicating is the automatic punching of information, carried by a master card, on one or a number of other cards. This method is often employed, for example, in the distribution of information to various departments of a business. The operations of duplication and selection of information for that purpose can be programmed into the card punch itself, so that additional machines are not necessarily required.

Another method of automatic punching is the automatic preparation of punched cards directly from original documents. This is accomplished by providing the salesman, timekeeper or other field worker with specially-positioned data cards and special pencils for marking them. The material of the pencil is electrically conducting so that the cards can be electrically read for the purpose of mark-sensed punching, which requires no initial typewriting or other manual operation.

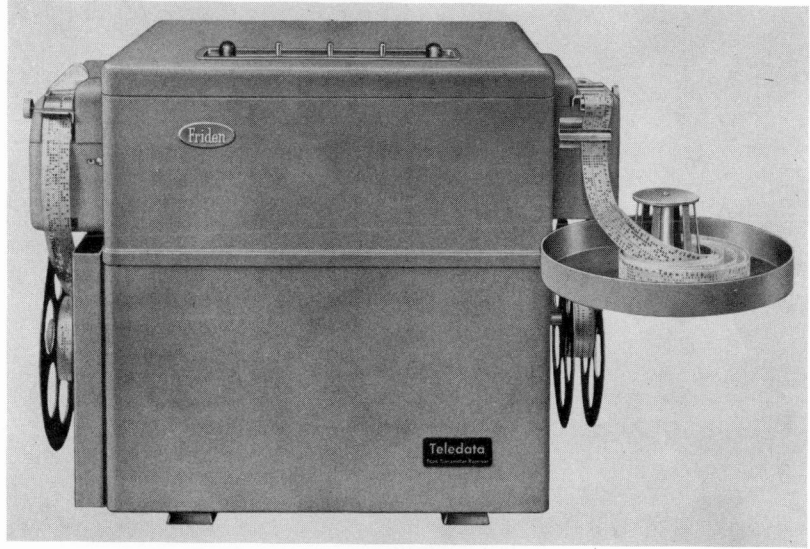

Figure 21-15. Friden Teledata Tape Transmitter and Receiver, which sends and simultaneously receives coded data over existing wire services. (Courtesy *Friden, Inc.*).

Verification is obviously an essential function of any information recording or communicating system. Machines for card or tape verification operate by retyping or otherwise rerecording the information upon the original punched cards or punched tape. The verifying devices are designed, however, not to punch holes, but to "read" by electrical or mechanical means, the holes that have already been punched, and to indicate, by stopping of the machine or by other signal, whenever a discrepancy occurs.

The operation of sorting is fundamental to practically any punched card system. The primary function is the selection from the entire group of cards of only those which have a certain common characteristic. Sorting machines operate to separate cards into groups on the basis of their punched information, or of certain details of it.   They are therefore essential in many of the uses of punched cards, including computation and tabulation functions.   Sorters operate mechanically or electrically by the use of rows of mechanically actuated or electrically-sensitive contacts over which the card passes.   In addition to these two types, electronic sorting machines are well developed, and can perform statistical functions as well as sorting.

Figure 21-16.   NCR 304 High-Speed Card Reader.   (Courtesy *National Cash Register Company*).

The function of selection is closely related to that of sorting, and may be performed, of course, by the same type of machine.   It is also done on a type of machine called the collator, which performs the function of merging, which is the converse process of selection.   In other words, merging is the combining of sets of cards into a single set.   Collators are usually arranged to maintain existing sequences.   Thus, if the cards in each of the sets to be merged are arranged in order of increasing amount of a given quantity, then the collator intersperses them so that the combined set is arranged in correct sequence by that quantity.   The function of matching is also performed by collating equipment.   The object of matching is to check the agreement by the two sets of cards and to indicate, usually by selection, the unmatched cards.

The major remaining functions of a punched card or punched tape system are obviously those of calculation and printing. While logically calculation should be discussed before printing, the converse order is followed here in order to correlate more closely the discussion of computation with that of the computers themselves. In essence, printing is the converse to punching, and the processes by which machines convert the information on punched cards or tape into printed accounting reports or typewritten descriptions is the converse of the method by which the

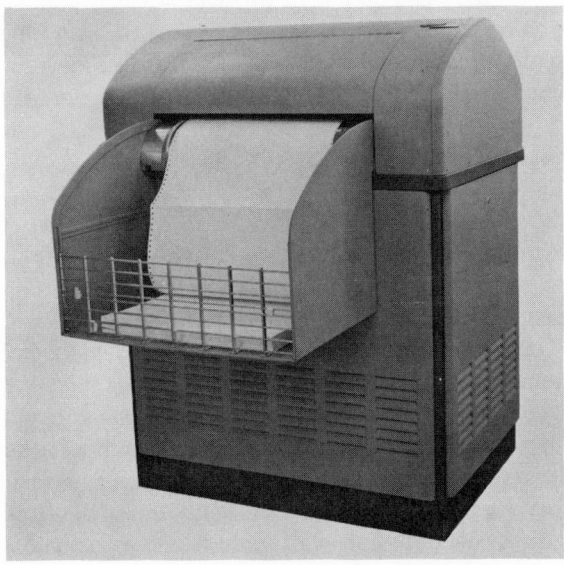

Figure 21-17.   NCR 304 High-Speed Printer.   (Courtesy *National Cash Register Company*).

punched records were originally prepared. It follows therefore that there are accounting machines designed to operate upon punched cards or tape, and to print accounting reports from them of identical character with those that would be produced upon the manually operated accounting machines discussed earlier in this chapter. There are automatic typewriters which are operated by punched cards to present selected items from them, or all of the information upon them in typewritten form. Finally there are devices for the interconversion of data from one coded form into another. For example, the tape reader is a device for preparing punched cards from punched tape. This device is especially useful in conjunction with the telegraphic transmission of punched tape data. The information received by telegraph is reproduced on punched tape, which is then transferred to punched cards for use in a punched card system.

The calculations in a punched card or punched tape system may be made, as indicated above, by using the cards or tape to actuate an accounting machine, which is essentially similar to those described for manual operation earlier in this chapter. The punched cards or tape may also be used to operate an automatic computer.

Automatic Computers—General

One of the most striking differences between an automatic computer and the machines discussed earlier in this chapter is the much more rapid operation of the computer. Its speed is so great, in fact, that it must be operated primarily by automatic input of data and instructions, in the form of punched cards, punched tape, magnetic tape, and other means which can be prepared in advance. While the manual keyboard is also an input device on computers, its main function is the insertion of special data or instructions or the location of malfunctioning components.

In nearly every instance the punched cards or tape used on computers are direct adaptations of the media already described, with one important added feature. For the data coded on tape has been discussed up to this point as consisting essentially of numerical information, with only such descriptive information as would be required to identify it. The tapes fed to an automatic computer, however, carry programs as well as data.

Automatic computers are divided into two general classes—digital computers and analog computers. In a digital computer the increments counted vary in discrete steps so that the computations are made in terms of integral numbers; while in an analog computer the computations are carried out in terms of continuous variables, which are usually direct representations of the physical quantities entering into the computation. Therefore, digital computers are the type used generally in business calculations.

In digital computers, the computations are not made merely in terms of integral numbers; they are further broken down into binary numbers. Note that the use of a binary number system does not exclude the use of a digital computer for the most complex arithmetical, or even mathematical calculations. It merely requires programming in terms of the binary system. Therefore, an understanding of the binary system is important in work with digital computers.

The Binary System

The binary system is a number system which uses two symbols (usually denoted by "0" and "1") and has two as its radix, just as the decimal system uses ten symbols ("0", 1, . . . 9") and has ten as its radix.   The binary system is applied widely to electronic computation where simple alternatives (i.e., binary conditions) can be reproduced by electrical or electronic devices, such as a relay open—("0") and closed—("1").

(1) *Conversion of Decimal to Binary Numbers.* The conversion from decimal to binary numbers is done by successive division by two and reading up the remainder column for the result.   For example, to express 13 as a binary number:

$$\tfrac{13}{2} = 6 \text{ with a remainder of } 1$$
$$\tfrac{6}{2} = 3 \text{ with a remainder of } 0$$
$$\tfrac{3}{2} = 1 \text{ with a remainder of } 1$$
$$\tfrac{1}{2} = 0 \text{ with a remainder of } 1$$

Reading up the remainder column gives the result, 1101.

(2) *Conversion of Binary to Decimal Numbers.* The conversion from binary to decimal numbers is done by multiplying the digits of the number by ascending powers of 2, and adding the result.   For example, to express the binary number 1101 in decimal system:

$$1 \times 2^0 = 1$$
$$0 \times 2^1 = 0$$
$$1 \times 2^2 = 4$$
$$1 \times 2^3 = 8$$

Addition given the result, 13.

(3) *Addition of Binary Numbers.* The method of adding two binary numbers is shown in the four possible two symbol additions below:

0	0	1	1
+0	+1	+0	+1
0	1	1	10 *

for example:

Augend	0111 = 0 + 4 + 2 + 1 =	7
	+0100 = 0 + 4 + 0 + 0 =	+4
	1011	11

Mechanically, binary addition can be accomplished in two ways: the parallel method and the serial method.   In the parallel method, all columns are added at the same time.   It is the faster of the two methods, but requires as many sets of carry and sum devices as there are columns to be added.

The serial method of binary addition requires as many pulse periods of time as there are columns of digits.   It is the most common method for

* 1 is carried to the next higher ordered column.

performing binary addition where time is not important. Numbers are fed into the input as a train of pulses ("0" represented by no pulses, and "1" by the presence of a pulse).

(4) *Subtraction of Binary Numbers.* The method of subtracting two binary numbers is shown in the four possible two symbol subtractions below:

$$
\begin{array}{cccc}
0 & 1 & 1 & 0 \\
\underline{-0} & \underline{-0} & \underline{-1} & \underline{-1} \\
0 & 1 & 0 & 0 \,*
\end{array}
$$

Example:

Minuend	011101 =	0 + 16 + 8 + 4 + 0 + 1 =	29
Subtrahend	−010101	−0 − 16 − 0 − 4 − 0 − 1 =	−21
	001000	0 + 0 + 8 + 0 + 0 + 0 =	8

(5) *Binary Multiplication.* The method of multiplying two binary numbers follows the same basic rules as decimal number multiplication, as is shown below:

Example:

$$
\begin{array}{lll}
1011 & = & 11 \\
\underline{\times 101} & & \underline{\times 5} \\
1011 \\
0000 \\
\underline{1011} \\
110111 & = & 55
\end{array}
$$

(6) *Binary Division.* The method of dividing two binary numbers follows the same basic rules as decimal number division, as is shown below:

Example:

$$
\begin{array}{ll}
000110 & 6 \\
111)\overline{101010} & 7)\overline{42}
\end{array}
$$

The Digital Computer

In addition to the differences in methods of control by punched or magnetic tape, punched cards, etc., containing data and instructions and to the binary system in which the data are coded, automatic computers have a far larger memory for data and instructions than the other types of computers. The term "data processing" encompasses all three major steps of digital computer operations—input of data to be processed: actual processing of data: and output of new data after processing. Due to the different physical requirements of these operations, a computer is not a single machine but a group of separate pieces of specialized equipment.

* 1 is borrowed from the next higher column.

All are interlinked and perform different data processing operations together as part of an integrated system.   This system basically consists of input and output equipment for physical handling of machine information and instructions, and a central unit which performs the actual electronic processing.

The central processing unit is made up of three basic components: the control unit; (memory) storage; and the arithmetic unit.   The control unit directs the step-by-step operation of the entire system, including peripheral equipment.   It directs selection of instructions from storage, interprets them, and directs their execution to fulfill the computer program.

Storage holds both data to be processed and the computer's program of operations, composed of processing instructions.   They are stored in such a way that they can readily be retrieved when needed.   Processed data also are stored until they are used for further processing or delivered to an output unit.

Actual processing of data is performed by the arithmetic unit, following program instructions.   The unit adds, subtracts, multiplies and divides. It also makes equality and less-than comparisons to establish whether data items meet certain conditions whose presence or absence may alter the schedule of instructions to be executed.

Input devices read data to be processed and programming instructions into the central processor memory.   The most common machine input media are: punched cards, punched paper tape, magnetically encoded documents, and magnetic tapes, drums and disks.   Output devices transcribe processed data into machine media and can also print it out as readable hard copy.   Besides the input devices, communications with the central processor may also be established through the computer console.   This manually-operated control device usually consists of a keyboard, switches and indicator lights.   It permits the human operator to manually enter additional information, maintain control over the system's operation, and to monitor the central processor and peripheral units.

Computer systems may operate in two major modes: on-line and off-line.   In an on-line system, processing is done in real-time, simultaneous with generation of source data.   Real-time on-line systems are widely used in savings banks.   There, transaction information is transmitted over telephone lines from a teller window machine to the central processor which instantly checks balance and other information stored in memory storage.   As they are located, the account records are updated to reflect the transaction and this information is retransmitted to the teller machine which automatically prints it in the customer's passbook.   On-line processing requires suitable data gathering equipment and communications facilities, and random access memory devices which permit instant location of the "address" at which any data item is stored.   In a sequential search, data items would have to be read in order until the item sought was located. Such a system which is fully automatic at all stages, from data origination through processing back to final implementation of control is called a *closed-loop system.*

Digital Computer Operation

All instructions issued to the system come from the control section of the central processing unit just as all data processed through the system must enter the central processor's arithmetic section.   The central processing unit thus controls and supervises the entire system and performs all logical and arithmetic operations on data.

All computer data and instructions must issue from memory storage prior to processing or execution.   Memory storage is of two types, main and auxiliary.   Main storage is generally the fastest storage device in a system.   It houses all instructions which usually take up the greater part of its capacity.   In addition, all input data to be stored in auxiliary storage or retrieved from the latter for processing must be routed through main storage.   Auxiliary storage consists of other storage devices such as magnetic tapes, drums and disks.   Its capacity is usually far greater than that of main storage, even though information thus stored is less rapidly accessible.

In binary notation (described previously) the smallest unit of operation is the bit, which is 1, while 0 is called no bit.   In computer codes, each numeric, alphabetic or special character is represented by a different combination of bits.   There are different codes in use, most of which are self-checking.   They are provided with a built-in method for automatically checking the validity of coded information as it is processed.   In some codes, each unit or character of data is represented by a specific number of bit positions which must always contain an even number of 1 bits.   A code character with an odd number of 1 bits is detected and an error is indicated.

The basic unit of computer information is the "word."   It consists of consecutive bit positions of information whose number varies according to computer models.   Common word lengths are 24, 36 or 48 bits.   If data positions are fewer than a word's length, excess positions can be filled with zeros or spaces.   Two or more short data items can also be packed into one word.   Extra steps are then required to unpack or separate them for individual processing.   An opposite situation occurs when an item is of greater-than-word length, requiring more than one word to express it.

Arithmetic Section

Data retrieved from memory for processing are handled by the arithmetic logical section of the central processor.   This section contains the circuitry for logical and binary arithmetic operations. The two basic arithmetic operations are addition and subtraction. Multiplication may be performed as a series of additions, and division as a series of subtraction and shifts. The logical portion carries out decision-making operations to change the sequence of instruction execution. The arithmetic circuits as well as most circuits for acting on control information are logic circuits, which operate by performing "logical operations" on the various "bits" of information, where a bit of information is a single electrical signal or other representation which may be either 1 or 0 at any given time. The basic logical operations are "and," "or," and "not," although the delay element and flip-flop storage are also of fundamental importance. Besides the adder, the arithmetic portion consists of several "registers." These electronic devices in the central processor are capable of receiving information, storing it, and transferring it elsewhere as directed. Registers differ in size, capacity and use and are named according to their functions.

Control Section

Instructions for logical and arithmetic operations are selected, interpreted and directed by the control unit. The order in which these instructions are transferred from memory to the control unit is generally controlled by a sequence register located in memory. At the start of program execution, the register is set to the address of the first instruction and from there it supplies the control unit with the address of the next instruction. During the sequence of each execution, the sequence register is automatically stepped up to the address of the next instruction and then supervises its execution.

An instruction basically consists of an *operand* and an *operation*. The operand can either be a storage address for data or instruction or can specify a control function. The operation indicates which function is to be performed, such as reading, writing, add or subtract. The execution of each instruction must therefore combine several machine operations. They are carried out in a sequence of machine cycles which varies according to the instruction, the first of which is called the *instruction cycle*.

For long and complex problems it is clearly tedious to prepare a program which must specify in detail each and every operation the digital computer is to perform. In fact the time consumed in preparing a program frequently exceeds by a large factor the time required by the machine to execute the program. The programming task is particularly great with the high-speed electronic computers, which are capable of performing 10,000 or more instructions per second. To reduce the programming effort required several "automatic programming" techniques have been developed. Automatic programming is accomplished by specifying the problem in a special notation and preparing a "coding" program which will interpret the problem and automatically prepare a set of instructions which will subsequently solve it.

It is to be emphasized that the great capacity of the storage unit of a computer for data and instructions makes possible a great reduction in the time required for the performance of calculations requiring stored information, once that information has been stored and the computer programmed to use it. Thus, the payroll information system of a business comprises much information that can be stored in a computer, including the wage rate for each employee and their various deductions. It is obvious, therefore, that the program which must be prepared for each pay period need not include this unchanging data, except indeed for those instances in which it does change. Moreover, programs can also be prepared for obtaining all the payroll summary figures required, ranging from the single pay period subtotals and totals, to periodic totals for individuals, departments and the entire business. Furthermore, the computer can be arranged to supply such data to other machines for printing the required statements and summaries.

The foregoing example of the use of computers in payroll work applies with equal validity to any other repeated operation in business information processing and documentation. The point to be stressed is that programming, and to a lesser degree, information storage, takes time. Therefore, the more frequently the particular task is to be performed, the greater is the saving to be effected in time and labor through the use of the fully-integrated computer system.

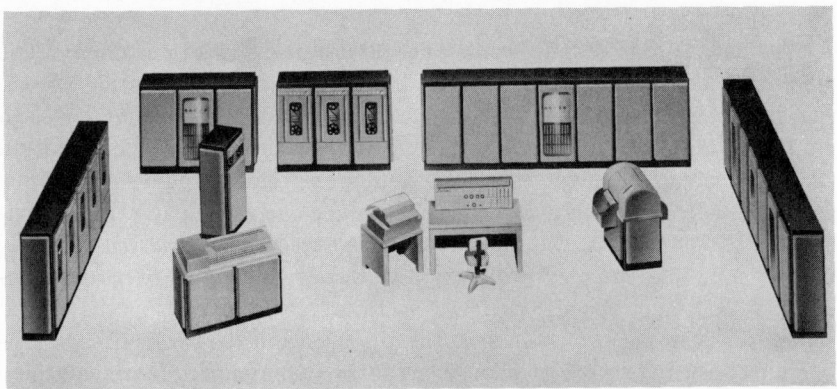

Figure 21-18. NCR Electronic Data Processing System. In this illustration the data processing system is shown separated into its component items of equipment. (Courtesy *National Cash Register Company*).

Figure 21-19.   Prototype Model of NCR 304 Electronic Data Processing System. In this illustration the data processing system is shown as it would be set up in an installation.   (Courtesy *National Cash Register Company*).

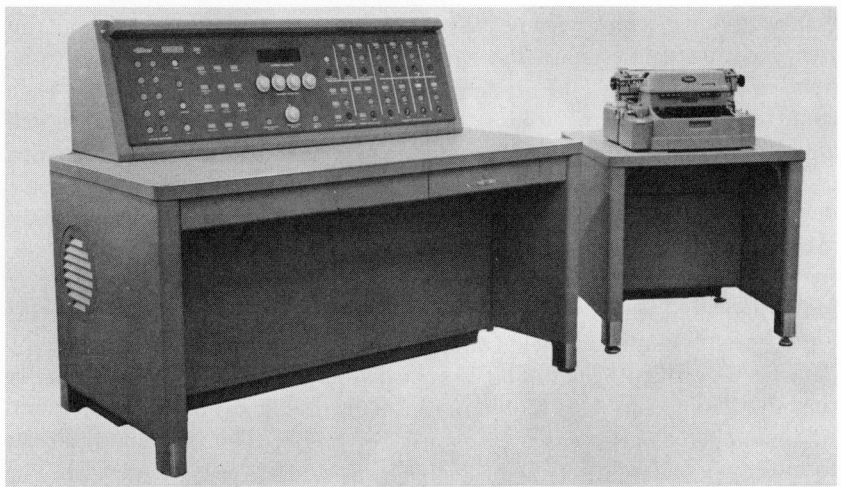

Figure 21-20.   NCR 304 Control Console and Electronic Typewriter.   In this illustration the control console of the data processing system shown in Figures 21-18 and 21-19 appears separately in an enlarged view.   (Courtesy *National Cash Register Company*).

Chapter 22

OPERATIONS RESEARCH

Origin and Nature

Operations research is a general method of attack upon complex problems, or more particularly, upon problems concerning complex systems, such as the modern business organization. The nature of the method can be seen readily from a brief review of its origin and development.

Operations research can be said to have had its beginning during World War II in Great Britain and, shortly thereafter, in the United States. At that time various urgent problems, arising from enemy action, confronted the governments and military leaders of those countries. Two of these problems were, for example, the heavy toll being taken by air and by submarine warfare, which were not then being checked sufficiently by available weapons and tactics. At the same time, there were available a great number of scientists and other research people, who were serving their countries in various capacities, notably for the development of new weapons and defense equipment. As the immediate war problems became more and more critical, it was felt that some of these scientists and engineers should devote their time to development of means for using more efficiently the existing weapons and defense equipment to meet the emergency then current. Moreover, the various problems to be solved were assigned, not to individuals, but rather to groups of scientists and engineers, who therefore represented a number of fields of specialization.

This diversified background is regarded as one of the chief reasons for the outstanding successes scored in the solution of many wartime problems by these operations research teams. They had at their command, for the formulation and solution of problems, a very wide variety of tools, developed in the course of their work in mathematics, statistics, physics, chemistry, the various branches of engineering and many other disciplines. Moreover, they were trained to formulate problems in the most general terms, to develop successive models (mathematical, statistical, mechanical or other) until they had one that justified preliminary testing, and to work from start to finish as a team.

Since World War II, the method of operations research has been applied to a great variety of peacetime problems. Many of which are business problems. In the course of this development, the method has, of course, undergone modification and extension. But its essential nature is unchanged from the procedure that proved so successful in wartime, and which was stated in the concluding sentence of the last paragraph. That procedure can be summarized in numbered steps as follows:

(1) Set up a group of experts representing various fields of knowledge or training.
(2) Formulate the problem in the form of a tentative hypothesis to serve as a basis for gathering data.
(3) Collect the data.
(4) Set up a model, which is the best representation, at the time, of the data. This model may be a mathematical formula, a statistical relationship, a logical statement or description, or an electrical or mechanical analogue. Its form is dictated by the nature of the problem; its purpose is to express the basic relationship involved.
(5) Test the hypothesis formulated in (2) by means of the model. From the test results, construct new models until a satisfactory representation of the data has been obtained.
(6) When a satisfactory model has been obtained, apply it to the solution of the problem.

Methods

In the course of this development of operations research, it has naturally evolved a number of methods which have proved particularly fruitful in their application. Many of these have originated from the fields of specialization of the members of operations research teams, but they have been so extended and modified in their application as to constitute a distinct discipline in itself. Consider, for example, the method of linear programming, which was derived from mathematics. There its definition is "the mathematical theory of the minimization or the maximization of a linear function subject to linear constraints." (As was pointed out in Chapter 8, the word linear means straight line, or algebraically, a function of the first degree in all variables. Thus, while a linear function may involve a number of variables, such as x, y, z, etc., they enter the relationship only to the first power, there being no terms in x^2, y^3, etc.)

Now in operations research the method of linear programming has been applied successfully to the solution of many types of broad-gauge problems. One of the most common is the transportation problem, which enters into various business situations. One such situation is the freight car problem, which is stated in the following form: Given a number of cities, or other points on a railroad from which freight is shipped, given the distribution of freight cars among the cities, and given the operating costs per car mile between the various cities, to minimize the total costs of hauling freight throughout the system by finding the optimal (best) routing of the cars throughout the system. This transportation problem or transportation-distribution problem obviously has broader applications than in this example of freight car routing. It can obviously be extended to the routing of a fleet of oil tankers, for which the boundary conditions, such as the routes to be followed, are not as restrictive as those applying to freight cars, which must follow the existing tracks. It can even be extended, for example, to the routing of traveling salesmen, and is, in fact, sometimes called the "traveling salesmen" problem.

Of course, the linear programming method is but one of the mathematical and statistical methods that have been used successfuly in operations research. Since programming of industrial production of assembled products involves decisions about reserve stocks of components, there has been developed the so-called "quequing theory" to study and optimize such processes. Quequing methods extend from those applicable to operations under strict control, to those involving chance or uncertainty, to which the Monte Carlo method has been applied. The latter is based upon the application, in statistical experiments, of mathematical operations to random numbers.

There is, however, another interesting example of an application of linear programming which illustrates the very broad applicability of the methods of operations research. It is the power distribution problem. This problem is stated in the following form: Given a number of electric power generating stations distributed throughout a region, given a number of power consuming points similarly distributed, given the cost-volume relationship for the production of power at each of the stations and given the cost of transmitting power per unit distance over the lines, what is the distribution of total load among the generating stations for minimum total cost of power for the system, including both production and distribution costs? In this problem, as can almost be inferred from its statement, the optimum load distribution among the stations varies with the total load, and also with its distribution among the individual consuming points. For that reason the operation of such a power system at minimum total cost requires the constant use of an automatic computer.

One such system is that of the Southern Company which uses an analog computer to control the loading of its electric generating plants, giving consideration to both generating costs and transmission losses. This problem is solved by a continuous transfer of load from high-cost stations to low-cost stations until the incremental costs of delivered power are equal. The equipment required includes means for measuring the power output of each station, for generating signals which represent the corresponding incremental costs, and for making adjustments to bring these costs into agreement.

Applications

Although the foregoing examples have involved models representing complete systems, the range of application of operations research methods is by no means so restricted. While the operations research team does take cognizance of the system or business as a whole, the problems to be solved often lie within a particular department of the business. Thus personnel problems may deal with the recruitment of new employees or the most effective utilization of present employees, and thus be concerned with the evaluation of wage plans, testing methods, employee benefits, training and promotion systems or any other (or all) of the personnel policies. Production problems may be concerned with the evaluation of production techniques, time-and-motion studies, production planning and scheduling, inventory control, quality control or any other (or all) of the production methods. The accounting and administration problems cover a very broad field indeed. They begin with the "operational functions" such as are necessary in the preparation of invoices and shipping instruction, in the maintenance of accounts receivable and accounts payable records (with the related activities of effecting collections and paying bills), and the keeping of personnel records (and the related activities of paying wages and wage deductions). They also include the "statistical office functions" of preparing the business reports, since these are based upon the operating office figures already indicated; and above all else, of providing management with the control figures necessary for decision making. Finally, they are coming to include part of the decision-making function itself, in so far as the latter can be reduced to solution by formula or other model. If the requirement of the minimum cost that is consistent with the desired efficiency is added to the foregoing, it is easy to understand why the operations research treatment of office functions is a complex problem, often resulting in a highly mechanized system, as discussed in Chapter 21.

Still another class of business problems which have proved profitable fields for the application of operations research are those relating to marketing. As might be inferred from the basic nature of operations research, the view it takes of marketing extends from fundamental economic principles to the evaluation of specific methods. As a result of this broad view, solutions to marketing problems have been effected not only by modification of selling or advertising procedures, but also by relocation of plants or warehouses, by modified purchasing and shipping methods, or by revamping of price structures. The last is of particular interest, since it touches immediately upon the element of competition, which can be approached effectively by the methods of one of the newer branches of mathematical statistics, the theory of games. The theory of games is clearly a very important tool of an operations research team; it also has other applications, and is the subject of Chapter 23 of this book.

As stated above, the approach of an operations research team to a marketing problem would proceed from the broadest view to the development of specific methods. That is, some of the problems have been found to lend themselves to formulation in terms of the more specific types of model. Since this later type of treatment can be presented in briefer form, it is better suited for use as an illustration in a general book such as this one. Therefore, two reports have been chosen to show the application of operations research to a field of business, namely that of marketing. The first report, by John F. Magee, is illustrated by graphs and charts, and so is an excellent introduction to the subject. The second report, by M. T. Vidale and H. B. Wolfe, uses algebraic as well as graphical methods, and so gives a somewhat more detailed view of these methods of model construction.

OPERATIONS RESEARCH AS APPLIED
TO MARKETING PROBLEMS

John F. Magee
Arthur D. Little, Inc.
Cambridge, Massachusetts

Most of the examples which have appeared in the literature about operations research have been concerned with work in production planning and inventory control, traffic and communications problems, military tactics, or data-handling methods. Not much has been said about work in problems with a strong marketing flavor. In some ways this is a compliment, indicating as it does the importance placed on it by the companies who have had operations research teams working in the marketing area, and their desire to keep details of what they are doing under cover. The only two companies that I know have mentioned their work in this area are the Lamp Division of the General Electric Company, and Imperial Oil. Actually, in our group we find ourselves putting more effort into problems centered about marketing than into any other single area. If the interest in and growth of work on marketing problems in our own group is any measure, I would predict that in the future, marketing will be one of the most fertile areas for use of the experimental and analytical skills of operations research to complement the knowledge and techniques of present-day marketing research.

Examples of Marketing Problems

Here, in brief, are some examples of what operations research teams have been doing in marketing problems.

The executive committee of a company making a line of light machines questioned the amount of money spent for missionary salesmen calling on customers. Studies and experiments were made which resulted in numerical statements of (1) the relation between the number and types of accounts called on and the effect on sales volume, and (2) the relation between sales and manufacturing and distribution costs. These were brought together, and by using the methods of differential calculus, tables were set up which could be used for picking the level of promotion in each area, depending on economic and marketing conditions, which would maximize company net profits. The results showed that nearly a 50% increase in promotional activity was economically feasible and would allow substantial profits.

An operations research team has been engaged in a continuing program of study for a manufacturer of chemical products. This has resulted in measurement of the sales impact of various types of trade advertising and promotion of a number of the company's products. The most important result has been the development of a pretest method. This allows the company to determine, using some short experiments, the responsiveness of new products to advertising, and their expected market life. These pretest results give the company a rational basis for setting up promotional campaigns on new products to get the degree of market penetration which will maximize long-run profits.

A research program was undertaken for a shoe manufacturer operating a captive chain of retail outlets. The job was to find out how the chain could best be operated to maximize the return on investment of the parent company. The studies resulted, among other things, in a cost control method based on statistical concepts similar to quality control. It also brought to light an important but previously unrecognized inconsistency between the basis for store manager compensation and the goals of the company. It turned out that store managers had a much greater incentive to sell clothing and accessories purchased on the outside than to sell the company's own manufactured products. This turned out to be just the wrong thing to do, from the point of view of company-wide return on investment.

One of the most difficult problems in many types of retail chain operations is getting an accurate estimate of what the potential volume of business at a particular site may be in the light of expected traffic and existing competition. An operations research team has been working on this problem for one chain operator and has developed a preliminary mathematical model or theory which appears to tie together a lot of hitherto unexplained marketing data, and on a trial basis appears to improve ability to predict volume very substantially. Work is continuing to test out the method, and if the initial promise holds up, it will represent a substantial breakthrough for this company in planning their marketing investments.

Another operations research team attacked price problems for a manufacturer of basic chemicals. This company is not the dominant figure in its field; and though demand is currently keeping capacity fully employed, the company was concerned about what would happen when new units of capacity were installed, in view of the existing price structure. The research team worked out a pricing basis which would permit the company to capitalize on certain location advantages it had, and to defend its market position against larger suppliers in the event of excess capacity. The company has implemented these results and has seized the pricing initiative in its field. For what it's worth, one of its major competitors had dismissed operations research until the results of this study went into effect. Since the word leaked out that the new pricing system was based on an operations research study, the competitor has moved rather quickly to plan its own operations research activity.

It is perhaps misleading to characterize these problems as marketing problems, if one implies that these are the sole or primary concern of a marketing function in a business. Attack on these problems characteristically requires not only a study of marketing operations and customers' reactions to marketing effort, but also an investigation of cost and operating characteristics in the production and distribution system. In short, while these problems have a strong marketing flavor, in the sense that detailed investigation of marketing operations is required and that the work frequently results in modification in marketing methods or plans, they are really company problems, and company-wide interests must be taken into account. This suggests an important objective of operations research—to reduce the pressures bearing on particular plans or decisions as far as possible to numerical quantities, so that company management will be in a position to reconcile these pressures to the best advantage of the company as a whole.

Several other companies, including a large financial house, a petroleum company, and one of the large food processors, have undertaken studies by operations research teams in the marketing area. These include studies of advertising effectiveness, competitive problems, location of facilities to improve market service and penetration, and product line.

What Is Operations Research

These illustrate some of the kinds of problems operations research teams have worked on. I would like to describe what operations research is and what it does, in terms of a typical marketing problem—budgeting sales effort. I realize that this covers only a small part of the complex of problems facing management in marketing. In many industrial concerns, this problem may not be important—for example, where products are sold on very long-term contracts, or where geography has an overwhelming effect on sales. I think it will illustrate the kinds of things operations research teams do. In the course of this discussion, I would like to use some illustrative charts and graphs. I have necessarily been forced to disguise the products and the scales used in these graphs; otherwise, the relationships and the data shown are real and are the result of work on real business problems.

Operations research teams use the techniques of experimental science and men trained in these techniques to do these things:

1. By experiment and observation, to define and measure important relationships needed for management planning and control—for example, the relation between the amount of selling effort and the payoff in sales;
2. Using numerical or mathematical techniques, to analyze these relationships to predict the effect of alternative operating methods and strategies—for example, changes in assignment of selling time, or changes in the promotional budget;
3. To check by experiment the accuracy of these predictions; and
4. To recommend to management improved operating methods, based on these tests and analyses.

I would like to look first at the problem of measuring experimentally basic relationships. For example, it is generally conceded that a salesman must put in effort to sell a prospect, and in many cases, the more effort put in, the more likely is the salesman or promotion to complete the sale.

One idea as to what the relation between selling effort and outcome or payoff might look like is illustrated in Figure 22-1. The vertical scale represents the chance that a sale will be made as a result of that amount of effort. Figure 22-1 is purely imaginative; the first job of an operations research study of many selling operations is to find out by experiment what this relation really looks like and how to measure the horizontal and vertical

scales.   What are the numbers that characterize this relationship?   What
is meant by "effort," or payoff?   How fast does it rise?   Does it level off?
When?   What does the relationship depend on?   Is it different, for example, for different types of products or for customers of different size, or
under different conditions of competition, or in different economic circumstances, or for different salesmen?

There are indeed many difficulties in trying to locate and measure any
relationship of this sort—difficulties due to differences in salesmen, in
customers, in economic and competitive conditions.   Happily, however,
the measurement difficulties that arise in this problem are not at all unique
to sales problems; they arise in other fields that are equally vague and
equally difficult to explore.   Techniques for designing experiments and

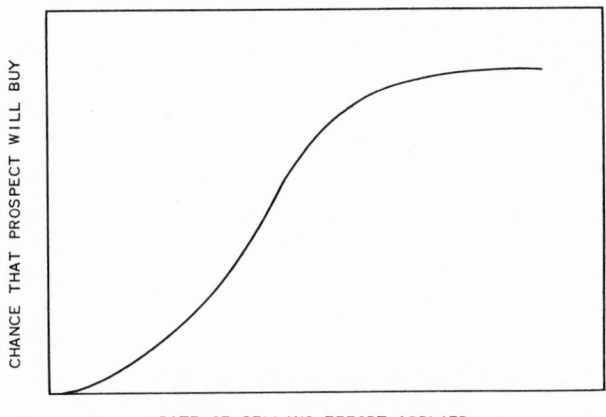

Figure 22-1.   Conceptual relation.

making measurements are being built up and are available for use.   Analysis of variance and covariance is one such type of technique that can be
used to sort out the various effects of different circumstances and conditions
on this fundamental relation between effort and results.

To illustrate, Figure 22-2 shows what was found in the case of a consumer product.   This product is sold door-to-door, and the estimate of
this payoff function was constructed by analysis of salemen's call records.
The horizontal scale in this case is the frequency of calling on a particular
customer, i.e., the number of calls per year; the vertical scale is the average
amount purchased per call.   The apparent relationship indicated by Figure
22-2 shows a characteristic form, similar to Figure 22-1—low return for
very small effort, a sharply rising area when effort really begins to pay off,
and the flattening out of results at high rates of effort.

In many cases, life is not as simple as indicated by the last example. A number of different selling approaches may be used, with the selling approach a combined effort on the part of salesmen and advertising campaigns. There is usually a line of products, and advertising and selling effort have different effects depending on the product characteristics. Display and availability are important, particularly in consumer retail items. Another important point is the question of who is to be sold— whether the dealer or consumer, in retail items, or the buyer or user, in industrial items. These may make measurement and experimentation more difficult, but the same experimental methods will still work. I don't want to leave with you the impression that I think running experiments of

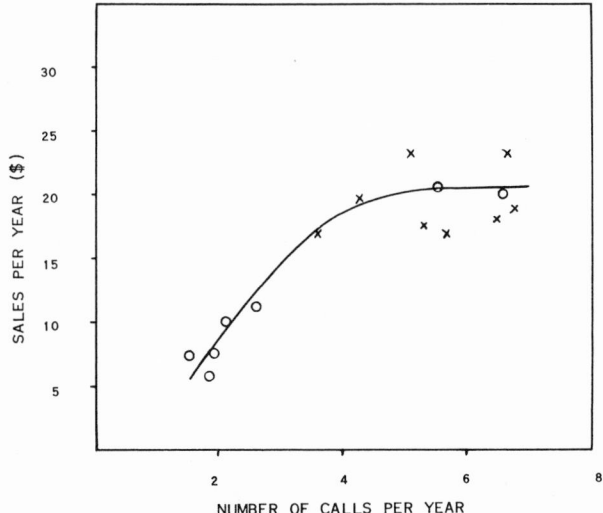

Figure 22-2.   Annual sales per customer vs. frequency of calls.

this type is easy; I don't. These experiments are time-consuming and delicate. On the other hand, they can be made, and meaningful results can be obtained. It is important that they be made, because getting a measure of the relation between effort put in and the results obtained from a particular customer or prospect is fundamental in getting a real grasp on selling problems.

Here is another dramatic illustration in Figure 22-3.   The product is a technical service type product, such as a grease, which is sold through promotion to equipment dealers who recommend the product for the equipment servicing which they do.   There are a number of competitive products, and it is fairly easy for a dealer to shift from one to another.   The result of the promotion is a rapid rise when dealers are converted to the use of the product promoted, and then a slow decay in sales as the dealers are gradually won away to competitive products.

Another type of experiment and measurement has to do with building a numerical picture of sales operations describing the customer population—in terms of number of customers, potential business, and other characteristics which may be identified as important. This, of course, is an area where market research methods are particularly valuable, where we have worked closely with market research groups and have relied heavily on their judgment. The detail required in characterizing the customer population depends on the circumstances.

As an illustration, let's take a company selling contract printing to

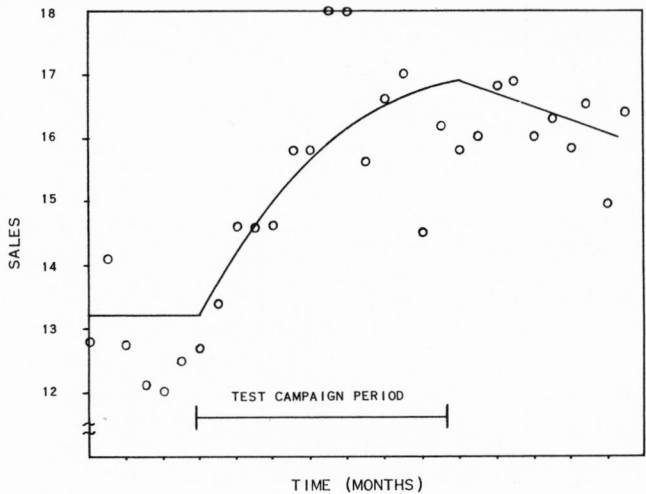

Figure 22-3. Growth in sales vs. time under promotion.

industrial customers. A market survey was made to determine the distribution of customers or potential customers in terms of the volume of contract printing which they let out. I won't attempt to go into the technical methods for making this survey; these are probably better known to most of you than to me. However, what we found was of some interest. The results are shown in Figure 22-4. Here we have plotted the cumulative distribution of customers according to estimated volume. The top line shows the percentage of customers at or below any given size and their estimated contract printing volume. The bottom line shows the percent of the total market potential accounted for by customers at or below a given size. For example, customers doing $500 or less per year make up over 70% of the total group but account for only 10% of the total potential.

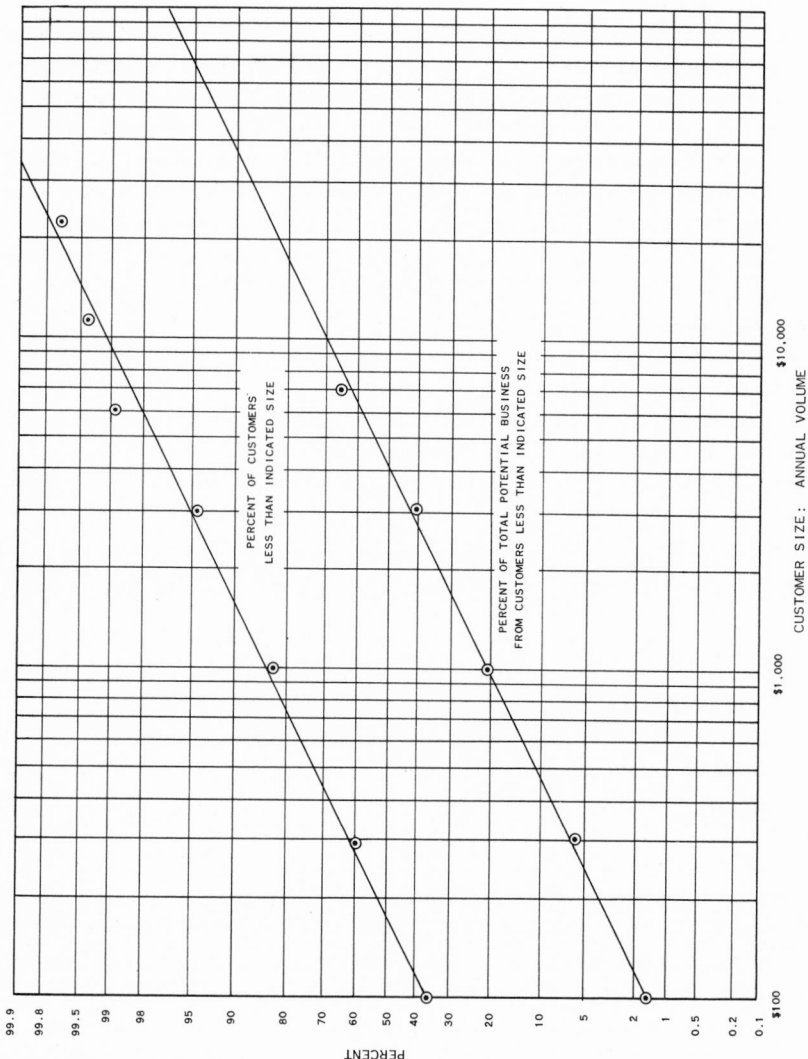

Figure 22-4. Distribution of customers by annual volume of contract printing.

589

On the other hand, the top 1% of the customer group—customers letting $10,000 or more contract printing business per year—account for over 30% of the total annual potential.

In itself this distribution of customers by potential size is not directly useful. It does have some suggestive value, indicating, for example, the tremendous importance of the few large printing buyers. However, combined with the results of the experiments and the experimental measurements of the relation between sales effort and payoff, this distribution puts us in a position to make some significant progress. On one hand, we have an estimate of the chance of gaining a customer or holding a customer, related to the amount of sales effort put in; on the other hand, we have a distribution of customers according to volume, which gives us a basis for knowing how many customers of any given size we have to work with. We can now begin to play these relationships one against another, to decide just how much of the market we should attempt to tap, how much of our effort should go into trying to gain large new customers vs. trying to hold moderate-sized existing customers. This brings us to the second job of an operations research team: to use numerical and mathematical methods to manipulate the relationships that have been found and measured, and in this way to uncover improved operating methods or strategies for management to consider.

For example, with the measurements and relationships described before, we are now in a position to begin to answer questions like these: How and where should sales effort be used? How much sales effort should be devoted to various types and sizes of customers? How many accounts and prospects should be assigned to a particular salesman? How many salesmen in total can be effectively employed in view of the estimated revenue they will produce and their cost?

There are a number of techniques for attacking these questions once the relation between effort and payoff is known, and we have some description of the customer population. These techniques range from arithmetic to more complex methods. The classical methods of the calculus may be used, and in some cases even more esoteric approaches such as game theory may have a place. In some cases it may be satisfactory to attack these problems with pencil and paper, while in others it may be productive to use computing equipment. An analyst who is well versed in a range of these techniques and has a good sense for the physical realities of the problem can use the ideas and basic principles which are common to these techniques fairly readily in getting at answers to operating questions of the type I have posed.

There is one principle which is fundamental to all of these; that is to adjust the use of effort in order to get an equal added profit or return on the advertising investment from the last dollar spent on each medium or customer. This is by no means a new principle; it is very similar to the principle underlying the economist's marginal analysis. What is new or added is this: first we have isolated and measured the relationships needed to apply this principle, and have changed these from abstract concepts to numerical quantities; second, we have techniques to manipulate the numerical relationships in order to apply marginal principles in practice.

For example, using mathematical or arithmetic techniques of the type mentioned, it is possible to construct a chart like Figure 22-5, relating sales obtained to promotional effort in total. This chart was derived for the problem I mentioned earlier of door-to-door selling of consumer products.

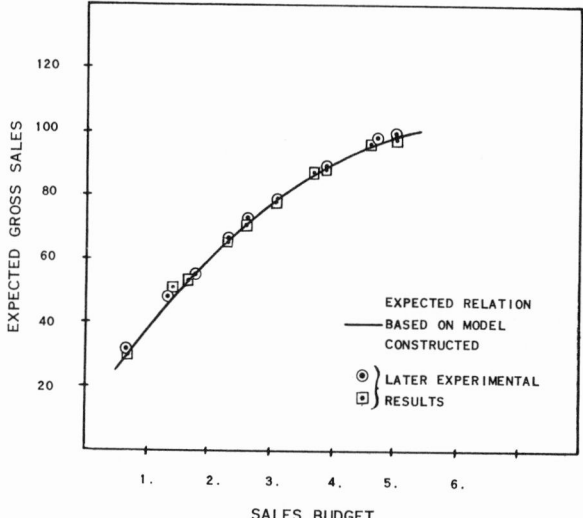

Figure 22-5.   Expected gross sales vs. sales budget.

The solid line shows the derived relationship based on the detailed measurements of results obtained vs. effort put in and on the statistical analysis of the customer population. The points show various experimental checks that were made in field trials.

One might ask: Why go to the bother of working out the derived relationship? Why not obtain the relationship directly from experimentation? There are at least three reasons why building up this relationship from detailed analysis was fruitful:

1. Any relation between effort expended on promotion and results obtained implies a determination of how different increments of promotional effort would be used. The preliminary analysis was necessary to arrive at an efficient answer to this question.

2. Preliminary analysis gave us a close enough understanding of individual customers' behavior to permit accurate adjustments for differences in sales results due to economic or geographical differences. Without the preliminary work, it would have been extremely difficult to interpret the experimental results to account for extraneous influences.

3. A check between the derived relationship based on detailed analysis and the experimentally observed relationship gave us confidence

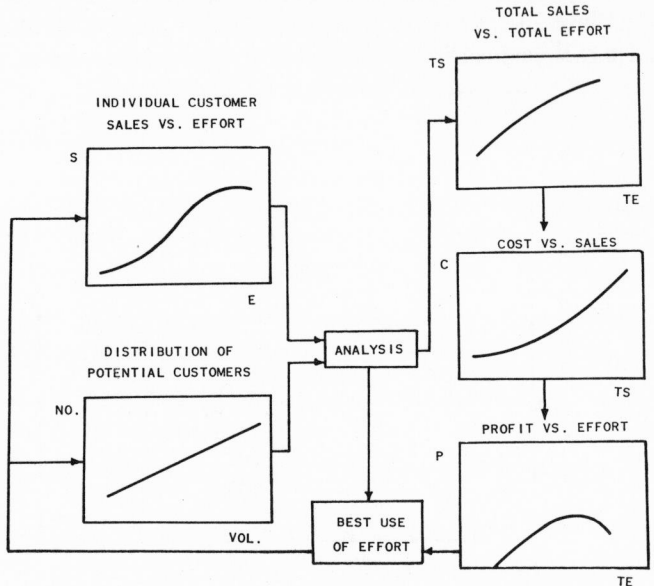

Figure 22-6.   Illustrative model of sales budgeting.

both in the analysis which had gone before and in the validity of the experimental results.

In Figure 22-6 I have tried to illustrate how these pieces tie together into a coherent picture of a marketing operation as a whole.

1. First, as shown by the graphs to the left, we must start with a measure of the relationship between effort spent on an individual customer or prospect and the payoff expected, and with measurement of the distribution of customers as a whole. These are measurements of the type first described.

2. Then, by numerical or mathematical analysis of these, we can measure the relation between total effort expended and total sales

expected, on the upper right.   This may be checked experimentally.

3. Analysis of operating and distribution costs related to volume, and knowledge of the effort required to get a given sales volume, gives the raw material for measuring total operating costs vs. sales volume or, alternatively, the total operating profit.

4. The relations between volume and profit, and between effort and volume, give the relation between effort and profit.   From this we can choose the optimum range of total effort.

5. The analysis which yielded a measure of total sales resulting from a given amount of effort can indicate how best to use the level of effort agreed on; i.e., which customers to concentrate on, and how much effort to spend on each type.

Digging out, measuring, and building up relationships of the types described is one of the prime jobs of an operations research team in helping business management program sales activities.   With relationships of this type stated and measured, together with analyses of production, distribution, and promotion costs, the team is in a position to look into such questions for management as: How big should the promotion budget be?   At what products or customers should it be directed?   What media or promotion methods should be used?   What sales and profits can be expected? How can tests be set up to measure and control results on existing products and sales areas, or to spot the characteristics of new products or customer markets which are developed?

Conclusion

The examples I have given illustrate the sorts of things operations research teams try to do in the marketing area: they experiment; they dig out relationships tying together action and outcome; they state these in numerical terms suitable for analysis and experimental verification; they use any methods they know, from simple arithmetic on up, using computers or pencil and paper—whatever is necessary to lay out in numerical terms what the expected outcome of various courses of action or decisions in a marketing problem will be; they back this up with experimentation, not only to find facts but also to prove out the predictions they have made. There is clearly much of common interest in this work with market research units in industry.   However, I don't think this means competition or duplication of effort.   I cannot back up this feeling with a logical argument— only with experience.   In our work, we have found that the stronger the market research unit that exists, the more effectively we can work and the greater the contribution we can make.

AN OPERATIONS-RESEARCH STUDY OF SALES RESPONSE TO ADVERTISING

M. L. VIDALE and H. B. WOLFE

Arthur D. Little, Inc., Cambridge, Massachusetts

(Received January 29, 1957)

Reprinted from Operations Research

Vol. 5, No. 3, June, 1957

This paper presents the results of studies for major industrial concerns on the sales response to advertising. A simple model of the interaction of advertising and sales is described that is consistent with the results of controlled experiments performed on a large number of products and several media. The model is based on three parameters: Sales Decay Constant, Saturation Level, and Response Constant. It has proved useful for analyses of advertising campaigns and for allocations of advertising appropriations.

Operations Research has not as yet found many applications in the field of advertising. Only a few papers (1–6, Page 605) on the subject have appeared in the literature. It is difficult to obtain reliable experimental data. It is probably true that designing original advertising copy and making *a priori* estimates of the behavior of the buying public are not promising material for operations research; there do exist, however, problems that are of great interest to the advertising man and that can be studied quantitatively. For example:

1. How does one evaluate the effectiveness of an advertising campaign?
2. How should the advertising budget be allocated among different products and media?
3. What criteria determine the size of the advertising budget?

The last two questions cannot be answered without a knowledge of advertising effectiveness; this is where most of the difficulties lie and where research is most needed. Once the relation between sales response and advertising has been established, the optimum budget size and allocation can be determined.

During the past few years, the Operations Research Group at Arthur D. Little, Inc., has studied these problems and examined sales promotions for several large industrial concerns. In this paper we wish to present some generalizations that have been suggested by the results of our experiments.

We shall first describe the type of experimental results we have obtained, and then discuss a simple mathematical model consistent with our observations.

Experimental Results: Advertising Parameters

In order to measure the sales response of individual products to advertising and to compare the effectiveness of various media, we have performed a large number of controlled experiments in which the intensity and type of promotion were varied.   With the cooperation of sales and advertising departments and their advertising agencies, we have been able to run large-scale tests over considerable portions of the U. S. market.   The results of the tests have in most cases been significant and reproducible.   In the analysis of advertising campaigns, we have found it helpful to describe the interaction of sales and advertising in terms of three parameters:

1. The Sales Decay Constant
2. The Saturation Level
3. The Response Constant

We shall introduce these parameters by means of a few sales histories that exemplify them.   The relations and the data in the examples are real.   However, for reasons of industrial security, it has been necessary to conceal the types of products tested and, in a few cases, to paraphrase the advertising media.

Sales Decay Constant

In the absence of promotion, sales tend to decrease because of product obsolescence, competing advertising, etc.   Under relatively constant market conditions, the rate of decrease is, in general, constant: that is, a constant per cent of sales is lost each year.   Figure 22-7 presents the eight-year sales history of product A, plotted on a semi-logarithmic scale.   This product exhibits a small seasonality in sales; however, over the years the sales have been decreasing exponentially.   Figure 22-8 presents the sales history of a very seasonal product, B.   Here again, the monthly sales, averaged over a full year, "decay" at a constant rate.

This behavior, which we have observed in a great number of unpromoted products, leads us to introduce as a parameter the exponential Sales Decay Constant λ; that is, the sales rate at time t of an unpromoted product is given by $S(t) = S(0) \exp(-\lambda t)$.   In the examples above, the Sales Decay Constants are 0.24 per year and 0.06 per year for products A and B respectively.   As might be expected, the sales decay rate ranges from large values for products that become quickly obsolescent or products in a highly competitive market to almost zero for noncompetitive, well-established products.

Product C (Figure 22-9) exhibits some interesting features when analyzed with this parameter in mind.   The sales of this product were "decaying" at a constant rate ($\lambda = 0.9$ per year) up to the beginning of 1953, when an article favorable to the product appeared in a popular magazine of wide circulation. Sales increased by a factor of five within a month. This level of sales, however, was not maintained, but began to decrease much more quickly ($\lambda = 4.7$ per year) than the original rate until it reached a new level, double that before the promotion. At this point, the Sales

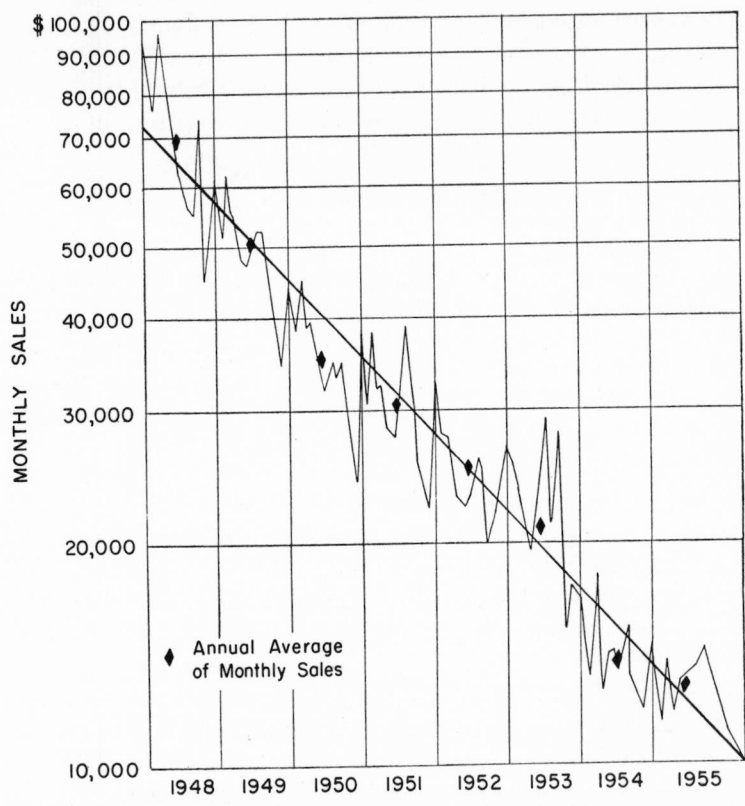

Figure 22-7.   Unpromoted product A—sales history.

Decay Constant returned to the original value of 0.9.   Eight months later, the product was mentioned favorably in another popular magazine, and the same phenomenon occurred.   Clearly, we are dealing here with two classes of customers: those who were induced to purchase after reading the magazine articles, but who soon lost interest in the product; and the "normal" customers, who behaved much like the original customer population.   Both articles succeeded in raising the number of "normal" customers.

Saturation Level

The concept of Saturation Level is illustrated by the sales history of product *D*, Figure 22-10. This product was promoted continuously for one year by weekly newspaper advertisements beginning in July, 1954. In the first six months, sales rose 30 per cent and then leveled off, although the advertising campaign was continued for another six months. This additional advertising may have helped to maintain sales at the new level, but this effect cannot have been large, because the decay rate both before

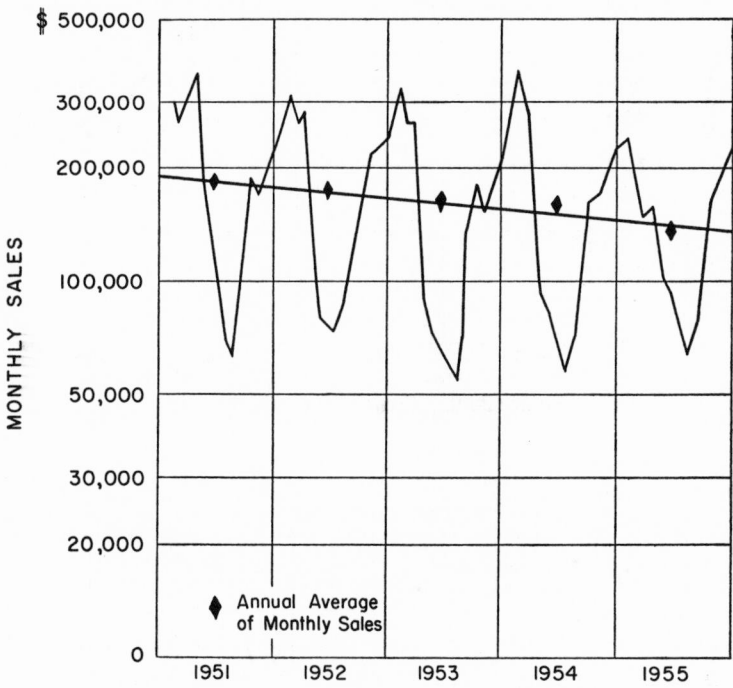

Figure 22-8. Unpromoted product B—sales history.

and after the advertising campaign was small. We conclude that this campaign could have been considerably shorter and equally effective, and that beyond a certain point, it lost its value.

Figure 22-11 presents the sales history of product *E*. Because of the complexity of the sales responses, sales are here plotted on a cumulative scale.

— Area 1 received a spot radio commercial campaign for six months.
— Beginning at the same time, Area 2 received the campaign for twelve months.

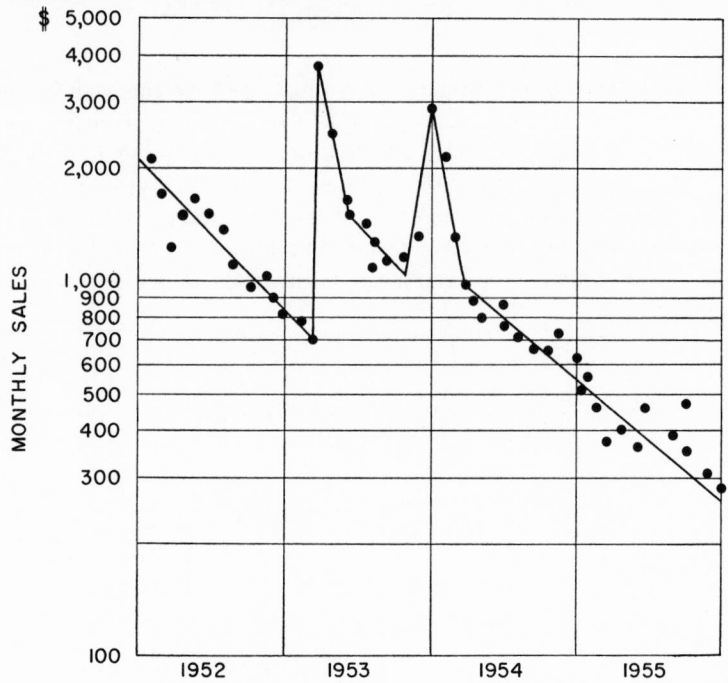

Figure 22-9.   Product C—sales history.

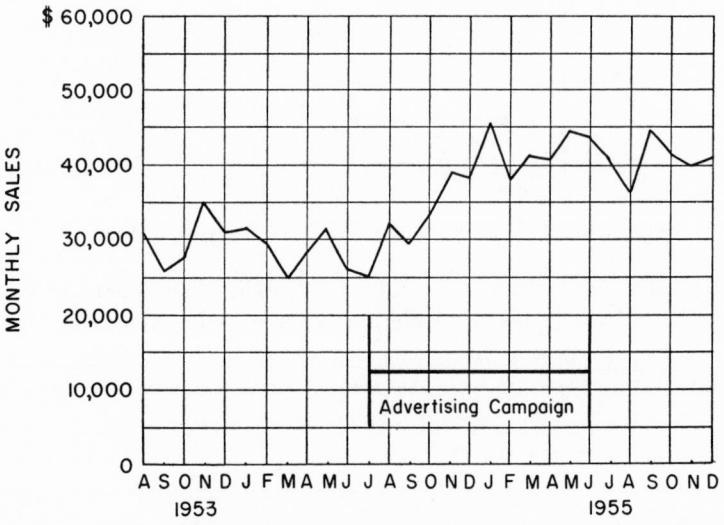

Figure 22-10.   Product D—sales history.

— At the end of the campaign in Area 1, Area 3 received the campaign for six months.

— Area 4 was kept as control and received no promotion.

In Areas 1 and 2, sales increased approximately 150 per cent over those in Area 4; the additional six months' promotion received by Area 2 did not increase sales further.   Area 3 experienced a similar sales increase after

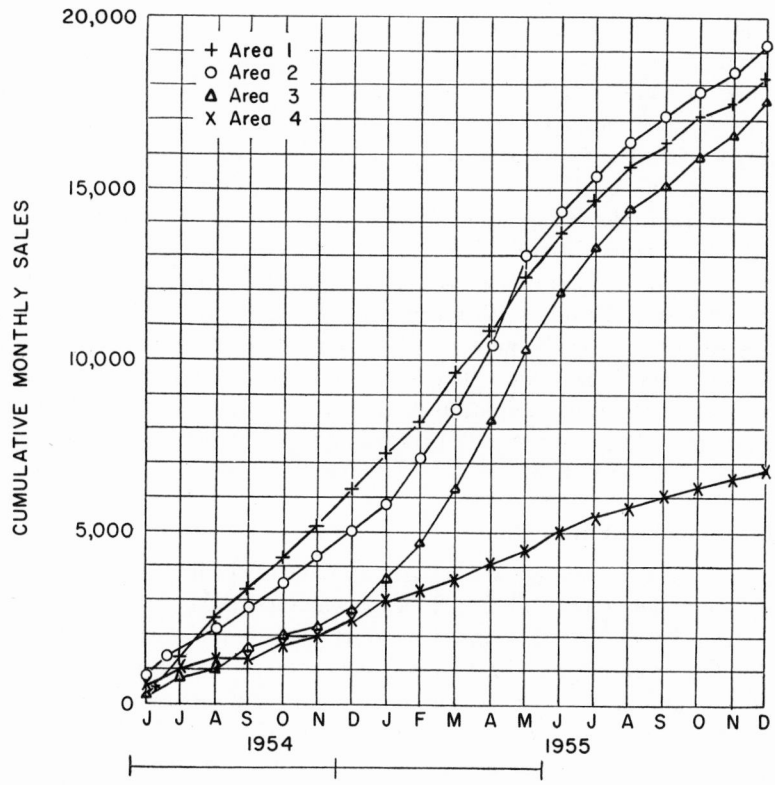

Figure 22-11.   Product E—sales history.

the promotion started.   Therefore, even though the advertising campaign was postponed for six months, it lost none of its effectiveness.

From the results exemplified in Figures 22-10 and 22-11, we are led to describe the interaction of advertising and sales in terms of a second parameter—the Saturation Level, M, or practical limit of sales that can be generated.   This Saturation Level depends not only on the product being promoted, but also on the advertising medium used; it represents the fraction of the market that the particular campaign can capture.

This Saturation Level can often be raised further by other advertising media.

Response Constant

In addition to the Decay Constant and the Saturation Level, we need a third parameter to describe the sales behavior of a product. We define the Response Constant, r, as the sales generated per advertising dollar when $S = 0$. We note that the number of new customers who are potential buyers decreases as sales approach saturation. When advertising is directed indiscriminately to both customers and noncustomers, the effectiveness of each advertising dollar in obtaining new customers also decreases as sales increase. In general, the sales generated per advertising dollar, when sales are at a level S, is given by $r(M - S)/M$, where M is the Saturation Level.

As an example, for product D the Saturation Level was \$42,000 per month (see Figure 22-10). The advertising expenditure was \$5,000 per month. In 1954, before the start of the advertising campaign, monthly sales averaged \$29,000 or 70 per cent of the Saturation Level. The unsaturated portion, or the percentage of the potential represented by noncustomers, was 30 per cent. The new customers converted to the product as a result of the July promotion increased sales by approximately \$3,000 per month. The Response Constant was therefore $r = (\$3,000/\text{mo})/(0.30 \times \$5,000) = 2/\text{mo}$.

Measurement of Parameters

In the next section, we will present a model of the interaction of advertising and sales, based on the three parameters: Sales Decay Constant, Saturation Level, and Response Constant. These parameters differ from product to product and must therefore be determined separately for individual products. The Sales Decay Constant can be measured from the sales data either before or after a promotion. The Saturation Level and Response Constant can be determined from a detailed analysis of the sales history, or when necessary, experimentally. We have found that test promotions, when carefully designed with experimental controls and on a sufficiently large scale, give results that are both significant and reproducible, though the degree of accuracy attainable is smaller than ordinarily considered acceptable in many other fields of research. Product advertising, when effective, shows results within days or at most weeks, so proposed advertising programs can be thoroughly pretested. When as large a market share as possible must be captured before competing products are developed and marketed, it may be necessary to forego pretests. In such cases, rough estimates of the three parameters can be made from a knowledge of past performances of similar products. As the campaign progresses and the estimates of the parameters are improved, the campaign can be modified accordingly.

Mathematical Model

We have seen that the response of sales to a promotional campaign can be described by three parameters: λ, the exponential Sales Decay Constant, M, the Saturation Level, and r, the Response Constant.

A mathematical model of sales response to advertising, based on these parameters, is represented by:

$$dS/dt = rA(t)(M - S)/M - \lambda S, \qquad (22\text{-}1)$$

where S is the rate of sales at time t, and $A(t)$ is the rate of advertising expenditure.   This equation has the following interpretation: the increase in the rate of sales, dS/dt, is proportional to the intensity of the advertising effort, A, reaching the fraction of potential customers, $(M - S)/M$, less the number of customers that are being lost, λS.

This model has been chosen because it describes in simple mathematical terms our experimental observations.   Undoubtedly the probability of losing customers is decreased by advertising.   Further experiments may prove that r and M are altered by changes in market conditions, by competing advertising, and by the introduction of new products.   However, every increase in complexity requires the introduction of one or more additional parameters into equation (22-1).   Since this model has been sufficient to describe the observed phenomena to the degree of accuracy allowed by the quality of our experimental data, there seems to be no reason at this time to complicate the picture unnecessarily.   As our knowledge of advertising increases, it should be possible to improve this model and to develop more sophisticated theories.

From equation (22-1) we can derive several results that have proved useful in the design and evaluation of advertising campaigns:

Steady-state solution.   We can determine the advertising effort required to maintain sales at a steady predetermined level by setting $dS/dt = 0$. From equation (22-1), we then have $A = (\lambda/r) SM(M - S)$.   We see that the closer sales are to the saturation level M, and the larger the ratio λ/r, the more expensive it is to maintain the required sales rate.

Solution of equation (22-1)—For a constant rate, A, of advertising expenditure, maintained for time T, the rate of sales is obtained by integration of equation (22-1):

$$S(t) = [M/(1 + \lambda M/rA)]\{1 - e^{-(rA/M+\lambda)t}\} + S_0 e^{-r(a/M+\lambda)t}, \quad (t < T)$$
$$(22\text{-}2)$$

where S_0 is the rate of sales at $t = 0$, the start of the advertising campaign. After advertising has stopped $(t > T)$, sales decrease exponentially:

$$S(t) = S(T)e^{-\lambda(t-T)}, \ (t > T) \tag{22-3}$$

The sales response to an advertising campaign of constant intensity and of duration T is shown in Figure 22-12.

The rate of sales increase is most rapid at $t = 0$; as saturation, M, is approached, this rate is reduced.   This means that the first advertising dollar expended is most effective, the second dollar is next most effective, and so on.

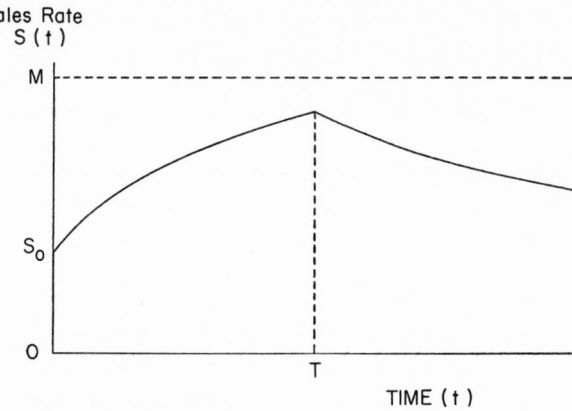

Figure 22-12.   Sales response to an advertising campaign of duration T.

Advertising Pulse

Many advertising campaigns are short and very intense.   To get an expression for a single-pulse campaign of negligible duration we can integrate equation (22-1) to obtain

$$S(t) = Me^{-\lambda t} - (M - S_0)e^{-(ra/M+\lambda)t}, \tag{22-4}$$

where S_0 is the rate of sales immediately preceding the promotion and a is the total advertising expenditure.   The immediate sales increase resulting from the promotion is

$$S(0) - S_0 = (M - S_0)(1 - e^{-ra/M}). \tag{22-5}$$

The total additional sales generated by this campaign are

$$\int_0^\infty [S(0) - S_0]e^{-\lambda t} \, dt = \frac{M - S_0}{\lambda}(1 - e^{-ra/M}),$$

which reduces to $(ra/\lambda)(M - S_0)/M$ for sales well below saturation.   The total extra sales generated by the advertising campaign are therefore the immediate sales increase, multiplied by the mean life of the product, λ^{-1}. Also, given a choice of several products, the advertising campaign will generate the most sales for the product with the largest value of (r/λ) $(M - S_0)/M$.

Allocation of Advertising Budget

We have discussed experimental results of sales response to advertising and have described a simple mathematical model that adequately fits our observations. Once the parameters are measured for individual products, the problems of advertising budget size and of the allocation of the budget among different products can be considered.

Advertising is a form of investment. Those products should be advertised that will result in a return on capital invested equal to or greater than the returns from other possible investments, such as new equipment and research.

As an example, let us consider the simple case of a family of products that might be advertised by short, intense campaigns. We define the following quantities:

a_k = total cost of the proposed advertising campaign for product k.

$R_k(t)$ = additional sales resulting from the advertising campaign.

$C_k(t)$ = rate of additional expenditures resulting from the advertising campaign. These include (a) the cost of the advertising campaign itself, (b) the cost of manufacturing and distributing the additional items sold.

I_k = return on capital invested in advertising product k. For example, \$100 at time t_1 is equivalent to \$100 $\exp[I_k(t_2 - t_1)]$ at time t_2.

The sum total of expenditures incurred by the promotion of product k discounted at the rate I_k from the start of the advertising campaign $(t = 0)$ is

$$\int_0^\infty C_k(t)\, e^{-I_k t}\, dt.$$

The additional sales resulting from the advertising campaign, also discounted at the rate I_k, are

$$\int_0^\infty R_k(t)\, e^{-I_k t}\, dt.$$

In order to determine the rate of return on capital invested in the promotion of product k, we equate expenditures and sales increases:

$$\int_0^\infty C_k(t)\, e^{-I_k t}\, dt = \int_0^\infty R_k(t)\, e^{I_k t}\, dt. \tag{22-6}$$

Under the assumption that production and distribution costs are proportional to sales, we have

$$C_k(t) = f_k R_k(t) + a_k, \qquad (22\text{-}7)$$

where f_k is the ratio of production and distribution costs to selling price. Assuming that the rate of sales of the unpromoted product decays exponentially at the rate λ_k, we have

$$R_k(t) = R_{0k}\, e^{-\lambda_k t}, \qquad (22\text{-}8)$$

where R_{0k} is the instantaneous sales increase resulting from the campaign. Substituting (22-7) and (22-8) into equation (22-6), we obtain

$$a_k + \int_0^\infty f_k R_{0k}\, e^{-\lambda_k t}\, e^{-I_k t}\, dt = \int_0^\infty R_{0k}\, e^{-\lambda_k t}\, e^{-I_k t}\, dt.$$

Integrating and solving for I_k:

$$I_k = (R_{0k}/a_k)(1 - f_k) - \lambda_k. \qquad (22\text{-}9)$$

It should be noted that the relation between R_{0k} and a_k is not linear, so the rate of return I_k is a function of the intensity of the advertising campaign.

Once the values of I_k are known, one can in principle select the products that may be advertised profitably. The rate of return considered acceptable by management varies considerably from company to company, but remains relatively constant in time.

We see that the amount of advertising appropriate to each product, and consequently the total advertising appropriation, can be determined once the I_k are known.

Summary

In summary, we wish to stress the following points:

1. When carefully designed and executed, advertising experiments give results that are both reliable and reproducible. The degree of accuracy attainable is, however, considerably smaller than would be considered acceptable in many other fields of research. Product advertising gives quick results; the pretesting of proposed product advertising campaigns, therefore, is especially attractive.

2. The response of sales to advertising varies widely from product to product, but some generalizations are possible. The response of individual products to an advertising promotion may be characterized by two parameters: Response Constant and Saturation Level. A third parameter, the Sales Decay Constant, gives the rate at which customers are lost.

3. A mathematical model of sales response, based on these three

parameters, has proved useful in the analysis of advertising campaigns. By means of this model one can compute the quantities needed to evaluate and compare alternate promotional campaigns.

4. A knowledge of sales response to advertising for each product permits one to evaluate the return that can be expected from capital invested in advertising for each product. With this information it is then possible to select profitable advertising programs and to estimate the optimum total size of the advertising budget.

We do not know whether the model of sales response discussed in this paper will prove applicable to all situations; our experience is limited to a few industries, and we have not tested all advertising media. It is our hope that as these studies progress and as the volume of experimental data grows, it will be possible to refine the model and thus increase its usefulness.

We wish to express our appreciation to Sherman Kingsbury, George E. Kimball, and Frank T. Hulswit, who in their studies of advertising effectiveness, first developed many of the ideas expressed in this paper and helped to demonstrate the value of the operations-research approach to sales problems.

References

1. HORACE C. LEVINSON, "Experiences in Commercial Operations Research," *Opns. Res.* 1, 220 (1953).
2. BERNARD O. KOOPMAN, "The Optimum Distribution of Effort," *Opns. Res.* 1, 52 (1953).
3. JOHN F. MAGEE, "The Effect of Promotional Effort on Sales," *Opns. Res.* 1, 64 (1953).
4. ROBERT DORFMAN and PETER O. STEINER, "Optimal Advertising and Optimal Quality," *Amer. Econ. Rev.* 44, 5 (1954).
5. R. S. WEINBERG, "Multiple Factor Break-Even Analysis," *Opns. Res.* 4, 152 (1956).
6. A. A. BROWN, F. T. HULSWIT, and J. D. KETTELLE, "A Study of Sales Operations," *Opns. Res.* 4, 296 (1956).

As stated earlier in this chapter, one of the most important mathematical methods used in operations research is that of linear programming. This method is of interest not only because of the wide range of problems to which it applies, but also because it can be carried out quite simply by the use of matrices. A matrix is an array of numbers, and it can be used to represent the effects of variables upon a quantity of interest. The determinants which were discussed in Chapter 5 of this book are a special kind of matrices. They are special in that they contain the same number of rows as of columns, that is, they are square matrices. As will be seen from the solution of the following problem, there are other rectangular matrices which are not square, and in which the number of rows and columns are not equal. This problem is illustrative of many of the simpler business and industrial calculations to which the method of linear programming can be applied by means of matrices.

Reprinted from LINEAR PROGRAMMING: THE SOLUTION
OF REFINERY PROBLEMS

By Gifford H. Symonds
Executive Secretary, Manufacturing Technical Committee
Esso Standard Oil Company

1955

Courtesy of Esso Standard Oil Company

A CRUDE ALLOCATION PROBLEM

The transportation model of linear programming can be used to determine an arrangement for allocating available crudes to several refineries in order to obtain the maximum possible profit. An illustrative example is presented herewith. In this example, ten crudes are available in stated quantities from 10,000 to 30,000 barrels per day each, with an aggregate availability of 200,000 barrels per day. Three refineries X, Y, Z have incremental operations with stated requirements totaling 180,000 barrels per day. Of the available crude, 20,000 barrels per day will not be used. One of the refineries has two incremental operations, X_1 and X_2, at different efficiency levels. The net profit or loss for each crude in each refinery operation is given. It is assumed that the crude evaluations will reflect the resulting product distribution from these incremental operations. However, if further debits are encountered in the solution because of lack of product quality or for transportation of surplus products, suitable corrections can be made in the crude evaluations and the problem reworked until a realistic solution is obtained. In large-scale problems, the calculations can be handled easily on high-speed computers.

The mathematical treatment used in this example is similar to the simplex method applied to a transportation problem. However, the crude allocation problem is worked to maximize the profit, whereas the transportation problem is worked to minimize the cost. A modified method of selecting the basic case is introduced. It is believed that this method will save about one-half of the trials required for the solution. A new method is also suggested to maintain the required number of elements in the quantity matrix (necessary for the simplex method). It is believed that this method, also, will save calculations and will prevent degeneracy of the solution.

The following calculations are shown in considerable detail so that the method can be used for the solution of current problems.

Crude evaluation, availability and requirement
  (Abbreviations: cpb = cents per barrel; bpd = barrels per day.)

Crude Refinery	a	b	c	d	e	f	g	h	i	j	Required M bpd
			(Profit or loss of each refinery cpb)								
X_1	−6	3	17	10	63	34	15	22	−2	15	30
X_2	−11	−7	−16	9	49	16	4	10	−8	8	40
Y	−7	3	16	13	60	25	12	19	4	13	50
Z	−1	0	13	3	48	15	7	17	9	3	60
N	0	0	0	0	0	0	0	0	0	0	20 Not Used
Available M bpd	30	30	20	20	10	20	20	10	30	10	200

Solution of Problem

Construct a basic feasible solution in the modified manner. Select the row and column containing the greatest profit from the table (63 cpb) and place this row X_1 and this column e as the first row and column of a new quantity table for the basic feasible solution.

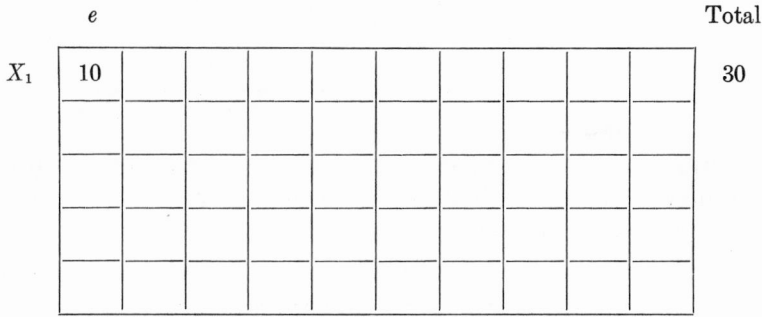

Enter the totals of 30 for X_1 and 10 for e. Place the smaller of these two numbers in box X_1e. Thus crude e is all assigned to refinery X_1.

Since refinery X_1 requires additional crude, select the next highest profit operation. This is crude f with a profit of 34 cpb. The second column on the quantity table is f, and all of crude f is assigned to refinery X_1, satisfying its requirements.

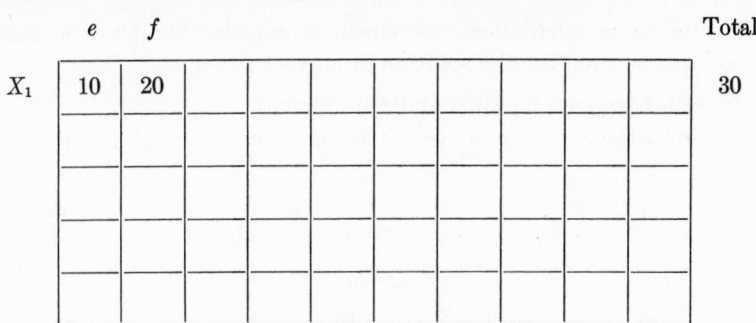

A new refinery and a new crude must be selected, again on the basis of greatest profit. The profit table shows crude h at refinery Y to be the next best operation at 19 cpb. The desired information is placed in the quantity table as before.

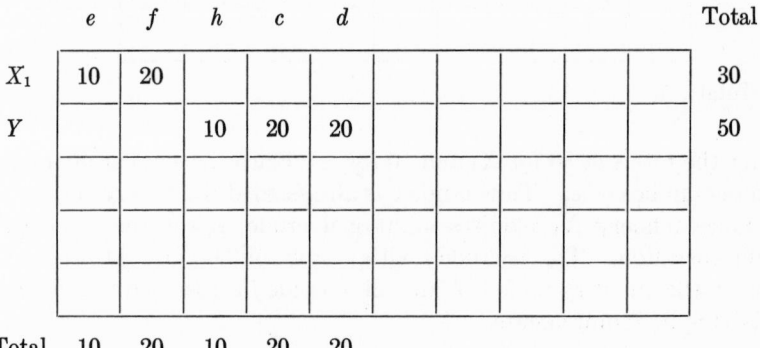

Additional crude supply is selected for refinery Y on the basis of greatest profit, namely, crudes c with 16 cpb and d with 13 cpb. This satisfies the crude requirement at refinery Y.

	e	f	h	c	d						Total
X_1	10	20									30
Y			10	20	20						50
Total	10	20	10	20	20						

A new refinery and a new crude must be selected.   Crude j at refinery X_2 is the next best operation, with a profit of 8 cpb.   Crudes g and b with profits of 4 cpb and -7 cpb are next in order of preference for refinery X_2.

	e	f	h	c	d	j	g	b			Total
X_1	10	20									30
Y			10	20	20						50
X_2						10	20	10			40
Total	10	20	10	20	20	10	20	10			

It will be noted that 20 M bpd of crude b is left unassigned until all the crudes available for the next refinery are considered.   The remaining refinery is Z, and the remaining crudes in order of preference are i, b, and a with profits of 9, 0, and -1 cpb respectively.   These assignments are made, and the leftover crude is placed in row N.

	e	f	h	c	d	j	g	b	i	a	Total
X_1	10	20									30
Y			10	20	20						50
X_2						10	20	10			40
Z								20	30	10	60
N										20	20
Total	10	20	10	20	20	10	20	30	30	30	200

Since the total number of elements placed in the boxes is only 12 and the number of elements required to apply the simplex method is $n + m - 1 = 10 + 5 - 1 = 14$, it is necessary to place 0 in two boxes.   For best results the selections should be made on the basis of highest profit* and they must "connect" the groups $e\,f$ and $h\,c\,d$ and $j\,g\,b\,i\,a$.   An inspection of the profit table shows that Ye and X_2e satisfy these requirements.   The modified basic feasible solution is now complete.

* Where the profit is equal for two or more competing elements, a definite order of preference must be established for all elements to be used in the calculations.

	e	f	h	c	d	j	g	b	i	a	Total
X_1	10	20									30
Y	0		10	20	20						50
X_2	0					10	20	10			40
Z								20	30	10	60
N										20	20
Total	10	20	10	20	20	10	20	30	30	30	200

For convenience, the table of real profits is rearranged to conform with the basic feasible solution.

	e	f	h	c	d	j	g	b	i	a
X_1	63	34	22	17	10	15	15	3	−2	−6
Y	60	25	19	16	13	13	12	3	4	−7
X_2	49	16	10	−16	9	8	4	−7	−8	−11
Z	48	15	17	13	3	3	7	0	9	−1
N	0	0	0	0	0	0	0	0	0	0

The profit for the basic feasible solution is

$$
\begin{array}{llllllllll}
 & e & f & h & c & d & j & g & b & i & a \\
X_1 & 630 + 680 & & & & & & & & & = 1310 \\
Y & & & + 190 + 320 + 260 & & & & & & & = 770 \\
X_2 & & & & & + 80 + 80 - 70 & & & & & = 90 \\
Z & & & & & & & 0 + 270 = 10 & & & = 260 \\
 & & & & & & & & & & \overline{2430}
\end{array}
$$

$\text{Profit}_1 = 2430(1000/100) = \$24,300$ per day

To determine whether this is a maximum profit feasible solution, it is necessary to calculate the C'_{ij} values (negative coefficients in the $f(C)$ row of the simplex matrix). Since it is desired to maximize the profit function $f(C)$, any A_{ij} with a positive C'_{ij} value should be introduced into the basis.

Since there are 36 vacant boxes in this problem $[(mn - m - n + 1)$ possible A_{ij} values not in the basis], it is unnecessary to compute all the C'_{ij}. Actually the C'_{ij} should be computed in turn until the first positive value appears, and then the corresponding A_{ij} should be substituted. New C'_{ij} can then be computed by continuing the same order of computation until no more substitution can be made with increased profit. This procedure will save materially on the amount of computing over the usually simplex procedure of choosing the largest C'_{ij} for each substitution. For this case

$$C'_{X2d} = C_{X2d} - C_{Yd} + C_{Ye} - C_{X2e} = 9 - 13 + 60 - 49 = 7,$$

indicating that X_2d should be introduced into the basis. Therefore, the quantity θ is inserted in the X_2d position and the new case is balanced.

	e	f	h	c	d	j	g	b	i	a	Total
X_1	10	20									30
Y	$0 + \theta$		10	20	$20 - \theta$						50
X_2	$0 - \theta$				θ	10	20	10			40
Z								20	30	10	60
N										20	20
Total	10	20	10	20	20	10	20	30	30	30	200

The value of θ is the smallest necessary to eliminate one of the existing elements. This is 0, and element $X_2e = 0 - 0$ is eliminated. The new feasible solution No. 2 becomes

	e	f	h	c	d	j	g	b	i	a	Total
X_1	10	20									30
Y	0		10	20	20						50
X_2					0	10	20	10			40
Z								20	30	10	60
N										20	20
Total	10	20	10	20	20	10	20	30	30	30	200

The profit for feasible solution No. 2 is the same as for the basic feasible solution, namely,

$$\text{Profit}_2 = \$24,300 \text{ per day.}$$

Continuing the search for positive C'_{ij} reveals that

$$C'_{Yb} = C_{Yb} - C_{X2b} + C_{X2d} - C_{Yd} = 3 + 7 + 9 - 13 = 6.$$

Therefore, Yb should be introduced into the basis.

The required adjustment is made by inserting θ in box Yb and balancing the case.

	e	f	h	c	d	j	g	b	i	a	Total
X_1	10	20									30
Y	0		10	20	$20 - \theta$			θ			50
X_2					$0 + \theta$	10	20	$10 - \theta$			40
Z								20	30	10	60
N										20	20
Total	10	20	10	20	20	10	20	30	30	30	200

Feasible solution No. 3 becomes

	e	f	h	c	d	j	g	b	i	a	Total
X_1	10	20									30
Y	0		10	20	10			10			50
X_2					10	10	20				40
Z								20	30	10	60
N										20	20
Total	10	20	10	20	10	10	20	30	30	30	200

The profit for feasible solution No. 3 is

	e	f	h	c	d	j	g	b	i	a	
X_1	630	+ 680									= 1310
Y	0		+ 190	+ 320	+ 130			+ 30			= 670
X_2					+ 90	+ 80	+ 80				= 250
Z								+ 0	+ 270	− 10	= 260
											2490

$$\text{Profit}_3 = 2490(1000/100) = \$24{,}900 \text{ per day}$$

Continuing the search for positive C'_{ij} reveals that

$$C'_{X1g} = C_{X1g} - C_{X2g} + C_{X2d} - C_{Yd} + C_{Ye} - C_{X1e}$$
$$= 15 - 4 + 9 - 13 + 60 - 63 = 4.$$

Therefore, X_{1g} should be introduced into the basis, and θ is inserted in box X_{1g}.

	e	f	h	c	d	j	g	b	i	a	Total
X_1	$10 - \theta$	20					θ				30
Y	$0 + \theta$		10	20	$10 - \theta$			10			50
X_2					$10 + \theta$	10	$20 - \theta$				40
Z								20	30	10	60
N										20	20
Total	10	20	10	20	20	10	20	30	30	30	200

Feasible solution No. 4 becomes

	e	f	h	c	d	j	g	b	i	a	Total
X_1	0	20					10				30
Y	10		10	20				10			50
X_2					20	10	10				40
Z								20	30	10	60
N										20	20
Total	10	20	10	20	20	10	20	30	30	30	200

Note that 0 has been restored in box X_1e since this is the highest profit element which will connect the two groups of elements.

The profit for feasible solution No. 4 is

	e	f	h	c	d	j	g	b	i	a	
X_1	0 + 680						+ 150				= 830
Y	600		+ 190 + 320								= 1140
X_2					+ 180 + 80 +		40				= 300
Z								+ 0 + 270 - 10 =			260
											2530

$$\text{Profit}_4 = 2530(1000/100) = \$25{,}300 \text{ per day}$$

The next A_{ij} to be introduced in the basis is X_2h since

$$C'_{X2h} = C_{X2h} - C_{X2b} + C_{Yb} - C_{Yh} = 17 - 10 + 13 - 19 = 1.$$

Therefore, θ is inserted in box Zh.

	e	f	h	c	d	j	g	b	i	a	Total
X_1	0	20					10				30
Y	10		$10-\theta$	20				$10+\theta$			50
X_2				20	10	10					40
Z			θ					$20-\theta$	30	10	60
N										20	20
Total	10	20	10	20	20	10	20	30	30	30	200

Feasible solution No. 5 becomes

	e	f	h	c	d	j	g	b	i	a	Total
X_1	0	20					10				30
Y	10			20				20			50
X_2				20	10	10					40
Z			10					10	30	10	60
N										20	20
Total	10	20	10	20	20	10	20	30	30	30	200

The profit for feasible solution No. 5 is

	e	f	h	c	d	j	g	b	i	a		

$$
\begin{array}{llllllllll}
 & e & f & h & c & d & j & g & b & i & a \\
X_1 & 0+680 & & & & & & +150 & & & & = & 830 \\
Y & 600 & & +320 & & & & & +60 & & & = & 980 \\
X_2 & & & & +180 + 80 + & 40 & & & & & = & 300 \\
Z & & +170 & & & & & +0 + 270 - 10 & = & \underline{430} \\
 & & & & & & & & & & & & 2540
\end{array}
$$

$$\text{Profit}_5 = 2540(1000/100) = \$25{,}400 \text{ per day}$$

The search for positive C'_{ij} at this time requires the calculation of all 36 values, since no positive values can be found. This is therefore an optimal solution. However, there are two C'_{ij} values which are zero, namely,

$$C'_{Yg} = C_{Yg} - C_{X1g} + C_{X1e} - C_{Ye} = 12 - 15 + 63 - 60 = 0$$

and

$$C'_{Zc} = C_{Zc} - C_{Zb} + C_{Yb} - C_{Yc} = 13 - 0 + 3 - 16 = 0$$

The substitution of Yg or Zc will result in different but equally profitable solutions known as alternate optima. These alternate solutions are shown as follows:

Alternate solution No. 5A

	e	f	h	c	d	j	g	b	i	a	Total
X_1	10	20									30
Y	0			20			10	20			50
X_2					20	10	10				40
Z			10					10	30	10	60
N										20	20
Total	10	20	10	20	20	10	20	30	30	30	200

and alternate solution No. 5B

	e	f	h	c	d	j	g	b	i	a	Total
X_1	0	20					10				30
Y	10			10				30			50
X_2					20	10	10				40
Z			10	10					30	10	60
N										20	20
Total	10	20	10	20	20	10	20	30	30	30	200

Any combination of these solutions would also be at maximal profit; for example, an equal mixture of all three solutions would be:

	e	f	h	c	d	j	g	b	i	a	Total
X_1	3	20					7				30
Y	7			17			3	23			50
X_2					20	10	10				40
Z			10	3				7	30	10	60
N										20	20
Total	10	20	10	20	20	10	20	30	30	30	200

The selection of the optimal crude allocation, in this case, can be made with some flexibility, possibly to improve some other criterion such as service or good will. The profit will remain at $25,400 per day with any optimal solution.

Chapter 23

THE THEORY OF GAMES

Introduction

The fundamental relationship to business mathematics of the theory of games is clearly apparent from the statement that this discipline made possible, for the first time, a mathematics of competition. In fact, the foundations of the theory of games are so broad that they apply, not only to business but also to war, politics and all other activities in which competitive situations play an important part.

The theory of games was presented comprehensively in the book, *Theory of Games and Economic Behavior*, written in 1944 by John von Neumann and Oskar Morgenstern,* although the subject was treated in earlier mathematical papers by those authors and others, and it has since been extended in many later publications. Its methods are essentially mathematical in character, in fact, the objective of the book by von Neumann and Morgenstern was to "mathematize" economics, not in the sense of formulating all economics, but rather of providing mathematical methods for the formulation and as far as possible, the solution, of certain economic problems. In fact, the authors considered those problems as being reducible to essentially a single problem, that of the "maximization of utility," or in the case of a business, of the "maximization of profit."

To appreciate the importance of this problem to economics, and incidentally, the role of the theory of games in business mathematics, consider the effect of successive increments in the number of businesses producing and/or marketing a particular product. When this number (in a closed economy, or isolated market) is 1, the situation is that described by the word monopoly as used in classical economics, and its optimum course of action is determined from the principles and logic of classical economics. In mathematical terms, the analysis of an isolated business may be made

---

* Currently in a Third Edition of 1953 (Princeton University Press).

in terms of certain physical data: such as resources, raw materials, demand (or demand-price relationship), etc., and the problem is to apply this data so as to obtain a maximum result. While, of course, even a monopoly cannot maximize interdependent variables, such as volume of production *and* gross income *and* profits, simultaneously, it can choose one of these, such as profits, and adjust the others to maximize the one. This is an ordinary maximum problem, in which the difficulties, however great, are purely technical.

Now, if the number of businesses making or selling the product in the market is increased by 1, so that there is a "duopoly" instead of a monopoly, the situation becomes entirely changed. Here are present, not only the variables of each business, but those arising from the relations between them. That is, since their actions affect each other, then the result for each one depends not merely upon its own actions, but also upon those of the other. Thus, each business endeavors to maximize a function of which it does not control all the variables. This, therefore, is no maximum problem, but a mixture of such problems, and there is no basis for its solution in classical economics.

When a third economic participant, e.g., a third business, is added to the two, the situation becomes still more complex, since there are now three sets of partial variables concerned. Furthermore, with each additional competitor that is added, the complexity continues to grow, until the number becomes so great that the influence of each becomes negligible, and the principles of statistics and probability are applicable, at least to the extent to which they have been elaborated for economic problems. This final condition would realize, of course, the free competition of classical economics. There is left, therefore, as the province of a new field of investigation, the gap between the monopoly (single enterprise economy) on one hand, and the N-enterprise economy on the other.

To make clear the practical business importance of this field of investigation, it must be emphasized that its application is by no means limited to very large enterprises, as the more restricted meaning of the word monopoly might seem to imply. A single grocery store in a remote hamlet is as truly a monopoly, in the sense of the theory of games, as the giant corporation that is the sole source of supply of a commodity for a nation— furthermore, the addition of a second grocery store in that hamlet constitutes a true duopoly, in the sense of this analysis. Moreover, an N-enterprise or N-individual aystem is not necessarily free competition, however large N may be, if the individual units act, to a greater or less degree, in unison.

This problem to which von Neumann and Morgenstern addressed themselves is therefore of very wide occurrence, in business as in other fields. Their approach utilized various mathematical procedures, notably those of set theory, functional analysis and mathematical logics. However, they and many of the later contributors to the subject have furnished many explanations and examples, whereby there is available a basis for a non-mathematical survey of the methods and results.

The basic approach is familiar from having been used before in exploring new fields or in attacking old unsolved problems. It is to simplify, to the utmost extent possible, the problem to be solved, while retaining its essential features. Since the distinguishing characteristic of this problem is that of competition between people, that characteristic can be understood by the study of competitive games. While it is true that games do not approach in complexity the many intricate elements of an economic or business problem, for that very reason they provide a means of attacking mathematically any such problem of conflicting interests and strategies.

As a further step in simplifying the analysis, the theory classifies games into two major groups—zero-sum games and non-zero-sum games. In a zero-sum game the sum of the payments between the players as of the end of the game is zero, that is, one player's gain is a loss to the other or the others. All games played for entertainment belong to this class, while competitive situations in business rarely do. The development of the theory of zero-sum games was found to provide methods of analysis which could be extended to the non-zero-sum ones.

This extension was made possible in part by von Neumann's demonstration that an N-person non-zero-sum game (variable sum game) could be reduced to a zero-sum N + 1-person game. Moreover, he was also able to base the theory of the zero-sum N-person game (or N + 1-person game) on the special case of the zero-sum two-person game. For while some elements are absent from two-person games that occur where more than two are involved, such as coalitions and related compensations, the zero-sum two-person games, by this very simplification, concentrate attention on the problems which are fundamental to all games, and indeed to all strategy. These problems include the following: How does each player plan his strategy? How much information is available to each player throughout the game? How does each player modify his strategy from information about the player's plan? Complete answers to these three questions embody a theory of games which can therefore be formulated most simply n terms of the zero-sum two-person game.

Two-Person Games

To illustrate the method of formulating the results of game-theory analysis, it is well to begin with a very simple game. Two players, A and B, play the game of matching pennies under rules whereby each player chooses the side of the penny he will show, and does not see, of course, the side shown by the opponent until the play is made. The payment is one penny won by A from B if the faces "match," and one penny won by B from A if they do not. Now, for mathematical convenience let us represent amounts won by A (losses by B) as positive numbers, and losses by A (winnings by B) as negative numbers. Then let us represent the plays of the game by a matrix* of numbers as follows

Player B

	Play #1 Heads	Play #2 Tails	Row Minimum
Play #1 Heads	1	−1	−1
Play #2 Tails	−1	1	−1
Column Maximum	1	1	

Player A

This matrix is effective in summarizing the results of the various plays in the game. Each row represents a play by Player A, each column a play by Player B, and the figures in the spaces formed by the intersection of rows and columns represent the payments for the plays. If both play heads or both play tails, A wins 1 penny (represented by the figure 1), whereas if A plays heads and B, tails, or *vice versa*, A loses 1 penny, represented by the figure −1.

The strategy of a player is the play, or the sequence of plays which he chooses. In this game there are only two plays available to each player, he can show heads or he can show tails. If A shows heads and B shows heads, A wins 1, whereas if A shows heads and B shows tails A loses one. In either case the value of the game is zero, just as it is if A shows tails, and B tails or heads. Therefore, this game is said to be a "fair" game, which presents to neither player the opportunity to maximize his gains unless he can discover in advance the moves of his opponent. But for either player to show consistently more heads than tails would expose him to certain loss, once the opponent discovered his strategy. Therefore, he should show heads and tails with equal frequency, (that is, he should distribute his plays in the proportion $\frac{1}{2}$, $\frac{1}{2}$) but in a distribution that cannot

* Matrix is a mathematical term for an array of numbers, rectangular (or square). The "Crude Allocation Problem", in Chapter 22, makes use of matrices.

be discovered by the opponent. The optimum strategy of this game is, therefore, for each player to choose his moves at random, as by flipping the coin (assuming that it is uniform) or by using a table of randomized numbers, selecting odd or even, at a point unknown to the opponent. This variable strategy is called a mixed strategy.

Now, suppose that this game is changed by giving A a payment of 2 pennies when heads match heads, but leaving the other payments unchanged. The matrix for the game then becomes the following:

Player B

		Play #1 Heads	Play #2 Tails	Row Minimum
	Play #1 Heads	2	−1	−1
Player A	Play #2 Tails	−1	1	−1
	Column Maximum	2	1	

Since A receives twice as much if he shows heads and matches, as he does if he shows tails and matches, superficial consideration of the problem would lead to a choice by A of a mixed strategy in which he would show heads more frequently than tails. However, the method of matrix analysis, as applied in the theory of games, shows that the optimum strategy for A is a random distribution averaging two calls of heads in every five plays, and that the same distribution would be B's optimum strategy also. The logical explanation of the result is to recall that the theory of games assumes that all players make the best choice possible to them. Therefore, B's optimum strategy is to show fewer heads, on which his loss is greater, than he shows tails. Therefore, A's optimum strategy is conditioned by B's to the extent that A, also, shows fewer heads. In other words, he chooses a strategy that does not promise maximum gains, but one that gives the greatest assurance of a minimum maximum, which is called the value of the game.

Thus the value of the foregoing game is found as follows:

Out of ten plays, A's expected winnings on head-head matches are 4(number of heads shown by A) $\times \frac{4}{10}$ (probability of B showing heads) $\times$ 2(payment) = 3.2 cents. Out of ten plays, A's average winnings on tail-

tail matches are 6(number of tails shown by A) $\times \frac{6}{10}$ (probability of B showing tails) $\times$ 1(payment) = 3.6 cents.   A's total winnings = 6.8 cents. Out of ten plays B's expected winnings on head-tail mismatches are 4(number of heads shown by B) $\times \frac{6}{10}$ (probability of A showing tails) $\times$ 1(payment) = 2.4 cents.   Out of ten plays, B's expected winnings on tail-head mismatches are 6(number of tails shown by B) $\times \frac{4}{10}$ (probability of A showing heads) $\times$ 1(payment) = 2.4 cents.   B's total winnings = 4.8.

A's net winnings = 6.8 − 4.8 = 2.0 cents in ten plays, so that the value of the game = $\frac{2}{10}$ or $\frac{1}{5}$.

In the foregoing example, it was shown that the optimum strategy is not concerned primarily with the possibility of maximum gain per play. This subject is developed further in the game represented by the following matrix:

Player B

		S_1B	S_2B	S_3B	Row Minimum
Player A	S_1A	5	4	5	4
	S_2A	6	3	2	2
	Column Maximum	6	4	5	4

The above matrix shows a generalized game between two players.   The figures in the columns represent the payments to Player A by Player B (the "banker" of the game) in the events of various strategies being adopted by them.   Player A makes no payments, since he has paid the banker for the right to play.   His sole object is, therefore, to maximize his winnings, while that of the banker is to minimize them.   Now, according to the theory of games, A should choose Strategy S_1A rather than S_2A, because, while his maximum possible payment is in the latter, his highest minimum is in the former.   By choosing S_1A, he is sure of the 4 payment, regardless of the strategy which B may adopt.   The figure 4 in the first row is shown in the last row to be the maximum minimum payment (called maxmin in the terminology of game theory).   By similar reasoning, B should prefer strategy S_2B, even though S_3B contains the lowest minimum payment, 2. For S_3B entails the risk by B of a payment of 5, while S_2B has a maximum payment of 4.   This Strategy S_2B is the minimum maximum, or minmax for player B.

Note that this relationship requires an inequality in the game, so that one player, in this case A, is the maximizing player, while the other B, is the minimizing one.   Moreover, whenever the maxmin value for the maximizing player is the same as the minmax value for the minimizing player, as here it is the value 4, at the intersection of row S_1A with column S_2B, that point is called a saddle point.   That value represents the optimum strategy for both players.   However, it is not always discoverable, even if present, and sometimes there is more than one such point, although usually they are equivalent.   It does, however, have the great merit, as already implied in the discussion of simpler games, of minimizing the risk of the discovery by an opponent of a player's strategy.   By choosing a strategy that provides, not indeed a possibility of maximum return, but the certainty of at least a maximum minimum return, he insures that he will receive the highest return possible on the assumption that his opponent knows his strategy.   In short, the maximizing player concedes the difference between the maximum that he can possibly obtain, and the maxmin, as insurance of receiving the latter.

A practical business application of this procedure is common in the specialty sales business, especially in those enterprises that sell directly to the public by mail order methods.   Their problem centers around the non-monopolistic character of their merchandise, so that the marketer introducing a new product knows that he will soon have competition. Moreover, since his sales are obtained to a considerable extent by advertisements, control figures of great importance to him are those representing the relative effectiveness of various advertisements and advertising media for the sales of the type of products he is selling.   This effectiveness can be measured in units of profit, or any other quantity of which profits are a known or direct function, such as advertising cost per dollar of sales.

Now, while the specialty sales business has no mathematical problem in determining by experience the advertising media which yield optimum profits for products of which it has a monopoly, the appearance of competing advertisements, or even the reasonable probability of their appearance, constitutes a somewhat complicated problem.   Data for the solution of that problem is often obtained by such companies from their experience with competing advertisements of similar products.   To show the applicability of the theory of games, let us consider the case of two-business (duopoly) competition in the same advertising media.   Let us set up the data obtained by Company A of the effect upon the profitability (as measured in dollars of sales per dollar of advertising expenditure) of its advertisements in four media as affected by advertisements of Company B in the same media.   This matrix is as follows:

Company B

	Medium #1	Medium #2	Medium #3	Medium #4	Row Minima
Medium #1	3	3	12	10	3
Medium #2	8	4	7	5	4
Medium #3	5	3	1	11	1
Medium #4	6	3	8	2	2
Column	8	4	12	11	

Note that the above matrix does not represent a zero-sum game, since the figures all represent profits to Company A obtained by advertising in various media, as conditioned by advertisements of Company B in those same media.   There is, however, no basis for believing that the profits of Company B would be represented by the same numbers.   Nevertheless, this matrix does have a saddle point, since the minimum maximum and the maximum minimum both are equal to four.   Therefore, by using Medium #2 for a single advertisement, Company A will be sure of an advertising profit of four units, even though Company B advertises in the same medium.   While the maximum return which Company A may secure by advertising in that medium is eight units, and its maximum possibility by the use of Media #1 or #3 are 12 and 11 respectively, the higher maxmin value assures Company A of a profit of 4 from Medium #2 if a competing advertisement is placed.

Now, of course, the foregoing example has been simplified to a great degree.   It deals with only a single advertisement, instead of a campaign— or in terms of game theory, it deals with only a single play, instead of a strategy.   In the planning of a complete advertising campaign from the foregoing matrix, Company A would be governed, of course, by all the figures, rather than by the single saddle point, although the latter might well weight the distribution of advertising expenditures in favor of Medium #2.

Furthermore, in planning a campaign on a game theory basis, great emphasis must be placed upon the knowledge available to the competitor. If Company A believes that Company B can learn of its campaign early enough to modify its own campaign, partly or entirely, then Company B must concentrate to a great extent upon maxmin strategy. On the other hand, if Company A feels that its advertisements as they appear will guide Company B only in planning the latter part of its campaign then Company A must make greater use of concealment strategy. A technique of this nature was used in the penny-matching game by means of random choices. A further method was developed by von Neumann in his analysis of the strategy of bluffing in the game of poker. There he showed that the poker player should also distribute his bluffs at random, but on a controlled probability basis. In the case of an advertising campaign, this effect could be realized by the use of a limited percentage of unprofitable media in the early stages of the campaign. They would be limited to a definite percentage so that the "cost of deception" could be held to a predetermined figure, but they would be distributed at random to avoid identification.

As an example of a matrix of strategies, consider the following case:

Company B

	S_1	S_2	S_3	S_4	S_5	Row Minimum
S_1	9	6	4	5	11	4
S_2	10	8	7	8	12	7
S_3	12	4	3	4	4	3
S_4	7	11	6	10	10	6
S_5	15	10	11	12	3	3
Column Maximum	15	11	11	12	12	

This matrix represents the profits of Company A obtained by the use of 5 strategies (e.g., complete advertising campaigns, pricing policies, model distributions, etc.) on the assumption that Company B may adopt essentially the same strategy. It is to be observed that this matrix does not have a saddle point, and therefore that method of simplification cannot be adopted. However, it is still possible to achieve simplification by use of another concept of game theory—the concept of dominance. Dominance is a method of eliminating certain strategies from consideration. Dominance is said to be strict when one strategy is superior to another term by term.   That is, in the above matrix strategy S_2 for Company A is strictly dominant to strategy S_1.   Also from the point of view of Company B, strategy S_3 is strictly dominant over strategy S_1 because each term of strategy number 3 is less than the corresponding term of strategy S_1. This second statement however, is predicated on the assumption that the profits obtained by Company B vary inversely with those of Company A because the above matrix represents only the profits of Company A. A more rigorous treatment is possible of course, if Company A can set up, for guidance in its decision, two matrices, one representing its own profits, and the other, those of Company B.   This complication, as well as many other types of dominance, such as non-strict dominance, or in the case of multiply matrices, matrix dominance, are beyond the scope of this treatment.

Three-Person Games

A three-person game introduces many complications which do not appear in the two-person game.   These complications arise from the possibility of coalitions, that is, a situation in which two of the players act in union to play against the third player.   From game theory it follows that for players A, B, and C, there are four possible situations: (1) A three-person game between A, B, and C; (2) A two-person game between A and B on one hand and C on the other; (3) A two-person game between the A-C combination and the player B; and (4) A two-person game between the B-C combination and player A.   Since the returns to the players will in all probability be different for all four of these games, the analysis of three-person games is far more complex than that of two-person games and the complexity increases, of course, with increasing numbers of players until, as indicated at the beginning of the chapter, that number increases to a point where the effect of each player is negligible.

The theory of games assumes the coalitions will be formed whenever they yield greater advantages to two of the players than they would obtain if each acted independently.   Matrices for the three-person games can also be set up.   Usually one of several simplifying assumptions is made, one of them being that gains for each individual player are possible only if he forms a coalition with another player.   In such cases the entire objective of the game for each player is to form a coalition with another. The solutions of such games consist, therefore, in determining which of the three possible coalitions yields the greatest return to its two members. A further complication of such games, however, is the possibility of one of the members of the coalition dealing with the third player.   For example, if A and B form a coalition whereby each profits by one unit at the expense of C who loses two units, then A might deal with C on the basis that C pay

A $1\frac{1}{2}$ units in all, on condition of A's withdrawal from the coalition with B—in this manner C would reduce his potential loss to $1\frac{1}{2}$ units, while A would extend his gain from the one unit to be obtained from his coalition with B, to the $1\frac{1}{2}$ units he would obtain directly from C.

To deal with this situation the concept of dominance may be extended from two-person games to three-person games. Thus, one of the possible distributions of payments in a three-person game is said to dominate another if it is more advantageous to both the members of the coalition (in the above example to both A and B).

It is apparent at once, however, that the extension of the concept of dominance to three-person games does not exclude multiple solutions, that is multiply distributions of payments which are of equal value. Assuming, for example, that the maximum payment which can be obtained by two players acting in coalition from the third player, is the same whether the third player be A, B or C, then the theory of games obviously will not return a single answer as to which players should form the coalition. In cases of this sort, especially as they occur outside of the field of elementary games, in real games, or more particularly, in economics or other fields of human activity, there are often external considerations which limit the choices by the players to a smaller number than that mathematically possible. Thus, in the field of business there is specific legal prohibition of certain forms of cartel action. Moreover, the moral or social effect of this legal prohibition is to discourage even smaller businesses, to which it does not apply directly, from combining for the complete exploitation of a third enterprise. Their actions of this nature result far more frequently from the independent discovery by each in his own enterprise and from the results of his own operations, of a course of action which promises to yield the maximum profit, or the maxmin profit.

It is for the foregoing reasons that so much attention has been paid to the mathematically programmed games of business strategy which form the subject of the next section.

Strategic Games

The use of game theory has been extended to decision making in business management by means of three games which are now regularly conducted: the IBM Management Decision-Making Model, the Executive Decision Games of the University of California, Los Angeles, and the AMA Top Management Model for Decision Making. Their general purpose is to develop means for the training of executives, so that the economy of the nation, as well as that of the individual business, can be strengthened by the establishment of means for reaching sounder executive decisions. This problem is, of course, closely related to that of business education, and it also provides means for testing a wide range of methods and policies with which business is concerned.   The extensive use of these methods reflects the realization that sound business policies are fundamental to the economic health of the nation.

The IBM Management Decision-Making Model is conducted as part of the IBM executive development program at Scarborough, New York. It assumes a situation in which three companies, all selling the same product, operate in four areas—each company being located in a different area, while the fourth area is external to all three companies.

In starting the game the size and level of operations of the companies are not usually assumed to be the same, but are different initially and variable thereafter.   Within that framework each company is free to adjust its regional marketing distribution, its price structure and the allocation of its expenditures between marketing, research and other activities. The game is planned to simulate operations extending over a considerable period of time, during which occur changes in policy, and many individual decisions on expenditures for research and advertising, on price changes, on plant expansion and other major considerations.   Obviously an ever-present element in making these decisions is the relative emphasis to be placed on present earnings and future earnings; while another controlling consideration is that of cash position in relation to investment in inventory, in promotion or in research and development.   Decisions for each "company" are made by a single manager or management group.   The time units are quarter-years, and the game may extend to cover a total period of 10 years. By the use of IBM computers the results of decisions for this entire period can be computed, by electronic data processing, in a few days or less by allowing ten to twenty minutes for making the decisions of each "quarter," usually with a summary at the end of each "year" to give the management of each company an opportunity to evaluate the results.

While many of the conditions of the game vary from time to time, the usual plan is to permit no change in capital during the game.   This enables a judgment to be made of the soundness of the use of cash reserves.   Moreover, as stated earlier in this article, the plant capacity is also a limiting factor, since it is usually decided at the beginning of the game for each competing company and can be changed thereafter, if at all, only at the expense of cash reserves.   In addition, it is generally limited by fixed policy.

The figures calculated include all the usual balance sheet and earnings statement items, in order to obtain data on the income and financial position of each participant.   Another class of figures which this game is useful in determining is those of transportation costs and their volume-distribution pattern for the four geographical areas.   In this way, the object of the game can be a study of the effect upon the operations of each company of the limitations imposed by geographical or regional marketing and distributing factors. In the process of obtaining this information, however, an opportunity is provided to evaluate the effects of many other considerations that enter into decision-making at the executive level.

The Executive Decision Games of the University of California, Los Angeles, are discussed at length in the article which concludes this chapter.

It should be emphasized that these business simulation operations do not consist only of the application of the methods of the theory of games, as might be inferred from their treatment in this chapter. While they do draw heavily on that theory, they also make extensive use of all operations-research techniques discussed in Chapter 22, as well as others that are not considered there.

It should be said, moreover, that the success of these simulation studies has been due in great measure to the skill which has been exercised in choosing controlling factors as they exist in economics as a background against which the effect of the decisions can be measured. While it is true that the effect of a new product, an advertising campaign, or a sales policy can be measured in the last analysis only in terms of its real results, the effects measured in these studies of projected economic conditions, of price structures in their relation to demand and competitive supply, and of the allocation of available resources to the various activities of a business, all have direct application to the solution of management problems in a competitive economy.

To summarize the results of these operations in a single statement, it might be said that simulation can not show how to decide upon the best presentation of a new product for maximum market acceptance, or how to write an advertisement for maximum response, but it can provide answers to the question of how rapidly a successful new product or new advertisement can be exploited.

An excellent picture of the operations of these business simulation games can be gathered from an actual run of the American Management Association Game that was made by twenty-one corporation executives in May, 1957. The players were divided into managing groups of five "companies," each of which began the game with 20% of the market, $10,200,000 in paper assets, consisting of $4,400,000 in cash, $675,000 in inventory (150,000 units), and a plant with an annual capacity of 1,000,000 units. Each "company" was given a specified time limit—usually about 20 minutes—in which to make its decisions for the succeeding quarter. There were eight of these decisions, including production rate, marketing program, selling price, expenditures for research and development, and level of operations.

At the end of that time each "company" entered its decisions upon a statement form for that purpose, which was then processed by the IBM 650 electronic computer.   As in the games discussed earlier, the bases of evaluation were fundamental economic formulas set up before the game began, and planned so as to show the effect upon the overall situation of the decisions of every "company."   Then, in light of these decisions, the computer determined the results obtained by each of the "companies," and the resulting operating statements were used as a basis for a new set of decisions to apply to the succeeding quarter.   The verisimilitude of these operations is made possible by the high speed of the electronic computer, which can process a number of decision figures sufficiently great to simulate real business conditions, and still report the effects upon each company of the decisions of all, within a matter of a few minutes.

In conclusion it should be stated that while the foregoing discussions of business simulation have stressed the effectiveness of their application to top level executive decisions, the technique need not be considered to be limited in this way.   Active studies have been made of its application at the junior executive or even foremanship level, and there is every indication that it will prove to be a valuable educational device at various levels of business operation.

The Executive Decision Games of the University of California, Los Angeles, are described in detail in an article which is reproduced in full below.

BUSINESS GAMING FOR GENERAL MANAGEMENT EDUCATION[1]

by James R. Jackson

Director, Management Sciences Research Project
Associate Professor of Business Administration
University of California, Los Angeles

The business decision games with which this article is concerned are designed as tools of education and training in business decision-making. They are "rule games," whose procedures, scoring systems, etc., are clearly defined and depend only slightly (if at all) upon the judgments of referees.

[1] The research underlying this article was supported by the Management Sciences Research Project (under contract to the Logistics Branch, Office of Naval Research, United States Navy), the Division of Research, and the Western Data Processing Center, all in the Graduate School of Business Administration, University of California, Los Angeles.   Reproduction in whole or in part is permitted for any purpose of the United states Government.   UCLA Executive Decision Game No. 2 was developed by several persons, including Tibor Fabian (who initiated work on it), James L. McKenney, and Kendall R. Wright.

Sequences of decisions are required from the players. Corresponding sequences of reports on results of the decisions are fed back to the players, often very soon after decisions are made. The players are given only incomplete advance information as to how their choices will influence operations and the consequent reports. A central problem is therefore to "learn from experience," while playing, how the game really works.

The first such game to become widely known was developed in 1956 for the American Management Association, by C. J. Craft, Richard Bellman (a Rand Corporation mathematician), D. G. Malcolm (of Booz, Allen and Hamilton), and others. In this "top management decision simulation," five teams of players control manufacturing firms, which compete in a hypothetical, one-product industry. Each team makes quarterly decisions for its firm, governing product price, production volume, and budgets for plant investment, research and development, marketing, and market information. The "scoring system," based upon an economic model, is coded so that an IBM 650 computer will work out the consequences of decisions and (with the help of an IBM 407 tabulator) quickly prepare reports on sales, revenues, costs, profits, etc. This game was made the central feature of a special two-week course at the AMA's Academy of Advanced Management, Saranac Lake, New York. It attracted many enthusiastic comments from executives and scholars who participated in the trial runs and in the two-week course. Its success has much influenced several researchers who have independently worked on games of the same general type. One of three such games developed at the University of California, Los Angeles, by my associates and myself, is described below in some detail, and a few others among the many existing "executive games" are discussed in general terms.

The executive games are the glamorous entries in the field of business decision-gaming. They represent big problems in a big way, and are often played by high level executives, who sometimes pay substantial sums for the privilege. But I feel that games of a far more down-to-earth sort are of equal interest to those seriously concerned with management education and training. For lack of a better term, I shall call them "specialized business decision games."

These games relate to restricted problems associated with functionally specialized areas in business management—including problems of inventory control, record maintenance, machine repair, production scheduling, and even bargaining. As an example, a game developed by J. F. Lubin, at the Wharton School, University of Pennsylvania, requires players to place purchase orders for future delivery, month-by-month, to control the inventory of an item whose sales vary in a partially unpredictable fashion. A competitive element is present because of the limited capacity of the supplier (who is not a player, but whose actions are determined by the rules of the game). The purpose of playing is to learn about the process of striking balances among the costs of carrying inventory, stock shortages, and placing, cancelling, and expediting orders. A simpler, "solitaire" inventory game, used in undergraduate and graduate courses at the University of California, Los Angeles, will be fully described in this article.

The specialized business decision games have received far less attention than I feel they deserve, perhaps mainly because they are usually unspectacular—even commonplace—in comparison with their glamorous relatives, the executive games. They do indeed present relatively limited and unexciting problems, but they present them relatively realistically. Consequently, although these games are not always pertinent to top management work, their value for specialized educational and training purposes is clear.

In recent months, there has been much interest in building complex games which will include many features of both the executive games and the specialized games which already exist. Researchers at several universities, including most notably the Carnegie Institute of Technology, are developing games which call for organizational hierarchies of players, some filling top management posts, and others occupying relatively specialized positions. Such games I am sure will assume great importance in the future, but it is still too soon to report on them except in the most general terms.

What Good Are Business Games?

Both players and administrators of executive games often describe them with such words as "absorbing" and "exciting." Excessive claims may be made for the games, in the flush of enthusiasm, and such claims may even be supported by "disinterested" players. I suspect myself as well as the next man, and hence must issue a warning that the next few paragraphs are full of personal conjectures. The games are too new to have been evaluated scientifically, or to have undergone the test of long use. Consequently, evaluations must for the moment be largely matters of opinion. I hope that a straightforward presentation of some of my ideas will help others to form their own conclusions.

The enthusiasm with which the games are played contributes to their potential worth. Whatever the players do, they do energetically and with a high degree of concentration. Good play requires lots of hard thinking. Those who believe that mental exercise is beneficial in itself may agree with many players who have said that there was ample compensation for the time and effort spent on a game in the stimulation of brainwork alone. Good play in the team games requires effective organization and intelligent cooperation.   The experience of working together is often mentioned as extremely worthwhile by those who play such games.

The concentration and involvement of players make business decision games ideal tools for creating interest in their subject matter.   By bringing the subject matter to life, a game encourages a high quality of work in related post-game study, and provides a focal point for thought and discussion.   It can help greatly toward establishing a common basis for communication among players and between players and teachers.   At the same time, a game will help to spark the critical analysis of specific assumptions upon which it is based.

Games can be used as demonstration pieces to teach and crystallize the significance of "principles," much as the laboratory experiments in science courses provide demonstrations of physical or chemical laws. Existing executive games are too hypothetical in structure for this application to be taken seriously, except in relation to some of the most general (and most important) requirements for effective management—good teamwork, careful planning and control, and balanced coordination of interacting factors, for instance.

For the present, highly realistic games have been designed only to represent relatively narrow, almost "technical" problems (including, though, problems of vast complexity).   These are most often problems which can be solved by systematic routines and which consequently do not really call for *individual* attention from managers.   The games are most useful as exercises in setting up appropriate systematic routines, each of which would presumably be applicable in real life to a variety of related individual problems.   Or, at a lower level (approaching that of the mere textbook exercise), such games can be used to give practice in applying specific techniques.   The specialized games mentioned before, and many others, have proved highly effective as means for developing ability to work with the everyday decision problems of middle and lower management and management staffs.

But what I perceive as the primary and unique value of business games as tools of education and training lies in their character as "exercises in learning from experience."   To one degree or another, depending upon the particular game concerned, the players must learn for themselves where their problems lie and how their choices relate to the solution of these problems.   Partly because the games are inevitably unrealistic in some regards, players cannot rely upon preconceptions, and the secret of "winning" is largely in being able efficiently to find out how things work in the unique situation at hand, and in being able to make effective use of what is learned to influence this situation.   Even the problems posed by quite artificial executive games may retain many of the most important aspects of real life, as information-handling problems: large amounts of data are pertinent to the dynamic solution of repetitively raised questions; the totality of problems is too complex to be comprehended in one sweep, but the sub-problems are too interdependent to be dealt with separately; empirical questions, as well as analytic ones, are raised; and problems are posed, such as those associated with risk-creating innovations, which are difficult even to formulate objectively.   In simpler ways, the information charac-teristics of specialized game problems also parallel those of their real-life counterparts.   Consequently, I feel that gaming is a technique on which can be based decision-making laboratories in which managers and manage-ment students and trainees can practice the process of gathering experience and making the most of it—laboratories which may well be as useful in the management education and training of the future as are practice sessions in sports and problem sets in mathematics.

An Inventory-Control Game

Specialized games are most straightforward in concept than are the complex executive games, and it is appropriate in getting down to specifics to start with one of them.   The one to be described is of interest as an example of its species, rather than for itself alone.   The description will be in two parts: instructions for players, and additional information on setting up the game.   Enough information is given so that the reader, if he wishes, will be able to set up and play the game himself, or administer it to others.

This game is a "solitaire" inventory-control game, designed in such a way that none of the standard, quantitative, order-reorder-policy models is directly applicable.   A moderately sophisticated analysis, however, will lead to a computational technique closely approximating optimal policies for the specific problem posed and others of the same type.   The accuracy of such a technique of course depends upon accurate estimates of the rele-vant parameters.   The player is required to start acting as an inventory manager with only a very brief "past history" available.   Thus, even if he is expert at analysis, he must work into the problem sequentially, as the progress of the game yields additional data.

Instructions for playing the inventory-control game.   This game is con-cerned with an inventory-management problem.   Table 23 summarizes thirteen weeks of the ALCU Company's inventory records for Vistascreen television sets.   *Initial Inventory, Sets Received, Total Inventory, Customer Orders Received,* and *Sales* are tabulated for each week.   Three cost items are also listed, as follows:

Inventory Carrying Cost.   Two dollars per set per week, figured on *Total Inventory* for the week.

Cost of Placing Orders.   One hundred dollars per order placed, regardless of quantity, incurred in the week when an order is placed. (This is not purchase cost, but the incidental cost of paperwork, etc., associated with the transaction.)

Cost of Lost Sales.   Forty dollars per sale lost due to shortage of stock, representing profits which would have been earned had the sales been made. Note that no backordering is possible.

These three costs are the *only* ones considered in the game.

In playing the game, you will spend two accelerated years as the Inventory Manager responsible for ALCU's Vistascreen line.   Demands on inventory will be determined by cutting a special deck of playing cards. You will need sheets of paper ruled and numbered as continuations of Table 23.   These ruled sheets will serve as tables on which the following entries are made "each week":

1. *Initial Inventory.*   Enter the difference between the previous week's *Total Inventory* and *Sales.*
2. *Total Inventory.*   Add *Goods Received* to *Initial Inventory*, and enter this sum.

TABLE 23—INITIAL "HISTORY," INVENTORY-CONTROL GAME

Week Number	Initial Inventory	Sets Received	Total Inventory	Customer Orders Received	Sales	Carrying Cost	Cost of Placing Orders	Cost of Lost Sales
1......	40	0	40	7	7	$ 80	$ 0	$ 0
2......	33	0	33	8	8	66	100	0
3......	25	0	25	5	5	50	0	0
4......	20	0	20	12	12	40	0	0
5......	8	0	8	10	8	16	0	80
6......	0	60	60	6	6	120	0	0
7......	54	0	54	7	7	108	0	0
8......	47	0	47	8	8	94	0	0
9......	39	0	39	6	6	78	0	0
10......	33	0	33	13	13	66	100	0
11......	20	0	20	6	6	40	0	0
12......	14	0	14	3	3	28	0	0
13......	11	0	11	4	4	22	0	0
14......	..	60	..	..	..	..	..	..
15......	..	0	..	..	..	..	..	..
16......	..	0	..	..	..	..	..	..

3. *Carrying Cost.* Enter twice the *Total Inventory* (the cost is $2 per set carried).

4. *Customer Orders Received.* This is a statistical quantity, determined by cutting the special deck of playing cards. The cards are valued as follows: Joker, 0; Ace, 1; Numbered cards, "face-value"; face-cards, 0. Proceed as follows, moving to Step 5 as soon as an entry is made:

    a. Cut one card. If it is not a face-card, enter its value. If it is a face-card, go to Step 4b.

    b. Cut two cards. If neither is a face-card, enter the sum of their values. If either or both are face-cards, go to Step 4c.

    c. Cut four cards, and enter the sum of their values.

5. *Sales.* Enter the smaller of *Customer Orders Received* and *Total Inventory.*

6. *Cost of Lost Sales.* Enter forty times the difference between *Customer Orders Received* and *Sales* (a lost sale implies a lost profit of $40).

7. *Cost of Placing Orders.* If you do not wish to place a purchase order this week, the entry is "0". If you do wish to place an order, enter "100" (the cost of actually placing an order is $100).

8. *Goods Received.* Count ahead four weeks from the present; this is the line on which the entry is to be made. If no order is being placed this week, enter "0". If you are placing an order this week, enter the quantity ordered.

"Zero" entries in Steps 6, 7, and 8 need not actually be written. It may be convenient to enter Initial Inventory for "next week" before carrying through Steps 7 and 8 for "this week." The playing cards should be thoroughly shuffled every few "weeks."

Your "moves" in the game are the choices described in Steps 7 and 8, above. You must decide when to place orders and in what quantities. The object of the game is not just to cut current costs, but to "zero in" as quickly as possible on a systematic, routine policy which is sure to provide optimal results, or nearly so, in the long run.

An optimal policy is technically defined as one which will in the long run result in the lowest average over-all costs. Such a policy must properly balance the cost of placing orders against the cost of carrying inventory, and the cost of lost sales against the cost of carrying reserve stock. A slightly more subtle relationship calls for balance between frequency of placing orders (and hence of low points in stock) and the cost of lost sales.

It is "cheating" to count through the special deck. You are allowed to know nothing about its make-up except what you can infer from the data given initially and what is developed in the course of play. And, of course, it is "cheating" to determine future sales orders before placing purchase orders.

Setting up the inventory-control game. The main omission from the instructions above is the make-up of the special deck of playing cards. This can, of course, be varied. The following deck has been used in classes: 1 Joker; 1 Ace; 2 Deuces; 4 Treys; 6 Fours; 8 each, Fives through Eights; 5 Nines; 3 Tens; 3 face-cards.

In presenting the game to a group, one person can do all the cutting of cards. It may be desirable to run through a few weeks, carrying out the calculations in detail, using some simple order-reorder policy. The last three paragraphs of the instructions should be modified to suit circumstances and purposes. In particular, if analytic treatment of the problem is desired from inexperienced students, additional hints may be called for. Also, informal comments are desirable to emphasize that the game is an exercise in method, based on a problem similar to many real inventory-management problems, but not necessarily identical with any one of them.

Experience with the inventory-control game. The game described above has been used in business-school courses to introduce inventory-control problems and arouse interest in them, to illustrate forcefully the difference between problems posed in terms of raw data and the more common text-book problems posed in terms of analytically convenient assumptions, and to provide practice in setting up and solving order-reorder policy problems, but with the central purpose of providing a laboratory experience akin to a real-life research experience aimed at management decision.

There is no need to describe the many ways in which the inventory-control game can be modified to include such factors as variable "pipeline time," quantity discounts, limited back-ordering, competition for the supplier's capacity, etc. Nor would any purpose be served through enumerating specialized games used at various universities, by the AMA, and in private industry. Such games are not difficult to devise in relation to any aspect of business operations which is well enough understood to be simulated computationally. I hope that this article will encourage others to design their own games and to use them for their own purposes in management education and training.

UCLA Executive Game No. 2

Three executive games have been developed at the University of California, Los Angeles. Game No. 1, which was first played in the spring of 1957, has been superseded by the more refined Game No. 2. Game No. 3, utilizing the Western Data Processing Center's IBM 709 computer is relatively new: Game No. 2, which has been used by a number of universities and also by several business firms, is the best suited of the three for detailed discussion, especially because it has been prepared in a manually computed version, as well as in the electronically computed version.

The bulk of the discussion is a straightforward description of the game, in the form of a condensed and slightly generalized version of the instructions given to players.

As a preliminary to the formal instructions, players are usually told briefly about business games in general and their purposes. What is said amounts to a capsule version of the preceding portions of this article. Questions are invited throughout the instruction period, but the administrator of the game reserves the right to give incomplete answers. As a substitute for more thorough instructions and the knowledge which would in a real business be inherited from past managements, a short, unscored practice period of play usually precedes the "main run" for a group.

General. Executive Game No. 2 simulates a multi-firm, one-product industry. There may be as few as two firms or as many as nine. Time is accelerated to a rate of approximately one year per hour or two of actual play. Five to seven years are simulated by one play of the game, sometimes in a single day, and sometimes in a series of one- or two-hour sessions.

A team of three to six players forms the top management of each firm, and guides it by making decisions on the following quarterly:

Price of product
Production volume
Advertising and selling budget
Research and development budget
Investment in plant and equipment
Dividend

The decisions are entered upon preprinted forms, which are designed to facilitate keeping track of past policies.

When decisions have been made, they are taken to a computing room and punched into cards which are fed, along with cards summarizing the state of the industry at the end of the preceding quarter, into an IBM 650 computer. This machine is programmed to simulate a quarter's operations and produce cards from which an IBM 407 tabulator prepares the following confidential reports for each firm:

Sales Volume
Percent Share of Industry Sales
Current Inventory Quantity
Production Capacity for the Next Quarter
Statement of Profit and Loss
Statement of Receipts and Disbursements
End-of-Quarter Statement of Financial Condition.

Table 24 is a facsimile set of reports. The Operating Statements covering a given quarter's operations are returned immediately after the decisions have been made, which will guide operations during the *following* quarter.

TABLE 24—TYPICAL REPORTS, *UCLA Executive Game No. 2*

OPERATING STATEMENTS
FIRM 3   PERIOD 14

Sales Volume	451,806
Per Cent Share of Industry Sale	14
Current Inventory Quantity	287,597
Production CPY Next Quarter	604,209

PROFIT AND LOSS

Income	Sales Revenue		$ 2,990,956
Expense			
	Manufacturing Costs	$1,676,478	
	Reduction in Inventory Value	444,582 —	
	Administration	393,348	
	Advertising and Selling	200,000	
	Research and Development	400,000	
	Depreciation	302,107	
	Miscellaneous	253,412	$ 2,780,763
Profit before Income Tax			210,193
Addition to Income Tax Fund			109,300
Net Profit after Income Tax			100,893
Dividends Paid			50,000
Addition to Owners Equity			50,893

RECEIPTS AND DISBURSEMENTS

Receipts	Sales Revenue		$ 2,990,956
Disbursements			
	Cash Expense	$2,923,238	
	Addition to Income Tax Fund	109,300	
	Dividends Paid	50,000	
	Investment in Plant	302,000	$ 3,384,538
Addition to Cash Assets			393,582 —

FINANCIAL CONDITION

Assets		
	Net Cash Assets	$ 758,889
	Inventory Value	862,791
	Plant Net Book Value	12,084,180
Owners Equity		13,705,860

NOTE: Dashes following entries indicate negative numbers. Totals of detail listings appear to the right of the last item.

In addition to these reports, the teams are notified of their competitors' prices immediately after each quarter's decisions are collected. They are also kept up-to-date on predicted and actual values of a general business index of special pertinence to the hypothetical industry of the game. Annual summaries of the operation of all firms are posted shortly after the end of each year. The game has usually been played in one large room, whose atmosphere, with these reports posted, has been compared to that of a wide-open book-making establishment. Espionage by eavesdropping is sometimes feasible.

It is usual to concentrate about half of the total time for a year's decision-making in the period when annual summaries are published. Over-all plans are then made, but may be modified at any time during the rest of the year. The time scale is firmly set by those who administer the game. Lunchbreaks are given, but intermediate breaks must be arranged within the teams, much like "vacations" in real life. The schedule usually allows two or three hours for pre-game discussion and the unscored practice period, as well as an hour or two for post-game analysis of results and the reasons therefore.

Management's job.   Management's job in Executive Game No. 2 is to balance the controllable factors in such a way as to make the most of available resources and potentialities. All firms start from the same position, with the same sales, inventories, prices, etc. The industry can raise itself up as a whole. At the same time, the firm whose management team learns most quickly what the essential problems of the game are, and how to cope with them, can pull far ahead of its competitors in the course of a few "years" of play.

Efforts to increase sales must be properly related to costs, both in terms of enlarged budgets for advertising and for research and development and reduced margins resulting from price cutting. Marketing efforts must be coordinated with plant capacity and production volume. Investment programs and dividend policies must be geared to available funds. All of these factors must be balanced in the face of continually changing competitive and general business conditions. The need for planning is emphasized by the fact that relatively stable policies are more effective, price for price, dollar for dollar budgeted, etc., than are policies involving much fluctuation.

Total industry market is affected both by business conditions and by the industry-wide constellation of prices and expenditures for advertising and research and development. Each firm's potential share of the total market is determined primarily by the competitors. The product's purchasers are fairly sensitive to price differentials, and in the short run to price changes as such. Market shares are also much influenced by advertising and by design improvements resulting from research and development expenditures. Advertising and research and development have effects which extend for several quarters. As might be expected, the impact of advertising is relatively intense but also relatively short-lived, compared with that of research and development.

Production at or below the "capacity" figure listed on the Operating Statements is accomplished at nearly fixed cost per unit, relatively small reductions being a consequence of vigorous research and development programs. Production over and above the capacity can be called for, but at an approximately doubled direct cost per unit. Normally, the largest nonbudgeted, indirect costs are those which are fixed and those, such as depreciation, which depend roughly upon plant size. (Exceptions occur if a firm expands its plant too rapidly, or if large cash deficits appear.) Advertising and research and development are costs as budgeted.

Fixed costs make large volume operation advantageous relative to total cost per unit. Cost depending upon plant size levy large penalties for overexpansion. Underproduction, relative to potential sales, results in loss of revenue through lost sales, rather than in added costs. Overproduction leads to excessive inventories and to correspondingly large carrying charges.

Plant and equipment deteriorate at a rate of 2.5 per cent per quarter and this deterioration is reflected immediately in reduced capacity. To maintain a given capacity, it is necessary to reinvest accordingly. Reduction in capacity is accomplished by allowing depreciation to take its course, without reinvestment. New capacity is purchased by allocating to "Investment in Plant and Equipment" twenty dollars per unit of quarterly capacity desired, over and above the sum needed to hold ground against depreciation. There are "incidental expenses" associated with purchases of plant and equipment, which are small for moderate rates of expansion, but which become significant when as much as one million dollars is allocated to plant investment in a single quarter, and which grow rapidly with larger investments. Plant and equipment whose purchase is budgeted at the beginning of one quarter is not available for production until the following quarter.

When net cash assets fall below zero, costs are incurred for loan negotiations, interest, factoring, etc. These costs become significant with a shortage of a few hundred thousand dollars, and grow rapidly with larger deficits. The administrators of the game may be willing to "buy into a firm" if its cash position becomes desperate, but will not pay more than about half the book value of the equity purchased.

Like all such reports in real life, the Operating Statements used in the game are to some degree "conventional." For instance, inventory value is figured on a standard cost basis, and certain costs are arbitrarily allocated to the "Administration" detail item and others to "Miscellaneous." These conventions and also some quantitative information concerning the factors governing various costs, which are discussed as part of the preparation of players, will not be taken up here.

Post-Mortem discussion. The goals to be sought by participants in this game are not spelled out in detail. Different teams may take different tasks. One may concentrate on expansion and increased sales, for instance, while another may focus more directly on the profit picture. Each team is required to keep track of its broad objectives and of its operating strategies during the course of the game.

The game itself is followed by a discussion of the objectives and strategies of the teams. Each team subjectively evaluates its own work, and is also given an objective "score," based upon over-all profitability, dividend policy, and the condition of its firm at the end of play. The discussion is facilitated by large size charts summarizing the progress of the game. Some of the charts used are shown by Figure 23-1.

The purpose of the post-mortem is less to reveal better strategies which might have been adopted than to show how better use could have been made of the available information. For example, in the game to which Figure 23-1 refers, the generally successful Firm 4 failed to cut its price in the "recession year" (Year 6), even though the downturn had been forecast and everyone was aware of competitive price cutting. This mistake should have been avoided in view of the available information concerning the consequences to Firm 1 of maintaining a high-price level through the earlier downturn in Year 3. Criticisms of this type help to refocus attention upon the game as an exercise in learning from experience.

Other executive games. A few paragraphs are in order to indicate how some of the other executive games differ from the game just described. Several of these games are discussed in detail elsewhere. The interested reader is referred to the list of papers at the end of this article.

The American Management Association game, mentioned at the start of this article, much influenced the development of *UCLA Executive Games No. 1* and *No. 2*, and these games are naturally somewhat similar to it. The biggest difference is that the teams in the AMA game are limited to relatively narrow ranges in their decisions, at each stage. The UCLA games allow almost unrestricted choices, but are designed in such a way that failure to follow reasonable and stable policies is penalized. ("Overspending" is permitted, but results in heavy interest charges, for example.) A second point of difference is the AMA game's provision for buying market information beyond that which is made available as a matter of course. The games are completely different in such minor details as report formats.

CHARTS SUMMARIZING A FOUR-FIRM "RUN" OF UCLA EXECUTIVE DECISION GAME NO. 2

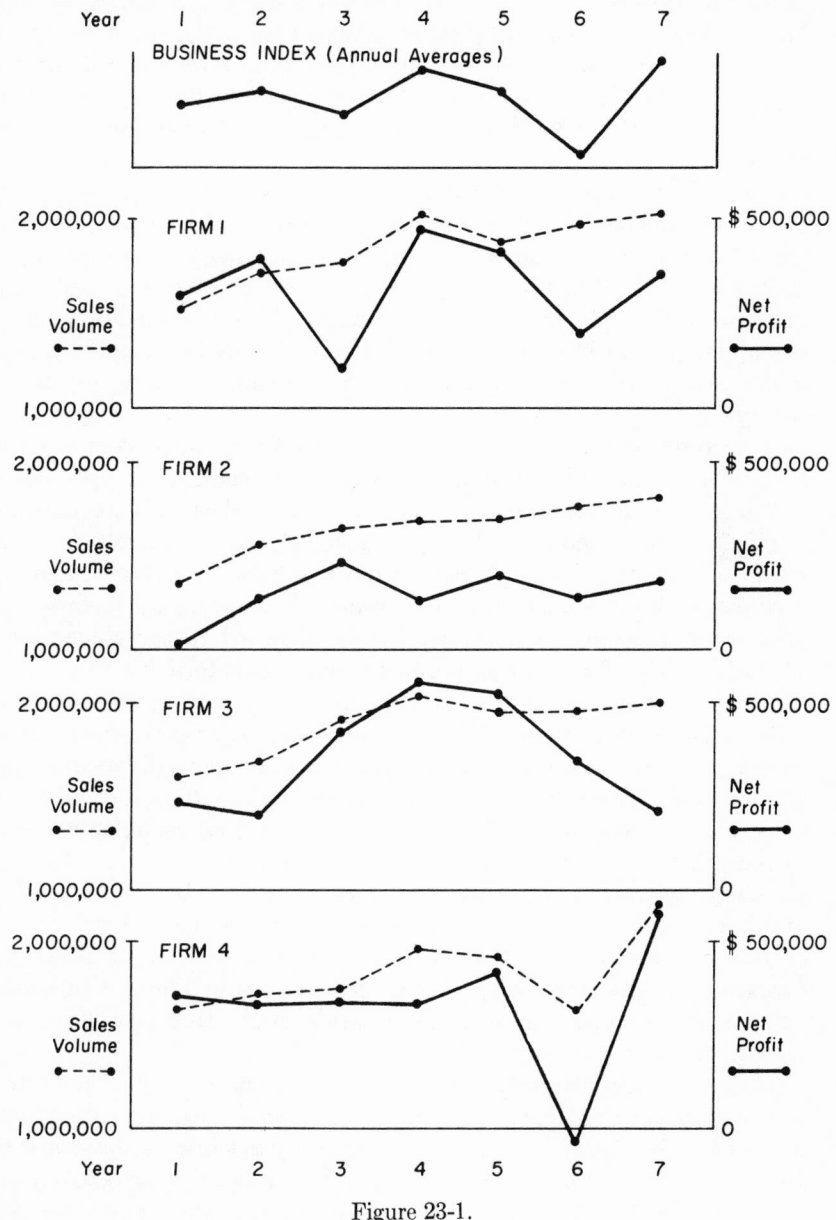

Figure 23-1.

Another similar game was developed for the International Business Machines Company, by G. T. Hunter and others. In this game, three firms compete in four geographically separate markets. One of these is a "home market" for each firm, and the fourth is normally the principle competitive battleground. A. N. Schrieber, of the University of Washington, has also developed fairly complex executive games for use in business courses.

The relatively new *UCLA Executive Game No. 3* is also a complicated one, in which each firm can manufacture several models of the same product—these being distinguished primarily in price and (correspondingly) in quality level. A diversity of products is made profitable by a multi-sector market. This game was developed primarily for slow-paced play (one or two moves per week) as a laboratory portion of curricular courses, and the initial experience with its application in this context has been very encouraging.

An interesting board game has been devised by G. R. Andlinger and J. R. Greene, for McKinsey and Company. This game, which is concerned with a hypothetical capital goods manufacturing industry, is unique among existing executive games in being economically hand-computable. Also, partly to compensate for a relatively uncomplicated underlying model, the progress of play depends relatively strongly upon statistical factors. The wide interest inspired by the McKinsey game led to the conversion of *UCLA Executive Game No. 2* into hand-computable form.

Milton Stone of the Electro-Data Division, Burroughs Corporation, and others have developed an interesting game especially for the purposes of a recent conference of supermarket executives. This game differs from those previously mentioned in being organized around the decisions and reports typical in supermarket operation, rather than general manufacturing and merchandising. G. J. Feeney, of General Electric Corporation, has designed a relatively generalized executive game, involving two products and three marketing areas, and focusing upon marketing problems broadly representative of one of the GE operating components. A number of executive games referring to various other types of business operations have been proposed, but little information about them has been made publicly available.

An extremely complex game developed at the Carnegie Institute of Technology, by R. M. Cyert and others provides a far more realistic simulation of business activity than do any of the games previously mentioned. In addition to such activities as over-all budgeting, the players will have to make a wide variety of specialized decisions. Because of the complexity of the game, it is run at a relatively slow pace, perhaps an hour or so of team activity per simulated month. A game with similar characteristics is being constructed at the University of California, Los Angeles, by Morris Asimow and R. C. Sprowls, and plans are being made to center a special seminar in data processing around this game. It is intended that these games be adaptable for the representation of actual firms and/or industries.

A Closing Comment

Business decision gaming is new, and the exploration of its possibilities has hardly begun. Consequently, this article, which is nominally in the most part a report on existing games and their past use, is really aimed toward the future. The directions which gaming may take, within the framework of general management education alone, cannot yet even be suspected. In this article, I have not gone into other areas of application —other educational uses (especially in management science education), research uses, and uses related directly to practical decision making. The possibilities are so varied, and their potential import so great, that business gaming seems certain to be one of the most fruitful inventions of recent years.

References

General. The following article is a broad discussion of the purposes and potentialities of executive games:

G. R. Andlinger, "Looking Around: What Can Business Games Do?" *Harvard Business Review* XXXVI, 4 (July-Aug., 1958), 147-160.

The AMA Game. The first of the following references is a fairly technical description of the game and its purposes, the second is aimed directly toward the businessman, and the third extensively discusses the relation of the game to modern, quantitative techniques in decision-making:

Richard Bellman, *et al.*, "On the Construction of a Multi-Stage, Multi-Person Business Game," *Operations Research*, V. 4 (Aug., 1957).

John McDonald and F. M. Ricciardi, "The Business Decision Game." *Fortune*, March, 1958.

F. M. Ricciardi, *et al.*, *Top Management Decision Simulation: The AMA Approach.* (New York: American Management Association, 1957).

The IBM Game. The following papers, both published by the International Business Machines Corporation, 590 Madison Avenue, New York City, provide full information for operating and playing the game, which requires an IBM 650 computer and 407 tabulator.

"IBM Management Decision-Making Laboratory, Model 1: Administrators Reference Manual." 1958.

"IBM Management Decision-Making Laboratory, Model 1: Instructions for Participants." 1958.

The McKinsey Game. The following article can also be obtained in reprints which represent the *McKinsey Game* in "do-it-yourself-kit" form:

G. R. Andlinger, "Business Games—Play One," *Harvard Business Review* XXXVI, 2 (March-April, 1958).

The UCLA Game. The instructions for players, and full technical details for the new, manually computed version as well as the original, IBM 650 version of this game are included in the following four papers, all published in mimeograph form by the Management Sciences Research Project, University of California, Los Angeles:

J. R. Jackson, "UCLA Executive Game No. 2: A Preliminary Report," 1958.
K. R. MacCrimmon and J. R. Jackson, "Hand Computed Version of UCLA Executive Game No. 2" 1959.
J. R. Jackson and K. R. Wright, "UCLA Executive Game No. 2: Mathematical Model and Computer Code," 1958, 13 pp.
K. R. Wright, J. R. Jackson and J. L. McKenney, "UCLA Executive Game No. 2: Computing Instructions," 1958.

The University of Washington Game. The following paper is a general description of the game and its uses:

A. N. Schrieber, "Gaming—A New Way to Teach Business Decision Making," *University of Washington Business Review*, April, 1958.

INDEX